# UNITED STATES
# Coast Pilot®

# 3

## Atlantic Coast:
## Sandy Hook, New Jersey
## to Cape Henry, Virginia

### 2022 (55th) Edition

This edition cancels the 54th Edition and includes all previously published corrections.

Weekly updates to this edition are available at:
*nauticalcharts.noaa.gov/publications/coast-pilot/index.html*

**U.S. Department of Commerce**
Gina M. Raimondo, Secretary of Commerce

**National Oceanic and Atmospheric Administration (NOAA)**
Richard W. Spinrad, Ph.D., Under Secretary of Commerce for Oceans and Atmosphere

**National Ocean Service**
Nicole R. LeBoeuf, Assistant Administrator for Ocean Services and Coastal Zone Management

D1294720

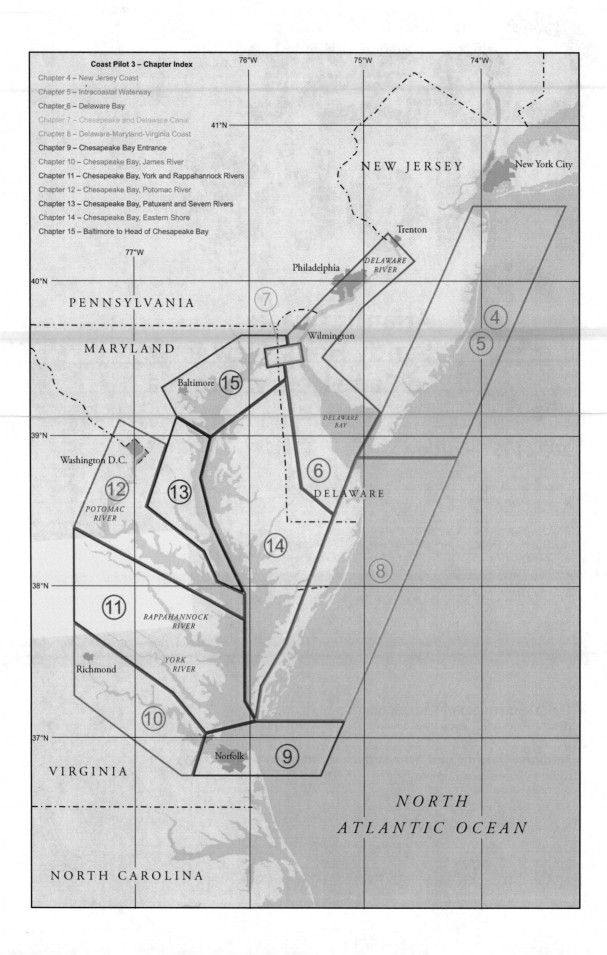

# Preface

The United States Coast Pilot is published by the National Ocean Service (NOS), National Oceanic and Atmospheric Administration (NOAA), pursuant to the Act of 6 August 1947 (33 U.S.C. 883a and b), and the Act of 22 October 1968 (44 U.S.C. 1310).

The Coast Pilot supplements the navigational information shown on NOAA nautical charts. The publication is continually updated and maintained from inspections conducted by NOAA survey vessels and field parties, corrections published in Notices to Mariners, information from other Federal agencies, State and local governments, maritime and pilots' associations, port authorities, and concerned mariners.

NOAA's Office of Coast Survey encourages public feedback regarding its suite of nautical charting products and services through **ASSIST**, Coast Survey's stakeholder engagement and feedback tool. This allows customers to submit questions or comments or to report an error with NOAA's nautical charts and products.
Customers can access **ASSIST** at *www.nauticalcharts.noaa.gov/customer-service/assist/*
Those who prefer to communicate by telephone can contact Coast Survey at 1–888–990–6622.

Coast Pilot corrections are no longer published in the NGA Notice to Mariners effective 01 January 2021. Additional information regarding the NGA policy change can be referenced at *msi.nga.mil/NTM* in the Notice to Mariners 52/20 Hydrogram and Marine Information sections.

---

**Coast Pilot Updates**

Check for weekly critical updates for this edition at *nauticalcharts.noaa.gov/publications/coast-pilot/index.html*
(See **33 CFR 164.33 Charts and Publications**, chapter 2, for regulations.)

Customers may print the specifically affected paragraphs to revise this book, or download an updated file (PDF) of the entire volume.

A *Weekly Record of Updates* is provided directly preceding the index.

# Contents

# General Information

(1)

## UNITED STATES COAST PILOT®

(2)      The United States Coast Pilot, published by the National Oceanic and Atmospheric Administration (NOAA), is a series of ten nautical books (volumes) that encompasses a wide variety of information important to navigators of U.S. coastal/intracoastal waters and the waters of the Great Lakes. The Coast Pilot is intended to be used as a supplement to NOAA nautical charts. Much of the content cannot be shown graphically on the charts and is not readily available elsewhere. Topics which are covered include environmental factors of weather, climate, ice conditions, tides, water levels, currents, prominent coastal features and landmarks. Specific information on vertical clearances, wharf descriptions, small-craft facilities, hazards, dredged channels and depths are also provided. Navigation services and regulations are also identified including pilotage, towing, anchorages, routes and traffic separation schemes, environmental protection, and other Federal laws.

(3)      New editions of each volume are issued annually. Fully updated files are posted weekly on the Internet, and are also available through NOAA Certified Chart Agents at *www.nauticalcharts.noaa.gov*.

(4)      **Amendments** to this publication are available at *nauticalcharts.noaa.gov/publications/coast-pilot/index. html*.

(5)

### Using the Coast Pilot

(5)      <Deleted Paragraph>

(6)      **Chapter 1** contains definitions of general and standard terms used throughout the volume, discussions of NOAA charting products and services, descriptions of maritime services by various U.S. Government agencies, Notices to Mariners and other information pertinent to safe navigation.

(7)      **Chapter 2** contains selected extracts from the Code of Federal Regulations (CFR) that affect mariners.

(8)      **Chapter 3** contains general information that is peculiar to the region covered by a particular Coast Pilot volume. For example, practical information regarding offshore currents and dangers, coastal aids to navigation, prominent landmarks and the general character of the coast and depths helpful in approaching the region.

(9)      In **Chapter 4 and the remaining numbered chapters**, the detailed description of the region begins. A map precedes each chapter and outlines the nautical charts used in the area to be discussed. In these chapters, as much as possible, the coastal description is in geographic sequence, north to south on the east coast, east to west on the gulf coast, clockwise around each of the Great Lakes and south to north on the west coast and Alaskan coast. Features are described as they appear on the largest scale chart, with that chart number prominently shown in blue.

(10)      **Appendix A** contains contact information regarding the various products, services and agencies detailed throughout the volume.

(11)      **Navigation Rules**— preceding Appendix A, contains the International (72 COLREGS) and Inland Navigation Rules, technical Annexes, and associated Federal rules and regulations.

(12)      The **Weekly Record of Updates** is intended as a log for critical updates applied to this volume.

(13)      The **Index** contains geographic names mentioned throughout a Coast Pilot volume. These names are boldfaced and indexed along with the number of the largest scale chart on which the entire feature appears. Asterisks preceding a chart number in the index of Coast Pilot 5 indicate charts published by the National Geospatial-Intelligence Agency, and in the index of Coast Pilot 6, charts published by the Canadian Hydrographic Service.

(14)

### Bearings

(15)      Bearings and courses are in degrees true and are measured clockwise from **000°** (north) to **359°**. The bearings of an aid to navigation (e.g., directional light, light sector, range) are given as viewed from the bridge of a vessel toward the light.

(16)

### Bridges and Cables

(17)      Vertical clearances of bridges and overhead cables are in feet above mean high water unless otherwise stated; clearances in Coast Pilot 6 are in feet above Low Water Datum unless otherwise stated. When the water level is above Low Water Datum, the bridge and overhead cable clearances given in the Coast Pilot and shown on the charts should be reduced accordingly. Clearances of drawbridges are for the closed position, although the open clearances are also given for vertical-lift bridges. Whenever a bridge span over a channel does not open fully to an unlimited clearance position, a minimum clearance for the sections over the channel is given; the same applies to swing and pontoon bridges with openings less than 50 feet horizontally. Clearances given in the Coast Pilot are those approved for nautical charting and are supplied by the U.S. Coast Guard (bridges) and U.S. Army Corps of

Engineers (cables). See charts for horizontal clearances of bridges, as these are generally given in the Coast Pilot only when they are less than 50 feet (15 meters). Tables listing structures across waterways, found in some Coast Pilots, show both horizontal and vertical clearances. Submarine cables are rarely mentioned.

(18)

### Cable ferries

(19) Cable ferries are guided by cables fastened to shore and sometimes propelled by a cable rig attached to the shore. Generally, the cables are suspended during crossings and dropped to the bottom when the ferries dock. Where specific operating procedures are known they are mentioned in the text. Since operating procedures vary, mariners are advised to exercise extreme caution and seek local knowledge. **DO NOT ATTEMPT TO PASS A MOVING CABLE FERRY.**

(20)

### Courses

(21) These are true and are given in degrees clockwise from **000°** (north) to **359°**. The courses given are the courses to be made good.

(22)

### Currents

(23) Stated current velocities are the averages at strength. Velocities are in knots, which are nautical miles per hour. Directions are the true directions to which the currents set (see chapter 3, this book).

(24)

### Depths

(25) Depth is the vertical distance from the chart datum to the bottom and is expressed in the same units (feet, meters or fathoms) as those soundings found on the chart. (See Chart Datum, this chapter, for further detail.) The **controlling depth** is the least known depth of a channel. This depth is determined by periodic hydrographic surveys and restricts use of the channel to drafts less than that depth. The **centerline controlling depth** applies only to the channel centerline or close proximity; lesser depths may exist in the remainder of the channel. The **midchannel controlling depth** is the controlling depth of only the middle half of the channel. **Federal project depth** is the original design dredging depth of a channel planned by the U.S. Army Corps of Engineers (USACE) and may be deeper than current conditions. For this reason, project depth must not be confused with controlling depth. **Depths alongside** wharves usually have been reported by owners and/or operators of the waterfront facilities and have not been verified by Government surveys. Since these depths may be subject to change, local authorities should be consulted for the latest controlling depths.

(26) For all maintained channels with controlling depths detailed on charts in tabular form, the Coast Pilot usually states only the project depths. For all other channels which may be depicted on charts with depth legends, notes or soundings, the Coast Pilot will list where to find the most recent information on the latest known surveys. Depths may vary considerably between maintenance dredging.

(27)

### Under-keel clearances

(28) It is becoming increasingly evident that economic pressures are causing mariners to navigate through waters of barely adequate depth, with under-keel clearances being finely assessed from the charted depths, predicted tide levels and depths recorded by echo sounders.

(29) It cannot be too strongly emphasized that even charts based on modern surveys may not show all seabed obstructions or the shoalest depths, and actual tide levels may be appreciably lower than those predicted.

(30) In many ships an appreciable correction must be applied to shoal soundings recorded by echo sounders due to the horizontal distance between the transducers. This separation correction, which is the amount by which recorded depths therefore exceed true depths, increases with decreasing depths to a maximum equal to half the distance apart of the transducers; at this maximum the transducers are aground. Ships whose transducers are more than 6 feet (1.8 meters) apart should construct a table of true and recorded depths using the Traverse Tables. (Refer to the topic on echo soundings elsewhere in chapter 1.)

(31) Other appreciable corrections, which must be applied to many ships, are for settlement and squat. These corrections depend on the depth of water below the keel, the hull form and the speed of the ship.

(32) Settlement causes the water level around the ship to be lower than would otherwise be the case. It will always cause echo soundings to be less than they would otherwise be. Settlement is appreciable when the depth is less than seven times the draft of the ship and increases as the depth decreases and the speed increases.

(33) Squat denotes a change in trim of a ship underway, relative to her trim when stopped. It usually causes the stern of a vessel to sit deeper in the water. However, it is reported that in the case of mammoth ships, squat causes the bow to sit deeper. Depending on the location of the echo sounding transducers, this may cause the recorded depth to be greater or less than it ought to be. **Caution and common sense are continuing requirements for safe navigation.**

(34)

### Distances

(35) These are in nautical miles unless otherwise stated. A nautical mile is one minute of latitude, or approximately 2,000 yards, and is about 1.15 statute miles.

(36) Coast Pilot 6 is in statute miles unless otherwise stated. A statute mile is 5,280 feet or about 0.87 nautical mile.

(37)

### Geographic Coordinates

(38) Geographic coordinates listed in the Coast Pilot are referred to North American Datum of 1983 (NAD 83)

unless otherwise noted for certain CFR extracts in chapter 2.

(39)

### Heights

(40)     These are in feet (meters) above the tidal datum used for that purpose on the charts, usually mean high water. However, the heights of the decks of piers and wharves are given in feet (meters) above the chart datum for depths.

(41)     Coast Pilot 6 is in feet (meters) above the chart datum used for that purpose on the charts, usually Low Water Datum.

(42)

### Light and Sound Signal Characteristics

(43)     These are not described in the Coast Pilot. Also, light sectors and visible ranges are generally not fully described. This information can be found in U.S. Coast Guard Light Lists.

(44)

### Obstructions

(45)     Wrecks and other obstructions are mentioned only if they are relatively permanent and in or near normal traffic routes.

(46)

### Radio Navigational Aids

(47)     For detailed information on Radio Navigation Aids see the **United States Coast Guard Light Lists** and the National Geospatial-Intelligence Agency's **Radio Navigational Aids, Publication 117.**

(48)

### Ranges

(49)     These are not fully described. "**A 339° Range**" means that the rear structure bears **339°** from the front structure. (See United States Coast Guard Light Lists.)

(50)

### Reported information

(51)     Information received by NOAA from various sources concerning depths, dangers, currents, facilities, and other topics, which has not been verified by Government surveys or inspections, is often included in the Coast Pilot; such **unverified information** is qualified as "reported" and should be regarded with caution.

(52)

### Tides

(53)     Tidal information, including real-time water levels, tide predictions and tidal current predictions are available at *tidesandcurrents.noaa.gov.*

(54)

### Time

(55)     Unless otherwise stated, all times are given in local standard time in the 24-hour system. (Noon is 1200, 2:00 p.m. is 1400 and midnight is 0000.)

(56)

### Winds

(57)     Directions are the true directions from which the winds blow; however, sometimes (rarely) compass points are used. Unless otherwise indicated, speeds are given in knots, which are nautical miles per hour.

(58)     <Deleted Paragraph>

(58)

## NAUTICAL CHARTS

(59)     <Deleted Paragraph>

(59)     NOAA produces and maintains a suite of over 1,000 nautical charts that cover the U.S. coastal waters, the Great Lakes and U.S. territories. These charts provide a graphic representation of water depths, the shoreline, prominent topographic and man-made features, aids to navigation and other navigational information useful to the mariner. NOAA's charts are available in a variety of digital formats designed to meet the specific requirements of all mariners. Paper copies may also be obtained through one of NOAA's Print-on-Demand partners.

(60)

### Paper Print on Demand Nautical Charts

(60)     <Deleted Paragraph>

(61)     The content of Print-On-Demand (POD) charts is updated weekly by NOAA with the most current U.S. Coast Guard Local Notice to Mariners and other critical safety information. POD charts are printed under the authority of NOAA and shipped through partnerships between NOAA and commercial providers. POD information and a list of participating POD chart agents can be found at *nauticalcharts.noaa.gov/publications/print-agents.html#paper-charts-mobile.*

(61)     <61-62 Deleted>

(62)

### Portable Document Format (PDF) Nautical Charts

(63)     <Deleted Paragraph>

(63)     Almost all of NOAA's nautical charts may be downloaded for free as Portable Document Format (PDF) files at *nauticalcharts.noaa.gov/charts/noaa-raster-charts.html#full-size-nautical-charts.* The PDF nautical charts are exact replicas of the images used to produce POD and Raster Navigational Charts (RNC). As such, they also have all the latest updates based on U.S. Coast Guard Local Notices to Mariners, National Geospatial-Intelligence Agency Notices to Mariners and other critical safety information.

(64)     Most PDF charts can be printed at the proper scale from any plotter accommodating a 36-inch paper width. When printed properly, PDF charts and POD charts are very similar, but PDF charts have not yet been approved to meet Federal regulations for paper chart carriage requirements as POD charts have.

(65)
### BookletCharts

(66)    The NOAA BookletChart™ is a product that can be printed by the users for free. They are made to help recreational boaters locate themselves on the water. BookletCharts are reduced in scale and divided into pages for convenience but otherwise contain all the information of the full-scale nautical charts and are updated weekly. For more information visit *nauticalcharts.noaa.gov/charts/noaa-raster-charts.html#booklet-charts*.

(67)
### Raster Navigational Charts (NOAA RNC®)

(68)    NOAA Raster Navigational Charts (NOAA RNC®) are geo-referenced digital images of NOAA's entire suite of paper charts. NOAA RNCs are official data that can be used in many types of electronic charting systems (ECS), including Raster Chart Display Systems (RCDS) and some Electronic Chart Display and Information Systems (ECDIS). Current regulations support the use of RNCs as a primary means of navigation when ENCs are not available, but they require an accompanying minimal set of up-to-date paper charts. They can integrate position information from the Global Positioning System (GPS) and other navigational sensors, such as radar and automatic identification systems (AIS) to show a vessel's track, waypoints, and planned routes. NOAA RNCs and their weekly updates are available free of charge at *nauticalcharts.noaa.gov/charts/noaa-raster-charts. html*.

(69)
### Electronic Navigational Charts (NOAA ENC®)

(70)    NOAA Electronic Navigational Charts (NOAA ENC®) are databases of charted objects and their attributes with standardized content, structure and format. They comply with International Hydrographic Organization (IHO) specifications stated in IHO Publication S-57. They may be used as an alternative to paper charts required on SOLAS class vessels.

(71)    ENCs are intended for use in electronic charting systems (ECS) as well as Electronic Chart Display and Information Systems (ECDIS). ECDIS are programmable to show as much or as little data as the user requires. They can integrate position information from the Global Positioning System (GPS) and other navigational sensors, such as radar and automatic identification systems (AIS) to show a vessel's track, waypoints and planned routes. Using this information ECDIS can use ENCs to give warning of impending danger in relation to the vessel's position and movement. NOAA ENCs and their updates are available free of charge at *nauticalcharts.noaa.gov/charts/noaa-enc.html*.

(72)
### Nautical Chart—New Editions and Corrections

(73)    New editions of paper Print-on-Demand (POD) charts are available on the Monday after NOAA clears a new edition for release. Once the authorized POD chart is available, it meets federal chart carriage requirements, and should be put into service immediately. It should be updated from the *last correction and cleared through* dates shown in the lower left corner of the chart.

(74)    The chart date is of vital importance to the navigator. When charted information becomes obsolete, further use of the chart for navigation is dangerous. Natural and artificial changes, many of them critical, are occurring constantly; therefore it is important that navigators use up-to-date charts. Nautical charts and publications are available for purchase from authorized POD agents and their sales outlets.

(75)    NOAA's "Nautical Chart Update" website allows mariners to update their nautical charts from one database that includes information from NOAA, NGA U.S. Notice to Mariners, U.S. Coast Guard Local Notices to Mariners and the Canadian Coast Guard Notices to Mariners at: *nauticalcharts.noaa.gov/charts/chart-updates.html*.

(76)
### Nautical Chart Numbering System

(77)    This chart numbering system, adopted by NOAA and National Geospatial-Intelligence Agency (NGA), provides for a uniform method of identifying charts published by both agencies. Nautical charts published by NGA and by the Canadian Hydrographic Service are identified in the Coast Pilot by an asterisk preceding the chart number.

(78)
### Chart Scale

(79)    The scale of a chart is the ratio of a given distance on the chart to the actual distance that it represents on the earth. For example, one unit of measurement on a 1:10,000 scale chart is equal to 10,000 of the same unit on the earth's surface. Large scale charts show greater detail of a relatively small area. Small scale charts show less detail but cover a larger area. Certain hydrographic information may be omitted on smaller scale charts. **Mariners should always obtain the largest scale coverage for near shore navigation**.

(80)    The scales of nautical charts range from 1:2,500 to about 1:5,000,000. Graphic scales are generally shown on charts with scales of 1:80,000 or larger, and numerical scales are given on smaller scale charts. NOAA charts are classified according to scale as follows:

(81)    **Sailing charts**, scales 1:600,000 and smaller, are for use in fixing the mariner's position approaching the coast from the open ocean or for sailing between distant coastwise ports. On such charts the shoreline and topography are generalized and only offshore soundings, principal lights, outer buoys and landmarks visible at considerable distances are shown.

(82)    **General charts**, scales 1:150,000 to 1:600,000, are for coastwise navigation outside of outlying reefs and shoals.

(83)    **Coast charts**, scales 1:50,000 to 1:150,000, are for inshore navigation leading to bays and harbors of considerable width and for navigating large inland waterways.

(84)     **Harbor charts**, scales larger than 1:50,000, are for harbors, anchorage areas and the smaller waterways.

(85)     **Special charts**, at various scales, cover the Intracoastal waterway and miscellaneous small-craft areas.

(86)
## Chart Projections

(87)     The **Mercator projection** used on most nautical charts has straight-line meridians and parallels that intersect at right angles. On any particular chart the distances between meridians are equal throughout, but distances between parallels increase progressively from the equator toward the poles so that a straight line between any two points is a rhumb line. This unique property of the Mercator projection is one of the main reasons why it is preferred by the mariner.

(88)     The **Polyconic projection** is used on most U.S. nautical charts of the Great Lakes. On this projection, parallels of latitude appear as non-concentric circles, and meridians appear as curved lines converging toward the pole and concave to the central meridian. The scale is correct along any parallel and along the central meridian of the projection. Along other meridians the scale increases with increased difference of longitude from the central meridian.

(89)
## Chart Datum, Tidal Waters

(90)     Chart Datum is the particular tidal level to which soundings and depth curves on a nautical chart or bathymetric map are referred. The tidal datum of **Mean Lower Low Water** is used on all NOAA charts, except for charts in the Great Lakes and non-tidal inland waterways. For information on **Chart Datum, Great Lakes System**, see Coast Pilot 6, chapter 3.

(91)
## Horizontal Datum

(92)     Nautical charts are constructed based on one of a number of horizontal datums which are adopted to best represent individual regions around the world. Note that the terms horizontal datum, horizontal geodetic datum, and horizontal control datum are synonymous.

(93)     The exact placement of lines of latitude and longitude on a nautical chart is dependent on the referenced horizontal datum. Charts of the United States are currently referenced primarily to the North American Datum of 1983 (NAD 83), and the World Geodetic System 1984 (WGS 84). WGS 84 is equivalent to the NAD 83 for charting purposes.

(94)     NAD 83 and WGS 84 have replaced the North American Datum of 1927 and other regional datums as the primary horizontal datum to which NOAA charts are referenced. Since some geographic positions may still be referenced to the older datums, NOAA has included notes on charts which show the amount to shift those positions in latitude and longitude to fit the chart's NAD 83 or WGS 84 projection.

(95)     It should be noted that the physical shift between positions on older datums and NAD 83/WGS 84 was significant. Mariners should always be certain the positions they are plotting on a nautical chart are on the same datum as the chart.

(96)
## Chart Accuracy

(97)     The value of a nautical chart depends upon the accuracy of the surveys on which it is based. The chart reflects what was found by field surveys and what has been reported to NOAA. It also represents general conditions at the time of surveys or reports and does not necessarily portray present conditions. Significant changes may have taken place since the date of the last survey or report.

(98)     Each sounding represents an actual measure of depth and location at the time the survey was made, and each bottom characteristic represents a sampling of the surface layer of the sea bottom at the time of the sampling. Areas where sand and mud prevail, especially the entrances and approaches to bays and rivers exposed to strong tidal current and heavy seas, are subject to continual change.

(99)     In coral regions and where rocks and boulders abound, it is always possible that surveys may have failed to find every obstruction. Thus, when navigating such waters, customary routes and channels should be followed, and areas where irregular and sudden changes in depth indicate conditions associated with pinnacle rocks, coral heads, or boulders should be avoided..

(100)     Information charted as "reported" should be treated with caution when navigating the area, because the actual conditions have not been verified by government surveys.

(101)
## Source Diagrams and Zone of Confidence Diagrams

(102)     The age and accuracy of hydrographic survey data that support nautical charts can vary. Depth information on nautical charts, paper or digital, is based on data from the latest available hydrographic survey, which in many cases may be quite old. Diagrams are provided on nautical charts to assist mariners in assessing hydrographic survey data and the associated level of risk to navigate in a particular area. There are currently two types of diagrams shown on NOAA paper and raster navigational charts (RNCs) of 1:500,000 scale and larger—**Zone of Confidence (ZOC) Diagrams** and **Source Diagrams**. ZOC information (designated CATZOC) is also found on electronic navigational charts (ENCs). This provides consistency in the display of source data between ENCs and newer paper charts.

(103)     Both types of diagrams consist of a graphic representation of the extents of hydrographic surveys within the chart and accompanying table of related survey quality categories. CATZOC information on an ENC, unlike the diagrams on a paper chart or RNC, is displayed over the ENC data using symbols rather than letters. These symbols are displayed on a separate layer, which can be viewed when planning a route, then switched off until needed again at another time.

(106)

## Zone of Confidence Diagrams

| ZOC CATEGORIES | | | | |
|---|---|---|---|---|
| ZOC | DATE | POSITION ACCURACY | DEPTH ACCURACY | SEAFLOOR COVERAGE |
| A1 | 2008–2016 | ± 16.4 ft | = 1.6 feet + 1% depth | All significant seafloor features detected |
| A2 | — | ± 65.6 ft | = 3.3 feet + 2% depth | All significant seafloor features detected |
| B | 2005 | ± 164.0 ft | = 3.3 feet + 2% depth | Uncharted features hazardous to surface navigation are not expected but may exist |
| C | — | ± 1640.4 ft | = 6.6 feet + 2% depth | Depth anomalies may be expected |
| D | — | Worse than ZOC C | Worse than ZOC C | Large depth anomolies may be expected |
| U | Unassessed – The quality of the bathymetric data has yet to be assessed. | | | |

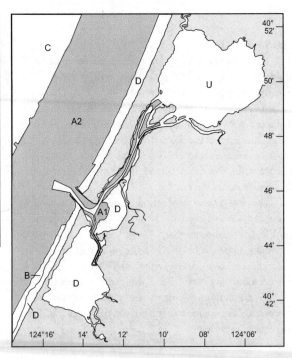

(104)       On **ZOC Diagrams**, the quality of the hydrographic data is assessed according to six categories; five quality categories for assessed data (A1, A2, B, C and D) and a sixth category (U) for data that has not yet been assessed. On the ENC, the categories are shown using a rating system of stars—the higher the quality, the greater the number of stars. Assessment of hydrographic data quality and classification into zones of confidence is based on a combination of: survey date, position accuracy, depth accuracy and sea floor coverage (the survey's ability to detect objects on the seafloor.)

(105)       **Source Diagrams** provide the mariner with additional information about the density and adequacy of the sounding data depicted on the chart. The adequacy with which sounding data reflects the configuration of the bottom depends on the following factors: survey technology employed (sounding and navigation equipment), survey specifications in effect (prescribed survey line spacing and sounding interval) and type of bottom (e.g., rocky with existence of submerged pinnacles, flat sandy, coastal deposits subject to frequent episodes of deposition and erosion). Source diagrams will be replaced with ZOC diagrams as new editions are created.

(108)

### Chart Symbols, Abbreviations and Terms

(109)       The standard symbols and abbreviations approved for use on nautical charts produced by the U.S. Government are described in **U.S. Chart No. 1: Symbols, Abbreviations and Terms used on Paper and Electronic Navigational Charts.** This reference, jointly maintained by the National Geospatial-Intelligence Agency (NGA) and NOAA, is available at *nauticalcharts.noaa.gov/publications/us-chart-1.html*.

(110)       The publication **Chart 1: Symbols, Abbreviations and Terms** published by the Canadian Hydrographic Service, is available online at *charts.gc.ca/publications/chart1-carte1/index-eng.asp*.

(111)       Some symbols and abbreviations used on foreign charts, including reproductions of foreign charts made by NGA, are different than those used on U.S. charts. It is recommended that mariners who use foreign charts also obtain the symbol sheet or Chart No. 1 produced by the appropriate foreign agency.

(112)       Mariners are warned that the buoyage systems, shapes and colors used by other countries often have a different significance than the U.S. system.

(113)

### Areas with Blue Tint

(114)       A blue tint is shown in water areas on many charts to accentuate shoals and other areas considered dangerous for navigation when using that particular chart. Since the danger curve varies with the intended purpose of a chart a careful inspection should be made to determine the contour depth of the blue tint areas.

(115)

### Bridge and Cable Clearances

(116)       For bascule bridges whose spans do not open to a full vertical position, unlimited overhead clearance is not

(107)

## Source Diagrams

Referring to the accompanying sample Source Diagram to the right and the previous discussion of survey methods over time, transiting from Point X to Point Y, along the track indicated by the dotted line, would have the following information available about the relative quality of the depth information shown on the chart.

Point X lies in an area surveyed by NOAA between 1900-1939. The sounding data in this area would have been collected by leadline. Depths between sounding points can only be inferred, and undetected features might exist between the sounding points in areas of irregular relief — caution should be exercised.

The transit then crosses an area surveyed by NOAA between 1940-1969. The sounding data in this area would have been collected by continuous recording single beam echo sounder. It is possible that features could have been missed between sounding lines, although echo sounders record all depths along a sounding line with varying beam widths.

The transit ends in an area charted from miscellaneous surveys. These surveys may be too numerous to depict or may vary in age, reliability, origin or technology used. No inferences about the fitness of the data can be made in this area from the diagram.

Referring again to the accompanying sample Source Diagram, and the previous discussion of survey methods over time, a mariner could choose to transit from Point X to Point Y, along the track shown with a dashed line.

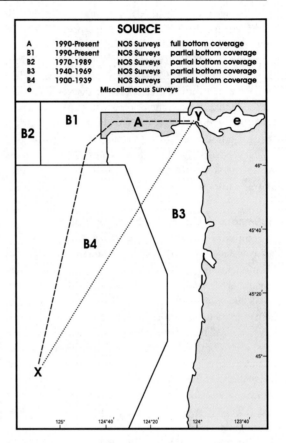

The transit starts again in an area surveyed by NOAA between 1900-1939. The sounding data in this area would have been collected by leadline. Depths between sounding points can only be inferred, and undetected features might still exist between the sounding points in areas of irregular relief — caution should be exercised.

The transit then crosses an area surveyed by NOAA between 1990–present, with partial bottom coverage. The data is collected in metric units and acquired by continuous recording single beam echo sounder. It is possible that features could have been missed between the sounding lines, although echo sounders record all depths along a sounding line with varying beam widths.

The transit then crosses into an area surveyed by NOAA etween 1990–present, having full bottom coverage. This area of the charted diagram is shaded with a blue screen to draw attention to the fact that full bottom coverage has been achieved. The data in this area would have been collected in metric units and acquired by side scan sonar or multibeam sonar technology. Undetected features in this area, at the time of the survey, would be unlikely.

The transit ends in an area charted from miscellaneous surveys. These surveys may be too numerous to depict or may vary in age, reliability, origin or technology used. No inferences about the fitness of the data can be made in this area from the diagram. By choosing to transit along the track shown by the dashed line, the mariner would elect to take advantage of survey information that is more recent and collected with modern technology.

available for the entire charted horizontal clearance when the bridge is open, due to the inclination of the drawspans over the channel.

(117) Charted in black text, vertical clearances of overhead cables are for the lowest wires at mean high water as authorized and permitted by the U.S. Army Corps of Engineers (USACE). Reported clearances received from sources other than the USACE are labeled as such. When provided, safe vertical clearances are shown in magenta text and indicate the highest points of a ship that can pass under an overhead power cable without risk of electrical discharge from the cable to the ship or without making contact with a bridge. **Vessels with masts, stacks, booms or antennas should allow sufficient clearance under power cables to avoid arcing.**

(118)

### Submarine Cables and Submerged Pipelines

(119) **Submarine cables** and **submerged pipelines** cross many waterways used by both large and small vessels, but all of them may not be charted. For inshore areas, they usually are buried beneath the seabed, but for offshore areas they may lie on the ocean floor. Warning signs are often posted to warn mariners of their existence.

(120) The installation of submarine cables or pipelines in U.S. waters or the Continental Shelf of the United States is under the jurisdiction of one or more Federal agencies, depending on the nature of the installation. They are shown on the charts when the necessary information is reported to NOAA and they have been recommended for charting by the responsible agency. The chart symbols for submarine cable and pipeline areas are usually shown for inshore areas, whereas chart symbols for submarine cable and pipeline routes may be shown for offshore areas. Submarine cables and pipelines are not described in the Coast Pilots.

(121) In view of the serious consequences resulting from damage to submarine cables and pipelines, vessel operators should take special care when anchoring, fishing or engaging in underwater operations near areas where these cables or pipelines may exist or have been reported to exist. Mariners are also warned that the areas where cables and pipelines were originally buried may have changed and they may be exposed; extreme caution should be used when operating vessels in depths of water comparable to the vessel's draft.

(122) Certain cables carry high voltage, while many pipelines carry natural gas under high pressure or petroleum products. Electrocution, fire or explosion with injury, loss of life or a serious pollution incident could occur if they are broached.

(123) Vessels fouling a submarine cable or pipeline should attempt to clear without undue strain. Anchors or gear that cannot be cleared should be slipped, but no attempt should be made to cut a cable or a pipeline.

(124)

### Artificial Obstructions to Navigation

(125) **Disposal areas** are designated by the U.S. Army Corps of Engineers for depositing dredged material where there is sufficient depth not to cause shoaling or create a danger to surface navigation. The areas are charted without blue tint, and soundings and depth curves are retained.

(126) **Disposal sites** are areas established by Federal regulation (**40 CFR 220** through **228**) in which dumping of dredged and fill material and other nonbuoyant objects is allowed with the issuance of a permit. Dumping of dredged and fill material is supervised by the U.S. Army Corps of Engineers and all other dumping by the Environmental Protection Agency (EPA). (See U.S. Army Corps of Engineers and Environmental Protection Agency, this chapter, and Appendix A for office addresses.)

(127) **Dumping grounds** are also areas that were established by Federal regulation (**33 CFR 205**). However, these regulations have been revoked and the use of the areas discontinued. These areas will continue to be shown on nautical charts until such time as they are no longer considered to be a danger to navigation.

(128) Disposal Sites and Dumping Grounds are rarely mentioned in the Coast Pilot, but are shown on nautical charts. **Mariners are advised to exercise caution in the vicinity of all dumping areas.**

(129) **Spoil areas** are for the purpose of depositing dredged material, usually near and parallel to dredged channels. Spoil areas are usually charted from survey drawings from U.S. Army Corps of Engineers after-dredging surveys, though they may originate from private or other Government agency surveys. On nautical charts, spoil areas are tinted blue, labeled and have all soundings and depth curves omitted from within their boundaries. Spoil areas present a hazard to navigation and even the smallest craft should avoid crossing them.

(130) **Fish havens** are artificial shelters constructed of various materials including rocks, rubble, derelict barges/oil rigs and specially designed precast structures. This material is placed on the sea floor to simulate natural reefs and attract fish. Fish havens are often located near fishing ports or major coastal inlets and are usually considered hazards to shipping. Before such a reef may be built, the U.S Army Corps of Engineers must issue a permit specifying the location and depth over the reef. Constructed of rigid material and projecting above the bottom, they can impede surface navigation and therefore represent an important feature for charting. Fish havens may be periodically altered by the addition of new material, thereby possibly increasing the hazard. They are outlined and labeled on charts and show the minimum authorized depth when known. Fish havens are tinted blue if they have a minimum authorized depth of 11 fathoms or less. If the minimum authorized depth is unknown and they are in depths greater than 11 fathoms, they are considered a danger to navigation. Navigators

(131) should be cautious about passing over fish havens or anchoring in their vicinity.

(131) **Fishtrap areas** are areas established by the U.S. Army Corps of Engineers, or State or local authority, in which traps may be built and maintained according to established regulations. The fish stakes that may exist in these areas are obstructions to navigation and may be dangerous. The limits of fishtrap areas and a cautionary note are usually charted. Navigators should avoid these areas.

(132)
### Local Magnetic Disturbances

(133) If measured values of magnetic variation differ from the expected (charted) values by several degrees, a magnetic disturbance note will be printed on the chart. The note will indicate the location and magnitude of the disturbance, but the indicated magnitude should not be considered as the largest possible value that may be encountered. Large disturbances are more frequently detected in the shallow waters near land masses than on the deep sea. Generally, the effect of a local magnetic disturbance diminishes rapidly with distance, but in some locations there are multiple sources of disturbances and the effects may be distributed for many miles.

(134)
### Compass Roses

(135) Each compass rose shows the date, magnetic variation and the annual change in variation. Prior to the new edition of a nautical chart, the compass roses are reviewed. Corrections for annual change and other revisions may be made as a result of newer and more accurate information. On some general and sailing charts, the magnetic variation is shown by isogonic lines in addition to the compass roses.

(136)
### Echo Soundings

(137) The echo sounder on a ship may indicate small variations from charted soundings; this may be due to the fact that various corrections (instrument corrections, settlement and squat, draft and velocity corrections) are made to echo soundings in surveying which are not normally made in ordinary navigation, or to observational errors in reading the echo sounder. Instrument errors vary between different equipment and must be determined by calibration aboard ship. Most types of echo sounders are factory calibrated for a velocity of sound in water of 800 fathoms per second, but the actual velocity may differ from the calibrated velocity by as much as 5 percent, depending upon the temperature and salinity of the waters in which the vessel is operating; the highest velocities are found in warm, highly saline water and the lowest in icy freshwater. Velocity corrections for these variations are determined and applied to echo soundings during hydrographic surveys. All echo soundings must be corrected for the vessel's draft, unless the draft observation has been set on the echo sounder.

(138) Observational errors include misinterpreting false echoes from schools of fish, seaweed, etc., but the most serious error that commonly occurs is where the depth is greater than the scale range of the instrument; a 400–fathom scale indicates 15 fathoms when the depth is 415 fathoms. Caution in navigation should be exercised when wide variations from charted depths are observed.

(139)
## NOTICES TO MARINERS

(140) **Notices to Mariners** are published to advise operators of marine information affecting the safety of navigation. The notices include changes in aids to navigation, depths in channels, bridge and overhead cable clearances, reported dangers and other useful marine information. They should be used routinely for updating the latest editions of nautical charts and related publications.

(141) **Local Notices to Mariners** are issued by each Coast Guard District Commander for the waters under their jurisdiction. (See Appendix A for Coast Guard district(s) covered by this volume.) These notices are usually published weekly and are available at *navcen.uscg.gov*.

(142) **U.S. Notice to Mariners**, published weekly by the National Geospatial-Intelligence Agency, are prepared jointly with NOAA and the Coast Guard. These notices contain selected items from the Local Notices to Mariners and other reported marine information required by oceangoing vessels operating in both foreign and domestic waters. Special items covering a variety of subjects and generally not discussed in the Coast Pilot or shown on nautical charts are published annually in Notice to Mariners No. 1. These items are important to the mariner and should be read for future reference. These notices are available at *msi.nga.mil/NGAPortal/ MSI.portal*.

(143) **Broadcast Notices to Mariners** are made by the Coast Guard to report deficiencies and important changes in aids to navigation. (See Navigational Warnings, Information and Weather, this chapter.)

(144) The **Special Notice to Mariners** is an annual publication containing important information for mariners on a variety of subjects which supplements information not usually found on charts and in navigational publications. It includes excerpts from various Federal laws and regulations regarding marine pollution reporting, aids to navigation and Vessel Traffic Service (VTS) procedures. There are tips for trip planning, updates to the Rules of the Road and information on local hazards. Also included are points of contact, phone numbers and email addresses for various subject matter experts to assist the mariner in locating further information.

(145) Vessels operating within the limits of the Coast Guard districts can obtain information affecting NOAA charts and related publications from the Local Notices to Mariners. Small craft using the Intracoastal Waterway and other waterways and small harbors within the United

States that are not normally used by oceangoing vessels will require the Local Notices to Mariners to keep charts and related publications up to date.

(146)
## AIDS TO NAVIGATION

(147)
### U.S. Aids to Navigation System

(148)    The navigable waters of the United States are marked to assist navigation using the U.S. Aids to Navigation System, a system consistent with the International Association of Marine Aids to Navigation and Lighthouse Authorities (IALA) Maritime Buoyage System. The **IALA Maritime Buoyage System** is followed by most of the world's maritime nations and will improve maritime safety by encouraging conformity in buoyage systems worldwide. IALA buoyage is divided into two regions made up of Region A and Region B. All navigable waters of the United States follow IALA Region B, except U.S. possessions west of the International Date Line and south of 10° north latitude, which follow IALA Region A. Lateral aids to navigation in Region A vary from those located within Region B. Nonlateral aids to navigation are the same as those used in Region B. Appropriate nautical charts and publications should be consulted to determine whether the Region A or Region B marking schemes are in effect for a given area.

(149)    As standard protocol, the U.S. Coast Guard reported assigned positions of aids to navigation uses the North American Datum of 1983 (NAD 83). Due to the development of new navigational systems and the retirement of old systems, the World Geodetic System 1984 (WGS 84) has become the preferred standard. In 2020, the U.S. Coast Guard Chief of the Office of Navigation Systems (CG-NAV) announced that all geographic coordinates for aids to navigation assigned positions will be reported using WGS 84.

(150)
### Reporting Defects in Aids to Navigation

(151)    Promptly notify the nearest Coast Guard District Commander if an aid to navigation is observed to be missing, sunk, capsized, out of position, damaged, extinguished or showing improper characteristics.

(152)    **Aids to navigation** in United States waters of the Great Lakes and their connecting waters, except for the St. Lawrence River, are maintained by the U.S. Coast Guard. Local jurisdiction for the region is assigned to the Commander, Ninth Coast Guard District. The Lake Champlain region and the Hudson River are under the jurisdiction of the Commander, First Coast Guard District. (See Appendix A for the addresses.)

(153)    It is unlawful to establish or maintain any aid similar to those maintained by the U.S. Coast Guard without first obtaining permission from the Coast Guard District Commander. The licensed officer in command of a vessel which collides with any aid must report the fact promptly to the nearest U.S. Coast Guard Sector.

(154)
### Lights

(155)    The range of visibility of lights as given in the U.S. Coast Guard Light Lists and as shown on the charts is the **nominal range**, which is the maximum distance at which a light may be seen in clear weather (meteorological visibility of 10 nautical miles) expressed in nautical miles. The Light Lists give the nominal ranges for all U.S. Coast Guard lighted aids except range and directional lights.

(156)    **Luminous range** is the maximum distance at which a light may be seen under the existing visibility conditions. By use of the diagram in the Light Lists, luminous range may be determined from the known nominal range, and the existing visibility conditions. Neither the nominal nor the luminous ranges do not take into account elevation, observer's height of eye, or the curvature of the earth.

(157)    **Geographic range** is a function of only the curvature of the earth and is determined solely from the heights above sea level of the light and the observer's eye; therefore, to determine the actual geographic range for a height of eye, the geographic range must be corrected by a distance corresponding to the height difference, the distance correction being determined from a table of "distances of visibility for various heights above sea level", found in the United States Coast Guard Light List.

(158)    The maximum distances at which lights can be seen may at times be increased by abnormal atmospheric refraction and may be greatly decreased by unfavorable weather conditions such as fog, rain, haze or smoke. All except the most powerful lights are easily obscured by such conditions. In some conditions of the atmosphere white lights may have a reddish hue. During weather conditions which tend to reduce visibility, colored lights are more quickly lost to sight than white lights. Navigational lights should be used with caution because of the following conditions that may exist.

(159)    A light may be extinguished and the fact not reported to the Coast Guard for correction, or a light may be located in an isolated area where it will take time to correct.

(160)    In regions where ice conditions prevail the lantern panes of unattended lights may become covered with ice or snow, which will greatly reduce the visibility and may also cause colored lights to appear white.

(161)    Brilliant shore lights used for advertising and other purposes, particularly those in densely populated areas, make it difficult to identify a navigational light.

(162)    At short distances flashing lights may show a faint continuous light between flashes.

(163)    The distance of an observer from a light cannot be estimated by its apparent intensity. The characteristics of lights in an area should always be checked in order that powerful lights visible in the distance not be mistaken for nearby lights showing similar characteristics at low intensity such as those on lighted buoys.

(164)    The apparent characteristic of a complex light may change with the distance of the observer, due to color and intensity variations among the different lights of the

group. The characteristic as charted and shown in the Light List may not be recognized until nearer the light.

(165) Motion of a vessel in a heavy sea may cause a light to alternately appear and disappear, and thus give a false characteristic.

(166) Where lights have different colored sectors, be guided by the correct bearing of the light; do not rely on being able to accurately observe the point at which the color changes. On either side of the line of demarcation of colored sectors there is always a small arc of uncertain color.

(167) On some bearings from the light, the range of visibility of the light may be reduced by obstructions. In such cases, the obstructed arc might differ with height of eye and distance. When a light is cut off by adjoining land and the arc of visibility is given, the bearing on which the light disappears may vary with the distance of the vessel from which observed and with the height of eye. When the light is cut off by a sloping hill or point of land, the light may be seen over a wider arc by a ship far off than by one closer.

(168) Arcs of circles drawn on charts around a light are not intended to give information as to the distance at which it can be seen, but solely to indicate, in the case of lights which do not show equally in all directions, the bearings between which the variation of visibility or obscuration of the light occurs.

(169) Lights of equal candlepower but of different colors may be seen at different distances. This fact should be considered not only in predicting the distance at which a light can be seen, but also in identifying it.

(170) Lights should not be passed close aboard, because in many cases riprap mounds are maintained to protect the structure against ice damage and scouring action.

(171) Many prominent towers, tanks, smokestacks, buildings and other similar structures, charted as landmarks, display flashing and/or fixed red aircraft obstruction lights. Lights shown from landmarks are charted only when they have distinctive characteristics to enable the mariner to positively identify the location of the charted structure.

(172)

### Articulated Lights

(173) An articulated light is a vertical pipe structure supported by a submerged buoyancy chamber and attached by a universal coupling to a weighted sinker on the seafloor. The light, allowed to move about by the universal coupling, is not as precise as a fixed aid. However, it has a much smaller watch circle than a conventional buoy, because the buoyancy chamber tends to force the pipe back to a vertical position when it heels over under the effects of wind, wave or current.

(174) Articulated lights are primarily designed to mark narrow channels with greater precision than conventional buoys.

(175)

### Daybeacons

(176) Daybeacons are unlighted aids affixed to stationary structures. They are marked with dayboards for daytime identification. The dayboards aid navigation by presenting one of several standard shapes and colors which have navigational significance. Dayboards are sometimes referred to as daymarks.

(177) Daybeacons are found on-shore and in shallow water. They are frequently used to mark channel edges.

(178)

### Articulated Daybeacons

(179) Articulated daybeacons are similar to articulated lights, described above, except they are unlighted.

(180)

### Buoys

(181) The aids to navigation depicted on charts comprise a system consisting of fixed and floating aids with varying degrees of reliability. Therefore, prudent mariners will not rely solely on any single aid to navigation, particularly a floating aid.

(182) The approximate position of a buoy is represented by the dot or circle associated with the buoy symbol. The approximate position is used because of practical limitations in positioning and maintaining buoys and their sinkers in precise geographical locations. These limitations include, but are not limited to, inherent imprecisions in position fixing methods, prevailing atmospheric and sea conditions, the slope of and the material making up the seabed, the fact that buoys are moored to sinkers by varying lengths of chain and the fact that buoy body and/or sinker positions are not under continuous surveillance, but are normally checked only during periodic maintenance visits which often occur more than a year apart. The position of the buoy body can be expected to shift inside and outside of the charting symbol due to the forces of nature. The mariner is also cautioned that buoys are liable to be carried away, shifted, capsized, sunk, etc. Lighted buoys may be extinguished or sound signals may not function as a result of ice, running ice or other natural causes, collisions or other accidents.

(183) For the foregoing reasons, a prudent mariner must not rely completely upon the charted position or operation of floating aids to navigation but will also utilize bearings from fixed objects and aids to navigation on shore. Further, a vessel attempting to pass close aboard always risks collision with a yawing buoy or with the obstruction the buoy marks.

(184) Buoys may not always properly mark shoals or other obstructions due to shifting of the shoals or of the buoys. Buoys marking wrecks or other obstructions are usually placed on the seaward or channelward side and not directly over a wreck. Since buoys may be located some distance from a wreck they are intended to mark, and since sunken wrecks are not always static, extreme caution should be exercised when operating in the vicinity of such buoys.

(185)

### Automatic Identification System (AIS) Aids to Navigation

(186)     AIS is an automatic communication and identification system intended to improve the safety of navigation by assisting the efficient operation of a Vessel Traffic Services (VTS), ship reporting, ship-to-ship and ship-to-shore operations. AIS is increasingly being used as an aid to navigation. An AIS-equipped aid to navigation may provide a positive identification of the aid. It may also have the capability to transmit an accurate position and provide additional information such as actual tide height and/or weather information.

(187)     The AIS message may represent an aid to navigation that physically exists (physical AIS Aid to Navigation) or the message, transmitted from a remote location, may represent an aid to navigation that does not physically exist (virtual AIS Aid to Navigation). A virtual aid to navigation is a digital information object promulgated by an authorized service provider that can be presented on navigational systems.

(188)     Physical AIS aids to navigation are charted with the symbol for the physical aid (such as a buoy or light) with a magenta circle surrounding the symbol and labeled AIS. Virtual aids to navigation are charted with a small central dot with a topmark symbol indicating the purpose of the aid, surrounded by a magenta circle and labeled V-AIS. Temporary AIS aids to navigation and stations remotely transmitting an AIS signal are not charted. See U.S. Chart No. 1, Section S, for additional information and examples.

(189)

### Examples of Charted AIS Aids to Navigation

Physical AIS      Virtual AIS Aid to Navigation
Aid to Navigation

(190)

### Bridge Lights and Clearance Gages

(191)     The Coast Guard regulates marine obstruction lights and clearance gages on bridges across navigable waters. Where installed, clearance gages are generally vertical numerical scales, reading from top to bottom, and show the actual vertical clearance between the existing water level and the lowest point of the bridge over the channel; the gages are normally on the right-hand pier or abutment of the bridge, on both the upstream and downstream sides.

(192)     Bridge lights are fixed red or green and are privately maintained; they are generally not charted or described in the text of the Coast Pilot. All bridge piers (and their protective fenders) and abutments that are in or adjacent to a navigation channel are marked on all channel sides by red lights. On each channel span of a fixed bridge,

there is a range of two green lights marking the center of the channel and a red light marking both edges of the channel, except that when the margins of the channel are confined by bridge piers, the red lights on the span are omitted, since the pier lights then mark the channel edges. For multiplespan fixed bridges, the main-channel span may also be marked by three white lights in a vertical line above the green range lights.

(193)     On all types of drawbridges, one or more red lights are shown from the drawspan (higher than the pier lights) when the span is closed; when the span is open, the higher red lights are obscured and one or two green lights are shown from the drawspan, higher than the pier lights. The number and location of the red and green lights depend upon the type of drawbridge.

(194)     Bridges and their lighting, construction and maintenance are set forth in **33 CFR 114**, **115**, **116**, and **118** (not carried in this Coast Pilot). Aircraft obstruction lights prescribed by the Federal Aviation Administration may operate at certain bridges.

(195)

### Sound Signals

(196)     Caution should be exercised in the use of sound signals for navigation purposes. They should be considered solely as warning devices.

(197)     Sound travels through the air in a variable manner, even without the effects of wind, and, therefore the hearing of sound signals cannot be implicitly relied upon.

(198)     Experience indicates that distances must not be judged only by the intensity of the sound; that occasionally there may be areas close to a sound signal in which it is not heard; and that fog may exist not far from a station, yet not be seen from it, so the signal may not be operating. It is not always possible to start a sound signal immediately when fog is observed.

(199)

### Channel Markers

(200)     Lights, daybeacons, and buoys along dredged channels do not always mark the bottom edges. Due to local conditions, aids may be located inside or outside the channel limits shown by dashed lines on a chart. The Light List tabulates the offset distances for these aids in many instances.

(201)     Aids may be moved, discontinued or replaced by other types to facilitate dredging operations. Mariners should exercise caution when navigating areas where dredges with auxiliary equipment are working.

(202)     Temporary changes in aids are not included on the charts.

(203)

### Light Lists

(204)     The Coast Guard Light Lists are a means for communicating aids to navigation information to the maritime public. They are updated weekly and available for download on the United States Coast Guard Navigation Center's website at *www.navcen.uscg.gov*. Mariners should refer to these lists for detailed

(201) information regarding the characteristics and visibility of lights, and the description of light structures, buoys, sound signals and electronic aids.

(205)

## ELECTRONIC POSITIONING SYSTEMS

(206)   **Global Positioning System (GPS)**permits land, sea, and airborne users to determine their three-dimensional position, velocity and time 24 hours a day, in all weather, anywhere in the world. The basic system is defined as a constellation of satellites, the navigation payloads which produce the GPS signals, ground stations, data links and associated command and control facilities, that are operated and maintained by the Department of Defense. Please report GPS problems or anomalies at *navcen.uscg. gov* or contact the USCG Navigation Information Service at 703–313–5900.

(207)

### LORAN-C

(208)   LORAN, an acronym for LOng RAnge Navigation, was an electronic aid to navigation consisting of shore-based radio transmitters. In accordance with the Department of Homeland Security Appropriations Act, the U.S. Coast Guard terminated the transmission of all LORAN-C signals as of August 2010, rendering them unusable and permanently discontinued. For more details, visit *navcen.uscg.gov*. The Coast Guard strongly urges mariners accustomed to using LORAN-C for navigation to shift to a GPS navigation system and become familiar with its operation. NOAA is removing LORAN-C lines of position from all of its charts as new editions are published.

(209)

## SEARCH AND RESCUE

(210)

### Coast Guard Search and Rescue

(211)   The Coast Guard conducts and/or coordinates search and rescue operations for surface vessels or aircraft that are in distress or overdue. Search and rescue vessels and aircraft have special markings, including a wide slash of red-orange and a small slash of blue on the forward portion of the hull or fuselage. Other parts of aircraft, normally painted white, may have other areas painted red to facilitate observation. The cooperation of vessel operators with Coast Guard helicopters, fixed-wing aircraft, and vessels may mean the difference between life and death for some seaman or aviator; such cooperation is greatly facilitated by the prior knowledge on the part of vessel operators of the operational requirements of Coast Guard equipment and personnel, of the international distress signals and procedures and of good seamanship.

(212)   <Deleted Paragraph>

(212)

### Search and Rescue Great Lakes

(213)   The United States Coast Guard has established a toll-free search and rescue telephone number for the Great Lakes. The number is intended for use when the telephone number of the nearest Coast Guard station is unknown or when that station cannot be contacted. The toll-free number should not be used without first attempting to contact the nearest Coast Guard station. In all Great Lakes States the telephone number is 800-321-4400. This number is to be used for public reports of distress incidents, suspicious sightings, pollution or other maritime concerns.

(214)

### Radiotelephone Distress Message

(215)   Distress calls indicate a vessel or aircraft is threatened by grave and imminent danger and requests immediate assistance. They have absolute priority over all other transmissions. All stations which hear a distress call must immediately cease any transmission capable of interfering with the distress traffic and continue to listen on the frequency used for the emission of the distress call. This call should not be addressed to a particular station, and acknowledgment of receipt should not be given before the distress message which follows it is sent.

(216)   Distress calls are made on VHF-FM channel 16 (MAYDAY). For less serious situations than warrant the distress procedure, the radiotelephone urgency signal consisting of three repetitions of the word PAN-PAN (pronounced PAWN-PAWN), or the safety signal SECURITE (pronounced SECURITAY) spoken three times, are used as appropriate. For complete information on emergency radio procedures, see **47 CFR 80** or **Radio Navigational Aids, Pub. 117**.

(217)

### Global Maritime Distress and Safety System (GMDSS)

(218)   This international system, developed by the International Maritime Organization (IMO), is based on a combination of satellite and terrestrial radio services and has changed international distress communications from being primarily ship-to-ship based to primarily ship-to-shore (Rescue Coordination Center) based. Prior to the GMDSS, the number and types of radio safety equipment required to be carried by vessels depended upon the tonnage. Under GMDSS, the number and type of radio safety equipment vessels are required to carry depend on the areas in which they travel; GMDSS sea areas are defined by governments. All GMDSS-regulated ships must carry a satellite Emergency Position Indicating Radio Beacon (EPIRB), a NAVTEX receiver (if they travel in any areas served by NAVTEX), an Inmarsat-C SafetyNET receiver (if they travel in any areas not served by NAVTEX), a DSC-equipped VHF radiotelephone, two or more VHF handhelds and a search and rescue radar transponder (SART).

(219)

## Automated Mutual Assistance Vessel Rescue System (AMVER)

(220)
AMVER is a worldwide voluntary ship reporting system operated by the United States Coast Guard to promote safety of life and property at sea. AMVER's mission is to quickly provide search and rescue (SAR) authorities, on demand, accurate information on the positions and characteristics of vessels near a reported distress. Any merchant vessel anywhere on the globe, on a voyage of greater than 24 hours duration, is welcome in the AMVER system and family. International participation is voluntary regardless of the vessel's flag of registry, the nationality of the owner or company or ports of call.

(221)
According to U.S. Maritime Administration (MARAD) regulations, U.S. flag merchant vessels of 1,000 gross tons or more operating in foreign commerce and foreign flag vessels of 1,000 gross tons or more for which an Interim War Risk Insurance Binder has been issued under the provisions of Title XII, Merchant Marine Act, 1936, must report and regularly update their voyages and positions to AMVER in accordance with instructions set forth in the AMVER Ship Reporting System Manual. For more information contact AMVER Maritime Relations U.S. Coast Guard, 1 South Street Battery Park Building, New York, NY 10004; Phone: 212–668–7764, Fax: 212-668-7684, Telex: 127594-AMVER NYK, or go to *amver.com*.

(222)

## COSPAS-SARSAT

(223)
COSPAS: Space System for Search of Distress Vessels - SARSAT: Search and Rescue Satellite-Aided Tracking. COSPAS-SARSAT is an international satellite system designed to provide distress alert and location data to assist search and rescue operations using satellites and ground facilities to detect and locate the signals of distress beacons operating on 406 MHz. For more information on the Cospas-Sarsat System go to *cospas-sarsat.int*.

(224)

## Digital Selective Calling (DSC)

(225)
The U.S. Coast Guard offers VHF and MF/HF radiotelephone service to mariners as part of the Global Maritime Distress and Safety System. This service, called digital selective calling (DSC), allows mariners to instantly send an automatically formatted distress alert to the Coast Guard or other rescue authority anywhere in the world. Digital selective calling also allows mariners to initiate or receive distress, urgency, safety and routine radiotelephone calls to or from any similarly equipped vessel or shore station, without requiring either party to be near a radio loudspeaker. Each ship or shore station equipped with a DSC terminal has a unique Maritime Mobile Station Identity (MMSI). This is a nine-digit number that specifically identifies a ship, coast station, or group of stations. The DSC system alerts an operator when a distress call is received. It will provide the operator with a pre-formatted message that can include the distressed vessel's nine-digit MMSI, location, nature of distress, desired mode of communication and preferred working frequency.

(226)

## Emergency Position Indicating Radiobeacons (EPIRB)

(227)
EPIRBs emit a radio signal that can be used to locate mariners in distress. SARSAT satellites can locate the position of a 406 MHz EPIRB which greatly increases a mariner's chances of survival. While orbiting the earth, the satellites continuously monitor EPIRB frequencies. When SARSAT receives an EPIRB signal, it determines the beacon's position that is ultimately relayed to the nearest Coast Guard Rescue Coordination Center where rescue units are dispatched to the scene.

(228)
Mariners should ensure that their EPIRB is in working condition and stowed properly at all times to avoid non-distress emissions. Mariners are required to register their 406 MHz EPIRBs for improved search and rescue response and keep the registration current at all times. Registration can be accomplished online at *beaconregistration.noaa.gov*.

(229)
<Deleted Paragraph>

(229)

| EPIRB Types | | |
| --- | --- | --- |
| Type | Frequency | Description |
| Cat I | 406 MHz | Float-free, automatically activated EPIRB. Detectable by satellite anywhere in the world. Recognized by the Global Maritime and Distress Safety System (GMDSS). |
| Cat II | 406 MHz | Similar to Category I, except is manually activated. Some models are also water activated. |

(230)
<Deleted Paragraph>

(230)

## Medical Advice

(231)
Ships at sea with no medical personnel embarked and experiencing a medical emergency onboard can receive medical advice via radiotelex, radiotelephony or Inmarsat. Messages are generally addressed RADIOMEDICAL followed by the name of the coast station to which the message is sent. The priority of the message should depend on the severity of the ailment. In extreme emergency, the urgency signal (PAN-PAN) should precede the address. Messages are sent using distress and safety frequencies.

(232)

## Vessel Identification

(233)
Coast Guard search and rescue aircraft and surface craft use radar to assist in locating disabled vessels. Wooden and fiberglass vessels are often poor radar targets. Operators of disabled craft that are the object of a search are requested to hoist, as high above the waterline as possible, a radar-reflecting device. If no special radar-reflecting device is aboard, an improvised device can be used. This should consist of metallic objects of irregular shape. The more irregular the shape, the better will be the

(241)

## U.S. VHF Channels

| Channel | Ship Frequency (MHz) Transmit | Receive | Channel Usage |
|---|---|---|---|
| 01A | 156.050 | 156.050 | Port Operations and Commercial, VTS (Available only in New Orleans/Lower Mississippi area) |
| 05A | 156.250 | 156.250 | Port Operations or VTS in the Houston, New Orleans and Seattle areas |
| 06 | 156.300 | 156.300 | Intership Safety |
| 07A | 156.350 | 156.350 | Commercial |
| 08 | 156.400 | 156.400 | Commercial (Intership only) |
| 09 | 156.450 | 156.450 | Boater Calling; Commercial and Non-commercial |
| 10 | 156.500 | 156.500 | Commercial |
| 11 | 156.550 | 156.550 | Commercial; VTS in selected areas |
| 12 | 156.600 | 156.600 | Port Operations; VTS in selected areas |
| 13 | 156.650 | 156.650 | Intership Navigation Safety (bridge-to-bridge) Ships greater than 20m maintain a listening watch on this channel in US waters. |
| 14 | 156.700 | 156.700 | Port Operations; VTS in selected areas |
| 15 | – | 156.750 | Environmental (Receive only) Used by Class C EPIRBs |
| 16 | 156.800 | 156.800 | International Distress, Safety and Calling. Ships required to carry radio, USCG, and most coast stations maintain a listening watch on this channel. |
| 17 | 156.850 | 156.850 | State and local government maritime control |
| 18A | 156.900 | 156.900 | Commercial |
| 19A | 156.950 | 156.950 | Commercial |
| 20 | 157.000 | 161.600 | Port Operations (duplex) |
| 20A | 157.000 | 157.000 | Port Operations |
| 21A | 157.050 | 157.050 | U.S. Coast Guard only |
| 22A | 157.100 | 157.100 | Coast Guard Liaison and Maritime Safety Information Broadcasts (Broadcasts announced on channel 16) |
| 23A | 157.150 | 157.150 | U.S. Coast Guard only |
| 24 | 157.200 | 161.800 | Public Correspondence (Marine Operator) |
| 25 | 157.250 | 161.850 | Public Correspondence (Marine Operator) |
| 26 | 157.300 | 161.900 | Public Correspondence (Marine Operator) |
| 27 | 157.350 | 161.950 | Public Correspondence (Marine Operator) |
| 28 | 157.400 | 162.000 | Public Correspondence (Marine Operator) |
| 63A | 156.175 | 156.175 | Port Operations and Commercial, VTS (Available only in New Orleans/Lower Mississippi area) |
| 65A | 156.275 | 156.275 | Port Operations |
| 66A | 156.325 | 156.325 | Port Operations |
| 67 | 156.375 | 156.375 | Commercial. Used for bridge-to-bridge communications in lower Mississippi River (Intership only.) |
| 68 | 156.425 | 156.425 | Non-Commercial |
| 69 | 156.475 | 156.475 | Non-Commercial |
| 70 | 156.525 | 156.525 | Digital Selective Calling (voice communications not allowed) |
| 71 | 156.575 | 156.575 | Non-Commercial |
| 72 | 156.625 | 156.625 | Non-Commercial (Intership only) |
| 73 | 156.675 | 156.675 | Port Operations |
| 74 | 156.725 | 156.725 | Port Operations |
| 77 | 156.875 | 156.875 | Port Operations (Intership only) |
| 78A | 156.925 | 156.925 | Non-Commercial |
| 79A | 156.975 | 156.975 | Commercial (Non-commercial in Great Lakes only) |
| 80A | 157.025 | 157.025 | Commercial (Non-commercial in Great Lakes only) |
| 81A | 157.075 | 157.075 | U.S. Government only (environmental protection operations) |
| 82A | 157.125 | 157.125 | U.S. Government only |
| 83A | 157.175 | 157.175 | U.S. Coast Guard only |
| 84 | 157.225 | 161.825 | Public Correspondence (Marine Operator) |
| 85 | 157.275 | 161.875 | Public Correspondence (Marine Operator) |
| 86 | 157.325 | 161.925 | Public Correspondence (Marine Operator) |
| 87 | 157.375 | 157.375 | Public Correspondence (Marine Operator) |
| 88A | 157.425 | 157.425 | Commercial (Intership only) |
| AIS 1 | 161.975 | 161.975 | Automatic Identification System (AIS) |
| AIS 2 | 162.025 | 162.025 | Automatic Identification System (AIS) |

Boaters should normally use channels listed as Non-Commercial. Channel 16 is used for calling other stations or for distress alerting. Channel 13 should be used to contact a ship when there is danger of collision. All ships of length 20m or greater are required to guard VHF-FM channel 13, in addition to VHF-FM channel 16, when operating within U.S. territorial waters.

Note that the letter "A" indicates simplex use of the ship station transmit side of an international duplex channel, and that operations are different than international operations on that channel. Some VHF transceivers are equipped with an *International - U.S.* switch for that purpose. "A" channels are generally only used in the United States, and use is normally not recognized or allowed outside the U.S. The letter "B" indicates simplex use of the coast station transmit side of an international duplex channel. The U.S. does not currently use "B" channels for simplex communications in this band.

(247)

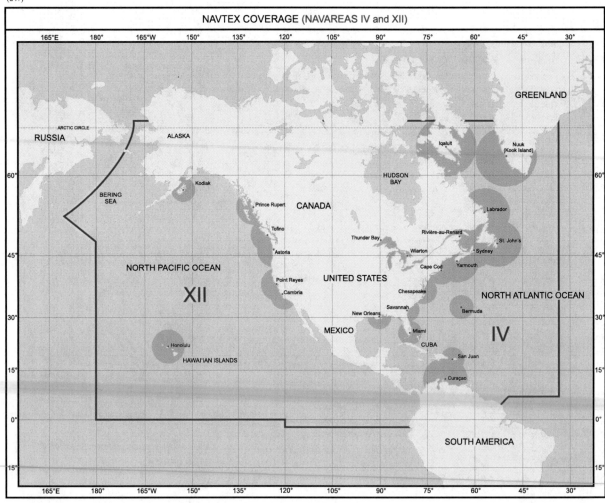

NAVTEX COVERAGE (NAVAREAS IV and XII)

radar-reflective quality. For quick identification at night, shine spotlights straight up. If aircraft are involved, once you are identified, turn lights away so as not to blind aircraft crew.

(234)

**Float Plan**

(235)    Small craft operators should prepare a float plan before starting a trip and leave it ashore with a yacht club, marina, friend or relative. It is advisable to regularly use a checking-in procedure by radio or telephone for each point specified in the float plan. A float plan is vital for determining if a boat is overdue and will assist in locating a missing vessel in the event search and rescue operations become necessary.

(236)

## NAVIGATIONAL WARNINGS, INFORMATION AND WEATHER

(237)    Marine radio warnings and weather are disseminated by many sources and through several types of transmissions. For complete information on radio warnings and weather, see **Radio Navigational Aids, Pub. 117** and the National Weather Service (NWS) publication **Worldwide Marine Radiofacsimile Broadcast Schedules**.

(238)    Radio navigational warning broadcasts are designed to provide the mariner with up-to-date marine information vital to safe navigation. There are three types of broadcasts: coastal and local, long range and worldwide.

(239)    Coastal and local warnings are generally restricted to ports, harbors and coastal waters and involve items of local interest. Usually, local or short-range warnings are broadcast from a single coastal station, frequently by voice and also radiotelegraph, to assist small craft operators in the area. The information is often quite detailed. Foreign area broadcasts are frequently in English as well as the native language. In the United States, short-range radio navigational warnings are broadcast by the U.S. Coast Guard Districts via NAVTEX and subordinate coastal radio stations.

(240)    Long range warnings are intended primarily to assist mariners on the high seas by promulgating navigational safety information concerning port and harbor approaches, coastlines and major ocean areas. Long-range radio navigational warnings are usually broadcast by means of radiotelegraphy and in many instances by radio-teletypewriter. A NAVAREA system of navigational warning areas has been developed providing worldwide coverage using standard format and procedures. The U.S.

(258)

## Standard Abbreviations Used in Broadcasts

### Aids to Navigation

AERO RBN — Aeronautical Radiobeacon
ART DBN — Articulated Daybeacon
ART LT — Articulated Light
DESTR — Destroyed
DISCONTD — Discontinued
ESTAB — Established
ELB — Exposed Location Buoy
FOG SIG — Fog Signal Station
LNB — Large Navigation Buoy

LT — Light
LLNR — Light List Number
LBB — Lighted Bell Buoy
LB — Lighted Buoy
LGB — Lighted Gong Buoy
LHB — Lighted Horn Buoy
LWB — Lighted Whistle Buoy
ODAS — Ocean Data Acquisition System
PRIV MAINTD — Privately Maintained

RACON — Radar Beacon
RA REF — Radar Reflector
TRUB — Temporarily Replaced by
   Unlighted Buoy
TRLB — Temporarily Replaced by
   Lighted Buoy
WHIS — Whistle

### Light Characteristics

AL — Alternating
CHAR — Characteristic
FL(2+1) — Composite Group-Flashing
OC(2+1) — Composite Group-Occulting
Q — Continuous Quick-Flashing

FFL — Fixed and Flashing
F — Fixed
FL(3) — Group-Flashing
OC(2) — Group-Occulting
IQ — Interrupted Quick-Flashing

ISO — Isophase
MO(A) — Morse Code
OC — Occulting
FL — Single-Flashing

### Colors (Color refers to light characteristics of Aids to Navigation only)

B — Black
BU — Blue
G — Green

OR — Orange
R — Red
W — White

Y — Yellow

### Organizations

CCGD(#) — Commander, Coast Guard
   District (#)
CG — Coast Guard

COE — Corps of Engineers
NGA — National Geospatial-Intelligence
   Agency

NOS — National Ocean Service
NWS — National Weather Service

### Vessels

A/C — Aircraft
F/V — Fishing Vessel
LNG — Liquified Natural Gas Carrier

M/V — Motor Vessel*
P/C — Pleasure Craft
R/V — Research Vessel

S/V — Sailing Vessel

* M/V includes: Steam Ship, Container Vessel,
Cargo Vessel, etc.

### Compass Directions

N — North
S — South
E — East

W — West
NE — Northeast
NW — Northwest

SE — Southeast
SW — Southwest

### Various

ANCH — Anchorage
ANCH PROHIB — Anchorage Prohibited
APPROX — Approximate
ATLC — Atlantic
AUTH — Authorized
AVG — Average
BRG — Bearing
BKW — Breakwater
BNM — Broadcast Notice to Mariners
CHAN — Channel
CFR — Code of Federal Regulations
CONT — Continue
DEG — Degrees (temp, geo-position)
DIA — Diameter
ED — Edition
EFF — Effect/Effective
ENTR — Entrance
EXPLOS ANCH — Explosive Anchorage
FM(S) — Fathoms
FT — Foot/Feet
HBR — Harbor
HT — Height
HZ — Hertz
HOR CL — Horizontal Clearance
HR — Hour
COLREGS — International Regulations for
   Preventing Collisions at Sea

KHZ — Kilohertz
KM — Kilometer
KT(S) — Knot(s)
LAT — Latitude
LNM — Local Notice to Mariners
LONG — Longitude
MAINTD — Maintained
MAX — Maximum
MHZ — Megahertz
MB — Millibar
MM — Millimeter
MIN — Minute (time, geo position)
MOD — Moderate
MT — Mountain, Mount
NM — Nautical Mile(s)
NTM — Notice to Mariners
OBSTR — Obstruction
OCCASION — Occasion/Occasionally
OPAREA — Operating Area
PAC — Pacific
PT(S) — Point(s)
POS — Position
PA — Position Approximate
PRES — Pressure
PRIV — Private/Privately
PROHIB — Prohibited
PUB — Publication

RGE — Range
REP — Reported
RESTR — Restricted
RK — Rock
ST — Saint
SEC — Second (time, geo position)
SIG STA — Signal Station
STA — Station
SM — Statute Mile(s)
S SIG STA — Storm Signal Station
TEMP — Temporary
TSTORM — Thunderstorm
THRU — Through
T — True
UNCOV — Uncovers
UTC — Universal Coordinate Time
UMIB — Urgent Marine Information
   Broadcast
VEL — Velocity
VERT CL — Vertical Clearance
VIS — Visibility
YD — Yard(s)
WARN — Warning
WX — Weather
WK — Wreck

(242)     participates as Area Coordinator for both NAVAREA IV (Western North Atlantic) and NAVAREA XII (Eastern North Pacific).

(242)     The United States also maintains worldwide coverage using the HYDROLANT/HYDROPAC Navigational Warning System outside of NAVAREAs IV and XII.

(243)
## NAVTEX

(244)     NAVTEX is a standard international method of broadcasting notices to mariners and marine weather forecasts using small, low cost receivers designed to be installed in the pilothouse of a vessel. NAVTEX receivers screen incoming messages, inhibiting those which had been previously received or are of a category not of interest to the user, and print the rest on adding machine-size paper. NAVTEX not only provides marine information previously available only to those knowledgeable in Morse code but also allows any mariner who cannot man a radio full time to receive safety information at any hour. All NAVTEX transmissions are made on 518 kHz. Mariners who do not have NAVTEX receivers but have Simplex Teletype Over Radio (SITOR) radio equipment can also receive these broadcasts by operating it in the Forward Error Correction (FEC) mode and tuning to 518 kHz.

(245)     Information broadcast over NAVTEX includes offshore weather forecasts, offshore marine advisory warnings, search and rescue information and navigational information that applies to waters from the line of demarcation (separating Inland Rules from COLREG Rule waters) to 200 miles offshore. Navigational information that affects the safety of navigation of deep draft (15 feet or more) vessels within the U.S. Inland Rules waters will also be included. Gulf Stream location is also included from Miami and Portsmouth. Coastal and high seas weather forecasts are not being broadcast over NAVTEX. The Safety of Life at Sea Convention, as amended in 1988, requires vessels regulated by that convention to carry NAVTEX receivers.

(246)     See Appendix A, U.S. NAVTEX Transmitting Stations, for a list of NAVTEX broadcast stations and message content covered by this Coast Pilot.

(248)
## Broadcast Notice to Mariners

(249)     The U.S. Coast Guard broadcasts marine safety information on VHF-FM channel 22A (157.1 MHz). These safety broadcasts contain information such as notices to mariners, storm warnings, distress warnings and other pertinent information that is vital for safe navigation. Following a preliminary call on VHF-FM channel 16 (156.8 MHz), mariners are instructed to shift to VHF-FM channel 22A simplex (157.1 MHz). Operators of vessels who plan to transit U.S. waters and who do not have VHF radios tunable to U.S. channel 22A are urged to obtain the necessary equipment.

(250)
## NOAA Weather Radio Broadcasts

(251)     NOAA Weather Radio provides continuous broadcasts of the latest weather information directly from (NWS) offices. In addition to general weather information, marine weather is provided by stations along the sea coasts and the Great Lakes. During severe weather, NWS forecasters can interrupt the regular broadcasts and substitute special warning messages. The stations operate 24 hours daily, and messages are repeated every 4 to 6 minutes and are routinely revised every 1 to 3 hours or more frequently if necessary. The broadcasts are made on seven VHF-FM frequencies, 162.40 to 162.55 MHz. The 162.475 MHz frequency is only used in special cases where needed to avoid channel interference. They can usually be heard as far as 40 miles from the antenna site, sometimes more. The effective range depends on many factors, including the height of the broadcast antenna, terrain, quality of the receiver and the type of receiving antenna. As a general rule, listeners close to or perhaps beyond the 40 mile range should have a good quality receiver system to get reliable reception. (See Appendix A for a list of these stations in the area covered by this Coast Pilot.)

(252)
## Commercial Maritime Coast Stations and Weather Nets

(253)     Commercial maritime coast stations, which provide communications services, broadcast weather information to ships at sea as a public service, or make forecast information available on demand, either free or for a nominal fee. These transmissions are most commonly performed using HF SITOR and Pactor/E-Mail; however, several of these stations also offer services via Inmarsat satellite and other means.

(254)     There are also a number of maritime weather *nets* operating on commercial marine VHF, MF and HF, where weather information is exchanged. These *nets* are extremely popular in areas of the world that have a large yachting population and where weather is dynamic, such as in the Caribbean, and typically incorporate volunteers ashore.

(255)     Information on commercial maritime coast stations, including schedules and frequencies, is available in the **Radio Navigational Aids, Pub. 117.**

(256)
## Standard Abbreviations for Broadcasts

(257)     A listing of Standard Abbreviations for Textual Maritime Safety Broadcasts can be found in this chapter. These abbreviations were jointly approved by the U.S. Coast Guard, National Weather Service, National Geospatial-Intelligence Agency and the Radio Technical Commission for Maritime Services. In addition to appearing in radio broadcasts of the U.S. Coast Guard and National Weather Service, they appear in Notices to Mariners of the U.S. Coast Guard and National Geospatial-Intelligence Agency and in NAVTEX.

(259)

### Voluntary Observing Ship Program (VOS)

(260)        The Voluntary Observing Ship program is organized for the purpose of obtaining weather and oceanographic observations from moving ships. An international program under World Meteorological Organization auspices, the VOS has over 5000 vessels participating from 23 countries. Any vessel willing to take and transmit observations in marine areas can join the program. Weather observations are essential to meteorologists preparing weather forecasts for coastal, offshore and high seas areas. For more information on the VOS, including a comprehensive observing handbook, visit *vos.noaa.gov.*

(261)

### National Institute of Standards and Technology (NIST)

(262)        The National Institute of Standards and Technology maintains the standards for time and frequency for most users in the United States. NIST provides a variety of services designed to deliver time and frequency signals to the people who need them. The signals are broadcast via several mediums, including high and low frequency radio, the Internet and telephone lines. Broadcasts of time and frequency signals are made by stations operating in the part of the radio spectrum that is properly known as high frequency (HF) but is commonly called shortwave. Station WWV is located just north of Fort Collins, Colorado, and station WWVH is located on the island of Kaua'i, Hawaii. Both stations broadcast continuous time and frequency signals on 2.5, 5, 10 and 15 MHz; WWV also broadcasts on 20 MHz.

(263)        **NIST Time and Frequency Services, Special Publication 432** gives a detailed description of the signals and services offered by NIST, how they work and how you can use them. The publication is available for download at *nist.gov/pml/div688/generalpubs.cfm.*

(264)

## CAUTIONARY INFORMATION

(265)

### Hurricanes and Tropical Storms

(266)        Hurricanes, tropical storms and other major storms may cause considerable damage to marine structures, aids to navigation and moored vessels, resulting in submerged debris in unknown locations. Fixed aids to navigation may have been damaged or destroyed. Buoys may have been moved from charted positions, damaged, sunk, extinguished or otherwise made inoperative. Mariners should not rely upon the position or operation of an aid to navigation. Charted soundings, channel depths and shoreline may not reflect actual conditions following these storms. Wrecks and submerged obstructions may have been displaced from charted locations. Pipelines may have become uncovered or moved. Mariners are urged to exercise extreme caution and are requested to report aids to navigation discrepancies and hazards to navigation to the U.S. Coast Guard.

(267)

### Destructive Waves

(268)        Unusual sudden changes in water level can be caused by tsunamis or violent storms. These two types of destructive waves have become commonly known as **tidal waves,** a name which is technically incorrect as they are not the result of tide-producing forces.

(269)        **Tsunamis** (seismic sea waves) are ocean waves generated by any rapid large-scale disturbance of the sea water. Most tsunamis are generated by earthquakes, but they may also be caused by volcanic eruptions, landslides, undersea slumps or meteor impacts.

(270)        The waves radiate outward in all directions from the disturbance and can propagate across entire ocean basins. Tsunami waves are distinguished from ordinary ocean waves by their great length between peaks, often exceeding 100 miles in the deep ocean, and by the long interval of time between these peaks, ranging from five minutes to an hour. The speed at which tsunamis travel depends on the ocean depth. A tsunami can exceed 500 knots in the deep ocean but slows to 20 or 30 knots in the shallow water near land. In less than 24 hours, a tsunami can cross the entire Pacific Ocean.

(271)        In the deep ocean, a tsunami is barely noticeable and will only cause a small and slow rising and falling of the sea surface as it passes. Only as it approaches land does a tsunami become a hazard. As the tsunami approaches land and shallow water, the waves slow down and become compressed, causing them to grow in height. In the best of cases, the tsunami comes onshore like a quickly rising tide and causes a gentle flooding of low-lying coastal areas. In the worst of cases, a bore will form.

(272)        A bore is a wall of turbulent water that can exceed several yards in height and can rush onshore with great destructive power. Behind the bore is a deep and fast-moving flood that can pick up and sweep away almost anything in its path. Minutes later, the water will drain away as the trough of the tsunami wave arrives, sometimes exposing great patches of the sea floor, then the water will rush in again as before, causing additional damage. This destructive cycle may repeat many times before the hazard finally passes. Sometimes the first noticeable part of the wave is the trough, which causes a recession of the water from shore, and people who have gone out to investigate this unusual exposure of the beach have been engulfed by the oncoming crest. Such an unexplained withdrawal of the sea should be considered as nature's warning of an approaching wave.

(273)        Tsunamis do not have a season and do not occur regularly or frequently. Yet they pose a major threat to the coastal populations of the Pacific and other world oceans and seas. Nothing can be done to prevent them, but their adverse impact can be reduced with proper planning. The loss of life and property can be lessened if shipmasters and others acquaint themselves with the behavior of these waves so that intelligent action can be taken when they become imminent.

(274)        <Deleted Paragraph>

(274)     NOAA oversees the U.S. Tsunami Program with its mission to provide a 24-hour detection and warning system and increase public awareness about the threat of tsunamis. The NOAA National Weather Service operates two tsunami warning centers The West Coast/Alaska Tsunami Warning Center in Palmer, Alaska: *wcatwc.arh.noaa.gov*, and the Richard H. Hagemeyer Pacific Tsunami Warning Center in 'Ewa Beach, Hawaii: *ptwc.weather.gov*. These centers continuously monitor data from seismological and tidal stations, evaluate earthquakes that have the potential to generate tsunamis and disseminate tsunami information and warning bulletins to government authorities and the public.

(275)     A tsunami warning is issued when a potential tsunami with significant inundation is imminent or expected. Warnings alert the public that widespread, dangerous coastal flooding accompanied by powerful currents is possible and may continue for several hours after arrival of the initial wave. Warnings also alert emergency management officials to take action for the entire tsunami hazard zone. When a tsunami warning has been issued, use a NOAA Weather Radio or stay tuned to a Coast Guard emergency frequency station or a local radio or television station for updated emergency information.

(276)

### Storm Surge

(277)     <Deleted Paragraph>

(277)     A considerable rise or fall in the level of the sea along a particular coast may result from strong winds and sharp change in barometric pressure. In cases where the water level is raised, higher waves can form with greater dept,h and the combination can be destructive to low regions, particularly at high stages of tide. Extreme low levels can result in depths which are considerably less than those shown on nautical charts. This type of wave occurs especially in coastal regions bordering on shallow waters which are subject to tropical storms.

(278)     **Seiche** is a stationary vertical wave oscillation with a period varying from a few minutes to an hour or more but somewhat less than the tidal periods. It is usually attributed to external forces such as strong winds, changes in barometric pressure, swells or tsunamis disturbing the equilibrium of the water surface. Seiche is found both in enclosed bodies of water and superimposed upon the tides of the open ocean. When the external forces cause a short-period horizontal oscillation on the water, it is called **surge**.

(279)     <Deleted Paragraph>

(279)     The combined effect of seiche and surge sometimes makes it difficult to maintain a ship in its position alongside a pier even though the water may appear to be completely undisturbed, and heavy mooring lines have been parted repeatedly under such conditions. Pilots advise taut lines to reduce the effect of the surge.

(280)     <Deleted Paragraph>

(280)

### Immersion Hypothermia

(281)     Immersion hypothermia is the loss of heat when a body is immersed in water. With few exceptions, humans die if their core temperature of approximately 99.7° F drops below 78.6° F. Cardiac arrest is the most common direct cause of death. During prolonged immersion, the main threat to life is cold or cold and drowning combined.

(282)

| SURVIVAL TIME VERSUS WATER TEMPERATURE | | |
| --- | --- | --- |
| Water Temperature (°F) | Exhaustion or Unconsciousness | Expected Time of Survival |
| 32 | 15 minutes | 15 to 45 minutes |
| 32 to 41 | 15-30 minutes | 30 to 90 minutes |
| 41 to 50 | 30-60 minutes | 1 to 3 hours |
| 50 to 59 | 1-2 hours | 1 to 6 hours |
| 59 to 68 | 2-7 hours | 2 to 40 hours |
| 68 to 77 | 3-12 hours | 3 hours to indefinite |
| 77 and above | indefinite | indefinite |

(283)     The length of time that a human survives in water depends on the water temperature and to a lesser extent on the person's behavior and body type. The table shows approximate human survival time in the sea. Body type can cause deviations, as small people become hypothermic more rapidly than large people. The cooling rate can be slowed by the person's behavior and insulated gear. The Heat Escape Lessening Posture (HELP) was developed for those in the water alone and the huddle for small groups. Both require a PFD (personal flotation device), or life preserver. HELP involves holding the arms close to the body, keeping the thighs together, and raising the knees to protect the groin area. In the huddle, people face each other and keep their bodies as close together as possible. These positions improve survival time to approximately two times that of a swimmer and one and a half times that of a person in the passive position.

(284)     Near-drowning victims in cold water (less than 70° F) are revivable for much longer periods than usual. Keys to a successful revival are immediate cardiopulmonary resuscitation (CPR) and administration of pure oxygen. Total re-warming is not necessary at first. The whole revival process may take hours and require medical help.

(285)

### Wind Chill and Frostbite

(286)     When the body is warmer than its surroundings, it begins to lose heat. The rate of loss depends on barriers such as clothing and insulation, the speed of air movement and air temperature. Heat loss increases dramatically in moving air that is colder than skin temperature (91.4° F). Even a light wind increases heat loss, and a strong wind can lower the body temperature if the rate of loss is greater than the body's heat replacement rate.

(287)     When skin temperature drops below 50° F, there is a marked constriction of blood vessels, leading to vascular stagnation, oxygen want and cellular damage. The first

(287) indication that something is wrong is a painful tingling. Swelling of varying extent follows, provided freezing has not occurred. Excruciating pain may be felt if the skin temperature is lowered rapidly, but freezing of localized portions of the skin may be painless when the rate of change is slow. Possible effects of cold include cold allergy (welts), chilblains, which appear as reddened, warm, itching, swollen patches on the fingers and toes, and trench foot and immersion foot, which present essentially the same picture. Both result from exposure to cold and lack of circulation. Wetness can add to the problem as water and wind soften the tissues and accelerate heat loss.

(288) Frostbite usually begins when the skin temperature falls within the range of 14° to 4° F. Ice crystals form in the tissues and small blood vessels. The rate of heat loss determines the rate of freezing, which is accelerated by wind, wetness, extreme cold and poor blood circulation. Parts of the body susceptible to freezing are those with surfaces large in relation to their volume, such as toes, fingers, ears, nose, chin and cheeks.

(289) Injuries from the cold may, to a large extent, be prevented by maintaining natural warmth through the use of proper footgear and adequate, dry clothing, by avoiding cramped positions and constricting clothing and by active exercise of the hands, legs and feet.

(290)
## MARINE POLLUTION

(290)     <Deleted Paragraph>

(291)
### The Federal Water Pollution Control Act (Clean Water Act)

(291)     <Deleted Paragraph>
(292)     The Federal Water Pollution Control Act (FWPCA) or Clean Water Act (CWA) was passed to restore and maintain the chemical, physical and biological integrity of the waters within the United States..

(293)
### No-Discharge Zones

(293)     <Deleted Paragraph>
(294)     Section 312 of the FWPCA gives the Environmental Protection Agency (EPA) and States the authority to designate certain areas as No-Discharge Zones (NDZ) for vessel sewage. Freshwater lakes, freshwater reservoirs or other freshwater impounds whose entrances and exits prohibit traffic by regulated vessels (vessels with installed toilets) are, by regulation, NDZs. Rivers that do not support interstate navigation vessel traffic are also NDZs by regulation. Water bodies that can be designated as NDZs by States and EPA include the Great Lakes and their connecting waterways, freshwater lakes and impoundments accessible through locks and other flowing waters that support interstate navigation by vessels subject to regulation.

(295)     Inside NDZ waters, discharge of any sewage, whether treated or untreated, is completely prohibited.

(296)     Discharge of sewage in waters not designated as NDZs is regulated by the Marine Sanitation Device Standard (see **40 CFR 140** in chapter 2.)

(297)     Additional information concerning the regulations may be obtained from *water.epa.gov*.

(298)
### Oil Spill Reporting

(299)     Reporting requirements for any oil discharge, noxious liquid substance or harmful substance occurring in waters under U.S. jurisdiction are found in **33 CFR 153**, subpart B (not in this Coast Pilot.) Any person in charge of a vessel or an onshore/offshore facility must, as soon as they have knowledge of any discharge of oil or a hazardous substance, immediately notify the National Response Center (NRC) at 800-424-8802 or NRC@uscg.mil.

(300)
### Ocean Dumping

(301)     The Marine Protection Research and Sanctuaries Act of 1972, as amended (33 USC 1401 et seq.), regulates the dumping of all material, except fish waste, into ocean waters. Radiological, chemical and biological warfare agents and other high level radioactive wastes are expressly banned from ocean disposal. The USACE issues permits for the disposal of dredged spoils; the EPA is authorized to issue permits for all other dumping activities. Surveillance and enforcement to prevent unlawful transportation of material for dumping or unlawful dumping under the Act has been assigned to the U.S. Coast Guard. The Act provides civil penalties of up to $50,000 and criminal penalties of up to $50,000 and/or one year imprisonment.

(302)
## SELECT NAVIGATION RULES

(303)
### Improper use of searchlights

(304)     No person shall flash or cause to be flashed the rays of a searchlight or other blinding light onto the bridge or into the pilothouse of any vessel underway. The International Code Signal "PG2" may be made by a vessel inconvenienced by the glare of a searchlight in order to apprise the offending vessel of the fact.

(305)
### Use of Radar

(306)     <Deleted Paragraph>
(306)     Navigation Rules, International-Inland, Rule 7, states, in part, that every vessel shall use all available means appropriate to the prevailing circumstances and conditions to determine if risk of collision exists. If there is any doubt such risk shall be deemed to exist. Proper use shall be made of radar equipment if fitted and operational, including long-range scanning to obtain early warning of risk of collision and radar plotting or equivalent systematic observation of detected objects.

(306)     <306-307 Deleted>

(321)

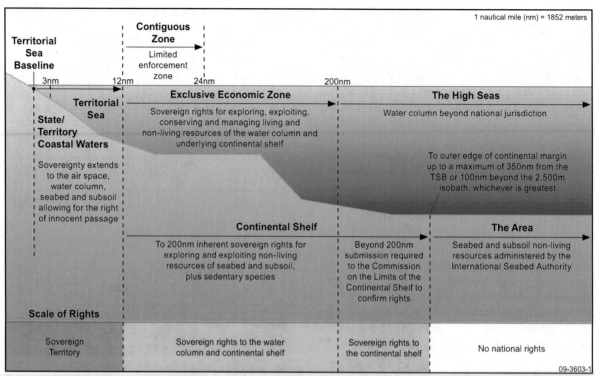

Figure 1: Offshore extent of the maritime zones recognized under international law

(307) This rule places an additional responsibility on vessels that are equipped and manned to use radar to do so while underway during periods of reduced visibility without in any way relieving commanding officers of the responsibility of carrying out normal precautionary measures.

(308) <Deleted Paragraph>

(308) Navigation Rules, International-Inland, Rules 6, 7, 8, and 19 apply to the use of radar.

(309)

### Danger signal

(310) Navigation Rules, International-Inland, Rule 34(d), states that when vessels in sight of one another are approaching each other and from any cause either vessel fails to understand the intentions or actions of the other or is in doubt whether sufficient action is being taken by the other to avoid collision, the vessel in doubt shall immediately indicate such doubt by giving at least five short and rapid blasts on the whistle. Such signal may be supplemented by a light signal of at least five short and rapid flashes.

(311)

### Narrow channels

(312) Navigation Rules, International-Inland, Rule 9(b) states that a vessel of less than 20 meters in length or a sailing vessel shall not impede the passage of a vessel that can safely navigate only within a narrow channel or fairway.

(313)

# REGULATED WATERS

(314)

### Traffic Separation Schemes (Traffic Lanes)

(315) To increase the safety of navigation, particularly in converging areas of high traffic density, routes incorporating traffic separation have been adopted by the IMO in certain areas of the world. In the interest of safe navigation, it is recommended that through traffic use these schemes, as far as circumstances permit, by day and by night and in all weather conditions. When approved or established, traffic separation scheme details are announced in Notice to Mariners and later depicted on appropriate charts and included in the U.S. Coast Pilot. See **33 CFR 167**, chapter 2, for regulations.

(316) The IMO is recognized as the only international body responsible for establishing and recommending measures on an international level concerning ships' routing. In deciding whether or not to adopt or amend a traffic separation scheme, IMO will consider whether the scheme complies with the design criteria for traffic separation schemes and with the established methods of routing. IMO also considers whether the aids to navigation proposed will enable mariners to determine their position with sufficient accuracy to navigate the scheme in accordance with Rule 10 of the International Regulations for Preventing Collisions at Sea (72 COLREGS).

(317) The IMO approved routing measures which affect shipping in or near U.S. waters are:

(318)

| IMO-Approved Traffic Separation Routes |
| --- |
| Portland, Maine (approaches to) |
| Boston, Massachusetts (approaches to) |
| Narragansett Bay, Rhode Island (approaches to) |
| Buzzards Bay, Massachusetts (approaches to) |
| New York, New York |
| Delaware Bay |
| Chesapeake Bay (approaches to) |
| Cape Fear River (approaches to) |
| Galveston Bay (approaches to) |
| Off San Francisco, California |
| Los Angeles/Long Beach, California (approaches to) |
| Strait of Juan de Fuca (approaches to and in) |
| Puget Sound (approaches to and in) |
| Haro Strait, Boundary Pass and the Strait of Georgia |
| Prince William Sound, Alaska |

(319)

## Maritime Zones

(320)     The maritime zones recognized under international law include internal waters, territorial sea, contiguous zone, exclusive economic zone, continental shelf, the high seas and the Area (see Figure 1). The following zones are depicted on NOAA's nautical charts: internal waters, territorial sea, contiguous zone and exclusive economic zone. The limits of these zones are subject to modification as depicted on future charts; limits shown on the most recent chart edition take precedence.

(322)

## Internal Waters

(323)     Internal waters are the waters (harbors, bays and rivers) on the landward side of the baseline from which the breadth of the territorial sea is measured. The United States has full sovereignty over its internal waters and ports as if they were part of its land territory. NOAA's nautical charts depict the baseline from which the limits of the U.S. territorial sea, contiguous zone and exclusive economic zone are measured as well as the Three Nautical Mile Line and Natural Resources Boundary, as described below.

(324)

## Territorial Sea

(325)     The territorial sea of the United States extends beyond the land territory and internal waters and also includes the Commonwealth of Puerto Rico, Guam, American Samoa, the U.S. Virgin Islands, the Commonwealth of the Northern Mariana Islands and any other territory or possession over which the United States exercises sovereignty. (Presidential Proclamation No. 5928. December 27, 1988.) The United States exercises sovereignty over the territorial sea that extends to the airspace over the area and to the bed and subsoil. Under customary international law as reflected in the 1982 United Nations Convention on the Law of the Sea (UNCLOS), the territorial sea of the United States extends to 12 nautical miles (nm) from the baseline from which the breadth of the territorial sea is measured; determined in accordance with international law except as otherwise established in a maritime boundary treaty of the United States. While the United States may adopt certain laws and regulations, vessels of all countries navigating through the territorial sea enjoy the right of innocent passage; vessels and aircraft of all countries enjoy the right of transit passage through international straits.

(326)

## Contiguous Zone

(327)     The contiguous zone of the United States is a zone measured 24 nm from the territorial sea baseline and is contiguous to the territorial sea of the United States, including the Commonwealth of Puerto Rico, Guam, American Samoa, the U.S. Virgin Islands, the Commonwealth of the Northern Mariana Islands and any other territory or possession over which the United States exercises sovereignty. (Presidential Proclamation No. 7219. August 2, 1999.) Under customary law as reflected in UNCLOS, the U.S. may exercise the control necessary to prevent infringement of its customs, fiscal, immigration or sanitary laws and regulations within its territory or territorial sea and to punish infringement of these laws and regulations committed within its territory or territorial sea. The United States may also prescribe and enforce laws against foreign flagged vessels and nationals to protect the underwater cultural heritage to the outer boundary of the contiguous zone (24 nm).

(328)

## Exclusive Economic Zone

(329)     The exclusive economic zone of the United States extends no more than 200 nm from the territorial sea baseline and is adjacent to the 12 nm territorial sea of the United States, including the Commonwealth of Puerto Rico, Guam, American Samoa, the U.S. Virgin Islands, the Commonwealth of the Northern Mariana Islands and any other territory or possession over which the United States exercises sovereignty. (Presidential Proclamation No. 5030 of March 10, 1983 and Federal Register, volume 60 - number 163, August 23, 1995, "Exclusive Economic Zone and Maritime Boundaries: Notice of Limits") As such, the exclusive economic zone overlaps the 12 nm-24 nm contiguous zone.

(330)     Within the EEZ, the U.S. has (a) sovereign rights for the purpose of exploring, exploiting, conserving and managing natural resources, whether living and nonliving, of the seabed and subsoil and the superjacent waters and with regard to other activities for the economic exploitation and exploration of the zone, such as the production of energy from the water, currents and winds; (b) jurisdiction as provided for in international and domestic laws with regard to the establishment and use of artificial islands, installations, and structures, marine scientific research, and the protection and preservation of

the marine environment; and (c) other rights and duties provided for under international and domestic laws.

(331)     Note: In certain U.S. fisheries laws, the term "exclusive economic zone" (EEZ) is used. While its outer limit is the same as the EEZ on NOAA charts, the inner limit generally extends landward to the seaward boundary of the coastal states of the U.S.

(332)
### Three Nautical Mile Line

(333)     The Three Nautical Mile Line, as measured from the territorial sea baseline and previously identified as the outer limit of the U.S. territorial sea, is retained on charts because it continues to be used in certain Federal laws.

(334)     Note: Since the "coast line," a term used in the Submerged Lands Act, and the baseline are determined using the same criteria under international law, the Three Nautical Mile Line is generally the same as the seaward boundary of states under the Submerged Lands Act. There are exceptions; therefore, the Three Nautical Mile Line does not necessarily depict the seaward limit of states under the Submerged Lands Act.

(335)
### Natural Resources Boundary

(336)     The 9 nm Natural Resources Boundary is the seaward limit of the submerged lands of Puerto Rico, Texas and the Gulf coast of Florida. It coincides with the inner limit of the U.S. outer continental shelf under the Outer Continental Shelf Lands Act.

(337)
### Notification of Arrival and Vessel Response Plans

(338)     A **Notification of Arrival (NOA)** must be submitted by all U.S. and foreign vessels bound for or departing from ports or places in the United States. (See **33 CFR 160 – Subpart C**, chapter 2). Additionally, tank vessels and non-tank vessels are required to submit an oil spill response plan. (See **33 CFR 155**– Subparts D and J, not contained in this Coast Pilot.)

(339)
### Marine Protected Area (MPA)

(340)     Marine Protected Areas (MPAs) are particular places in ocean, coastal and estuarine ecosystems where vital natural and cultural resources are given greater protection than in surrounding waters. MPAs have been established in the U.S. for more than a century. Currently, there are over 1,700 MPAs in U.S. marine waters and the Great Lakes, with levels of protection ranging from a few "no-take" areas that prohibit all extractive uses to the more common multiple use areas that allow vessel access, anchoring, fishing and non-consumptive activities. MPAs are managed by dozens of Federal, state, tribal and local authorities. For detailed information on MPA locations, types, interactive map, purposes and legal restrictions, visit *marineprotectedareas.noaa.gov.*

(341)
### Archaeological Resource Preservation

(342)     Under Federal and state laws it is illegal to destroy, deface, collect, transport, sell or trade archaeological, cultural, submerged and historic resources without authorization. Applicable laws include, but are not limited to, the Historic Sites Act, the Archaeological Resource Protection Act, the National Historic Preservation Act the Abandoned Shipwreck Act, and the Sunken Military Craft Act. These laws protect archaeological resources on lands administered by the National Park Service, U.S. Fish and Wildlife Service, Bureau of Land Management, and National Marine Sanctuaries as well as state, private and Native lands.

(343)
# DEPARTMENT OF AGRICULTURE

(344)
### Animal and Plant Health Inspection Service

(345)     The Animal and Plant Health Inspection Service is responsible for protecting the Nation's animal population, food and fiber crops and forests from invasion by foreign pests. They administer agricultural quarantine and restrictive orders issued under authority provided in various acts of Congress. The regulations prohibit or restrict the importation or interstate movement of live animals, meats, animal products, plants, plant products, soil, injurious insects, and associated items that may introduce or spread plant pests and animal diseases which may be new to or not widely distributed within the United States or its territories. Inspectors examine imports at ports of entry as well as the vessel, its stores and crew or passenger baggage.

(346)     The Service also provides an inspection and certification service for exporters to assist them in meeting the quarantine requirements of foreign countries. (See **Appendix A** for a list of ports where agricultural inspectors are located and inspections conducted.)

(347)
# DEPARTMENT OF COMMERCE

(348)
### National Oceanic and Atmospheric Administration (NOAA)

(349)     The National Oceanic and Atmospheric Administration (NOAA) conducts research and gathers data about the global oceans, atmosphere, space and sun, and applies this knowledge to improve our understanding and stewardship of the environment.

(350)     NOAA provides services to the nation and the public through five major organizations: the National Ocean Service; the National Weather Service; the National Marine Fisheries Service; the National Environmental Satellite, Data and Information Service (NESDIS); and NOAA Research; and numerous special program units. In addition, NOAA research and operational activities are

supported by the Nation's seventh uniformed service, the NOAA Corps, a commissioned officer corps of men and women who operate NOAA ships and aircraft and serve in scientific and administrative positions.

(351)
### National Ocean Service (NOS)

(352)      The National Ocean Service's primary concern is the health and safety of our Nation's coastal and oceanic environment. Within NOS, the **Office of Coast Survey** is responsible for producing and maintaining the suite of over 1000 nautical charts and the Coast Pilots that cover the coastal waters of the U.S. and its territories. Nautical charts are published primarily for the use of the mariner but serve the public interest in many other ways. Cartographers in Coast Survey receive and compile information from a variety of government and non-governmental sources for portrayal on nautical charts and the Coast Pilots. In addition, Coast Survey hydrographers, as well as private contractors, conduct new surveys that are used to update these products. The principal facilities of Coast Survey are located at NOAA headquarters in Silver Spring, MD; Norfolk, VA (Marine Operations Center Atlantic); and Seattle, WA (Western Regional Center).

(353)      The **Center for Operational Oceanographic Products and Services (CO-OPS)** collects and distributes observations and predictions of water levels and currents to ensure safe, efficient and environmentally sound maritime commerce. Users can find a variety of information, including observed water level and currents data, tide and current predictions, sea level trends and coastal inundation information. TIdes and Currents information is available at *tidesandcurrents.noaa.gov.*

(354)      **PORTS® (Physical Oceanographic Real-Time System)** is a decision support tool that improves the safety and efficiency of maritime commerce and coastal resource management. Data from PORTS® supports navigation safety, improves the efficiency of U.S. ports and harbors, and ensures the protection of coastal marine resources. PORTS® collects and disseminates observations of water levels, currents, salinity, bridge air gap and meteorological parameters (e.g., winds, atmospheric pressure, air and water temperatures) that mariners need to navigate safely and allows seaport and terminal facilities to make good decisions. PORTS® data and information is provided via the internet at *tidesandcurrents.noaa.gov/ports_info.html* and, in some areas, via telephone voice response.

(354.001)
### NOAA Tide Predictions and Tidal Current Predictions

(354.002)      NOAA discontinued the annual printed Tide Tables and Tidal Current Tables in 2020, and has transitioned to providing this information digitally online. The online prediction service equals or exceeds the accuracy of the historically printed publications. Tide and tidal current predictions needed for navigation can be generated in real-time for any time period required by the mariner, for as short as one day, or as long as an entire year. All predictions for U.S. waters are available at *tidesandcurrents.noaa.gov.*

(354.003)      U.S. Coast Guard regulations do not consider access to NOAA's online prediction service "while navigating" as meeting carriage requirements. In order to use predictions from these services, the predictions must be generated in advance and either be stored on the user's device as an electronic file (PDF, screen image, data table, etc.), or as a printed page.

(354.004)      **NOAA Tide Predictions** - *tidesandcurrents.noaa.gov/tide_predictions.html* - allows the generation of predicted tides for more than 3000 locations along the U.S. coastline. Tide predictions may be generated as times and heights of high and low tides for all locations, or as interval predictions (hourly, 15-minute, 6-minute, etc.) for many locations. Tide predictions may be generated for past, present, or future dates; with lengths of 1 day to 1 month, or the full calendar year. The Users Guide - *tidesandcurrents.noaa.gov/PageHelp.html* - describes the displays, formats, additional capabilities, and uses of this online service.

(354.005)      **Caution** –When using Tide Predictions, slack water should not be confused with high or low water. For ocean stations there is often little difference between the time of high or low water and the start of flood/ebb currents; but for places in narrow channels, landlocked harbors or on tidal rivers, the time of slack current may differ by several hours from the time of high or low water. The relationship of the times of high or low water to the flood and ebb of the current depends upon a number of factors unique to each location; no simple general rule can be given which applies to every location. For navigation or other activities which depend on slack water, tidal current predictions should be used to provide times of slack water.

(354.006)      **NOAA Tidal Current Predictions** –*tidesandcurrents.noaa.gov/noaacurrents/Regions* - allows the generation of predicted currents for more than 2500 locations along the U.S. coastline. Tidal current predictions may be generated as times and speeds of flood/ebb currents and times of slack water for all locations; or as interval predictions of speed (hourly, 30-minute, 6-minute) for many locations. Tidal current predictions may be generated for past, present or future dates; with length of 1 day to 2 weeks, or the full calendar year. The Users Guide - *tidesandcurrents.noaa.gov/noaacurrents/Help* - describes the displays, formats, additional capabilities, and uses of this online service.

(363)      <Deleted Paragraph>

<sub>(367)</sub>
### National Weather Service (NWS)

<sub>(368)</sub>
### National Data Buoy Center Meteorological Buoys

<sub>(369)</sub>
The National Data Buoy Center (NDBC) deploys moored meteorological buoys that provide weather data directly to the mariner as well as to marine forecasters.

<sub>(370)</sub>
These buoys have a watch circle radius (WCR) of 2,000 to 4,000 yards from assigned position (AP). In addition, any mooring in waters deeper than 1,000 feet will have a floating "loop" or catenary that may be as little as 500 feet below the surface. This catenary could be anywhere within the buoy's WCR. Any underwater activity within this radius may contact the mooring, causing a failure.

<sub>(371)</sub>
To avoid cutting or damaging a mooring, mariners are urged to exercise extreme caution when navigating in the vicinity of meteorological buoys and to remain well clear of the watch circle. If a mooring is accidentally contacted or cut, please notify NDBC at 228-688-2835 or 228-688-2436.

<sub>(372)</sub>
For further information relating to these buoys visit *ndbc.noaa.gov*.

<sub>(373)</sub>
### Marine Weather Forecasts

<sub>(374)</sub>
The NWS provides marine weather forecasts and warnings for the U.S. coastal waters, the Great Lakes, offshore waters and high seas areas. Scheduled marine forecasts are issued four times daily from **National Weather Service Offices** with local areas of responsibility around the United States, Guam, American Samoa and Puerto Rico. (See Appendix A for NWS Offices located in the area covered by this Coast Pilot.)

<sub>(375)</sub>
Typically, the forecasts contain information on wind speed and direction, wave heights, visibility, weather and a general synopsis of weather patterns affecting the region. The forecasts are supplemented with special marine warnings and statements, radar summaries, marine observations, small-craft advisories, gale warnings, storm warnings and various categories of tropical cyclone warnings, e.g., tropical depression, tropical storm and hurricane warnings. Specialized products such as coastal flood, seiche, and tsunami warnings, heavy surf advisories, low water statements, ice forecasts and outlooks and lake shore warnings and statements are issued as necessary. (For further information, go to *nws.noaa.gov/om/marine/home.htm*.)

<sub>(376)</sub>
The principal means of disseminating marine weather services and products in coastal areas is **NOAA Weather Radio**. This network of more than 900 transmitters, covering all 50 states, adjacent coastal waters, Puerto Rico, the U.S. Virgin Islands and the U.S. Pacific Territories, is operated by the NWS and provides continuous broadcasts of weather information for the general public. These broadcasts repeat recorded messages every 4 to 6 minutes. Messages are updated periodically, usually every 2-3 hours and amended as required to include the latest information. When severe weather threatens, routine transmissions are interrupted and the broadcast is devoted to emergency warnings. (See Appendix A for NOAA Weather Radio Stations covered by this Coast Pilot.)

<sub>(377)</sub>
In coastal areas, the programming is tailored to the needs of the marine community. Each coastal marine forecast covers a specific area. For example, "Cape Henlopen to Virginia Beach, out 20 miles." The broadcast range is about 40 miles from the transmitting antenna site, depending on terrain and quality of the receiver used. When transmitting antennas are on high ground, the range is somewhat greater, reaching 60 miles or more. Some receivers are equipped with a warning alert device that can be turned on by means of a tone signal controlled by the NWS office concerned. This signal is transmitted for 13 seconds preceding an announcement of a severe weather warning.

<sub>(378)</sub>
Marine weather warnings are displayed to small-craft operators and others within sight of the shore by the flags, pennants and lights of the **Coastal Warning Display** program. These displays are meant to warn the public of approaching storm conditions and visually communicate that citizens should take personal responsibility for individual safety in the face of an approaching storm. Anyone observing the signals displayed by the program is urged to tune to the NWS radio broadcasts for the latest information. (See **National Weather Service Coastal Warning Displays** illustration for additional information.)

<sub>(380)</sub>
NWS marine weather products are also disseminated to marine users through the broadcast facilities of the Coast Guard, Navy and commercial marine radio stations. Details on these broadcasts including times, frequencies and broadcast content are listed on the NWS internet site, **Marine Product Dissemination Information**, *nws.noaa.gov/om/marine/home.htm*.

<sub>(381)</sub>
Ships of all nations share equally in the effort to report weather observations. These reports enable meteorologists to create a detailed picture of wind, wave and weather patterns over the open waters that no other data source can provide and upon which marine forecasts are based. The effectiveness and reliability of these forecasts and warnings plus other services to the marine community are strongly linked to the observations received from mariners. There is an especially urgent need for ship observations in the coastal waters, and the NWS asks that these be made and transmitted whenever possible. Many storms originate and intensify in coastal areas. There may be a great difference in both wind direction and speed between the open sea, the offshore waters and on the coast itself.

<sub>(382)</sub>
Information on how ships, commercial fishermen, offshore industries and others in the coastal zone may participate in the marine observation program is available from **National Weather Service Port Meteorological Officers (PMOs)**. PMOs are located in major U.S. port cities where they visit ships in port to assist masters

(379)

# NATIONAL WEATHER SERVICE COASTAL WARNING DISPLAYS

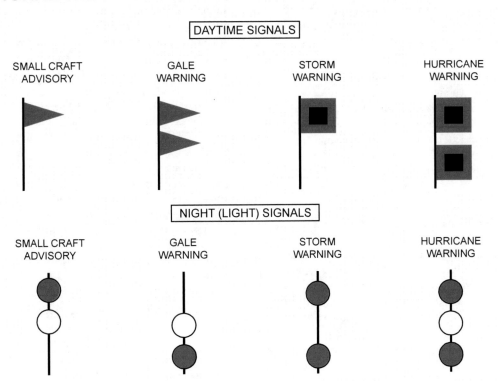

**SMALL CRAFT ADVISORY**: An advisory issued by coastal and Great Lakes Weather Forecast Offices (WFO) for areas included in the Coastal Waters Forecast or Nearshore Marine Forecast (NSH) products. Thresholds governing the issuance of small craft advisories are specific to geographic areas. A Small Craft Advisory may also be issued when sea or lake ice exists that could be hazardous to small boats. There is no precise definition of a small craft. Any vessel that may be adversely affected by Small Craft Advisory criteria should be considered a small craft. Other considerations include the experience of the vessel operator, and the type, overall size, and sea worthiness of the vessel. There is no legal definition of "small craft". The Small Craft Advisory is an advisory in Coastal Waters and Nearshore forecasts for sustained winds, frequent gusts, or sea/wave conditions, exceeding defined thresholds specific to geographic areas. A Small Craft Advisory may also be issued when sea or lake ice exists that could be hazardous to small boats.

Eastern (ME to SC, Lake Erie, Lake Ontario) – Sustained winds or frequent gusts ranging between 25 and 33 knots (except 20 to 25 knots, lower threshold area dependent, to 33 knots for harbors, bays, etc.) and/or seas or waves 5 to 7 feet and greater, area dependent.

Central (MN to OH) – Sustained winds or frequent gusts (on the Great Lakes) between 22 and 33 knots inclusive, and/or seas or waves greater than 4 feet.

Southern (GA to TX and Caribbean) – Sustained winds of 20 to 33 knots, and/or forecast seas 7 feet or greater that are expected for more than 2 hours.

Western (WA..CA) - Sustained winds of 21 to 33 knots, potentially in combination with wave heights exceeding 10 feet (or wave steepness values exceeding local thresholds).

Alaska (AK) – Sustained winds or frequent gusts of 23 to 33 knots. A small craft advisory for rough seas may be issued for sea/wave conditions deemed locally significant, based on user needs, and should be no lower than 8 feet.

Hawaii (HI), Samoa – Sustained winds 25 knots or greater and seas 10 feet or greater.

Guam and the Northern Mariana Islands – Sustained winds 22 to 33 knots and/or combined seas of 10 feet or more. "Frequent gusts"are typically long duration conditions (greater than 2 hours).

For a list of NWS Weather Offices by Region, refer to the following web-site: http://www.nws.noaa.gov/organization.php

**GALE WARNING**: To indicate winds within the range 34 to 47 knots are forecast for the area.

**STORM WARNING**: To indicate winds 48 knots and above, no matter how high the speed, are forecast for the area. However, if the winds are associated with a tropical cyclone (hurricane), the STORM WARNING indicates that winds within the range 48-63 knots are forecast.

**HURRICANE WARNING**: Issued only in connection with a tropical cyclone (hurricane) to indicate that winds 64 knots and above are forecast for the area.

NOTE: A "HURRICANE WATCH" is an announcement issued by the National Weather Service via press and television broadcasts whenever a tropical storm or hurricane becomes a threat to a coastal area. The "Hurricane Watch" announcement is not a warning, rather it indicates that the hurricane is near enough that everyone in the area covered by the "Watch" should listen to their radios for subsequent advisories and be ready to take precautionary action in case hurricane warnings are issued.

NOTE: A SPECIAL MARINE WARNING is issued whenever a severe local storm or strong wind of brief duration is imminent and is not covered by existing warnings or advisories. No visual displays will be used in connection with the Special Marine Warning Bulletin; boaters will be able to receive thesespecial warnings by keeping tuned to a NOAA Weather Radio station or to Coast Guard and commercial radio stations that transmit marine weather information.

and mates with the weather observation program, provide instruction on the interpretation of weather charts, calibrate barometers and other meteorological instruments and discuss marine weather communications and marine weather requirements affecting the ships' operations. (For further information on the Voluntary Observing Ship Program and PMOs, go to *vos.noaa.gov*.)

### Space Weather Prediction Center (SWPC)

(383)

(383)       <Deleted Paragraph>

(384)       The Space Weather Prediction Center provides real-time monitoring and forecasting of solar and geophysical events that impact satellites, power grids, communications, navigation and many other technological systems. (See Space Weather Prediction Center in Appendix A.)

(385)

### National Environmental Satellite, Data, and Information Service (NESDIS)

(386)       Among its functions, NESDIS archives, processes and disseminates the non-real-time meteorological and oceanographic data collected by government agencies and private institutions. Marine weather observations are collected from ships at sea on a voluntary basis. About one million observations are received annually at NESDIS's National Climatic Center. They come from vessels representing every maritime nation. These observations, along with land data, are returned to the mariners in the form of climatological summaries and atlases for coastal and ocean areas. They are available in such NOAA publications as the **U.S. Coast Pilot, Mariners Weather Log** and **Local Climatological Data, Annual Summary**. They also appear in the National Geospatial-Intelligence Agency's **Pilot Chart Atlases** and **Sailing Directions Planning Guides**.

(387)

## DEPARTMENT OF DEFENSE

(388)

### National Geospatial-Intelligence Agency (NGA)

(389)       The National Geospatial-Intelligence Agency provides hydrographic, navigational, topographic, and geodetic data, charts, maps and related products and services to the Armed Forces, other Federal Agencies, the Merchant Marine and mariners in general. Publications include Sailing Directions, List of Lights, Distances Between Ports, Radio Navigational Aids, International Code of Signals, American Practical Navigator (Bowditch) and Notice to Mariners. (See NGA Procurement Information in Appendix A.)

(390)

### Army Corps of Engineers

(391)       The U.S. Army Corps of Engineers has charge of the improvement of the rivers and harbors of the United States and of miscellaneous other civil works, which include the administration of certain Federal laws enacted for the protection and preservation of navigable waters of the United States; the establishment of regulations for the use, administration, and navigation of navigable waters; the establishment of harbor lines; the removal of sunken vessels obstructing or endangering navigation; and the granting of permits for structures or operations in navigable waters and for discharges and deposits of dredged and fill materials in these waters.

(392)       **Restricted areas** in most places are defined and regulations governing them are established by the USACE. The regulations are enforced by the authority designated in the regulations, and the areas are shown on the large-scale charts of the National Ocean Service. Copies of the regulations may be obtained at the District offices of the USACE. The regulations also are included in the appropriate Coast Pilot.

(393)       Information concerning the various ports, improvements, channel depths, navigable waters and the condition of the Intracoastal Waterways in the areas under their jurisdiction may be obtained direct from the District Engineer Offices. (See Appendix A for addresses.)

(394)       The USACE has general supervision of location, construction and manner of maintenance of all **fishtraps,** weirs, pounds or other fishing structures in the navigable waters of the United States. Where state and/or local controls are sufficient to regulate these structures, including that they do not interfere with navigation, the USACE leaves such regulation to the state or local authority. (See **33 CFR 330** (not carried in this Pilot) for applicable Federal regulations.) Construction permits issued by the Engineers specify the lights and signals required for the safety of navigation.

(395)       **Fish havens**, artificial reefs constructed to attract fish, can be established in U.S. coastal waters only as authorized by a USACE permit; the permit specifies the location, extent and depth over these mounds of rubble.

(396)

### Naval Observatory

(397)       The United States Naval Observatory (USNO) provides a wide range of astronomical data and products and serves as the official source of time for the U.S. Department of Defense and a standard of time for the entire United States. The USNO provides earth orientation products such as the latest 24-hour and 48-hour sets of GPS satellite orbits, the latest determinations and predictions for polar motion and information for GPS users. The USNO also maintains a reference for precise time (USNO Master Clock) and monitors the GPS constellation. For extensive information on the USNO products available, visit: *https://www.public.navy.mil/fltfor/cnmoc/Pages/usno_test_page.aspx* or contact by telephone at 202-762-1467.

(398)
# DEPARTMENT OF HEALTH AND HUMAN SERVICES

(399)
### Food and Drug Administration (FDA)

(400) Under the provisions of the Control of Communicable Diseases Regulations (**21 CFR 1240**) and Interstate Conveyance Sanitation Regulations (**21 CFR 1250**), vessel companies operating in interstate traffic must obtain potable water for drinking and culinary purposes only at watering points found acceptable to the FDA. Water supplies used in watering point operations must also be inspected to determine compliance with applicable Interstate Quarantine Regulations (**42 CFR 72**). These regulations are based on authority contained in the Public Health Service Act (PL 78–410). Penalties for violation of any regulation prescribed under authority of the Act are provided for under Section 368 (42 USC 271) of the Act.

(401)
### Public Health Service

(402) The Public Health Service administers foreign quarantine procedures at U.S. ports of entry.

(403) All vessels arriving in the United States are subject to public health inspection. Vessels subject to routine boarding for quarantine inspection are only those which have had on board during the 15 days preceding the date of expected arrival or during the period since departure (whichever period of time is shorter) the occurrence of any death or ill person among passengers or crew (including those who have disembarked or have been removed). The master of a vessel must report such occurrences immediately by radio to the quarantine station at or nearest the port at which the vessel will arrive.

(404) In addition, the master of a vessel carrying 13 or more passengers must report by radio 24 hours before arrival the number of cases (including zero) of diarrhea in passengers and crew recorded in the ship's medical log during the current cruise. All cases that occur after the 24 hour report must also be reported not less than 4 hours before arrival.

(405) *Ill person* means a person who:

(406) 1. Has a temperature of 100°F (or 38°C) or greater, accompanied by a rash, glandular swelling or jaundice, or which has persisted for more than 48 hours; or

(407) 2. Has diarrhea, defined as the occurrence in a 24 hour period of three or more loose stools or of a greater than normal (for the person) amount of loose stools.

(408) Vessels arriving at ports under control of the United States are subject to sanitary inspection to determine whether measures should be applied to prevent the introduction, transmission or spread of communicable disease.

(409) Specific public health laws, regulations, policies and procedures may be obtained by contacting U.S. Quarantine Stations, U.S. Consulates or the Chief Program Operations, Division of Quarantine, Centers for Disease Control, Atlanta, GA 30333. (See Appendix A for addresses of U.S. Public Health Service Quarantine Stations.)

(410)
# DEPARTMENT OF HOMELAND SECURITY

(411)
### Citizenship and Immigration Services

(412) The **U.S. Citizenship and Immigration Service** (USCIS) is the federal agency that oversees lawful immigration to the United States. the Service enhances security and improves the efficiency of national immigration services by exclusively focusing on the administration of benefit applications. No person may enter the United States until they have been inspected by an immigration officer. A list of the offices covered by this Coast Pilot is given in Appendix A.

(413)
### U.S. Coast Guard

(414) The U.S. Coast Guard has among its duties the enforcement of the laws of the United States on the high seas and in coastal and inland waters of the U.S. and its possessions; enforcement of navigation and neutrality laws and regulations; establishment and enforcement of navigational regulations upon the Inland Waters of the United States, including the establishment of a demarcation line separating the high seas from waters upon which U.S. navigational rules apply; administration of the Oil Pollution Act of 1990, as amended; establishment and administration of vessel anchorages; approval of bridge locations and clearances over navigable waters; administration of the alteration of obstructive bridges; regulation of drawbridge operations; inspection of vessels of the Merchant Marine; admeasurement of vessels; documentation of vessels; preparation and publication of merchant vessel registers; registration of stack insignia; port security; issuance of Merchant Marine licenses and documents; search and rescue operations; investigation of marine casualties and accidents and suspension and revocation proceedings; destruction of derelicts; operation of aids to navigation; maintenance and issuance of Light Lists and Local Notices to Mariners; and operation of ice-breaking facilities.

(415) Issuance of certificates of registry (more commonly referred to as Certificates of Documentation) with endorsements indicating eligibility of vessels that measure at least 5 net tons to engage in various trades for commercial vessels and certain recreational vessels that are numbered either by the Coast Guard or by a state having an approved numbering system (the latter is the most common) and the administration of the various laws pertaining thereto are functions of the Coast Guard and specifically the National Vessel Documentation Center. Owners of vessels may obtain the necessary information from the National Vessel Documentation Center either by mail to the National Vessel Documentation Center, 792

T.J. Jackson Drive, Falling Waters, WV 25419-9502; via toll free number: 800-799-8362; or via online at: *dco. uscg.mil/Our-Organization/Deputy-for-Operations-Policy-and-Capabilities-DCO-D/National-Vessel-Documentation-Center/.*

(416)

### U.S. Customs and Border Protection

(417)     The U.S. Customs and Border Protection administers certain laws relating to:

(418)     – entry and clearance of vessels and permits for certain vessel movements between points in the United States

(419)     – prohibitions against coastwise transportation of passengers and merchandise

(420)     – salvage

(421)     – dredging and towing by foreign vessels

(422)     – certain activities of vessels in the fishing trade

(423)     – regular and special tonnage taxes on vessels

(424)     – landing and delivery of foreign merchandise (including unlading, appraisement, lighterage, drayage, warehousing and shipment in bond)

(425)     – collection of customs duties, including duty on imported pleasure boats and yachts and 50% duty on foreign repairs to American vessels engaged in trade

(426)     – customs treatment of sea and ship's stores while in port and the baggage of crewmen and passengers

(427)     – illegally imported merchandise

(428)     – remission of penalties or forfeiture if customs or navigation laws have been violated.

(429)     Customs and Border Protection also cooperates with many other Federal agencies in the enforcement of statutes for which they are responsible for. Customs districts and ports of entry are listed in Appendix A.

(430)     The Customs and Border Protection office may issue, without charge, a **cruising license**, normally valid for one year, to a yacht of a foreign country that has a reciprocal agreement with the United States. A foreign yacht holding a cruising license is exempt from having to undergo formal entry and clearance procedures such as filing manifests and obtaining permits to proceed as well as from payment of tonnage tax and entry and clearance fees at all but the first port of entry. These vessels must not engage in trade, violate the laws of the United States or visit a vessel not yet inspected by a Customs Agent and does, within 24 hours of arrival at each port or place in the United States, report the fact of arrival to the nearest customhouse. Countries that have reciprocal agreements granting these privileges to U.S. yachts are:

(431)

| Countries with U.S. Cruising License Reciprocity | |
|---|---|
| Argentina | Honduras |
| Australia | Ireland |
| Austria | Italy |
| Bahama Islands | Jamaica |
| Belguim | Liberia |
| Bermuda | Marshall Islands |
| Canada | Netherlands |
| Denmark | New Zealand |
| Finland | Norway |
| France | Sweden |
| Germany | Switzerland |
| Great Britain | Turkey |
| Greece | |

(432)     Further information concerning cruising licenses may be obtained from the headquarters port for the customs district in which the license is desired or at *cbp. gov*. U.S. yacht owners planning cruises to foreign ports may contact the nearest customs district headquarters as to customs requirements.

(433)

## ENVIRONMENTAL PROTECTION AGENCY (EPA)

(434)     The U.S. EPA provides coordinated governmental action to ensure the protection of the environment by abating and controlling pollution on a systematic basis. The ocean dumping permit program of the EPA provides that except when authorized by permit, the dumping of any material into the ocean is prohibited by the "Marine Protection, Research, and Sanctuaries Act of 1972, Public Law 92–532," as amended (33 USC 1401 et seq.).

(435)     Permits for the **dumping of dredged material** into waters of the United States, including the territorial sea, and into ocean waters are issued by the U.S. Army Corps of Engineers. Permits for the dumping of fill material into waters of the United States, including the territorial sea, are also issued by the U.S. Army Corps of Engineers. Permits for the dumping of other material in the territorial sea and ocean waters are issued by the EPA.

(436)     U.S. Army Corps of Engineers regulations relating to the above are contained in **33 CFR 323** and **324**; EPA regulations are in **40 CFR 220** though **228**. (See Disposal Sites, this chapter.)

(437)     Persons or organizations who want to file for an application for an ocean dumping permit should write the EPA Regional Office for the region in which the port of departure is located. (See Appendix A for addresses of regional offices and States in the EPA coastal regions.)

(438)     The letter should contain the name and address of the applicant, name and address of person or firm, the name and usual location of the conveyance to be used in the transportation and dumping of the material involved, a physical description where appropriate, and the quantity to be dumped and proposed dumping site.

(439)     Everyone who writes EPA will be sent information about a final application for a permit as soon as possible. This final application is expected to include questions about the description of the process or activity giving rise to the production of the dumping material, information on past activities of applicant or others with respect to the disposal of the type of material involved, and a description about available alternative means of disposal

of the material with explanations about why an alternative is thought by the applicant to be inappropriate.

<sup>(440)</sup>
## FEDERAL COMMUNICATIONS COMMISSION (FCC)

<sup>(441)</sup>　　The Federal Communications Commission controls non-government radio communications in the United States, Guam, Puerto Rico and the Virgin Islands. Commission inspectors have authority to board ships to determine whether their radio stations comply with international treaties, Federal laws and Commission regulations. The commission has field offices in the principal U.S. ports. (See Appendix A for addresses.) Information concerning ship radio regulations and service documents may be obtained from the Federal Communications Commission, Washington, DC 20554, or from any of the field offices.

<sup>(452)</sup>　　<452-456 Deleted>

(442)

## Measurements and Equivalencies

nautical mile — 1,852 meters / 6,076.12 feet
statute mile — 5,280 feet / 1,609.3 meters / 1.6093 kilometers
cable — 0.1 nautical mile (CN) / 720 feet (US)
fathom — 6 feet / 1.8288 meters
foot — 0.3048 meter
inch — 2.54 centimeters
pound (avoirdupois) — 453.59 gram
kilometer — 1,000 meters
knot — 1.6877 feet per second / 0.5144 meters per second
miles/hour (statute) — 1.466 feet per second / 0.44704 meters per second

acre — 43,560 square feet / 4,046.82 square meters
gram — 0.0022046 pound (avoirdupois) / 0.035274 ounce
meter — 39.37 inches / 3.281 feet / 1.0936 yards
short ton — 2,000 pounds
long ton — 2,240 pounds
metric ton — 2,204.6 pounds
kilogram — 2.2 pounds
liter — 1.0567 quarts
barrel (petroleum) — 42 gallons (US)

## Conversion Factors

### Linear

inches — muiltiply by 25.40 — millimeters
inches — multiply by 2.540 — centimeters
centimeters — multiply by 0.032808 — feet
feet — multiply by 30.48 — centimeters
feet — multiply by 0.3048 — meters
feet — multiply by 0.00016458 — nautical miles
yard — multiply by 0.9144 — meters

meters — multiply by 3.2808 — feet
meters — multiply by 1.094 — yards
meters — multiply by 0.0005399 — nautical miles
statute miles — multiply by 0.86897 — nautical miles
statute miles — multiply by 1.6093 — kilometers
statute miles — multiply by 1,609.3 — meters
nautical miles — multiply by 1.151 — statute miles

### Area

acres — multiply by 4,046.9 — square meters
acres — multiply by 43,560 — square feet
acres — multiply by 0.404685 — hectare
hectare — multiply by 2.471054 — acres
hectare — multiply by 10,000 — square meters
hectare — multiply by $1.07639 \times 10^5$ — square feet

square feet — multiply by 0.0929 — square meters
square feet — multiply by 0.00002296 — acres
square meters — multiply by 10.764 — square feet
square meters — multiply by 0.0002471 — acres

### Depths

fathoms — multiply by 1.8288 — meters
feet — multiply by 0.3048 — meters

meters — multiply by 0.54681 — fathoms
meters — multiply by 3.2808 — feet

### Rate

feet/second — multiply by 0.5925 — knots
feet/second — multiply by 0.6818 — miles/hour
feet/second — multiply by 30.48 — centimeters/second
statute miles/hour — multiply by 0.8689 — knots
statute miles/hour — multiply by 1.467 — feet/second
statute miles/hour — multiply by 0.447 — meters/second

knots — multiply by 1.151 — miles/hour
knots — multiply by 0.5144 — meters/second
knots — multiply by 1.6878 — feet/second
centimeters/second — multiply by 0.01944 — miles/hour
centimeters/second — multiply by 0.02237 — miles/hour
centimeters/second — multiply by 0.032808 — feet/second

### Mass

grams — multiply by 0.035275 — ounces
grams — multiply by 0.002205 — pounds
ounces — multiply by 28.349 — grams
pounds — multiply by 0.45359 — kilograms
short tons — multiply by 2,000 — pounds
short tons — multiply by 0.89286 — long tons
short tons — multiply by 0.9072 — metric tons

long tons — multiply by 2,240 — pounds
long tons — multiply by 1.12 — short tons
long tons — multiply by 1.016 — metric tons
metric tons — multiply by 1,000 — kilograms
metric tons — multiply by 0.9842 — long tons
metric tons — multiply by 1.1023 — short tons
metric tons — multiply by 2,204.6 — pounds

### Volume

barrels (petroleum) — multiply by 42 — gallons (US)
barrels (petroleum) — multiply by 158.99 — liters
barrels (liquid, US) — multiply by 31.5 — gallons (US)
barrels (liquid, US) — multiply by 26.229 — gallons (British)
barrels (liquid, US) — multiply by 119.24 — liters

gallons (US) — multiply by 0.02381 — barrels (petroleum)
gallons (US) — multiply by 3.7854 — liters
liters — multiply by 0.26417 — gallons (US)

(443)

*Tips for*
# BOATING CLEAN AND GREEN

### Practice preventative engine maintenance
Keep your engine well tuned and practice preventative engine maintenance by regularly checking hoses and lines for chaffing or deterioration.

### Use oil absorbents
Place and secure an oil absorbent under the engine and in the bilge. Avoid using bilge cleaners as they may get discharged overboard. It is illegal to use soap to disperse fuel and oil spills. Report oil and chemical spills by calling the EPA National Response Center at 800–424–8802.

### Spill-proof your fueling practices
Use a spill proof system like a portable oil change pump to change your oil. Use oil absorbents when fueling and changing the oil. Do not top-off your fuel tank; leave it 10 percent empty to allow fuel to expand as it warms.

### Reduce greywater discharges
Use shore-side facilities for laundry, showers, and dish washing whenever possible. Use only phosphate-free and biodegradable soaps. The legality of discharging greywater into a marina or within three miles off the coast varies from place to place. In some areas, there are local ordinances and codes that allow harbor patrol to issue citations for any discharge that is not "clean and clear." To avoid any potential fines and to protect the aquatic environment, do not discharge greywater overboard.

### Dispose of hazardous waste properly
Recycle and properly dispose of absorbents, used oil, oil filters, paint, and batteries at your local household hazardous waste collection site.

### Minimize boat cleaning and maintenance conducted on the water
• Use more elbow grease.
• Use products that are water-based, biodegradable, phosphate-free, and labeled as less toxic.
• Check out less toxic cleaning alternatives for all types of uses. Visit **http://dbw.parks.ca.gov/?page_id=29184**.
• Buy only the amount that you need and use products for spot cleaning only.
• Properly handle and store materials. Dispose of hazardous waste legally and safely.

### Reduce discharges from bottom paints
• Consider alternative, non-biocide hull coatings.
• Clean the bottom with a soft, non-abrasive sponge.
• Use hull cleaning companies who use green management practices such as monitoring their divers and using non-abrasive scrubbing agents that do not release paint into the water. For more information visit **https://www3.epa.gov/npdes/pubs/vgp_hull_husbandry.pdf**.

### Stow it, don't throw it
Keep your trash on-board. Recycle plastic, glass, metal, and paper. Avoid excess packaging.

### Dump at the pump!
It is illegal to discharge untreated sewage anywhere within the three-mile territorial limit including lakes, rivers, reservoirs or coastal waters. Never discharge treated sewage into "restricted waters" such as a marina, swimming/wading areas, a sanctuary, poorly flushed areas, lakes, reservoirs, or freshwater impoundments and federal No Discharge Zones. Use sewage pumpouts, dump stations, or mobile-pumpout services.

### Prevent the spread of aquatic invasive species
Before leaving any body of water, examine your boat and equipment and remove any visible mud, plants, or animals before transporting equipment. Never release plants or animals into a body of water or storm drains unless they came out of that body of water. Use cleaning procedures for anything that contacts the water. Visit **https://invasivemusselcollaborative.net/wp-content/uploads/2018/11/NOAA-Decon-Watercraft.pdf**.

For hazardous waste recycling or collection centers call 800–CLEAN–UP or visit **http://www.earth911.com**

# Navigation Regulations

(1)     This chapter contains extracts from **Code of Federal Regulations (CFR)** that are of importance to mariners in the area covered by this Coast Pilot. Sections of little value to the mariner are sometimes omitted. Omitted sections are signified by the following [...]

(2)     Extracts from the following titles are contained in this chapter.

(3)

**Title 15: Commerce and Foreign Trade**
  Part 922—National Marine Sanctuary Program Regulations
**Title 33: Navigation and Navigable Waters**
  Part 26—Vessel Bridge-to-Bridge Radiotelephone Regulations
  Part 80—COLREGS Demarcation Lines
  Part 81—72 COLREGS: Implementing Rules
  Part 82—72 COLREGS: Interpretive Rules
  Part 88—Annex V: Pilot Rules
  Part 89—Inland Navigation Rules: Implementing Rules
  Part 90—Inland Rules: Interpretive Rules
  Part 110—Anchorage Regulations
  Part 117—Drawbridge Operation Regulations
  Part 157—Rules for the Protection of the Marine Environment Relating to Tank Vessels Carrying Oil in Bulk (in part)
  Part 160—Ports and Waterways Safety-General
  Part 162—Inland Waterways Navigation Regulations
  Part 164—Navigation Safety Regulations (in part)
  Part 165—Regulated Navigation Areas and Limited Access Areas
  Part 166—Shipping Safety Fairways
  Part 167—Offshore Traffic Separation Schemes
  Part 169—Ship Reporting Systems
  Part 207—Navigation Regulations
  Part 334—Danger Zones and Restricted Area Regulations
**Title 40: Protection of Environment**
  Part 140—Marine Sanitation Device Standard
**Title 46: Shipping**
  Part 15—Manning Requirements
**Title 50: Wildlife and Fisheries**
  Part 222—General Endangered and Threatened Marine Species
  Part 224—Endangered Marine and Anadromous Species
  Part 226—Designated Critical Habitat

(4)     These regulations can only be amended by the enforcing agency or other authority cited in the regulations. Accordingly, requests for changes to these regulations should be directed to the appropriate agency for action. In those regulations where the enforcing agency is not cited or is unclear, recommendations for changes should be directed to the following Federal agencies for action:

(5)     **National     Oceanic     and     Atmospheric Administration**—15 CFR 922, and 50 CFR 222, 224 and 226

(6)     **United States Coast Guard**—33 CFR 26, 80, 81, 82, 88, 89, 90, 110, 117, 157, 160, 162, 164, 165, 166, 167 and 169; 46 CFR 15

(7)     **United States Army Corps of Engineers**—33 CFR 207 and 334

(8)     **Environmental Protection Agency**—40 CFR 140

(9)
## TITLE 15–COMMERCE AND FOREIGN TRADE

(10)
## Part 922–National Marine Sanctuary Program Regulations

(11)
## Subpart A–General

(12)
### §922.1 Applicability of regulations.

(13)     Unless noted otherwise, the regulations in subparts A, D, and E of this part apply to all National Marine Sanctuaries and related site-specific regulations set forth in this part. Subparts B and C of this part apply to the sanctuary nomination process and to the designation of future Sanctuaries.

(14)
### §922.2 Mission, goals, and special policies.

(15)     (a) In accordance with the standards set forth in title III of the Marine Protection, Research, and Sanctuaries Act of 1972, as amended, also known as the National Marine Sanctuaries Act (Act) the mission of the National Marine Sanctuary program (Program) is to identify, designate and manage areas of the marine environment of special national, and in some cases international, significance due to their conservation, recreational, ecological, historical, research, educational, or aesthetic qualities.

(16)     (b) The goals of the Program are to carry out the mission to:

(17)     (1) Identify and designate as National Marine Sanctuaries areas of the marine environment which are of special national significance;

(18)     (2) Provide authority for comprehensive and coordinated conservation and management of these marine areas, and activities affecting them, in a manner which complements existing regulatory authorities;

(19)     (3) Support, promote, and coordinate scientific research on, and monitoring of, the resources of these

marine areas, especially long-term monitoring and research of these areas;

(20) (4) Enhance public awareness, understanding, appreciation, and wise use of the marine environment;

(21) (5) Facilitate to the extent compatible with the primary objective of resource protection, all public and private uses of the resources of these marine areas not prohibited pursuant to other authorities;

(22) (6) Develop and implement coordinated plans for the protection and management of these areas with appropriate Federal agencies, State and local governments, Native American tribes and organizations, international organizations, and other public and private interests concerned with the continuing health and resilience of these marine areas;

(23) (7) Create models of, and incentives for, ways to conserve and manage these areas;

(24) (8) Cooperate with global programs encouraging conservation of marine resources; and

(25) (9) Maintain, restore, and enhance living resources by providing places for species that depend upon these marine areas to survive and propagate.

(26) (c) To the extent consistent with the policies set forth in the Act, in carrying out the Program's mission and goals:

(27) (1) Particular attention will be given to the establishment and management of marine areas as National Marine Sanctuaries for the protection of the area's natural resource and ecosystem values; particularly for ecologically or economically important or threatened species or species assemblages, and for offshore areas where there are no existing special area protection mechanisms;

(28) (2) The size of a National Marine Sanctuary, while highly dependent on the nature of the site's resources, will be no larger than necessary to ensure effective management;

(29) (d) Management efforts will be coordinated to the extent practicable with other countries managing marine protected areas;

(30) (e) Program regulations, policies, standards, guidelines, and procedures under the Act concerning the identification, evaluation, registration, and treatment of historical resources shall be consistent, to the extent practicable, with the declared national policy for the protection and preservation of these resources as stated in the National Historic Preservation Act of 1966, 16 U.S.C. 470 *et seq.*, the Archeological and Historical Preservation Act of 1974, 16 U.S.C. 469 *et seq.*, and the Archeological Resources Protection Act of 1979 (ARPA), 16 U.S.C. 470aa *et seq.* The same degree of regulatory protection and preservation planning policy extended to historical resources on land shall be extended, to the extent practicable, to historical resources in the marine environment within the boundaries of designated National Marine Sanctuaries. The management of historical resources under the authority of the Act shall be consistent, to the extent practicable, with the Federal archeological program by consulting the Uniform Regulations, ARPA (43 CFR part 7) and other relevant Federal regulations. The Secretary of the Interior's Standards and Guidelines for Archeology may also be consulted for guidance. These guidelines are available from the Office of Ocean and Coastal Management at (301) 713-3125.

(31)

## § 922.3 Definitions.

(32) *Act* means title III of the Marine Protection, Research, and Sanctuaries Act of 1972, as amended, 16 U.S.C. 1431 et seq., also known as the National Marine Sanctuaries Act.

(33) *Assistant Administrator* means the Assistant Administrator for Ocean Services and Coastal Zone Management, National Oceanic and Atmospheric Administration (NOAA), or designee.

(34) *Benthic community* means the assemblage of organisms, substrate, and structural formations found at or near the bottom that is periodically or permanently covered by water.

(35) *Commercial fishing* means any activity that results in the sale or trade for intended profit of fish, shellfish, algae, or corals.

(36) *Conventional hook and line gear* means any fishing apparatus operated aboard a vessel and composed of a single line terminated by a combination of sinkers and hooks or lures and spooled upon a reel that may be hind- or electrically operated, hand-held or mounted. This term does not include bottom longlines.

(37) *Cultural resources* means any historical or cultural feature, including archaeological sites, historic structures, shipwrecks, and artifacts.

(38) *Director* means, except where otherwise specified, the Director of the Office of Ocean and Coastal Resource Management, NOAA, or designee

(39) *Exclusive economic zone* means the exclusive economic zone as defined in the Magnuson Fishery Conservation and Management Act, 16 U.S. 1801 et seq.

(40) *Fish wastes* means waste materials resulting from commercial fish processing operations.

(41) *Historical resource* means any resource possessing historical, cultural, archaeological or paleontological significance, including sites, contextual information, structures, districts, and objects significantly associated with or representative of earlier people, cultures, maritime heritage, and human activities and events. Historical resources include "submerged cultural resources", and also include "historical properties," as defined in the National Historic Preservation Act, as amended, and its implementing regulations, as amended.

(42) *Indian tribe* means any American Indian tribe, band, group, or community recognized as such by the Secretary of the Interior.

(43) *Injure* means to change adversely, either in the short or long term, a chemical, biological or physical attribute of, or the viability of. This includes, but is not limited to, to cause the loss of or destroy.

(44)     *Inventory* means a list of nominated areas selected by the Director as qualifying for future consideration of designation as a national marine sanctuary.

(45)     *Lightering* means at-sea transfer of petroleum-based products, materials, or other matter from vessel to vessel.

(46)     *Marine* means those areas of coastal and ocean waters, the Great Lakes and their connecting waters, and submerged lands over which the United States exercises jurisdiction, including the exclusive economic zone, consistent with international law.

(47)     *Mineral* means clay, stone, sand, gravel, metalliferous ore, non-metalliferous ore, or any other solid material or other matter of commercial value.

(48)     *National historic landmark* means a district, site, building, structure or object designated as such by the Secretary of the Interior under the National Historic Landmarks Program (36 CFR part 65).

(49)     *National Marine Sanctuary* means an area of the marine environment of special national significance due to its resource or human-use values, which is designated as such to ensure its conservation and management.

(50)     *Person* means any private individual, partnership, corporation or other entity; or any officer, employee, agent, department, agency or instrumentality of the Federal government, of any State or local unit of government, or of any foreign government.

(51)     *Regional Fishery Management Council* means any fishery council established under section 302 of the Magnuson Fishery Conservation and Management Act, 16 U.S.C. 1801 et seq.

(52)     *Sanctuary quality* means any of those ambient conditions, physical-chemical characteristics and natural processes, the maintenance of which is essential to the ecological health of the Sanctuary, including, but not limited to, water quality, sediment quality and air quality.

(53)     *Sanctuary resource* means any living or non-living resource of a National Marine Sanctuary that contributes to the conservation, recreational, ecological, historical, research, educational, or aesthetic value of the Sanctuary, including, but not limited to, the substratum of the area of the Sanctuary, other submerged features and the surrounding seabed, carbonate rock, corals and other bottom formations, coralline algae and other marine plants and algae, marine invertebrates, brineseep biota, phytoplankton, zooplankton, fish, seabirds, sea turtles and other marine reptiles, marine mammals and historical resources. For Thunder Bay National Marine Sanctuary and Underwater Preserve, Sanctuary resource means an underwater cultural resource as defined at §922.191. For Mallows Bay-Potomac River National Marine Sanctuary, Sanctuary resource is defined at §922.201(a).

(54)     *Secretary* means the Secretary of the United States Department of Commerce, or designee.

(55)     *Shunt* means to discharge expended drilling cuttings and fluids near the ocean seafloor.

(56)     *State* means each of the several States, the District of Columbia, the Commonwealth of Puerto Rico, the Commonwealth of the Northern Mariana Islands, American Samoa, the United States Virgin Islands, Guam, and any other commonwealth, territory, or possession of the United States.

(57)     *Subsistence use* means the customary and traditional use by rural residents of areas near or in the marine environment for direct personal or family consumption as food, shelter, fuel, clothing, tools, or transportation; for the making and selling of handicraft articles; and for barter, if for food or non-edible items other than money, if the exchange is of a limited and non-commercial nature.

(58)     *Take or taking* means: (1) For any marine mammal, sea turtle, or seabird listed as either endangered or threatened pursuant to the Endangered Species Act, to harass, harm, pursue, hunt, shoot, wound, kill, trap, capture, collect or injure, or to attempt to engage in any such conduct; (2) For any other marine mammal, sea turtle, or seabird, to harass, hunt, capture, kill, collect or injure, or to attempt to engage in any such conduct. For the purposes of both (1) and (2) of this definition, this includes, but is not limited to, to collect any dead or injured marine mammal, sea turtle or seabird, or any part thereof; to restrain or detain any marine mammal, sea turtle or seabird, or any part thereof, no matter how temporarily; to tag any sea turtle, marine mammal or seabird; to operate a vessel or aircraft or to do any other act that results in the disturbance or molestation of any marine mammal, sea turtle or seabird.

(59)     *Tropical fish* means fish or minimal sport and food value, usually brightly colored, often used for aquaria purposes and which lives in a direct relationship with live bottom communities.

(60)     *Vessel* means a watercraft of any description capable of being used as a means of transportation in/on the waters of a Sanctuary.

(61)

## §922.4 Effect of National Marine Sanctuary designation.

(62)     The designation of a National Marine Sanctuary, and the regulations implementing it, are binding on any person subject to the jurisdiction of the United States. Designation does not constitute any claim to territorial jurisdiction on the part of the United States for designated sites beyond the U.S. territorial sea, and the regulations implementing the designation shall be applied in accordance with generally recognized principles of international law, and in accordance with treaties, conventions, and other agreements to which the United States is a party. No regulation shall apply to a person who is not a citizen, national, or resident alien of the United States, unless in accordance with:

(63)     (a) Generally recognized principles of international law;

(64)     (b) An agreement between the United States and the foreign state of which the person is a citizen; or

(65)     (c) An agreement between the United States and the flag state of the foreign vessel, if the person is a crew member of the vessel.

(66)
## Subpart B—Sanctuary Nomination Process

(67)
### §922.10 General.

(68)
(a) *Nomination process.* The sanctuary nomination process (see National Marine Sanctuaries Web site *www.sanctuaries.noaa.gov*) is the means by which the public can submit areas of the marine and Great Lakes environments for consideration by NOAA as a national marine sanctuary.

(69)
(b) *National significance criteria.* The Director will consider the following in determining if a nominated area is of special national significance:

(70)
(1) The area's natural resources and ecological qualities are of special significance and contribute to: Biological productivity or diversity; maintenance or enhancement of ecosystem structure and function; maintenance of ecologically or commercially important species or species assemblages; maintenance or enhancement of critical habitat, representative biogeographic assemblages, or both; or maintenance or enhancement of connectivity to other ecologically significant resources.

(71)
(2) The area contains submerged maritime heritage resources of special historical, cultural, or archaeological significance, that: Individually or collectively are consistent with the criteria of eligibility or listing on the National Register of Historic Places; have met or which would meet the criteria for designation as a National Historic Landmark; or have special or sacred meaning to the indigenous people of the region or nation.

(72)
(3) The area supports present and potential economic uses, such as: Tourism; commercial and recreational fishing; subsistence and traditional uses; diving; and other recreational uses that depend on conservation and management of the area's resources.

(73)
(4) The publicly-derived benefits of the area, such as aesthetic value, public recreation, and access to places depend on conservation and management of the area's resources.

(74)
(c) *Management considerations.* The Director will consider the following in determining the manageability of a nominated area:

(75)
(1) The area provides or enhances opportunities for research in marine science, including marine archaeology.

(76)
(2) The area provides or enhances opportunities for education, including the understanding and appreciation of the marine and Great Lakes environments.

(77)
(3) Adverse impacts from current or future uses and activities threaten the area's significance, values, qualities, and resources.

(78)
(4) A national marine sanctuary would provide unique conservation and management value for this area that also have beneficial values for adjacent areas.

(79)
(5) The existing regulatory and management authorities for the area could be supplemented or complemented to meet the conservation and management goals for the area.

(80)
(6) There are commitments or possible commitments for partnerships opportunities such as cost sharing, office space or exhibit space, vessel time, or other collaborations to aid conservation or management programs for the area.

(81)
(7) There is community-based support for the nomination expressed by a broad range of interests, such as: Individuals or locally-based groups (e.g., friends of group, chamber of commerce); local, tribal, state, or national agencies; elected officials; or topic-based stakeholder groups, at the local, regional or national level (e.g., a local chapter of an environmental organization, a regionally-based fishing group, a national-level recreation or tourism organization, academia or science-based group, or an industry association).

(82)
(d) Following evaluation of a nomination against the national significance criteria and management considerations, the Director may place nominated areas in a publicly available inventory for future consideration of designation as a national marine sanctuary.

(83)
(e) A determination that a site is eligible for national marine sanctuary designation, by itself shall not subject the site to any regulatory control under the Act. Such controls may only be imposed after designation.

(84)
### §922.11 Selection of nominated areas for national marine sanctuary designation.

(85)
(a) The Director may select a nominated area from the inventory for future consideration as a national marine sanctuary.

(86)
(b) Selection of a nominated area from the inventory shall begin the formal sanctuary designation process. A notice of intent to prepare a draft environmental impact statement shall be published in the Federal Register and posted on the Office of National Marine Sanctuaries Web site. Any designation process will follow the procedures for designation and implementation set forth in section 304 of the Act.

(87)
## Subpart C—Designation of National Marine Sanctuaries

(88)
### §922.20 Standards and procedures for designation.

(89)
In designating a National Marine Sanctuary, the Secretary shall apply the standards and procedures set forth in section 303 and section 304 of the Act.

(90)
### §922.21 [Reserved]

(91)
### §922.22 Development of designation materials.

(92)
(a) In designating a National Marine Sanctuary, the Secretary shall prepare the designation materials described in section 304 of the Act.

(93)     (b) If a proposed Sanctuary includes waters within the exclusive economic zone, the Secretary shall notify the appropriate Regional Fishery Management Council(s) which shall have one hundred and twenty (120) days from the date of such notification to make recommendations and, if appropriate, prepare draft fishery regulations and to submit them to the Secretary. In preparing its recommendations and draft regulations, the Council(s) shall use as guidance the national standards of section 301(a) of the Magnuson Act (16 U.S.C. 1851) to the extent that they are consistent and compatible with the goals and objectives of the proposed Sanctuary designation. Fishery activities not proposed for regulation under section 304(a)(5) of the Act may be listed in the draft Sanctuary designation document as potentially subject to regulation, without following the procedures specified in section 304(a)(5) of the Act. If the Secretary subsequently determines that regulation of any such fishery activity is necessary, then the procedures specified in section 304(a)(5) of the Act shall be followed.

(94)
### §922.23 [Reserved]

(95)
### §922.24 Congressional documents.

(96)     In designating a National Marine Sanctuary, the Secretary shall prepare and submit to Congress those documents described in section 304 of the Act.

(97)
### §922.25 Designation determination and findings.

(98)     (a) In designating a National Marine Sanctuary, the Secretary shall prepare a written Designation Determination and Findings which shall include those findings and determinations described in section 303 of the Act.

(99)     (b) In addition to those factors set forth in section 303 of the Act, the Secretary, when making a designation determination, shall consider the Program's fiscal capability to manage the area as a National Marine Sanctuary.

(100)
## Subpart D—Management Plan Development and Implementation

(101)
### §922.30 General.

(102)     (a) The Secretary shall implement each management plan, and applicable regulations, including carrying out surveillance and enforcement activities and conducting such research, monitoring, evaluation, and education programs as are necessary and reasonable to carry out the purposes and policies of the Act.

(103)     (b) Consistent with Sanctuary management plans, the Secretary shall develop and implement site-specific contingency and emergency-response plans designed to protect Sanctuary resources. The plans shall contain alert procedures and actions to be taken in the event of an emergency such as a shipwreck or an oil spill.

(104)
### §922.31 Promotion and coordination of Sanctuary use.

(105)     The Secretary shall take such action as is necessary and reasonable to promote and coordinate the use of National Marine Sanctuaries for research, monitoring, and education purposes. Such action may include consulting with Federal agencies, or other persons to promote use of one or more Sanctuaries for research, monitoring and education, including coordination with the National Estuarine Research Reserve System.

(106)
## Subpart E—Regulations of General Applicability

(107)
### §922.40 Purpose.

(108)     The purpose of the regulations in this subpart and in the site-specific subparts in this part is to implement the designations of the National Marine Sanctuaries by regulating activities affecting them, consistent with their respective terms of designation in order to protect, preserve and manage and thereby ensure the health, integrity and continued availability of the conservation, ecological, recreational, research, educational, historical and aesthetic resources and qualities of these areas. Additional purposes of the regulations implementing the designation of the Florida Keys and Hawaiian Islands Humpback Whale National Marine Sanctuaries are found at §§922.160 and 922.180, respectively.

(109)
### §922.41 Boundaries.

(110)     The boundary for each of the National Marine Sanctuaries is set forth in the site-specific regulations covered by this part.

(111)
### §922.42 Allowed activities.

(112)     All activities (*e.g.*, fishing, boating, diving, research, education) may be conducted unless prohibited or otherwise regulated in the site-specific regulations covered by this part, subject to any emergency regulations promulgated under this part, subject to all prohibitions, regulations, restrictions, and conditions validly imposed by any Federal, State, or local authority of competent jurisdiction, including but not limited to, Federal, Tribal, and State fishery management authorities, and subject to the provisions of section 312 of the National Marine Sanctuaries Act (NMSA) (16 U.S.C. 1431 *et seq.*). The Assistant Administrator may only directly regulate fishing activities pursuant to the procedure set forth in section 304(a)(5) of the NMSA.

(113)

### §922.43 Prohibited or otherwise regulated activities.

(114) The site-specific regulations applicable to the activities specified therein are set forth in the subparts covered by this part.

(115)

### §922.44 Emergency regulations.

(116) (a) Where necessary to prevent or minimize the destruction of, loss of, or injury to a Sanctuary resource or quality, or minimize the imminent risk of such destruction, loss, or injury, any and all such activities are subject to immediate temporary regulation, including prohibition.

(117) (b) The provisions of this section do not apply to the following national marine sanctuaries with site-specific regulations that establish procedures for issuing emergency regulations:

(118) (1) Cordell Bank National Marine Sanctuary, **§922.112(e)**.

(119) (2) Florida Keys National Marine Sanctuary, **§922.165**.

(120) (3) Hawaiian Islands Humpback Whale National Marine Sanctuary, **§922.185**.

(121) (4) Thunder Bay National Marine Sanctuary, **§922.196**.

(122) (5) Mallows Bay-Potomac River National Marine Sanctuary, **§922.204**.

(123) (6) [Reserved].

(124)

### §922.45 Penalties.

(125) (a) Each violation of the NMSA or FKNMSPA, any regulation in this part, or any permit issued pursuant thereto, is subject to a civil penalty of not more than $ 100,000. Each day of a continuing violation constitutes a separate violation.

(126) (b) Regulations setting forth the procedures governing administrative proceedings for assessment of civil penalties, permit sanctions, and denials for enforcement reasons, issuance and use of written warnings, and release or forfeiture of seized property appear at 15 CFR part 904.

(127)

### §922.46 Response costs and damages.

(128) Under section 312 of the Act, any person who destroys, causes the loss of, or injures any Sanctuary resource is liable to the United States for response costs and damages resulting from such destruction, loss or injury, and any vessel used to destroy, cause the loss of, or injure any Sanctuary resource is liable in rem to the United States for response costs and damages resulting from such destruction, loss or injury.

(129)

### §922.47 Pre-existing authorizations or rights and certifications of pre-existing authorizations or rights.

(130) (a) Leases, permits, licenses, or rights of subsistence use or access in existence on the date of designation of any National Marine Sanctuary shall not be terminated by the Director. The Director may, however, regulate the exercise of such leases, permits, licenses, or rights consistent with the purposes for which the Sanctuary was designated.

(131) (b) The prohibitions listed in subparts F through P and R through T of this part do not apply to any activity authorized by a valid lease, permit, license, approval or other authorization in existence on the effective date of Sanctuary designation, or in the case of the Florida Keys National Marine Sanctuary the effective date of the regulations in subpart P, and issued by any Federal, State or local authority of competent jurisdiction, or by any valid right of subsistence use or access in existence on the effective date of Sanctuary designation, or in the case of the Florida Keys National Marine Sanctuary the effective date of the regulations in subpart P, provided that the holder of such authorization or right complies with certification procedures and criteria promulgated at the time of Sanctuary designation, or in the case of the Florida Keys National Marine Sanctuary the effective date of the regulations in subpart P, and with any terms and conditions on the exercise of such authorization or right imposed by the Director as a condition of certification as the Director deems necessary to achieve the purposes for which the Sanctuary was designated.

(132)

### §922.48 National Marine Sanctuary permits—application procedures and issuance criteria.

(133) (a) A person may conduct an activity prohibited by subparts F through O and S and T of this part, if conducted in accordance with the scope, purpose, terms and conditions of a permit issued under this section and subparts F through O and S and T, as appropriate. For the Florida Keys National Marine Sanctuary, a person may conduct an activity prohibited by subpart P of this part if conducted in accordance with the scope, purpose, terms and conditions of a permit issued under **§922.166**. For the Thunder Bay National Marine Sanctuary and Underwater Preserve, a person may conduct an activity prohibited by subpart R of this part in accordance with the scope, purpose, terms and conditions of a permit issued under **§922.195**.

(134) (b) Applications for permits to conduct activities otherwise prohibited by subparts F through O and S and T of this part, should be addressed to the Director and sent to the address specified in subparts F through O of this part, or subparts R through T of this part, as appropriate. An application must include:

(135) (1) A detailed description of the proposed activity including a timetable for completion;

(136) (2) The equipment, personnel and methodology to be employed;

(137) (3) The qualifications and experience of all personnel;

(138) (4) The potential effects of the activity, if any, on Sanctuary resources and qualities; and

(139) (5) Copies of all other required licenses, permits, approvals or other authorizations.

(140)     (c) Upon receipt of an application, the Director may request such additional information from the applicant as he or she deems necessary to act on the application and may seek the views of any persons or entity, within or outside the Federal government, and may hold a public hearing, as deemed appropriate.

(141)     (d) The Director, at his or her discretion, may issue a permit, subject to such terms and conditions as he or she deems appropriate, to conduct a prohibited activity, in accordance with the criteria found in subparts F through O of this part, or subparts R through T of this part, as appropriate. The Director shall further impose, at a minimum, the conditions set forth in the relevant subpart.

(142)     (e) A permit granted pursuant to this section is nontransferable.

(143)     (f) The Director may amend, suspend, or revoke a permit issued pursuant to this section for good cause. The Director may deny a permit application pursuant to this section, in whole or in part, if it is determined that the permittee or applicant has acted in violation of the terms and conditions of a permit or of the regulations set forth in this section or subparts F through O of this part, or subparts R through T of this part or for other good cause. Any such action shall be communicated in writing to the permittee or applicant by certified mail and shall set forth the reason(s) for the action taken. Procedures governing permit sanctions and denials for enforcement reasons are set forth in subpart D of 15 CFR part 904.

(144)

### §922.49 Notification and review of applications for leases, licenses, permits, approvals, or other authorizations to conduct a prohibited activity.

(145)     (a) A person may conduct an activity prohibited by subparts L through P of this part, or subparts R through T of this part, if such activity is specifically authorized by any valid Federal, State, or local lease, permit, license, approval, or other authorization issued after the effective date of Sanctuary designation, or in the case of the Florida Keys National Marine Sanctuary after the effective date of the regulations in subpart P, provided that:

(146)     (1) The applicant notifies the Director, in writing, of the application for such authorization (and of any application for an amendment, renewal, or extension of such authorization) within fifteen (15) days of the date of filing of the application or the effective date of Sanctuary designation, or in the case of the Florida Keys National Marine Sanctuary the effective date of the regulations in subpart P, whichever is later;

(147)     (2) The applicant complies with the other provisions of this section;

(148)     (3) The Director notifies the applicant and authorizing agency that he or she does not object to issuance of the authorization (or amendment, renewal, or extension); and

(149)     (4) The applicant complies with any terms and conditions the Director deems reasonably necessary to protect Sanctuary resources and qualities.

(150)     (b) Any potential applicant for an authorization described in paragraph (a) of this section may request the Director to issue a finding as to whether the activity for which an application is intended to be made is prohibited by subparts L through P of this part, or subparts R through T of this part, as appropriate.

(151)     (c) Notification of filings of applications should be sent to the Director, Office of National Marine Sanctuaries at the address specified in subparts L through P of this part, or subparts R through T of this part, as appropriate. A copy of the application must accompany the notification.

(152)     (d) The Director may request additional information from the applicant as he or she deems reasonably necessary to determine whether to object to issuance of an authorization described in paragraph (a) of this section, or what terms and conditions are reasonably necessary to protect Sanctuary resources and qualities. The information requested must be received by the Director within 45 days of the postmark date of the request. The Director may seek the views of any persons on the application.

(153)     (e) The Director shall notify, in writing, the agency to which application has been made of his or her pending review of the application and possible objection to issuance. Upon completion of review of the application and information received with respect thereto, the Director shall notify both the agency and applicant, in writing, whether he or she has an objection to issuance and what terms and conditions he or she deems reasonably necessary to protect Sanctuary resources and qualities, and reasons therefor.

(154)     (f) The Director may amend the terms and conditions deemed reasonably necessary to protect Sanctuary resources and qualities whenever additional information becomes available justifying such an amendment.

(155)     (g) Any time limit prescribed in or established under this section may be extended by the Director for good cause.

(156)     (h) The applicant may appeal any objection by, or terms or conditions imposed by, the Director to the Assistant Administrator or designee in accordance with the provisions of **§922.50**.

(157)

### §922.50 Appeals of administrative action.

(158)     (a)(1) Except for permit actions taken for enforcement reasons (see subpart D of 15 CFR part 904 for applicable procedures), an applicant for, or a holder of, a National Marine Sanctuary permit; an applicant for, or a holder of, a Special Use permit issued pursuant to section 310 of the Act; a person requesting certification of an existing lease, permit, license or right of subsistence use or access under § 922.47; or, for those Sanctuaries described in subparts L through P and R through T of this part, an applicant for a lease, permit, license or other authorization issued by any Federal, State, or local authority of competent jurisdiction (hereinafter appellant) may appeal to the Assistant Administrator:

(159)     (i) The granting, denial, conditioning, amendment, suspension or revocation by the Director of a National Marine Sanctuary or Special Use permit;

(160)     (ii) The conditioning, amendment, suspension or revocation of a certification under §922.47; or

(161)     (iii) For those Sanctuaries described in subparts L through P and R through T of this part, the objection to issuance of or the imposition of terms and conditions on a lease, permit, license or other authorization issued by any Federal, State, or local authority of competent jurisdiction.

(162)     (2) For those National Marine Sanctuaries described in subparts F through K and S and T of this part, any interested person may also appeal the same actions described in paragraphs (a)(1)(i) and (ii) of this section. For appeals arising from actions taken with respect to these National Marine Sanctuaries, the term "appellant" includes any such interested persons.

(163)     (b) An appeal under paragraph (a) of this section must be in writing, state the action(s) by the Director appealed and the reason(s) for the appeal, and be received within 30 days of receipt of notice of the action by the Director. Appeals should be addressed to the Assistant Administrator for Ocean Services and Coastal Zone Management, NOAA 1305 East-West Highway, 13th Floor, Silver Spring, MD 20910.

(164)     (c)(1) The Assistant Administrator may request the appellant to submit such information as the Assistant Administrator deems necessary in order for him or her to decide the appeal. The information requested must be received by the Assistant Administrator within 45 days of the postmark date of the request. The Assistant Administrator may seek the views of any other persons. For the Monitor National Marine Sanctuary, if the appellant has requested a hearing, the Assistant Administrator shall grant an informal hearing. For all other National Marine Sanctuaries, the Assistant Administrator may determine whether to hold an informal hearing on the appeal. If the Assistant Administrator determines that an informal hearing should be held, the Assistant Administrator may designate an officer before whom the hearing shall be held.

(165)     (2) The hearing officer shall give notice in the **Federal Register** of the time, place and subject matter of the hearing. The appellant and the Director may appear personally or by counsel at the hearing and submit such material and present such arguments as deemed appropriate by the hearing officer. Within 60 days after the record for the hearing closes, the hearing officer shall recommend a decision in writing to the Assistant Administrator.

(166)     (d) The Assistant Administrator shall decide the appeal using the same regulatory criteria as for the initial decision and shall base the appeal decision on the record before the Director and any information submitted regarding the appeal, and, if a hearing has been held, on the record before the hearing officer and the hearing officer's recommended decision. The

Assistant Administrator shall notify the appellant of the final decision and the reason(s) therefore in writing. The Assistant Administrator's decision shall constitute final agency action for the purpose of the Administrative Procedure Act.

(167)     (e) Any time limit prescribed in or established under this section other than the 30-day limit for filing an appeal may be extended by the Assistant Administrator or hearing office for good cause.

(168)
## Subpart S–Mallows Bay–Potomac River National Marine Sanctuary

(169)
### §922.200 Boundary.

(170)     The Mallows Bay-Potomac River National Marine Sanctuary consists of an area of approximately 18 square miles of waters of the state of Maryland and the submerged lands thereunder, over, around, and under the underwater cultural resources in the Potomac River. The precise boundary coordinates are listed in appendix A to this subpart. The western boundary of the sanctuary approximates the border between the Commonwealth of Virginia and the State of Maryland along the western side of the Potomac River and begins at Point 1 north of the mouth of Aquia Creek in Stafford County, Virginia, near Brent Point. From this point the boundary continues to the north approximating the border between Virginia and Maryland cutting across the mouths of streams and creeks passing through the points in numerical order until it reaches Point 40 north of Tank Creek. From this point the sanctuary boundary continues east across the Potomac River in a straight line towards Point 41 until it intersects the Maryland shoreline just north of Sandy Point in Charles County, Maryland. From this intersection the sanctuary boundary then follows the Maryland shoreline south around Mallows Bay, Blue Banks, and Wades Bay cutting across the mouths of creeks and streams along the eastern shoreline of the Potomac River until it intersects the line formed between Point 42 and Point 43 just south of Smith Point. Finally, from this intersection the sanctuary boundary crosses the Potomac River to the west in a straight line until it reaches Point 43 north of the mouth of Aquia Creek in Stafford County, Virginia, near Brent Point.

(171)
### §922.201 Definitions.

(172)     (a) The following terms are defined for purposes of this subpart:

(173)     (1) *Sanctuary resource* means any historical resource with the Sanctuary boundaries, as defined in §922.3. This includes, but is not limited to, any sunken watercraft and any associated rigging, gear, fittings, trappings, and equipment; the personal property of the officers, crew, and passengers, and any cargo; and any submerged or partially submerged prehistoric, historic, cultural remains, such as docks, piers, fishing-related remains (e.g., weirs,

fish-traps) or other cultural heritage materials. Sanctuary resource also means any archaeological, historical, and cultural remains associated with or representative of historic or prehistoric American Indians and historic groups or peoples and their activities.

(174)    (2) *Traditional fishing* means those commercial, recreational, and subsistence fishing activities that were customarily conducted within the Sanctuary prior to its designation or expansion, as identified in the relevant Final Environmental Impact Statement and Management Plan for this Sanctuary.

(175)    (b) All other terms appearing in the regulations in this subpart are defined at 15 CFR 922.3, and/or in the Marine Protection, Research, and Sanctuaries Act, as amended, 33 U.S.C. 1401 *et seq.*, and 16 U.S.C. 1431 *et seq.*

(176)
### §922.202 Joint management.

(177)    NOAA has primary responsibility for the management of the Sanctuary pursuant to the Act. However, NOAA shall co-manage the Sanctuary in collaboration with the State of Maryland and Charles County. The Director shall enter into a Memorandum of Agreement regarding this collaboration that shall address, but not be limited to, such aspects as areas of mutual concern, including Sanctuary programs, permitting, activities, development, and threats to Sanctuary resources.

(178)
### §922.203 Prohibited or otherwise regulated activities.

(179)    (a) Except as specified in paragraphs (b) and (c) of this section, the following activities are prohibited and thus are unlawful for any person to conduct or to cause to be conducted:

(180)    (1) Moving, removing, recovering, altering, destroying, possessing, or otherwise injuring, or attempting to move, remove, recover, alter, destroy, possess or otherwise injure a Sanctuary resource, except as an incidental result of traditional fishing. This prohibition does not apply to possessing historical resources removed from the Sanctuary area before the effective date of the Sanctuary designation.

(181)    (2) Marking, defacing, or damaging in any way, or displacing or removing or tampering with any signs, notices, or placards, whether temporary or permanent, or with any monuments, stakes, posts, buoys, or other boundary markers related to the Sanctuary.

(182)    (3) Interfering with, obstructing, delaying or preventing an investigation, search, seizure or disposition of seized property in connection with enforcement of the Act or any regulation or any permit issued under the Act.

(183)    (b) The prohibitions in paragraphs (a)(1) through (3) of this section do not apply to any activity necessary to respond to an emergency threatening life, property or the environment; or to activities necessary for valid law enforcement purposes.

(184)    (c)(1) All military activities shall be carried out in a manner that avoids to the maximum extent practicable any adverse impact on sanctuary resources and qualities.

(185)    (2) Any existing military activity conducted by DoD prior to the effective date of the regulations in this subpart and as specifically identified in the Final Environmental Impact Statement and Final Management Plan for the Sanctuary (FEIS/FMP) is allowed to continue in the Sanctuary. The prohibitions in paragraphs (a)(1) through (3) of this section do not apply to those existing military activities or to the following military activities conducted by DoD:

(186)    (i) Low-level overflight of military aircraft operated by DoD;

(187)    (ii) The designation of new units of special use airspace;

(188)    (iii) The use or establishment of military flight training routes;

(189)    (iv) Air or ground access to existing or new electronic tracking communications sites associated with special use airspace or military flight training routes; or

(190)    (v) Activities to reduce or eliminate a threat to human life or property presented by unexploded ordnances or munitions.

(191)    (3) New military activities that do not violate the prohibitions in paragraphs (a)(1) through (3) of this section are allowed. Any new military activity that is likely to violate sanctuary prohibitions may become exempt through consultation between the Director and DoD pursuant to section 304(d) of the NMSA. For purposes of this paragraph (c)(3), the term "new military activity" includes but is not limited to, any existing military activity that is modified in any way (including change in location, frequency, duration, or technology used) that is likely to destroy, cause the loss of, or injure a sanctuary resource, or is likely to destroy, cause the loss of, or injure a sanctuary resource in a manner or to an extent that was not considered in a previous consultation under section 304(d) of the NMSA.

(192)    (4) In the event of destruction of, loss of, or injury to a sanctuary resource or quality resulting from an incident, including but not limited to spills and groundings caused by DoD, the cognizant component shall promptly coordinate with the Director for the purpose of taking appropriate actions to prevent, respond to or mitigate the harm and, if possible, restore or replace the sanctuary resource or quality.

(193)
### §922.204 Emergency regulations.

(194)    (a) Where necessary to prevent or minimize the destruction of, loss of, or injury to a Sanctuary resource, or to minimize the imminent risk of such destruction, loss, or injury, any and all activities, other than DoD activities, are subject to immediate temporary regulation, including prohibition. An emergency regulation shall not take effect without the approval of the Governor of Maryland or her/his designee or designated agency.

(195)    (b) Emergency regulations remain in effect until a date fixed in the rule or six months after the effective date, whichever is earlier. The rule may be extended once for not more than six months.

(196)
### §922.205 Permit procedures and review criteria.

(197)    (a) *Authority to issue general permits.* The Director may allow a person to conduct an activity that would otherwise be prohibited by this subpart, through issuance of a general permit, provided the applicant complies with:

(198)    (1) The provisions of subpart E of this part; and

(199)    (2) The relevant site-specific regulations appearing in this subpart.

(200)    (b) *Sanctuary general permit categories.* The Director may issue a sanctuary general permit under this subpart, subject to such terms and conditions as he or she deems appropriate, if the Director finds that the proposed activity falls within one of the following categories:

(201)    (1) Research—activities that constitute scientific research on or scientific monitoring of national marine sanctuary resources or qualities;

(202)    (2) Education—activities that enhance public awareness, understanding, or appreciation of a national marine sanctuary or national marine sanctuary resources or qualities; or

(203)    (3) Management—activities that assist in managing a national marine sanctuary.

(204)    (c) *Review criteria.* The Director shall not issue a permit under this subpart, unless he or she also finds that:

(205)    (1) The proposed activity will be conducted in a manner compatible with the primary objective of protection of national marine sanctuary resources and qualities, taking into account the following factors:

(206)    (i) The extent to which the conduct of the activity may diminish or enhance national marine sanctuary resources and qualities; and

(207)    (ii) Any indirect, secondary or cumulative effects of the activity.

(208)    (2) It is necessary to conduct the proposed activity within the national marine sanctuary to achieve its stated purpose.

(209)    (3) The methods and procedures proposed by the applicant are appropriate to achieve the proposed activity's stated purpose and eliminate, minimize, or mitigate adverse effects on sanctuary resources and qualities as much as possible.

(210)    (4) The duration of the proposed activity and its effects are no longer than necessary to achieve the activity's stated purpose.

(211)    (5) The expected end value of the activity to the furtherance of national marine sanctuary goals and purposes outweighs any potential adverse impacts on sanctuary resources and qualities from the conduct of the activity.

(212)    (6) The applicant is professionally qualified to conduct and complete the proposed activity.

(213)    (7) The applicant has adequate financial resources available to conduct and complete the proposed activity and terms and conditions of the permit.

(214)    (8) There are no other factors that would make the issuance of a permit for the activity inappropriate.

(215)
### §922.206 Certification of preexisting leases, licenses, permits, approvals, other authorizations, or rights to conduct a prohibited activity.

(216)    (a) A person may conduct an activity prohibited by **§922.203(a)(1)** through **(3)** if such activity is specifically authorized by a valid Federal, state, or local lease, permit, license, approval, or other authorization, or tribal right of subsistence use or access in existence prior to the effective date of sanctuary designation and within the sanctuary designated area and complies with **§922.49** and provided that the holder of the lease, permit, license, approval, or other authorization complies with the requirements of paragraph (e) of this section.

(217)    (b) In considering whether to make the certifications called for in this section, the Director may seek and consider the views of any other person or entity, within or outside the Federal government, and may hold a public hearing as deemed appropriate.

(218)    (c) The Director may amend, suspend, or revoke any certification made under this section whenever continued operation would otherwise be inconsistent with any terms or conditions of the certification. Any such action shall be forwarded in writing to both the holder of the certified permit, license, or other authorization and the issuing agency and shall set forth reason(s) for the action taken.

(219)    (d) Requests for findings or certifications should be addressed to the Director, Office of National Marine Sanctuaries; ATTN: Sanctuary Superintendent, Mallows Bay-Potomac National Marine Sanctuary, 1305 East West Hwy., 11th Floor, Silver Spring, MD 20910. A copy of the lease, permit, license, approval, or other authorization must accompany the request.

(220)    (e) For an activity described in paragraph (a) of this section, the holder of the authorization or right may conduct the activity prohibited by § 922.203(a)(1) through (3) provided that:

(221)    (1) The holder of such authorization or right notifies the Director, in writing, within 180 days of the **Federal Register** notification announcing of effective date of the Sanctuary designation, of the existence of such authorization or right and requests certification of such authorization or right;

(222)    (2) The holder complies with the other provisions of this section; and

(223)    (3) The holder complies with any terms and conditions on the exercise of such authorization or right imposed as a condition of certification, by the Director, to achieve the purposes for which the Sanctuary was designated.

(224)    (f) The holder of an authorization or right described in paragraph (a) of this section authorizing an activity

prohibited by § 922.203 may conduct the activity without being in violation of applicable provisions of § 922.203, pending final agency action on his or her certification request, provided the holder is otherwise in compliance with this section.

(225)     (g) The Director may request additional information from the certification requester as he or she deems reasonably necessary to condition appropriately the exercise of the certified authorization or right to achieve the purposes for which the Sanctuary was designated. The Director must receive the information requested within 45 days of the postmark date of the request. The Director may seek the views of any persons on the certification request.

(226)     (h) The Director may amend any certification made under this section whenever additional information becomes available that he/she determines justifies such an amendment.

(227)     (i) Upon completion of review of the authorization or right and information received with respect thereto, the Director shall communicate, in writing, any decision on a certification request or any action taken with respect to any certification made under this section, in writing, to both the holder of the certified lease, permit, license, approval, other authorization, or right, and the issuing agency, and shall set forth the reason(s) for the decision or action taken.

(228)     (j) The holder may appeal any action conditioning, amending, suspending, or revoking any certification in accordance with the procedures set forth in § 922.50.

(229)     (k) Any time limit prescribed in or established under this section may be extended by the Director for good cause.

(230)

### Appendix A to Subpart S of Part 922—Mallows Bay-Potomac River Marine Sanctuary Boundary Description and Coordinates of the Lateral Boundary Closures and Excluded Areas

(231)     Table 1—Coordinates for Sanctuary

(232)

**Table 1—Coordinates for Sanctuary**
Coordinates listed in this Appendix are unprojected (Geographic) and based on the North American Datum of 1983.

| Point | Latitude (N) | Longitude (W) |
|---|---|---|
| 1 | 38.39731 | −77.31008 |
| 2 | 38.39823 | −77.31030 |
| 3 | 38.39856 | −77.31059 |
| 4 | 38.39886 | −77.31074 |
| 5 | 38.39917 | −77.31067 |
| 6 | 38.40014 | −77.31074 |
| 7 | 38.40090 | −77.31145 |
| 8 | 38.40138 | −77.31215 |
| 9 | 38.40197 | −77.31236 |
| 10 | 38.40314 | −77.31278 |
| 11 | 38.40658 | −77.31377 |
| 12 | 38.40984 | −77.31465 |

**Table 1—Coordinates for Sanctuary**
Coordinates listed in this Appendix are unprojected (Geographic) and based on the North American Datum of 1983.

| Point | Latitude (N) | Longitude (W) |
|---|---|---|
| 13 | 38.41388 | −77.31692 |
| 14 | 38.41831 | −77.31913 |
| 15 | 38.41974 | −77.31930 |
| 16 | 38.42352 | −77.31971 |
| 17 | 38.42548 | −77.32030 |
| 18 | 38.42737 | −77.32081 |
| 19 | 38.43091 | −77.32240 |
| 20 | 38.43163 | −77.32242 |
| 21 | 38.43350 | −77.32263 |
| 22 | 38.43384 | −77.32269 |
| 23 | 38.43430 | −77.32265 |
| 24 | 38.43461 | −77.32229 |
| 25 | 38.43498 | −77.32146 |
| 26 | 38.43526 | −77.32057 |
| 27 | 38.43522 | −77.32040 |
| 28 | 38.47321 | −77.31845 |
| 29 | 38.47434 | −77.31874 |
| 30 | 38.47560 | −77.31752 |
| 31 | 38.47655 | −77.31686 |
| 32 | 38.47748 | −77.31666 |
| 33 | 38.47821 | −77.31604 |
| 34 | 38.47871 | −77.31554 |
| 35 | 38.47885 | −77.31563 |
| 36 | 38.47905 | −77.31559 |
| 37 | 38.47921 | −77.31578 |
| 38 | 38.47943 | −77.31592 |
| 39 | 38.47985 | −77.31592 |
| 40 | 38.48493 | −77.31335 |
| 41* | 38.48554. | −77.27298 |
| 42* | 38.39793 | −77.25704 |
| 43 | 38.39731 | −77.31008 |

(233)     Note 1 to table 1 of this appendix: The coordinates in the table above marked with an asterisk (*) are not a part of the sanctuary boundary. These coordinates are landward reference points used to draw a line segment that intersects with the shoreline.

(234)

### Appendix B to Subpart S of Part 922—Mallows Bay-Potomac River Marine Sanctuary Terms of Designation

(235)     **Terms of Designation for the Mallows Bay-Potomac River National Marine Sanctuary**

(236)     Under the authority of the National Marine Sanctuaries Act, as amended (the "Act" or "NMSA"), 16 U.S.C. 1431 *et seq.*, certain waters and submerged lands located off the Nanjemoy Peninsula of Charles County, Maryland, and along the tidal Potomac River and its surrounding waters are hereby designated as a National Marine Sanctuary for the purposes of providing

long-term protection and management of the historical resources and recreational, research, educational, and aesthetic qualities of the area.

(237)     *Article I: Effect of Designation*

(238)     The NMSA authorizes the issuance of such regulations as are necessary and reasonable to implement the designation, including managing and protecting the historical resources and recreational, research, and educational qualities of the Mallows Bay-Potomac River National Marine Sanctuary (the "Sanctuary"). Section 1 of Article IV of this appendix lists those activities that may have to be regulated on the effective date of designation, or at some later date, in order to protect Sanctuary resources and qualities. Listing an activity does not necessarily mean that it will be regulated; however, if an activity is not listed it may not be regulated, except on an emergency basis, unless Section 1 of Article IV is amended by the same procedures by which the original Sanctuary designation was made.

(239)     *Article II: Description of the Area*

(240)     The Mallows Bay-Potomac River National Marine Sanctuary consists of an area of approximately 18 square miles of waters of the State of Maryland and the submerged lands thereunder, over, around, and under the underwater cultural resources in the Potomac River between Stafford County, Virginia, and Charles County, Maryland. The western boundary of the sanctuary approximates the border between the Commonwealth of Virginia and the State of Maryland for roughly 6 miles along the Potomac River, beginning north of the mouth of Aquia Creek in Stafford County, Virginia, near Brent Point and continuing north past Widewater, VA, and Clifton Point to a point north of Tank Creek. From this point the sanctuary boundary crosses the Potomac to the east until it intersects the Maryland shoreline just north of Sandy Point in Charles County, MD. From this point the eastern boundary of the sanctuary, approximately 8 miles in total length, follows the Maryland shoreline south past Mallows Bay, Blue Banks, and Wades Bay to a point just south of Smith Point. From this location the sanctuary boundary crosses the Potomac River to the west back to its point of origin north of the mouth of Aquia Creek near Brent Point on the Virginia side of the river.

(241)     *Article III: Special Characteristics of the Area*

(242)     Mallows Bay-Potomac River National Marine Sanctuary and its surrounding waters contain a diverse collection more than 100 known historic shipwreck vessels dating back to the Civil War and potentially dating back to the Revolutionary War, as well as archaeological artifacts dating back 12,000 years indicating the presence of some of the region's earliest American Indian cultures, including the Piscataway Indian Nation and the Piscataway Conoy Confederacy and Sub-Tribes of Maryland. The area is most renowned for the remains of over 100 wooden steamships, known as the "Ghost Fleet," that were built for the U.S. Emergency Fleet between 1917-1919 as part of U.S. engagement in WWI. Their construction at more than 40 shipyards in 17 states

reflects the massive national wartime effort that drove the expansion and economic development of communities and related maritime service industries including the present-day Merchant Marines. The area is contiguous to the Captain John Smith Chesapeake National Historic Trail, the Star Spangled Banner National Historic Trail, the Potomac Heritage National Scenic Trail and the Lower Potomac Water Trail which offer meaningful educational and recreational opportunities centered on the region's culture, heritage and history. Additionally, the structure provided by the vessels and related infrastructure serve as important habitat to thriving populations of recreational fisheries, bald eagles, and other aquatic species. The area's listing on the National Historical Register of Places in 2015 codifies the historical, archaeological and recreational significance of the Ghost Fleet and related maritime cultural heritage sites in and around Mallows Bay-Potomac River National Marine Sanctuary.

(243)     *Article IV: Scope of Regulations*

(244)     Section 1. Activities Subject to Regulation. The following activities are subject to regulation, including prohibition, to the extent necessary and reasonable to ensure the protection and management of the historical resources and recreational, research and educational qualities of the area:

(245)     a. Moving, removing, recovering, altering, destroying, possessing, or otherwise injuring, or attempting to move, remove, recover, alter, destroy, possess or otherwise injure a Sanctuary resource, except as an incidental result of traditional fishing (as defined in the regulations).

(246)     b. Marking, defacing, or damaging in any way, or displacing or removing or tampering with any signs, notices, or placards, whether temporary or permanent, or with any monuments, stakes, posts, buoys, or other boundary markers related to the Sanctuary.

(247)     c. Interfering with, obstructing, delaying or preventing an investigation, search, seizure or disposition of seized property in connection with enforcement of the Act or any regulation issued under the Act.

(248)     Section 2. NOAA will not exercise its authority under the NMSA to regulate fishing in the Sanctuary.

(249)     Section 3. Emergencies. Where necessary to prevent or minimize the destruction of, loss of, or injury to a Sanctuary resource; or minimize the imminent risk of such destruction, loss, or injury, any activity, including those not listed in Section 1, is subject to immediate temporary regulation. An emergency regulation shall not take effect without the approval of the Governor of Maryland or her/his designee or designated agency.

(250)     *Article V: Relation to Other Regulatory Program*

(251)     Section 1. Fishing Regulations, Licenses, and Permits. Fishing in the Sanctuary shall not be regulated as part of the Sanctuary management regime authorized by the Act. However, fishing in the Sanctuary may be regulated by other Federal, State, Tribal and local authorities of competent jurisdiction, and designation

of the Sanctuary shall have no effect on any regulation, permit, or license issued thereunder.

(252)  Section 2. Other Regulations, Licenses, and Permits. If any valid regulation issued by any federal, state, Tribal, or local authority of competent jurisdiction, regardless of when issued, conflicts with a Sanctuary regulation, the regulation deemed by the Director of the Office of National Marine Sanctuaries, National Oceanic and Atmospheric Administration, or designee, in consultation with the State of Maryland, to be more protective of Sanctuary resources and qualities shall govern. Pursuant to section 304(c)(1) of the Act, 16 U.S.C. 1434(c)(1), no valid lease, permit, license, approval, or other authorization issued by any federal, state, Tribal, or local authority of competent jurisdiction, or any right of subsistence use or access, may be terminated by the Secretary of Commerce, or designee, as a result of this designation, or as a result of any Sanctuary regulation, if such lease, permit, license, approval, or other authorization, or right of subsistence use or access was issued or in existence as of the effective date of this designation. However, the Secretary of Commerce or designee, in consultation with the State of Maryland, may regulate the exercise of such authorization or right consistent with the purposes for which the Sanctuary is designated.

(253)  Section 3. Department of Defense Activities. DoD activities shall be carried out in a manner that avoids to the maximum extent practicable any adverse impacts on sanctuary resources and qualities. Any existing military activity conducted by DoD prior to the effective date of the regulations in this subpart and as specifically identified in the Final Environmental Impact Statement and Final Management Plan for the Sanctuary (FEIS/FMP) is allowed to continue in the Sanctuary. The prohibitions in **§922.203(a)(1)** through (3) do not apply to those existing military activities listed in the FEIS/FMP or the military activities conducted by DoD listed in **§922.203(c)(2)**. New military activities that do not violate the prohibitions in paragraphs (a)(1) through (3) of this section are allowed. Any new military activity that is likely to violate sanctuary prohibitions may become exempt through consultation between the Director and DoD pursuant to section 304(d) of the NMSA. The term "new military activity" includes but is not limited to, any existing military activity that is modified in any way (including change in location, frequency, duration, or technology used) that is likely to destroy, cause the loss of, or injure a sanctuary resource, or is likely to destroy, cause the loss of, or injure a sanctuary resource in a manner or to an extent that was not considered in a previous consultation under section **304(d)** of the NMSA. In the event of destruction of, loss of, or injury to a sanctuary resource or quality resulting from an incident, including but not limited to spills and groundings caused by DoD, the cognizant component shall promptly coordinate with the Director for the purpose of taking appropriate

actions to prevent, respond to or mitigate the harm and, if possible, restore or replace the sanctuary resource or quality.

(254)  *Article VI. Alteration of This Designation*

(255)  The terms of designation may be modified only by the same procedures by which the original designation is made, including public meetings, consultation according to the NMSA.

(256)

## §922.10 General.

(257)  (a) *Nomination process.* The sanctuary nomination process (see National Marine Sanctuaries Web site *www.sanctuaries.noaa.gov*) is the means by which the public can submit areas of the marine and Great Lakes environments for consideration by NOAA as a national marine sanctuary.

(258)  (b) *National significance criteria.* The Director will consider the following in determining if a nominated area is of special national significance:

(259)  (1) The area's natural resources and ecological qualities are of special significance and contribute to: Biological productivity or diversity; maintenance or enhancement of ecosystem structure and function; maintenance of ecologically or commercially important species or species assemblages; maintenance or enhancement of critical habitat, representative biogeographic assemblages, or both; or maintenance or enhancement of connectivity to other ecologically significant resources.

(260)  (2) The area contains submerged maritime heritage resources of special historical, cultural, or archaeological significance, that: Individually or collectively are consistent with the criteria of eligibility or listing on the National Register of Historic Places; have met or which would meet the criteria for designation as a National Historic Landmark; or have special or sacred meaning to the indigenous people of the region or nation.

(261)  (3) The area supports present and potential economic uses, such as: Tourism; commercial and recreational fishing; subsistence and traditional uses; diving; and other recreational uses that depend on conservation and management of the area's resources.

(262)  (4) The publicly-derived benefits of the area, such as aesthetic value, public recreation, and access to places depend on conservation and management of the area's resources.

(263)  (c) *Management considerations.* The Director will consider the following in determining the manageability of a nominated area:

(264)  (1) The area provides or enhances opportunities for research in marine science, including marine archaeology.

(265)  (2) The area provides or enhances opportunities for education, including the understanding and appreciation of the marine and Great Lakes environments.

(266)  (3) Adverse impacts from current or future uses and activities threaten the area's significance, values, qualities, and resources.

(267)      (4) A national marine sanctuary would provide unique conservation and management value for this area that also have beneficial values for adjacent areas.

(268)      (5) The existing regulatory and management authorities for the area could be supplemented or complemented to meet the conservation and management goals for the area.

(269)      (6) There are commitments or possible commitments for partnerships opportunities such as cost sharing, office space or exhibit space, vessel time, or other collaborations to aid conservation or management programs for the area.

(270)
## TITLE 33–NAVIGATION AND NAVIGABLE WATERS

(271)
## Part 26–VesselBridge-to-Bridge Radiotelephone Regulations

(272)
### §26.01 Purpose

(273)      (a) The purpose of this part is to implement the provisions of the Vessel Bridge-to-Bridge Radiotelephone Act. This part–

(274)      (1) Requires the use of the vessel bridge-to-bridge radiotelephone;

(275)      (2) Provides the Coast Guard's interpretation of the meaning of important terms in the Act;

(276)      (3) Prescribes the procedures for applying for an exemption from the Act and the regulations issued under the Act and a listing of exemptions.

(277)      (b) Nothing in this part relieves any person from the obligation of complying with the rules of the road and the applicable pilot rules.

(278)
### §26.02 Definitions.

(279)      For the purpose of this part and interpreting the Act–

(280)      *Act* means the "Vessel Bridge-to-Bridge Radiotelephone Act", 33 U.S.C. sections 1201–1208;

(281)      *Length* is measured from end to end over the deck excluding sheer;

(282)      *Power-driven vessel* means any vessel propelled by machinery; and

(283)      *Secretary* means the Secretary of the Department in which the Coast Guard is operating;

(284)      *Territorial sea* means all waters as defined in §2.22(a)(1) of this chapter.

(285)      *Towing vessel* means any commercial vessel engaged in towing another vessel astern, alongside, or by pushing ahead.

(286)      *Vessel Traffic Services (VTS)* means a service implemented under Part 161 of this chapter by the United States Coast Guard designed to improve the safety and efficiency of vessel traffic and to protect the environment. The VTS has the capability to interact with marine traffic and respond to traffic situations developing in the VTS area.

(287)      *Vessel Traffic Service Area* or *VTS Area* means the geographical area encompassing a specific VTS area of service as described in Part 161 of this chapter. This area of service may be subdivided into sectors for the purpose of allocating responsibility to individual Vessel Traffic Centers or to identify different operating requirements.

(288)      **Note:** Although regulatory jurisdiction is limited to the navigable waters of the United States, certain vessels will be encouraged or may be required, as a condition of port entry, to report beyond this area to facilitate traffic management within the VTS area.

(289)
### §26.03 Radiotelephone required.

(290)      (a) Unless an exemption is granted under §26.09 and except as provided in paragraph (a)(4) of this section, this part applies to:

(291)      (1) Every power-driven vessel of 20 meters or over in length while navigating;

(292)      (2) Every vessel of 100 gross tons and upward carrying one or more passengers for hire while navigating;

(293)      (3) Every towing vessel of 26 feet or over in length while navigating; and

(294)      (4) Every dredge and floating plant engaged in or near a channel or fairway in operations likely to restrict or affect navigation of other vessels except for an unmanned or intermittently manned floating plant under the control of a dredge.

(295)      (b) Every vessel, dredge, or floating plant described in paragraph (a) of this section must have a radiotelephone on board capable of operation from its navigational bridge, or in the case of a dredge, from its main control station, and capable of transmitting and receiving on the frequency or frequencies within the 156–162 Mega-Hertz band using the classes of emissions designated by the Federal Communications Commission for the exchange of navigational information.

(296)      (c) The radiotelephone required by paragraph (b) of this section must be carried on board the described vessels, dredges, and floating plants upon the navigable waters of the United States.

(297)      (d) The radiotelephone required by paragraph (b) of this section must be capable of transmitting and receiving on VHF–FM channel 22A (157.1 MHz).

(298)      (e) While transiting any of the following waters, each vessel described in paragraph (a) of this section also must have on board a radiotelephone capable of transmitting and receiving on VHF–FM channel 67 (156.375 MHz):

(299)      (1) The lower Mississippi River from the territorial sea boundary, and within either the Southwest Pass safety fairway or the South Pass safety fairway specified in 33 CFR 166.200, to mile 242.4 AHP (Above Head of Passes) near Baton Rouge;

(300)      (2) The Mississippi River-Gulf Outlet from the territorial sea boundary, and within the Mississippi River-Gulf outlet Safety Fairway specified in 33 CFR

(301) 166.200, to that channel's junction with the Inner Harbor Navigation Canal; and

(301) (3) The full length of the Inner Harbor Navigation Canal from its junction with the Mississippi River to that canal's entry to Lake Pontchartrain at the New Seabrook vehicular bridge.

(302) (f) In addition to the radiotelephone required by paragraph (b) of this section, each vessel described in paragraph (a) of this section while transiting any waters within a Vessel Traffic Service Area, must have on board a radiotelephone capable of transmitting and receiving on the VTS designated frequency in Table 161.12(c) (VTS and VMRS Centers, Call Signs/MMSI, Designated Frequencies, and Monitoring Areas).

(303) **Note:** A single VHF–FM radio capable of scanning or sequential monitoring (often referred to as "dual watch" capability) will not meet the requirements for two radios.

(304)
### §26.04 Use of the designated frequency.

(305) (a) No person may use the frequency designated by the Federal Communications Commission under section 8 of the Act, 33 U.S.C. 1207 (a), to transmit any information other than information necessary for the safe navigation of vessels or necessary tests.

(306) (b) Each person who is required to maintain a listening watch under section 5 of the Act shall, when necessary, transmit and confirm, on the designated frequency, the intentions of his vessel and any other information necessary for the safe navigation of vessels.

(307) (c) Nothing in these regulations may be construed as prohibiting the use of the designated frequency to communicate with shore stations to obtain or furnish information necessary for the safe navigation of vessels.

(308) (d) On the navigable waters of the United States, channel 13 (156.65 MHz) is the designated frequency required to be monitored in accordance with §26.05(a) except that in the area prescribed in §26.03(e), channel 67 (156.375 MHz) is the designated frequency.

(309) (e) On those navigable waters of the United States within a VTS area, the designated VTS frequency is an additional designated frequency required to be monitored in accordance with §26.05.

(310)
### §26.05 Use of radiotelephone.

(311) Section 5 of the Act states that the radiotelephone required by this Act is for the exclusive use of the master or person in charge of the vessel, or the person designated by the master or person in charge to pilot or direct the movement of the vessel, who shall maintain a listening watch on the designated frequency. Nothing herein shall be interpreted as precluding the use of portable radiotelephone equipment to satisfy the requirements of this act.

(312)
### §26.06 Maintenance of radiotelephone; failure of radiotelephone.

(313) Section 6 of the Act states–(a) Whenever radiotelephone capability is required by this Act, a vessel's radiotelephone equipment shall be maintained in effective operating condition. If the radiotelephone equipment carried aboard a vessel ceases to operate, the master shall exercise due diligence to restore it or cause it to be restored to effective operating condition at the earliest practicable time. The failure of a vessel's radiotelephone equipment shall not, in itself, constitute a violation of this Act, nor shall it obligate the master of any vessel to moor or anchor his vessel; however, the loss of radiotelephone capability shall be given consideration in the navigation of the vessel.

(314)
### §26.07 Communications.

(315) No person may use the service of, and no person may serve as, a person required to maintain a listening watch under section 5 of the Act, 33 U.S.C. 1204, unless the person can communicate in the English language.

(316)
### §26.08 Exemption procedures.

(317) (a) The Commandant has redelegated to the Assistant Commandant for Prevention Policy, U.S. Coast Guard Headquarters, with the reservation that this authority shall not be further redelegated, the authority to grant exemptions from provisions of the Vessel Bridge-to-Bridge Radiotelephone Act and this part.

(318) (b) Any person may petition for an exemption from any provision of the Act or this part;

(319) (c) Each petition must be submitted in writing to Commandant (CG–DCO–D), Attn: Deputy for Operations Policy and Capabilities, U.S. Coast Guard Stop 7318, 2703 Martin Luther King Jr. Avenue SE., Washington, DC 20593–7318, and must state:

(320) (1) The provisions of the Act or this part from which an exemption is requested; and

(321) (2) The reasons why marine navigation will not be adversely affected if the exemption is granted and if the exemption relates to a local communication system how that system would fully comply with the intent of the concept of the Act but would not conform in detail if the exemption is granted.

(322)
### §26.09 List of exemptions.

(323) (a) All vessels navigating on those waters governed by the navigation rules for Great Lakes and their connecting and tributary waters (33 U.S.C. 241 et seq.) are exempt from the requirements of the Vessel Bridge-to-Bridge Radiotelephone Act and this part until May 6, 1975.

(324) (b) Each vessel navigating on the Great Lakes as defined in the Inland Navigational Rules Act of 1980 (33 U.S.C. 2001 et seq.) and to which the Vessel Bridge-to-Bridge Radiotelephone Act (33 U.S.C. 1201–1208)

applies is exempt from the requirements in 33 U.S.C. 1203, 1204, and 1205 and the regulations under §26.03, 26.04, 26.05, 26.06, and 26.07. Each of these vessels and each person to whom 33 U.S.C. 1208(a) applies must comply with Articles VII, X, XI, XII, XIII, XV, and XVI and Technical Regulations 1–9 of "The Agreement Between the United States of America and Canada for Promotion of Safety on the Great Lakes by Means of Radio, 1973."

<sup>(325)</sup>

## Part 80–COLREGSDemarcation Lines

<sup>(326)</sup>

### §80.01 General basis and purpose of demarcation lines.

<sup>(327)</sup>     (a) The regulations in this part establish the lines of demarcation delineating those waters upon which mariners shall comply with the International Regulations for Preventing Collisions at Sea, 1972 (72 COLREGS) and those waters upon which mariners shall comply with the Inland Navigation Rules.

<sup>(328)</sup>     (b) The waters inside of the lines are Inland Rules waters. The waters outside the lines are COLREGS waters.

<sup>(329)</sup>     (c) Geographic coordinates expressed in terms of latitude or longitude, or both, are not intended for plotting on maps or charts whose referenced horizontal datum is the North American Datum of 1983 (NAD 83), unless such geographic coordinates are expressly labeled NAD 83. Geographic coordinates without the NAD 83 reference may be plotted on maps or charts referenced to NAD 83 only after application of the appropriate corrections that are published on the particular map or chart being used.

<sup>(330)</sup>

### §80.165 New York Harbor.

<sup>(331)</sup>     A line drawn from 40°34'56.600"N., 073°45'17.200"W. (East Rockaway Inlet Breakwater Light) to 40°27'42.177"N., 074°00'07.309"W. (Sandy Hook Light).

<sup>(332)</sup>

### §80.501 Sandy Hook, NJ to Tom's River, NJ.

<sup>(333)</sup>     (a) A line drawn across the seaward extremity of Shark River Inlet.

<sup>(334)</sup>     (b) A line drawn across the seaward extremity of Manasquan Inlet.

<sup>(335)</sup>     (c) A line drawn across the seaward extremity of Barnegat Inlet.

<sup>(336)</sup>

### §80.502 Tom's River, NJ to Cape May, NJ.

<sup>(337)</sup>     (a) A line drawn from the seaward tangent of Long Beach Island to the seaward tangent to Pullen Island across Beach Haven and Little Egg Inlet, thence across Brigantine Inlet to Brigantine Island.

<sup>(338)</sup>     (b) A line drawn from the seaward extremity of Absecon Inlet.

<sup>(339)</sup>     (c) A line drawn parallel with the general trend of highwater shoreline from the southernmost point of Longport at latitude 39°17.6'N., longitude 74°33.1'W. across Great Egg Harbor Inlet.

<sup>(340)</sup>     (d) A line drawn parallel with the general trend of highwater shoreline across Corson Inlet.

<sup>(341)</sup>     (e) A line formed by the centerline of the Townsend Inlet Highway Bridge.

<sup>(342)</sup>     (f) A line formed by the shoreline of Seven Mile Beach to 39°00'23.757"N., 074°47'28.017"W. (Hereford Inlet Light).

<sup>(343)</sup>     (g) A line drawn across the seaward extremity of Cape May Inlet.

<sup>(344)</sup>

### §80.503 Delaware Bay.

<sup>(345)</sup>     A line drawn from Cape May Light to Harbor of Refuge Light; thence to the northernmost extremity of Cape Henlopen.

<sup>(346)</sup>

### §80.505 Cape Henlopen, DE, to Cape Charles, VA.

<sup>(347)</sup>     (a) A line drawn from the seaward extremity of Indian River Inlet North Jetty to Indian River Inlet South Jetty Light.

<sup>(348)</sup>     (b) A line drawn from Ocean City Inlet Light 6, 225° true across Ocean City Inlet to the submerged south breakwater.

<sup>(349)</sup>     (c) A line drawn from Assateague Beach Tower Light to the tower charted at 37°52.6'N., 75°26.7'W.

<sup>(350)</sup>     (d) A line formed by the range of Wachapreague Inlet Light 3 and Parramore Beach Lookout Tower drawn across Wachapreague Inlet.

<sup>(351)</sup>     (e) A line drawn from the lookout tower charted on the northern end of Hog Island to the seaward tangent of Parramore Beach.

<sup>(352)</sup>     (f) A line drawn 207° true from the lookout tower charted on the southern end of Hog Island across Great Machipongo Inlet.

<sup>(353)</sup>     (g) A line formed by the range of the two cupolas charted on the southern end of Cobb Island drawn across Sand Shoal Inlet.

<sup>(354)</sup>     (h) Except as provided elsewhere in this section from Cape Henlopen to Cape Charles, lines drawn parallel with the general trend of the highwater shoreline across the entrances to small bays and inlets.

<sup>(355)</sup>

### §80.510 Chesapeake Bay Entrance, VA.

<sup>(356)</sup>     A line drawn from Cape Charles Light to Cape Henry Light.

<sup>(357)</sup>

## Part 81–72 COLREGS: IMPLEMENTING RULES

<sup>(358)</sup>

### §81.1 Definitions.

<sup>(359)</sup>     As used in this part:

<sup>(360)</sup>     *72 COLREGS* refers to the International Regulations for Preventing Collisions at Sea, 1972, done at London,

(361) October 20, 1972, as rectified by the Proces-Verbal of December 1, 1973, as amended.

(361) *A vessel of special construction or purpose* means a vessel designed or modified to perform a special function and whose arrangement is thereby made relatively inflexible.

(362) *Interference with the special function of the vessel* occurs when installation or use of lights, shapes, or sound-signaling appliances under 72 COLREGS prevents or significantly hinders the operation in which the vessel is usually engaged.

(363)
### §81.3 General.

(364) Vessels of special construction or purpose which cannot fully comply with the light, shape, and sound signal provisions of 72 COLREGS without interfering with their special function may instead meet alternative requirements. The Chief of the Prevention Division in each Coast Guard District Office makes this determination and requires that alternative compliance be as close as possible with the 72 COLREGS. These regulations set out the procedure by which a vessel may be certified for alternative compliance. The information collection and recordkeeping requirements in §§81.5 and 81.18 have been approved by the Office of Management and Budget under OMB control No. 1625-0019.

(365)
### Alternative Compliance

(366)
### §81.5 Application for a Certificate of Alternative Compliance.

(367) (a) The owner, builder, operator, or agent of a vessel of special construction or purpose who believes the vessel cannot fully comply with the 72 COLREGS light, shape, or sound signal provisions without interference with its special function may apply for a determination that alternative compliance is justified. The application must be in writing, submitted to the Chief of the Prevention Division of the Coast Guard District in which the vessel is being built or operated, and include the following information:

(368) (1) The name, address, and telephone number of the applicant.

(369) (2) The identification of the vessel by its:

(370) (i) Official number;

(371) (ii) Shipyard hull number;

(372) (iii) Hull identification number; or

(373) (iv) State number, if the vessel does not have an official number or hull identification number.

(374) (3) Vessel name and home port, if known.

(375) (4) A description of the vessel's area of operation.

(376) (5) A description of the provision for which the Certificate of Alternative Compliance is sought, including:

(377) (i) The 72 COLREGS Rule or Annex section number for which the Certificate of Alternative Compliance is sought;

(378) (ii) A description of the special function of the vessel that would be interfered with by full compliance with the provision of that Rule or Annex section; and

(379) (iii) A statement of how full compliance would interfere with the special function of the vessel.

(380) (6) A description of the alternative installation that is in closest possible compliance with the applicable 72 COLREGS Rule or Annex section.

(381) (7) A copy of the vessel's plans or an accurate scale drawing that clearly shows:

(382) (i) The required installation of the equipment under the 72 COLREGS,

(383) (ii) The proposed installation of the equipment for which certification is being sought, and

(384) (iii) Any obstructions that may interfere with the equipment when installed in:

(385) (A) The required location; and

(386) (B) The proposed location.

(387) (b) The Coast Guard may request from the applicant additional information concerning the application.

(388)
### §81.9 Certificate of Alternative Compliance: Contents.

(389) The Chief of the Prevention Division issues the Certificate of Alternative Compliance to the vessel based on a determination that it cannot comply fully with 72 COLREGS light, shape, and sound signal provisions without interference with its special function. This Certificate includes—

(390) (a) Identification of the vessel as supplied in the application under §81.5(a)(2);

(391) (b) The provision of the 72 COLREGS for which the Certificate authorizes alternative compliance;

(392) (c) A certification that the vessel is unable to comply fully with the 72 COLREGS lights, shape, and sound signal requirements without interference with its special function;

(393) (d) A statement of why full compliance would interfere with the special function of the vessel;

(394) (e) The required alternative installation;

(395) (f) A statement that the required alternative installation is in the closest possible compliance with the 72 COLREGS without interfering with the special function of the vessel;

(396) (g) The date of issuance;

(397) (h) A statement that the Certificate of Alternative Compliance terminates when the vessel ceases to be usually engaged in the operation for which the certificate is issued.

(398)
### §81.17 Certificate of Alternative Compliance: Termination.

(399) The Certificate of Alternative Compliance terminates if the information supplied under §81.5(a) or the Certificate issued under §81.9 is no longer applicable to the vessel.

(400)

### §81.18 Notice and record of certification of vessels of special construction or purpose.

(401)     (a) In accordance with 33 U.S.C. 1605(c), a notice is published in the Federal Register of the following:

(402)     (1) Each Certificate of Alternative Compliance issued under §81.9; and

(403)     (2) Each Coast Guard vessel determined by the Commandant to be a vessel of special construction or purpose.

(404)     (b) Copies of Certificate of Alternative Compliance and documentation concerning Coast Guard vessels are available for inspection at Marine Transportation Systems Directorate, U.S. Coast Guard Headquarters, (CG-5PW), Stop 7509, 2703 Martin Luther King Avenue SE., Washington, DC 20593-7509.

(405)     (c) The owner or operator of a vessel issued a Certificate shall ensure that the vessel does not operate unless the Certificate of Alternative Compliance or a certified copy of that Certificate is on board the vessel and available for inspection by Coast Guard personnel.

(406)

### Exemptions

(407)

### §81.20 Lights and sound signal appliances.

(408)     Each vessel under the 72 COLREGS, except the vessels of the Navy, is exempt from the requirements of the 72 COLREGS to the limitation for the period of time stated in Rule 38 (a), (b), (c), (d), (e), (f), and (g) if:

(409)     (a) Her keel is laid or is at a corresponding stage of construction before July 15, 1977; and

(410)     (b) She meets the International Regulations for Preventing Collisions at Sea, 1960 (77 Stat. 194, 33 U.S.C. 1051-1094).

(411)

## Part 82–72 COLREGS: INTERPRETATIVE RULES

(412)

### §82.1 Purpose.

(413)     This part contains the interpretative rules concerning the 72 COLREGS that are adopted by the Coast Guard for the guidance of the public.

(414)

### §82.3 Pushing vessel and vessel being pushed: Composite unit.

(415)     Rule 24(b) of the 72 COLREGS states that when a pushing vessel and a vessel being pushed ahead are rigidly connected in a composite unit, they are regarded as a power-driven vessel and must exhibit the lights under Rule 23. A "composite unit" is interpreted to be a pushing vessel that is rigidly connected by mechanical means to a vessel being pushed so they react to sea and swell as one vessel. "Mechanical means" does not include the following:

(416)     (a) Lines.

(417)     (b) Hawsers.

(418)     (c) Wires.

(419)     (d) Chains.

(420)

### §82.5 Lights for moored vessels.

(421)     For the purposes of Rule 30 of the 72 COLREGS, a *vessel at anchor* includes a barge made fast to one or more mooring buoys or other similar device attached to the sea or river floor. Such a barge may be lighted as a vessel at anchor in accordance with Rule 30, or may be lighted on the corners in accordance with 33 CFR 83.30(h) through (l).

(422)

### §82.7 Sidelights for unmanned barges.

(423)     An unmanned barge being towed may use the exception of COLREGS Rule 24(h). However, this exception only applies to the vertical sector requirements.

(424)

## Part 88—ANNEX V: PILOT RULES

(425)

### §88.01 Purpose and applicability.

(426)     This part applies to all vessels operating on United States inland waters and to United States vessels operating on the Canadian waters of the Great Lakes to the extent there is no conflict with Canadian law.

(427)

### §88.03 Definitions.

(428)     The terms used in this part have the same meaning as the terms defined in part 83 of this subchapter.

(429)

### §88.05 Law enforcement vessels.

(430)     (a) Law enforcement vessels may display a flashing blue light when engaged in direct law enforcement or public safety activities. This light must be located so that it does not interfere with the visibility of the vessel's navigation lights.

(431)     (b) The blue light described in this section may be displayed by law enforcement vessels of the United States and the States and their political subdivisions.

(432)

### §88.07 Public safety activities.

(433)     (a) Vessels engaged in government sanctioned public safety activities, and commercial vessels performing similar functions, may display an alternately flashing red and yellow light signal. This identification light signal must be located so that it does not interfere with the visibility of the vessel's navigation lights. The identification light signal may be used only as an identification signal and conveys no special privilege. Vessels using the identification light signal during public safety activities must abide by the Inland Navigation Rules, and must not presume that the light or the exigency gives them precedence or right of way.

(434)     (b) Public safety activities include but are not limited to patrolling marine parades, regattas, or special water celebrations; traffic control; salvage; firefighting;

(435) medical assistance; assisting disabled vessels; and search and rescue.

## Part 89—INLAND NAVIGATION RULES: IMPLE-MENTING RULES

(436)
### Subpart A—Certificate of Alternative Compliance

(437)
### §89.1 Definitions.

(438)     As used in this subpart:

(439)     *Inland Rules* refers to the Inland Navigation Rules contained in the Inland Navigational Rules Act of 1980 (Pub. L. 96-591) and the technical annexes established under that act.

(440)     *A vessel of special construction or purpose* means a vessel designed or modified to perform a special function and whose arrangement is thereby made relatively inflexible.

(441)     *Interference with the special function of the vessel* occurs when installation or use of lights, shapes, or sound-signaling appliances under the Inland Rules prevents or significantly hinders the operation in which the vessel is usually engaged.

(442)
### §89.3 General.

(443)     Vessels of special construction or purpose which cannot fully comply with the light, shape, and sound signal provisions of the Inland Rules without interfering with their special function may instead meet alternative requirements. The Chief of the Prevention Division in each Coast Guard District Office makes this determination and requires that alternative compliance be as close as possible with the Inland Rules. These regulations set out the procedure by which a vessel may be certified for alternative compliance. The information collection and recordkeeping requirements in §§89.5 and 89.18 have been approved by the Office of Management and Budget under OMB control No. 1625-0019.

(444)
### §89.5 Application for a Certificate of Alternative Compliance.

(445)     (a) The owner, builder, operator, or agent of a vessel of special construction or purpose who believes the vessel cannot fully comply with the Inland Rules light, shape, or sound signal provisions without interference with its special function may apply for a determination that alternative compliance is justified. The application must be in writing, submitted to the Chief of the Prevention Division of the Coast Guard District in which the vessel is being built or operated, and include the following information:

(446)     (1) The name, address, and telephone number of the applicant.

(447)     (2) The identification of the vessel by its:

(448)     (i) Official number;

(449)     (ii) Shipyard hull number;

(450)     (iii) Hull identification number; or

(451)     (iv) State number, if the vessel does not have an official number or hull identification number.

(452)     (3) Vessel name and home port, if known.

(453)     (4) A description of the vessel's area of operation.

(454)     (5) A description of the provision for which the Certificate of Alternative Compliance is sought, including:

(455)     (i) The Inland Rules Rule or Annex section number for which the Certificate of Alternative Compliance is sought;

(456)     (ii) A description of the special function of the vessel that would be interfered with by full compliance with the provision of that Rule or Annex section; and

(457)     (iii) A statement of how full compliance would interfere with the special function of the vessel.

(458)     (6) A description of the alternative installation that is in closest possible compliance with the applicable Inland Navigation Rules Rule or Annex section.

(459)     (7) A copy of the vessel's plans or an accurate scale drawing that clearly shows:

(460)     (i) The required installation of the equipment under the Inland Rules,

(461)     (ii) The proposed installation of the equipment for which certification is being sought, and

(462)     (iii) Any obstructions that may interfere with the equipment when installed in:

(463)     (A) The required location; and

(464)     (B) The proposed location.

(465)     (b) The Coast Guard may request from the applicant additional information concerning the application.

(466)
### §89.9 Certificate of Alternative Compliance: Contents.

(467)     The Chief of the Prevention Division issues the Certificate of Alternative Compliance to the vessel based on a determination that it cannot comply fully with Inland Rules light, shape, and sound signal provisions without interference with its special function. This Certificate includes:

(468)     (a) Identification of the vessel as supplied in the application under §89.5(a)(2);

(469)     (b) The provision of the Inland Rules for which the Certificate authorizes alternative compliance;

(470)     (c) A certification that the vessel is unable to comply fully with the Inland Rules light, shape, and sound signal requirements without interference with its special function;

(471)     (d) A statement of why full compliance would interfere with the special function of the vessel;

(472)     (e) The required alternative installation;

(473)     (f) A statement that the required alternative installation is in the closest possible compliance with the Inland Rules without interfering with the special function of the vessel;

(474)     (g) The date of issuance;

(475) (h) A statement that the Certificate of Alternative Compliance terminates when the vessel ceases to be usually engaged in the operation for which the certificate is issued.

(476)
### §89.17 Certificate of Alternative Compliance: Termination.

(477) The Certificate of Alternative Compliance terminates if the information supplied under §89.5(a) or the Certificate issued under §89.9 is no longer applicable to the vessel.

(478)
### §89.18 Record of certification of vessels of special construction or purpose.

(479) (a) Copies of Certificates of Alternative Compliance and documentation concerning Coast Guard vessels are available for inspection at the offices of the Marine Transportation Systems Directorate, U.S. Coast Guard Headquarters (CG-5PW), Stop 7509, 2703 Martin Luther King Avenue SE., Washington, DC 20593-7509.

(480) (b) The owner or operator of a vessel issued a Certificate shall ensure that the vessel does not operate unless the Certificate of Alternative Compliance or a certified copy of that Certificate is on board the vessel and available for inspection by Coast Guard personnel.

(481)
### Subpart B—Waters Upon Which Certain Inland Navigation Rules Apply

(482)
### §89.21 Purpose.

(483) Inland Navigation Rules 9(a)(ii), 14(d), and 15(b) apply to the Great Lakes, and along with 24(i), apply on the "Western Rivers" as defined in Rule 3(1), and to additional specifically designated waters. The purpose of this Subpart is to specify those additional waters upon which Inland Navigation Rules 9(a)(ii), 14(d), 15(b), and 24(i) apply.

(484)
### §89.23 Definitions.

(485) As used in this subpart:

(486) *Inland Rules* refers to the Inland Navigation Rules contained in the Inland Navigational Rules Act of 1980 (Pub. L. 96-591, 33 U.S.C. 2001 et. seq.) and the technical annexes established under that Act.

(487)
### §89.25 Waters upon which Inland Rules 9(a)(ii), 14(d), and 15(b) apply.

(488) Inland Rules 9(a)(ii), 14(d), and 15(b) apply on the Great Lakes, the Western Rivers, and the following specified waters:

(489) (a) Tennessee-Tombigbee Waterway.

(490) (b) Tombigbee River.

(491) (c) Black Warrior River.

(492) (d) Alabama River.

(493) (e) Coosa River.

(494) (f) Mobile River above the Cochrane Bridge at St. Louis Point.

(495) (g) Flint River.

(496) (h) Chattahoochee River.

(497) (i) The Apalachicola River above its confluence with the Jackson River.

(498)
### §89.27 Waters upon which Inland Rule 24(j) applies.

(499) (a) Inland Rule 24(j) applies on the Western Rivers and the specified waters listed in §89.25 (a) through (i).

(500) (b) Inland Rule 24(j) applies on the Gulf Intracoastal Waterway from St. Marks, Florida, to the Rio Grande, Texas, including the Morgan City-Port Allen Alternate Route and the Galveston-Freeport Cutoff, except that a power-driven vessel pushing ahead or towing alongside shall exhibit the lights required by Inland Rule 24(c), while transiting within the following areas:

(501) (1) St. Andrews Bay from the Hathaway Fixed Bridge at Mile 284.6 East of Harvey Locks (EHL) to the DuPont Fixed Bridge at Mile 295.4 EHL.

(502) (2) Pensacola Bay, Santa Rosa Sound and Big Lagoon from the Light "10" off of Trout Point at Mile 176.9 EHL to the Pensacola Fixed Bridge at Mile 189.1 EHL.

(503) (3) Mobile Bay and Bon Secour Bay from the Dauphin Island Causeway Fixed Bridge at Mile 127.7 EHL to Little Point Clear at Mile 140 EHL.

(504) (4) Mississippi Sound from Grand Island Waterway Light "1" at Mile 53.8 EHL to Light "40" off the West Point of Dauphin Island at Mile 118.7 EHL.

(505) (5) The Mississippi River at New Orleans, Mississippi River-Gulf Outlet Canal and the Inner Harbor Navigation Canal from the junction of the Harvey Canal and the Algiers Alternate Route at Mile 6.5 West of Harvey Locks (WHL) to the Michoud Canal at Mile 18 EHL.

(506) (6) The Calcasieu River from the Calcasieu Lock at Mile 238.6 WHL to the Ellender Lift Bridge at Mile 243.6 WHL.

(507) (7) The Sabine Neches Canal from mile 262.5 WHL to mile 291.5 WHL.

(508) (8) Bolivar Roads from the Bolivar Assembling Basin at Mile 346 WHL to the Galveston Causeway Bridge at Mile 357.3 WHL.

(509) (9) Freeport Harbor from Surfside Beach Fixed Bridge at Mile 393.8 WHL to the Bryan Beach Pontoon Bridge at Mile 397.6 WHL.

(510) (10) Matagorda Ship Channel area of Matagorda Bay from Range "K" Front Light at Mile 468.7 WHL to the Port O'Connor Jetty at Mile 472.2 WHL.

(511) (11) Corpus Christi Bay from Redfish Bay Day Beacon "55" at Mile 537.4 WHL when in the Gulf Intracoastal Waterway main route or from the north end of Lydia Ann Island Mile 531.1A when in the Gulf Intracoastal Waterway Alternate Route to Corpus Christi Bay LT 76 at Mile 543.7 WHL.

(512)      (12) Port Isabel and Brownsville Ship Channel south of the Padre Island Causeway Fixed Bridge at Mile 665.1 WHL.

(513)
## Part 90—INLAND RULES: INTERPRETATIVE RULES

(514)
### §90.1 Purpose.
(515)      This part contains the interpretative rules for the Inland Rules. These interpretative rules are intended as a guide to assist the public and promote compliance with the Inland Rules.

(516)
### §90.3 Pushing vessel and vessel being pushed: Composite unit.
(517)      Rule 24(b) of the Inland Rules states that when a pushing vessel and a vessel being pushed ahead are rigidly connected in a composite unit, they are regarded as a power-driven vessel and must exhibit the lights prescribed in Rule 23. A "composite unit" is interpreted to be the combination of a pushing vessel and a vessel being push ahead that are rigidly connected by mechanical means so they react to sea and swell as one vessel. Mechanical means does not include lines, wires, hawsers, or chains.

(518)
### §90.5 Lights for moored vessels.
(519)      A *vessel at anchor* includes a vessel made fast to one or more mooring buoys or other similar device attached to the ocean floor. Such vessels may be lighted as a vessel at anchor in accordance with Rule 30, or may be lighted on the corners in accordance with 33 CFR 88.30(h) through (l).

(520)
### §90.7 Sidelights for unmanned barges.
(521)      An unmanned barge being towed may use the exception of COLREGS Rule 24(h). However, this exception only applies to the vertical sector requirements for sidelights.

(522)
## Part 110–Anchorage Regulations

(523)
### §110.1 General.
(524)      (a) The areas described in subpart A of this part are designated as special anchorage areas for the purposes of rule 30 (**33 CFR 83.30**) and rule 35 (**33 CFR 83.35**) of the Inland Navigation Rules, 33 CFR chapter I, subchapter E. Vessels of less than 20 meters in length; and barges, canal boats, scows, or other nondescript craft, are not required to sound signals required by rule 35 of the Inland Navigation Rules. Vessels of less than 20 meters are not required to exhibit anchor lights or shapes required by rule 30 of the Inland Navigation Rules.

(525)      (b) The anchorage grounds for vessels described in Subpart B of this part are established, and the rules and regulations in relation thereto adopted, pursuant to the authority contained in section 7 of the act of March 4, 1915, as amended (38 Stat. 1053; 33 U.S.C. 471).

(526)      (c) All bearings in the part are referred to true meridian.

(527)      (d) Geographic coordinates expressed in terms of latitude or longitude, or both, are not intended for plotting on maps or charts whose referenced horizontal datum is the North American Datum of 1983 (NAD 83), unless such geographic coordinates are expressly labeled NAD 83. Geographic coordinates without the NAD 83 reference may be plotted on maps or charts referenced to NAD 83 only after application of the appropriate corrections that are published on the particular map or chart being used.

(528)
## Subpart A–Special Anchorage Areas

(529)
### §110.65 [Removed].

(530)
### §110.67 Delaware River, Essington, PA.
(531)      North of Little Tinicum Island, between the mouth of Darby Creek and Jansen Avenue, Essington, bounded as follows: Beginning at a point (approximately 39°51'31"N., 75°17'43"W.) on a line in prolongation of the westerly line of Jansen Avenue 135 yards southerly from the mean high water line; thence 184°, 300 yards; thence 274°30', 1,700 yards; thence 04°, 425 yards; thence 100°, 1,225 yards; and thence 95°, 490 yards, to the point of beginning.

(532)
### §110.70 [Removed].

(533)      .

(534)
### §110.70a Northeast River, North East, MD.
(535)      The water area west of North East Heights, Maryland enclosed by a line beginning on the shoreline at
(536)      39°34'26"N., 75°57'18"W.; thence westerly to
(537)      39°34'26"N., 75°57'29"W.; thence northeasterly to
(538)      39°34'30"N., 75°57'27"W.; thence easterly to the shoreline at
(539)      39°34'30"N., 75°57'18"W.; thence southerly following the shoreline to the point of beginning.

(540)
### §110.71 Jacobs Nose Cove, Elk River, MD.
(541)      The water area of Jacobs Nose Cove, on the west side of the mouth of Elk River, Maryland, comprising the entire cove south of Jacobs Nose as defined by the shoreline and a line bearing **046°–226°** true across the entrance of the cove tangent to the shore on both the north and south sides.

(542)

### §110.71a [Removed].

(543)

### §110.71b Wye River, Wye, MD.

(544) The waters of a cove on the western shore of Wye River opposite Drum Point enclosed by a line drawn from

(545) 38°53'17"N., 76°11'23"W., to

(546) 38°53'18"N., 76°11'23"W., to

(547) 38°53'18"N., 76°11'13"W.; thence following the shoreline to the point of beginning.

(548)

### §110.72 Blackhole Creek, MD.

(549) The waters on the west side of Blackhole Creek, a tributary of Magothy River, southwest of a line bearing 310°30' from the most northerly tip of an unnamed island located 0.16 mile upstream from the mouth of the creek approximately 660 feet to the west shore of the creek; northwest of a line ranging from the southwesterly tip of the island toward the point of land on the west shore of the creek immediately southwest thereof; and north of a line 100 feet from and parallel to the shore of the creek to its intersection with the south property line extended of the Potapskut Sailing Association, Inc., thence northwesterly along the said property line extended to the shore.

(550)

### §110.72a Chester River, southeast of Chestertown, MD.

(551) The waters of the Chester River enclosed by a line beginning at a point on the Rolph Marina pier at 39°10'25"N., 76°02'17"W.; thence 327° to a point 400 feet southwest of the entrance to Hambleton Creek at 39°10'55"N., 76°02'40"W.; thence northeasterly to the eastern side of the entrance to Hambleton Creek; thence southerly following the shoreline to the Rolph Point Marina pier; thence southwesterly along the Rolph Point Marina pier to the point of beginning.

(552)

## Subpart B–Anchorage Grounds

(553)

### §110.157 Delaware Bay and River.

(554) (a) *The anchorage grounds*–(1) *Anchorage A off the entrance to Mispillion River.* In Delaware Bay southwest of Brandywine Channel beginning at

(555) 38°53'57"N., 75°08'00"W., thence northwesterly to

(556) 39°01'22"N., 75°13'25"W., thence southwesterly to

(557) 39°00'49"N., 75°14'57"W., thence southeasterly to

(558) 38°53'22"N., 75°09'26"W., thence northeasterly to the point of beginning. Supervision over the anchoring of vessels and over all cargo transfer operations in Anchorage A is exercised by the Captain of the Port, Philadelphia. The regulations of paragraphs (b)(1) and (b)(2) of this section do not apply to this anchorage.

(559) (2) *Anchorage 1 off Bombay Hook Point.* On the southwest side of the channel along Liston Range, in the waters bounded by a line connecting the following points:

(560)

| Latitude | Longitude |
|---|---|
| 39°17'14.0"N | 075°22'21.0"W |
| 39°16'55.2"N | 075°22'50.5"W |
| 39°20'34.1"N | 075°26'56.8"W |
| 39°20'53.5"N | 075°26'28.0"W |
| (DATUM: NAD 83) | |

(561) (3) *Anchorage 2 northwest of Artificial Island.* On the east side of the channel along Reedy Island Range, bounded as follows: Beginning at a point bearing 105° from the northernmost point of Reedy Island, 167 yards easterly of the east edge of the channel along Reedy Island Range; thence 105°, 800 yards; thence 195°, 4,500 yards; thence 285°, 800 yards to a point (at approximately 39°28'58"N., 75°33'37"W.,) opposite the intersection of Reedy Island and Baker Ranges; and thence 15°, 4,500 yards, to the point of beginning.

(562) (4) *Anchorage 3 southeast of Reedy Point.* Southeast of the entrance to the Chesapeake and Delaware Canal at Reedy Point, in the waters bounded by a line connecting the following points:

(563)

| Latitude | Longitude |
|---|---|
| 39°33'09.0"N | 075°32'38.0"W |
| 39°32'34.6"N | 075°32'38.2"W |
| 39°31'29.0"N | 075°33'01.0"W |
| 39°31'31.8"N | 075°33'16.2"W |
| 39°32'14.6"N | 075°33'08.3"W |
| 39°33'09.0"N | 075°33'10.0"W |
| (DATUM: NAD 83) | |

(564) (5) *Anchorage 4 north of Reedy Point.* North of the entrance to the Chesapeake and Delaware Canal at Reedy Point, on the west side of the river, bounded as follows: Beginning at a point (approximately 39°33'51"N., 75°33'35"W.) 344°58' true, 160 yards from Chesapeake and Delaware Canal Light 2; thence 306°26', 1,442 yards; thence 36°26', 377 yards; thence 126°26', 1,442 yards; thence 216°26', 377 yards to the point of beginning.

(565) (6) *Anchorage 5 southeast of Pea Patch Island.* On the northeast side of the channel along New Castle Range, bounded as follows: Beginning at 39°34'28"N., 75°33'06"W.; thence 334°, 2,343 yards; thence 64°, 512 yards; thence 154°, 2,343 yards; and thence 244°, 512 yards, to the point of beginning.

(566) (7) *Anchorage 6 off Deepwater Point.* East of the entrance to Christina River, in the waters bounded by a line connecting the following points:

(567)

| Latitude | Longitude |
|---|---|
| 39°43'00.0"N | 075°30'20.0"W |
| 39°42'51.5"N | 075°29'44.9"W |
| 39°42'05.4"N | 075°30'25.2"W |
| 39°41'47.3"N | 075°30'37.5"W |

| Latitude | Longitude |
|---|---|
| 39°41'34.7"N | 075°30'39.9"W |
| 39°41'36.6"N | 075°30'51.1"W |
| (DATUM: NAD 83) | |

(568)    (8) *Anchorage 7 off Marcus Hook*. (i) On the southeast side of the channel along Marcus Hook Range, bounded by a line connecting the following points:

(569)    39°49'17"N., 75°22'50"W.

(570)    39°48'39"N., 75°23'17"W.

(571)    39°47'45"N., 75°25'01"W.

(572)    39°47'43"N., 75°26'00"W.

(573)    (DATUM: NAD 83)

(574)    (ii) A vessel that is arriving from or departing for sea and that requires an examination by public health, customs, or immigration authorities shall anchor in the preferential area of this anchorage designated for the use of vessels awaiting quarantine inspection, this area being the waters bounded by the arc of a circle with a radius of 366 yards and with the center located at:

(575)    39°48'46"N., 75°23'26"W.

(576)    (DATUM: NAD 83)

(577)    (iii) Should the remainder of the anchorage be in use, the preferential area, when available, may be used by vessels not subject to quarantine inspection.

(578)    (9) *Anchorage 8 off Thompson Point*. On the south side of the channel along Tinicum Range, between Thompson Point and the east side of Crab Point, in the waters bounded by a line connecting the following points:

(579)

| Latitude | Longitude |
|---|---|
| 39°50'52.0"N | 075°18'23.0"W |
| 39°50'51.1"N | 075°17'41.0"W |
| 39°50'44.5"N | 075°17'41.6"W |
| 39°50'46.0"N | 075°18'23.0"W |
| (DATUM: NAD 83) | |

(580)    (10) *Anchorage 9 near entrance to Mantua Creek*. On the southeast side of the channel along Mifflin Range, bounded as follows: Beginning at a point on the southeast edge of the channel at longitude 75°14'26"; thence northeasterly along the edge of the channel to longitude 75°12'01.5"; thence 203°30', 933 yards; thence 233°30', 3,058 yards; and thence 263°30', 933 yards, to the point of beginning. Vessels must not cast anchor in this anchorage in such manner as to interfere unreasonably with the passage of other vessels to and from Mantua Creek.

(581)    (11) *Anchorage 10 at Naval Base, Philadelphia*. On the north side of the channel along Eagle Point Range, bounded as follows: Beginning off of the southeasterly corner of Pier 1 at 39°53'07"N., 075°10'30"W., thence south to the to the north edge of the channel along Eagle Point Range to 39°52'58"N., 075°10'29"W., thence east along the edge of the channel to 39°52'56"N., 075°09'53"W., thence north to 39°53'07"N., 075°09'54"W., thence

continuing west to the beginning point at 39°53'07"N., 075°10'30"W. These coordinates are based on WGS 84.

(582)    (12) *Anchorage 11 at Gloucester*. (i) East of the channel south of the Walt Whitman Bridge at Gloucester, in the waters bounded by a line connecting the following points:

(583)

| Latitude | Longitude |
|---|---|
| 39°54'10.0"N | 075°07'45.0"W |
| 39°54'09.4"N | 075°07'43.0"W |
| 39°54'03.0"N | 075°07'41.0"W |
| 39°53'30.5"N | 075°07'57.7"W |
| 39°53'09.6"N | 075°08'17.0"W |
| 39°53'36.6"N | 075°08'00.6"W |
| (DATUM: NAD 83) | |

(584)    (ii) The area between Pier 124S and 122S, along the west side of the Delaware River, is restricted to facilitate vessel movements. The areas adjacent to working piers are restricted to facilitate the movement of vessels to and from these piers. Should the anchorage become so congested that vessels are compelled to anchor in these restricted areas, they must move immediately when another berth is available.

(585)    (13) *Anchorage 12 between Gloucester and Camden*. (i) East of the channel beginning north of the Walt Whitman Bridge at Gloucester and ending south of the Benjamin Franklin Bridge at Camden, bounded as follows: Beginning at a point at 39°54'26.0"N., 75°07'41"W., bounded on the west by a line perpendicular to the channel, 210 yards from the east edge of the channel, 5,536 yards north to a point at 39°57'05.0"N., 75°08'04.2"W., and then bounded by a line connecting the following points, connecting to the point of beginning:

(586)

| Latitude | Longitude |
|---|---|
| 39°57'04.3"N | 075°07'57.3"W |
| 39°56'51.7"N | 075°08'01.3"W |
| 39°56'35.5"N | 075°08'03.1"W |
| 39°56'02.8"N | 075°08'02.0"W |
| 39°55'34.7"N | 075°07'54.5"W |
| 39°54'45.7"N | 075°07'32.5"W |
| 39°54'33.8"N | 075°07'32.9"W |
| 39°54'25.2"N | 075°07'36.1"W |
| (DATUM: NAD 83) | |

(587)    (ii) The area between No.2 Broadway pier and No.1 Broadway pier is restricted to facilitate vessel movements. The areas adjacent to working piers are restricted to facilitate the movement of vessels to and from these piers. Should the anchorage become so congested that vessels are compelled to anchor in these restricted areas, they must move immediately when another berth is available.

(588)    (14) *Anchorage 13 at Camden*. East of the channel, north of the Benjamin Franklin Bridge to Cooper Point,

Camden, NJ, in the waters bounded by a line connecting the following points:

| Latitude | Longitude |
|----------|-----------|
| 39°57'17.0"N | 075°07'58.0"W |
| 39°57'22.3"N | 075°07'55.9"W |
| 39°57'32.0"N | 075°07'49.4"W |
| 39°57'39.2"N | 075°07'39.7"W |
| 39°57'34.9"N | 075°07'34.7"W |
| 39°57'21.2"N | 075°07'49.8"W |
| 39°57'15.1"N | 075°07'52.7"W |
| (DATUM: NAD 83) | |

(590)     (15) *Anchorage 14 opposite Port Richmond.* On the southeast side of the channel, north of Petty Island, bounded as follows: Beginning at a point on the southeast edge of the channel at longitude 75°05'43"; thence 163°, 248 yards; thence 253°, 1,978 yards, to the southeast edge of the channel; and thence northeasterly along the edge of the channel to the point of beginning. Vessels having a draft of less than 20 feet must anchor southwest of Pier No. 11, Port Richmond. The area off the Cities Service Oil Company wharves, Petty Island, shall be restricted to facilitate the movement of vessels to and from the wharves.

(591)     (16) *Anchorage 15 off northeasterly end of Petty Island.* On the southeast side of the channel, bounded as follows: Beginning at a point on the southeast edge of the channel at longitude 75°05'34.7"; thence northeasterly along the southeast edge of the channel to longitude 75°05'09.5"; thence 171°, 198 yards; thence 260°30', 667 yards; and thence 351°, 198 yards, to the point of beginning. When necessary, this anchorage will be reserved for vessels under the custody of the United States, at which time other vessels may be required by the Captain of the Port to shift position.

(592)     (17) *Anchorage 16 between Port Richmond and Five Mile Point.* On the northwest side of the channel, bounded as follows: Beginning at a point on the northwest edge of the channel at longitude 75°05'35"; thence northeasterly along the edge of the channel to longitude 75°04'20"; thence 328°, 125 yards; thence 243°, 450 yards; thence 251°, 475 yards; thence 257°, 1,042 yards; thence 174°30', 122 yards, to the point of beginning. When necessary, this anchorage will be reserved for vessels under the custody of the United States, at which time other vessels may be required by the Captain of the Port to shift position.

(593)     (b) *General regulations.* (1) Except in cases of great emergency, no vessel shall be anchored in Delaware Bay and River between Ship John Light and The Pennsylvania Railroad Company bridge at Delair, New Jersey, outside of the anchorage areas established in this section, or within a cable or pipe line area shown on a Government chart, or be moored, anchored, or tied up to any pier, wharf, or other vessel in such manner as to obstruct or endanger the passage of any vessel. When an emergent condition exists due to congestion in the prescribed anchorage areas in the Delaware River, the Captain of the Port may authorize the anchorage of vessels in locations other than the prescribed areas. Vessels so anchored must not be anchored within the channel limits. Any vessel anchored outside of the prescribed anchorage limits must move to a prescribed anchorage area when space becomes available.

(594)     (2) No vessel shall occupy any prescribed anchorage for a longer period than 48 hours without a permit from the Captain of the Port. Vessels expecting to be at anchor more than 48 hours shall obtain a permit from the Captain of the Port for that purpose. No vessel in such condition that it is likely to sink or otherwise become a menace or obstruction to navigation or anchorage of other vessels shall occupy an anchorage except in an emergency, and then only for such period as may be permitted by the Captain of the Port.

(595)     (3) Whenever, in the opinion of the Captain of the Port such action may be necessary, he may require any or all vessels in any designated anchorage area to moor with two or more anchors.

(596)     (4) (Reserved)

(597)     (5) Anchors shall be placed well within the anchorage areas, so that no portion of the hull or rigging will at any time extend outside of the anchorage area.

(598)     (6) Light-draft barges using the anchorages shall be anchored away from the deeper portions of the anchorages, so as not to interfere with the anchoring of deep-draft vessels. Any barges towed in tandem to an anchorage area shall be bunched together when anchoring.

(599)     (7) Upon approval of the District Engineer, Corps of Engineers, the Captain of the Port may permit wrecking plant or other vessels legally engaged in recovering sunken property, or in laying or repairing pipe lines or cables, or plant engaged in dredging operations, to anchor in channels. Such permission is not necessary for plant engaged upon works of river and harbor improvement under the supervision of the District Engineer, but the District Engineer will notify the Captain of the Port in advance of all such proposed work.

(600)     (8) (Reserved)

(601)     (9) A vessel upon being notified to shift its position shall get under way at once or signal for a tug and shall change position as directed with reasonable promptness.

(602)     (10) Nothing in this section shall be construed as relieving any vessel or the owner or person in charge of any vessel from the penalties of law for obstructing navigation or for obstructing or interfering with range lights, or for not complying with the laws relating to lights and fog signals or other navigation laws and regulations.

(603)     (11) Annually from September 1 until December 31, additional requirements and restrictions in this paragraph for the use of anchorages defined in paragraphs (a)(7), (a)(8), and (a)(10) of this section apply.

(604)     (i) Before anchoring in Anchorage 7 off Marcus Hook, as described in paragraph (a)(8) of this section, a vessel must first obtain permission from the Captain of the Port, Philadelphia, at least 24 hours in advance of arrival. Permission to anchor will be granted on a

"first-come, first-served" basis. The Captain of the Port, Philadelphia, will allow only one vessel at a time to be at anchor in Anchorage 7, and no vessel may remain within Anchorage 7 for more than 12 hours. Any vessel arriving from or departing to sea that requires an examination by the public health service, customs or immigration authorities will be directed to an anchorage for the required inspection by the Captain of the Port on a case-by-case basis.

(605)    (ii) For Anchorage 6 off Deepwater Point, as described in paragraph (a)(7) of this section, and Anchorage 9 as described in paragraph (a)(10) of this section.

(606)    (A) Any vessel 700 feet or greater in length requesting anchorage shall obtain permission from the Captain of the Port, Philadelphia, Pennsylvania, at least 24 hours in advance.

(607)    (B) Any vessel from 700 to 750 feet in length shall have one tug alongside at all times while the vessel is at anchor.

(608)    (C) Any vessel greater than 750 feet in length shall have two tugs alongside at all times while the vessel is at anchor.

(609)    (D) The Master, owner or operator of a vessel at anchor shall ensure that any tug required by this section is of sufficient horsepower to assist with necessary maneuvers to keep the vessel clear of the navigation channel.

(610)    (iii) As used in this section, Captain of the Port means the Commander of Sector Delaware Bay or any Coast Guard commissioned, warrant or petty officer who has been authorized by the Captain of the Port to act on his behalf. The Captain of the Port may be contacted by telephone at 215–271–4807 or via VHF marine band radio, channel 16.

(611)    (c) *Regulations for vessels carrying and handling explosives.* (1) All vessels carrying explosives as defined in and subject to, Title 49 Code of Federal Regulations, Parts 171–177, or on which such explosives are to be loaded, shall obtain a permit from the Captain of the Port, except as provided in paragraph (c)(5) of this section. The maximum amount of explosives for which a permit is required in 49 CFR Parts 171–177, which may be carried or loaded at any time by a vessel shall not exceed 800 tons, except in cases of great emergency or by special permit from the Captain of the Port. This written permit shall be obtained from the Captain of the Port before vessels carrying explosives or on which explosives are to be loaded within the weight limit specified in paragraph (c)(1) of this section, may anchor in any anchorage. Permits will not be issued for Anchorage 2 under any circumstances. Such permit may be revoked at any time. All vessels used in connection with loading, or unloading explosives shall carry written permits from the Captain of the Port, and shall show such permit whenever required by him or his representative.

(612)    (2) Vessels handling explosives shall be anchored so as to be at least 2,200 feet from any other vessel, but the number of vessels which may anchor in an anchorage at any one time shall be at the discretion of the Captain of the Port. This provision is not intended to prohibit barges or lighters from tying up alongside the vessels for the transfer of cargo.

(613)    (3) Whenever a vessel or barge not mechanically self-propelled anchors while carrying explosives or while awaiting the loading of explosives, the Captain of the Port may require the attendance of a tug upon such vessel or barge when in his judgment such action is necessary.

(614)    (4) Fishing and navigation are prohibited within an anchorage whenever occupied by an anchored vessel displaying a red flag.

(615)    (5) The District Engineer, U.S. Army Corps of Engineers, may authorize, in writing, a vessel carrying explosives for use on river and harbor works or on other work under Department of the Army permit, to anchor in or near the vicinity of such work. The Captain of the Port will prescribe the conditions under which explosives shall be stored and handled in such cases.

(616)    (6) Vessels carrying explosives or on which explosives are to be loaded, within the weight limit specified in paragraph (c)(1) of this section, shall comply with the general regulations in paragraph (b) of this section when applicable.

(617)    (7) Nothing in this section shall be construed as relieving any vessel or the owner or person-in-charge of any vessel, and all others concerned, of the duties and responsibilities imposed upon them to comply with the regulations governing the handling, loading or discharging of explosives entitled "Subchapter C-Hazardous Materials Regulations" (49 CFR Parts 171 through 177).

(618)

### §110.158 Baltimore Harbor, MD.

(619)    (a) *Anchorage Grounds—*

(620)    (1) *No. 1, general anchorage.*

(621)    (i) All waters of the Patapsco River, bounded by a line connecting the following points:

(622)    *Latitude, Longitude*

(623)    39°15′13.51″N., 76°34′07.76′′′′W.

(624)    39°15′11.01″N., 76°34′11.69″W.

(625)    39°14′52.98″N., 76°33′52.67″W.

(626)    39°14′47.90″N., 76°33′40.73″W.

(627)    (ii) No vessel shall remain in this anchorage for more than 12 hours without permission from the Captain of the Port.

(628)    (2) *Anchorage No. 2, general anchorage.*

(629)    (i) All waters of the Patapsco River, bounded by a line connecting the following points:

(630)    *Latitude, Longitude*

(631)    39°14′50.06″N., 76°33′29.86″W.

(632)    39°14′57.53″N., 76°33′37.74″W.

(633)    39°15′08.56″N., 76°33′37.66″W.

(634)    39°15′15.77″N., 76°33′28.81″W.

(635)    39°15′18.87″N., 76°33′12.82″W.

(636)    39°15′17.71″N., 76°33′09.09″W.

(637)    39°14′50.35″N., 76°32′40.43″W.

(638)  39°14'45.28"N., 76°32'48.68"W.

(639)  39°14'46.27"N., 76°32'49.69"W.

(640)  39°14'43.76"N., 76°32'53.63"W.

(641)  39°14'57.51"N., 76°33'08.14"W.

(642)  39°14'55.60"N., 76°33'11.14"W.

(643)  39°14'59.42"N., 76°33'15.17"W.

(644)  (ii) No vessel shall remain in this anchorage for more than 72 hours without permission from the Captain of the Port.

(645)  (3) *Anchorage No. 3A, general anchorage.*

(646)  (i) All waters of the Patapsco River, bounded by a line connecting the following points:

(647)  *Latitude, Longitude*

(648)  39°14'15.66"N., 76°32'53.59"W.

(649)  39°14'32.48"N., 76°33'11.31"W.

(650)  39°14'46.27"N., 76°32'49.69"W.

(651)  39°14'32.50"N., 76°32'35.18"W.

(652)  39°14'22.37"N., 76°32'43.07"W.

(653)  (ii) No vessel shall remain in this anchorage for more than 24 hours without permission from the Captain of the Port.

(654)  (4) *Anchorage No. 3B, general anchorage.*

(655)  (i) All waters of the Patapsco River, bounded by a line connecting the following points:

(656)  *Latitude, Longitude*

(657)  39°14'32.48"N., 76°33'11.31"W.

(658)  39°14'46.23"N., 76°33'25.83"W.

(659)  39°14'57.51"N., 76°33'08.14"W.

(660)  39°14'43.76"N., 76°32'53.63"W.

(661)  (ii) No vessel shall remain in this anchorage for more than 24 hours without permission from the Captain of the Port.

(662)  (5) *Anchorage No. 3C, general anchorage.*

(663)  (i) All waters of the Patapsco River, bounded by a line connecting the following points:

(664)  *Latitude, Longitude*

(665)  39°14'46.23"N., 76°33'25.83"W.

(666)  39°14'50.06"N., 76°33'29.86"W.

(667)  39°14'59.42"N., 76°33'15.17"W.

(668)  39°14'55.60"N., 76°33'11.14"W.

(669)  (ii) No vessel shall remain in this anchorage for more than 72 hours without permission from the Captain of the Port.

(670)  (6) *Anchorage No. 4, general anchorage.*

(671)  (i) All waters of the Patapsco River, bounded by a line connecting the following points:

(672)  *Latitude, Longitude*

(673)  39°13'52.92"N., 76°32'29.60"W.

(674)  39°14'04.38"N., 76°32'41.69"W.

(675)  39°14'09.35"N., 76°32'39.89"W.

(676)  39°14'17.96"N., 76°32'26.44"W.

(677)  39°14'05.32"N., 76°32'13.09"W.

(678)  39°14'00.05"N., 76°32'17.77"W.

(679)  (ii) No vessel shall remain in this anchorage for more than 24 hours without permission from the Captain of the Port.

(680)  (7) *Anchorage No. 5, general anchorage.*

(681)  (i) All waters of the Patapsco River, bounded by a line connecting the following points:

(682)  *Latitude, Longitude*

(683)  39°14'07.89"N., 76°32'58.23"W.

(684)  39°13'34.82"N., 76°32'23.66"W.

(685)  39°13'22.25"N., 76°32'28.90"W.

(686)  39°13'21.20"N., 76°33'11.94"W.

(687)  (ii) No vessel shall remain in this anchorage for more than 72 hours without permission from the Captain of the Port.

(688)  (8) *Anchorage No. 6, general anchorage.*

(689)  (i) All waters of the Patapsco River, bounded by a line connecting the following points:

(690)  *Latitude, Longitude*

(691)  39°13'42.98"N., 76°32'19.11"W.

(692)  39°13'20.65"N., 76°31'55.58"W.

(693)  39°13'34.00"N., 76°31'33.50"W.

(694)  39°14'01.95"N., 76°32'02.65"W.

(695)  39°13'51.01"N., 76°32'18.71"W.

(696)  (ii) No vessel shall remain in this anchorage for more than 72 hours without permission from the Captain of the Port.

(697)  (9) Anchorage No. 7, Dead ship anchorage.

(698)  (i) All waters of Curtis Bay, bounded by a line connecting the following points:

(699)  Latitude, Longitude

(700)  39°13'00.40"N., 76°34'10.40"W.

(701)  39°13'13.40"N., 76°34'10.81"W.

(702)  39°13'13.96"N., 76°34'05.02"W.

(703)  39°13'14.83"N., 76°33'29.80"W.

(704)  39°13'00.40"N., 76°33'29.90"W.

(705)  (ii) The primary use of this anchorage is to lay up dead ships. Such use has priority over other uses. Permission from the Captain of the Port must be obtained prior to the use of this anchorage for more than 72 hours.

(706)  (b) *Definitions.* As used in this section—

(707)  *Certain dangerous cargo* means certain dangerous cargo as defined in **§160.202** of this chapter.

(708)  *COTP* means Captain of the Port Sector Maryland—National Capital Region.

(709)  (c) *General regulations.* (1) Except as otherwise provided, this section applies to vessels over 20 meters long and all vessels carrying or handling certain dangerous cargo while anchored in an anchorage ground described in this section.

(710)  (2) Except in cases where unforeseen circumstances create conditions of imminent peril, or with the permission of the Captain of the Port, no vessel shall be anchored in Baltimore Harbor or the Patapsco River outside of the anchorage areas established in this section for more than 24 hours. No vessel shall anchor within a tunnel, cable or pipeline area shown on a government chart. No vessel shall be moored, anchored, or tied up to any pier, wharf, or other vessel in such manner as to extend into established channel limits. No vessel shall be positioned so as to obstruct or endanger the passage of any other vessel.

(711)  (3) Except in an emergency, a vessel that is likely to sink or otherwise become an obstruction to navigation

or the anchoring of other vessels may not occupy an anchorage, unless the vessel obtains permission from the Captain of the Port.

(712)     (4) Upon notification by the Captain of the Port to shift its position, a vessel at anchor must get underway and shall move to its new designated position within two hours after notification.

(713)     (5) The Captain of the Port may prescribe specific conditions for vessels anchoring within the anchorages described in this section, including, but not limited to, the number and location of anchors, scope of chain, readiness of engineering plant and equipment, usage of tugs, and requirements for maintaining communication guards on selected radio frequencies.

(714)     (6) No vessel at anchor or at a mooring within an anchorage may transfer oil to or from another vessel unless the vessel has given the Captain of the Port the four hours advance notice required by **§156.118** of this chapter.

(715)     (7) No vessel shall anchor in a "dead ship" status (propulsion or control unavailable for normal operations) without prior approval of the Captain of the Port.

(716)
### §110.159 Annapolis Harbor, MD.

(717)     (a) *The Anchorage Grounds*–(1) *Naval Anchorage for Deep Draft Vessels*. In the Chesapeake Bay, bounded on the north by latitude 38°58'00"; on the east by a line bearing 203° from latitude 38°58'00", longitude 76°24'00"; on the south by latitude 38°56'30"; and on the west by a line bearing 139° from Greenbury Point Shoal Light. This anchorage is reserved for deep draft naval vessels. Berths in the area will be assigned on application to the Superintendent, U.S. Naval Academy.

(718)     (2) *Middle Ground Anchorage*. Beginning at a point in the Severn River 139°, 620 yards from Triton Light (located at the intersection of the northeast and southeast seawall of the Naval Academy grounds); thence easterly to a point 112°30', 970 yards from Triton Light; thence southeasterly to a point 274°, 1,045 yards from the radio tower at the tip of Greenbury Point; thence south-southeasterly to a point 233°30', 925 yards from the radio tower at the tip of Greenbury Point; thence west to a point 295°, 1,015 yards from Greenbury Point Shoal Light; thence northwesterly to the point of beginning.

(719)     (3) *South Anchorage*. In the Severn River, beginning at a point on the shoreline at Horn Point, Eastport, 168°, 1,190 yards from Triton Light; thence east to a point 294°, 1,075 yards from Greenbury Point Shoal Light; thence northwest to a point 143°, 595 yards from Triton Light; thence westerly to a point 209°, 700 yards from Triton Light; thence 180° to a point on the shoreline at Eastport. No vessel shall anchor within 100 feet of any wharf, marine railway, or other structure without the permission of the owner thereof.

(720)     (4) *Naval Anchorage for Small Craft*. In the Severn River, beginning at a point 80 feet off the southeast seawall of the Naval Academy bearing 132° from Triton

Light; thence easterly to a point 072°30', 285 yards from Triton Light; thence southeasterly to a point 109°, 785 yards from Triton Light; thence westerly to a point 211°, 537 yards from Triton Light; thence northwesterly to a point 45 yards off the southeast seawall of the Naval Academy bearing 214°, 535 yards from Triton Light; thence northeasterly to the point of beginning. Except in the case of emergency, no vessel shall be anchored in this area without the permission of the Superintendent, U.S. Naval Academy. Anchorages will be assigned upon request to the Superintendent, U.S. Naval Academy.

(721)     (5) *Spa Creek Anchorage*. In Spa Creek, those waters bounded by a line connecting the following points:
(722)     38°58'37.3"N., 76°28'48.1"W.
(723)     38°58'36.1"N., 76°28'57.8"W.
(724)     38°58'31.6"N., 76°29'03.3"W.
(725)     38°58'26.7"N., 76°28'59.5"W.
(726)     Datum: NAD 83
(727)     **Note.**–The City Council of Annapolis has promulgated local ordinances to control the building of structures, and mooring and anchorage of vessels in anchorages (a)(3), and (a)(5). These local ordinances will be enforced by the local harbormaster.

(728)     (b) The regulations. (1) Except in the case of emergency, no vessel shall be anchored in the area to the north and east of the Annapolis Channel bounded on the east by Greenbury Point; on the south by a line bearing 270° from the southern tip of Greenbury Point; on the west by the Annapolis Channel; on the north by the southern boundary of the cable area and the shoreline of the Government reservation and Carr Creek.

(729)     (2) Except in the case of emergency, no vessel shall be anchored in Annapolis Harbor to the westward of the dredged channel and northward of the southern boundary of the South Anchorage outside of the established anchorage areas, except in Spa Creek and the area to the southwestward of the Naval anchorage for small craft. No vessel shall be so anchored that any part of the vessel extends at any time within this area. Any vessel anchoring, under great emergency, within this area shall be placed as close to an anchorage area as practicable, and shall move away immediately after the emergency ceases.

(730)     (3) No vessel shall be anchored in the cable and pipeline area, lying between the Naval Academy and the Naval Ship Research and Development Laboratory and having the following limits: Southeastern limit, from Triton Light 072° to white "Cable Crossing" sign at the Naval Ship Research and Development Laboratory; northwestern limit, a line bearing 054° from the Capitol Dome.

(731)     (4) Except in the case of emergency, no vessel shall be anchored, without permission of the Superintendent, U.S. Naval Academy, in the Naval Academy Drill area described as follows:

(732)     That portion of the Severn River lying to the northeastward of the Naval Academy, bounded on the north by the State Highway Bridge and on the south

by the northern limit of the cable and pipeline area, excluding that area off the eastern shoreline enclosed by a line bearing approximately 131° from the eastern abutment of the State Highway Bridge to the vicinity of Ferry Point. This drill area also includes the lower part of Dorseys Creek below the Naval Academy Drawbridge. Requests to anchor in this drill area shall be made to the Superintendent, U.S. Naval Academy.

(733)     (5) The restrictions in this section do not apply to the anchoring or marking by buoys or apparatus used for the purpose of taking seafood, except within the cable or pipeline area described in paragraph (b)(3) of this subsection.

(734)     (6) The regulations in paragraph (b) shall be enforced by the Superintendent, U.S. Naval Academy, and such agencies as he may designate.

(735)

### §110.166 York River, VA, naval anchorage.

(736)     (a) *The anchorage grounds.* Between Yorktown and the Naval Mine Depot, beginning at

(737)     37°15'34"N., 76°31'25"W.; thence to

(738)     37°15'25"N., 76°31'39.5"W.; thence to

(739)     37°16'21.5"N., 76°32'46"W.; thence to

(740)     37°17'07.5"N., 76°34'17"W.; thence to

(741)     37°17'55"N., 76°35'14.5"W.; thence to

(742)     37°18'05"N., 76°35'01"W.; thence to

(743)     37°17'20"N., 76°34'07"W.; thence to

(744)     37°16'33.5"N., 76°32'34"W., and thence to the point of beginning.

(745)     (b) *The regulations.* This anchorage is reserved for the exclusive use of naval vessels and except in cases of emergency, no other vessel shall anchor therein without permission from the local naval authorities, obtained through the Captain of the Port, Norfolk, Virginia. Movement of vessels through the anchorage will not be restricted.

(746)

### §110.168 Hampton Roads, Virginia, and adjacent waters.

(747)     (a) *Anchorage Grounds.* Unless otherwise stated, all coordinates in this section for anchorage grounds are based on North American Datum of 1983 (NAD 83). (1) *Anchorage A [Naval Anchorage].* The waters bounded by the shoreline and a line connecting the following points:

(748)     36°55'36.2"N., 76°02'46.3"W.

(749)     36°57'03.3"N., 76°03'01.4"W.

(750)     36°56'45.5"N., 76°01'28.8"W.

(751)     36°55'55.7"N., 76°01'35.7"W.

(752)     (2) *Chesapeake Bay, Thimble Shoals Channel Anchorages.*

(753)     (i) *Anchorage B [Naval Anchorage].* The waters bounded by a line connecting the following points:

(754)     36°57'58.5"N., 76°06'05.8"W.

(755)     36°57'11.5"N., 76°03'00.9"W.

(756)     36°55'49.3"N., 76°03'12.8"W.

(757)     36°56'32.3"N., 76°06'05.8"W.

(758)     36°57'04.5"N., 76°06'05.8"W.

(759)     36°57'09.0"N., 76°06'23.3"W.

(760)     (ii) *Anchorage C [Naval Anchorage].* The waters bounded by a line connecting the following points:

(761)     36°58'55.3"N., 76°09'40.3"W.

(762)     36°58'19.3"N., 76°07'16.8"W.

(763)     36°57'27.5"N., 76°07'36.3"W.

(764)     36°58'04.5"N., 76°09'58.8"W.

(765)     (iii) *Anchorage D [Naval Anchorage].* The waters bounded by the shoreline a line connecting the following points:

(766)     36°55'49.5"N., 76°10'31.6"W.

(767)     36°58'04.5"N., 76°10'00.9"W.

(768)     36°57'31.7"N., 76°07'53.6"W.

(769)     36°55'24.6"N., 76°08'27.6"W.

(770)     (iv) *Anchorage E [Commercial Explosives Anchorage].* The waters bounded by a line connecting the following points:

(771)     36°59'59.2"N., 76°13'45.8"W.

(772)     36°59'08.7"N., 76°10'32.6"W.

(773)     36°58'13.5"N., 76°10'50.6"W.

(774)     36°59'02.5"N., 76°14'08.9"W.

(775)     (v) *Explosives Handling Berth E–1 [Explosives Anchorage Berth].* The waters bounded by the arc of a circle with a radius of 500 yards and the center located at:

(776)     36°59'05.5"N., 76°11'21.8"W.

(777)     (3) *Hampton Roads Anchorages.* (i) *Anchorage F, Hampton Bar.* The waters bounded by a line connecting the following points:

(778)     36°59'25.5"N., 76°20'05.8"W.

(779)     36°59'52.1"N., 76°19'10.8"W.

(780)     36°59'25.7"N., 76°18'47.3"W.

(781)     36°58'49.6"N., 76°19'32.6"W.

(782)     (ii) *Anchorage Berth F–1.* The waters bounded by the arc of a circle with a radius of 500 yards and the center located at:

(783)     36°59'29.6"N., 76°19'13.9"W.

(784)     (iii) *Anchorage G, Hampton Flats (Naval Explosives Anchorage).* The waters bounded by a line connecting the following points:

(785)     36°59'25.0"N., 76°20'07.0"W.

(786)     36°58'49.1"N., 76°19'33.8"W.

(787)     36°57'41.4"N., 76°21'07.7"W.

(788)     36°57'34.6"N., 76°21'26.7"W.

(789)     36°57'31.1"N., 76°22'01.9"W.

(790)     36°58'07.0"N., 76°22'03.0"W.

(791)     36°58'54.8"N., 76°21'42.6"W.

(792)     (iv) *Explosives Handling Berth G–1.* The waters bounded by the arc of a circle with a radius of 500 yards and the center located at:

(793)     36°57'50.5"N., 76°21'37.8"W.

(794)     (v) *Explosives Handling Berth G–2.* The waters bounded by the arc of a circle with a radius of 500 yards and the center located at:

(795)     36°58'14.5"N., 76°21'00.3"W.

(796)     (vi) *Explosives Handling Berth G–3.* The waters bounded by the arc of a circle with a radius of 500 yards and with the center located at:

(797)     36°58'34.2"N., 76°20'31.4"W.

(798)     (vii) *Explosives Handling Berth G–4*. The waters bounded by the arc of a circle with a radius of 500 yards and with the center located at:

(799)     36°58'54.9"N., 76°20'03.2"W.

(800)     (viii) *Anchorage H, Newport News Bar*. The waters bounded by a line connecting the following points:

(801)     36°57'38.8"N., 76°24'18.5"W.

(802)     36°57'52.3"N., 76°22'29.7"W.

(803)     36°58'07.4"N., 76°22'01.8"W.

(804)     36°57'31.6"N., 76°22'00.6"W.

(805)     36°57'18.7"N., 76°24'10.1"W.

(806)     (4) *James River Anchorages*. (i) *Anchorage I, Newport News*. The waters bounded by a line connecting the following points:

(807)     36°58'49.0"N., 76°27'09.8"W.

(808)     36°58'35.9"N., 76°26'37.2"W.

(809)     36°57'52.2"N., 76°26'01.6"W.

(810)     36°57'31.1"N., 76°25'33.3"W.

(811)     36°57'07.2"N., 76°24'43.1"W.

(812)     36°56'23.1"N., 76°24'26.8"W.

(813)     36°56'03.5"N., 76°24'35.8"W.

(814)     36°57'54.2"N., 76°26'40.3"W.

(815)     36°58'23.5"N., 76°27'09.8"W.

(816)     (ii) *Anchorage Berth I–1*. The waters bounded by the arc of a circle with a radius of 400 yards and the center located at:

(817)     36°57'09.0"N., 76°25'20.4"W.

(818)     (iii) *Anchorage Berth I–2*. The waters bounded by the arc of a circle with a radius of 400 yards and with the center located at:

(819)     36°57'23.8"N., 76°25'46.0"W.

(820)     (iv) *Anchorage J, Newport News Middle Ground*. The waters bounded by a line connecting the following points:

(821)     36°55'59.9"N., 76°22'11.7"W.

(822)     36°55'59.9"N., 76°24'00.0"W.

(823)     36°56'25.3"N., 76°23'48.0"W.

(824)     36°57'10.2"N., 76°24'09.9"W.

(825)     36°57'12.0"N., 76°23'47.3"W.

(826)     36°56'38.5"N., 76°21'39.1"W.

(827)     36°56'38.5"N., 76°20'47.0"W.

(828)     (v) *Anchorage K, Newport News Middle Ground*. The waters bounded by a line connecting the following points:

(829)     36°57'56.4"N., 76°20'30.5"W.

(830)     36°57'08.5"N., 76°20'31.0"W.

(831)     36°56'48.8'N., 76°20'22.5"W.

(832)     36°56'45.0"N., 76°20'32.0"W.

(833)     36°56'45.0"N., 76°21'37.7"W.

(834)     36°57'14.1"N., 76°23'29.1"W.

(835)     36°57'28.1"N., 76°21'11.7"W.

(836)     (vi) *Anchorage Berth K–1*. The waters bounded by the arc of a circle with a radius of 400 yards and with the center located at:

(837)     36°57'30.5"N., 76°20'45.3"W.

(838)     (vii) *Anchorage Berth K–2*. The waters bounded by the arc of a circle with a radius of 400 yards and with the center located at:

(839)     36°57'16.8"N., 76°21'09.5"W.

(840)     (viii) *Anchorage Berth L, Craney Island Flats*. The waters bounded by a line connecting the following points:

(841)     36°55'59.9"N., 76°22'11.7"W.

(842)     36°56'38.5"N., 76°20'45.5"W.

(843)     36°56'30.0"N., 76°20'24.3"W.

(844)     36°56'04.2"N., 76°20'26.2"W.

(845)     (5) *Elizabeth River Anchorages*. (i) Anchorage M, Port Norfolk. The waters bounded by a line connecting the following points:

(846)     36°51'45.7"N., 76°19'31.5"W.

(847)     36°51'45.8"N., 76°19'20.7"W.

(848)     36°51'37.8"N., 76°19'24.3"W.

(849)     36°51'32.5"N., 76°19'31.1"W.

(850)     36°51'40.7"N., 76°19'37.3"W.

(851)     36°51'45.7"N., 76°19'31.5"W.

(852)     (ii) *Anchorage N, Hospital Point*. The waters bounded by a line connecting the following points:

(853)     36°51'05.4"N., 76°18'22.4"W.

(854)     36°50'50.0"N., 76°18'00.0"W.

(855)     36°50'36.7"N., 76°17'52.8"W.

(856)     36°50'33.6"N., 76°17'58.8"W.

(857)     36°50'49.3"N., 76°18'09.0"W.

(858)     36°50'50.3"N., 76°18'07.8"W.

(859)     36°50'56.2"N., 76°18'12.5"W.

(860)     36°51'01.8"N., 76°18'32.3"W.

(861)     (iii) *Anchorage O, The Hague*. The waters of the basin known as 'The Hague', north of the Brambleton Avenue Bridge, except for the area within 100 feet of the bridge span that provides access to and from the Elizabeth River.

(862)     (6) *Anchorage Q. Quarantine Anchorage*. The waters bounded by a line connecting the following points, which are based on the World Geodetic System (WGS84)::

(863)     37°05'40"N., 76°08'12"W.

(864)     37°05'40"N., 76°07'19"W.

(865)     37°03'46"N., 76°05'58"W.

(866)     37°03'46"N., 76°06'51"W.

(867)     (i) *Anchorage Berth Q–1*. The waters bounded by the arc of a circle with a radius of 500 yards and with the center located at:

(868)     37°17'05.7"N., 76°06'08.9"W.

(869)     (ii) *Anchorage Berth Q–2*. The waters bounded by the arc of a circle with a radius of 500 yards with the center located at:

(870)     37°16'33.0"N., 76°05'51.1"W.

(871)     (7) *Anchorage R*. The waters bound by a line connecting the following points, which are based on the World Geodetic System (WGS84):

(872)     37°19'10"N., 76°05'00"W.

(873)     37°12'00"N., 76°05'00"W.

(874)     37°09'08"N., 76°08'19"W.

(875)     37°11'23"N., 76°08'49"W.

(876)     37°19'10"N., 76°05'46"W.

(877)     (b) *Definitions*. As used in this section–

(878)     *Class 1 (explosive) materials* means Division 1.1, 1.2, 1.3, and 1.4 explosives, as defined in 49 CFR 173.50.

(879)     *Dangerous cargo* means "certain dangerous cargo" as defined in §160.202 of this chapter.

(880)     *U.S. naval vessel* means any vessel owned, operated, chartered, or leased by the U.S. Navy; any pre-commissioned vessel under construction for the U.S. Navy, once launched into the water; and any vessel under the operational control of the U.S. Navy or a Combatant Command.

(881)     (c) *General regulations.* (1) Except as otherwise provided, this section applies to vessels over 20 meters long and vessels carrying or handling dangerous cargo or Class 1 (explosive) materials while anchored in an anchorage ground described in this section.

(882)     (2) Except as otherwise provided, a vessel may not occupy an anchorage for more than 30 days, unless the vessel obtains permission from the Captain of the Port.

(883)     (3) Except in an emergency, a vessel that is likely to sink or otherwise become a menace or obstruction to navigation or to the anchoring of other vessels, may not occupy an anchorage, unless the vessel obtains permission from the Captain of the Port.

(884)     (4) The Captain of the Port may, upon application, assign a vessel to a specific berth within an anchorage for a specified period of time.

(885)     (5) The Captain of the Port may grant a revocable permit to a vessel for a habitual use of a berth. Only the vessel that holds the revocable permit may use the berth during the period that the permit is in effect.

(886)     (6) The Commander, Fifth Coast Guard District, may authorize the establishment and placement of temporary mooring buoys within a berth. Placement of a fixed structure within an anchorage may be authorized by the District Engineer, U.S. Army Corps of Engineers.

(887)     (7) If an application is for the long-term lay up of a vessel, the Captain of the Port may establish special conditions in the permit with which the vessel must comply.

(888)     (8) Upon notification by the Captain of the Port to shift its position within an anchorage, a vessel at anchor must get underway at once or signal for a tug. The vessel must move to its new location within 2 hours after notification.

(889)     (9) The Captain of the Port may prescribe specific conditions for vessels anchoring within the anchorages described in this section, including, but not limited to, the number and location of anchors, scope of chain, readiness of engineering plant and equipment, usage of tugs, and requirements for maintaining communications guards on selected radio frequencies.

(890)     (10) A vessel that does not have a sufficient crew on board to weigh anchor at any time must have two anchors in place, unless the Captain of the Port waives this requirement. Members of the crew may not be released until the required anchors have been set.

(891)     (11) No vessel at anchor or at a mooring within an anchorage may transfer oil to another vessel unless the vessel has given the Captain of the Port the four hours advance notice required by §156.118 of this title.

(892)     (12) Barges may not anchor in the deeper portions of anchorages or interfere with the anchoring of deep-draft vessels.

(893)     (13) Barges towed in tandem to an anchorage must be nested together when anchored.

(894)     (14) Any vessel anchored or moored in an anchorage adjacent to the Chesapeake Bay Bridge Tunnel or Monitor-Merrimac Bridge Tunnel (MMBT) must be capable of getting underway within 30 minutes with sufficient power to keep free of the bridge tunnel complex.

(895)     (15) A vessel may not anchor or moor in an anchorage adjacent to the Chesapeake Bay Bridge Tunnel or Monitor-Merrimac Bridge Tunnel (MMBT) if its steering or main propulsion equipment is impaired.

(896)     (d) *Regulations for vessels handling or carrying dangerous cargoes or Class 1 (explosive) materials.* This paragraph applies to every vessel, except a naval vessel, handling or carrying dangerous cargoes or Class 1 (explosive) materials.

(897)     (1) Unless otherwise directed by the Captain of the Port, each commercial vessel handling or carrying dangerous cargoes or Class 1 (explosive) materials must be anchored or moored within Anchorage Berth E–1.

(898)     (2) Each vessel, including each tug and stevedore boat, used for loading or unloading dangerous cargoes or Class 1 (explosive) materials in an anchorage, must have permission issued by the Captain of the Port.

(899)     (3) The Captain of the Port may require every person having business aboard a vessel handling or carrying dangerous cargoes or Class 1 (explosive) materials while in an anchorage, other than a member of the crew, to hold a form of valid identification.

(900)     (4) Each person having business aboard a vessel handling or carrying dangerous cargoes or Class 1 (explosive) materials while in an anchorage, other than a member of the crew, must present the identification prescribed by paragraph (d)(3) of this section to any Coast Guard boarding officer who requests it.

(901)     (5) Each non-self-propelled vessel handling or carrying dangerous cargoes or Class 1 (explosive) materials must have a tug in attendance at all times while at anchor.

(902)     (6) Each vessel handling or carrying dangerous cargoes or Class 1(explosive) materials while at anchor must display by day a red flag (Bravo flag) in a prominent location and by night a fixed red light.

(903)     (e) *Regulations for Specific Anchorages.* (1) *Anchorages A, B, C, and D.* Except for a naval vessel, military support vessel, or vessel in an emergency situation, a vessel may not anchor in Anchorages A, B, C, or D without the permission of the Captain of the Port. The Captain of the Port must consult with the Commander, Naval Amphibious Base Little Creek, before granting a vessel permission to anchor in Anchorages A, B, C, or D.

(904)　　　(2) *Anchorage E.* (i) A vessel may not anchor in Anchorage E without permission from the Captain of the Port.

(905)　　　(ii) The Captain of the Port must give commercial vessels priority over naval and public vessels.

(906)　　　(iii) The Captain of the Port may at any time revoke permission to anchor in Anchorage E issued under the authority of paragraph (e)(4)(i) of this section.

(907)　　　(iv) A vessel may not anchor in Anchorage Berth E–1, unless it is handling or carrying dangerous cargoes or Class 1 (explosive) materials.

(908)　　　(v) A vessel may not anchor within 500 yards of Anchorage Berth E–1 without the permission of the Captain of the Port, if the berth is occupied by a vessel handling or carrying dangerous cargoes or Class 1 (explosive) materials.

(909)　　　(3) *Anchorage F.* A vessel having a draft less than 45 feet may not anchor in Anchorage F without the permission of the Captain of the Port. No vessel may anchor in Anchorage F for a longer period than 72 hours without permission from the Captain of the Port. Vessels expecting to be at anchor for more than 72 hours must obtain permission from the Captain of the Port.

(910)　　　(4) *Anchorage G.* (i) Except for a naval vessel, a vessel may not anchor in Anchorage G without the permission of the Captain of the Port.

(911)　　　(ii) When handling or transferring Class 1 (explosive) materials in Anchorage G, naval vessels must comply with Department of Defense Ammunition and Explosives Safety Standards, or the standards in this section, whichever are the more stringent.

(912)　　　(iii) When barges and other vessels are berthed at the Ammunition Barge Mooring Facility, located at 36°58'34"N., 76°21'12"W., no other vessel, except a vessel that is receiving or offloading Class 1 (explosive) materials, may anchor within 1,000 yards of the Ammunition Barge Mooring Facility. Vessels transferring class 1 (explosive) materials must display by day a red flag (Bravo flag) in a prominent location and by night a fixed red light.

(913)　　　(iv) Whenever a vessel is handling or transferring Class 1 (explosive) materials while at anchor in Anchorage G, no other vessel may anchor in Anchorage G without the permission of the Captain of the Port. The Captain of the Port must consult with the Commander, Naval Station Norfolk, before granting a vessel permission to anchor in Anchorage G.

(914)　　　(v) A vessel located within Anchorage G may not handle or transfer Class 1 (explosive) materials within 400 yards of Norfolk Harbor Entrance Reach.

(915)　　　(vi) A vessel may not handle or transfer Class 1 (explosive) materials within 850 yards of another anchored vessel, unless the other vessel is also handling or transferring Class 1 (explosive) materials.

(916)　　　(vii) A vessel may not handle or transfer Class 1 (explosive) materials within 850 yards of Anchorage F or H.

(917)　　　(5) *Anchorage I: Anchorage Berths I–1 and I–2.* A vessel that is 500 feet or less in length or that has a draft of 30 feet or less may not anchor in Anchorage Berth I–1 or I–2 without the permission of the Captain of the Port.

(918)　　　(6) *Anchorage K: Anchorage Berths K–1 and K–2.* A vessel that is 500 feet or less in length or that has a draft of 30 feet or less may not anchor in Anchorage Berth K–1 or K–2 without the permission of the Captain of the Port.

(919)　　　(7) *Anchorage N.* Portions of this anchorage are a special anchorage area under §110.72aa of this part during marine events regulated under Sec. 100.501 of this chapter.

(920)　　　(8) *Anchorage O.* (i) A vessel may not anchor in Anchorage O unless it is a recreational vessel.

(921)　　　(ii) No float, raft, lighter, houseboat, or other craft may be laid up for any reason in Anchorage O without the permission of the Captain of the Port.

(922)　　　(9) *Anchorage Q: Quarantine Anchorage.* (i) A vessel that is arriving from or departing for sea and that requires an examination by public health, customs, or immigration authorities shall anchor in Anchorage Q. Vessels not needing examination may use Anchorage Q at any time.

(923)　　　(ii) Every vessel using Anchorage Q must be prepared to move promptly under its own power to another location when directed by the Captain of the Port, and must promptly vacate Anchorage Q after being examined and released by authorities.

(924)　　　(iii) Any non-self-propelled vessel using Anchorage Q must have a tugboat in attendance while undergoing examination by quarantine, customs, or immigration authorities, except with the permission of the Captain of the Port.

(925)　　　(10) *Anchorage R.* (i) No vessel using Anchorage R may conduct oil or hazardous material transfer operations subject to 33 CFR part 156 except with permission of the COTP.

(926)　　　(ii) Any non-self-propelled vessel using Anchorage R must have a towing vessel in attendance except with permission of the COTP not to have a towing vessel in attendance.

(927)
# Part 117–Drawbridge Operation Regulations

(928)
## Subpart A–General Requirements

(929)
### §117.1 Purpose.

(930)　　　(a) This part prescribes the general and special drawbridge operating regulations that apply to the drawbridges across the navigable waters of the United States and its territories. The authority to regulate drawbridges across the navigable waters of the United States is vested in the Secretary of Homeland Security.

(931)     (b) Subpart A contains the general operation requirements that apply to all drawbridges.

(932)     (c) Subpart B contains specific requirements for operation of individual drawbridges. These requirements are in addition to or vary from the general requirements in Subpart A. Specific sections in subpart B that vary from a general requirement in Subpart A supersede the general requirement. All other general requirements in Subpart A, that are not at variance, apply to the drawbridges and removable span bridges listed in Subpart B.

(933)
### §117.3 [Removed].

(934)
### §117.4 Definitions.

(935)     The following definitions apply to this part:

(936)     *Appurtenance* means an attachment or accessory extending beyond the hull or superstructure that is not an integral part of the vessel and is not needed for a vessel's piloting, propelling, controlling, or collision avoidance capabilities.

(937)     *Automated drawbridge* means a drawbridge that is operated by an automated mechanism, not a drawtender. An automated drawbridge is normally kept in the open to navigation position and closes when the mechanism is activated.

(938)     *Deviation* means a District Commander's action authorizing a drawbridge owner to temporarily not comply with the drawbridge opening requirements in this part.

(939)     *Drawbridge* means a bridge with an operational span that is intended to be opened for the passage of waterway traffic.

(940)     *Drawspan* means the operational span of a drawbridge.

(941)     *Lowerable* means a non-structural vessel appurtenance that is or can be made flexible, hinged, collapsible, or telescopic so that it can be mechanically or manually lowered.

(942)     *Nonstructural* means that the item is not rigidly fixed to the vessel and can be relocated or altered.

(943)     *Not essential to navigation* means that a nonstructural vessel appurtenance, when in the lowered position, would not adversely affect the vessel's piloting, propulsion, control, or collision-avoidance capabilities.

(944)     *Public vessel* means a vessel that is owned and operated by the United States Government and is not engaged in commercial service, as defined in 46 U.S.C. 2101.

(945)     *Remotely operated drawbridge* means a drawbridge that is operated by remote control from a location away from the drawbridge.

(946)     *Removable span bridge* means a bridge that requires the complete removal of a span by means other than machinery installed on the bridge to open the bridge to navigation.

(947)     *Untended* means that there is no drawtender at the drawbridge.

(948)
### §117.5 When the drawbridge must open.

(949)     Except as otherwise authorized or required by this part, drawbridges must open promptly and fully for the passage of vessels when a request or signal to open is given in accordance with this subpart.

(950)
### §117.7 General requirements of drawbridge owners.

(951)     Except for drawbridges that have been authorized, before January 3, 2007, to remain closed to navigation or as otherwise specified in subpart B, drawbridge owners must:

(952)     (a) Provide the necessary drawtender(s) for the safe and prompt opening of the drawbridge.

(953)     (b) Maintain the working machinery of the drawbridge in good operating condition.

(954)     (c) Cycle the drawspan(s) periodically to ensure operation of the drawbridge.

(955)     (d) Ensure that the drawbridge operates in accordance with the requirements of this part.

(956)     (e) Any drawbridge allowed to remain closed to navigation prior to January 3, 2007, when necessary, must be returned to operable condition within the designated time set forth by the District Commander and will become subject to the requirements of this part.

(957)
### §117.8 Permanent changes to drawbridge operation.

(958)     (a) Anyone may submit a written request to the District Commander for a permanent change to a drawbridge operating requirement. The request must include documentation supporting or justifying the requested change.

(959)     (b) If after evaluating the request, the District Commander determines that the requested change is not needed, he or she will respond to the request in writing and provide the reasons for denial of the requested change.

(960)     (c) If the District Commander decides that a change may be needed, he or she will begin a rulemaking to implement the change.

(961)
### §117.9 Delaying opening of a draw.

(962)     No person shall unreasonably delay the opening of a draw after the signals required by §117.15 have been given.

(963)     **Note.**–Trains are usually controlled by the block method. That is, the track is divided into blocks or segments of a mile or more in length. When a train is in a block with a drawbridge, the draw may not be able to open until the train has passed out of the block and the yardmaster or other manager has "unlocked" the drawbridge controls. The maximum time permitted for delay is defined in Subpart B for each affected bridge. Land and water traffic should pass over or through the draw as soon as possible in order to prevent unnecessary delays in the opening and closure of the draw.

(964)
### §117.11 Unnecessary opening of the draw.

(965)     No vessel owner or operator shall–

(966)     (a) Signal a drawbridge to open if the vertical clearance is sufficient to allow the vessel, after all lowerable nonstructural vessel appurtenances that are not essential to navigation have been lowered, to safely pass under the drawbridge in the closed position; or

(967)     (b) Signal a drawbridge to open for any purpose other than to pass through the drawbridge opening.

(968)
### §117.15 Signals.

(969)     (a) *General.* (1) The operator of each vessel requesting a drawbridge to open shall signal the drawtender and the drawtender shall acknowledge that signal. The signal shall be repeated until acknowledged in some manner by the drawtender before proceeding.

(970)     (2) The signals used to request the opening of the draw and to acknowledge that request shall be sound signals, visual signals, or radiotelephone communications described in this subpart.

(971)     (3) Any of the means of signaling described in this subpart sufficient to alert the party being signaled may be used.

(972)     (b) *Sound signals.* (1) Sound signals shall be made by whistle, horn, megaphone, hailer, or other device capable of producing the described signals loud enough to be heard by the drawtender.

(973)     (2) As used in this section, "prolonged blast" means a blast of four to six seconds duration and "short blast" means a blast of approximately one second duration.

(974)     (3) The sound signal to request the opening of a draw is one prolonged blast followed by one short blast sounded not more than three seconds after the prolonged blast. For vessels required to be passed through a draw during a scheduled closure period, the sound signal to request the opening of the draw during that period is five short blasts sounded in rapid succession.

(975)     (4) When the draw can be opened immediately, the sound signal to acknowledge a request to open the draw is one prolonged blast followed by one short blast sounded not more than 30 seconds after the requesting signal.

(976)     (5) When the draw cannot be opened immediately, or is open and shall be closed promptly, the sound signal to acknowledge a request to open the draw is five short blasts sounded in rapid succession not more than 30 seconds after the vessel's opening signal. The signal shall be repeated until acknowledged in some manner by the requesting vessel.

(977)     (c) *Visual signals.* (1) The visual signal to request the opening of a draw is–

(978)     (i) A white flag raised and lowered vertically; or

(979)     (ii) A white, amber, or green light raised and lowered vertically.

(980)     (2) When the draw can be opened immediately, the visual signal to acknowledge a request to open the draw, given not more than 30 seconds after the vessel's opening signal, is–

(981)     (i) A white flag raised and lowered vertically;

(982)     (ii) A white, amber, or green light raised and lowered vertically, or

(983)     (iii) A fixed or flashing white, amber, or green light or lights.

(984)     (3) When the draw cannot be opened immediately, or is open and must be closed promptly, the visual signal to acknowledge a request to open the draw is–

(985)     (i) A red flag or red light swung back and forth horizontally in full sight of the vessel given not more than 30 seconds after the vessel's opening signal; or

(986)     (ii) A fixed flashing red light or lights given not more than 30 seconds after the vessel's opening signal.

(987)     (4) The acknowledging signal when the draw cannot open immediately or is open and must be closed promptly shall be repeated until acknowledged in some manner by the requesting vessel.

(988)     (d)   *Radiotelephone   communications.*   (1) Radiotelephones may be used to communicate the same information provided by sound and visual signals.

(989)     (2) The vessel and the drawtender shall monitor the frequency used until the vessel has cleared the draw.

(990)     (3) When radiotelephone contact cannot be initiated or maintained, sound or visual signals under this section shall be used.

(991)
### §117.17 Signalling for contiguous drawbridges.

(992)     When a vessel must pass two or more drawbridges close together, the opening signal is given for the first bridge. After acknowledgment from the first bridge that it will promptly open, the opening signal is given for the second bridge, and so on until all bridges that the vessel must pass have been given the opening signal and have acknowledged that they will open promptly.

(993)
### §117.19 Signaling when two or more vessels are approaching a drawbridge.

(994)     When two or more vessels are approaching the same drawbridge at the same time, or nearly the same time, whether from the same or opposite directions, each vessel shall signal independently for the opening of the draw and the drawtender shall reply in turn to the signal of each vessel. The drawtender need not reply to signals by vessels accumulated at the bridge for passage during a scheduled open period.

(995)
### §117.21 Signalling for an opened drawbridge.

(996)     When a vessel approaches a drawbridge with the draw in the open position, the vessel shall give the opening signal. If no acknowledgment is received within 30 seconds, the vessel may proceed, with caution, through the open draw.

(997)
### §117.23 Installation of radiotelephones.

(998)     (a) When the District Commander deems it necessary for reasons of safety of navigation, the District Commander may require the installation and operation of a radiotelephone on or near a drawbridge.

(999)     (b) The District Commander gives written notice of the proposed requirement to the bridge owner.

(1000)     (c) All comments the owner wishes to submit shall be submitted to the District Commander within 30 days of receipt of the notice under paragraph (b) of this section.

(1001)     (d) If, upon consideration of the comments received, the District Commander determines that a radiotelephone is necessary, the District Commander notifies the bridge owner that a radiotelephone shall be installed and gives a reasonable time, not to exceed six months, to install the radiotelephone and commence operation.

(1002)
### §117.24 Radiotelephone installation identification.

(1003)     (a) The Coast Guard authorizes, and the District Commander may require the installation of a sign on drawbridges, on the upstream and downstream sides, indicating that the bridge is equipped with and operates a VHF radiotelephone in accordance with §117.23.

(1004)     (b) The sign shall give notice of the radiotelephone and its calling and working channels–

(1005)     (1) In plain language; or

(1006)     (2) By a sign consisting of the outline of a telephone handset with the long axis placed horizontally and a vertical three-legged lightning slash superimposed over the handset. The slash shall be as long vertically as the handset is wide horizontally and normally not less than 27 inches and no more than 36 inches long. The preferred calling channel should be shown in the lower left quadrant and the preferred working channel should be shown in the lower right quadrant.

(1007)     **Note.**–It is recommended that the radio-telephone sign be similar in design to the Service Signs established by the Federal Highway Administration (FHWA) in U.S. Road Symbol Signs using Reflective Blue and Reflective White colors. Color and design information is available from the District Commander of the Coast Guard District in which the bridge is located.

(1008)
### §117.31 Drawbridge operations for emergency vehicles and emergency vessels.

(1009)     (a) Upon receiving notification that an emergency vehicle is responding to an emergency situation, a drawtender must make all reasonable efforts to have the drawspan closed at the time the emergency vehicle arrives.

(1010)     (b) When a drawtender receives notice, or a proper signal as provided in §117.15 of this part, the drawtender shall take all reasonable measures to have the draw opened, regardless of the operating schedule of the draw, for passage of the following, provided this opening does not conflict with local emergency management

procedures which have been approved by the cognizant Coast Guard Captain of the Port:

(1011)     (1) Federal, State, and local government vessels used for public safety;

(1012)     (2) Vessels in distress where a delay would endanger life or property;

(1013)     (3) Commercial vessels engaged in rescue or emergency salvage operations; and

(1014)     (4) Vessels seeking shelter from severe weather.

(1015)
### §117.33 Closure of draw for natural disasters or civil disorders.

(1016)     Drawbridges need not open for the passage of vessels during periods of natural disasters or civil disorders declared by the appropriate authorities unless otherwise provided for in Subpart B or directed to do so by the District Commander.

(1017)
### §117.35 Temporary change to a drawbridge operating schedule.

(1018)     (a) For any temporary change to the operating schedule of a drawbridge, lasting less than or equal to 180 days, the District Commander may issue a deviation approval letter to the bridge owner and publish a "Notice of temporary deviation from regulations" in the **Federal Register**.

(1019)     (b) If the time period for a temporary change to the operating schedule of a drawbridge will be greater then 180 days, the District Commander will follow appropriate rulemaking procedures and publish a temporary rule in the **Federal Register** prior to the start of the action.

(1020)     (c) *Request for change.* (1) To temporarily change the drawbridge-operating requirements the bridge owner must submit a written request to the District Commander for approval of the change.

(1021)     (2) The request must describe the reason for the deviation and the dates and times scheduled for the start and end of the change.

(1022)     (3) Requests should be submitted as early as possible, preferably 90 days before the start of the action. District Commanders have discretion to accept requests submitted less than 90 days before a needed change if those requests can be processed before the date of the needed change.

(1023)     (d) *Determination.* The District Commander's determination to allow the schedule change is normally forwarded to the bridge owner within ten working days after receipt of the request. If the request is denied, the reasons for the denial will be set out in the District Commander's decision letter.

(1024)     (e) The drawbridge must return to its regular operating schedule immediately at the end of the designated time period.

(1025)     (f) If the authorized deviation period for an event is broken into separate time periods on the same day or on consecutive days, the drawbridge must provide openings for navigation between authorized schedule changes.

(1026)　　(g) The District Commander will also announce the change to the operating schedule in the Local Notice to Mariners and other appropriate local media.

(1027)
### §117.36 Closure of drawbridge for emergency repair.

(1028)　　(a) When a drawbridge unexpectedly becomes inoperable, or should be immediately rendered inoperable because of mechanical failure or structural defect, the drawbridge owner must notify the District Commander of the closure without delay and give the reason for the emergency closure of the drawbridge and an estimated time when the drawbridge will be returned to operating condition.

(1029)　　(b) The District Commander will notify mariners about the drawbridge status through Broadcast Notices to Mariners, Local Notice to Mariners and any other appropriate local media.

(1030)　　(c) Repair work under this section must be performed with all due speed in order to return the drawbridge to operation as soon as possible.

(1031)
### §117.37 [Removed].

(1032)
### §117.39 Authorized closure of drawbridge due to infrequent requests for openings.

(1033)　　(a) When there have been no requests for drawbridge openings for at least two years, a bridge owner may request in writing that the District Commander authorize the drawbridge to remain closed to navigation and to be untended.

(1034)　　(b) The District Commander may:

(1035)　　(1) Authorize the closure of the drawbridge;

(1036)　　(2) Set out any conditions in addition to the requirement in paragraph (d): and

(1037)　　(3) Revoke an authorization and order the drawbridge returned to operation when necessary.

(1038)　　(c) All drawbridges authorized to remain closed to navigation, under this section, must be maintained in operable condition.

(1039)　　(d) Authorization under this section does not:

(1040)　　(1) Authorize physical changes to the drawbridge structure, or

(1041)　　(2) Authorize removal of the operating machinery.

(1042)　　(e) Drawbridges authorized under this section to remain closed to navigation and to be untended are identified in subpart B of this part.

(1043)
### §117.40 Advance notice for drawbridge opening.

(1044)　　(a) Upon written request by the owner of a drawbridge, the District Commander may authorize a drawbridge to operate under an advance notice for opening. The drawbridge tender, after receiving the advance notice, must open the drawbridge at the requested time and allow for a reasonable delay in arrival of the vessel giving the advance notice.

(1045)　　(b) If the request is approved, a description of the advanced notice for the drawbridge will be added to subpart B of this part.

(1046)
### §117.41 Maintaining drawbridges in the fully open position.

(1047)　　(a) Drawbridges permanently maintained in the fully open to navigation position may discontinue drawtender service as long as the drawbridge remains fully open to navigation. The drawbridge must remain in the fully open position until drawtender service is restored.

(1048)　　(b) If a drawbridge is normally maintained in the fully open to navigation position, but closes to navigation for the passage of pedestrian, vehicular, rail, or other traffic, the drawbridge must be tended unless:

(1049)　　(1) Special operating requirements are established in subpart B of this part for that drawbridge; or

(1050)　　(2) The drawbridge is remotely operated or automated.

(1051)
### §117.42 Remotely operated and automated drawbridges.

(1052)　　(a) Upon written request by the owner of a drawbridge, the District Commander may authorize a drawbridge to operate under an automated system or from a remote location.

(1053)　　(b) If the request is approved, a description of the full operation of the remotely operated or automated drawbridge will be added to subpart B of this part.

(1054)
### §117.43 [Removed].

(1055)
### §117.45 [Removed].

(1056)
### §117.47 Clearance gauges.

(1057)　　(a) Clearance gauges are required for drawbridges across navigable waters of the United States discharging into the Atlantic Ocean south of Delaware Bay (including the Lewes and Rehoboth Canal, DE) or into the Gulf of Mexico (including coastal waterways contiguous thereto and tributaries to such waterways and the Lower Atchafalaya River, LA), except the Mississippi River and its tributaries and outlets.

(1058)　　(b) Except for provisions in this part which specify otherwise for particular drawbridges, clearance gauges shall be designed, installed, and maintained according to the provisions of 33 CFR 118.160 (not carried in this Coast Pilot).

(1059)　　**Note.**–Clearance gauge requirements, if any, for drawbridges other than those referred to in this section are listed in Subpart B under the appropriate bridge.

(1060)
### §117.49 Process of violations.

(1061)　　(a) Complaints of alleged violations under this part are submitted to the District Commander of the Coast Guard District in which the drawbridge is located.

(1062)     (b) Penalties for violations under this part are assessed and collected under Subpart 1.07 of Part 1 of this chapter (not published in this Coast Pilot; see 33 CFR 1.07).

(1063)
## Subpart B–Specific Requirements

(1064)
### §117.51 General.

(1065)     The drawbridges in this subpart are listed by the state in which they are located and by the waterway they cross. Waterways are arranged alphabetically by state. The drawbridges listed under a waterway are generally arranged in order from the mouth of the waterway moving upstream. The drawbridges on the Atlantic Intracoastal Waterway are listed from north to south and on the Gulf Intracoastal Waterway from east to west.

(1066)
### §117.53 [Removed].

(1067)
### §117.55 Posting of requirements.

(1068)     (a) The owner of each drawbridge under this subpart, other than removable span bridges, must ensure that a sign summarizing the requirements in this subpart applicable to the drawbridge is posted both upstream and downstream of the drawbridge. The requirements to be posted need not include those in Subpart A or §§117.51 through 117.59 of this part.

(1069)     (b) The signs shall be of sufficient size and so located as to be easily read at any time from an approaching vessel.

(1070)     (c) If advance notice is required to open the draw, the signs shall also state the name, address, and telephone number of the person to be notified.

(1071)
### §117.57 [Removed].

(1072)
### §117.59 Special requirements due to hazards.

(1073)     For the duration of occurrences hazardous to safety or navigation, such as floods, freshets, and damage to the bridge or fender system, the District Commander may require the owner of an operational drawbridge listed in this subpart to have the bridge attended full time and open on signal.

(1074)
## DELAWARE

(1075)
### §117.231 Brandywine Creek.

(1076)     The draw of the Conrail bridge, mile 1.1, the Church Street bridge, mile 1.3, and the Sixteenth Street bridge, mile 1.7, all at Wilmington, need not be opened for the passage of vessels.

(1077)
### §117.233 Broad Creek.

(1078)     The draws of the Norfolk Southern bridge, mile 8.0, the Poplar Street Bridge, mile 8.2 and the U.S. 13A Bridge, mile 8.25, all in Laurel, need not open for the passage of vessels.

(1079)
### §117.234 Cedar Creek.

(1080)     The SR 36 Bridge, mile 0.5 in Cedar Beach, shall open on signal. From April 1 through November 30 from 2 a.m. to 4 a.m.; and from December 1 through March 31 from 6:30 p.m. to 6 a.m., the draw shall open on signal if at least four hours notice is given.

(1081)
### §117.235 Chesapeake and Delaware Canal.

(1082)     The draw of the Conrail bridge, mile 7.7, is operated by the Delmarva Central Railroad Company and shall open on signal. The following light signals, located in the center of the drawspan on both sides of the bridge, shall be used:

(1083)     (a) When the draw is to be opened immediately, one fixed amber light.

(1084)     (b) When the draw is not ready to be opened, one flashing red light.

(1085)
### §117.237 Christina River.

(1086)     (a) The owners of the bridges on this waterway:

(1087)     (1) Shall provide and keep in good legible condition two board gages painted white with black figures not less than six inches high, to indicate the vertical clearance under the closed draw at all stages of the tide. The gages shall be so placed on the bridges that they are plainly visible to the operator of each vessel approaching the bridges either up or downstream.

(1088)     (2) Shall open on signal except that the draw of a railroad bridge need not be opened when a train is in the bridge block, approaching the bridge, or within 5 minutes of the passage of a passenger train; but in no event shall the opening of the draw be delayed more than 10 minutes.

(1089)     (b) The draw of the Norfolk Southern Railroad Bridge, mile 1.4 at Wilmington, shall operate as follows:

(1090)     (1) The draw shall remain in the open position for navigation. The draw shall only be closed for train crossings or periodic maintenance authorized in accordance with subpart A of this part.

(1091)     (2) The bridge shall be operated by the controller at the Harrisburg, PA Dispatcher's Office. The controller shall monitor vessel traffic with closed circuit cameras and infrared sensors covering the swing radius. Operational information will be provided 24 hours a day on marine channel 13 and via telephone 717–541–2140.

(1092)     (3) The bridge shall not be operated from the remote location in the following events: Failure or obstruction of the infrared sensors, closed-circuit cameras or marine-radio communications, or anytime controller's visibility is inhibited. In these situations, a bridge tender with

Norfolk Southern must be called and on-site within 30 minutes.

(1093)  (4) Before the bridge closes for any reason, the remote operator will monitor waterway traffic in the area. The bridge shall only be closed if the off-site remote operator's visual inspection shows that the channel is clear and there are no vessels transiting in the area. While the bridge is moving, the operator shall maintain constant surveillance of the navigation channel.

(1094)  (5) Before closing the draw, the channel traffic lights would change from flashing green to flashing red, the horn will sound five short blasts, and an audio voice warning stating, "Attention, Attention. Norfolk Southern Railroad Bridge over Christina River at milepost 1.4 will be closing to river traffic." Five short blasts of the horn will continue until the bridge is seated and locked down to vessels. The channel traffic lights will continue to flash red.

(1095)  (6) When the rail traffic has cleared, the horn will sound one prolonged blast followed by one short blast to indicate the draw is opening to vessel traffic. During the opening swing movement, the channel traffic lights would flash red until the bridge returns to the fully open position. In the full open position to vessels, the bridge channel lights will flash green followed by an announcement stating, "Security, security, security. Norfolk Southern Railroad Bridge over Christina River at mile 1.4 is open for river traffic." Vessels shall stay clear of both channels as to not interfere with infrared detectors, until green lights are displayed on the swing span.

(1096)  (c) In Wilmington DE, the draw of the Third Street Bridge at mile 2.3, shall open on signal, the draws of the Walnut Street Bridge at mile 2.8, and the Market Street Bridge at mile 3.0, shall open on signal if at least eight hours notice is given. From 7 a.m. to 8 a.m. and 4:30 p.m. to 5:30 p.m., Monday through Saturday except holidays, the draws of these three bridges need not be opened for the passage of vessels. Any vessel which has passed through one or more of these bridges immediately prior to a closed period and which requires passage through the other bridge or bridges in order to continue to its destination shall be passed through the draw or draws of the bridge or bridges without delay.

(1097)  (d) The draws of the Norfolk Southern Railroad bridges, at miles 4.1 and 4.2, both at Wilmington, shall open on signal from 6 a.m. to 8 p.m. if at least 24 hours notice is given. From 8 p.m. to 6 a.m., the draws need not be opened for the passage of vessels.

(1098)  ### §117.239 Lewes and Rehoboth Canal.

(1099)  (a) The draw of the Savannah Road/SR 18 Bridge, at mile 1.7, in Lewes shall open on signal if at least four hours notice is given.

(1100)  (b) The draw of the SR 14A Bridge, at mile 6.7, in Rehoboth shall open on signal if at least 24 hours notice is given.

(1101)

### §117.241 Mispillion River.

(1102)  The draw of the Route 1/Rehoboth Blvd. Bridge, at mile 11.0, at Milford shall open on signal if at least 24 hours notice is given.

(1103)  ### §117.243 Nanticoke River.

(1104)  (a) The draw of the Norfolk Southern Railway Bridge, mile 39.4 in Seaford, will operate as follows:

(1105)  (1) From March 15 through November 15, the draw will open on signal for all vessels except that from 11 p.m. to 5 a.m. at least 2.5 hours notice will be required.

(1106)  (2) At all times, from November 16 through March 14, the draw will open on signal if at least 2.5 hours notice is given.

(1107)  (3) When notice is required, the owner operator of the vessel must contact the bridge operator (Delmarva Central Railroad Company) with an estimated time of passage by calling 1-802-774-0305.

(1108)  (b) The draw of the SR 13 Bridge, mile 39.6, in Seaford shall:

(1109)  (1) Open on signal, except from 6 p.m. to 8 a.m., from April 1 through October 31; from November 1 through March 31, Monday to Friday and on Saturday and Sunday from 3:30 p.m. to 7:30 a.m., if at least four hours notice is given.

(1110)  (2) Open on signal, on Saturday and Sunday, from 7:31 a.m. through 3:29 p.m., from November 1 through March 31, if at least 24 hours notice is given.

(1111)

## DISTRICT OF COLUMBIA

(1112)  ### §117.253 Anacostia River.

(1113)  (a) The draw of the Frederick Douglass Memorial (South Capitol Street) bridge, mile 1.2, need not be opened for the passage of vessels.

(1114)  (b) The CSX Railroad Bridge, mile 3.4.

(1115)  (1) The draw of the bridge to be operated by the controller at the Benning Yard office shall open on signal;

(1116)  (i) At all times for public vessels of the United States, state and local government vessels, commercial vessels and any vessels in an emergency involving danger to life or property.

(1117)  (ii) Between 9 a.m. and 12 p.m. and between 1 p.m. and 6 p.m. from May 15 through September 30.

(1118)  (iii) Between 6 p.m. and 7 p.m. from May 15 through September 30 if notice is given to the controller at the Benning Yard office not later than 6 p.m. on the day for which the opening is requested.

(1119)  (iv) At all other times, if at least 48 hours of notice is given to the controller at the Benning Yard office.

(1120)  (2) The CSX Railroad Bridge shall not be operated by the controller at the Benning Yard office in the event of failure or obstruction of the motion sensors, laser scanners, video cameras or marine-radio communications. In these situations, a bridge tender must be called to operate the bridge on-site.

(1121)    (3) Except as provided in §117.31(b), opening of the draw shall not exceed ten minutes after clearance of rail traffic.

(1122)    (4) A horn will sound one prolonged blast followed by one short blast to indicate that the CSX Railroad Bridge is moving to the full open position for vessel traffic. During open span movement, the channel traffic lights will flash red until the bridge is in the full open position to vessels. In the full open position to vessels, the bridge channel traffic lights will flash green.

(1123)    (5) A horn will sound five short blasts, the channel traffic lights will flash red, and an audio voice-warning device will announce bridge movement during closing span movement. Five short blasts of the horn will continue until the bridge is seated in and locked down. When the bridge is seated and in locked down position to vessels, the channel traffic lights will continue to flash red.

(1124)    (6) The owners of the bridge shall provide and keep in good legible condition two board gauges painted white with black figures not less than six inches high to indicate the vertical clearance under the closed draw at all stages of the tide. The gauges shall be placed on the bridge so that they are plainly visible to the operator of any vessel approaching the bridge from either upstream or downstream.

(1125)

### §117.255 Potomac River.

(1126)    (a) The draw of the Woodrow Wilson Memorial (I–95) bridge, mile 103.8, between Alexandria, Virginia, and Oxon Hill, Maryland–

(1127)    (1) Shall open on signal at any time only for a vessel in distress, notwithstanding the provisions of §117.31:

(1128)    (2) Shall open for the passage of a commercial vessel at any time except:

(1129)    (i) From Monday through Friday (except Federal holidays), 5 a.m. to 8 p.m.

(1130)    (ii) Saturday, Sunday, and Federal holidays, 2 p.m. to 7 p.m.

(1131)    (3) Need not open for the passage of a commercial vessel under paragraph (a)(2) of this section unless–

(1132)    (i) The owner or operator of the vessel provides the bridge tender with an estimate of the approximate time of that passage at least 12 hours in advance at 703–836–2396; and

(1133)    (ii) The owner or operator of the vessel notifies the bridge tender at least 4 hours in advance of the requested time for that passage.

(1134)    (4) Shall open for the passage of a recreational vessel at any time except:

(1135)    (i) Monday through Friday (except Federal holidays), 5 a.m. to 12 midnight;

(1136)    (ii) Saturday, Sunday, and Federal holidays, 7 a.m. to 12 midnight, except as provided in paragraph (a)(4)(iii) of this section;

(1137)    (iii) Notwithstanding paragraph (a)(4)(ii) of this section, the bridge may open beginning at 10 p.m. on Saturday, Sunday, or a Federal holiday for the passage of

a recreational vessel if the owner or operator of the vessel notifies the Bridge Tender of the time of that passage by not later than 12 hours before that time.

(1138)    (5) Need not open for the passage of a recreational vessel under paragraph (a)(4) of this section unless–

(1139)    (i) The owner or operator of the vessel provides the bridge tender with an estimate of the approximate time of the passage at least 12 hours in advance at 703–736–2396; and

(1140)    (ii) the owner or operator of the vessel notifies the bridge tender at least 4 hours in advance of the requested time for that passage.

(1141)    (6) A recreational vessel may pass through the drawspan at any time it is open for passage of a commercial vessel.

(1142)    (b) The draws of all other bridges need not be opened for the passage of vessels.

(1143)    (c) This section is also issued under the authority of Pub. L. 102–587, 106 Stat. 5039.

(1144)

## MARYLAND

(1145)

### §117.543 Bear Creek.

(1146)    (a) The draw of the Peninsula Parkway Bridge, mile 2.1, between Dundalk and Sparrows Point, shall open on signal; except that, from April 16 through November 15 from 12 midnight to 8 a.m. except Saturdays and Sundays, and Federal and State holidays, at least one half hour notice is required.

(1147)    (b) The draw of the Baltimore County highway bridge, mile 3.4 at Wise Avenue between Dundalk and Sparrows Point, shall open on signal if at least four hours notice is given.

(1148)

### §117.547 Bush River.

(1149)    The draw of the Amtrak Bridge, mile 6.8 at Perryman, shall operate as follows:

(1150)    (a) Shall open twice a day from May 1 through October 31, on Saturdays, Sundays, and Federal holidays that fall on a Friday or a Monday, when a proper request has been received.

(1151)    (b) Request for an opening is given to the Amtrak Assistant Division Engineer at 410–642–1588 and or email at BridgeOpeningRequest@Amtrak.com by an authorized representative of the Bush River Yacht Club no later than noon on the Friday just preceding the day of opening or, if that Friday is a Federal holiday, no later than noon on the preceding Thursday.

(1152)    (c) Amtrak determines the times for openings and shall schedule the times:

(1153)    (1) During daylight hours, six to ten hours apart; and

(1154)    (2) One opening before noon and one after noon.

(1155)    (3) In emergent situations after notification is given to the numbers indicated in paragraph (b) of this section it can take up to six hours for the bridge to open.

(1156)    (d) Amtrak shall notify a representative of the Bush River Yacht Club of the times of all openings for the weekend (or extended weekend) in question no later than 6 p.m., on the Friday just preceding the weekend or, if that Friday is a Federal holiday, no later than 6 p.m., on the preceding Thursday.

(1157)    (e) Each opening shall be of sufficient duration to pass waiting vessels.

(1158)    (f) At all other times the draw need not open for the passage of vessels.

(1159)
### §117.549 Cambridge Harbor.

(1160)    The draw of the S342 bridge, mile 0.1 at Cambridge, shall open on signal from 6 a.m. to 8 p.m.; except that, from 12 noon to 1 p.m. Monday through Friday, the draw need not be opened. The draw need not be opened from 8 p.m. to 6 a.m.

(1161)
### §117.551 Chester River.

(1162)    The draw of the S213 Bridge, mile 26.8 at Chestertown, shall open on signal if at least six hours notice is given.

(1163)
### §117.553 Choptank River.

(1164)    (a) The draw of the Maryland 331 bridge, mile 35.3, at Dover, shall open on signal from 6 a.m. to 6 p.m. year-round, and the draw shall remain closed from 6 p.m. to 6 a.m., year-round, unless 24 hours advance notice is given by calling 301–820–8592 or 301–745–2096.

(1165)    (b) The draw of the Conrail bridge, mile 50.9 at Denton, shall open on signal from May 30 through September 30 from sunrise to sunset and at all other times if at least four hours notice is given.

(1166)
### §117.555 College Creek.

(1167)    The draws of the Naval Academy highway bridge, mile 0.3 at Annapolis, and the Maryland highway bridge, mile 0.4 at Annapolis, need not be opened for the passage of vessels.

(1168)
### §117.557 Curtis Creek.

(1169)    The draw of the I695 bridge, mile 1.0 at Baltimore, shall open on signal if at least a one-hour notice is given to the Maryland Transportation Authority in Baltimore.

(1170)
### §117.559 Isle of Wight (Sinepuxent) Bay.

(1171)    The draw of the US 50 Bridge, mile 0.5, at Ocean City, shall open on signal, except:

(1172)    (a) From October 1 through April 30, from 6 p.m. to 6 a.m., the draw shall open if notice has been given to the bridge tender before 6 p.m.

(1173)    (b) From May 25 through September 15, from 9:25 a.m. to 9:55 p.m., the draw shall open at 25 minutes after and 55 minutes after the hour for a maximum of five minutes to let accumulated vessels pass, except that on Saturdays, from 1 p.m. to 5 p.m., the draw shall open on the hour for all waiting vessels and shall remain in the open position until all waiting vessels pass.

(1174)    (c) On July 4, the draw need not open from 10 p.m. until 11 p.m. to accommodate the annual July 4th fireworks show. Should inclement weather prevent the fireworks event from taking place as planned, the draw need not open from 10 p.m. until 11 p.m. on July 5th to accommodate the annual July 4th fireworks show.

(1175)
### §117.561 Kent Island Narrows.

(1176)    The draw of the U.S. Route 50/301 bridge, mile 1.0, Kent Island Narrows, operates as follows:

(1177)    (a) From November 1 through April 30, the draw shall open on signal from 6 a.m. to 6 p.m. but need not be opened from 6 p.m. to 6 a.m.

(1178)    (b) From May 1 through October 31, the draw shall open on signal on the hour and half-hour from 6 a.m. to 9 p.m., but need not be opened from 9 p.m. to 6 a.m.

(1179)    (c) The draw shall open on signal for public vessels of the United States, state and local government vessels used for public safety purposes, and vessels in distress. Operational information will be available 24 hours a day by calling 800–543–2515

(1180)
### §117.563 Marshyhope Creek.

(1181)    The draw of the S14 bridge, mile 5.8 at Brookview, need not be opened for the passage of vessels. The operating machinery shall be maintained in a serviceable condition.

(1182)
### §117.565 Miles River.

(1183)    The draw of the Route S370 bridge, mile 10.0 at Easton, Maryland, shall open on signal; except that from November 1 through March 31, 24 hours a day, and from April 1 through October 31, from 6 p.m. to 6 a.m., a six-hour advance notice to the drawtender is required for bridge openings.

(1184)
### §117.566 Patapsco River—Middle Branch.

(1185)    (a) The draw of the Hanover Street S2 bridge, mile 12.0 across the Middle Branch of the Patapsco River at Baltimore, will open on signal from 5 a.m. to 6:30 a.m., 9:30 a.m. to 4 p.m., and 6 p.m. to 9:00 p.m. The draw need not be opened from 6:30 a.m. to 9:30 a.m. and 4 p.m. to 6 p.m.; however, fire boats, police boats, and other vessels engaged in emergency operations will be passed immediately during this period. When a vessel desires to pass the draw from 9 p.m. to 5 a.m., notice will be given to the superintendent of the bridge, either at the bridge before 9 p.m. or at the superintendent's residence after 9 p.m. If the notice is given from 5 a.m. to 9 p.m. or if at least one half hour has elapsed since the notice was given, the draw will open promptly at the time requested.

(1186)    (b) The draw of the Western Maryland railroad bridge, mile 12.5 across the Middle Branch of the Patapsco River at Baltimore, shall open on signal from 7 a.m. to 12 noon and 1 p.m. to 4 p.m. Monday through Friday except legal holidays. At all other times, the draw shall open if at least six hours notice is given. Marine firefighting equipment and pollution control vessels shall be passed as soon as possible but in no event more than 15 minutes after notice is given.

(1187)

### §117.567 Patuxent River.

(1188)    The draw of S231 bridge, mile 18.5 at Benedict, shall open on signal; except that, from 6 p.m. to 6 a.m., the draw shall open on signal if notice is given to the Toll Captain at the Administration Building at the east end of the bridge before 6 p.m.

(1189)

### §117.569 Pocomoke River.

(1190)    (a) The Conrail railroad bridge, mile 15.2, at Pocomoke City, shall open on signal, except between November 1 and March 31 the draw must open only if at least five hours advance notice is given to the bridge operator (Delmarva Central Railroad Company) by calling 1-802-774-0305.

(1191)    (b) The draw of the Route 675 bridge, mile 15.6, at Pocomoke City, shall open on signal, except between November 1 and March 31 the draw must open only if at least five hours advance notice is given.

(1192)    (c) The draw of the S12 bridge, mile 29.9, at Snow Hill, shall open on signal if at least five hours notice is given.

(1193)

### §117.570 Sassafras River.

(1194)    The draw of the Sassafras River (Route 213) bridge, mile 10.0 at Georgetown, Maryland, shall open on signal; except that from November 1 through March 31, from midnight to 8 a.m., the draw need only open if at least a six-hour advance notice is given.

(1195)

### §117.571 Spa Creek.

(1196)    The S181 bridge, mile 0.4, at Annapolis, Maryland:

(1197)    (a) From May 1 to October 31, Monday through Friday, except Federal and State holidays:

(1198)    (1) The draw shall remain closed from 7:30 a.m. to 9:00 a.m. and from 4:30 p.m. to 7:30 p.m., except the draw shall open at 6:00 p.m. and 7:00 p.m. for any vessels waiting to pass.

(1199)    (2) The draw shall open on the hour and the half-hour, from 9:00 a.m. to 4:30 p.m.

(1200)    (3) The draw shall open on the hour and half hour, from 7:30 p.m. to 7:30 a.m.

(1201)    (b) From November 1 to April 30, Monday through Friday, except Federal and State holidays:

(1202)    (1) The draw shall remain closed from 7:30 a.m. to 9:00 a.m. and from 4:30 p.m. to 6:00 p.m.

(1203)    (2) The draw shall open on signal from 9:00 a.m. to 4:30 p.m. and from 6:00 p.m. to 7:30 a.m.

(1204)    (c) On Saturdays, Sundays, and holidays year-round, the draw shall open on the hour and half-hour for vessels waiting to pass. Except on July 4th of every year from 8:30 p.m. to 11 p.m., the draw need not open for vessels,

and in the event of inclement weather, the alternate date is July 5th.

(1205)    (d) The drawspan must always open on signal for public vessels of the United States.

(1206)

### §117.573 Stoney Creek.

(1207)    The draw of the Stoney Creek (S173) bridge, mile 0.9, in Riviera shall open on signal, except:

(1208)    (a) From 6:30 a.m. to 9 a.m. and from 3:30 p.m. to 6:30 p.m., Monday through Friday except Federal and State holidays, the draw need be opened only at 7:30 a.m. and 5 p.m. if any vessels are waiting to pass.

(1209)    (b) From 11 a.m. to 7 p.m. on Saturday and from 12 p.m. to 5 p.m. on Sunday, the draw need be opened only on the hour and half hour.

(1210)    (c) Public vessels of the United States must be passed as soon as possible.

(1211)

### §117.575 Susquehanna River.

(1212)    The draw of the Conrail bridge, mile 1.0 at Havre de Grace, shall open on signal if at least 24 hours notice is given.

(1213)

### §117.577 Weems Creek.

(1214)    The draw of the S437 bridge, mile 0.7 at West Annapolis, shall open on signal from sunrise to sunset from May 1 through September 30. At all other times, the draw shall open on signal if at least five hours notice is given.

(1215)

### §117.579 Wicomico River (North Prong).

(1216)    The draws of the Main Street and U.S. 50 bridges, mile 22.4, Salisbury, Maryland shall open on signal if at least four hours notice is given by calling the telephone contact number at 410–430–7461.

(1217)

### NEW JERSEY

(1218)

### §117.701 Alloway Creek.

(1219)    (a) The draws of the Salem County bridges, miles 5.1 at Hancocks Bridge, and 6.5 at New Bridge, shall open on signal if at least 24 hours notice is given.

(1220)    (b) The draw of the S49 bridge, mile 9.5 at Quinton, need not be opened for the passage of vessels.

(1221)

### §117.705 Beaver Dam Creek.

(1222)    The draw of the Ocean County bridge, mile 0.5 at Point Pleasant, shall open on signal from June 1 through September 30 and from 8 a.m. to 4 p.m. during April, May, October, and November. At all other times, the draw shall open on signal if at least 24 hours notice is given.

(1223)

### §117.711 Cohansey River.

(1224)    The draw of the Broad Street bridge, mile 18.2 at Bridgeton, need not be opened for the passage of vessels.

(1225)
### §117.713 Cooper River.

(1226)    (a) The drawspans for the State Street Drawbridge, mile 0.3 and the Conrail Drawbridge at North River Avenue, mile 0.9, must open on signal if at least four hours notice is given.

(1227)    (b) The draw of the Admiral Wilson Boulevard bridge, mile 1.1 at Camden, need not be opened for the passage of vessels. However, the draw shall be returned to operable condition within six months after notification by the District Commander to do so.

(1228)
### §117.714 Corson Inlet.

(1229)    The draw of the Corson Inlet Bridge, mile 0.9, at Strathmere, shall open on signal; except that from October 1 through May 15 from 10 p.m. to 6 a.m. and from 6 a.m. to 10 p.m. on December 25 the draw need open only if at least two hours notice is given.

(1230)
### §117.716 Delaware River.

(1231)    (a) The following apply to all drawbridges across the Delaware River:

(1232)    (1) The draws of railroad bridges need not be opened when there is a train in the bridge block approaching the bridge with the intention of crossing or within five minutes of the known time of the passage of a scheduled passenger train.

(1233)    (2) The opening of a bridge may not be delayed more than five minutes for a highway bridge or 10 minutes for a railroad bridge after the signal to open is given.

(1234)    (3) The owners of drawbridges shall provide and keep in good legible condition two board gages painted white with black figures not less than six inches high to indicate the vertical clearance under the closed draw at all stages of the tide. The gages shall be so placed on the bridge that they are plainly visible to operators of vessels approaching the bridge either up or downstream.

(1235)    (b) The draw of the Conrail Memorial Railroad Bridge, mile 104.6, at Pennsauken Township, NJ shall be operated as follows:

(1236)    (1) The bridge will be remotely operated from the Conrail South Jersey dispatch center in Mount Laurel, NJ, unless the remote operation system is in a failed condition.

(1237)    (2) An AIS transmitter has been installed on the New Jersey side of the bridge at the bridge and land intersection in approximate position 39°58′50.52″ N (39.9807), 75°03′58.75″ (-75.06632). The AIS transmitter is assigned maritime mobile service identity (MMSI) number 993663001. The status of the bridge (open/closed/inoperative) will be provided via the name transmitted by the AIS private aids to navigation as DELAIR BRG–OPEN (fully open and locked position, channel light green), DELAIR BRG–CLOSED (other than fully open, not inoperative), or DELAIR BRG–INOP (other than fully open, inoperative). The AIS transmitter

will transmit the bridge status every two minutes and upon a change in the bridge status.

(1238)    (3) The remote operation system will be considered in a failed condition and qualified personnel will return and operate the bridge within 60 minutes if any of the following conditions are found:

(1239)    (i) The remote operation system becomes incapable of safely and effectively operating the bridge from the remote operation center; or

(1240)    (ii) Visibility of the waterway or bridge is degraded to less than equal that of an on-site bridge tender; or

(1241)    (iii) Signals (communications) via sound or visual signals or radio telephone (voice) via VHF–FM channels 13 or 16 become inoperative; or

(1242)    (iv) AIS becomes inoperative.

(1243)    (4) Vessels that require an opening shall continue to request an opening via the methods defined in § 117.15(b) through (d) (sound or visual signals or radio telephone (VHF–FM) voice communications), via telephone at (856) 231–2301, or via push-to-talk (PTT) on VHF–FM channel 13. Vessels may push the PTT button five times while on VHF–FM channel 13 to request an opening.

(1244)    (5) The signals for the remote operation center or on-site bridge tender to respond to a sound signal for a bridge opening include:

(1245)    (i) When the draw can be opened immediately—a sound signal of one prolonged blast followed by one short blast and illumination of a fixed white light not more than 30 seconds after the requesting signal; or

(1246)    (ii) When the draw cannot be opened immediately—five short blasts sounded in rapid succession and illumination of a fixed red light not more 30 seconds after the vessel's opening signal.

(1247)    (6) The signals for the remote operation center or on-site bridge tender to respond to a visual signal for a bridge opening include:

(1248)    (i) When the draw can be opened immediately—illumination of a fixed white light not more than 30 seconds after the requesting signal; or

(1249)    (ii) When the draw cannot be opened immediately—illumination of a fixed red light not more 30 seconds after the vessel's opening signal.

(1250)    (7) The fixed white light will remain illuminated until the bridge reaches the fully open position. The fixed white and red lights will be positioned on the east (New Jersey) bridge abutment adjacent to the navigation span.

(1251)
### §117.719 Glimmer Glass (Debbie's Creek).

(1252)    (a) The draw of the Monmouth County highway bridge, mile 0.4 at Manasquan, shall open on signal, except as follows:

(1253)    (1) From 4:30 p.m. January 1 through 8 a.m. April 1, from 4:30 p.m. to 8 a.m., the draw need open only if at least four-hours advance notice is given.

(1254)    (2) From Memorial Day through Labor Day from 7 a.m. to 8 p.m., the draw need open only on the hour and half hour if any vessels are waiting to pass.

(1255)　　(b) The owners of the bridge shall provide and keep in good legible condition two board gauges painted white with black figures not less than eight inches high to indicate the vertical clearance under the closed draw at all stages of the tide. The gauges shall be so placed on the bridge that they are plainly visible to operators of vessels approaching the bridge either up or downstream.

(1256)
### §117.720 Great Channel.

(1257)　　The draw of the County of Cape May bridge, mile 0.7, between Stone Harbor and Nummy Island, shall open on signal except that:

(1258)　　(a) From May 15 through October 15 from 10 p.m. to 6 a.m., the draw need only open if at least four hours advance notice is given.

(1259)　　(b) [Suspended]

(1260)　　(c) from 9:15 a.m. to 2:30 p.m. on the fourth Sunday in March of every year, the draw need not open for vessels. If the fourth Sunday falls on a religious holiday, the draw need not open from 9:15 a.m. to 2:30 p.m. on the third Sunday of March of every year.

(1261)
### §117.721 Grassy Sound Channel.

(1262)　　The draw of the Grassy Sound Channel Bridge, mile 1.0 in Middle Township, shall open on signal from 6 a.m. to 8 p.m. from May 15 through September 30. From 9:15 a.m. to 2:30 p.m. on the fourth Sunday in March of every year, the draw need not open for vessels. If the fourth Sunday falls on a religious holiday, the draw need not open from 9:15 a.m. to 2:30 p.m. on the third Sunday of March of every year. Two hours advance notice is required for all other openings by calling 609–368–4591.

(1263)
### §117.722 Great Egg Harbor Bay.

(1264)　　The draw of the U.S. Route 9/Beesleys Point Bridge, mile 3.5, shall open if at least two hours' notice is given from October 1 to May 14 from 8 p.m. to 6 a.m., from May 15 to September 30 from 10 p.m. to 6 a.m., and from 8 p.m. on December 24 until and including 6 a.m. on December 26 of every year; and shall open on signal at all other times.

(1265)
### §117.725 Manantico Creek.

(1266)　　The draw of the highway bridge, mile 0.5 at Millville, need not be opened for the passage of vessels.

(1267)
### §117.729 Mantua Creek.

(1268)　　(a) The draw of the Conrail automated railroad bridge, mile 1.4, at Paulsboro, NJ shall operate as follows:

(1269)　　(1) The bridge will be operated remotely by the South Jersey Train Dispatcher located in Mt. Laurel, NJ. Operational information will be provided 24 hours a day by telephone at 856–231–2282.

(1270)　　(2) From March 1 through November 30, the draw shall be left in the open position and will only be lowered for the passage of trains and to perform periodic maintenance authorized in accordance with subpart A of this part.

(1271)　　(3) From December 1 through the last day of February, the draw will open on signal if at least 4 hours notice is given by telephone at 856–231–2282.

(1272)　　(4) The timeframe to initiate the bridge closure will be not more than 15 minutes before a train will arrive at the bridge location. If a train moving toward the bridge has crossed the home signal for the bridge, the train may continue across the bridge and must clear the bridge prior to stopping for any reason. Trains shall be controlled so that any delay in opening of the draw shall not exceed ten minutes except as provided in §117.31(b).

(1273)　　(5) The bridge will be equipped with cameras and channel sensors to visually and electronically ensure the waterway is clear before the bridge closes. The video and sensors are located and monitored at the remote operating location in Mt. Laurel, NJ. The channel sensors signal will be a direct input to the bridge control system. In the event of failure or obstruction of the infrared channel sensors, the bridge will automatically stop closing and the South Jersey Train Dispatcher will return the bridge to the open position. In the event of video failure the bridge will remain in the full open position.

(1274)　　(6) The Conrail Railroad center span light will change from fixed green to flashing red anytime the bridge is not in the full open position.

(1275)　　(7) Prior to downward movement of the span, the horn will sound two prolonged blasts, followed by a pause, and then two short blasts until the bridge is seated and locked down. At the time of movement, the center span light will change from fixed green to flashing red and remain flashing until the bridge has returned to its full open position.

(1276)　　(8) When the train controller at Mt. Laurel has verified that rail traffic has cleared, they will sound the horn five times to signal the draw is about to return to its full open position.

(1277)　　(9) During upward movement of the span, the horn will sound two prolonged blasts, followed by a pause, and then sound two short blasts until the bridge is in the full open position. The center span light will continue to flash red until the bridge is in the fully open position.

(1278)　　(10) When the draw cannot be operated from the remote site, a bridge tender must be called to operate the bridge in the traditional manner. Personnel shall be dispatched to arrive at the bridge as soon as possible, but not more than one hour after malfunction or disability of the remote system.

(1279)　　(b) The draw of the S.R. 44 bridge, mile 1.7, at Paulsboro, shall open on signal from May 1 through October 31 from 7 a.m. to 11 p.m., and shall open on signal at all other times upon four hours notice.

(1280)
### §117.730 Maurice River.

(1281) The draw of the Cumberland County bridge, mile 12.1 at Mauricetown, need not be opened for the passage of vessels.

(1282)
### §117.733 New Jersey Intracoastal Waterway.

(1283) (a) The draw of the Route 35 Bridge, mile 1.1 across Manasquan River at Brielle, shall open on signal except as follows:

(1284) (1) From May 15 through September 30:

(1285) (i) On Saturdays, Sundays and Federal holidays, from 8 a.m. to 10 p.m., the draw need only open 15 minutes before the hour and 15 minutes after the hour.

(1286) (ii) On Mondays to Thursdays from 4 p.m. to 7 p.m., and on Fridays, except Federal holidays from 12 p.m. to 7 p.m., the draw need only open 15 minutes before the hour and 15 minutes after the hour.

(1287) (2) Year-round from 11 p.m. to 8 a.m., the draw need only open if at least four hours notice is given.

(1288) (b) The draw of the Route 88 Bridge, mile 3.0, across Point Pleasant Canal at Point Pleasant, shall operate as follows:

(1289) (1) From 7 a.m. to 11 p.m. the draw shall open on signal.

(1290) (2) From 11:01 p.m. to 6:59 a.m. the draw shall open on signal, if at least four hours advance notice is given.

(1291) (c) The draw of the Route 13 Bridge, mile 3.9, across Point Pleasant Canal at Point Pleasant, shall operate as follows:

(1292) (1) From 7 a.m. to 11 p.m. the draw shall open on signal.

(1293) (2) From 11:01 p.m. to 6:59 a.m. the draw shall open on signal, if at least

(1294) (d) The draw of the County Route 528 Bridge, mile 6.3 across Barnegat Bay at Mantoloking, shall open on signal; except that from Memorial Day through Labor Day on Saturdays, Sundays and Federal holidays from 9 a.m. to 6 p.m., the draw need only open on the hour, twenty minutes after the hour, and forty minutes after the hour.

(1295) (e) The draw of the S37 Bridge across Barnegat Bay, mile 14.1 at Seaside Heights, shall open on signal except as follows:

(1296) (1) From December 1 through March 31, the draw need only open if at least four hours notice is given.

(1297) (2) From April 1 through November 30 from 11 p.m. to 8 a.m., the draw need only open if at least four hours notice is given.

(1298) (3) From Memorial Day through Labor Day from 8 a.m. to 8 p.m., the draw need only open on the hour and half hour.

(1299) (f) The draw of the AMTRAK New Jersey Transit Rail Operations (NJTRO) automated railroad swing bridge across Beach Thorofare, mile 68.9 at Atlantic City shall operate as follows:

(1300) (1) Open on signal from 11 p.m. to 6 a.m. From 6 a.m. to 11 p.m., the draw shall open on signal from 20 minutes to 30 minutes after each hour and remain open for all waiting vessels.

(1301) (2) Opening of the draw span may be delayed for ten minutes except as provided in §117.31(b). However, if a train is moving toward the bridge and has crossed the home signal for the bridge before the signal requesting opening of the bridge is given, that train may continue across the bridge and must clear the bridge interlocks before stopping.

(1302) (3) When the bridge is not tended locally and/or is operated from a remote location, sufficient closed circuit TV cameras shall be operated and maintained at the bridge site to enable the remotely located bridge/train controller to have full view of both river traffic and the bridge.

(1303) (4) Radiotelephone Channel 13 (156.65 MHz) VHF–FM, shall be maintained and utilized to facilitate communication in both remote and local control locations. The bridge shall also be equipped with directional microphones and horns to receive and deliver signals to vessels within a mile that are not equipped with radiotelephones.

(1304) (5) Whenever the remote control system equipment is partially disabled or fails for any reason, the bridge shall be physically tended and operated by local control. Personnel shall be dispatched to arrive at the bridge as soon as possible, but not more that one hour after malfunction or disability of the remote system. Mechanical bypass and override capability of the remote operation system shall be provided and maintained.

(1305) (6) When the draw is opening and closing, or is closed, yellow flashing lights located on the ends of the center piers shall be displayed continuously until the bridge is returned to the fully open position.

(1306) (g) The draw of the Route 30 Bridge across Beach Thorofare, mile 67.2 at Atlantic City, shall open on signal but only if at least four hours of notice is given; except that:

(1307) (1) From April 1 through October 31, from 7 a.m. to 11 p.m. the draw need only open on the hour.

(1308) (2) On July 4, the draw need not open from 9:40 p.m. until 11:15 p.m. to accommodate the annual July 4th fireworks show. Should inclement weather prevent the fireworks event from taking place as planned, the draw need not open from 9:40 p.m. until 11:15 p.m. on July 5th to accommodate the annual July 4th fireworks show.

(1309) (3) On the third or fourth Wednesday of August the draw will open every two hours on the hour from 10 a.m. until 4 p.m. and need not open from 4 p.m. until 8 p.m. to accommodate the annual Air Show.

(1310) (4) From 8 a.m. on March 3, 2021, through 5 p.m. on March 31, 2021; from 8 a.m. on November 1, 2021, through 5 p.m. on March 31, 2022; and from 8 a.m. on November 1, 2022, through 5 p.m. on March 31, 2023, the drawbridge will be maintained in the closed-to-navigation position. A work platform will reduce the horizontal clearance of the navigation channel to approximately 30 feet and temporary shielding will reduce the vertical clearance of the entire bridge to approximately 19 feet above mean high water in the closed position. Vessels that can safely transit through the bridge in the closed position with the reduced clearances may do so, if at least 30 minutes notice is given, to allow for safe navigation.

(1311)    (h) The draw of the US40–322 (Albany Avenue) Bridge, mile 70.0 across Inside Thorofare, at Atlantic City, shall open on signal except that:

(1312)    (1) Year-round, from 11 p.m. to 7 a.m.; and from November 1 through March 31 from 3 p.m. to 11 p.m., the draw need only open if at least four hours notice is given;

(1313)    (2) From June 1 through September 30:

(1314)    (i) From 9 a.m. to 4 p.m. and from 6 p.m. to 9 p.m. the draw need only open on the hour and half hour; and

(1315)    (ii) From 4 p.m. to 6 p.m. the draw need not open.

(1316)    (3) On July 4, the draw need not open from 9:40 p.m. until 11:15 p.m. to accommodate the annual July 4th fireworks show. Should inclement weather prevent the fireworks event from taking place as planned, the draw need not open from 9:40 p.m. until 11:15 p.m. on July 5th to accommodate the annual July 4th fireworks show.

(1317)    (4) On the third or fourth Wednesday of August, the draw will open every two hours on the hour from 10 a.m. until 4 p.m. and need not open from 4 p.m. until 8 p.m. to accommodate the annual Air Show.

(1318)    (i) The draw of the Dorset Avenue Bridge across Inside Thorofare, mile 72.1 at Ventnor City, shall open on signal except that from June 1 through September 30, from 9:15 a.m. to 9:15 p.m., the draw need only open at 15 and 45 minutes after the hour.

(1319)    (j) The draw of the Stone Harbor Boulevard Bridge, mile 102.0 across Great Channel, at Stone Harbor, shall open on signal except that:

(1320)    (1) From October 1 through March 31 from 10 p.m. to 6 a.m. the draw need only open if at least eight hours notice is given.

(1321)    (2) From Memorial Day through Labor Day from 6 a.m. to 6 p.m. on Saturdays, Sundays and Federal holidays, the draw need open only on the hour, 20 minutes after the hour, and 20 minutes before the hour.

(1322)    (3) From 10 p.m. on December 24 until 6 a.m. on December 26, the draw need open only if at least two hours notice is given.

(1323)    (k) The draw of Two-Mile Bridge, mile 112.2, across Middle Thorofare in Wildwood Crest, shall open on signal except:

(1324)    (1) From 9:15 a.m. to 10:30 a.m. on the fourth Sunday in March of every year, the draw need not open for vessels. If the fourth Sunday falls on a religious holiday, the draw need not open for vessels from 9:15 a.m. to 10:30 a.m. on the third Sunday of March of every year.

(1325)    (2) From 10:30 p.m. on December 24 until 10:30 p.m. on December 26, the draw need open only if at least two hours notice is given.

(1326)    (l) The draw of Cape May Canal Railroad Bridge across Cape May Canal, mile 115.1, at Cape May shall operate as follows:

(1327)    (1) The draw shall be maintained in the open position; the draw may close only for the crossing of trains and maintenance of the bridge. When the draw is closed for a train crossing a bridge tender shall be present to reopen the draw after the train has cleared the bridge. When the draw is closed for maintenance a bridge tender shall be present to open the draw upon signal.

(1328)    (2) Train service generally operates as follows (please contact Cape May Seashore Lines for current train schedules):

(1329)    (i) Winter (generally December through March): In general, there is no train service, therefore the bridge is unmanned and placed in the full open position.

(1330)    (ii) Spring (generally April through May and Fall (generally September through November): Generally weekend service only: Friday through Sunday train service starts at 10 a.m. and ends at 7:30 p.m. Monday thru Thursday the bridge generally unmanned and in the open position.

(1331)    (iii) Summer Service (generally June through August): Daily train service starting at 10 a.m. and ending 7:30 p.m.

(1332)    (3) When a vessel approaches the drawbridge with the draw in the open position, the vessel shall give the opening signal. If no acknowledgment is received within 30 seconds, the vessel may proceed, with caution, through the open draw. When the draw is open and will be closing promptly, the drawbridge will generally signal using sound signals or radio telephone.

(1333)    (4) Opening of the draw span may be delayed for ten minutes after a signal to open except as provide in (117.31(b). However, if a train is moving toward the bridge and has crossed the home signal for the bridge before the signal requesting opening of the bridge is given, the train may continue across the bridge and must clear the bridge interlocks as soon possible in order to prevent unnecessary delays in the opening of the draw.

(1334)

### §117.737 Oldmans Creek.

(1335)    The draws of the US30 bridge, mile 3.1 at Nortonville, the Conrail railroad bridge, mile 4.0 at Jumbo, and the Salem County bridge, mile 5.1 at Pedricktown, need not be opened for the passage of vessels. However, the draws of any of these bridges shall be restored to operable condition within six months after notification by the District Commander to do so.

(1336)

### §117.741 Raccoon Creek.

(1337)    (a) The draw of the Route 130 highway bridge, mile 1.8 at Bridgeport, shall open on signal:

(1338)    (1) May 1 through October 31, from 7 a.m. to 11 p.m.

(1339)    (2) At all other times, if at least four hours notice is given.

(1340)    (b) The draw of the CONRAIL Railroad Bridge, mile 2.0 at Bridgeport, shall operate as follows:

(1341)    (1) From March 1 through November 30, the draw shall be left in the open position at all times and will only be closed for the passage of trains and to perform periodic maintenance authorized in accordance with subpart A of this part.

(1342)    (i) Trains shall be controlled so that any delay in opening of the draw shall not exceed ten minutes except as provided in § 117.31(b).

(1343)    (ii) Before the bridge closes for any reason, a train crewmember will observe the waterway for approaching craft, which will be allowed to pass. A train crewmember will then operate the bridge by radiophone. The bridge shall only be closed if a train crewmember's visual inspection shows that the channel is clear and there are no vessels transiting in the area.

(1344)    (iii) While the CONRAIL Railroad Bridge is moving from the full open to the full closed position, a train crewmember will maintain constant surveillance of the navigational channel to ensure no conflict with maritime traffic exists. In the event of failure or obstruction, the train crewmember will stop the bridge and return the bridge to the open position.

(1345)    (iv) The CONRAIL Railroad channel traffic lights will change from flashing green to flashing red anytime the bridge is not in the full open position.

(1346)    (v) During closing of the span, the channel traffic lights will change from flashing green to flashing red, the horn will sound four times, followed by a pause, then the four blasts will be repeated and the bridge will close. When the rail traffic has cleared the swing span, the horn will automatically sound five times to signal the draw of the CONRAIL Railroad Bridge is about to return to its full open position.

(1347)    (vi) During open span movement, the channel traffic lights will be flashing red, the horn will sound four times, followed by a pause, then four blasts will be repeated until the bridge is in the full open position. In the full open position, the channel traffic lights will then turn from flashing red to flashing green.

(1348)    (2) At all other times, the draw may be left in the closed position and opened on signal if at least four hours notice is given by telephone at 856–231–2393.

(1349)
### §117.745 Rancocas Creek.

(1350)    (a) The following requirements apply to all bridges across the Rancocas River (Creek):

(1351)    (1) Public vessels of the United States must be passed through the drawspan of each drawbridge as soon as possible without delay at anytime. The opening signal from these vessels is four or more short blasts of a whistle or horn, or a radio request.

(1352)    (2) The owners of these bridges shall provide and keep in good legible condition clearance gauges for each draw with figures not less than 12 inches high designed,

installed and maintained according to the provisions of §118.160 of this chapter.

(1353)    (3) Trains and locomotives shall be controlled so that any delay in opening the draw span shall not exceed ten minutes. However, if a train moving toward the bridge has crossed the home signal for the bridge before the signal requesting opening of the bridge is given, that train may continue across the bridge and must clear the bridge interlocks before stopping or reversing.

(1354)    (b) The drawspans for the Riverside-Delanco/SR #543 Drawbridge, mile 1.3 at Riverside must operate as follows:

(1355)    (1) From April 1 through October 31 open on signal from 7 a.m. to 11 p.m.

(1356)    (2) From November 1 through March 31 from 7 a.m. to 11 p.m., open on signal if at least 24 hours notice is given, except as provided in paragraph (a)(1) of this section.

(1357)    (3) Year round from 11 p.m. to 7 a.m. need not open for the passage of vessels, except as provided in paragraph (a)(1) of this section.

(1358)    (c) The draw of the Centerton County Route 635 Bridge, mile 7.8, at Mt. Laurel, need not open for the passage of vessels.

(1359)
### §117.749 Salem River.

(1360)    The draw of the S49 bridge, mile 3.5 at Salem, shall open on signal if at least 24 hours notice is given.

(1361)
### §117.751 Shark River (South Channel).

(1362)    The draws of the S71 Bridge, mile 0.8, and the Railroad Bridge, mile 0.9, both at Avon, operate as follows:

(1363)    (a) The bridges operate as one unit. The owners shall provide signal systems so connected that the operator of either bridge may simultaneously notify the operator of the other bridge. The operator of the first bridge to be passed shall be responsible for observing the approach vessels, for receiving and acknowledging signals, and for coordinating the opening of the other draw.

(1364)    (b) The draws shall open on signal; except that, from May 15 through September 30 from 4 p.m. to 7 p.m. Monday through Friday except Federal holidays and from 9 a.m. to 9 p.m. Saturdays, Sundays, and holidays, the draw need be opened only on the hour and half hour if a vessel is waiting to pass.

(1365)    (c) The owners of the bridges shall provide and keep in good legible condition two board gages painted white with black figures not less than eight inches high to indicate the vertical clearance under the closed draw at all stages of the tide. The gages shall be so placed on the bridges that they are plainly visible to operators of vessels approaching the bridges either up or downstream.

(1366)
### §117.757 Townsend Inlet.

(1367)    The draw of Townsend Inlet Bridge, mile 0.3 in Avalon, shall open on signal except:

(1368)　　(a) From 9:15 a.m. to 2:30 p.m. on the fourth Sunday in March of every year, the draw need not open for vessels. If the fourth Sunday falls on a religious holiday, the draw need not open from 9:15 a.m. to 2:30 p.m. on the third Sunday of March of every year.

(1369)　　(b) From 11 p.m. on December 24 until 11 p.m. on December 25, the draw need open only if at least two hours notice is given.

(1370)

### §117.758 Tuckahoe River.

(1371)　　The draw of the State highway bridge, mile 8.0 at Tuckahoe, shall open on signal if at least 24 hours notice is given.

(1372)

## PENNSYLVANIA

(1373)

### §117.901 Chester Creek.

(1374)　　The draw of the Front Street bridge, mile 0.1 at Chester, shall open on signal if at least 24 hours notice is given.

(1375)

### §117.904 Delaware River.

(1376)　　See §117.716, Delaware River, listed under New Jersey.

(1377)

### §117.905 Schuylkill River.

(1378)　　(a) The following requirements apply to all drawbridges across the Schuylkill River:

(1379)　　(1) The draws of railroad bridges need not be opened when there is a train in the bridge block approaching the bridge with the intention of crossing, or within five minutes of the known time of the passage of a scheduled passenger train.

(1380)　　(2) The opening of a bridge may not be delayed more than five minutes for a highway bridge or 10 minutes for a railroad bridge, after the signal to open is given.

(1381)　　(3) The owners of drawbridges shall provide and keep in good legible condition two board gages painted white with black figures not less than six inches high to indicate the vertical clearance under the closed draw at all stages of the tide. The gages shall be so placed on the bridge that they are plainly visible to operators of vessels approaching the bridge either up or downstream.

(1382)　　(b) The Passyunk Avenue bridge, mile 3.5 at Philadelphia, shall open on signal at all times if at least four hours notice is given. Public vessels of the United States shall be passed as soon as possible at any time.

(1383)　　(c) The draw of the Conrail bridge, mile 5.5 at Grays Ferry Avenue, Philadelphia, shall open on signal; except that, on Saturdays and Sundays, the draw shall open on signal if at least two hours notice is given. Public vessels of the United States shall be passed as soon as possible at any time.

(1384)　　(d) The draw of the University Avenue bridge, mile 6.2 at Philadelphia, shall open on signal at all times if at least two hours notice is given. Public vessels of the United States shall be passed as soon as possible at any time.

(1385)　　(e) The draw of the CSX Bridge, mile 6.4 near Christian Street, Philadelphia, need not be opened for the passage of vessels.

(1386)

## VIRGINIA

(1387)

### §117.995 Appomattox River.

(1388)　　The draw of the Seaboard System Railroad bridge, mile 2.5 at Hopewell, shall open on signal if at least 24 hours notice is given to the Seaboard System Agent at Hopewell. However, a drawtender shall be in constant attendance and the draw shall open on signal upon 30 days notice, in writing, to do so from the District Commander.

(1389)

### §117.997 Atlantic Intracoastal Waterway, South Branch of the Elizabeth River to the Albemarle and Chesapeake Canal.

(1390)　　(a) The draw of the Belt Line Railroad Bridge, mile 2.6, in Portsmouth and Chesapeake will operate as follows:

(1391)　　(1) The bridge will be left in the open position at all times and will only be lowered for the passage of trains and to perform periodic maintenance authorized in accordance with Subpart A of this part.

(1392)　　(2) The bridge will be operated by the controller at the Berkley Yard office.

(1393)　　(3) The controller will monitor waterway traffic in the bridge and directly beneath the bridge with closed circuit cameras mounted on top of the bridge and with surface navigational radar.

(1394)　　(4) When the bridge closes for any reason, the controller will announce 30 minutes in advance, 15 minutes in advance, immediately proceeding the actual lowering, over marine channel 13, that the Belt Line Railroad Bridge is closing for river traffic. In each of these three announcements, the bridge/train controller will request all concerned river traffic to please acknowledge on marine channel 13.

(1395)　　(5) The bridge shall only be operated from the remote site if closed circuit visual and radar information shows there are no vessels in the area and no opposing radio communications have been received.

(1396)　　(6) While the Belt Line Bridge is moving from the full open position to the full closed position, the bridge/train controller will maintain constant surveillance of the navigational channel to ensure no conflict with maritime traffic exists. In the event of failure of a camera or the radar system, or loss of marine-radio communications, the bridge shall not be operated by the off-site bridge/train controller from the remote location.

(1397)　　(7) If the off-site bridge/train controller's visibility of the navigational channel is less than ¾ of a mile, the bridge shall not be operated from the remote location.

(1398)     (8) When the draw cannot be operated from the remote site, a bridgetender must be called to operate the bridge in the traditional on- site manner.

(1399)     (9) The Belt Line mid-channel lights will change from green to red anytime the bridge is not in the full open position.

(1400)     (10) During the downward and upward span movement, a warning alarm will sound until the bridge is seated and locked down or in the full open position.

(1401)     (11) When the bridge has returned to its full up position, the mid-channel light will turn from red to green, and the controller will announce over marine radio channel 13, "Security, security, security, the Belt Line bridge is open for river traffic." Operational information will be provided 24 hours a day on marine channel 13 and via telephone 757-271-1741 or 757-633-2241.

(1402)     (b) The draw of the Norfolk and Western railroad bridge across the South Branch of the Elizabeth River, mile 3.6 at Portsmouth-Chesapeake, shall be maintained in the open position; except the draw may close for the crossing of trains and maintenance of the bridge. When the draw is closed, a drawtender shall be present and draw shall open on signal.

(1403)     (c) The draw of the Gilmerton (US13/460) bridge, mile 5.8, in Chesapeake:

(1404)     (1) Shall open on signal at any time for commercial vessels carrying liquefied flammable gas or other hazardous materials.

(1405)     (2) From 6:30 a.m. to 8:30 a.m. and from 3:30 p.m. to 5:30 p.m., Monday through Friday, except Federal holidays:

(1406)     (i) Need not open for the passage of recreational or commercial vessels that do not qualify under paragraph (d)(2)(ii) of this section.

(1407)     (ii) Need not open for commercial cargo vessels, including tugs, and tugs with tows, unless 2 hours advance notice has been given to the Gilmerton Bridge at 757-485-5567.

(1408)     (3) Shall open on signal at all other times.

(1409)     (d) The draw of the Norfolk Southern #7 Railroad Bridge, mile 5.8 in Chesapeake, shall operate as follows:

(1410)     (1) The draw shall be remotely controlled by the operator at the Norfolk Southern #5 Railroad Bridge office over the Eastern Branch of the Elizabeth River, at mile 1.1, in Norfolk.

(1411)     (2) The draw shall be left in the open position to vessels and will only be closed for the passage of trains and to perform periodic maintenance authorized in accordance with subpart A of this part.

(1412)     (3) Trains shall be controlled so that any delay in opening of the draw shall not exceed ten minutes except as provided in §117.31(b).

(1413)     (4) Before the bridge closes for any reason, the off-site remote operator will monitor waterway traffic in the area with closed circuit cameras and motion sensors mounted on the bridge. The bridge will only be closed if the off-site remote operator's visual inspection shows that the channel is clear and there are no vessels transiting in the area.

(1414)     (5) While the bridge is moving from the full open position to the full closed position, the off-site remote operator will maintain constant surveillance of the navigation channel to ensure that no conflict with maritime traffic exists. In the event of failure or obstruction, the off-site remote operator will stop and return the bridge to the full open position to vessels. In the event of a failure or obstruction, a bridge tender must be called by the off-site remote operator and must be on-site within 30 minutes of the call to operate the bridge.

(1415)     (6) During closing of the span, the channel traffic lights will change from flashing green to flashing red, the horn will sound twice, and an audio voice warning device will announce bridge movement, then two repeat blasts of the horn will sound until the bridge is seated and locked down. When the bridge is seated and locked down to vessels, the channel traffic lights will flash red.

(1416)     (7) During the open span movement, the channel traffic lights will flash red, the horn will sound twice, followed by a pause, and then five repeat blasts of the horn will sound until the bridge is in the full open position to vessels. In the full open position to vessels, the bridge channel traffic lights will turn from flashing red to flashing green then an audio warning device will announce bridge movement by stating "Security, security, security, the Norfolk Southern #7 Railroad Bridge at mile 5.8 is open for river traffic".

(1417)     (8) Operational information will be provided 24 hours a day on marine channel 13 and via telephone 757–924–5320.

(1418)     (e) The draw of the I–64 bridge across the South Branch of the Elizabeth River, mile 7.1 at Chesapeake, shall open on signal if at least 24 hours notice is given.

(1419)     (f) The draw of the Dominion Boulevard (US 17) bridge, mile 8.8 in Chesapeake:

(1420)     (1) Shall open on signal at any time for commercial vessels carrying liquefied flammable gas or other hazardous materials.

(1421)     (2) From 7 a.m. to 9 a.m. and 4 p.m. to 6 p.m., Monday through Friday, need not open for the passage of recreational vessels, and need open for commercial cargo vessels not carrying hazardous materials, including tugs and tugs with tows, only when notice has been given at least 2 hours in advance to the Dominion Boulevard Bridge at 757–547–0521.

(1422)     (3) From 6 a.m. to 7 a.m. and from 9 a.m. to 4 p.m., Monday to Friday, and from 6 a.m. to 6 p.m. on Saturdays, Sundays, and Federal holidays, the draw need only be opened every hour on the hour, except the draw shall open on signal for commercial vessels that qualify under paragraphs (g)(1) or (g)(2) of this section.

(1423)     (4) If any vessel is approaching the bridge and cannot reach the draw exactly on the half hour, the drawtender may delay the opening up to ten minutes past the half hour for the passage of the approaching vessel and any other vessels that are waiting to pass.

(1424)    (5) Shall open on signal at all other times.

(1425)    (g) The draw of the S168 bridge, mile 12 at Chesapeake (Great Bridge), shall open on signal; except that, from 6 a.m. to 7 p.m., the draw need be opened only on the hour. If any vessel is approaching the bridge and cannot reach the draw exactly on the hour, the drawtender may delay the hourly opening up to 10 minutes past the hour for the passage of the approaching vessel and any other vessels that are waiting to pass. Vessels in an emergency condition which presents danger to life or property shall be passed at any time.

(1426)    (h) The draw of the Albemarle & Chesapeake Railroad bridge, mile 13.9, in Chesapeake, Virginia, shall be maintained in the open position; the draw may close only for the crossing of trains and maintenance of the bridge. When the draw is closed, a bridgetender shall be present to reopen the draw after the train has cleared the bridge.

(1427)    (i) The draw of the Centerville Turnpike (SR170) bridge across the Albemarle and Chesapeake Canal, mile 15.2, at Chesapeake:

(1428)    (1) Shall open on signal at any time for commercial vessels carrying liquefied flammable gas or other hazardous materials.

(1429)    (2) From 6:30 a.m. to 8:30 a.m. and from 4 p.m. to 6 p.m., Monday through Friday, except Federal holidays:

(1430)    (i) Need not open for the passage of recreational or commercial vessels that do not qualify under paragraph (i)(2)(ii) of this section.

(1431)    (ii) Need not open for commercial cargo vessels, including tugs, and tugs with tows, unless 2 hours advance notice has been given to the Centerville Turnpike bridge at 757–547–3632.

(1432)    (3) From 8:30 a.m. to 4 p.m., Monday through Friday, except Federal holidays, the draw need only be opened on the hour and half hour.

(1433)    (4) If any vessel is approaching the bridge and cannot reach the draw exactly on the hour or half hour, the drawtender may delay the opening ten minutes past the hour or half hour for the passage of the approaching vessel and any other vessels that are waiting to pass.

(1434)    (5) Shall open on signal at all other times.

(1435)    **§117.1001 Cat Point Creek.**

(1436)    The draw of the S634 bridge, mile 0.3 at Naylors, need not be opened for the passage of vessels.

(1437)    **§117.1003 Chickahominy River.**

(1438)    The draw of the highway bridge, mile 1.5 at Barrets Ferry, shall open on signal; except that, from 11 p.m. to 7 a.m., the draw shall open on signal if at least 12 hours notice is given.

(1439)    **§117.1005 Chincoteague Channel.**

(1440)    The draw of the SR 175 Bridge, mile 3.5, at Chincoteague shall open on demand; except from 7 a.m. to 5 p.m. on the last consecutive Wednesday and Thursday in July, the draw need not be opened.

(1441)    **§117.1007 Elizabeth River–Eastern Branch.**

(1442)    (a) The draw of the Norfolk Southern Railroad Bridge (NS #V2.8), mile 2.7 at Norfolk, shall operate as follows:

(1443)    (1) The draw shall remain in the open position for navigation. The draw shall only be closed for train crossings or periodic maintenance authorized in accordance with subpart A of this part.

(1444)    (2) The bridge shall be operated by the controller at the Norfolk Southern Railroad Bridge (NS #5), mile 1.1, over the Eastern Branch of the Elizabeth River in Norfolk, VA. The controller shall monitor vessel traffic with closed circuit cameras and infrared sensors covering the swing radius. Operational information will be provided 24 hours a day on marine channel 13 and via telephone 757–446–5320.

(1445)    (3) The bridge shall not be operated from the remote location in the following events: Failure or obstruction of the infrared sensors, closed-circuit cameras or marine-radio communications, or anytime controller's visibility is inhibited. In these situations, a bridge tender with Norfolk Southern must be called to operate the bridge on-site.

(1446)    (4) Before the bridge closes for any reason, the remote operator will monitor waterway traffic in the area. The bridge shall only be closed if the off-site remote operator's visual inspection shows that the channel is clear and there are no vessels transiting in the area. While the bridge is moving, the operator shall maintain constant surveillance of the navigation channel.

(1447)    (5) Before closing the draw, the channel traffic lights will change from flashing green to flashing red, the horn will sound five short blasts, and an audio voice warning stating, "Attention, Attention. Norfolk Southern's Railroad Bridge over the Eastern Branch of the Elizabeth River at milepost 2.7 will be closing to river traffic." Five short blasts of the horn will continue until the bridge is seated and locked down to vessels, the channel traffic lights will continue to flash red.

(1448)    (6) When the rail traffic has cleared, the horn will sound one prolonged blast followed by one short blast to indicate that the draw is opening to vessel traffic. During the opening swing movement, the channel traffic lights will flash red until the bridge returns to the fully open position. In the full open position to vessels, the bridge channel lights will flash green followed by an announcement stating, "Security, security, security. Norfolk Southern Railroad Bridge at mile 2.7 is open for river traffic." Vessels shall stay clear of both channels as to not interfere with infrared detectors, until green lights are displayed on the swing span.

(1449)    (b) The draw of the Berkley Bridge, mile 0.4 in Norfolk:

(1450)    (1) Shall remain closed one hour prior to the published start of a scheduled marine event regulated under §100.501 of this chapter, and shall remain closed until one hour following the completion of the event unless the Patrol Commander designated under § 100.501 of this chapter allows the bridge to open for commercial vessel traffic.

(1451)    (2) Shall open on signal at any time for vessels carrying, in bulk, cargoes regulated by 46 CFR subchapters D or O, or Certain Dangerous Cargoes as defined in 33 CFR 160.202.

(1452)    (3) For all other vessels, the draw shall open on signal at any time, except from 5 a.m. to 7 p.m., Monday through Friday, except Federal holidays. During these times, the draw shall:

(1453)    (i) Open for commercial vessels with a draft of 18 feet or more, provided at least 6 hours notice was given to the Berkley Bridge Traffic Control room at 757–494–2490.

(1454)    (ii) Open on signal at 9 a.m., 11 a.m., 1 p.m. and 2:30 p.m.

(1455)    (4) If the bridge is not opened during a particular scheduled opening per paragraph (b)(3)(ii) of this section and a vessel has made prior arrangements for a delayed opening, the draw tender may provide a single opening up to 30 minutes past that scheduled opening time for that signaling vessel, except at 2:30 p.m. The draw tender may provide a single opening up to 20 minutes past the 2:30 p.m. scheduled opening time for a signaling vessel that made prior arrangements for a delayed opening. A vessel may make prior arrangements for a delayed opening by contacting the Berkley Bridge Traffic Control room at 757–494–2490.

(1456)
#### §117.1013 Kinsale Creek.
(1457)    The draw of the state highway bridge, mile 4.0, at Kinsale need not be opened for the passage of vessels.

(1458)
#### §117.1015 Mattaponi River.
(1459)    The draws of the Lord Delaware (S33) bridge, mile 0.8 at West Point, and the S629 bridge, mile 28.5 at Walkerton, shall open on signal if at least 24 hours notice is given. The drawtender service for either bridge shall be increased to the degree determined to be adequate within 30 days after written notice is received from the District Commander to do so.

(1460)
#### §117.1021 North Landing River.
(1461)    The draw of the S165 bridge, mile 20.2 at Chesapeake, shall open on signal; except that, from 6 a.m. to 7 p.m., the draw need be opened only on the hour and half hour for the passage of pleasure craft. Public vessels of the United States, commercial vessels, and vessels in an emergency endangering life or property shall be passed at any time.

(1462)    **Note:** Call signs and radio channels for drawbridges equipped with radiotelephones are included with the bridge descriptions in chapters 4 through 15.

(1463)
#### §117.1023 Pamunkey River.
(1464)    The draw of the Eltham Bridge (SR33/30) mile 1.0, located at West Point, Virginia shall open on signal if at least four hours notice is given at all times.

(1465)
#### §117.1025 York River.
(1466)    (a) The Coleman Memorial Bridge, mile 7.0 at Yorktown, shall open on signal; except from 5 a.m. to 8 a.m. and 3 p.m. to 7 p.m., Monday through Friday, except Federal holidays, the bridge shall remain closed to navigation.

(1467)    (b) The bridge shall be opened at anytime for vessels in an emergency which presents danger to life or property.

(1468)
## Part 157–Rules for the Protection of the Marine Environment relating to Tank Vessels carrying Oil in Bulk (in part).

(1469)
**For a complete description of this part see 33 CFR 157.**

(1470)
## Subpart A–General

(1471)
#### §157.01 Applicability.
(1472)    (a) Unless otherwise indicated, this part applies to each vessel that carries oil in bulk as cargo and that is:

(1473)    (1) Documented under the laws of the United States (a U.S. vessel); or

(1474)    (2) Any other vessel that enters or operates in the navigable waters of the United States, or that operates, conducts lightering under 46 U.S.C 3715, or receives cargo from or transfers cargo to a deepwater port under 33 U.S.C. 1501 et seq, in the United States Exclusive Economic Zone, as defined in 33 U.S.C. 2701(8).

(1475)    (b) This part does not apply to a vessel exempted under 46 U.S.C. 2109 or 46 U.S.C. 3702.

(1476)
#### §157.03 Definitions.
(1477)    Except as otherwise stated in a subpart:

(1478)    *Amidships* means the middle of the length.

(1479)    *Animal fat* means a non-petroleum oil, fat, or grease derived from animals and not specifically identified elsewhere in this part.

(1480)    *Ballast voyage* means the voyage that a tank vessel engages in after it leaves the port of final cargo discharge.

(1481)    *Breadth* or *B* means the maximum molded breadth of a vessel in meters.

(1482)    *Cargo tank length* means the length from the forward bulkhead of the forwardmost cargo tanks, to the after bulkhead of the aftermost cargo tanks.

(1483)    *Center tank* means any tank inboard of a longitudinal bulkhead.

(1484)     *Clean ballast* means ballast which:

(1485)     (1) If discharged from a vessel that is stationary into clean, calm water on a clear day, would not–

(1486)     (i) Produce visible traces of oil on the surface of the water or on adjoining shore lines; or

(1487)     (ii) Cause a sludge or emulsion to be deposited beneath the surface of the water or upon adjoining shore lines; or

(1488)     (2) If verified by an approved oil discharge monitoring and control system, has an oil content that does not exceed 15 p.m.

(1489)     *Combination carrier* means a vessel designed to carry oil or solid cargoes in bulk.

(1490)     *Crude oil* means any liquid hydrocarbon mixture occurring naturally in the earth, whether or not treated to render it suitable for transportation, and includes crude oil from which certain distillate fractions may have been removed, and crude oil to which certain distillate fractions may have been added.

(1491)     *Deadweight or DWT* means the difference in metric tons between the lightweight displacement and the total displacement of a vessel measured in water of specific gravity 1.025 at the load waterline corresponding to the assigned summer freeboard.

(1492)     *Dedicated clean ballast tank* means a cargo tank that is allocated solely for the carriage of clean ballast.

(1493)     *Domestic trade* means trade between ports or places within the United States, its territories and possessions, either directly or via a foreign port including trade on the navigable rivers, lakes, and inland waters.

(1494)     *Double bottom* means watertight protective spaces that do not carry any oil and which separate the bottom of tanks that hold any oil within the cargo tank length from the outer skin of the vessel.

(1495)     *Double hull* means watertight protective space that do not carry any oil and which separate the sides, bottom, forward end, and aft and aft end of tanks that hold any oil within the cargo tank length from the outer skin of the vessel as prescribed in §157.10d.

(1496)     *Doubles sides* means watertight protective spaces that do not carry any oil and which separate the sides of tanks that hold any oil within the cargo tank length from the outer skin of the vessel.

(1497)     *Existing vessel* means any vessel that is not a new vessel.

(1498)     *Fleeting or assist towing vessel* means any commercial vessel engaged in towing astern, alongside, or pushing ahead, used solely within a limited geographic area, such as a particular barge fleeting area or commercial facility, and used solely for restricted service, such as making up or breaking up larger tows.

(1499)     *Foreign trade* means any trade that is not domestic trade.

(1500)     *From the nearest land* means from the baseline from which the territorial sea of the United States is established in accordance with international law.

(1501)     *Fuel oil* means any oil used as fuel for machinery in the vessel in which it is carried.

(1502)     *Inland vessel* means a vessel that is not oceangoing and that does not operate on the Great Lakes.

(1503)     *Instantaneous rate of discharge of oil content* means the rate of discharge of oil in liters per hour at any instant, divided by the speed of the vessel in knots at the same instant.

(1504)     *Integrated tug barge* means a tug and a tank barge with a mechanical system that allows the connection of the propulsion unit (the tug) to the stern of the cargo carrying unit (the tank barge) so that the two vessels function as a single self-propelled vessel.

(1505)     Large primary structural member includes any of the following:

(1506)     (1) Web frames.

(1507)     (2) Girders.

(1508)     (3) Webs.

(1509)     (4) Main brackets.

(1510)     (5) Transverses.

(1511)     (6) Stringers.

(1512)     (7) Struts in transverse web frames when there are 3 or more struts and the depth of each is more than 1/15 of the total depth of the tank.

(1513)     *Length or L* means the distance in meters from the fore side of the stem to the axis of the rudder stock on a waterline at 85 percent of the least molded depth measured from the molded baseline, or 96 percent of the total length on that waterline, whichever is greater. In vessels designed with drag, the waterline is measured parallel to the designed waterline.

(1514)     *Lightweight* means the displacement of a vessel in metric tons without cargo, fuel oil, lubricating oil, ballast water, fresh water, and feedwater in tanks, consumable stores, and any persons and their effects.

(1515)     *Major conversion* means a conversion of an existing vessel that:

(1516)     (1) Substantially alters the dimensions or carrying capacity of the vessel, except a conversion that includes only the installation of segregated ballast tanks, dedicated clean ballast tanks, a crude oil washing system, double sides, a double bottom, or a double hull;

(1517)     (2) Changes the type of vessel;

(1518)     (3) Substantially prolongs the vessel's service life; or

(1519)     (4) Otherwise so changes the vessel that it is essentially a new vessel, as determined by the Commandant (CG–CVC).

(1520)     *MARPOL 73/78* means the International Convention for the Prevention of Pollution from Ships 1973, as modified by the Protocol of 1978 relating to that Convention. A copy of MARPOL 73/78 is available from the International Maritime Organization, 4 Albert Embankment, London, SE1

(1521)     *New vessel* means:

(1522)     (1) A U.S. vessel in domestic trade that:

(1523)     (i) Is constructed under a contract awarded after December 31, 1974;

(1524)　　(ii) In the absence of a building contract, has the keel laid or is at a similar stage of construction after June 30, 1975;

(1525)　　(iii) Is delivered after December 31, 1977; or

(1526)　　(iv) Has undergone a major conversion for which:

(1527)　　(A) The contract is awarded after December 31, 1974;

(1528)　　(B) In the absence of a contract, conversion is begun after June 30, 1975; or

(1529)　　(C) Conversion is completed after December 31, 1977; and

(1530)　　(2) A foreign vessel or a U.S. vessel in foreign trade that;

(1531)　　(i) Is constructed under a contract awarded after December 31, 1975;

(1532)　　(ii) In the absence of a building contract, has the keel laid or is at a similar stage of construction after June 30, 1976;

(1533)　　(iii) Is delivered after December 31, 1979; or

(1534)　　(iv) Has undergone a major conversion for which:

(1535)　　(A) The contract is awarded after December 31, 1975;

(1536)　　(B) In the absence of a contract, conversion is begun after June 30, 1976; or

(1537)　　(C) Conversion is completed after December 31, 1979.

(1538)　　*Non-petroleum oil* means oil of any kind that is not petroleum-based. It includes, but is not limited to, animal fat and vegetable oil.

(1539)　　*Oceangoing* has the same meaning as defined in §151.05 of this chapter.

(1540)　　*Officer in charge of a navigational watch* means any officer employed or engaged to be responsible for navigating or maneuvering the vessel and for maintaining a continuous vigilant watch during his or her periods of duty and following guidance set out by the master, international or national regulations, and company policies.

(1541)　　*Oil* means oil of any kind or in any form including, but not limited to, petroleum, fuel oil, sludge, oil refuse, and oil mixed with wastes other than dredged spoil. This includes liquid hydrocarbons as well as animal and vegetable oils.

(1542)　　*Oil cargo residue* means any residue of oil cargo whether in solid, semi-solid, emulsified, or liquid form from cargo tanks and cargo pump room bilges, including but not limited to, drainages, leakages, exhausted oil, muck, clingage, sludge, bottoms, paraffin (wax), and any constituent component of oil. The term "oil cargo residue" is also known as "cargo oil residue".

(1543)　　*Oil residue* means–

(1544)　　(1) Oil cargo residue; and

(1545)　　(2) Other residue of oil whether in solid, semi-solid, emulsified, or liquid form, resulting from drainages, leakages, exhausted oil, and other similar occurrences from machinery spaces.

(1546)　　*Oil spill response vessel* means a vessel that is exclusively dedicated to operations to prevent or mitigate environmental damage due to an actual or impending accidental oil spill. This includes a vessel that performs routine service as an escort for a tank vessel, but excludes a vessel that engages in any other commercial activity, such as the carriage of any type of cargo.

(1547)　　*Oil tanker* means a vessel that is constructed or adapted primarily to carry crude oil or products in bulk as cargo. This includes a tank barge, a tankship, and a combination carrier, as well as a vessel that is constructed or adapted primarily to carry noxious liquid substances in bulk as cargo and which also carries crude oil or products in bulk as cargo.

(1548)　　*Oily mixture* means a mixture, in any form, with any oil content. "Oily mixture" includes, but is not limited to–

(1549)　　(1) Slops from bilges;

(1550)　　(2) Slops from oil cargoes (such as cargo tank washings, oily waste, and oily refuse);

(1551)　　(3) Oil residue; and

(1552)　　(4) Oily ballast water from cargo or fuel oil tanks, including any oil cargo residue.

(1553)　　*Other non-petroleum oil* means an oil of any kind that is not petroleum oil, an animal fat, or a vegetable oil.

(1554)　　*Permeability of a space* means the ratio of volume within a space that is assumed to be occupied by water to the total volume of that space.

(1555)　　*Petroleum oil* means petroleum in any form, including but not limited to, crude oil, fuel oil, sludge, oil residue, and refined products.

(1556)　　*Primary towing vessel* means any vessel engaged in towing astern, alongside, or pushing ahead and includes the tug in an integrated tug barge. It does not include fleeting or assist towing vessels.

(1557)　　*Product* means any liquid hydrocarbon mixture in any form, except crude oil, petrochemicals, and liquefied gases.

(1558)　　*Segregated ballast* means the ballast water introduced into a tank that is completely separated from the cargo oil and fuel oil system and that is permanently allocated to the carriage of ballast.

(1559)　　*Slop tank* means a tank specifically designed for the collection of cargo drainings, washings, and other oily mixtures.

(1560)　　*Tank* means an enclosed space that is formed by the permanent structure of a vessel, and designated for the carriage of liquid in bulk.

(1561)　　*Tank barge* means a tank vessel not equipped with a means of self-propulsion.

(1562)　　*Tank vessel* means a vessel that is constructed or adapted primarily to carry, or that carries, oil or hazardous material in bulk as cargo or cargo residue, and that–

(1563)　　(1) Is a vessel of the United States;

(1564)　　(2) Operates on the navigable waters of the United States; or

(1565)　　(3) Transfers oil or hazardous material in a port or place subject to the jurisdiction of the United States. This does not include an offshore supply vessel, or a fishing vessel or fish tender vessel of not more than 750 gross tons when engaged only in the fishing industry.

(1566)     *Tankship* means a tank vessel propelled by mechanical power or sail.

(1567)     *Vegetable oil* means a non-petroleum oil or fat not specifically identified elsewhere in this part that is derived from plant seeds, nuts, kernels, or fruits.

(1568)     *Wing tank* means a tank that is located adjacent to the side shell plating.

(1569)

## Subpart B–Design, Equipment, and Installation

(1570)

### §157.08 Applicability of Subpart B.

(1571)     **NOTE:** An "oil tanker" as defined in §157.03 includes barges as well as self-propelled vessels.

(1572)     (a) Sections 157.10d and 157.11(g) apply to each vessel to which this part applies.

(1573)     (b) Sections 157.11 (a) through (f), 157.12, 157.15, 157.19(b)(3), 157.33, and 157.37 apply to each vessel to which this part applies that carries 200 cubic meters or more of crude oil or products in bulk as cargo, as well as to each oceangoing oil tanker to which this part applies of 150 gross tons or more. These sections do not apply to a foreign vessel which remains beyond the navigable waters of the United States and does not transfer oil cargo at a port or place subject to the jurisdiction of the United States.

(1574)     (c) Section 157.21 applies to each oil tanker to which this part applies of 150 gross tons or more that is oceangoing or that operates on the Great Lakes. This section does not apply to a foreign vessel which remains beyond the navigable waters of the United States and does not transfer oil cargo at a port or place subject to the jurisdiction of the United States.

(1575)     (d) Sections in subpart B of 33 CFR part 157 that are not specified in paragraphs (a) through (c) of this section apply to each oceangoing oil tanker to which this part applies of 150 gross tons or more, unless otherwise indicated in paragraphs (e) through (m) of this section. These sections do not apply to a foreign vessel which remains beyond the navigable waters of the United States and does not transfer oil cargo at a port or place subject to the jurisdiction of the United States.

(1576)     (e) Sections 157.11 (a) through (f), 157.12, and 157.15 do not apply to a vessel, except an oil tanker, that carries less than 1,000 cubic meters of crude oil or products in bulk as cargo and which retains oil mixtures on board and discharges them to a reception facility.

(1577)     (f) Sections 157.11 (a) through (f), 157.12, 157.13, and 157.15 do not apply to a tank vessel that carries only asphalt, carbon black feedstock, or other products with similar physical properties, such as specific gravity and cohesive and adhesive characteristics, that inhibit effective product/water separation and monitoring.

(1578)     (g) Sections 157.11 (a) through (f), 157.12, 157.13, 157.15, and 157.23 do not apply to a tank barge that cannot ballast cargo tanks or wash cargo tanks while underway.

(1579)     (h) Sections 157.19 and 157.21 do not apply to a tank barge that is certificated by the Coast Guard for limited short protected coastwise routes if the barge is otherwise constructed and certificated for service exclusively on inland routes.

(1580)     (i) Section 157.09(d) does not apply to any:

(1581)     (1) U.S. vessel in domestic trade that is constructed under a contract awarded before January 8, 1976;

(1582)     (2) U.S. vessel in foreign trade that is constructed under a contract awarded before April 1, 1977; or

(1583)     (3) Foreign vessel that is constructed under a contract awarded before April 1, 1977.

(1584)     (j) Sections 157.09 and 157.10a do not apply to a new vessel that:

(1585)     (1) Is constructed under a building contract awarded after June 1, 1979;

(1586)     (2) In the absence of a building contract, has the keel laid or is at a similar stage of construction after January 1, 1980;

(1587)     (3) Is delivered after June 1, 1982; or

(1588)     (4) Has undergone a major conversion for which:

(1589)     (i) The contract is awarded after June 1, 1979;

(1590)     (ii) In the absence of a contract, conversion is begun after January 1, 1980; or

(1591)     (iii) Conversion is completed after June 1, 1982.

(1592)     (k) Sections 157.09(b)(3), 157.10(c)(3), 157.10a(d)(3), and 157.10b(b)(3) do not apply to tank barges.

(1593)     (l) Section 157.10b does not apply to tank barges if they do not carry ballast while they are engaged in trade involving the transfer of crude oil from an offshore oil exploitation or production facility on the Outer Continental Shelf of the United States.

(1594)     (m) Section 157.12 does not apply to a U.S. vessel that:

(1595)     (1) Is granted an exemption under Subpart F of this part; or

(1596)     (2) Is engaged solely in voyages that are:

(1597)     (i) Between ports or places within the United States, its territories or possessions;

(1598)     (ii) Of less than 72 hours in length; and

(1599)     (iii) At all times within 50 nautical miles of the nearest land.

(1600)     (n) Section 157.10d does not apply to:

(1601)     (1) A vessel that operates exclusively beyond the navigable waters of the United States and the United States Exclusive Economic Zone, as defined in 33 U.S.C. 2701(8);

(1602)     (2) An oil spill response vessel;

(1603)     (3) Before January 1, 2015–

(1604)     (i) A vessel unloading oil in bulk as cargo at a deepwater port licensed under the Deepwater Port Act of 1974 (33 U.S.C. 1501 et seq.); or

(1605)     (ii) A delivering vessel that is offloading oil in bulk as cargo in lightering activities–

(1606)     (A) Within a lightering zone established under 46 U.S.C. 3715(b)(5); and

(1607)     (B) More than 60 miles from the territorial sea base line, as defined in 33 CFR 2.20.

(1608)    (4) A vessel documented under 46 U.S.C., chapter 121, that was equipped with a double hull before August 12, 1992;

(1609)    (5) A barge of less than 1,500 gross tons as measured under 46 U.S.C., chapter 145, carrying refined petroleum in bulk as cargo in or adjacent to waters of the Bering Sea, Chuckchi Sea, and Arctic Ocean and waters tributary thereto and in the waters of the Aleutian Islands and the Alaskan Peninsula west of 155 degrees west longitude; or

(1610)    (6) A vessel in the National Defense Reserve Fleet pursuant to 50 App. U.S.C. 1744.

(1611)    (o) Section 157.11(h) applies to every oil tanker delivered on or after January 1, 2010, meaning an oil tanker—

(1612)    (1) For which the building contract is placed on or after January 1, 2007;

(1613)    (2) In the absence of a building contract, the keel of which is laid or which is at a similar stage of construction on or after July 1, 2007;

(1614)    (3) The delivery of which is on or after January 1, 2010; or

(1615)    (4) That has undergone a major conversion—

(1616)    (i) For which the contract is placed on or after January 1, 2007;

(1617)    (ii) In the absence of a contract, the construction work of which is begun on or after July 1, 2007; or

(1618)    (iii) That is completed on or after January 1, 2010.

(1619)
### §157.10d Double hulls on tank vessels.

(1620)    (a) With the exceptions stated in §157.08(n), this section applies to a tank vessel–

(1621)    (1) For which the building contract is awarded after June 30, 1990;

(1622)    (2) That is delivered after December 31, 1993;

(1623)    (3) That undergoes a major conversion for which;

(1624)    (i) The contract is awarded after June 30, 1990; or

(1625)    (ii) Conversion is completed after December 31, 1993; or

(1626)    (4) That is otherwise required to have a double hull by 46 U.S.C. 3703a(c).

(1627)    (b) Each vessel to which this section applies must be fitted with:

(1628)    (1) A double hull in accordance with this section; and

(1629)    (2) If §157.10 applies, segregated ballast tanks and a crude oil washing system in accordance with that section.

(1630)    (c) Except on a vessel to which §157.10d(d) applies, tanks within the cargo tank length that carry any oil must be protected by double sides and a double bottom as follows:

(1631)    (1) Double sides must extend for the full depth of the vessel's side or from the uppermost deck, disregarding a rounded gunwale where fitted, to the top of the double bottom. At any cross section, the molded width of the double side, measured at right angles to the side shell plating, from the side of tanks containing oil to the side shell plating, must not be less than the distance w as shown in Figure 157.10d(c) and specified as follows:

(1632)    (i) For a vessel of 5,000 DWT and above: w=[0.5+(DWT/20,000)] meters; or, w=2.0 meters (79 in.)., whichever is less, but in no case less than 1.0 meter (39 in.).

(1633)    (ii) For a vessel of less than 5,000 DWT; w=[0.4+(2.4)(DWT/20,000)] meters, but in no case less than 0.76 meter (30 in.).

(1634)    (iii) For a vessel to which paragraph (a)(4) of this section applies: w=0.76 meter (30 in.), provided that the double side was fitted under a construction or conversion contract awarded prior to June 30, 1990.

(1635)    (2) At any cross section, the molded depth of the double bottom, measured at right angles to the bottom shell plating, from the bottom of tanks containing oil to the bottom shell plating, must not be less than the distance h as shown in Figure 157.10d(c) and specified as follows:

(1636)    (i) For a vessel of 5,000 DWT and above: h=B/15; or, h=2.0 meters (79 in.), whichever is less, but in no case less than 1.0 meter (39 in.).

(1637)    (ii) For a vessel of less than 5,000 DWT: h=B/15, but in no case less than 0.76 meter (30 in.).

(1638)    (iii) For a vessel to which paragraph (a)(4) of this section applies: h=B/15; or, h=2.0 meters (79 in.), whichever is the lesser, but in no case less than 0.76 meter (30 in.), provided that the double bottom was fitted under a construction or conversion contract awarded prior to June 30, 1990.

(1639)    (3) For a vessel built under a contract awarded after September 11, 1992, within the turn of the bilge or at cross sections where the turn of the bilge is not clearly defined, tanks containing oil must be located inboard of the outer shell–

(1640)    (i) For a vessel of 5,000 DWT and above: At levels up to 1.5h above the base line, not less than distance h, as shown in Figure 157.10d(c) and specified in paragraph (c)(2) of this section. At levels greater than 1.5h above the base line, not less than the distance w, as shown in Figure 157.10d(c) and specified in paragraph (c)(1) of this section.

(1641)    (ii) For a vessel of less than 5,000 DWT: Not less the distance h above the line of the mid-ship flat bottom, as shown in Figure 157.10d(c)(3)(ii) and specified in paragraph (c)(2) of this section. At levels greater than h above the line of the mid-ship flat bottom, not less than the distance w, as shown in Figure 157.10d(c)(3)(ii) and specified in paragraph (c)(1) of this section.

(1642)    (4) For a vessel to which §157.10(b) applies that is built under a contract awarded after September 11, 1992.

(1643)    (i) The aggregate volume of the double sides, double bottom, forepeak tanks, and afterpeak tanks must not be less than the capacity of segregated ballast tanks required under §157.10(b). Segregated ballast tanks that may be provided in addition to those required under §157.10(b) may be located anywhere within the vessel.

(1644)    (ii) Double side and double bottom tanks used to meet the requirements of §157.10(b) must be located as uniformly as practicable along the cargo tank length. Large inboard extensions of individual double side and double bottom tanks, which result in a reduction of overall side or bottom protection, must be avoided.

(1645)     (d) A vessel of less than 10,000 DWT that is constructed and certificated for service exclusively on inland or limited short protected coastwise routes must be fitted with double sides and a double bottom as follows:

(1646)     (1) A minimum of 61 cm. (2 ft.) from the inboard side of the side shell plate, extending the full depth of the side or from the main deck to the top of the double bottom, measured at right angles to the side shell; and

(1647)     (2) A minimum of 61 cm. (2 ft.) from the top of the bottom shell plating, along the full breadth of the vessel's bottom, measured at right angles to the bottom shell.

(1648)     (3) For a vessel to which paragraph (a)(4) of this section applies, the width of the double sides and the depth of the double bottom may be 38 cm. (15 in.), in lieu of the dimensions specified in paragraphs (d)(1) and (d)(2) of this section, provided that the double side and double bottom tanks were fitted under a construction or conversion contract awarded prior to June 30, 1990.

(1649)     (4) For a vessel built under a contract awarded after September 11, 1992, a minimum 46 cm. (18 in.) clearance for passage between framing must be maintained throughout the double sides and double bottom.

(1650)     (e) Except as provided in paragraph (e)(3) of this section, a vessel must not carry any oil in any tank extending forward of:

(1651)     (1) The collision bulkhead; or

(1652)     (2) In the absence of a collision bulkhead, the transverse plane perpendicular to the centerline through a point located:

(1653)     (i) The lesser of 10 meters (32.8 ft.) or 5 percent of the vessel length, but in no case less than 1 meter (39 in.), aft of the forwarded perpendicular;

(1654)     (ii) On a vessel of less than 10,000 DWT tons that is constructed and certificated for service exclusively on inland or limited short protected coastwise routes, the lesser of 7.62 meters (25 ft.) or 5 percent of the vessel length, but in no case less than 61 cm. (2 ft.), aft of the headlog or stem at the freeboard deck; or

(1655)     (iii) On each vessel which operates exclusively as a box or trail barge, 61 cm. (2 ft.) aft of the headlog.

(1656)     (3) This paragraph does not apply to independent fuel oil tanks that must be located on or above the main deck within the areas described in paragraphs (e)(1) and (e)(2) of this section to serve adjacent deck equipment that cannot be located further aft. Such tanks must be as small and as far aft as is practicable.

(1657)     (f) On each vessel, the cargo tank length must not extend aft to any point closer to the stern than the distance equal to the required width of the double side, as prescribed in §157.10d(c)(1) or §157.10d(d)(1).

(1658)
## Subpart G–Interim Measures for Certain Tank

## Vessels Without Double Hulls Carrying Petroleum Oils

(1659)
### §157.400 Purpose and applicability.
(1660)     (a) The purpose of this subpart is to establish mandatory safety and operational requirements to reduce environmental damage resulting from petroleum oil spills.

(1661)     (b) This subpart applies to each tank vessels specified in §157.01 of this part that–

(1662)     (1) Is 5,000 gross tons or more;

(1663)     (2) Carries petroleum oil in bulk as cargo or oil cargo residue; and

(1664)     (3) Is not equipped with a double hull meeting §157.10d of this part, or an equivalent to the requirements of §157.10d, but required to be equipped with a double hull at a date set forth in 46 U.S.C. 3703a (b)(3) and (c)(3).

(1665)
### §157.455 Minimum under-keel clearance.
(1666)     (a) The owner or operator of a tankship, that is not fitted with a double bottom that covers the entire cargo tank length, shall provide the tankship master with written under-keel clearance guidance that includes–

(1667)     (1) Factors to consider when calculating the ship's deepest navigational draft;

(1668)     (2) Factors to consider when calculating the anticipated controlling depth;

(1669)     (3) Consideration of weather or environmental conditions; and

(1670)     (4) Conditions which mandate when the tankship owner or operator shall be contacted prior to port entry or getting underway; if no such conditions exist, the guidance must contain a statement to that effect.

(1671)     (b) Prior to entering the port or place of destination and prior to getting underway, the master of a tankship that is not fitted with the double bottom that covers the entire cargo tank length shall plan the ship's passage using guidance issued under paragraph (a) of this section and estimate the anticipated under-keel clearance. The tankship master and the pilot shall discuss the ship's planned transit including the anticipated under-keel clearance. An entry must be made in the tankship's official log or in other onboard documentation reflecting discussion of the ship's anticipated passage.

(1672)     (c) The owner or operator of a tank barge, that is not fitted with a double bottom that covers the entire cargo tank length, shall not permit the barge to be towed unless the primary towing vessel master or operator has been provided with written under-keel clearance guidance that includes–

(1673)     (1) Factors to consider when calculating the tank barge's deepest navigational draft;

(1674)     (2) Factors to consider when calculating the anticipated controlling depth;

(1675)     (3) Consideration of weather or environmental conditions; and

(1676)     (4) Conditions which mandate when the tank barge owner or operator shall be contacted prior to port entry or getting underway; if no such conditions exist, the guidance must contain a statement to that effect.

(1677)
## Part 160–Portsand Waterways Safety–General

(1678)
## Subpart A–General:

(1679)
### §160.1 Purpose.
(1680)     This subchapter contains regulations implementing 46 U.S.C. chapter 700 "Ports and Waterways Safety" and related statutes.

(1681)
### §160.3 Definitions.
(1682)     For the purposes of this subchapter:

(1683)     *Bulk* means material in any quantity that is shipped, stored, or handled without the benefit of package, label, mark or count and carried in integral or fixed independent tanks.

(1684)     *Captain of the Port* means the Coast Guard officer designated by the Commandant to command a Captain of the Port Zone as described in part 3 of this chapter.

(1685)     *Commandant* means the Commandant of the United States Coast Guard.

(1686)     *Deviation* means any departure from any rule in this subchapter.

(1687)     *Director, Vessel Traffic Services* means the Coast Guard officer designated by the Commandant to command a Vessel Traffic Service (VTS) as described in part 161 of this chapter.

(1688)     *District Commander* means the Coast Guard officer designated by the Commandant to command a Coast Guard District as described in part 3 of this chapter.

(1689)     *ETA* means estimated time of arrival.

(1690)     *Length of Tow* means, when towing with a hawser, the length in feet from the stern of the towing vessel to the stern of the last vessel in tow. When pushing ahead or towing alongside, length of tow means the tandem length in feet of the vessels in tow excluding the length of the towing vessel.

(1691)     *Person* means an individual, firm, corporation, association, partnership, or governmental entity.

(1692)     *State* means each of the several States of the United States, the District of Columbia, the Commonwealth of Puerto Rico, Guam, American Samoa, the United States Virgin Islands, the Trust Territories of the Pacific Islands, the Commonwealth of the Northern Marianas Islands, and any other commonwealth, territory, or possession of the United States.

(1693)     *Tanker* means a self-propelled tank vessel constructed or adapted primarily to carry oil or hazardous materials in bulk in the cargo spaces.

(1694)     *Tank Vessel* means a vessel that is constructed or adapted to carry, or that carries, oil or hazardous material in bulk as cargo or cargo residue.

(1695)     *Vehicle* means every type of conveyance capable of being used as a means of transportation on land.

(1696)     *Vessel* means every description of watercraft or other artificial contrivance used, or capable of being used, as a means of transportation on water.

(1697)     *Vessel Traffic Services (VTS)* means a service implemented under part 161 of this chapter by the United States Coast Guard designed to improve the safety and efficiency of vessel traffic and to protect the environment. The VTS has the capability to interact with marine traffic and respond to traffic situations developing in the VTS area.

(1698)     *Vessel Traffic Service Area or VTS Area* means the geographical area encompassing a specific VTS area of service as described in part 161 of this chapter. This area of service may be subdivided into sectors for the purpose of allocating responsibility to individual Vessel Traffic Centers or to identify different operating requirements.

(1699)     **Note:** Although regulatory jurisdiction is limited to the navigable waters of the United States, certain vessels will be encouraged or may be required, as a condition of port entry, to report beyond this area to facilitate traffic management within the VTS area.

(1700)     *VTS Special Area* means a waterway within a VTS area in which special operating requirements apply.

(1701)
### §160.5 Delegations.
(1702)     (a) District Commanders and Captains of the Ports are delegated the authority to establish safety zones.

(1703)     (b) Under the provisions of 33 CFR 6.04–1 and 6.04–6, District Commanders and Captains of the Ports have been delegated authority to establish security zones.

(1704)     (c) Under the provisions of 33 CFR §1.05–1, District Commanders have been delegated authority to establish regulated navigation areas.

(1705)     (d) Subject to the supervision of the cognizant Captain of the Port and District Commander, Directors, Vessel Traffic Services are delegated authority under 33 CFR 1.01–30 to discharge the duties of the Captain of the Port that involve directing the operation, movement and anchorage of vessels within a Vessel Traffic Service area including management of vessel traffic within anchorages, regulated navigation areas and safety zones, and to enforce Vessel Traffic Service and ports and waterways safety regulations. This authority may be exercised by Vessel Traffic Center personnel. The Vessel Traffic Center may, within the Vessel Traffic Service area, provide information, make recommendations, or to a vessel required under part 161 of this chapter to participate in a Vessel Traffic Service, issue an order, including an order to operate or anchor as directed;

require the vessel to comply with orders issued; specify times of entry, movement or departure; restrict operations as necessary for safe operation under the circumstances; or take other action necessary for control of the vessel and the safety of the port or of the marine environment.

(1706)
### §160.7 Appeals.

(1707)    (a) Any person directly affected by a safety zone or an order or direction issued under this subchapter (33 CFR subchapter P) may request reconsideration by the official who issued it or in whose name it was issued. This request may be made orally or in writing, and the decision of the official receiving the request may be rendered orally or in writing.

(1708)    (b) Any person directly affected by the establishment of a safety zone or by an order or direction issued by, or on behalf of, a Captain of the Port may appeal to the District Commander through the Captain of the Port. The appeal must be in writing, except as allowed under paragraph (e) of this section, and shall contain complete supporting documentation and evidence which the appellant wishes to have considered. Upon receipt of the appeal, the District Commander may direct a representative to gather and submit documentation or other evidence which would be necessary or helpful to a resolution of the appeal. A copy of this documentation and evidence is made available to the appellant. The appellant is afforded five working days from the date of receipt to submit rebuttal materials. Following submission of all materials, the District Commander issues a ruling, in writing, on the appeal. Prior to issuing the ruling, the District Commander may, as a matter of discretion, allow oral presentation on the issues.

(1709)    (c) Any person directly affected by the establishment of a safety zone or by an order or direction issued by, or on behalf of, a District Commander, or who receives an unfavorable ruling on an appeal taken under paragraph (b) of this section may appeal to the Area Commander through the District Commander. The appeal must be in writing, except as allowed under paragraph (e) of this section, and shall contain complete supporting documentation and evidence which the appellant wishes to have considered. Upon receipt of the appeal, the Area Commander may direct a representative to gather and submit documentation or other evidence which would be necessary or helpful to a resolution of the appeal. A copy of this documentation and evidence is made available to the appellant. The appellant is afforded five working days from the date of receipt to submit rebuttal materials. Following submission of all materials, the Area Commander issues a ruling, in writing, on the appeal. Prior to issuing the ruling, the Area Commander may, as a matter of discretion, allow oral presentation on the issues.

(1710)    (d) Any person who receives an unfavorable ruling on an appeal taken under paragraph (c) of this section, may appeal to the Commandant (CG–5P), Attn: Assistant Commandant for Prevention, U.S. Coast Guard Stop 7501, 2703 Martin Luther King Jr. Avenue SE., Washington, DC 20593–7501. The appeal must be in writing, except as allowed under paragraph (e) of this section. The Area Commander forwards the appeal, all the documents and evidence which formed the record upon which the order or direction was issued or the ruling under paragraph (c) of this section was made, and any comments which might be relevant, to the Assistant Commandant for Prevention. A copy of this documentation and evidence is made available to the appellant. The appellant is afforded 5 working days from the date of receipt to submit rebuttal materials to the Assistant Commandant for Prevention. The decision of the Assistant Commandant for Prevention is based upon the materials submitted, without oral argument or presentation. The decision of the Assistant Commandant for Prevention is issued in writing and constitutes final agency action.

(1711)    (e) If the delay in presenting a written appeal would have significant adverse impact on the appellant, the appeal under paragraphs (b) and (c) of this section may initially be presented orally. If an initial presentation of the appeal is made orally, the appellant must submit the appeal in writing within five days of the oral presentation to the Coast Guard official to whom the presentation was made. The written appeal must contain, at a minimum, the basis for the appeal and a summary of the material presented orally. If requested, the official to whom the appeal is directed may stay the effect of the action while the ruling is being appealed.

(1712)
## Subpart B–Control of Vessel and Facility Operations

(1713)
### §160.101 Purpose.

(1714)    This subpart describes the authority exercised by District Commanders and Captains of the Ports to insure the safety of vessels and waterfront facilities, and the protection of the navigable waters and the resources therein. The controls described in this subpart are directed to specific situations and hazards.

(1715)
### §160.103 Applicability.

(1716)    (a) This subpart applies to any–

(1717)    (1) Vessel on the navigable waters of the United States, except as provided in paragraphs (b) and (c) of this section;

(1718)    (2) Bridge or other structure on or in the navigable waters of the United States; and

(1719)    (3) Land structure or shore area immediately adjacent to the navigable waters of the United States.

(1720)    (b) This subpart does not apply to any vessel on the Saint Lawrence Seaway.

(1721)    (c) Except pursuant to international treaty, convention, or agreement, to which the United States is a party, this subpart does not apply to any foreign vessel that is not destined for, or departing from, a port or place subject to the jurisdiction of the United States and that is in–

(1722)    (1) Innocent passage through the territorial sea of the United States;

(1723)    (2) Transit through the navigable waters of the United States which form a part of an international strait.

(1724)
### §160.105 Compliance with orders.

(1725)    Each person who has notice of the terms of an order issued under this subpart must comply with that order.

(1726)
### §160.107 Denial of entry.

(1727)    Each district Commander or Captain of the Port, subject to recognized principles of international law, may deny entry into the navigable waters of the United States or to any port or place under the jurisdiction of the United States, and within the district or zone of that district Commander or Captain of the Port, to any vessel not in compliance with the provisions of the Port and Tanker Safety Act (46 U.S.C. chapter 700) or the regulations issued thereunder.

(1728)
### §160.109 Waterfront facility safety.

(1729)    (a) To prevent damage to, or destruction of, any bridge or other structure on or in the navigable waters of the United States, or any land structure or shore area immediately adjacent to those waters, and to protect the navigable waters and the resources therein from harm resulting from vessel or structure damage, destruction, or loss, each District Commander or Captain of the Port may–

(1730)    (1) Direct the handling, loading, unloading, storage, and movement (including the emergency removal, control, and disposition) of explosives or other dangerous articles and substances, including oil or hazardous material as those terms are defined in 46 U.S.C. 2101 on any structure on or in the navigable waters of the United States, or any land structure or shore area immediately adjacent to those waters; and

(1731)    (2) Conduct examinations to assure compliance with the safety equipment requirements for structures.

(1732)
### §160.111 Special orders applying to vessel operations.

(1733)    Each District Commander or Captain of the Port may order a vessel to operate or anchor in the manner directed when–

(1734)    (a) The District Commander or Captain of the Port has reasonable cause to believe that the vessel is not in compliance with any regulation, law or treaty;

(1735)    (b) The District Commander or Captain of the Port determines that the vessel does not satisfy the conditions for vessel operation and cargo transfers specified in §160.113; or

(1736)    (c) The District Commander or Captain of the Port has determined that such order is justified in the interest of safety by reason of weather, visibility, sea conditions, temporary port congestion, other temporary hazardous circumstances, or the condition of the vessel.

(1737)
### §160.113 Prohibition of vessel operation and cargo transfers.

(1738)    (a) Each District Commander or Captain of the Port may prohibit any vessel subject to the provisions of chapter 37 of Title 46, U.S. Code, from operating in the navigable waters of the United States, or from transferring cargo or residue in any port or place under the jurisdiction of the United States, and within the district or zone of that District Commander or Captain of the Port, if the District Commander or the Captain of the Port determines that the vessel's history of accidents, pollution incidents, or serious repair problems creates reason to believe that the vessel may be unsafe or pose a threat to the marine environment.

(1739)    (b) The authority to issue orders prohibiting operation of the vessels or transfer of cargo or residue under paragraph (a) of this section also applies if the vessel:

(1740)    (1) Fails to comply with any applicable regulation;

(1741)    (2) Discharges oil or hazardous material in violation of any law or treaty of the United States;

(1742)    (3) Does not comply with applicable vessel traffic service requirements;

(1743)    (4) While underway, does not have at least one deck officer on the navigation bridge who is capable of communicating in the English language.

(1744)    (c) When a vessel has been prohibited from operating in the navigable waters of the United States under paragraphs (a) or (b) of this section, the District Commander or Captain of the Port may allow provisional entry into the navigable waters of the United States, or into any port or place under the jurisdiction of the United States and within the district or zone of that District Commander or Captain of the Port, if the owner or operator of such vessel proves to the satisfaction of the district Commander or Captain of the Port, that the vessel is not unsafe or does not pose a threat to the marine environment, and that such entry is necessary for the safety of the vessel or the persons on board.

(1745)    (d) A vessel which has been prohibited from operating in the navigable waters of the United States, or from transferring cargo or residue in a port or place under the jurisdiction of the United States under the provisions of paragraph (a) or (b)(1), (2), or (3) of this section, may be allowed provisional entry if the owner or operator proves, to the satisfaction of the District Commander or Captain of the Port that has jurisdiction, that the vessel is no longer unsafe or a threat to the environment, and that the condition which gave rise to the prohibition no longer exists.

(1746)
### §160.115 Withholding of clearance.

(1747)    (a) Each District Commander or Captain of the Port may request the Secretary of the Treasury, or the authorized representative thereof, to withhold or revoke the clearance required by 46 U.S.C. App. 91 of any vessel, the owner or operator of which is subject to any penalties under 46 U.S.C. 70036.

(1748)
## Subpart C–Notification of Arrival, Hazardous Conditions, and Certain Dangerous Cargoes

(1749)
### §160.201 General.

(1750)    This subpart contains requirements and procedures for submitting a notice of arrival (NOA), and a notice of hazardous condition. The sections in this subpart describe:

(1751)    (a) Applicability and exemptions from requirements in this subpart;

(1752)    (b) Required information in an NOA;

(1753)    (c) Required updates to an NOA;

(1754)    (d) Methods and times for submission of an NOA, and updates to an NOA;

(1755)    (e) How to obtain a waiver; and

(1756)    (f) Requirements for submission of the notice of hazardous condition.

(1757)    Note to §160.201. For notice-of-arrival requirements for the U.S. Outer Continental Shelf, see 33 CFR part 146.

(1758)
### §160.202 Definitions.

(1759)    Terms in this subpart that are not defined in this section or in §160.3 have the same meaning as those terms in 46 U.S.C. 2101. As used in this subpart—

(1760)    *Agent* means any person, partnership, firm, company or corporation engaged by the owner or charterer of a vessel to act in their behalf in matters concerning the vessel.

(1761)    *Barge* means a non-self propelled vessel engaged in commerce.

(1762)    *Boundary waters* mean the waters from main shore to main shore of the lakes and rivers and connecting waterways, or the portions thereof, along which the international boundary between the United States and the Dominion of Canada passes, including all bays, arms, and inlets thereof, but not including tributary waters which in their natural channels would flow into such lakes, rivers, and waterways, or waters flowing from such lakes, rivers, and waterways, or the waters of rivers flowing across the boundary.

(1763)    *Carried in bulk* means a commodity that is loaded or carried on board a vessel without containers or labels and received and handled without mark or count.

(1764)    *Certain dangerous cargo (CDC)* includes any of the following:

(1765)    (1) Division 1.1 or 1.2 explosives as defined in 49 CFR 173.50.

(1766)    (2) Division 1.5D blasting agents for which a permit is required under 49 CFR 176.415 or, for which a permit is required as a condition of a Research and Special Programs Administration exemption.

(1767)    (3) Division 2.3 "poisonous gas", as listed in 49 CFR 172.101 that is also a "material poisonous by inhalation" as defined in 49 CFR 171.8, and that is in a quantity in excess of 1 metric ton per vessel.

(1768)    (4) Division 5.1 oxidizing materials for which a permit is required under 49 CFR 176.415 or for which a permit is required as a condition of a Research and Special Programs Administration exemption.

(1769)    (5) A liquid material that has a primary or subsidiary classification of Division 6.1 "poisonous material" as listed 49 CFR 172.101 that is also a "material poisonous by inhalation," as defined in 49 CFR 171.8 and that is in a bulk packaging, or that is in a quantity in excess of 20 metric tons per vessel when not in a bulk packaging.

(1770)    (6) Class 7, "highway route controlled quantity" radioactive material or "fissile material, controlled shipment," as defined in 49 CFR 173.403.

(1771)    (7) All bulk liquefied gas cargo carried under 46 CFR 151.50–31 or listed in 46 CFR 154.7 that is flammable and/or toxic and that is not carried as certain dangerous cargo residue (CDC residue).

(1772)    (8) The following bulk liquids except when carried as CDC residue:

(1773)    (i) Acetone cyanohydrin;

(1774)    (ii) Allyl alcohol;

(1775)    (iii) Chlorosulfonic acid;

(1776)    (iv) Crotonaldehyde;

(1777)    (v) Ethylene chlorohydrin;

(1778)    (vi) Ethylene dibromide;

(1779)    (vii) Methacrylonitrile;

(1780)    (viii) Oleum (fuming sulfuric acid); and

(1781)    (ix) Propylene oxice, alone or mixed with ethylene oxide.

(1782)    (9) The following bulk solids:

(1783)    (i) Ammonium nitrate listed as Division 5.1 (oxidizing) material in 49 CFR 172.101 except when carried as CDC residue; and

(1784)    (ii) Ammonium nitrate based fertilizer listed as a Division 5.1 (oxidizing) material in 49 CFR 172.101 except when carried as CDC residue.

(1785)    *Certain dangerous cargo residue (CDC residue)* includes any of the following:

(1786)    (1) Ammonium nitrate in bulk or ammonium nitrate based fertilizer in bulk remaining after all saleable cargo is discharged, not exceeding 1,000 pounds in total and not individually accumulated in quantities exceeding two cubic feet.

(1787)    (2) For bulk liquids and liquefied gases, the cargo that remains onboard in a cargo system after discharge that is not accessible through normal transfer procedures, with the exception of the following bulk liquefied gas cargoes carried under 46 CFR 151.50–31 or listed in 46 CFR 154.7:

(1788)  (i) Ammonia, anhydrous;

(1789)  (ii) Chlorine;

(1790)  (iii) Ethane;

(1791)  (iv) Ethylene oxide;

(1792)  (v) Methane (LNG);

(1793)  (vi) Methyl bromide;

(1794)  (vii) Sulfur dioxide; and

(1795)  (viii) Vinyl chloride.

(1796)  *Charterer* means the person or organization that contracts for the majority of the carrying capacity of a ship for the transportation of cargo to a stated port for a specified period. This includes "time charterers" and "voyage charterers."

(1797)  *Crewmember* means all persons carried on board the vessel to provide navigation and maintenance of the vessel, its machinery, systems, and arrangements essential for propulsion and safe navigation or to provide services for other persons on board.

(1798)  *Embark* means when a crewmember or a person in addition to the crew joins the vessel.

(1799)  *Ferry schedule* means a published document that:

(1800)  (1) Identifies locations a ferry travels to and from;

(1801)  (2) Lists the times of departures and arrivals; and

(1802)  (3) Identifies the portion of the year in which the ferry maintains this schedule.

(1803)  *Foreign vessel* means a vessel of foreign registry or operated under the authority of a country except the United States.

(1804)  *Great Lakes* means Lakes Superior, Michigan, Huron, Erie, and Ontario, their connecting and tributary waters, the Saint Lawrence River as far as Saint Regis, and adjacent port areas.

(1805)  *Gross tons* means the tonnage determined by the tonnage authorities of a vessel's flag state in accordance with the national tonnage rules in force before the entry into force of the International Convention on Tonnage Measurement of Ships, 1969 ("Convention"). For a vessel measured only under Annex I of the Convention, gross tons means that tonnage. For a vessel measured under both systems, the higher gross tonnage is the tonnage used for the purposes of the 300-gross-ton threshold.

(1806)  *Hazardous condition* means any condition that may adversely affect the safety of any vessel, bridge, structure, or shore area or the environmental quality of any port, harbor, or navigable waterway of the United States. It may, but need not, involve collision, allision, fire, explosion, grounding, leaking, damage, injury or illness of a person aboard, or manning-shortage.

(1807)  *Nationality* means the state (nation) in which a person is a citizen or to which a person owes permanent allegiance.

(1808)  *Operating exclusively within a single Captain of the Port zone* refers to vessel movements within the boundaries of a single COTP zone, e.g., from one dock to another, one berth to another, one anchorage to another, or any combination of such transits. Once a vessel has arrived in a port in a COPT zone, it would not be considered as departing from a port or place simply because of its movements within that specific port.

(1809)  *Operator* means any person including, but not limited to, an owner, a charterer, or another contractor who conducts, or is responsible for, the operation of a vessel.

(1810)  *Persons in addition to crewmembers* mean any person onboard the vessel, including passengers, who are not included on the list of crewmembers.

(1811)  *Port or place of departure* means any port or place in which a vessel is anchored or moored.

(1812)  *Port or place of destination* means any port or place in which a vessel is bound to anchor or moor.

(1813)  *Public vessel* means a vessel that is owned or demise-(bareboat) chartered by the government of the United States, by a State or local government, or by the government of a foreign country and that is not engaged in commercial service.

(1814)  *Time charterer* means the party who hires a vessel for a specific amount of time. The owner and his crew manage the vessel, but the charterer selects the ports of destination.

(1815)  *Voyage charterer* means the party who hires a vessel for a single voyage. The owner and his crew manage the vessel, but the charterer selects the ports of destination.

(1816)

## §160.203 Applicability.

(1817)  (a) This subpart applies to the following vessels that are bound for or departing from ports or places within the navigable waters of the United States, as defined in 33 CFR 2.36(a), which includes internal waters and the territorial seas of the United States, and any deepwater port as defined in 33 CFR 148.5:

(1818)  (1) U.S. vessels in commercial service, and

(1819)  (2) All foreign vessels.

(1820)  (b) Unless otherwise specified in this subpart, the owner, agent, master, operator, or person in charge of a vessel regulated by this subpart is responsible for compliance with the requirements in this subpart.

(1821)  (c) Towing vessels controlling a barge or barges required to submit an NOA under this subpart must submit only one NOA containing the information required for the towing vessel and each barge under its control.

(1822)

## §160.204 Exemptions and exceptions.

(1823)  (a) Except for reporting notice of hazardous conditions, the following vessels are exempt from requirements in this subpart:

(1824)  (1) A passenger or offshore supply vessel when employed in the exploration for or in the removal of oil, gas, or mineral resources on the continental shelf.

(1825)  (2) An oil spill response vessel (OSRV) when engaged in actual spill response operations or during spill response exercises.

(1852)

## Table 160.206 – NOA Information Items

| Required Information | Vessels neither carrying CDC nor controlling another vessel carrying CDC | Vessels carrying CDC or controlling another vessel carrying CDC |
|---|:---:|:---:|
| **(1) Vessel Information** | | |
| (i) Name | X | X |
| (ii) Name of the registered owner | X | X |
| (iii) Country of registry | X | X |
| (iv) Call sign | X | X |
| (v) International Maritime Organization (IMO) international number or, if vessel does not have an assigned IMO international number, substitute with official number | X | X |
| (vi) Name of the operator | X | X |
| (vii) Name of the charterer | X | X |
| (viii) Name of classification society or recognized organization | X | X |
| (ix) Maritime Mobile Service Identity (MMSI) number, if applicable | X | X |
| (x) Whether the vessel is 300 gross tons or less (yes or no) | X | X |
| (xi) USCG Vessel Response Plan Control Number, if applicable | X | X |
| **(2) Voyage Information** | | |
| (i) Names of last five foreign ports or places visited | X | X |
| (ii) Dates of arrival and departure for last five foreign ports or places visited | X | X |
| (iii) For the port or place of the United States to be visited, list the names of the receiving facility, the port or place, the city, and the state | X | X |
| (iv) For the port or place in the United States to be visited, the estimated date and time of arrival | X | X |
| (v) For the port or place in the United States to be visited, the estimated date and time of departure | X | X |
| (vi) The location (port or place and country) or position (latitude and longitude or waterway and mile marker) of the vessel at the time of reporting | X | X |
| (vii) The name and telephone number of a 24-hour point of contact | X | X |
| (viii) Whether the vessel's voyage time is less than 24 hours (yes or no) | X | X |
| (ix) Last port or place of departure | X | X |
| (x) Dates of arrival and departure for last port or place of departure | X | X |
| **(3) Cargo Information** | | |
| (i) A general description of cargo, other than CDC, on board the vessel (e.g. grain, container, oil, etc.) | X | X |
| (ii) Name of each CDC carried, including cargo UN number, if applicable | – | X |
| (iii) Amount of each CDC carried | – | X |
| **(4) Information for each Crewmember On Board** | | |
| (i) Full name | X | X |
| (ii) Date of birth | X | X |
| (iii) Nationality | X | X |
| (iv) Passport* or mariners document number (type of identification and number) | X | X |
| (v) Position or duties on the vessel | X | X |
| (vi) Where the crewmembers embarked (list port or place and country) | X | X |
| **(5) Information for each Person On Board in Addition to Crew** | | |
| (i) Full name | X | X |
| (ii) Date of birth | X | X |
| (iii) Nationality | X | X |
| (iv) Passport number* | X | X |
| (v) Where the person embarked (list port or place and country) | X | X |
| **(6) Operational condition of equipment required by 33 CFR part 164 of this chapter (see note to table)** | **X** | **X** |
| **(7) International Safety Management (ISM) Code Notice** | | |
| (i) The date of expiration for the company's Document of Compliance certificate that covers the vessel | X | X |
| (ii) The date of expiration for the vessel's Safety Management Certificate | X | X |
| (iii) The name of the Flag Administration, or the recognized organization(s) representing the vessel Flag Administration, that issued those certificates | X | X |
| **(8) International Ship and Port Facility Code (ISPS) Notice** | | |
| (i) The date of issuance for the vessel's International Ship Security Certificate (ISSC), if any | X | X |
| (ii) Whether the ISSC, if any, is an initial Interim ISSC, subsequent and consecutive Interim ISSC, or final ISSC | X | X |
| (iii) Declaration that the approved ship security plan, if any, is being implemented | X | X |
| (iv) If a subsequent and consecutive Interim ISSC, the reasons therefore | X | X |
| (v) The name and 24-hour contact information for the Company Security Officer | X | X |
| (vi) The name of the Flag Administration, or the recognized security organization(s) representing the vessel Flag Administration that issued the ISSC | X | X |

**Note to Table 160.206**. For items with an asterisk (*), see paragraph (b) of this section. Submitting a response for item 6 indicating that navigation equipment is not operating properly does not serve as notice to the District Commander, Captain of the Port, or Vessel Traffic Center, under 33 CFR 164.53.

(1826)    (3) After December 31, 2015, a vessel required by 33 CFR 165.830 or 165.921 to report its movements, its cargo, or the cargo in barges it is towing.

(1827)    (4) A United States or Canadian vessel engaged in the salving operations of any property wrecked, or rendering aid and assistance to any vessels wrecked, disabled, or in distress, in waters specified in Article II of the 1908 Treaty of Extradition, Wrecking and Salvage (35 Stat. 2035; Treaty Series 502).

(1828)    (5) The following vessels neither carrying certain dangerous cargo nor controlling another vessel carrying certain dangerous cargo:

(1829)    (i) A foreign vessel 300 gross tons or less not engaged in commercial service.

(1830)    (ii) A vessel operating exclusively within a single Captain of the Port zone. Captain of the Port zones are defined in 33 CFR part 3.

(1831)    (iii) A U.S. towing vessel and a U.S. barge operating solely between ports or places of the contiguous 48 states, Alaska, and the District of Columbia.

(1832)    (iv) A public vessel.

(1833)    (v) Except for a tank vessel, a U.S. vessel operating· solely between ports or places of the United States on the Great Lakes.

(1834)    (vi) A U.S. vessel 300 gross tons or less, engaged in commercial service not coming from a foreign port or place.

(1835)    (vii) Each ferry on a fixed route that is described in an accurate schedule that is submitted by the ferry operator, along with information in paragraphs (a)(5)(vii)(A) through (J) of this section, to the Captain of the Port for each port or place of destination listed in the schedule at least 24 hours in advance of the first date and time of arrival listed on the schedule. At least 24 hours before the first date and time of arrival listed on the ferry schedule, each ferry operator who submits a schedule under paragraph (a)(5)(vii) of this section must also provide the following information to the Captain of the Port for each port or place of destination listed in the schedule for the ferry, and if the schedule or the following submitted information changes, the ferry operator must submit an updated schedule at least 24 hours in advance of the first date and time of arrival listed on the new schedule and updates on the following items whenever the submitted information is no longer accurate:

(1836)    (A) Name of the vessel;

(1837)    (B) Country of registry of the vessel;

(1838)    (C) Call sign of the vessel;

(1839)    (D) International Maritime Organization (IMO) international number or, if the vessel does not have an assigned IMO international number, the official number of the vessel;

(1840)    (E) Name of the registered owner of the vessel;

(1841)    (F) Name of the operator of the vessel;

(1842)    (G) Name of the vessel's classification society or recognized organization, if applicable;

(1843)    (H) Each port or place of destination;

(1844)    (I) Estimated dates and times of arrivals at and departures from these ports or places; and

(1845)    (J) Name and telephone number of a 24-hour point of contact.

(1846)    (b) A vessel less than 500 gross tons is not required to submit the International Safety Management (ISM) Code Notice (Entry 7 in Table 160.206 of §160.206).

(1847)    (c) A U.S. vessel is not required to submit the International Ship and Port Facility Security (ISPS) Code Notice information (Entry 8 in Table 160.206 of §160.206).

(1848)

### §160.205 Notices of arrival.

(1849)    The owner, agent, Master, operator, or person in charge of a vessel must submit notices of arrival consistent with the requirements in this subpart.

(1850)

### §160.206 Information required in an NOA.

(1851)    (a) Information required. With the exceptions noted in paragraph (b) of this section, each NOA must contain all of the information items specified in Table 160.206. Vessel owners and operators should protect any personal information they gather in preparing notices for transmittal to the National Vessel Movement Center (NVMC) to prevent unauthorized disclosure of that information.

(1853)    (b) Exceptions. If a crewmember or person on board other than a crewmember is not required to carry a passport for travel, then passport information required in Table 160.206 by items (4)(iv) and (5)(iv) need not be provided for that person.

(1854)

### §160.208 Updates to a submitted NOA.

(1855)    (a) Unless otherwise specified in this section, whenever events cause NOA information submitted for a vessel to become inaccurate, or the submitter to realize that data submitted was inaccurate, the owner, agent, Master, operator, or person in charge of that vessel must submit an update within the times required in §160.212.

(1856)    (b) Changes in the following information need not be reported:

(1857)    (1) Changes in arrival or departure times that are less than six (6) hours;

(1858)    (2) Changes in vessel location or position of the vessel at the time of reporting (entry (2)(vi) to Table 160.206); and

(1859)    (3) Changes to crewmembers' position or duties on the vessel (entry (4)(vii) to Table 160.206).

(1860)    (c) When reporting updates, revise and resubmit the NOA.

(1861)

### §160.210 Methods for submitting an NOA.

(1862)    (a) *National Vessel Movement Center (NVMC)*. Except as otherwise provided in this paragraph or paragraph (b) of this section, vessels must submit NOA information required by §160.206 to the NVMC using methods currently specified at *www.nvmc.uscg.gov*, which includes submission through the NVMC electronic Notice of Arrival and Departure (eNOAD) World Wide Web site, and XML, which includes the Excel Workbook format. These data may also be submitted using other methods that may be added as future options on *www. nvmc.uscg.gov*. XML spreadsheets may be submitted via email to *enoad@nvmc.uscg.gov*. If a vessel operator must submit an NOA or an update, for a vessel in an area without internet access or when experiencing technical difficulties with an onboard computer, and he or she has no shore-side support available, the vessel operator may fax or phone the submission to the NVMC. Fax at 1–800–547–8724 or 304–264–2684. Workbook available at *www.nvmc.uscg.gov*; or, telephone at 1–800–708–9823 or 304–264–2502.

(1863) (b) *Saint Lawrence Seaway*. Those vessels transiting the Saint Lawrence Seaway inbound, bound for a port or place in the United States, may meet the submission requirements of paragraph (a) of this section by submitting the required information to the Saint Lawrence Seaway Development Corporation and the Saint Lawrence Seaway Management Corporation of Canada using methods specified at *www.nvmc.uscg.gov*.

(1864)
### §160.212 When to submit an NOA.

(1865) (a) *Submission of an NOA*. (1) Except as set out in paragraphs (a)(2) and (a)(3) of this section, all vessels must submit NOAs within the times required in paragraph (a)(4) of this section.

(1866) (2) Towing vessels, when in control of a vessel carrying CDC and operating solely between ports or places of the contiguous 48 states, Alaska, and the District of Columbia, must submit an NOA before departure but at least 12 hours before arriving at the port or place of destination.

(1867) (3) U.S. vessels 300 gross tons or less, arriving from a foreign port or place, and whose voyage time is less than 24 hours must submit an NOA at least 60 minutes before departure from the foreign port or place. Also, Canadian vessels 300 gross tons or less, arriving directly from Canada, via boundary waters, to a United States port or place on the Great Lakes, whose voyage time is less than 24 hours must submit an NOA at least 60 minutes before departure from the Canadian port or place.

(1868) (4) Times for submitting NOAs are as follows:

(1869)

| If your voyage time is – | Then you must submit an NOA – |
| --- | --- |
| (i) 96 hours or more; or | At least 96 hours before arriving at the port or place of destination; or |
| (ii) Less than 96 hours | Before departure but at least 24 hours before arriving at the port or place of destination. |

(1870) (b) *Submission of updates to an NOA*. (1) Except as set out in paragraphs (b)(2) and (b)(3) of this section, vessels must submit updates in NOA information within the times required in paragraph (b)(4) of this section.

(1871) (2) Towing vessels, when in control of a vessel carrying CDC and operating solely between ports or places in the contiguous 48 states, Alaska, and the District of Columbia, must submit updates to an NOA as soon as practicable but at least 6 hours before entering the port or place of destination.

(1872) (3) U.S. vessels 300 gross tons or less, arriving from a foreign port or place, whose voyage time is—

(1873) (i) Less than 24 hours but greater than 6 hours, must submit updates to an NOA as soon as practicable, but at least 6 hours before entering the port or place of destination.

(1874) (ii) Less than or equal to 6 hours, must submit updates to an NOA as soon as practicable, but at least 60 minutes before departure from the foreign port or place.

(1875) (4) Times for submitting updates to NOAs are as follows:

(1877)
### §160.214 Waivers.

(1878) The Captain of the Port may waive, within that Captain

(1876)

| If your remaining voyage time is – | Then you must submit updates to an NOA – |
| --- | --- |
| (i) 96 hours or more; | As soon as practicable, but at least 24 hours before arriving at the port or place of destination; |
| (ii) Less than 96 hours but not less than 24 hours; or | As soon as practicable, but at least 24 hours before arriving at the port or place of destination; or |
| (iii) Less than 24 hours | As soon as practicable, but at least 12 hours before arriving at the port or place of destination. |

of the Port's designated zone, any of the requirements of this subpart for any vessel or class of vessels upon finding that the vessel, route area of operations, conditions of the voyage, or other circumstances are such that application of this subpart is unnecessary or impractical for purposes of safety, environmental protection, or national security.

(1879)
### §160.215 Force majeure.

(1880) When a vessel is bound for a port or place of the United States under force majeure, it must comply with the requirements in this section, but not other sections of this subpart. The vessel must report the following information to the nearest Captain of the Port as soon as practicable:

(1881) (a) The vessel Master's intentions;

(1882) (b) Any hazardous conditions as defined in §160.202; and

(1883) (c) If the vessel is carrying certain dangerous cargo or controlling a vessel carrying certain dangerous cargo, the amount and name of each CDC carried, including cargo UN number if applicable.

(1884)
### §160.216 Notice of hazardous conditions.

(1885) (a) Whenever there is a hazardous condition either on board a vessel or caused by a vessel or its operation, the owner, agent, master, operator, or person in charge must immediately notify the nearest Coast Guard Sector

Office or Group Office, and in addition submit any report required by 46 CFR 4.05-10.

(1886) (b) When the hazardous condition involves cargo loss or jettisoning as described in 33 CFR 97.115, the notification required by paragraph (a) of this section must include—

(1887) (1) What was lost, including a description of cargo, substances involved, and types of packages;

(1888) (2) How many were lost, including the number of packages and quantity of substances they represent;

(1889) (3) When the incident occurred, including the time of the incident or period of time over which the incident occurred;

(1890) (4) Where the incident occurred, including the exact or estimated location of the incident, the route the ship was taking, and the weather (wind and sea) conditions at the time or approximate time of the incident; and

(1891) (5) How the incident occurred, including the circumstances of the incident, the type of securing equipment that was used, and any other material failures that may have contributed to the incident.

(1892)
## Part 162–Inland Waterways Navigation Regulations

(1893)
### §162.1 General.

(1894) Geographic coordinates expressed in terms of latitude or longitude, or both, are not intended for plotting on maps or charts whose referenced horizontal datum is the North American Datum of 1983 (NAD 83), unless such geographic coordinates are expressly labeled NAD 83. Geographic coordinates without the NAD 83 reference may be plotted on maps or charts referenced to NAD 83 only after application of the appropriate corrections that are published on the particular map or chart being used.

(1895)
### §162.5 Definitions.

(1896) The following definitions apply to this part:

(1897) *Merchant mariner credential or MMC* means the credential issued by the Coast Guard under 46 CFR part 10. It combines the individual merchant mariner's document, license, and certificate of registry enumerated in 46 U.S.C. subtitle II part E as well as the STCW endorsement into a single credential that serves as the mariner's qualification document, certificate of identification, and certificate of service.

(1898)
### §162.30 Channel of Tuckerton Creek, NJ; navigation.

(1899) (a) Power boats or other vessels propelled by machinery shall not proceed at any time within the limits of these waters at a greater speed than 8 statute miles per hour.

(1900)
### §162.35 Channel of Christina River, DE; navigation.

(1901) (a) That vessels of over 20 tons capacity, propelled by machinery, shall not proceed at any time within the limits of these waters at a greater speed than 8 statute miles per hour.

(1902)
### §162.40 Inland waterway from Delaware River to Chesapeake Bay, DE and MD (Chesapeake and Delaware Canal).

(1903) These regulations are given in the description of the canal in chapter 7 of this Coast Pilot.

(1904)
### §162.270 Restricted areas in vicinity of Maritime Administration Reserve Fleets.

(1905) (a) The regulations in this section shall govern the use and navigation of waters in the vicinity of the following National Defense Reserve Fleets of the Maritime Administration, Department of Transportation:

(1906) (1) James River Reserve Fleet, Fort Eustis, Virginia.

(1907) (2) Beaumont Reserve Fleet, Neches River near Beaumont, Texas.

(1908) (3) Suisun Bay Reserve Fleet near Benicia, California.

(1909) (b) No vessels or other watercraft, except those owned or controlled by the United States Government, shall cruise or anchor between Reserve Fleet units within 500 feet of the end vessels in each Reserve Fleet unit, or within 500 feet of the extreme units of the fleets, unless specific permission to do so has first been granted in each case by the enforcing agency.

(1910) (c) The regulations in this section shall be enforced by the respective Fleet Superintendents and such agencies as they may designate.

(1911)
## Part 164–Navigation Safety Regulations (in part).

(1912)
### For a complete description of this part see 33 CFR 164.

(1913)
### §164.01 Applicability.

(1914) (a) This part (except as specifically limited by this section) applies to each self-propelled vessel of 1600 or more gross tons (except as provided in paragraphs (c) and (d) of this section, or for foreign vessels described in §164.02) when it is operating in the navigable waters of the United States except the St. Lawrence Seaway.

(1915) (b) Sections 164.70 through 164.82 of this part apply to each towing vessel of 12 meters (39.4 feet) or more in length operating in the navigable waters of the United States other than the St. Lawrence Seaway; except that a towing vessel is exempt from the requirements of §164.72 if it is–

(1916)     (1) Used solely within a limited geographic area, such as a fleeting-area for barges or a commercial facility, and used solely for restricted service, such as making up or breaking up larger tows;

(1917)     (2) Used solely for assistance towing as defined by 46 CFR 10.103;

(1918)     (3) Used solely for pollution response; or

(1919)     (4) Any other vessel exempted by the Captain of the Port (COTP). The COTP, upon written request, may, in writing, exempt a vessel from §164.72 for a specified route if he or she decides that exempting it would not allow its unsafe navigation under anticipated conditions.

(1920)     (c) Provisions of §§164.11(a)(2) and (c), 164.30, 164.33, and 164.46 do not apply to warships or other vessels owned, leased, or operated by the United States Government and used only in government noncommercial service when these vessels are equipped with electronic navigation systems that have met the applicable agency regulations regarding navigation safety.

(1921)     (d) Provisions of §164.46 apply to some self-propelled vessels of less than 1600 gross tonnage.

(1922)
### §164.02 Applicability exception for foreign vessels.

(1923)     (a) Except for §164.46(c) none of the requirements of this part apply to foreign vessels that:

(1924)     (1) Are not destined for, or departing from, a port or place subject to the jurisdiction of the United States; and

(1925)     (2) Are in:

(1926)     (i) Innocent passage through the territorial sea of the United States; or

(1927)     (ii) Transit through navigable waters of the United States which form a part of an international strait.

(1928)
### §164.03 Incorporation by reference.

(1929)     (a) Certain material is incorporated by reference into this part with the approval of the Director of the Federal Register under 5 U.S.C. 552(a) and 1 CFR part 51. To enforce any edition other than that specified in this section, the Coast Guard must publish notice of the change in the Federal Register and the material must be available to the public. All approved material is available for inspection at the National Archives and Records Administration (NARA). For more information on the availability of this material at NARA, call 202-741-6030, or go to: *www.archives.gov/federal-register/cfr/ibr-locations.html*. Also, it is available for inspection at the Commandant (CG-NAV), U.S. Coast Guard Stop 7418, Attn: Office of Navigation Systems, 2703 Martin Luther King Jr. Ave. SE., Washington, DC 20593-7418, telephone 202–372–1565, and is available from the sources listed below.

(1930)     (b) American Petroleum Institute (API), 1220 L Street NW., Washington, DC 20005-4070, 202–682–8000, *www.api.org*:

(1931)     (1) API Specification 9A, Specification for Wire Rope, Section 3, Properties and Tests for Wire and Wire Rope, May 28, 1984, IBR approved for §164.74.

(1932)     (2) [Reserved]

(1933)     (c) ASTM International, 100 Barr Harbor Drive, West Conshohocken, PA 19428-2959, 610-832-9585, *www.astm.org*:

(1934)     (1) ASTM D4268-93, Standard Test Method for Testing Fiber Rope, IBR approved for §164.74.

(1935)     (2) [Reserved]

(1936)     (d) Cordage Institute, 350 Lincoln Street, Hingham, MA 02043.

(1937)     (1) CIA-3, Standard Test Methods for Fiber Rope Including Standard Terminations, Revised, June 1980, IBR approved for §164.74.

(1938)     (2) [Reserved]

(1939)     (e) International Maritime Organization (IMO), 4 Albert Embankment, London SE1 7SR, United Kingdom, *www.imo.org*:

(1940)     (1) IMO Resolution A342(IX), Recommendation on Performance Standards for Automatic Pilots, November 12, 1975, IBR approved for §164.13.

(1941)     (2) IMO Resolution A.917(22), Guidelines for the Onboard Operational Use of Shipborne Automatic Identification System (AIS), January 25, 2002, IBR approved for §164.46.

(1942)     (3) SN/Circ.227, Guidelines for the Installation of a Shipborne Automatic Identification System (AIS), January 6, 2003, IBR approved for §164.46.

(1943)     (4) SN/Circ.244, Guidance on the Use of the UN/LOCODE in the Destination Field in AIS Messages, December 15, 2004, IBR approved for §164.46.

(1944)     (5) SN/Circ.245, Amendments to the Guidelines for the Installation of a Shipborne Automatic Identification System (AIS)(SN/Circ.227), December 15, 2004, IBR approved for §164.46.

(1945)     (6) SOLAS, International Convention for the Safety of Life at Sea, 1974, and 1988 Protocol relating thereto, 2000 Amendments, effective January and July 2002, (SOLAS 2000 Amendments), IBR approved for §164.46.

(1946)     (7) Conference resolution 1, Adoption of amendments to the Annex to the International Convention for the Safety of Life at Sea, 1974, and amendments to chapter V of SOLAS 1974, adopted on December 12, 2002, IBR approved for §164.46.

(1947)     (8) SN.1/Circ.289, Guidance on the Use of AIS Application-Specific Messages, June 2, 2010, IBR approved for §164.46.

(1948)     (f) National Marine Electronics Association (NMEA), 7 Riggs Avenue, Severna Park, MD 21146, 800–808–6632, *www.nmea.org*:

(1949)     (1) NMEA 0400, Installation Standard for Marine Electronic Equipment used on Moderate-Sized Vessels, Version 3.10, February 2012, IBR approved for §164.46.

(1950)     (2) [Reserved]

(1951)     (g) Radio Technical Commission for Maritime Services (RTCM), 1611 N. Kent St., Suite 605, Arlington, VA 22209, 703–527–2000, *www.rtcm.org*:

(1952)     (1) RTCM Paper 12-78/DO-100, Minimum Performance Standards, Loran C Receiving Equipment, 1977, IBR approved for §164.41.

(1953)    (2) RTCM Paper 71-95/SC112-STD, RTCM Recommended Standards for Marine Radar Equipment Installed on Ships of Less Than 300 Tons Gross Tonnage, Version 1.1, October 10, 1995, IBR approved for §164.72.

(1954)    (3) RTCM Paper 191-93/SC112-X, RTCM Recommended Standards for Maritime Radar Equipment Installed on Ships of 300 Tons Gross Tonnage and Upwards, Version 1.2, December 20, 1993, IBR approved for **§164.72**.

(1955)    (h) International Electrotechnical Commission (IEC), 3, rue de Varembe, Geneva, Switzerland, +41 22 919 02 11, *http://www.iec.ch/*. Email: info@iec.ch.

(1956)    (1) IEC 62065 (IEC 62065 2002–03), Maritime navigation and radiocommunication equipment and systems—Track control systems— Operational and performance requirements, methods of testing and required test results, First Edition, dated 2002, IBR approved for **§ 164.13(d)**.

(1957)    (2) IEC 62065 (IEC 62065 2014–02), Maritime navigation and radiocommunication equipment and systems—Track control systems— Operational and performance requirements, methods of testing and required test results, Edition 2.0, dated 2014, IBR approved for **§ 164.13(d)**.

(1958)

### §164.11 Navigation underway: General.

(1959)    The owner, master, or person in charge of each vessel underway shall ensure that:

(1960)    (a) The wheelhouse is constantly manned by persons who–

(1961)    (1) Direct and control the movement of the vessel; and

(1962)    (2) Fix the vessel's position;

(1963)    (b) Each person performing a duty described in paragraph (a) of this section is competent to perform that duty;

(1964)    (c) The position of the vessel at each fix is plotted on a chart of the area and the person directing the movement of the vessel is informed of the vessel's position;

(1965)    (d) Electronic and other navigational equipment, external fixed aids to navigation, geographic reference points, and hydrographic contours are used when fixing the vessel's position;

(1966)    (e) Buoys alone are not used to fix the vessel's position;

(1967)    **Note:** Buoys are aids to navigation placed in approximate positions to alert the mariner to hazards to navigation or to indicate the orientation of a channel. Buoys may not maintain an exact position because strong or varying currents, heavy seas, ice, and collisions with vessels can move or sink them or set them adrift. Although buoys may corroborate a position fixed by other means, buoys cannot be used to fix a position: however, if no other aids are available, buoys alone may be used to establish an estimated position.

(1968)    (f) The danger of each closing visual or each closing radar contact is evaluated and the person directing the movement of the vessel knows the evaluation;

(1969)    (g) Rudder orders are executed as given;

(1970)    (h) Engine speed and direction orders are executed as given;

(1971)    (i) Magnetic variation and deviation and gyrocompass errors are known and correctly applied by the person directing the movement of the vessel;

(1972)    (j) A person whom he has determined is competent to steer the vessel is in the wheelhouse at all times (See also 46 U.S.C. 8702(d), which requires an able seaman at the wheel on U.S. vessels of 100 gross tons or more in narrow or crowded waters during low visibility.);

(1973)    (k) If a pilot other than a member of the vessel's crew is employed, the pilot is informed of the draft, maneuvering characteristics, and peculiarities of the vessel and of any abnormal circumstances on the vessel that may affect its safe navigation.

(1974)    (1) Current velocity and direction for the area to be transited are known by the person directing the movement of the vessel;

(1975)    (m) Predicted set and drift are known by the person directing movement of the vessel;

(1976)    (n) Tidal state for the area to be transited is known by the person directing movement of the vessel;

(1977)    (o) The vessel's anchors are ready for letting go;

(1978)    (p) The person directing the movement of the vessel sets the vessel's speed with consideration for–

(1979)    (1) The prevailing visibility and weather conditions;

(1980)    (2) The proximity of the vessel to fixed shore and marine structures;

(1981)    (3) The tendency of the vessel underway to squat and suffer impairment of maneuverability when there is small underkeel clearance;

(1982)    (4) The comparative proportions of the vessel and the channel;

(1983)    (5) The density of marine traffic;

(1984)    (6) The damage that might be caused by the vessel's wake;

(1985)    (7) The strength and direction of the current; and

(1986)    (8) Any local vessel speed limit;

(1987)    (q) The tests required by §164.25 are made and recorded in the vessel's log; and

(1988)    (r) The equipment required by this part is maintained in operable condition.

(1989)    (s) Upon entering U.S. waters, the steering wheel or lever on the navigating bridge is operated to determine if the steering equipment is operating properly under manual control, unless the vessel has been steered under manual control from the navigating bridge within the preceding 2 hours, except when operating on the Great Lakes and their connecting and tributary waters.

(1990)    (t) At least two of the steering-gear power units on the vessel are in operation when such units are capable of simultaneous operation, except when the vessel is sailing on the Great Lakes and their connecting and tributary waters, and except as required by paragraph (u) of this section.

(1991)    (u) On each passenger vessel meeting the requirements of the International Convention for the Safety of Life at Sea, 1960 (SOLAS 60) and on each cargo vessel meeting the requirements of SOLAS 74 as amended in 1981, the number of steering-gear power units necessary to move the rudder from 35° on either side to 30° on the other in not more than 28 seconds must be in simultaneous operation.

(1992)

### §164.13 Navigation underway: tankers.

(1993)    (a) As used in this section, "tanker" means a self-propelled tank vessel, including integrated tug barge combinations, constructed or adapted primarily to carry oil or hazardous material in bulk in the cargo spaces and inspected and certificated as a tanker.

(1994)    (b) Each tanker must have an engineering watch capable of monitoring the propulsion system, communicating with the bridge, and implementing manual control measures immediately when necessary. The watch must be physically present in the machinery spaces or in the main control space and must consist of at least an engineer with an appropriately endorsed license or merchant mariner credential.

(1995)    (c) Each tanker must navigate with at least two deck officers with an appropriately endorsed license or merchant mariner credential on watch on the bridge, one of whom may be a pilot. In waters where a pilot is required, the second officer, must be an individual holding an appropriately endorsed license or merchant mariner credential and assigned to the vessel as master, mate, or officer in charge of a navigational watch, who is separate and distinct from the pilot.

(1996)    (d) This paragraph (d) has preemptive effect over State or local regulation within the same field. A tanker may navigate using a heading or track control system only if:

(1997)    (1) The tanker is at least one-half nautical mile (1,012 yards) beyond the territorial sea baseline, as defined in **33 CFR 2.20**;

(1998)    (i) Not within waters specified in **33 CFR part 110** (anchorages), or; (ii) Not within waters specified as precautionary areas in **33 CFR part 167**, and;

(1999)    (2) There is a person, competent to steer the vessel, present to assume manual control of the steering station at all times including, but not limited to, the conditions listed in **46 CFR 35.20–45(a)** through **(c)**; and

(2000)    (3) The system meets the heading or track control specifications of either IEC 62065 (2002–03) or IEC 62065 (2014–02) (incorporated by reference, see **§ 164.03**).

(2001)

### §164.15 Navigation bridge visibility.

(2002)    (a) The arrangement of cargo, cargo gear, and trim of all vessels entering or departing from U.S. ports must be such that the field of vision from the navigation bridge conforms as closely as possible to the following requirements:

(2003)    (1) From the conning position, the view of the sea surface must not be obscured by more than the lesser of two ship lengths or 500 meters (1,640 feet) from dead ahead to 10 degrees on either side of the vessel. Within this arc of visibility any blind sector caused by cargo, cargo gear, or other permanent obstruction must not exceed 5 degrees.

(2004)    (2) From the conning position, the horizontal field of vision must extend over an arc from at least 22.5 degrees abaft the beam on one side of the vessel, through dead ahead to at least 22.5 degrees abaft the beam on the other side of the vessel. Blind sectors forward of the beam caused by cargo, cargo gear, or other permanent obstruction must not exceed 10 degrees each, nor total more than 20 degrees, including any blind sector within the arc of visibility described in paragraph (a)(1) of this section.

(2005)    (3) From each bridge wing, the field of vision must extend over an arc from at least 45 degrees on the opposite bow, through dead ahead, to at least dead astern.

(2006)    (4) From the main steering position, the field of vision must extend over an arc from dead ahead to at least 60 degrees on either side of the vessel.

(2007)    (b) A clear view must be provided through at least two front windows at all times regardless of weather conditions.

(2008)

### §164.19 Requirements for vessels at anchor.

(2009)    The master or person in charge of each vessel that is anchored shall ensure that–

(2010)    (a) A proper anchor watch is maintained;

(2011)    (b) Procedures are followed to detect a dragging anchor; and

(2012)    (c) Whenever weather, tide, or current conditions are likely to cause the vessel's anchor to drag, action is taken to ensure the safety of the vessel, structures, and other vessels, such as being ready to veer chain, let go a second anchor, or get underway using the vessel's own propulsion or tug assistance.

(2013)

### §164.25 Tests before entering or getting underway.

(2014)    (a) Except as provided in paragraphs (b) and (c) of this section no person may cause a vessel to enter into or get underway on the navigable waters of the United States unless no more than 12 hours before entering or getting underway, the following equipment has been tested:

(2015)    (1) Primary and secondary steering gear. The test procedure includes a visual inspection of the steering gear and its connecting linkage, and, where applicable, the operation of the following:

(2016)    (i) Each remote steering gear control system.

(2017)    (ii) Each steering position located on the navigating bridge.

(2018)    (iii) The main steering gear from the alternative power supply, if installed.

(2019)　　(iv) Each rudder angle indicator in relation to the actual position of the rudder.

(2020)　　(v) Each remote steering gear control system power failure alarm.

(2021)　　(vi) Each remote steering gear power unit failure alarm.

(2022)　　(vii) The full movement of the rudder to the required capabilities of the steering gear.

(2023)　　(2) All internal vessel control communications and vessel control alarms.

(2024)　　(3) Standby or emergency generator, for as long as necessary to show proper functioning, including steady state temperature and pressure readings.

(2025)　　(4) Storage batteries for emergency lighting and power systems in vessel control and propulsion machinery spaces.

(2026)　　(5) Main propulsion machinery, ahead and astern.

(2027)　　(b) Vessels navigating on the Great Lakes and their connecting and tributary waters, having once completed the test requirements of this sub-part, are considered to remain in compliance until arriving at the next port of call on the Great Lakes.

(2028)　　(c) Vessels entering the Great Lakes from the St. Lawrence Seaway are considered to be in compliance with this sub-part if the required tests are conducted preparatory to or during the passage of the St. Lawrence Seaway or within one hour of passing Wolfe Island.

(2029)　　(d) No vessel may enter, or be operated on the navigable waters of the United States unless the emergency steering drill described below has been conducted within 48 hours prior to entry and logged in the vessel logbook, unless the drill is conducted and logged on a regular basis at least once every three months. This drill must include at a minimum the following:

(2030)　　(1) Operation of the main steering gear from within the steering gear compartment.

(2031)　　(2) Operation of the means of communications between the navigating bridge and the steering compartment.

(2032)　　(3) Operation of the alternative power supply for the steering gear if the vessel is so equipped.

(2033)

### §164.30 Charts, publications, and equipment: General.

(2034)　　No person may operate or cause the operation of a vessel unless the vessel has the marine charts, publications, and equipment as required by §§164.33 through 164.41 of this part.

(2035)

### §164.33 Charts and publications.

(2036)　　(a) Each vessel must have the following:

(2037)　　(1) Marine charts of the area to be transited, published by the National Ocean Service, U.S. Army Corps of Engineers, or a river authority that–

(2038)　　(i) Are of a large enough scale and have enough detail to make safe navigation of the area possible; and

(2039)　　(ii) Are currently corrected.

(2040)　　(2) For the area to be transited, a currently corrected copy of, or applicable currently corrected extract from, each of the following publications:

(2041)　　(i) U.S. Coast Pilot.

(2042)　　(ii) Coast Guard Light List.

(2043)　　(3) For the area to be transited, the current edition of, or applicable current extract from:

(2044)　　(i) Tide tables published by private entities using data provided by the National Ocean Service.

(2045)　　(ii) Tidal current tables published by private entities using data provided by the National Ocean Service, or river current publication issued by a river authority.

(2046)　　(b) As an alternative to the requirements for paragraph (a) of this section, a marine chart or publication, or applicable extract, published by a foreign government may be substituted for a U.S. chart and publication required by this section. The chart must be of large enough scale and have enough detail to make safe navigation of the area possible, and must be currently corrected. The publication, or applicable extract, must singly or in combination contain similar information to the U.S. Government publication to make safe navigation of the area possible. The publication, or applicable extract must be currently corrected, with the exceptions of tide and tidal current tables, which must be the current editions.

(2047)　　(c) As used in this section, "currently corrected" means corrected with changes contained in all Notices to Mariners published by National Geospatial-Intelligence Agency, or an equivalent foreign government publication, reasonably available to the vessel, and that is applicable to the vessel's transit.

(2048)

### §164.35 Equipment: All vessels.

(2049)　　Each vessel must have the following:

(2050)　　(a) A marine radar system for surface navigation.

(2051)　　(b) An illuminated magnetic steering compass, mounted in a binnacle, that can be read at the vessel's main steering stand.

(2052)　　(c) A current magnetic compass deviation table or graph or compass comparison record for the steering compass, in the wheelhouse.

(2053)　　(d) A gyrocompass.

(2054)　　(e) An illuminated repeater for the gyrocompass required by paragraph (d) of this section that is at the main steering stand, unless that gyrocompass is illuminated and is at the main steering stand.

(2055)　　(f) An illuminated rudder angle indicator in the wheelhouse.

(2056)　　(g) The following maneuvering information prominently displayed on a fact sheet in the wheelhouse:

(2057)　　(1) A turning circle diagram to port and starboard that shows the time and distance and advance and transfer required to alter course 90 degrees with maximum rudder angle and constant power settings, for either full and half speeds, or for full and slow speeds. For vessels whose turning circles are essentially the same for both directions, a diagram showing a turning circle in one direction, with a note on the diagram stating that turns to port and starboard are essentially the same, may be substituted.

(2058)    (2) The time and distance to stop the vessel from either full and half speeds, or from full and slow speeds, while maintaining approximately the initial heading with minimum application of rudder.

(2059)    (3) For each vessel with a fixed propeller, a table of shaft revolutions per minute for a representative range of speeds.

(2060)    (4) For each vessel with a controllable pitch propeller, a table of control settings for a representative range of speeds.

(2061)    (5) For each vessel that is fitted with an auxiliary device to assist in maneuvering, such as a bow thruster, a table of vessel speeds at which the auxiliary device is effective in maneuvering the vessel.

(2062)    (6) The maneuvering information for the normal load and normal ballast condition for–

(2063)    (i) Calm weather-wind 10 knots or less, calm sea;

(2064)    (ii) No current;

(2065)    (iii) Deep water conditions-water depth twice the vessel's draft or greater; and

(2066)    (iv) Clean hull.

(2067)    (7) At the bottom of the fact sheet, the following statement:

(2068)

**WARNING**

The response of the (name of the vessel) may be different from that listed above if any of the following conditions, upon which the maneuvering information is based, are varied:
(1) Calm weather—wind 10 knots or less, calm sea;
(2) No current;
(3) Water depth twice the vessel's draft or greater;
(4) Clean hull; and
(5) Intermediate drafts or unusual trim.

(2069)    (h) An echo depth sounding device.

(2070)    (i) A device that can continuously record the depth readings of the vessel's echo depth sounding device, except when operating on the Great Lakes and their connecting and tributary waters.

(2071)    (j) Equipment on the bridge for plotting relative motion.

(2072)    (k) Simple operating instructions with a block diagram, showing the change-over procedures for remote steering gear control systems and steering gear power units, permanently displayed on the navigating bridge and in the steering gear compartment.

(2073)    (l) An indicator readable from the centerline conning position showing the rate of revolution of each propeller, except when operating on the Great Lakes and their connecting and tributary waters.

(2074)    (m) If fitted with controllable pitch propellers, an indicator readable from the centerline conning position showing the pitch and operational mode of such propellers, except when operating on the Great Lakes and their connecting and tributary waters.

(2075)    (n) If fitted with lateral thrust propellers, an indicator readable from the centerline conning position showing the direction and amount of thrust of such propellers,

except when operating on the Great Lakes and their connecting and tributary waters.

(2076)    (o) A telephone or other means of communication for relaying headings to the emergency steering station. Also, each vessel of 500 gross tons and over and constructed on or after June 9, 1995 must be provided with arrangements for supplying visual compass-readings to the emergency steering station.

(2077)

### §164.37 Equipment: Vessels of 10,000 gross tons or more.

(2078)    (a) Each vessel of 10,000 gross tons or more must have, in addition to the radar system under §164.35(a), a second marine radar system that operates independently of the first.

(2079)    **Note:** Independent operation means two completely separate systems, from separate branch power supply circuits or distribution panels to antennas, so that failure of any component of one system will not render the other system inoperative.

(2080)    (b) On each tanker of 10,000 gross tons or more that is subject to 46 U.S.C. 3708, the dual radar system required by this part must have a short range capability and a long range capability; and each radar must have true north features consisting of a display that is stabilized in azimuth.

(2081)

### §164.38 Automatic radar plotting aids (ARPA).

(2082)    (See 33 CFR 164.)

(2083)

### §164.39 Steering gear: Foreign tankers.

(2084)    (a) This section applies to each foreign tanker of 10,000 gross tons or more, except a public vessel, that–

(2085)    (1) Transfers oil at a port or place subject to the jurisdiction of the United States; or

(2086)    (2) Otherwise enters or operates in the navigable waters of the United States, except a vessel described by §164.02 of this part.

(2087)    (b) Definitions. The terms used in this section are as follows:

(2088)    Constructed means the same as in chapter II–1, Regulations 1.1.2 and 1.1.3.1, of SOLAS 74.

(2089)    Existing tanker means a tanker–

(2090)    (1) For which the building contract is placed on or after June 1, 1979;

(2091)    (2) In the absence of a building contract, the keel of which is laid or which is at a similar stage of construction on or after January 1, 1980;

(2092)    (3) The delivery of which occurs on or after June 1, 1982; or

(2093)    (4) That has undergone a major conversion contracted for on or after June 1, 1979; or construction of which was begun on or after January 1, 1980, or completed on or after June 1, 1982.

(2094)    Public vessel, oil, hazardous materials, and foreign vessel mean the same as in 46 U.S.C. 2101.

(2095)       SOLAS 74 means the International Convention for the Safety of Life at Sea, 1974, as amended.

(2096)       Tanker means a self-propelled vessel defined as a tanker by 46 U.S.C. 2101(38) or as a tank vessel by 46 U.S.C. 2101(39).

(2097)       (c) Each tanker constructed on or after September 1, 1984, must meet the applicable requirements of chapter II–1, Regulations 29 and 30, of SOLAS 74.

(2098)       (d) Each tanker constructed before September 1, 1984, must meet the requirements of chapter II–1, Regulation 29.19, of SOLAS 74.

(2099)       (e) Each tanker of 40,000 gross tons or more, constructed before September 1, 1984, that does not meet the single-failure criterion of chapter II–1, Regulation 29.16, of SOLAS 74, must meet the requirements of chapter II–1, Regulation 29.20, of SOLAS 74.

(2100)       (f) Each tanker constructed before September 1, 1984, must meet the applicable requirements of chapter II–1, Regulations 29.14 and 29.15, of SOLAS 74.

(2101)

### §164.40 Devices to indicate speed and distance.

(2102)       (a) Each vessel required to be fitted with an Automatic Radar Plotting Aid (ARPA) under §164.38 must be fitted with a device to indicate speed and distance of the vessel either through the water, or over the ground.

(2103)       (b) The device must meet the following specifications:

(2104)       (1) The display must be easily readable on the bridge by day or night.

(2105)       (2) Errors in the indicated speed, when the vessel is operating free from shallow water effect, and from the effects of wind, current, and tide, should not exceed 5 percent of the speed of the vessel, or 0.5 knot, whichever is greater.

(2106)       (3) Errors in the indicated distance run, when the vessel is operating free from shallow water effect, and from the effects of wind, current, and tide, should not exceed 5 percent of the distance run of the vessel in one hour or 0.5 nautical mile in each hour, whichever is greater.

(2107)

### §164.41 Electronic position fixing devices.

(2108)       (a) Each vessel calling at a port in the continental United States, including Alaska south of Cape Prince of Wales, except each vessel owned or bareboat chartered and operated by the United States, or by a state or its political subdivision, or by a foreign nation, and not engaged in commerce, must have a satellite navigation receiver with–

(2109)       (1) Automatic acquisition of satellite signals after initial operator settings have been entered; and

(2110)       (2) Position updates derived from satellite information during each usable satellite pass.

(2111)       (b) A system that is found by the Commandant to meet the intent of the statements of availability, coverage, and accuracy for the U.S. Coastal Confluence Zone (CCZ) contained in the U.S. "Federal Radionavigation Plan" (Report No. DOD–NO 4650.4–P, I or No. DOT–TSC–RSPA–80–16, 1). A person desiring a finding by the Commandant under this subparagraph must submit a written application describing the device to the Commandant (CG–DCO–D), Attn: Deputy for Operations Policy and Capabilities, U.S. Coast Guard Stop 7318, 2703 Martin Luther King Jr. Avenue SE., Washington, DC 20593–7318. After reviewing the application, the Commandant may request additional information to establish whether or not the device meets the intent of the Federal Radionavigation Plan.

(2112)       **Note.**–The Federal Radionavigation Plan is available from the National Technical Information Service, Springfield, VA 22161, with the following Government Accession Numbers:

(2113)       Vol 1, ADA 116468

(2114)       Vol 2, ADA 116469

(2115)       Vol 3, ADA 116470

(2116)       Vol 4, ADA 116471

(2117)

### §164.42 Rate of turn indicator.

(2118)       Each vessel of 100,000 gross tons or more constructed on or after September 1, 1984, shall be fitted with a rate of turn indicator.

(2119)

### §164.43 [Removed]

(2120)

### §164.46 Automatic Identification System.

(2121)       (a) *Definitions.* As used in this section—Automatic Identification Systems or AIS means a maritime navigation safety communications system standardized by the International Telecommunication Union (ITU), adopted by the International Maritime Organization (IMO), that—

(2122)       (1) Provides vessel information, including the vessel's identity, type, position, course, speed, navigational status and other safety-related information automatically to appropriately equipped shore stations, other ships, and aircraft;

(2123)       (2) Receives automatically such information from similarly fitted ships, monitors and tracks ships; and

(2124)       (3) Exchanges data with shore-based facilities.

(2125)       *Gross tonnage* means tonnage as defined under the International Convention on Tonnage Measurement of Ships, 1969.

(2126)       *International voyage* means a voyage from a country to which the present International Convention for the Safety of Life at Sea applies to a port outside such country, or conversely.

(2127)       *Properly installed, operational* means an Automatic Identification System (AIS) that is installed and operated using the guidelines set forth by the International Maritime Organization (IMO) Resolution A.917(22) and Safety of Navigation Circulars (SN/Circ.) 227, 244, 245, and SN.1/Circ.289; or National Marine Electronics Association (NMEA) Installation Standard 0400-3.10 in lieu of SN/Circ.227 and 245 (incorporated by reference, see §164.03).

(2128) (b) *AIS carriage*—(1) *AIS Class A device.* The following vessels must have on board a properly installed, operational Coast Guard type-approved AIS Class A device:

(2129) (i) A self-propelled vessel of 65 feet or more in length, engaged in commercial service.

(2130) (ii) A towing vessel of 26 feet or more in length and more than 600 horsepower, engaged in commercial service.

(2131) (iii) A self-propelled vessel that is certificated to carry more than 150 passengers.

(2132) (iv) A self-propelled vessel engaged in dredging operations in or near a commercial channel or shipping fairway in a manner likely to restrict or affect navigation of other vessels.

(2133) (v) A self-propelled vessel engaged in the movement of—

(2134) (A) Certain dangerous cargo as defined in subpart C of part 160 of this chapter, or

(2135) (B) Flammable or combustible liquid cargo in bulk that is listed in 46 CFR 30.25-1, Table 30.25-1.

(2136) (2) *AIS Class B device.* Use of a Coast Guard type-approved AIS Class B device in lieu of an AIS Class A device is permissible on the following vessels if they are not subject to pilotage by other than the vessel Master or crew:

(2137) (i) Fishing industry vessels;

(2138) (ii) Vessels identified in paragraph (b)(1)(i) of this section that are certificated to carry less than 150 passengers and that—

(2139) (A) Do not operate in a Vessel Traffic Service (VTS) or Vessel Movement Reporting System (VMRS) area defined in Table 161.12(c) of §161.12 of this chapter, and

(2140) (B) Do not operate at speeds in excess of 14 knots; and

(2141) (iii) Vessels identified in paragraph (b)(1)(iv) of this section engaged in dredging operations.

(2142) *Note to paragraph (b):* Under 46 U.S.C. 70002 and 33 CFR 160.111, a Coast Guard Captain of the Port (COTP) may restrict the operation of a vessel if he or she determines that by reason of weather, visibility, sea conditions, port congestion, other hazardous circumstances, or the condition of such vessel, the restriction is justified in the interest of safety. In certain circumstances, if a COTP is concerned that the operation of a vessel not subject to §164.46 would be unsafe, the COTP may determine that voluntary installation of AIS by the operator would mitigate that concern. Fishing industry vessels include fishing vessels, fish processing vessels, and fish tender vessels as defined in 46 U.S.C. 2101.

(2143) (c) *SOLAS provisions.* The following self-propelled vessels must comply with International Convention for Safety of Life at Sea (SOLAS), as amended, chapter V, regulation 19.2.1.6 (Positioning System), 19.2.4 (AIS Class A), and 19.2.3.5 (Transmitting Heading Device) or 19.2.5.1 (Gyro Compass) as applicable (Incorporated by reference, see §164.03):

(2144) (1) A vessel of 300 gross tonnage or more, on an international voyage.

(2145) (2) A vessel of 150 gross tonnage or more, when carrying more than 12 passengers on an international voyage.

(2146) (d) Operations. The requirements in this paragraph are applicable to any vessel equipped with AIS.

(2147) (1) Use of AIS does not relieve the vessel of the requirements to sound whistle signals or display lights or shapes in accordance with the International Regulations for Preventing Collisions at Sea, 1972 (72 COLREGS), 28 U.S.T. 3459, T.I.A.S. 8587, or Inland Navigation Rules, 33 CFR part 83; nor of the radio requirements of the Vessel Bridge-to-Bridge Radiotelephone Act, 33 U.S.C. 1201-1208, part 26 of this chapter, and 47 CFR part 80.

(2148) (2) AIS must be maintained in effective operating condition, which includes—

(2149) (i) The ability to reinitialize the AIS, which requires access to and knowledge of the AIS power source and password;

(2150) (ii) The ability to access AIS information from the primary conning position of the vessel;

(2151) (iii) The accurate broadcast of a properly assigned Maritime Mobile Service Identity (MMSI) number;

(2152) (iv) The accurate input and upkeep of all AIS data fields and system updates; and

(2153) (v) For those vessels denoted in paragraph (b) of this section, the continual operation of AIS and its associated devices (*e.g.*, positioning system, gyro, converters, displays) at all times while the vessel is underway or at anchor, and, if moored, at least 15 minutes prior to getting underway; except when its operation would compromise the safety or security of the vessel or a security incident is imminent. The AIS should be returned to continuous operation as soon as the compromise has been mitigated or the security incident has passed. The time and reason for the silent period should be recorded in the ship's official log and reported to the nearest Captain of the Port or Vessel Traffic Center (VTC).

(2154) (3) AIS safety-related text messaging must be conducted in English and solely to exchange or communicate pertinent navigation safety information (analogous to a SECURITE broadcast). Although not prohibited, AIS text messaging should not be relied upon as the primary means for broadcasting distress (MAYDAY) or urgent (PAN PAN) communications. (47 CFR 80.1109, Distress, urgency, and safety communications).

(2155) (4) AIS application-specific messaging (ASM) is permissible, but is limited to applications adopted by the International Maritime Organization (such as IMO SN.1/Circ.289) or those denoted in the International Association of Marine Aids to Navigation and Lighthouse Authorities' (IALA) ASM Collection for use in the United States or Canada, and to no more than one ASM per minute.

(2156) *Note to paragraph (d):* The Coast Guard has developed the "U.S. AIS Encoding Guide" to help ensure consistent and accurate data encoding (input) by AIS users. This Guide is available at our "AIS Frequently Asked Questions" (FAQ #2) World Wide Web page at www.navcen.uscg.gov. Although of great benefit, the interfacing or installation of other external devices or displays (*e.g.*, transmitting heading device, gyro, rate of turn indicator, electronic charting systems, and radar), is not currently required except as denoted in §164.46(c). Most application-specific messages require interfacing to an external system that is capable of their portrayal, such as equipment certified to meet Radio Technical Commission for Maritime Services (RTCM) electronic chart system (ECS) standard 10900 series.

(2157)    (e) Watchkeeping. AIS is primarily intended for use by the Master or person in charge of the vessel, or by the person designated by the Master or person in charge to pilot or direct the movement of the vessel, who must maintain a periodic watch for AIS information.

(2158)    (f) Portable AIS. The use of a portable AIS is permissible only to the extent that electromagnetic interference does not affect the proper function of existing navigation and communication equipment on board and such that only one AIS device may be transmitting on board a vessel at any one time.

(2159)    (g) AIS Pilot Plug. The AIS Pilot Plug on any vessel subject to pilotage by other than the vessel Master or crew must be readily available and easily accessible from the primary conning position of the vessel and permanently affixed (not an extension cord) and adjacent (within 3 feet) to a 120-volt 50/60 Hz AC power receptacle (NEMA 5-15).

(2160)    (h) Exceptions. The following vessels may seek up to a 5-year deviation from the AIS requirements of this section by requesting a deviation under §164.55.

(2161)    (1) Vessels that operate solely within a very confined area (*e.g.*, less than a 1 nautical-mile radius, shipyard, or barge fleeting facility);

(2162)    (2) Vessels that conduct only short voyages (less than 1 nautical mile) on a fixed schedule (*e.g.*, a bank-to-bank river ferry service or a tender vessel);

(2163)    (3) Vessels that are not likely to encounter other AIS-equipped vessels;

(2164)    (4) Vessels whose design or construction makes it impracticable to operate an AIS device (e.g., those that lack electrical power, have an exposed or open cabin, or are submersible); or

(2165)    (5) Vessels denoted in paragraph (b)(2) that seek a deviation from requirements in paragraphs (d)(2)(ii) and (e) of this section because their AIS Class B device lacks a display.

(2166)    (i) Prohibition. Except for maritime support stations (see 47 CFR 80.5) licensed by the Federal Communications Commission (FCC), broadcasts from AIS Class A or B devices on aircraft, non-self propelled vessels or from land are prohibited.

(2167)    (j) Implementation date. Those vessels identified in paragraphs (b) and (c) of this section that were not previously subject to AIS carriage must install AIS no later than March 1, 2016.

(2168)

**§164.51 Deviations from rules: Emergency.**

(2169)    Except for the requirements of §164.53(b), in an emergency, any person may deviate from any rule in this part to the extent necessary to avoid endangering persons, property, or the environment.

(2170)

**§164.53 Deviations from rules and reporting: Non-operating equipment.**

(2171)    (a) If during a voyage any equipment required by this part stops operating properly, the person directing the movement of the vessel may continue to the next port of call, subject to the directions of the District Commander or the Captain of the Port, as provided by 33 CFR 160.

(2172)    (b) If the vessel's automatic identification system (AIS), radar, radio navigation receivers, gyrocompass, echo depth sounding device, or primary steering gear stops operating properly, the person directing the movement of the vessel must report or cause to be reported that it is not operating properly to the nearest Captain of the Port, District Commander, or, if participating in a Vessel Traffic Service, to the Vessel Traffic Center, as soon as possible.

(2173)

**§164.55 Deviations from rules: Continuing operation or period of time.**

(2174)    The Captain of the Port, upon written application, may authorize a deviation from any rule in this part if he determines that the deviation does not impair the safe navigation of the vessel under anticipated conditions and will not result in a violation of the rules for preventing collisions at sea. The authorization may be issued for vessels operating in the waters under the jurisdiction of the Captain of the Port for any continuing operation or period of time the Captain of the Port specifies.

(2175)

**§164.61 Marine casualty reporting and record retention.**

(2176)    When a vessel is involved in a marine casualty as defined in 46 CFR 4.03–1, the master or person in charge of the vessel shall–

(2177)    (a) Ensure compliance with 46 CFR 4.05, "Notice of Marine Casualty and Voyage Records," and

(2178)    (b) Ensure that the voyage records required by 46 CFR 4.05–15 are retained for–

(2179)    (1) 30 days after the casualty if the vessel remains in the navigable waters of the United States; or

(2180)    (2) 30 days after the return of the vessel to a United States port if the vessel departs the navigable waters of the United States within 30 days after the marine casualty.

(2181)

**§164.70 Definitions.**

(2182)    For purposes of §§164.72 through 164.82, the term–

(2183)    *Current edition* means the most recent published version of a publication, chart, or map required by §164.72.

(2184)      *Currently corrected edition* means a current or previous edition of a publication required by §164.72, corrected with changes that come from Notice to Mariners (NTMs) or Notices to Navigation reasonably available and that apply to the vessel's transit. Hand-annotated river maps from U.S. Army Corps of Engineers (ACOE) are currently corrected editions if issued within the previous 5 years.

(2185)      *Great Lakes* means the Great Lakes and their connecting and tributary waters including the Calumet River as far as the Thomas J. O'Brien Lock and Controlling Works (between miles 326 and 327), the Chicago River as far as the east side of the Ashland Avenue Bridge (between miles 321 and 322), and the Saint Lawrence River as far east as the lower exit of Saint Lambert Lock.

(2186)      *Merchant mariner credential or MMC* means the credential issued by the Coast Guard under 46 CFR part 10. It combines the individual merchant mariner's document, license, and certificate of registry enumerated in 46 U.S.C. subtitle II part E as well as the STCW endorsement into a single credential that serves as the mariner's qualification document, certificate of identification, and certificate of service.

(2187)      *Swing-meter* means an electronic or electric device that indicates that rate of turn of the vessel on board which it is installed.

(2188)      *Towing vessel* means a commercial vessel engaged in or intending to engage in pulling, pushing or hauling alongside, or any combination of pulling, pushing, or hauling alongside.

(2189)      *Western Rivers* means the Mississippi River, its tributaries, South Pass, and Southwest Pass, to the navigational-demarcation lines dividing the high seas from harbors, rivers, and other inland waters of the United States, and the Port Allen-Morgan City Alternative Route, and that part of the Atchafalaya River above its junction with the Port Allen-Morgan City Alternative Route including the Old River and the Red River and those waters specified by §§89.25 and 89.27 of this chapter, and such other, similar waters as are designated by the COTP.

(2190)

### §164.72 Navigational-safety equipment, charts or maps, and publications required on towing vessels.

(2191)      (a) Except as provided by §164.01(b), each towing vessel must be equipped with the following navigational-safety equipment:

(2192)      (1) *Marine Radar.* By August 2, 1997, a marine radar that meets the following applicable requirements:

(2193)      (i) For a vessel of less than 300 tons gross tonnage that engages in towing on navigable waters of the U.S., including Western Rivers, the radar must meet–

(2194)      (A) The requirements of the Federal Communications Commission (FCC) specified by 47 CFR part 80; and

(2195)      (B) RTCM Standard for Marine Radar Equipment Installed on Ships of Less Than 300 Tons Gross Tonnage, RTCM Paper 71–95/SC112–STD, Version 1.1, display Category II and stabilization Category Bravo.

(2196)      (ii) For a vessel of less than 300 tons gross tonnage that engages in towing seaward of navigable waters of the U.S. or more than three nautical miles from shore on the Great Lakes, the radar must meet–

(2197)      (A) The requirements of the FCC specified by 47 CFR part 80; and

(2198)      (B) RTCM Standard for Marine Radar Equipment Installed on Ships of Less Than 300 Tons Gross Tonnage, RTCM Paper 71–95/SC112–STD, Version 1.1, display Category I and stabilization Category Alpha.

(2199)      (iii) For a vessel of 300 tons gross tonnage or more that engages in towing on navigable waters of the U.S., including Western rivers, the radar must meet–

(2200)      (A) The requirements of the Federal Communications Commission (FCC) specified by 47 CFR part 80; and

(2201)      (B) RTCM Recommended Standards for Marine Radar Equipment Installed on Ships of 300 Tons Gross Tonnage and Upwards, RTCM Paper 191–93/SC112–X, Version 1.2 except the requirements for azimuth stabilization in paragraph 3.10.

(2202)      (iv) For a vessel of 300 tons gross tonnage or more that engages in towing seaward of navigable waters of the U.S. or more than three nautical miles from shore on the Great Lakes, the radar must meet–

(2203)      (A) The requirements of the FCC specified by 47 CFR Part 80; and

(2204)      (B) RTCM Recommended Standards for Marine Radar Equipment Installed on Ships of 300 Tons Gross Tonnage and upwards, RTCM Paper 191–93/ SC112–X, Version 1.2.

(2205)      (v) A towing vessel with an existing radar must meet the applicable requirements of paragraphs (a)(1)(i) through (iv) of this section by August 2, 1998; except that a towing vessel with an existing radar must meet the display and stabilization requirements of paragraph (a)(1)(ii)(B) of this section by August 2, 2001.

(2206)      (2) *Searchlight.* A searchlight, directable from the vessel's main steering station and capable of illuminating objects at a distance of at least two times the length of the tow.

(2207)      (3) *VHF–FM Radio.* An installation or multiple installations of VHF–FM radios as prescribed by part 26 of this chapter and 47 CFR part 80, to maintain a continuous listening watch on the designated calling channel, VHF–FM channel 13 (except on portions of the Lower Mississippi River, where VHF–FM channel 67 is the designated calling channel), and to separately monitor the International Distress and Calling Channel, VHF–FM channel 16, except when transmitting or receiving traffic on other VHF–FM channels or when participating in a Vessel Traffic Service (VTS) or monitoring a channel of a VTS. (Each U.S. towing vessel of 26 feet (about 8 meters) or more in length, except a public vessel, must hold a ship-radio-station license for radio transmitters (including radar and EPIRBs), and each operator must hold a restricted operator's license or higher. To get an

(2232)

### TABLE 164.72 – Equipment, Charts or Maps, and Publications of Towing Vessels for 12 Meters or More in Length

| | Western Rivers | U.S. Navigable Waters (other than Western Rivers) | Waters seaward of Navigable Waters and 3 NM or more from shore on the Great Lakes |
|---|---|---|---|
| Marine Radar: Towing Vessels of less than 300 GT | RTCM Paper 71-95/SC112-STD Version 1.1 Display Category II[1] Stabilization Category BRAVO | RTCM Paper 71-95/SC112-STD Version 1.1 Display Category II[1] Stabilization Category BRAVO | RTCM Paper 71-95/SC112-STD Version 1.1 Display Category I[2] Stabilization Category ALPHA |
| Towing Vessels of 300 GT or more | RTCM Paper 191-93/SC112-X Version 1.2 (except the Azimuth stabilization requirement in paragraph 3.10)[1] | RTCM Paper 191-93/SC112-X Version 1.2 (except the Azimuth stabilization requirement in paragraph 3.10)[1] | RTCM Paper 191-93/SC112-X Version 1.2[1] |
| Searchlight | X | X | X |
| VHF-FM Radio | X | X | X |
| Magnetic Compass | X[3] | X | X |
| Swing Meter | X[3] | | |
| Echo Depth-sounding Device | | X | X |
| Electronic Position Fixing Device | | | X |
| Charts or Maps | (1) Large enough scale (2) Current edition or currently corrected edition | (1) Large enough scale (2) Current edition or currently corrected edition | (1) Large enough scale (2) Currently corrected edition |
| General Publications | (1) U.S. Coast Guard Light List (2) Notices to Navigation or Local Notices to Mariners (3) River-current Tables | (1) U.S. Coast Guard Light List (2) Local Notices to Mariners (3) Tidal-current Tables (4) Tide Tables (5) U.S. Coast Pilot | (1) U.S. Coast Guard Light List (2) Local Notices to Mariners (3) Tidal-current Tables (4) Tide Tables (5) U.S. Coast Pilot |

Notes:
[1] Towing vessels with existing radar must meet this requirement by August 2, 1998.
[2] Towing vessels with existing radar must meet this requirement by August 2, 1998 but do not need to meet the display and stabilization requirements until August 2, 2001.
[3] A towing vessel may carry either a swing-meter or a magnetic compass.

(2207) application for either license, call (800) 418–FORM or (202) 418–FORM, or write to the FCC; Wireless Bureau, Licensing Division; 1270 Fairfield Road; Gettysburg, PA 17325–7245.)

(2208)     (4) *Magnetic Compass*. Either–

(2209)     (i) An illuminated swing-meter or an illuminated card-type magnetic steering compass readable from the vessel's main steering station, if the vessel engages in towing exclusively on Western Rivers; or

(2210)     (ii) An illuminated card-type magnetic steering compass readable from the vessel's main steering station.

(2211)     (5) *Echo Depth-Sounding Device*. By August 2, 2001, an echo depth-sounding device readable from the vessel's main steering station, unless the vessel engages in towing exclusively on Western Rivers.

(2212)     (6) *Electronic Position-Fixing Device*. An electronic position-fixing device, a satellite navigational system such as the Global Positioning System (GPS) as required by §164.41, if the vessel engages in towing seaward of navigable waters of the U.S. or more than three nautical miles from shore on the Great Lakes.

(2213)     (b) Each towing vessel must carry on board and maintain the following:

(2214)     (1) *Charts or maps*. Marine charts or maps of the areas to be transited, published by the National Ocean Service (NOS), the ACOE, or a river authority that satisfy the following requirements.

(2215)     (i) The charts or maps must be of a large enough scale and have enough detail to make safe navigation of the areas possible.

(2216)     (ii) The charts or maps must be either–

(2217)     (A) Current editions or currently corrected editions, if the vessel engages in towing exclusively on navigable waters of the U.S., including Western Rivers; or

(2218)     (B) Currently corrected editions, if the vessel engages in towing seaward of navigable waters of the U.S. or more than three nautical miles from shore on the Great Lakes.

(2219)     (iii) The charts or maps may be, instead of charts or maps required by paragraphs (b)(1) (i) and (ii) of this section, currently corrected marine charts or maps, or applicable extracts, published by a foreign government. These charts or maps, or applicable extracts, must contain information similar to that on the charts or maps required by paragraphs (b)(1) (i) and (ii) of the section, be of large enough scale, and have enough detail to make safe navigation of the areas possible, and must be currently corrected.

(2220)     (2) *General publications*. A currently corrected edition of, or an applicable currently corrected extract from, each of the following publications for the area to be transited:

(2221)     (i) If the vessel is engaged in towing exclusively on Western Rivers–

(2222)    (A) U.S. Coast Guard Light List;

(2223)    (B) Applicable Notices to Navigation published by the ACOE, or Local Notices to Marines (LNMs) published by the Coast Guard, for the area to be transited, when available; and

(2224)    (C) River-current tables published by a river authority, if available.

(2225)    (ii) if the vessel is engaged other than in towing exclusively on Western Rivers–

(2226)    (A) Coast Guard Light List;

(2227)    (B) Notices to Mariners published by the National Geospatial-Intelligence Agency, or LNMs published by the Coast Guard;

(2228)    (C) Tidal-Current tables published by private entities using data provided by the NOS, or river-current tables published by the ACOE or a river authority;

(2229)    (D) Tide tables published by private entities using data provided by the NOS; and

(2230)    (E) U.S. Coast Pilot.

(2231)    (c) Table 164.72, following, summarizes the navigational-safety equipment, charts or maps, and publications required for towing vessels of 12 meters or more in length engaged in towing:

(2233)
### §164.74 Towline and terminal gear for towing astern.

(2234)    (a) *Towline.* The owner, master, or operator of each vessel towing astern shall ensure that the strength of each towline is adequate for its intended service, considering at least the following factors:

(2235)    (1) The size and material of each towline must be–

(2236)    (i) Appropriate for the horsepower or bollard pull of the vessel;

(2237)    (ii) Appropriate for the static loads and dynamic loads expected during the intended service;

(2238)    (iii) Appropriate for the sea conditions expected during the intended service;

(2239)    (iv) Appropriate for exposure to the marine environment and to any chemicals used or carried on board the vessel;

(2240)    (v) Appropriate for the temperatures of normal stowage and service on board the vessel;

(2241)    (vi) Compatible with associated navigational-safety equipment; and

(2242)    (vii) Appropriate for the likelihood of mechanical damage.

(2243)    (2) Each towline as rigged must be–

(2244)    (i) Free of knots;

(2245)    (ii) Spliced with a thimble, or have a poured socket at its end; and

(2246)    (iii) Free of wire clips except for temporary repair, for which the towline must have a thimble and either five wire clips or as many wire clips as the manufacturer specifies for the nominal diameter and construction of the towline, whichever is more.

(2247)    (3) The condition of each towline must be monitored through the–

(2248)    (i) Keeping on board the towing vessel or in company files of a record of the towline's initial minimum breaking strength as determined by the manufacturer, by a classification ("class") society authorized in §157.04 of this chapter, or by a tensile test that meets API Specifications 9A, Specification for Wire Rope, Section 3; ASTM D 4268 (incorporated by reference, see §164.03), Standard Test Method for Testing Fiber Ropes; or Cordage Institute CIA 3, Standard Test Methods for Fiber Rope Including Standard Terminations;

(2249)    (ii) If the towline is purchased from another owner, master, or operator of a vessel with the intent to use it as a towline or if it is retested for any reason, keeping on board the towing vessel or in company files of a record of each retest of the towline's minimum breaking strength as determined by a class society authorized in §157.04 of this chapter or by a tensile test that meets API Specifications 9A, Section 3; ASTM D 4268 (incorporated by reference, see §164.03); or Cordage Institute CIA 3, Standard Test Methods;

(2250)    (iii) Conducting visual inspections of the towline in accordance with the manufacturer's recommendations, or at least monthly, and whenever the serviceability of the towline is in doubt (the inspections being conducted by the owner, master, or operator, or by a person on whom the owner, master, or operator confers the responsibility to take corrective measures appropriate for the use of the towline);

(2251)    (iv) Evaluating the serviceability of the whole towline or any part of the towline, and removing the whole or part from service either as recommended by the manufacturer or a class society authorized in §157.04 of this chapter or in accordance with a replacement schedule developed by the owner, master, or operator that accounts for at least the–

(2252)    (A) Nautical miles on, or time in service of, the towline;

(2253)    (B) Operating conditions experienced by the towline;

(2254)    (C) History of loading of the towline;

(2255)    (D) Surface condition, including corrosion and discoloration, of the towline;

(2256)    (E) Amount of visible damage to the towline;

(2257)    (F) Amount of material deterioration indicated by measurements of diameter and, if applicable, measurements of lay extension of the towline; and

(2258)    (G) Point at which a tensile test proves the minimum breaking strength of the towline inadequate by the standards of paragraph (a)(1) of this section, if necessary; and

(2259)    (v) Keeping on board the towing vessel or in company files of a record of the material condition of the towline when inspected under paragraphs (a)(3)(iii) and (iv) of this section. Once this record lapses for three months or more, except when a vessel is laid up or out of service or has not deployed its towline, the owner, master, or operator shall retest the towline or remove it from service.

(2260)    (b) *Terminal gear.* The owner, master, or operator of each vessel towing astern shall ensure that the gear used to control, protect, and connect each towline meets the following criteria:

(2261)    (1) The material and size of the terminal gear are appropriate for the strength and anticipated loading of the towline and for the environment;

(2262)    (2) Each connection is secured by at least one nut with at least one cotter pin or other means of preventing its failure;

(2263)    (3) The lead of the towline is appropriate to prevent sharp bends in the towline from fairlead blocks, chocks, or tackle;

(2264)    (4) There is provided a method, whether mechanical or non-mechanical, that does not endanger operating personnel but that easily releases the towline;

(2265)    (5) The towline is protected from abrasion or chafing by chafing gear, lagging, or other means;

(2266)    (6) Except on board a vessel towing in ice on Western Rivers or one using a towline of synthetic or natural fiber, there is fitted a winch that evenly spools and tightly winds the towline; and

(2267)    (7) If a winch is fitted, there is attached to the main drum a brake that has holding power appropriate for the horsepower or bollard pull of the vessel and can be operated without power to the winch.

(2268)
### §164.76 Towline and terminal gear for towing alongside and pushing ahead.

(2269)    The owner, master, or operator of each vessel towing alongside or pushing ahead shall ensure the face wires, spring lines, and push gear used–

(2270)    (a) Are appropriate for the vessel's horsepower;

(2271)    (b) Are appropriate for the arrangement of the tow;

(2272)    (c) Are frequently inspected; and

(2273)    (d) Remain serviceable.

(2274)
### §164.78 Navigation underway: Towing vessels.

(2275)    (a) The owner, master, or operator of each vessel towing shall ensure that each person directing and controlling the movement of the vessel–

(2276)    (1) Understands the arrangement of the tow and the effects of maneuvering on the vessel towing and on the vessel, barge, or object being towed;

(2277)    (2) Can fix the position of the vessel using installed navigational equipment, aids to navigation, geographic reference-points, and hydrographic contours;

(2278)    (3) Does not fix the position of the vessel using buoys alone (Buoys are aids to navigation placed in approximate positions either to alert mariners to hazards to navigation or to indicate the orientation of a channel. They may not maintain exact charted positions, because strong or varying currents, heavy seas, ice and collisions with vessels can move or sink them or set them adrift. Although they may corroborate a position fixed by other means, they cannot fix a position; however, if no other aids are available, buoys alone may establish an estimated position.);

(2279)    (4) Evaluates the danger of each closing visual or radar contact;

(2280)    (5) Knows and applies the variation and deviation, where a magnetic compass is fitted and where charts or maps have enough detail to enable this type of correction;

(2281)    (6) Knows the speed and direction of the current, and the set, drift, and tidal state for the area to be transited;

(2282)    (7) Proceeds at a safe speed taking into account the weather, visibility, density of traffic, draft of tow, possibility of wake damage, speed and direction of the current, and local speed-limits; and

(2283)    (8) Monitors the voyage plan required by §164.80.

(2284)    (b) The owner, master, or operator of each vessel towing shall ensure that the tests and inspections required by §164.80 are conducted and that the results are entered in the log or other record carried on board.

(2285)
### §164.80 Tests, inspections, and voyage planning.

(2286)    (a) The owner, master, or operator of each towing vessel of less than 1,600 GT shall ensure that the following tests and inspections of gear occur before the vessel embarks on a voyage of more than 24 hours or when each new master or operator assumes command:

(2287)    (1) *Steering-systems.* A test of the steering-gear-control system; a test of the main steering gear from the alternative power supply, if installed; a verification of the rudder-angle indicator relative to the actual position of the rudder; and a visual inspection of the steering gear and its linkage.

(2288)    (2) *Navigational equipment.* A test of all installed navigational equipment.

(2289)    (3) *Communications.* Operation of all internal vessel control communications and vessel-control alarms, if installed.

(2290)    (4) *Lights.* Operation of all navigational lights and all searchlights.

(2291)    (5) *Terminal gear.* Visual inspection of tackle; of connections of bridle and towing pendant, if applicable; of chafing gear; and the winch brake, if installed.

(2292)    (6) *Propulsion systems.* Visual inspection of the spaces for main propulsion machinery, of machinery, and of devices for monitoring machinery.

(2293)    (b) The owner, master, or operator of each towing vessel of 1,600 GT or more shall ensure that the following tests of equipment occur at the frequency required by §164.25 and that the following inspections of gear occur before the vessel embarks on a voyage of more than 24 hours or when each new master or operator assumes command:

(2294)    (1) *Navigational equipment.* Tests of onboard equipment as required by §164.25.

(2295)    (2) *Terminal gear.* Visual inspection of tackle; of connections of bridle and towing pendant, if applicable; of chafing gear; and of the winch brake, if installed.

(2296) (c)(1) The voyage-planning requirements outlined in this section do not apply to you if your towing vessel is–

(2297) (i) Used solely for any of the following services or any combination of these services–

(2298) (A) Within a limited geographic area, such as fleeting-area for barges or a commercial facility, and used for restricted service, such as making up or breaking up larger tows:

(2299) (B) For harbor assist;

(2300) (C) For assistance towing as defined by 46 CFR 10.103;

(2301) (D) For response to emergency or pollution;

(2302) (ii) A public vessel that is both owned, or demise chartered, and operated by the United States Government or by a government of a foreign country; and that is not engaged in commercial service;

(2303) (iii) A foreign vessel engaged in innocent passage; or

(2304) (iv) Exempted by the Captain of the Port (COTP).

(2305) (2) If you think your towing vessel should be exempt from these voyage planning requirements for a specified route, you should submit a written request to the appropriate COTP. The COTP will provide you with a written response granting or denying your request.

(2306) (3) If any part of a towing vessel's intended voyage is seaward of the baseline (i.e. the shoreward boundary) of the territorial sea of the U.S., then the owner, master, or operator of the vessel, employed to tow a barge or barges, must ensure that the voyage with the barge or barges is planned, taking into account all pertinent information before the vessel embarks on the voyage. The master must check the planned route for proximity to hazards before the voyage begins. During a voyage, if a decision is made to deviate substantially from the planned route, then the master or mate must plan the new route before deviating from the planned route. The voyage plan must follow company policy and consider the following (related requirements noted in parentheses):

(2307) (i) Applicable information from nautical charts and publication (also see paragraph (b) of section 164.72), including Coast Pilot, Coast Guard Light List, and Coast Guard Local Notice to Mariners for the port of departures, all ports of call, and the destination;

(2308) (ii) Current and forecast weather, including visibility, wind, and sea state for the port of departure, all ports of call, and the destination (also see paragraphs (a)(7) of section 164.78 and (b) of section 164.82);

(2309) (iii) Data on tides and currents for the port of departure, all ports of call, and the destination, and the river staged and forecast, if appropriate;

(2310) (iv) Forward and after drafts of the barge or barges and under-keel and vertical clearances (air-gaps) for all bridges, ports, and berthing areas;

(2311) (v) Pre-departure checklists;

(2312) (vi) Calculated speed and estimated time of arrival at proposed waypoints;

(2313) (vii) Communication contacts at any Vessel Traffic Services, bridges, and facilities, and any port specific requirements for VHF radio;

(2314) (viii) Any master's or operator's standings orders detailing closest points of approach, special conditions, and critical maneuvers; and

(2315) (ix) Whether the towing vessel has sufficient power to control the tow under all foreseeable circumstances.

(2316) **§164.82 Maintenance, failure, and reporting.**

(2317) (a) *Maintenance.* The owner, master, or operator of each towing vessel shall maintain operative the navigational-safety equipment required by §164.72.

(2318) (b) *Failure.* If any of the navigational-safety equipment required by §164.72 fails during a voyage, the owner, master, or operator of the towing vessel shall exercise due diligence to repair it at the earliest practicable time. He or she shall enter its failure in the log or other record carried on board. The failure of equipment, in itself, does not constitute a violation of this rule; nor does it constitute unseaworthiness; nor does it obligate an owner, master, or operator to moor or anchor the vessel. However, the owner, master, or operator shall consider the state of the equipment-along with such factors as weather, visibility, traffic, and the dictates of good seamanship-in deciding whether it is safe for the vessel to proceed.

(2319) (c) *Reporting.* The owner, master, or operator of each towing vessel whose equipment is inoperative or otherwise impaired while the vessel is operating within a Vessel Traffic Service (VTS) Area shall report the fact as required by 33 CFR Table 161.18(a) row Q.

(2320) (d) *Deviation and authorization.* The owner, master, or operator of each towing vessel unable to repair within 96 hours an inoperative marine radar required by §164.72(a) shall so notify the Captain of the Port (COTP) and shall seek from the COTP both a deviation from the requirements of this section and an authorization for continued operation in the area to be transited. Failure of redundant navigational-safety equipment, including but not limited to failure of one of two installed radars, where each satisfies §164.72(a), does not necessitate either a deviation or an authorization.

(2321) (1) The initial notice and request for a deviation and an authorization may be spoken, but the request must also be written. The written request must explain why immediate repair is impracticable, and state when and by whom the repair will be made.

(2322) (2) The COTP, upon receiving even a spoken request, may grant a deviation and an authorization from any of the provisions of §§164.70 through 164.82 for a specified time if he or she decides that they would not impair the safe navigation of the vessel under anticipated conditions.

(2323)
## Part 165–RegulatedNavigation Areas and Limited Access Areas

(2324)
## Subpart A–General

(2325)
### §165.1 Purpose of part.

(2326)    The purpose of this part is to–

(2327)    (a) Prescribe procedures for establishing different types of limited or controlled access areas and regulated navigation areas;

(2328)    (b) Prescribe general regulations for different types of limited or controlled access areas and regulated navigation areas;

(2329)    (c) Prescribe specific requirements for established areas; and

(2330)    (d) List of specific areas and their boundaries.

(2331)
### §165.3 Definitions.

(2332)    The following definitions apply to this part:

(2333)    *Credential* means any or all of the following:

(2334)    (1) Merchant mariner's document.

(2335)    (2) Merchant mariner's license.

(2336)    (3) STCW endorsement.

(2337)    (4) Certificate of registry.

(2338)    (5) Merchant mariner credential.

(2339)    *Merchant mariner credential or MMC* means the credential issued by the Coast Guard under 46 CFR part 10. It combines the individual merchant mariner's document, license, and certificate of registry enumerated in 46 U.S.C. subtitle II part E as well as the STCW endorsement into a single credential that serves as the mariner's qualification document, certificate of identification, and certificate of service.

(2340)
### §165.5 Establishment procedures.

(2341)    (a) A safety zone, security zone, or regulated navigation area may be established on the initiative of any authorized Coast Guard official authorized to issue such an order in accordance with 33 CFR 1.05-1.

(2342)    (b) Any person may request that a safety zone, security zone, or regulated navigation area be established. Except as provided in paragraph (c) of this section, each request must be submitted in writing to either the Captain of the Port or District Commander having jurisdiction over the location as described in 33 CFR 3, and include the following:

(2343)    (1) The name of the person submitting the request;

(2344)    (2) The location and boundaries of the safety zone, security zone, or regulated navigation area;

(2345)    (3) The date, time, and duration that the safety zone, security zone, or regulated navigation area should be established;

(2346)    (4) A description of the activities planned for the safety zone, security zone, or regulated navigation area;

(2347)    (5) The nature of the restrictions or conditions desired; and

(2348)    (6) The reason why the safety zone, security zone, or regulated navigation area is necessary.

(2349)    (c) *Safety Zones and Security Zones.* If, for good cause, the request for a safety zone or security zone is made less than 5 working days before the zone is to be established, the request may be made orally, but it must be followed by a written request within 24 hours.

(2350)    (Requests for safety zones, security zones, and regulated navigation areas are approved by the Office of Management and Budget under control number 1625–0020.)

(2351)
### §165.7 Notification.

(2352)    (a) The establishment of these limited access areas and regulated navigation areas is considered rulemaking. The procedures used to notify persons of the establishment of these areas vary depending upon the circumstances and emergency conditions. Notification may be made by marine broadcasts, local notice to mariners, local news media, distribution in leaflet form, and on-scene oral notice, as well as publication in the Federal Register.

(2353)    (b) Notification normally contains the physical boundaries of the area, the reasons for the rule, its estimated duration, and the method of obtaining authorization to enter the area, if applicable, and special navigational rules, if applicable.

(2354)
### §165.8 Geographic coordinates.

(2355)    Geographic coordinates expressed in terms of latitude or longitude, or both, are not intended for plotting on maps or charts whose referenced horizontal datum is the North American Datum of 1983 (NAD 83), unless such geographic coordinates are expressly labeled NAD 83. Geographic coordinates without the NAD 83 reference may be plotted on maps or charts referenced to NAD 83 only after application of the appropriate corrections that are published on the particular map or chart being used.

(2356)
### §165.9 Geographic application of limited and controlled access areas and regulated navigation areas.

(2357)    (a) *General.* The geographic application of the limited and controlled access areas and regulated navigation areas in this part are determined based on the statutory authority under which each is created.

(2358)    (b) *Safety zones and regulated navigation areas.* These zones and areas are created under the authority of 46 U.S.C. 70001–70041. Safety zones established under 46 U.S.C. 70116 and regulated navigation areas may be established in waters subject to the jurisdiction of the United States as defined in §2.38 of this chapter, including the territorial sea to a seaward limit of 12 nautical miles from the baseline.

(2359)　　(c) *Security zones*. These zones have two sources of authority–46 U.S.C. chapter 700, and the Act of June 15, 1917, as amended by both the Magnuson Act of August 9, 1950 ("Magnuson Act"), 46 U.S.C. 70051–54, and sec. 104 the Maritime Transportation Security Act of 2002 (Pub. L. 107–295, 116 Stat. 2064). Security zones established under either 46 U.S.C. 70116 or 46 U.S.C. 70051 may be established in waters subject to the jurisdiction of the United States as defined in §2.38 of this chapter, including the territorial sea to a seaward limit of 12 nautical miles from the baseline.

(2360)　　(d) *Naval vessel protection zones*. These zones are issued under the authority of 14 U.S.C. 503 and 527 and may be established in waters subject to the jurisdiction of the United States as defined in §2.38 of this chapter, including the territorial sea to a seaward limit of 3 nautical miles from the baseline.

(2361)
## Subpart B–Regulated Navigation Areas

(2362)
### §165.10 Regulated navigation area.

(2363)　　A regulated navigation area is a water area within a defined boundary for which regulations for vessels navigating within the area have been established under this part.

(2364)
### §165.11 Vessel operating requirements (regulations).

(2365)　　Each District Commander may control vessel traffic in an area which is determined to have hazardous conditions, by issuing regulations–

(2366)　　(a) Specifying times of vessel entry, movement, or departure to, from, within, or through ports, harbors, or other waters;

(2367)　　(b) Establishing vessel size, speed, draft limitations, and operating conditions; and

(2368)　　(c) Restricting vessel operation, in a hazardous area or under hazardous conditions, to vessels which have particular operating characteristics or capabilities which are considered necessary for safe operation under the circumstances.

(2369)
### §165.13 General regulations.

(2370)　　(a) The master of a vessel in a regulated navigation area shall operate the vessel in accordance with the regulations contained in Subpart F.

(2371)　　(b) No person may cause or authorize the operation of a vessel in a regulated navigation area contrary to the regulations in this Part.

(2372)
## Subpart C–Safety Zones

(2373)
### §165.20 Safety zones.

(2374)　　A Safety Zone is a water area, shore area, or water and shore area to which, for safety or environmental purposes, access is limited to authorized persons, vehicles, or vessels. It may be stationary and described by fixed limits or it may be described as a zone around a vessel in motion.

(2375)
### §165.23 General regulations.

(2376)　　Unless otherwise provided in this part–

(2377)　　(a) No person may enter a safety zone unless authorized by the COTP or the District Commander;

(2378)　　(b) No person may bring or cause to be brought into a safety zone any vehicle, vessel, or object unless authorized by the COTP or the District Commander;

(2379)　　(c) No person may remain in a safety zone or allow any vehicle, vessel, or object to remain in a safety zone unless authorized by the COTP or the District Commander; and

(2380)　　(d) Each person in a safety zone who has notice of a lawful order or direction shall obey the order or direction of the COTP or District Commander issued to carry out the purposes of this subpart.

(2381)
## Subpart D–Security Zones

(2382)
### §165.30 Security zones.

(2383)　　(a) A security zone is an area of land, water, or land and water which is so designated by the Captain of the Port or District Commander for such time as is necessary to prevent damage or injury to any vessel or waterfront facility, to safeguard ports, harbors, territories, or waters of the United States or to secure the observance of the rights and obligations of the United States.

(2384)　　(b) The purpose of a security zone is to safeguard from destruction, loss, or injury from sabotage or other subversive acts, accidents, or other causes of a similar nature:

(2385)　　(1) Vessels,

(2386)　　(2) Harbors,

(2387)　　(3) Ports, and

(2388)　　(4) Waterfront facilities–in the United States and all territory and water, continental or insular, that is subject to the jurisdiction of the United States.

(2389)
### §165.33 General regulations.

(2390)　　Unless otherwise provided in the special regulations in Subpart F of this part:

(2391)　　(a) No person or vessel may enter or remain in a security zone without the permission of the Captain of the Port;

(2392)     (b) Each person and vessel in a security zone shall obey any direction or order of the Captain of the Port;

(2393)     (c) The Captain of the Port may take possession and control of any vessel in the security zone;

(2394)     (d) The Captain of the Port may remove any person, vessel, article, or thing from a security zone;

(2395)     (e) No person may board, or take or place any article or thing on board, any vessel in a security zone without the permission of the Captain of the Port; and

(2396)     (f) No person may take or place any article or thing upon any waterfront facility in a security zone without the permission of the Captain of the Port.

(2397)
## Subpart E–Restricted Waterfront Areas

(2398)
### §165.40 Restricted Waterfront Areas.

(2399)     The Commandant, may direct the COTP to prevent access to waterfront facilities, and port and harbor areas, including vessels and harbor craft therein. This section may apply to persons who do not possess the credentials outlined in 33 CFR 125.09 when certain shipping activities are conducted that are outlined in 33 CFR 125.15.

(2400)
## Subpart F–Specific Regulated Navigation Areas and Limited Access Areas

(2401)
### §165.100 Regulated Navigation Area: Navigable waters within the First Coast Guard District.

(2402)     (a) *Regulated navigation area.* All navigable waters of the United States, as that term is used in 33 CFR 2.36, within the geographic boundaries of the First Coast Guard District, as defined in 33 CFR 3.05-1(b).

(2403)     (b) *Definitions.* Terms used in this section have the same meaning as those found in 33 CFR 157.03. Single-hull identifies any tank barge that is not a double-hull tank barge.

(2404)     (c) *Applicability.* This section applies to primary towing vessels engaged in towing tank barges carrying petroleum oil in bulk as cargo in the regulated navigation area, or as authorized by the District commander.

(2405)     (d) *Regulations*–(1) *Positive control for barges.* (i) Except as provided in paragraph (d)(1)(iii) and paragraph 5 of this section, each single hull tank barge, unless being towed by a primary towing vessel with twin-screw propulsion and with a separate system for power to each screw, must be accompanied by an escort tug of sufficient capability to promptly push or tow the tank barge away from danger of grounding or collision in the event of–

(2406)     (A) A propulsion failure;

(2407)     (B) A parted towing line;

(2408)     (C) A loss of tow;

(2409)     (D) A fire;

(2410)     (E) Grounding;

(2411)     (F) A loss of steering; or

(2412)     (G) Any other time a vessel may be operating in a Hazardous Vessel Operating Condition as defined in §161.2 of this chapter.

(2413)     (ii) Double-hull tank barges are exempt from paragraph (d)(1)(i) of this section.

(2414)     (iii) The cognizant Captain of the Port (COTP), upon written application, may authorize an exemption from the requirements of paragraph (d)(1)(i) of this section for–

(2415)     (A) Any tank barge with a capacity of less than 25,000 barrels, operating in an area with limited depth or width such as a creek or small river; or

(2416)     (B) Any tank barge operating on any waters within the COTP Zone, if the operator demonstrates to the satisfaction of the COTP that the barge employs an equivalent level of safety to that provided by the positive control provisions of this section. Each request for an exemption under this paragraph must be submitted in writing to the cognizant COTP no later than 7 days before the intended transit.

(2417)     (iv) The operator of a towing vessel engaged in towing any tank barge must immediately call for an escort or assist tug to render assistance in the event of any of the occurrences identified in paragraph (d)(1)(i) of this section.

(2418)     (2) *Enhanced communications.* Each vessel engaged in towing a tank barge must communicate by radio on marine band or Very High Frequency (VHF) channel 13 or 16, and issue security calls on marine band or VHF channel 13 or 16, upon approach to the following places:

(2419)     (i) Execution Rocks Light (USCG Light List No. [LLNR] 21440).

(2420)     (ii) Matinecock Point Shoal Lighted Gong Buoy 21 (LLNR 21420).

(2421)     (iii) 32A Buoy (LLNR 21380).

(2422)     (iv) Cable and Anchor Reef Lighted Bell Buoy 28C (LLNR 21330).

(2423)     (v) Stratford Shoal (Middle Ground) Light (LLNR 21260).

(2424)     (vi) Old Field Point Light (LLNR 21275).

(2425)     (vii) Approach to Stratford Point from the south (NOAA Chart 12370).

(2426)     (viii) Falkner Island Light (LLNR 21170).

(2427)     (ix) TE Buoy (LLNR 21160).

(2428)     (x) PI buoy (LLNR 21080).

(2429)     (xi) Race Rock Light (LLNR 19815).

(2430)     (xii) Valiant Rock Lighted Whistle Buoy 11 (LLNR 19825).

(2431)     (xiii) Approach to Point Judith in vicinity of Block Island ferry route.

(2432)     (xiv) Buzzards Bay Entrance Light (LLNR 630).

(2433)     (xv) Buzzards Bay Midchannel Lighted Buoy (LLNR 16055)

(2434)     (xvi) Cleveland East Ledge Light (LLNR 016080).

(2435)     (xvii) Hog Island Channel Lighted Buoys 1 (LLNR 16130) and 2 (LLNR 16135).

(2436)     (xviii) Approach to the Bourne Bridge.

(2437)     (xix) Approach to the Sagamore Bridge.

(2438)     (xx) Approach to the eastern entrance of Cape Cod Canal.

(2439)     (3) *Voyage planning.* (i) Each owner or operator of a towing vessel employed to tow a tank barge shall prepare a written voyage plan for each transit of the tank barge.

(2440)     (ii) The watch officer is authorized to make modifications to the plan and validate it as necessary.

(2441)     (iii) Except as provided in paragraph (d)(3)(iv) of this section, each voyage plan must contain:

(2442)     (A) A description of the type, volume, and grade of cargo.

(2443)     (B) Applicable information from nautical charts and publications, including Coast Pilot, Coast Guard Light List, and Coast Guard Local Notice to Mariners, for the destination(s).

(2444)     (C) Current and forecasted weather, including visibility, wind, and sea state for the destination(s).

(2445)     (D) Data on tides and tidal currents for the destination(s).

(2446)     (E) Forward and after drafts of the tank barge, and under-keel and vertical clearances for each port and berthing area.

(2447)     (F) Pre-departure checklists.

(2448)     (G) Calculated speed and estimated times of arrival at proposed waypoints.

(2449)     (H) Communication contacts at Vessel Traffic Service (VTS) (If applicable), bridges, and facilities, and port-specific requirements for VHF radio.

(2450)     (I) The master's standing orders detailing closest points of approach, special conditions, and critical maneuvers.

(2451)     (iv) Each owner or operator of a tank barge on an intra-port transit of not more than four hours may prepare a voyage plan that contains:

(2452)     (A) The information described in paragraphs (d)(3)(iii)(D) and (E) of this section.

(2453)     (B) Current weather conditions including visibility, wind, and sea state. This information may be entered in either the voyage plan or towing vessel's log book.

(2454)     (C) The channels of VHF radio to monitor.

(2455)     (D) Other considerations such as availability of pilot, assist tug, berth, and line-handlers, depth of berth at mean low water, danger areas, and security calls.

(2456)     (4) *Navigation restriction areas.* Unless authorized by the cognizant COTP, no tank barge may operate in–

(2457)     (i) The waters of Cape Cod Bay south of latitude 42°05' North and east of longitude 70°25' West; or

(2458)     (ii) The waters of Fishers Island Sound east of longitude 72°02' West, and west of longitude 71°55' West.

(2459)     (5) *Special Buzzards Bay regulations.* (i) For the purposes of this section, "Buzzards Bay" is the body of water east and north of a line drawn from the southern tangent of Sakonnet Point, Rhode Island, in approximate position 41°27.2'N., 71°11.7'W., to the Buzzards Bay Entrance Light in approximate position 41°23.48'N., 71°02.5'W., and then to the southwestern tangent of

Cuttyhunk Island, Massachusetts, at approximate position 41°24.6'N., 70°57.0'W., and including all of the Cape Cod Canal to its eastern entrance, except that the area of New Bedford harbor within the confines (north) of the hurricane barrier, and the passages through the Elizabeth Islands, is not considered to be "Buzzards Bay".

(2460)     (ii) *Additional Positive Control for Barges.* Except as provided in paragraph (d)(1)(iii) of this section, each single hull tank barge transiting Buzzards Bay and carrying 5,000 or more barrels of oil or other hazardous material must, in addition to its primary tug, be accompanied by an escort tug of sufficient capability to promptly push or tow the tank barge away from danger of grounding or collision in the event of–

(2461)     (A) A propulsion failure;

(2462)     (B) A parted tow line;

(2463)     (C) A loss of tow;

(2464)     (D) A fire;

(2465)     (E) Grounding;

(2466)     (F) A loss of steering; or

(2467)     (G) Any other time a vessel may be operating in a Hazardous Vessel Operating Condition as defined in §161.2 of this subchapter.

(2468)     (iii) *Federal Pilotage.* Each single hull tank barge transiting Buzzards Bay and carrying 5,000 or more barrels of oil or other hazardous material must be under the direction and control of a pilot, who is not a member of the crew, operating under a valid, appropriately endorsed, Federal first class pilot's license issued by the Coast Guard ("federally licensed pilot"). Pilots are required to embark, direct, and control from the primary tug during transits of Buzzards Bay.

(2469)     (iv) In addition to the vessels denoted in §161.16 of this chapter, requirements set forth in subpart B of 33 CFR part 161 also apply to any vessel transiting VMRS Buzzards Bay required to carry a bridge-to-bridge radiotelephone by part 26 of this chapter.

(2470)     (A) VMRS Buzzards Bay user must:

(2471)     (1) Not enter or get underway in the area without first notifying the VMRS Center;

(2472)     (2) Not enter VMRS Buzzards Bay if a Hazardous Vessel Operating Condition or circumstance per §161.2 of this subchapter exists:

(2473)     (3) If towing astern, do so with as short a hawser as safety and good seamanship permits;

(2474)     (4) Not meet, cross, or overtake any other VMRS user in the area without first notifying the VMRS center;

(2475)     (5) Before meeting, crossing, or overtaking any other VMRS user in the area, communicate on the designated vessel bridge-to-bridge radiotelephone frequency, intended navigation movements, and any other information necessary in order to make safe passing arrangements. This requirement does not relieve a vessel of any duty prescribed by the Navigation Rules (COLREGS and their associated Annexes and Inland Navigation Rules (33 CFR subchapter E)).

(2476)     (B) [Reserved]

(2477)     (e) In addition to the authority for this part 165, this section is also authorized under authorized under authority of section 311, Pub. L. 105–383.

(2478)
## §165.500 Safety/Security Zones; Chesapeake Bay, Maryland.

(2479)     (a) *Definitions.* (1) Certain Dangerous Cargo (CDC) means a material defined in 33 CFR part 160.

(2480)     (2) Liquefied Hazardous Gas (LHG) means a material defined in 33 CFR part 127.

(2481)     (3) Liquefied Natural Gas (LNG) means a material defined in 33 CFR part 127.

(2482)     (4) Cruise ship means a vessel defined as a "passenger vessel" in 46 U.S.C. 2101 (22).

(2483)     (b) *Location.* The following areas are a safety/security zone: All waters of the Chesapeake Bay and its tributaries, from surface to bottom, within a 500 yard radius around cruise ships and vessels transporting CDC, LNG, or LHG while transiting, anchored, or moored within the COTP Maryland-National Capital Region zone.

(2484)     (c) *Regulations.* (1) The COTP will notify the maritime community of affected vessels and the periods during which the safety/security zones will be enforced by providing notice to mariners in accordance with 33 CFR 165.7.

(2485)     (2) Entry into or remaining in this zone is prohibited unless authorized by the Coast Guard COTP, Maryland-National Capital Region or his designated representative.

(2486)     (3) Persons desiring to transit the area of the security zone may contact the COTP at telephone number 410–576–2693 or on VHF channel 16 (156.8 MHz) to seek permission to transit the area. If permission is granted, all persons and vessels must comply with the instructions of the COTP or his or her designated representative.

(2487)     (d) *Authority.* In addition to 46 U.S.C. 70034, the authority for this section includes 46 U.S.C. 70051.

(2488)
## §165.501 Chesapeake Bay entrance and Hampton Roads, VA and adjacent waters–Regulated Navigation Area.

(2489)     (a) *Location.* The waters enclosed by the shoreline and the following lines are a Regulated Navigation Area:

(2490)     (1) *Offshore zone.* A line drawn due East from the mean low water mark at the North Carolina and Virginia border at 36°33'03"N., 75°52'00"W., to the Territorial Seas boundary line at 36°33'05"N., 75°36'51"W., thence generally Northeastward along the Territorial Seas boundary line to 38°01'39"N., 74°57'18"W., thence due West to the mean low water mark at the Maryland and Virginia border at 38°01'39"N., 75°14'30"W., thence South along the mean low water mark on the Virginia coast, and eastward of the Colregs Demarcation Lines across Chincoteague Inlet, Assawoman Inlet, Gargathy Inlet, Metompkin Inlet, Wachapreague Inlet, Quinby Inlet, Great Machipongo Inlet, Sand Shoal Inlet, New Inlet, Ship Shoal Inlet and Little Inlet, to the Colregs Demarcation Line across the mouth of Chesapeake Bay, continuing south along the Virginia low water mark and eastward of the Colregs Demarcation Line across Rudee Inlet to the point of beginning. All positions reference NAD 83.

(2491)     (2) *Inland zone.* The waters enclosed by the shoreline and the following lines:

(2492)     (i) A line drawn across the entrance to Chesapeake Bay between Wise Point and Cape Charles Light, and then continuing to Cape Henry Light.

(2493)     (ii) A line drawn across the Chesapeake Bay between Old Point Comfort Light and Cape Charles City Range "A" Rear Light.

(2494)     (iii) A line drawn across the James River along the eastern side of U.S. Route 17 highway bridge, between Newport News and Isle of Wight County, Virginia.

(2495)     (iv) A line drawn across Chuckatuck Creek along the northern side of the north span of the U.S. Route 17 highway bridge, between Isle of Wight County and Suffolk, Virginia.

(2496)     (v) A line drawn across the Nansemond River along the northern side of the Mills Godwin (U.S. Route 17) Bridge, Suffolk, Virginia.

(2497)     (vi) A line drawn across the mouth of Bennetts Creek, Suffolk, Virginia.

(2498)     (vii) A line drawn across the Western Branch of the Elizabeth River along the eastern side of the West Norfolk Bridge, Portsmouth, Virginia.

(2499)     (viii) A line drawn across the Southern Branch of the Elizabeth River along the northern side of the I–64 highway bridge, Chesapeake, Virginia.

(2500)     (ix) A line drawn across the Eastern Branch of the Elizabeth River along the western side of the west span of the Campostella Bridge, Norfolk, Virginia.

(2501)     (x) A line drawn across the Lafayette River along the western side of the Hampton Boulevard Bridge, Norfolk, Virginia.

(2502)     (xi) A line drawn across Little Creek along the eastern side of the Ocean View Avenue (U.S. Route 60) Bridge, Norfolk, Virginia.

(2503)     (xii) A line drawn across Lynnhaven Inlet along the northern side of Shore Drive (U.S. Route 60) Bridge, Virginia Beach, Virginia.

(2504)     (b) *Definitions.* In this section:

(2505)     *CBBT* means the Chesapeake Bay Bridge Tunnel.

(2506)     Coast Guard Patrol Commander is a Coast Guard commissioned, warrant or petty officer who has been designated by the Commander, Coast Guard Sector Virginia.

(2507)     *Designated representative of the Captain of the Port* means a person, including the duty officer at the Coast Guard Sector Virginia, the Joint Harbor Operations Center watchstander, or the Coast Guard or Navy Patrol Commander who has been authorized by the Captain of the Port to act on his or her behalf and at his or her request to carry out such orders and directions as needed. All patrol vessels shall display the Coast Guard Ensign at all times when underway.

(2508) *I–664 Bridge Tunnel* means the Monitor Merrimac Bridge Tunnel.

(2509) *Inland waters* means waters within the COLREGS Line of Demarcation.

(2510) *Thimble Shoal Channel* consists of the waters bounded by a line connecting Thimble Shoal Channel Lighted Bell Buoy 1TS, thence to Thimble Shoal Lighted Gong Buoy 17, thence to Thimble Shoal Lighted Buoy 19, thence to Thimble Shoal Lighted Buoy 21, thence to Thimble Shoal Lighted Buoy 22, thence to Thimble Shoal Lighted Buoy 18, thence to Thimble Shoal Lighted Buoy 2, thence to the beginning.

(2511) *Thimble Shoal North Auxiliary Channel* consists of the waters in a rectangular area 450 feet wide adjacent to the north side of Thimble Shoal Channel, the southern boundary of which extends from Thimble Shoal Channel Lighted Buoy 2 to Thimble Shoal Lighted Buoy 18.

(2512) *Thimble Shoal South Auxiliary Channel* consists of the waters in a rectangular area 450 feet wide adjacent to the south side of Thimble Shoal Channel, the northern boundary of which extends from Thimble Shoal Channel Lighted Bell Buoy 1TS, thence to Thimble Shoal Lighted Gong Buoy 17, thence to Thimble Shoal Lighted Buoy 19, thence to Thimble Shoal Lighted Buoy 21.

(2513) (c) *Applicability*. This section applies to all vessels operating within the Regulated Navigation Area, including naval and public vessels, except vessels that are engaged in the following operations:

(2514) (1) Law enforcement.

(2515) (2) Servicing aids to navigation.

(2516) (3) Surveying, maintenance, or improvement of waters in the Regulated Navigation Area.

(2517) (d) *Regulations*.

(2518) (1) *Anchoring restrictions*. No vessel over 65 feet long may anchor or moor in the inland waters of the Regulated Navigation Area outside an anchorage designated in §110.168 of this title, with these exceptions:

(2519) (i) The vessel has the permission of the Captain of the Port.

(2520) (ii) Only in an emergency, when unable to proceed without endangering the safety of persons, property, or the environment, may a vessel anchor in a channel.

(2521) (iii) A vessel may not anchor within the confines of Little Creek Harbor, Desert Cove, or Little Creek Cove without the permission of the Captain of the Port. The Captain of the Port shall consult with the Commander, Naval Amphibious Base Little Creek, before granting permission to anchor within this area.

(2522) (2) *Anchoring detail requirements*. A self-propelled vessel over 100 gross tons, which is equipped with an anchor or anchors (other than a tugboat equipped with bow fenderwork of a type of construction that prevents an anchor being rigged for quick release), that is underway within two nautical miles of the CBBT or the I–664 Bridge Tunnel shall station its personnel at locations on the vessel from which they can anchor the vessel without delay in an emergency.

(2523) (3) *Secondary towing rig requirements on inland waters*.

(2524) (i) A vessel over 100 gross tons may not be towed in the inland waters of the Regulated Navigation Area unless it is equipped with a secondary towing rig, in addition to its primary towing rig, that:

(2525) (A) Is of sufficient strength for towing the vessel.

(2526) (B) Has a connecting device that can receive a shackle pin of at least two inches in diameter.

(2527) (C) Is fitted with a recovery pickup line led outboard of the vessel's hull.

(2528) (ii) A tow consisting of two or more vessels, each of which is less than 100 gross tons, that has a total gross tonnage that is over 100 gross tons, shall be equipped with a secondary towing rig between each vessel in the tow, in addition to its primary towing rigs, while the tow is operating within this Regulated Navigation Area. The secondary towing rig must:

(2529) (A) Be of sufficient strength for towing the vessels.

(2530) (B) Have connecting devices that can receive a shackle pin of at least two inches in diameter.

(2531) (C) Be fitted with recovery pickup lines led outboard of the vessel's hull.

(2532) (4) *Thimble Shoals Channel controls*.

(2533) (i) A vessel drawing less than 25 feet may not enter the Thimble Shoal Channel, unless the vessel is crossing the channel. Masters should consider the squat of their vessel based upon vessel design and environmental conditions. Channel crossings shall be made as perpendicular to the channel axis as possible.

(2534) (ii) Except when crossing the channel, a vessel in the Thimble Shoal North Auxiliary Channel shall proceed in a westbound direction.

(2535) (iii) Except when crossing the channel, a vessel in the Thimble Shoal South Auxiliary Channel shall proceed in an eastbound direction.

(2536) (5) *Restrictions on vessels with impaired maneuverability*.

(2537) (i) *Before entry*. A vessel over 100 gross tons, whose ability to maneuver is impaired by heavy weather, defective steering equipment, defective main propulsion machinery, or other damage, may not enter the Regulated Navigation Area without the permission of the Captain of the Port.

(2538) (ii) *After entry*. A vessel over 100 gross tons, which is underway in the Regulated Navigation Area, that has its ability to maneuver become impaired for any reason, shall, as soon as possible, report the impairment to the Captain of the Port.

(2539) (6) *Requirements for navigation charts, radars, and pilots*. No vessel over 100 gross tons may enter the Regulated Navigation Area, unless it has on board:

(2540) (i) *Corrected charts of the Regulated Navigation Area*. Instead of corrected paper charts, warships or other vessels owned, leased, or operated by the United States Government and used only in government noncommercial service may carry electronic charting and navigation

(2540) systems that have met the applicable agency regulations regarding navigation safety.

(2541)  (ii) An operative radar during periods of reduced visibility;

(2542)  (iii) When in inland waters, a pilot or other person on board with previous experience navigating vessels on the waters of the Regulated Navigation Area.

(2543)  (7) *Emergency procedures.*

(2544)  (i) Except as provided in paragraph (d)(7)(ii) of this section, in an emergency any vessel may deviate from the regulations in this section to the extent necessary to avoid endangering the safety of persons, property, or the environment.

(2545)  (ii) A vessel over 100 gross tons with an emergency that is located within two nautical miles of the CBBT or I–664 Bridge Tunnel shall notify the Captain of the Port of its location and the nature of the emergency, as soon as possible.

(2546)  (8) *Vessel speed limits.*

(2547)  (i) *Little Creek.* A vessel may not proceed at a speed over five knots between the Route 60 bridge and the mouth of Fishermans Cove (Northwest Branch of Little Creek).

(2548)  (ii) *Southern Branch of the Elizabeth River.* A vessel may not proceed at a speed over six knots between the junction of the Southern and Eastern Branches of the Elizabeth River and the Norfolk and Portsmouth Belt Line Railroad Bridge between Chesapeake and Portsmouth, Virginia.

(2549)  (iii) *Norfolk Harbor Reach.* Nonpublic vessels of 300 gross tons or more may not proceed at a speed over 10 knots between the Elizabeth River Channel Lighted Gong Buoy 5 of Norfolk Harbor Reach (southwest of Sewells Point) at approximately 36°58'00"N., 076°20'00"W, and gated Elizabeth River Channel Lighted Buoys 17 and 18 of Craney Island Reach (southwest of Norfolk International Terminal at approximately 36°54'17"N., and 076°20'11"W.

(2550)  (9) *Port security requirements.* Vessels in excess of 300 gross tons, including tug and barge combinations in excess of 300 gross tons (combined), shall not enter the Regulated Navigation Area, move within the Regulated Navigation Area, or be present within the Regulated Navigation Area, unless they comply with the following requirements:

(2551)  (i) Obtain authorization to enter the Regulated Navigation Area from the designated representative of the Captain of the Port prior to entry. All vessels entering or remaining in the Regulated Navigation Area may be subject to a Coast Guard boarding.

(2552)  (ii) Ensure that no person who is not a permanent member of the vessel's crew, or a member of a Coast Guard boarding team, boards the vessel without a valid purpose and photo identification.

(2553)  (iii) Report any departure from or movement within the Regulated Navigation Area to the designated representative of the Captain of the Port prior to getting underway.

(2554)  (iv) The designated representative of the Captain of the Port is the Sector Command Center (SCC)– Joint Harbor Operations Center (JHOC) which shall be contacted on VHF–FM channel 12, or by calling 757–668–5555.

(2555)  (v) In addition to the authorities listed in this part, this paragraph is promulgated under the authority under 46 U.S.C. 70116.

(2556)  (e) *Waivers.*

(2557)  (1) The Captain of the Port may, upon request, waive any regulation in this section.

(2558)  (2) An application for a waiver must state the need for the waiver and describe the proposed vessel operations.

(2559)  (f) Control of vessels within the regulated navigation area.

(2560)  (1) When necessary to prevent damage, destruction or loss of any vessel, facility or port infrastructure, the Captain of the Port may direct the movement of vessels or issue orders requiring vessels to anchor or moor in specific locations.

(2561)  (2) If needed for the maritime, commercial or security interests of the United States, the Captain of the Port may order a vessel to move from the location in which it is anchored to another location within the Regulated Navigation Area.

(2562)  (3) The master of a vessel within the Regulated Navigation Area shall comply with any orders or directions issued to the master's vessel by the Captain of the Port.

(2563)
### §165.502 Safety and Security Zone; Cove Point Liquefied Natural Gas Terminal, Chesapeake Bay, Maryland.

(2564)  (a) *Location.* The following area is a safety and security zone: All waters of the Chesapeake Bay, from surface to bottom, encompassed by lines connecting the following points, beginning at

(2565)  38°24'27"N., 76°23'42"W., thence to

(2566)  38°24'44"N., 76°23'11"W., thence to

(2567)  38°23'55"N., 76°22'27"W., thence to

(2568)  38°23'37"N., 76°22'58"W., thence to beginning at

(2569)  38°24'27"N., 76°23'42"W. These coordinates are based upon North American Datum (NAD) 1983. This area is 500 yards in all directions from the Cove Point LNG terminal structure.

(2570)  (b) *Regulations.* (1) In accordance with the general regulations in §§165.23 and 165.33 of this part, entry into or movement within this zone is prohibited unless authorized by the Coast Guard Captain of the Port, Maryland-National Capital Region or his designated representative. Designated representatives include any Coast Guard commissioned, warrant, or petty officer.

(2571)  (2) Persons desiring to transit the area of the zone may contact the Captain of the Port at telephone number 410–576–2693 or via VHF Marine Band Radio Channel 16 (156.8 MHz) to seek permission to transit the area. If permission is granted, all persons and vessels must comply with the instructions of the Captain of the Port or his designated representative.

(2572) (c) *Enforcement*. The U.S. Coast Guard may be assisted in the patrol and enforcement of the zone by Federal, State, local, and private agencies.

(2573)

### §165.503 Security Zone; Captain of the Port Hampton Roads Zone.

(2574) (a) *Definitions*. As used in this section–

(2575) *Certain dangerous cargo* or *CDC* means a material defined as CDC in 33 CFR 160.202.

(2576) *Designated Representative* of the Captain of the Port is any U.S. Coast Guard commissioned, warrant or petty officer who has been authorized by the Captain of the Port (COTP), Virginia to act on his or her behalf.

(2577) *Passenger vessel* means a vessel defined as a passenger vessel in 46 CFR part 70.

(2578) (b) *Location*. All navigable waters of the Captain of the Port Virginia zone (defined in 33 CFR 3.25-10) within 500 yards around a passenger vessel or vessel carrying a CDC, while the passenger vessel or vessel carrying CDC is transiting, moored or anchored.

(2579) (c) *Regulations*. (1) No vessel may approach within 500 yards of a passenger vessel or vessel carrying a CDC within the Captain of the Port Virginia zone, unless traveling at the minimum speed necessary to navigate safely.

(2580) (2) Under §165.33, no vessel or person may approach within 100 yards of a passenger vessel or vessel carrying a CDC within the Captain of the Port Virginia zone, unless authorized by the COTP Virginia or his or her designated representative.

(2581) (3) The COTP Virginia may notify the maritime and general public by marine information broadcast of the periods during which individual security zones have been activated by providing notice in accordance with 33 CFR 165.7.

(2582) (4) A security zone in effect around a moving or anchored vessel will be enforced by a law enforcement vessel. A security zone in effect around a moored vessel will be enforced by a law enforcement agent shoreside, a law enforcement vessel waterside, or both.

(2583) (5) Persons desiring to transit the area of the security zone within 100 yards of a passenger vessel or vessel carrying a CDC must contact the COTP Virginia on VHF–FM channel 16 (156.8 MHz) or telephone number 757–668–5555 or 757–484–8192 to seek permission to transit the area. All persons and vessels must comply with the instructions of the COTP or the COTP's designated representative.

(2584) (d) *Enforcement*. The COTP will enforce these zones and may enlist the aid and cooperation of any Federal, state, county, or municipal law enforcement agency to assist in the enforcement of the regulation.

(2585)

### §165.504 Newport News Shipbuilding and Dry

### Dock Company Shipyard, James River, Newport News, VA.

(2586) (a) *Location*. The following is a security zone: The waters of the James River encompassed by a line beginning at the intersection of the shoreline with the northernmost property line of the Newport News Shipbuilding and Dry Dock Co. at

(2587) 37°00'38.1"N., 76°27'05.7"W., thence southerly to

(2588) 36°59'58.4"N., 76°27'16.7"W., thence southeasterly to

(2589) 36°59'23.0"N., 76°26'54.6"W., thence westerly to

(2590) 36°59'21.5"N., 76°26'58.4"W., thence southeasterly to

(2591) 36°59'12.9"N., 76°26'52.4"W., thence easterly to

(2592) 36°59'14.2"N., 76°26'49.1"W., thence southeasterly to

(2593) 36°58'37.8"N., 76°26'26.3"W., thence easterly to

(2594) 36°58'43.5"N., 76°26'13.7"W., thence northerly to the intersection of the shoreline with the southernmost property line of the Newport News Shipbuilding and Dry Dock Co. at

(2595) 36°58'48.0"N., 76°26'11.2"W., thence northwesterly along the shoreline to the point of beginning.

(2596) (b) *Security zone anchorage*. The following is a security zone anchorage: The waters of the James River encompassed by a line beginning at the intersection of the shoreline with the northernmost property line of the Newport News Shipbuilding and Dry Dock Company shipyard at

(2597) 37°00'38.1"N., 76°27'05.7"W., thence southerly to

(2598) 36°59'58.4"N., 76°27'16.7"W., thence easterly to the shoreline at

(2599) 36°59'58.5"N., 76°27'11.6"W., thence along the shoreline to the point of beginning.

(2600) (c) *Special Regulations*.

(2601) (1) Section 165.33 (a), (e), and (f) do not apply to the following vessels or individuals on board those vessels:

(2602) (i) Public vessels of the United States.

(2603) (ii) Public vessels owned or operated by the Commonwealth of Virginia or its subdivisions for law enforcement or firefighting purposes.

(2604) (iii) Vessels owned by, operated by, or under charter to Newport News Shipbuilding and Dry Dock Co.

(2605) (iv) Vessels that are performing work at Newport News Shipbuilding and Dry Dock Co., including the vessels of subcontractors and other vendors of Newport News Shipbuilding and Dry Dock Co. or other persons that have a contractual relationship with Newport News Shipbuilding and Dry Dock Co.

(2606) (v) Vessels that are being built, rebuilt, repaired, or otherwise worked on at or by Newport News Shipbuilding and Dry Dock Co. or another person authorized to perform work at the shipyard.

(2607) (vi) Vessels that are authorized by Newport News Shipbuilding and Dry Dock Company to moor at and use its facilities.

(2608) (vii) Commercial shellfish harvesting vessels taking clams from the shellfish beds within the zone, if

(2609)    (A) The owner of the vessel has previously provided the Captain of the Port, Virginia, information about the vessel, including:

(2610)    (1) The name of the vessel;

(2611)    (2) The vessel's official number, if documented, or state number, if numbered by a state issuing authority;

(2612)    (3) A brief description of the vessel, including length, color, and type of vessel;

(2613)    (4) The name, Social Security number, current address, and telephone number of the vessel's master, operator, or person in charge; and

(2614)    (5) Upon request, information the vessel's crew.

(2615)    (B) The vessel is operated in compliance with any specific orders issued to the vessel by the Captain of the Port or other regulations controlling the operation of vessels within the security zone that may be in effect.

(2616)    (d) *Enforcement.* The U.S. Coast Guard may be assisted in the enforcement of this zone by the U.S. Navy.

(2617)
### §165.505 Security Zone; Calvet Cliffs Nuclear Power Plant, Chesapeake Bay, Calvet County, MD.

(2618)    (a) *Location.* The following area is a security zone: All waters of the Chesapeake Bay, from surface to bottom, encompassed by lines connecting the following points, beginning at

(2619)    38°26'06"N., 076°26'18"W., thence to

(2620)    38°26'10"N., 076°26'12"W., thence to

(2621)    38°26'21"N., 076°26'28"W., thence to

(2622)    38°26'14"N., 076°26'33"W., thence to beginning at

(2623)    38°26'06"N., 076°26'18"W. These coordinates are based upon North American Datum (NAD) 1983.

(2624)    (b) *Regulations.* (1) Entry into or remaining in this zone is prohibited unless authorized by the Coast Guard Captain of the Port, Maryland-National Capital Region.

(2625)    (2) Persons desiring to transit the area of the security zone may contact the Captain of the Port at telephone number 410–576–2693 or on VHF channel 16 (156.8 MHz) to seek permission to transit the area. If permission is granted, all persons and vessels must comply with the instructions of the Captain of the Port or his or her designated representative.

(2626)    (c) *Authority:* In addition to 46 U.S.C. 70034 and 46 U.S.C. 70051, the authority for this section includes 46 U.S.C. 70116.

(2627)
### §165.508 Security Zone; Potomac River and Anacostia River, and adjacent waters; Washington, DC.

(2628)    (a) *Location.* Coordinates used in this paragraph are based on NAD83. The following areas are security zones:

(2629)    (1) *Zone 1.* All navigable waters of the Potomac River, from shoreline to shoreline, bounded to the north by the Francis Scott Key (US–29) Bridge, at mile 113, and bounded to the south by a line drawn from the Virginia shoreline at Ronald Reagan Washington National Airport, at 38°51'21.3"N., 077°02'00.0"W., eastward across the Potomac River to the District of Columbia shoreline at Hains Point at position 38°51'24.3"N., 077°01'19.8"W., including the waters of the Boundary Channel, Pentagon Lagoon, Georgetown Channel Tidal Basin, and Roaches Run;

(2630)    (2) *Zone 2.* All navigable waters of the Anacostia River, from shoreline to shoreline, bounded to the north by the John Philip Sousa (Pennsylvania Avenue) Bridge, at mile 2.9, and bounded to the south by a line drawn from the District of Columbia shoreline at Hains Point at position 38°51'24.3"N., 077°01'19.8"W., southward across the Anacostia River to the District of Columbia shoreline at Giesboro Point at position 38°50'52.4"N., 077°01'10.9"W., including the waters of the Washington Channel;

(2631)    (3) *Zone 3.* All navigable waters of the Potomac River, from shoreline to shoreline, bounded to the north by a line drawn from the Virginia shoreline at Ronald Reagan Washington National Airport, at 38°51'21.3"N., 077°02'00.0"W., eastward across the Potomac River to the District of Columbia shoreline at Hains Point at position 38°51'24.3"N., 077°01'19.8"W., thence southward across the Anacostia River to the District of Columbia shoreline at Giesboro Point at position 38°50'52.4"N., 077°01'10.9"W., and bounded to the south by the Woodrow Wilson Memorial (I-95/I-495) Bridge, at mile 103.8.

(2632)    (4) *Zone 4.* All navigable waters of the Georgetown Channel of the Potomac River, 75 yards from the eastern shore measured perpendicularly to the shore, between the Long Railroad Bridge (the most eastern bridge of the 5-span, Fourteenth Street Bridge Complex) to the Theodore Roosevelt Memorial Bridge; and all waters in between, totally including the waters of the Georgetown Channel Tidal Basin.

(2633)    (5) *Zone 5.* All navigable waters in the Potomac River, including the Boundary Channel and Pentagon Lagoon, bounded on the west by a line running north to south from points along the shoreline at 38°52'50"N., 077°03'25"W., thence to 38°52'49"N., 077°03'25"W.; and bounded on the east by a line running from points at 38°53'10"N., 077°03'30"W., thence northeast to 38°53'12"N., 077°03'26"W., thence southeast to 38°52'31"N., 077°02'34"W., and thence southwest to 38°52'28"N., 077°02'38"W.

(2634)    (6) *Zone 6.* All navigable waters described in paragraphs (a)(1) through (a)(3) of this section.

(2635)    (b) *Regulations.* The general security zone regulations found in 33 CFR 165.33 apply to the security zones created by this section, §165.508.

(2636)    (1) Entry into or remaining in a zone listed in paragraph (a) in this section is prohibited unless authorized by the Coast Guard Captain of the Port Maryland-National Capital Region. Public vessels and vessels already at berth at the time the security zone is implemented do not have to depart the security zone. All vessels underway within the security zone at the time it is implemented are to depart the zone at the time the security zone is implemented.

(2637)    (2) Persons desiring to transit the area of the security zone must first obtain authorization from the Captain of the Port Maryland-National Capital Region or his or her designated representative. To seek permission to transit the area, the Captain of the Port Maryland-National Capital Region and his or her designated representatives can be contacted at telephone number 410–576–2693 or on Marine Band Radio, VHF-FM channel 16 (156.8 MHz). The Coast Guard vessels enforcing this section can be contacted on Marine Band Radio, VHF-FM channel 16 (156.8 MHz). Upon being hailed by a U.S. Coast Guard vessel, or other Federal, State, or local agency vessel, by siren, radio, flashing light, or other means, the operator of a vessel shall proceed as directed. If permission is granted, all persons and vessels must comply with the instructions of the Captain of the Port Maryland-National Capital Region or his designated representative and proceed at the minimum speed necessary to maintain a safe course while within the zone.

(2638)    (3) The U.S. Coast Guard may be assisted in the patrol and enforcement of the security zones listed in paragraph (a) in this section by Federal, State, and local agencies.

(2639)    (c) *Definitions*. As used in this section:

(2640)    *Captain of the Port Maryland-National Capital Region* means the Commander, U.S. Coast Guard Sector Maryland-National Capital Region or any Coast Guard commissioned, warrant or petty officer who has been authorized by the Captain of the Port to act on his or her behalf.

(2641)    *Designated representative* means any Coast Guard commissioned, warrant, or petty officer who has been authorized by the Captain of the Port Maryland-National Capital Region to assist in enforcing the security zones described in paragraph (a) of this section.

(2642)    *Public vessel* means a vessel that is owned or demise-(bareboat) chartered by the government of the United States, by a State or local government, or by the government of a foreign country and that is not engaged in commercial service.

(2643)    (d) *Enforcement*. (1) In addition to the specified times in paragraphs (d)(2) through (4) of this section, the security zones created by this section will be enforced only upon issuance of a notice of enforcement by the Captain of the Port Maryland-National Capital Region. The Captain of the Port Maryland-National Capital Region will cause notice of enforcement of these security zones to be made by all appropriate means to the affected segments of the public of the enforcement dates and times of the security zones including publication in the **Federal Register**, in accordance with 33 CFR 165.7(a). Such means of notification may also include, but are not limited to Broadcast Notice to Mariners or Local Notice to Mariners.

(2644)    (2) Security Zone 4, established in paragraph (a)(4) of this section, will be enforced annually, from 12:01 a.m. to 11:59 p.m. on July 4.

(2645)    (3) Security Zone 5, established in paragraph (a)(5) of this section, will be enforced annually on three dates: Memorial Day (observed), September 11, and November 11. Security Zone 5 will be enforced from 10 a.m. until 1 p.m. on Memorial Day (observed); from 8 a.m. until 11:59 a.m. on September 11; and from 10 a.m. until 1 p.m. on November 11.

(2646)    (4) Security Zone 6, established in paragraph (a)(6) of this section, will be enforced annually on the day the State of the Union Address is delivered. Security Zone 6 will be enforced from 9 a.m. on the day of the State of the Union Address until 2 a.m. on the following day.

(2647)    (e) *Suspension of enforcement*. (1) The Captain of the Port Maryland-National Capital Region may suspend enforcement of the enforcement period in paragraphs (d)(1) through (4) in this section earlier than listed in the notice of enforcement. Should the Captain of the Port Maryland-National Capital Region suspend the zone earlier than the duration listed, he or she will make the public aware of this suspension by Broadcast Notice to Mariners and/or onscene notice by his or her designated representative.

(2648)

### §165.510 Delaware Bay and River, Salem River, Christina River and Schuylkill River–Regulated Navigation Area.

(2649)    (a) *Regulated Navigation Area*. The following is a Regulated Navigation Area: The navigable waters of Delaware Bay and River, Salem River, Christina River, and Schuylkill River, in an area bounded on the south by a line drawn across the entrance to the Delaware Bay between Cape May Light and Harbor of Refuge Light and then continuing to the northernmost extremity of Cape Henlopen, and bounded on the north by a line drawn across the Delaware River between Trenton, NJ and Morinville, PA along the southern side of the U.S. Route 1 Bridge.

(2650)    (b) *Definitions*. As used in this section:

(2651)    *COTP* means the Captain of the Port, Delaware Bay and any Coast Guard commissioned, warrant or petty officer who has been authorized by the COTP to act on his or her behalf.

(2652)    *Dangerous Cargo* means those cargoes listed in §160.202 of this chapter when carried in bulk, but does not include cargoes listed in table 1 of 46 CFR part 153.

(2653)    *Underway* means that a vessel is not at anchor, made fast to the shore, or aground.

(2654)    (c) *Applicability*. This section applies to any vessel operating within the Regulated Navigation Area, including a naval or public vessel, except a vessel engaged in:

(2655)    (1) Law enforcement;

(2656)    (2) Servicing aids to navigation; or

(2657)    (3) Surveying, maintaining, or improving waters within the Regulated Navigation Area.

(2658)    (d) *Draft limitation*. Unless otherwise authorized by the COTP, no vessel with a draft greater than 55 feet may enter this regulated navigation area.

(2659)    **Note:** The project depth in many areas of the Regulated Navigation Area is less than 55 feet.

(2660)    (e) *Oil transfer operations.* Unless otherwise authorized by the COTP, no vessel to vessel oil transfer operations, excluding bunkering, may be conducted within the area between the southern boundary of this regulated navigation area and the southern span of the Delaware Memorial Bridge except within the anchorage ground designated in §110.157(a)(1) of this chapter.

(2661)    (f) *Requirements for vessels carrying dangerous cargoes.* The master, owner, or operator of a vessel carrying a dangerous cargo shall:

(2662)    (1) Notify the COTP at least 72 hours before the vessel enters or departs the regulated navigation area and at least 12 hours before the vessel moves within the regulated navigation area. The notice must include a report of the vessel's propulsion and machinery status and, for foreign flag vessels, the notice must include any outstanding deficiencies identified by the vessel's flag state or classification society;

(2663)    (2) Not enter, get or remain underway within the regulated navigation area if visibility is or is expected to be less than two (2) miles. If during the transit visibility becomes less than two (2) miles, the vessel must seek safe anchorage and notify the COTP immediately;

(2664)    (3) Not anchor in any area within the regulated navigation area unless in times of emergency or with COTP permission;

(2665)    (4) Not transfer dangerous cargo while the vessel is at anchor or bunkering;

(2666)    (5) Maintain a manned watch in the steering compartment whenever the vessel is underway within the regulated navigation area unless the vessel has two separate and independent steering control systems with duplicate pilothouse steering gear control systems which meet the requirements of 46 CFR 58.25-70.

(2667)    (6) When anchored within the regulated navigation area and:

(2668)    (i) Sustained winds are greater than 25 knots but less than 40 knots, ensure the main engines are ready to provide full power in five minutes or less; and

(2669)    (ii) Sustained winds are 40 knots or over, ensure that the main engines are on line to immediately provide propulsion;

(2670)    (7) While moored within the regulated navigation area, ensure that at least two wire cable mooring lines (firewarps) are rigged and ready for use as emergency towing hookups fore and aft on the outboard side of the vessel;

(2671)    (8) While underway or anchored within the regulated navigation area, ensure that at least two wire cable mooring lines (firewarps) are rigged and ready for use as emergency towing hookups fore and aft on the vessel; and,

(2672)    (9) Proceed as directed by the COTP.

(2673)    (g) *Requirements for vessels operating in the vicinity of a vessel carrying dangerous cargoes.* (1) Except for a vessel that is attending a vessel carrying dangerous cargo with permission from the master of the vessel carrying dangerous cargo or a vessel that is anchored or moored at a marina, wharf, or pier, and which remains moored or at anchor, no vessel may, without the permission of the COTP:

(2674)    (i) Come or remain within 500 yards of the port or starboard side or within 1,000 yards of the bow or stern of an underway vessel that is carrying dangerous cargo; or

(2675)    (ii) Come or remain within 100 yards of a moored or anchored vessel carrying dangerous cargo.

(2676)    (2) The master, owner, or operator of any vessel receiving permission under paragraph (g)(1) of this section shall;

(2677)    (i) Maintain a continuous radio guard on VHF–FM channels 13 and 16;

(2678)    (ii) Operate at "no wake" speed or the minimum speed needed to maintain steerage; and

(2679)    (iii) Proceed as directed by the COTP.

(2680)    (3) No vessel may overtake a vessel carrying dangerous cargoes unless the overtaking can be completed before reaching any bend in the channel. Before any overtaking, the pilots, masters or operators of both the overtaking vessel and the vessel being overtaken must clearly agree on the circumstances of the overtaking, including vessel speeds, time and location of overtaking.

(2681)    (h) *Additional restrictions above the C&D Canal.* When operating on the Delaware River above the C&D Canal:

(2682)    (1) A vessel carrying dangerous cargo must be escorted by at least one commercial tug; and

(2683)    (2) Meeting situations shall be avoided on river bends to the maximum extent possible.

(2684)    (i) The COTP will issue a Broadcast Notice to Mariners to inform the marine community of scheduled vessel movements during which the restrictions imposed by paragraphs (g) and (h) of this section will be in effect.

(2685)

### §165.511 Security Zone; Atlantic Ocean, Chesapeake & Delaware Canal, Delaware Bay, Delaware River and its tributaries.

(2686)    (a) *Location.* A 500-yard radius around escorted passenger vessels in the Captain of the Port, Delaware Bay zone as defined in 33 CFR 3.25-05.

(2687)    (b) *Regulations.* (1) All persons are required to comply with the general regulations governing security zones in §165.33 of this part.

(2688)    (2) All persons or vessels operating at the minimum safe speed necessary to maintain navigation may transit within 500 yards of an escorted passenger vessel without the permission of the Captain of the Port Delaware Bay, PA or designated representative while the escorted passenger vessel is in the Captain of the Port Delaware Bay zone.

(2689)    (3) No person or vessel may transit or remain within 100 yards of an escorted passenger vessel without the permission of the Captain of the Port Delaware Bay or designated representative while the passenger vessel is in the Captain of the Port Philadelphia zone.

(2690) (4) Any person or vessel authorized to enter the security zone must operate in strict conformance with any directions given by the Captain of the Port Delaware Bay or designated representative and leave the security zone immediately if the Captain of the Port Delaware Bay or designated representative so orders.

(2691) (5) When an escorted passenger vessel approaches within 100 yards of any vessel that is moored or anchored, the stationary vessel must stay moored or anchored while it remains within 100 yards of the passenger vessel unless it is either ordered by or given permission by the Captain of the Port, Delaware Bay or designated representative to do otherwise.

(2692) (6) The Coast Guard designated representative enforcing this section can be contacted on VHF Marine Band Radio, channels 13 and 16. The Captain of the Port can be contacted at 215–271–4807.

(2693) (c) *Maneuver-restricted vessels.* When conditions permit, the Captain of the Port or designated representative should:

(2694) (1) Permit vessels constrained by their navigational draft or restricted in their ability to maneuver to pass within the 100 yards of the passenger vessel in order to ensure safe passage in accordance with the Navigation Rules(COLREGS and their associated Annexes and Inland Navigation Rules (33 CFR subchapter E)); and

(2695) (2) Permit vessels constrained by their navigational draft or restricted in their ability to maneuver that must transit via a navigable channel or waterway to pass within 100 yards of an anchored passenger vessel.

(2696) (d) *Definitions.* As used in this section–

(2697) *Captain of the Port* means the Commanding Officer of the Coast Guard Sector Delaware Bay or any Coast Guard commissioned, warrant, or petty officer who has been authorized by the Captain of the Port to act as a designated representative on his behalf.

(2698) *Escort* means assets (surface or air) with the Coast Guard insignia that accompany and protect the escorted vessel, armed with crew-served weapons that are manned and ready.

(2699) *Passenger Vessels* means vessels greater than 100 feet in length, over 100 gross tons that are authorized to carry 500 or more passengers, making voyages lasting more than 24 hours, except for ferries.

(2700) **§165.516 Safety Zones; Waterway Training Areas, Captain of the Port Maryland-National Capital Region Zone.**

(2701) (a) *Regulated areas.* The following areas are established as safety zones (these coordinates are based on Datum NAD 83):

(2702) (1) *Waterway training area Alpha.* All waters of the Patapsco River, encompassed by a line connecting the following points beginning at 39°14′07.98″N., 076°32′58.50″W.; thence to 39°13′34.98″N.,

076°32′24.00″W.; thence to 39°13′22.50″N., 076°32′28.98″W.; thence to 39°13′21.00″N., 076°33′12.00″W.; and back to the beginning point.

(2703) (2) *Waterway training area Bravo.* All waters of the Chesapeake Bay, encompassed by a line connecting the following points beginning at 39°05′25.98″N., 076°20′20.04″W.; thence to 39°04′40.02″N, 076°19′28.98″W.; thence to 39°02′45.00″N., 076°22′09.00″W.; thence to 39°03′30.00″N., 076°23′00.00″W.; and back to the beginning point.

(2704) (3) *Waterway training area Charlie.* All waters of the Potomac River, encompassed by a line connecting the following points beginning at 38°00′28.80″N., 076°22′43.80″W,; thence to 38°01′18.00″N., 076°21′54.00″W.; thence to 38°05′06.00″N., 076°27′43.20″W.; thence to 38°04′40.20″N., 076°28′34.20″W.; and back to the beginning point.

(2705) (4) *Waterway training area Delta.* All waters of the Potomac River, encompassed by a line connecting the following points beginning at 38°32′31.14″N., 077°15′29.82″W.; thence to 38°32′48.18″N., 077°15′54.24″W.; thence to 38°33′34.56″N., 077°15′07.20″W.; thence to 38°33′15.06″N., 077°14′39.54″W.; and back to the beginning point.

(2706) (b) *Definitions.* As used in this section—

(2707) *Captain of the Port (COTP)* means the Commander, U.S. Coast Guard Sector Maryland-National Capital Region.Designated representative means a Coast Guard commissioned, warrant, or petty officer designated by or assisting the COTP in the enforcement of the safety zones.

(2708) *Training participant* means a person or vessel authorized by the COTP as participating in the training event or otherwise designated by the COTP or the COTP's designated representative as having a function tied to the training event.

(2709) (c) *Regulations.* (1) Under the general safety zone regulations in subpart C of this part, you may not enter the safety zones described in paragraph (a) of this section unless authorized by the COTP or the COTP's designated representative.

(2710) (2) Except for training participants, all vessels underway within this safety zone at the time it is activated are to depart the zone. To seek permission to enter, contact the COTP or the COTP's designated representative by telephone number 410–576–2693 or on Marine Band Radio VHF–FM channel 16 (156.8 MHz). The Coast Guard vessels enforcing this section can be contacted on Marine Band Radio VHF–FM channel 16 (156.8 MHz). Those in the safety zone must comply with all lawful orders or directions given to them by the COTP or the COTP's designated representative.

(2711) (3) The U.S. Coast Guard may be assisted in the patrol and enforcement of the safety zone by Federal, State, and local agencies.

(2712) (d) *Enforcement.* The safety zones created by this section will be enforced only upon issuance of a Broadcast Notice to Mariners (BNM) by the COTP or the COTP's representative, as well as on-scene notice or other appropriate means in accordance with **§165.7.**

(2713)

## §165.518 Security Zone; Waters of the Fifth Coast Guard District.

(2714)    (a) *Definitions.* As used in this section–

(2715)    *Designated Representative* means any U.S. Coast Guard commissioned, warrant or petty officer who has been authorized by the District Commander or local Captain of the Port (COTP), as defined in 33 CFR part 3, subpart 3.25, to act on his or her behalf.

(2716)    *Escorted vessel* means a vessel, other than a U.S. naval vessel as defined in §165.2015, that is accompanied by one or more Coast Guard assets or Federal, State or local law enforcement agency assets as listed below:

(2717)    (1) Coast Guard surface or air asset displaying the Coast Guard insignia.

(2718)    (2) Coast Guard Auxiliary surface asset displaying the Coast Guard Auxiliary insignia.

(2719)    (3) State and/or local law enforcement asset displaying the applicable agency markings and or equipment associated with the agency.

(2720)    *State and/or local law enforcement officers* means any State or local government law enforcement officer who has authority to enforce State criminal laws.

(2721)    (b) *Location.* The following area is a security zone: 500-yard radius around escorted vessels in the navigable waters of the Fifth Coast Guard District as defined in 33 CFR 3.25–1, from surface to bottom.

(2722)    (c) *Regulations.* (1) No vessel may approach within 500 yards of an escorted vessel within the navigable waters of the Fifth Coast Guard District, unless traveling at the minimum speed necessary to navigate safely.

(2723)    (2) No vessel may enter within a 100-yard radius of an escorted vessel within the navigable waters of the Fifth Coast Guard District, without approval from the District Commander, Captain of the Port or their designated representatives.

(2724)    (3) Moored or anchored vessels, which are overtaken by a moving zone, must remain stationary at their location until the escorted vessel maneuvers at least 500 yards past.

(2725)    (4) Vessels restricted in their ability to maneuver may request permission of the District Commander, Captain of the Port or designated representative to enter the security zone in order or ensure safe passage in accordance with the Navigation Rules (COLREGS and their associated Annexes and Inland Navigation Rules (33 CFR subchapter E)).

(2726)    (5) The local COTP may notify the maritime and general public by marine information broadcast of the periods during which individual security zones have been activated by providing notice in accordance with 33 CFR 165.7.

(2727)    (6) When moored, a security zone around an escorted vessel may also be enforced by Coast Guard, State or Local law enforcement personnel shoreside.

(2728)    (7) Persons desiring to transit within 100 yards of an escorted vessel in the Fifth Coast Guard District must contact the local Captain of the Port on VHF channel 16 (156.800 MHz), VHF channel 13 (156.650 MHz) or at telephone numbers:

(2729)    Philadelphia: 215–271–4807

(2730)    Maryland-National Capital Region: 410–576–2693

(2731)    Virginia: 757–668–5555 or 757–484–8192

(2732)    North Carolina: 910–772–2200 or 910–254–1500

(2733)    (8) If permission is granted to transit within 100 yards of an escorted vessel, all persons and vessels must comply with the instructions of the District Commander, Captain of the Port or their designated representative.

(2734)

## §165.552 Security Zone; Oyster Creek Generation Station, Forked River, Ocean County, New Jersey.

(2735)    (a) *Location.* The following area is a security zone: Starting at the south branch of the Forked River in the vicinity of the Oyster Creek Generation Station, bounded by a line beginning at

(2736)    39°49'12.0"N., 074°12'13.0"W.; thence to

(2737)    39°48'39.7"N., 074°12'0"W.; along the shoreline, thence to

(2738)    39°48'40.0"N., 074°12'0.3"W.; thence to

(2739)    39°49'11.8"N., 074°12'10.5"W.; thence back along the shoreline to the beginning point. All coordinates reference Datum: NAD 1983.

(2740)    (b) *Regulations.* (1) All persons are required to comply with the general regulations governing security zones in §165.33 of this part.

(2741)    (2) No person or vessel may enter or navigate within this security zone unless authorized to do so by the Coast Guard or designated representative. Any person or vessel authorized to enter the security zones must operate in strict conformance with any directions given by the Coast Guard or designated representative and leave the security zone immediately if the Coast Guard or designated representative so orders.

(2742)    (3) The Coast Guard or designated representative enforcing this section can be contacted on VHF Marine Band Radio, channels 13 and 16. The Captain of the Port can be contacted at 215–271–4807.

(2743)    (4) The Captain of the Port will notify the public of any changes in the status of this security zone by Marine Safety Radio Broadcast on VHF–FM marine band radio, channel 22 (157.1 MHz).

(2744)    (c) *Definitions.* For the purposes of this section, Captain of the Port means the Commanding Officer of the Coast Guard sector Delaware Bay or any Coast Guard commissioned, warrant, or petty officer who has been authorized by the Captain of the Port to act as a designated representative on his behalf.

(2745)

## §165.553 Security Zone; Salem and Hope Creek

**Generation Stations, Delaware River, Salem County, New Jersey.**

(2746)   (a) *Location.* The following area is a security zone: the waters of the Delaware River in the vicinity of the Salem and Hope Creek Generation Stations bounded by a line drawn from a point located at

(2747)   39°28'08.0"N., 075°32'31.7"W. to

(2748)   39°28'06.5"N., 075°32'47.4"W., thence to

(2749)   39°27'28.4"N., 075°32'15.8"W., thence to

(2750)   39°27'28.8"N., 075°31'56.6"W., thence to

(2751)   39°27'39.9"N., 075°31.51.6"W., thence along the shoreline to the point of

(2752)   39°28'08.0"N., 075°32'31.7"W. All coordinates reference Datum: NAD 1983.

(2753)   (b) *Regulations.* (1) All persons are required to comply with the general regulations governing security zones in §165.33 of this part.

(2754)   (2) No person or vessel may enter or navigate within this security zone unless authorized to do so by the Coast Guard or designated representative. Any person or vessel authorized to enter the security zones must operate in strict conformance with any directions given by the Coast Guard or designated representative and leave the security zone immediately if the Coast Guard or designated representative so orders.

(2755)   (3) The Coast Guard or designated representative enforcing this section can be contacted on VHF Marine Band Radio, channels 13 and 16. The Captain of the Port can be contacted at 215–271–4807.

(2756)   (4) The Captain of the Port will notify the public of any changes in the status of this security zone by Marine Safety Radio Broadcast on VHF–FM marine band radio, channel 22 (157.1 MHz).

(2757)   (c) *Definitions.* For the purposes of this section, Captain of the Port means the Commanding Officer of the Coast Guard Sector Delaware Bay, or any Coast Guard commissioned, warrant, or petty officer who has been authorized by the Captain of the Port to act as a designated representative on his behalf.

(2758)   **§165.555 Safety Zone; Delaware River.**

(2759)   (a) *Definition.* As used in this section, Captain of the Port means the Commander of Sector Delaware Bay or any Coast Guard commissioned, warrant or petty officer who has been authorized by the Captain of the Port to act on his behalf. The Captain of the Port may be contacted by telephone at 215–271–4807 or via VHF marine band radio, channel 16.

(2760)   (b) *Location.* The following area is a safety zone: All waters located within a 150-yard radius around the dredging operation and barge, conducting dredging operations in or near the Marcus Hook Range in the vicinity of Anchorage 7.

(2761)   (c) *Enforcement.* This safety zone will be enforced annually beginning on September 1 through December 31.

(2762)   (d) *Regulations.*

(2763)   (1) All persons are required to comply with the general regulations governing safety zones in 33 CFR 165.23 of this part.

(2764)   (2) All Coast Guard vessels enforcing this safety zone or watch officers aboard the Dredge and Barge can be contacted on VHF marine band radio, channel 16. The Captain of the Port may be contacted by telephone at 215–271–4807 or via VHF marine band radio, channel 16.

(2765)

**§165.556 Regulated Navigation Area; Chesapeake and Delaware Canal, Chesapeake City Anchorage Basin, MD.**

(2766)   (a) *Location.* The following area is a regulated navigation area: All waters of the Chesapeake and Delaware (C&D) Canal within the anchorage basin at Chesapeake City, Maryland, bounded by a line drawn across the entrance to the basin from position

(2767)   39°31'39.6"N., 075°48'36.5"W., to position

(2768)   39°31'40.6"N., 075°48'43.3"W. All coordinates refer to NAD 1983.

(2769)   (b) *Definitions.* For the purposes of this section:

(2770)   *District Commander* means the Commander, Fifth Coast Guard District or any Coast Guard commissioned, warrant, or petty officer who has been authorized by the Commander, Fifth Coast Guard District, to act on his or her behalf, or his or her designated representative.

(2771)   (c) *Regulations.* The general regulations governing regulated navigation areas, found in 33 CFR 165.13, apply to the regulated navigation area described in paragraph (a) of this section.

(2772)   (1) All vessels and persons are prohibited from entering and accessing this regulated navigation area, except as authorized by the District Commander or his or her designated representative.

(2773)   (2) Persons or vessels requiring entry into or passage within the regulated navigation area must request authorization from the District Commander or his or her designated representative, by telephone at 410–576–2693 or by marine band radio on VHF–FM channel 16 (156.8 MHz), from 12:01 a.m. until 11:59 p.m. on the last Saturday in June, annually. All Coast Guard vessels enforcing this regulated navigation area can be contacted on marine band radio VHF–FM channel 16 (156.8 MHz).

(2774)   (3) The operator of any vessel entering or located within this navigation area shall:

(2775)   (i) Travel at no-wake speed,

(2776)   (ii) Stop the vessel immediately upon being directed to do so by any commissioned, warrant or petty officer on board a vessel displaying a Coast Guard Ensign, and

(2777)   (iii) Proceed as directed by any commissioned, warrant or petty officer on board a vessel displaying a Coast Guard Ensign.

(2778)   (4) All vessels and persons within this regulated navigation area must comply with any additional instructions of the District Commander or the designated representative.

(2779)      (d) *Enforcement.* The U.S. Coast Guard may be assisted in the patrol and enforcement of the regulated navigation area by any Federal, State, and local agencies.

(2780)      (e) *Enforcement period.* This section will be enforced from 12:01 a.m. until 11:59 p.m. on the last Saturday in June, annually.

(2781)

### § 165.557 Security Zone; Potomac River, Montgomery County, MD.

(2782)      (a) *Definitions.* As used in this section:

(2783)      *Captain of the Port (COTP)* means the Commander, U.S. Coast Guard Sector Maryland-National Capital Region or any Coast Guard commissioned, warrant or petty officer who has been authorized by the Captain of the Port to act on his or her behalf.

(2784)      *Designated representative* means a Coast Guard commissioned, warrant, or petty officer who has been authorized by the Captain of the Port to enforce the security zone described in paragraph (b)(1) of this section.

(2785)      *Public vessel* has the same meaning as that term is defined under **46 U.S.C. 2101.**

(2786)      (b) *Location.* Coordinates used in this section are based on datum NAD 83.

(2787)      (1) *Security zone.* The following area is a security zone: All navigable waters of the Potomac River, from shoreline to shoreline, within an area bounded on the west by a line connecting the following points: 39°03′44.7″N., 077°21′47″W., thence north to 39°04′03″ N., 077°21′47″W., and bounded on the east by a line connecting the following points: 39°04′04″N., 077°19′58″W., thence south to 39°03′41.35″N., 077°20′05.30″W.

(2788)      (2) *Transit lane.* All waters within the Potomac River, contiguous with the Maryland shoreline and extending out into the Potomac River approximately 250 yards, within an area bounded by a line connecting the following points: Beginning at the Maryland shoreline at 39°04′03″N., 077°21′47″ W., thence south to 39°03′55.3″ N., 077°21′47″ W., thence east to 39°03′56.8″ N., 077°20′00.3″ W., thence north to the Maryland shoreline at 39°04′04″ N., 077°19′58″ W., thence back along the shoreline to the originating point.

(2789)      (c) *Regulations.* The general security zone regulations found in **§ 165.33** apply to the security zone created by this section.

(2790)      (1) Except for public vessels, entry into or remaining in the security zone described in paragraph (b)(1) of this section is prohibited unless authorized by the COTP or designated representative when the aforementioned security zone is being enforced. At the start of each enforcement, all persons and vessels within the security zone must depart the zone immediately or obtain authorization from the COTP or designated representative to remain within the zone. All vessels authorized to remain in the zone shall proceed as directed by the COTP or designated representative.

(2791)      (2) Persons and vessel operators who intend to enter or transit the security zone while the zone is being enforced must obtain authorization from the VerDate Sep<11>2014 16:02 May 15, 2020 Jkt 250001 PO 00000 Frm 00028 Fmt 4700 Sfmt 4700 E:\FR\FM\18MYR1. SGM 18MYR1 jbell on DSKJLSW7X2PROD with RULES Federal Register / Vol. 85, No. 96 / Monday, May 18, 2020 / Rules and Regulations 29621 COTP or designated representative. Access to the zone will be determined by the COTP or designated representative on a case-by-case basis when the zone is enforced. Persons and vessel operators requesting permission to enter or transit the security zone may contact the COTP or designated representative at telephone number 410–576–2675, on marine band radio VHF–FM channel 16 (156.8 MHz), or by visually or verbally hailing the on-scene law enforcement vessel enforcing the zone. On-scene Coast Guard personnel enforcing this section can be contacted on marine band radio, VHF–FM channel 16 (156.8 MHz). The operator of a vessel shall proceed as directed upon being hailed by a U.S. Coast Guard vessel, or ther Federal, State, or local law enforcement agency vessel, by siren, radio, flashing light, or other means. When authorized by the COTP or designated representative to enter the security zone all persons and vessels must comply with the instructions of the COTP or designated representative and proceed at the minimum speed necessary to maintain a safe course while within the security zone.

(2792)      (3) The transit lane, described in paragraph (b)(2) of this section, is the only part of the security zone through which persons and vessels may travel. Before entering the transit lane, persons or vessels must have authorization as described in paragraph (c)(2) of this section. All persons and vessels shall operate at bare steerage or no-wake speed while transiting through the lane, and must not loiter, stop, or anchor, unless authorized or otherwise instructed by the COTP or a designated representative.

(2793)      (4) The U.S. Coast Guard may secure the entire security zone, including transit lane, if deemed necessary to address security threats or concerns.

(2794)      (5) The U.S. Coast Guard may be assisted by Federal, State, and local law enforcement agencies in the patrol and enforcement of the security zone described in paragraph (b)(1) of this section.

(2795)      (d) *Enforcement.* The Coast Guard activates the security zone when requested by the U.S. Secret Service for the protection of individuals who qualify for protection under 18 U.S.C 3056(a) or Presidential memorandum. The COTP will provide the public with notice of enforcement of security zone by Broadcast Notice to Mariners (BNM), information release at the website: www.news.uscg.mil/Baltimore/ and via a recorded message at telephone number (410) 576–2675 as well as on-scene notice by designated representative or other appropriate means in accordance with **§ 165.7.**

(2796)

## § 165.558 Security Zone; Delaware River, and Schuylkill River, Philadelphia, PA.

(2797)     (a) *Location.* The following area is a security zone: All waters of the Delaware River in the vicinity of Philadelphia International Airport, within an area bound to the west by a line drawn from the New Jersey shoreline at Thompson Point, latitude 39°50′37″N, longitude 75°18′23″W, thence northwest to the Pennsylvania shoreline at latitude 39°51′45″N, longitude 75°18′46″W; thence up river and bound shoreline to shoreline; bound to the east by a line drawn from the New Jersey shoreline at latitude 39°52′28″ N, longitude 75°11′14″W, and thence northwest to the Pennsylvania shoreline near the eastern side of mouth to the Schuylkill River at latitude 39°53′05″N, longitude 75°11′34″W; the security zone extends north into the waters of Schuylkill River, bound from shoreline to shoreline, including the waters of Schuylkill River adjacent to the Navy Yard Reserve Basin Bridge, and terminates along a line drawn from latitude 39°54′04″N, longitude 75°12′56″W, thence eastward across the Schuylkill River to latitude 39°54′07″N, longitude 75°12′48″W, located approximately 500 yards northwest and parallel with the George C. Platt Memorial—Penrose Avenue lift-bridge. These coordinates are based on North American Datum 83 (NAD83).

(2798)     (b) *Definitions.* As used in this section—

(2799)     *Designated representative* means any Coast Guard commissioned, warrant or petty officer who has been designated by the COTP to act on his or her behalf. The designated representative may be on an official patrol vessel or may be on shore and will communicate with vessels via VHF–FM radio or loudhailer. In addition, members of the Coast Guard Auxiliary may be present to inform vessel operators of this regulation.

(2800)     *Official patrol vessel* means any Coast Guard, Coast Guard Auxiliary, State, or local law enforcement vessel assigned or approved by the COTP.

(2801)     *Very important person (VIP)* means any person for whom the United States Secret Service requests implementation of a security zone in order to supplement protection of said person(s).

(2802)     (c) *Regulations.* (1) In accordance with the general regulations contained in §165.33, entry into or movement within this zone is prohibited unless authorized by the COTP, Sector Delaware Bay, or designated representative.

(2803)     (2) Only vessels or people specifically authorized by the Captain of the Port, Delaware Bay, or designated representative, may enter or remain in the regulated area. To request permission to enter or remain in the regulated area contact the COTP or the COTP's representative on VHF–FM channel 13 or 16. Vessel operators and persons within the security zone must comply with all lawful orders or directions given to them by the COTP or the COTP's designated representative. No person may swim upon or below the surface of the water of this security zone unless authorized by the COTP or his designated representative.

(2804)     (3) Upon being hailed by an official patrol vessel or the designated representative, by siren, radio, flashing light or other means, the operator of the vessel shall proceed as directed. Failure to comply with lawful direction may result in expulsion from the regulated area, citation for failure to comply, or both.

(2805)     (d) *Enforcement.* This security zone will be enforced with actual notice by the U.S. Coast Guard representatives on scene, as well as other methods listed in §165.7. The Coast Guard will enforce the security zone created by this section only when it is necessary for the protection of VIPs traveling to or from the Philadelphia International Airport. The U.S. Coast Guard may be additionally assisted in the patrol and enforcement of the zone by Federal, State, and local agencies.

(2806)

## § 165.560 Security Zone; Christina River, Newport, DE.

(2807)     (a) *Location.* The following area is a security zone: All waters of the Christina River, from shoreline to shoreline bounded on the east by a line drawn from 39°42.55′ North Latitude (N), 075°35.88′ West Longitude (W), thence southerly to 39°42.50′ N, 075°35.87′ W thence along the Christina River in a westerly direction and bounded by the South James Street Bridge at 39°42.63′ N, 075°36.53′ W. These coordinates are based on North American Datum 83 (NAD83).

(2808)     b) *Definitions.* As used in this section—Designated representative means a Coast Guard Patrol Commander, including a Coast Guard coxswain, petty officer, or other officer operating a Coast Guard vessel and a Federal, State, and local officer designated by or assisting the Captain of the Port Delaware Bay (COTP) in the enforcement of the security zone. Official patrol vessel means any Coast Guard, Coast Guard Auxiliary, State, or local law enforcement vessel assigned or approved by the COTP. USSS protectee means any person for whom the United States Secret Service (USSS) requests implementation of a security zone in order to supplement protection of said person(s).

(2809)     (c) *Regulations.* (1) In accordance with the general regulations contained in § 165.33, entry into or movement within this zone is prohibited unless authorized by the COTP, Delaware Bay, or designated representative.

(2810)     (2) Only vessels or people specifically authorized by the Captain of the Port, Delaware Bay, or designated representative, may enter or remain in the regulated area. To seek permission to enter, contact the COTP or the COTP's representative on VHF–FM channel 13 or 16. Those in the security zone must comply with all lawful orders or directions given to them by the COTP or the COTP's designated representative. No person may swim upon or below the surface of the water of this security zone unless authorized by the COTP or his designated representative.

(2811)     (3) Upon being hailed by an official patrol vessel or the designated representative, by siren, radio, flashing light or other means, the operator of the vessel shall proceed as directed. Failure to comply with lawful direction may result in expulsion from the regulated area, citation for failure to comply, or both.

(2812)     (d) *Enforcement.* This security zone will be enforced with actual notice by the U.S. Coast Guard representatives on scene, as well as other methods listed in § 165.7. The Coast Guard will enforce the security zone created by this section only when it is necessary for the protection of a USSS protectee traveling across the route 141 bridge in Newport, Delaware. The U.S. Coast Guard may be additionally assisted in the patrol and enforcement of the zone by Federal, State, and local agencies.

(2813)     **§ 165.561 Security Zones; Lewes and Rehoboth Canal and Atlantic Ocean, Rehoboth Beach, DE.**

(2814)     (a) *Location.* The following areas are security zones; these coordinates are based on North American Datum 83 (NAD83):

(2815)     (1) *Security zone one:* All waters of the Lewes and Rehoboth Canal bounded on the north by a line drawn from 38° 44.35′ North Latitude (N), 075°5.32′ West Longitude (W), thence easterly to 38°44.37′ N, 075°5.31′ W proceeding from shoreline to shoreline on the Lewes and Rehoboth Canal in a Southeasterly direction where it is bounded by a line drawn from 38°43.89′ N, 075°5.31′ W, thence easterly to 38°43.90′ N, 075°5.07′ W thence northerly across the entrance to the yacht basin to 38°43.93′ N, 075° 5.09′ W

(2816)     (2) *Security zone two*: All waters of the Atlantic Ocean extending 500 yards seaward from a line beginning at 38°44.86′ N, 075°4.86′ W, proceeding southerly along the shoreline to 38°43.97′ N, 075°4.70′ W.

(2817)     (b) *Definitions.* As used in this section—

(2818)     *Designated representative* means a Coast Guard Patrol Commander, including a Coast Guard coxswain, petty officer, or other officer operating a Coast Guard vessel and a Federal, State, and local officer designated by or assisting the Captain of the Port Delaware Bay (COTP) in the enforcement of the security zone.

(2819)     *USSS protectee* means any person for whom the United States Secret Service requests implementation of a security zone in order to supplement protection of said person(s).

(2820)     *Official patrol vessel* means any Coast Guard, Coast Guard Auxiliary, State, or local law enforcement vessel assigned or approved by the COTP.

(2821)     (c) *Regulations.* (1) In accordance with the general regulations contained in § 165.33 of this part, entry into or movement within this zone is prohibited unless authorized by the COTP, Sector Delaware Bay, or designated representative.

(2822)     (2) Entry into or remaining in a security zone described in paragraph (a) of this section is prohibited unless authorized by the COTP or designated representative when the security zones are being enforced. At the start of each enforcement, all persons and vessels within

the security zone must depart the zones immediately or obtain authorization from the COTP or designated representative to remain within either zone. All vessels authorized to remain in the zone(s) must proceed as directed by the COTP or designated representative.

(2823)     (3) A person or vessel operator who intends to enter or transit the security zones while the zones are being enforced must obtain authorization from the COTP or designated representative. While the zones are being enforced the COTP or designated representative will determine access to the zones on a case-by-case basis. A person or vessel operator requesting permission to enter or transit the security zone may contact the COTP or designated representative at 215–271–4807 or on marine band radio VHF–FM channel 16 (156.8 MHz), or by visually or verbally hailing the onscene law enforcement vessel enforcing the zone. On-scene Coast Guard personnel enforcing this section can be contacted on marine band radio, VHF– FM channel 16 (156.8 MHz). The operator of a vessel must proceed as directed upon being hailed by a U.S. Coast Guard vessel, or other Federal, State, or local law enforcement agency vessel, by siren, radio, flashing light, or other means. When authorized by the COTP or designated representative to enter the security zone all persons and vessels must comply with the instructions of the COTP or designated representative and proceed at the minimum speed necessary to maintain a safe course while within the security zone.

(2824)     (4) Upon being hailed by a U.S. Coast Guard vessel, or other Federal, State, or local law enforcement agency vessel, by siren, radio, flashing light or other means, a person or operator of a vessel must proceed as directed. Failure to comply with lawful direction may result in expulsion from the regulated area, citation for failure to comply, or both.

(2825)     (5) Unless specifically authorized by on-scene enforcement vessels, no vessel or person will be permitted to stop or anchor in the security zone. A vessel granted permission to enter or transit within the security zone(s) must do so without delay or pause for the entirety of its time within the boundaries of the security zone(s). At times, for limited duration, it is anticipated that vessels may be prohibited from entering the zone due to movement of persons protected by USSS. During those times, the Coast Guard will provide actual notice to vessels in the area.

(2826)     (6) The U.S. Coast Guard may secure the entirety of either or both security zones if deemed necessary to address security threats or concerns.

(2827)     (7) The U.S. Coast Guard may be assisted by Federal, State, and local law enforcement agencies in the patrol and enforcement of the security zone described in paragraph (a) of this section.

(2828)     (d) *Enforcement.* (1) The Coast Guard activates the security zones when requested by the U.S. Secret Service for the protection of individuals who qualify for protection under 18 U.S.C 3056(a) or Presidential memorandum. The COTP will provide the public with notice of enforcement of security zone by Broadcast Notice to Mariners (BNM), information release at the website: https://homeport.uscg.mil/myhomeport/coast-guard-prevention/ waterway-management?cotpid=40 as well as on-scene notice by designated VerDate Sep<11>2014 16:08 Aug 25, 2021 Jkt 253001 PO 00000 Frm 00039 Fmt 4700 Sfmt 4700 E:\FR\FM\26AUR1. SGM 26AUR1 jbell on DSKJLSW7X2PROD with RULES 47580 Federal Register / Vol. 86, No. 163 / Thursday, August 26, 2021 / Rules and Regulations 1 86 FR 30204. 2 86 FR 30234. representative or other appropriate means in accordance with 33 CFR 165.7

(2829)    (2) These security zones may be enforced individually or simultaneously.

(2830)
### §165.823 Allegheny River, Monongahela River, and Ohio River, Pittsburgh, Pennsylvania; Regulated Navigation Area.

(2831)    (a) *Location*. The following is a regulated navigation area (RNA): The waters of the Allegheny, Monongahela, and Ohio Rivers between the Ninth Street Highway Bridge at mile marker (MM) 0.8 on the Allegheny River, Fort Pitt Highway Bridge at MM 0.22 on the Monongahela River, and West End- North Side Highway Bridge at MM 0.8 on the Ohio River.

(2832)    (b) *Applicability*. This section applies to any vessel operating within the RNA, including a naval or public vessel, except a vessel engaged in:

(2833)    (1) Law enforcement;

(2834)    (2) Servicing aids to navigation; or

(2835)    (3) Surveying, maintaining, or improving waters within the RNA.

(2836)    (c) *Regulations*. (1) No vessel shall loiter, anchor, stop, moor, remain or drift at any time more than 100 feet from any river bank within the RNA without permission of the Captain of the Port (COTP), or any Coast Guard commissioned, warrant, or petty officer who has been designated by the COTP to act on his or her behalf.

(2837)    (2) No vessel shall loiter, anchor, stop, moor, remain or drift in any manner as to impede safe passage of another vessel to any launching ramp, marina, or fleeting area.

(2838)
## Subpart G–Protection of Naval Vessels

(2839)
### §165.2010 Purpose.

(2840)    This subpart establishes the geographic parameters of naval vessel protection zones surrounding U.S. naval vessels in the navigable waters of the United States. This subpart also establishes when the U.S. Navy will take enforcement action in accordance with the statutory guidelines of 14 U.S.C. 91. Nothing in the rules and regulations contained in this subpart shall relieve any vessel, including U.S. naval vessels, from the observance of the Navigation Rules. The rules and regulations contained in this subpart supplement, but do not replace

or supercede, any other regulation pertaining to the safety or security of U.S. naval vessels.

(2841)
### §165.2015 Definitions.

(2842)    The following definitions apply to this subpart:

(2843)    *Atlantic Area* means that area described in 33 CFR 3.04–1 Atlantic Area.

(2844)    *Large U.S. naval vessel* means any U.S. naval vessel greater than 100 feet in length overall.

(2845)    *Naval defensive sea area* means those areas described in 32 CFR part 761.

(2846)    Naval vessel protection zone is a 500-yard regulated area of water surrounding large U.S. naval vessels that is necessary to provide for the safety or security of these U.S. naval vessels.

(2847)    *Navigable waters of the United States* means those waters defined as such in 33 CFR part 2.

(2848)    *Navigation rules* means the Navigation Rules, International-Inland.

(2849)    *Official patrol* means those personnel designated and supervised by a senior naval officer present in command and tasked to monitor a naval vessel protection zone, permit entry into the zone, give legally enforceable orders to persons or vessels within the zone, and take other actions authorized by the U.S. Navy.

(2850)    *Pacific Area* means that area described in 33 CFR 3.04–3 Pacific Area.

(2851)    *Restricted area* means those areas established by the Army Corps of Engineers and set out in 33 CFR part 334.

(2852)    Senior naval officer present in command is, unless otherwise designated by competent authority, the senior line officer of the U.S. Navy on active duty, eligible for command at sea, who is present and in command of any part of the Department of Navy in the area.

(2853)    *U.S. naval vessel* means any vessel owned, operated, chartered, or leased by the U.S. Navy; any pre-commissioned vessel under construction for the U.S. Navy, once launched into the water; and any vessel under the operational control of the U.S. Navy or a Combatant Command.

(2854)    *Vessel* means every description of watercraft or other artificial contrivance used, or capable of being used, as a means of transportation on water, except U.S. Coast Guard or U.S. naval vessels.

(2855)
### §165.2020 Enforcement authority.

(2856)    (a) *Coast Guard*. Any Coast Guard commissioned, warrant or petty officer may enforce the rules and regulations contained in this subpart.

(2857)    (b) *Senior naval officer present in command*. In the navigable waters of the United States, when immediate action is required and representatives of the Coast Guard are not present or not present in sufficient force to exercise effective control in the vicinity of large U.S. naval vessels, the senior naval officer present in command is responsible for the enforcement of the rules and regulations contained in this subpart to ensure the safety and security of all large naval vessels present. In meeting this responsibility, the senior naval officer present in command may directly assist any Coast Guard enforcement personnel who are present.

(2858)
### §165.2025 Atlantic Area.

(2859)    (a) This section applies to any vessel or person in the navigable waters of the United States within the boundaries of the U.S. Coast Guard Atlantic Area, which includes the First, Fifth, Seventh, Eighth and Ninth U.S. Coast Guard Districts.

(2860)    **Note to §165.2025 paragraph (a):** The boundaries of the U.S. Coast Guard Atlantic Area and the First, Fifth, Seventh, Eighth and Ninth U.S. Coast Guard Districts are set out in 33 CFR part 3.

(2861)    (b) A naval vessel protection zone exists around U.S. naval vessels greater than 100 feet in length overall at all times in the navigable waters of the United States, whether the large U.S. naval vessel is underway, anchored, moored, or within a floating dry dock, except when the large naval vessel is moored or anchored within a restricted area or within a naval defensive sea area.

(2862)    (c) The Navigation Rules shall apply at all times within a naval vessel protection zone.

(2863)    (d) When within a naval vessel protection zone, all vessels shall operate at the minimum speed necessary to maintain a safe course, unless required to maintain speed by the Navigation Rules, and shall proceed as directed by the Coast Guard, the senior naval officer present in command, or the official patrol. When within a naval vessel protection zone, no vessel or person is allowed within 100 yards of a large U.S. naval vessel unless authorized by the Coast Guard, the senior naval officer present in command, or official patrol.

(2864)    (e) To request authorization to operate within 100 yards of a large U.S. naval vessel, contact the Coast Guard, the senior naval officer present in command, or the official patrol on VHF–FM channel 16.

(2865)    (f) When conditions permit, the Coast Guard, senior naval officer present in command, or the official patrol should:

(2866)    (1) Give advance notice on VHF-FM channel 16 of all large U.S. naval vessel movements; and

(2867)    (2) Permit vessels constrained by their navigational draft or restricted in their ability to maneuver to pass within 100 yards of a large U.S. naval vessel in order to ensure a safe passage in accordance with the Navigation Rules; and

(2868)    (3) Permit commercial vessels anchored in a designated anchorage area to remain at anchor when within 100 yards of passing large U.S. naval vessels; and

(2869)    (4) Permit vessels that must transit via a navigable channel or waterway to pass within 100 yards of a moored or anchored large U.S. naval vessel with minimal delay consistent with security.

(2870)    **Note to §165.2025 paragraph (f):** The listed actions are discretionary and do not create any additional right

to appeal or otherwise dispute a decision of the Coast Guard, the senior naval officer present in command, or the official patrol.

(2871)
## Part 166–ShippingSafety Fairways

(2872)
## Subpart A–General

(2873)
### §166.100 Purpose.

(2874)    The purpose of these regulations is to establish and designate shipping safety fairways and fairway anchorages to provide unobstructed approaches for vessels using U.S. ports.

(2875)
### §166.103 Geographic coordinates.

(2876)    Geographic coordinates expressed in terms of latitude or longitude, or both, are not intended for plotting on maps or charts whose referenced horizontal datum is the North American Datum of 1983 (NAD 83), unless such geographic coordinates are expressly labeled NAD 83. Geographic coordinates without the NAD 83 reference may be plotted on maps or charts referenced to NAD 83 only after application of the appropriate corrections that are published on the particular map or chart being used.

(2877)
### §166.105 Definitions.

(2878)    (a) Shipping safety fairway or fairway means a lane or corridor in which no artificial island or fixed structure, whether temporary or permanent, will be permitted. Temporary underwater obstacles may be permitted under certain conditions described for specific areas in Subpart B. Aids to navigation approved by the U.S. Coast Guard may be established in a fairway.

(2879)    (b) Fairway anchorage means an anchorage area contiguous to and associated with a fairway, in which fixed structures may be permitted within certain spacing limitations, as described for specific areas in Subpart B.

(2880)
### §166.110 Modification of areas.

(2881)    Fairways and fairway anchorages are subject to modification in accordance with 46 U.S.C. 70003.

(2882)
## Subpart B–Designation of Fairways and Fairway Anchorages (in part)

(2883)
### §166.500 Areas along the Atlantic Coast.

(2884)    (a) *Purpose.* Fairways, as described in this section are established to control the erection of structures therein to provide safe vessel routes along the Atlantic Coast.

(2885)    (b) *Designated areas.–*

(2886)    (1) *Off New York Shipping Safety Fairway.*

(2887)    (i) *Ambrose to Nantucket Safety Fairway.* The area enclosed by rhumb lines, (North American Datum of 1927 (NAD–27)), joining points at:
(2888)    40°32'20"N., 73°04'57"W.
(2889)    40°30'58"N., 72°58'25"W.
(2890)    40°34'07"N., 70°19'23"W.
(2891)    40°35'37"N., 70°14'09"W.
(2892)    40°30'37"N., 70°14'00"W.
(2893)    40°32'07"N., 70°19'19"W.
(2894)    40°28'58"N., 72°58'25"W.
(2895)    40°27'20"N., 73°04'57"W.
(2896)    (ii) *Nantucket to Ambrose Safety Fairway.* The area enclosed by rhumb lines, NAD–27, joining points at:
(2897)    40°24'20"N., 73°04'58"W.
(2898)    40°22'58"N., 72°58'26"W.
(2899)    40°26'07"N., 70°19'09"W.
(2900)    40°27'37"N., 70°13'46"W.
(2901)    40°22'37"N., 70°13'36"W.
(2902)    40°24'07"N., 70°19'05"W.
(2903)    40°20'58"N., 72°58'26"W.
(2904)    40°19'20"N., 73°04'58"W.

(2905)
## Part 167–Offshore Traffic Separation Schemes

(2906)
## Subpart A–General

(2907)
### §167.1 Purpose.
(2908)    The purpose of the regulations in this part is to establish and designate traffic separation schemes and precautionary areas to provide access routes for vessels proceeding to and from U.S. ports.

(2909)
### §167.3 Geographic coordinates.
(2910)    Geographic coordinates are defined using North American 1927 Datum (NAD 27) unless indicated otherwise.

(2911)
### §167.5 Definitions.
(2912)    (a) *Area to be avoided* means a routing measure comprising an area within defined limits in which either navigation is particularly hazardous or it is exceptionally important to avoid casualties and which should be avoided by all ships or certain classes of ships.
(2913)    (b) *Traffic separation scheme (TSS)* means a designated routing measure which is aimed at the separation of opposing streams of traffic by appropriate means and by the establishment of traffic lanes.
(2914)    (c) *Traffic lane* means an area within defined limits in which one-way traffic is established. Natural obstacles, including those forming separation zones, may constitute a boundary.
(2915)    (d) *Separation zone or line* means a zone or line separating the traffic lanes in which ships are proceeding in opposite or nearly opposite directions; or separating a traffic lane from the adjacent sea area; or separating traffic lanes designated for particular classes of ships proceeding in the same direction.
(2916)    (e) *Precautionary area* means a routing measure comprising an area within defined limits where ships must navigate with particular caution and within which the direction of traffic flow may be recommended.
(2917)    (f) *Deep-water route* means an internationally recognized routing measure primarily intended for use by ships that, because of their draft in relation to the available depth of water in the area concerned, require the use of such a route.
(2918)    (g) *Two-way route* means a route within defined limits inside which two-way traffic is established, aimed at providing safe passage of ships through waters where navigation is difficult or dangerous.

(2919)
### §167.10 Operating rules.
(2920)    The operator of a vessel in a TSS shall comply with Rule 10 of the International Regulations for Preventing Collisions at Sea, 1972, as amended.

(2921)
### §167.15 Modification of schemes.
(2922)    (a) A traffic separation scheme or precautionary area described in this part may be permanently amended in accordance with 46 U.S.C. 70003, and with international agreements.
(2923)    (b) A traffic separation scheme or precautionary area in this part may be temporarily adjusted by the Commandant of the Coast Guard in an emergency, or to accommodate operations which would create an undue hazard for vessels using the scheme or which would contravene Rule 10 of the International Regulations for Preventing Collisions at Sea, 1972. Adjustment may be in the form of a temporary traffic lane shift, a temporary suspension of a section of the scheme, a temporary precautionary area overlaying a lane, or other appropriate measure. Adjustments will only be made where, in the judgment of the Coast Guard, there is no reasonable alternative means of conducting an operation and navigation safety will not be jeopardized by the adjustment. Notice of adjustments will be made in the appropriate Notice to Mariners and in the Federal Register. Requests by members of the public for temporary adjustments to traffic separation schemes must be submitted 150 days prior to the time the adjustment is desired. Such Requests, describing the interference that would otherwise occur to a TSS, should be submitted to the District Commander of the Coast Guard District in which the TSS is located.

(2924)

## Subpart B–Description of Traffic Separation Schemes and Precautionary Areas.

(2925)

### Atlantic East Coast

(2926)

### §167.150 Off New York Traffic Separation Scheme: General.

(2927)     The specific areas in the Off New York Traffic Separation Scheme and Precautionary Areas are described in §§167.151, 167.152, 167.153, 167.154, and 167.155 of this chapter.

(2928)

### §167.151 Off New York: Precautionary areas.

(2929)     (a) A circular precautionary area with a radius of 7 miles is established centered upon 40°27'30"N., 73°49'54"W.

(2930)     (b) A precautionary area is established between the traffic separation scheme "Eastern Approach, off Nantucket" and the traffic separation scheme "In the Approach to Boston, Massachusetts."

(2931)     (1) The precautionary area is bounded to the east by a circle of radius 15.5 miles, centered upon geographic position 40°35.00'N., 69°00.00'W., and is intersected by the traffic separation scheme "In the Approach to Boston, Massachusetts" and "Off New York" at the following geographic positions:

(2932)     40°50.33'N., 68°57.00'W.

(2933)     40°23.75'N., 69°14.63'W.

(2934)     (2) The precautionary area is bounded to the west by a line connecting the two traffic separation schemes between the following geographic positions:

(2935)     40°36.75'N., 68°15.16'W.

(2936)     40°48.00'N., 69°03.33'W.

(2937)

### §167.152 Off New York: Eastern approach, off Nantucket.

(2938)     (a) A separation zone is established bounded by a line connecting the following geographic positions:

(2939)     40°28.75'N., 69°14.83'W.

(2940)     40°27.62'N., 70°13.77'W.

(2941)     40°30.62'N., 70°14.00'W.

(2942)     40°31.75'N., 69°14.97'W.

(2943)     (b) A traffic lane for westbound traffic is established between the separation zone and a line connecting the following geographic positions:

(2944)     40°36.75'N., 69°15.17'W.

(2945)     40°35.62'N., 70°15.15'W.

(2946)     (c) A traffic lane for eastbound traffic is established between the separation zone and a line connecting the following geographic positions:

(2947)     40°22.62'N., 70°13.60'W.

(2948)     40°23.75'N., 69°14.63'W.

(2949)

### §167.153 Off New York: Eastern approach.

(2950)     (a) A separation zone is established bounded by a line connecting the following geographic positions:

(2951)     40°24.33'N., 73°04.97'W.

(2952)     40°24.20'N., 73°11.50'W.

(2953)     40°26.00'N., 73°40.93'W.

(2954)     40°27.00'N., 73°40.75'W.

(2955)     40°27.20'N., 73°11.50'W.

(2956)     40°27.33'N., 73°04.95'W.

(2957)     (b) A traffic lane for westbound traffic is established between the separation zone and a line connecting the following geographic positions:

(2958)     40°32.33'N., 73°04.95'W.

(2959)     40°32.20'N., 73°11.50'W.

(2960)     40°28.00'N., 73°40.73'W.

(2961)     (c) A traffic lane for eastbound traffic is established between the separation zone and a line connecting the following geographic positions:

(2962)     40°25.05'N., 73°41.32'W.

(2963)     40°19.20'N., 73°11.50'W.

(2964)     40°19.33'N., 73°04.97'W.

(2965)

### §167.154 Off New York: South-eastern approach.

(2966)     (a) A separation zone is established bounded by a line connecting the following geographic positions:

(2967)     40°03.10'N., 73°17.93'W.

(2968)     40°06.50'N., 73°22.73'W.

(2969)     40°22.45'N., 73°43.55'W.

(2970)     40°23.20'N., 73°42.70'W.

(2971)     40°08.72'N., 73°20.10'W.

(2972)     40°05.32'N., 73°15.28'W.

(2973)     (b) A traffic lane for northwest-bound traffic is established between the separation zone and a line connecting the following geographic positions:

(2974)     40°08.98'N., 73°10.87'W.

(2975)     40°12.42'N., 73°15.67'W.

(2976)     40°24.02'N., 73°41.97'W.

(2977)     (c) A traffic lane for southeast-bound traffic is established between the separation zone and a line connecting the following geographic positions:

(2978)     40°21.82'N., 73°44.55'W.

(2979)     40°02.80'N., 73°27.15'W.

(2980)     39°59.43'N., 73°22.35'W.

(2981)

### §167.155 Off New York: Southern approach.

(2982)     (a) A separation zone is established bounded by a line connecting the following geographic positions:

(2983)     39°45.70'N., 73°48.00'W.

(2984)     40°20.63'N., 73°48.33'W.

(2985)     40°20.87'N., 73°47.07'W.

(2986)     39°45.70'N., 73°44.00'W.

(2987)     (b) A traffic lane for northbound traffic is established between the separation zone and a line connecting the following geographic positions:

(2988)     39°45.70'N., 73°37.70'W.

(2989)     40°21.25'N., 73°45.85'W.

(2990) (c) A traffic lane for southbound traffic is established between the separation zone and a line connecting the following geographic positions:
(2991) 40°20.53'N., 73°49.65'W.
(2992) 39°45.70'N., 73°54.40'W.

(2993)
### §167.170 Off Delaware Bay Approach Traffic Separation Scheme: General.
(2994) The Off Delaware Bay Traffic Separation Scheme consists of an Eastern approach, a South-eastern approach, a Two-Way Traffic Route, and a Precautionary Area. The specific areas of the Off Delaware Bay Traffic Separation Scheme and precautionary Area are described in §167.171, §167.172, §167.173, and §167.174 of this chapter.

(2995)
### §167.171 Eastern approach.
(2996) (a) A separation zone is established bounded by a line connecting the following points:
(2997) 38°46'18"N., 74°34'27"W.
(2998) 38°46'20"N., 74°55'45"W.
(2999) 38°47'27"N., 74°55'24"W.
(3000) 38°47'21"N., 74°34'30"W.
(3001) (b) A traffic lane for westbound traffic is established between the northen side of the separation zone and a line connecting the following points:
(3002) 38°48'19"N., 74°55'18"W.
(3003) 38°49'48"N., 74°34'36"W.
(3004) (c) A traffic lane for eastbound traffic is established between the south side of the separation zone and a line connecting the following points:
(3005) 38°45'27"N., 74°56'12"W.
(3006) 38°44'27"N., 74°34'21"W.

(3007)
### §167.172 Southeastern approach.
(3008) (a) A separation zone is established bounded by a line connecting the following points:
(3009) 38°27'00"N., 74°42'18"W.
(3010) 38°43'24"N., 74°58'00"W.
(3011) 38°44'12"N., 74°57'12"W.
(3012) 38°27'36"N., 74°41'18"W.
(3013) (b) A traffic lane for north-westbound traffic is established between the northeastern side of the separation zone and a line connecting the following points:
(3014) 38°28'48"N., 74°39'18"W.
(3015) 38°45'06"N., 74°56'36"W.
(3016) (c) A traffic lane for south-eastbound traffic is established between the southwestern side of the separation zone and a line connecting the following points:
(3017) 34°42'48"N., 74°58'54"W.
(3018) 34°27'00"N., 74°45'24"W.

(3019)
### §167.173 The Two-Way Traffic Route.
(3020) The Two-Way Traffic Route is established bounded on the west and south by a line connecting the following points:

(3021) 38°50'45"N., 75°03'24"W.
(3022) 38°47'30"N., 75°01'48"W.
(3023) 38°48'19"N., 74°55'18"W.
(3024) 38°50'12"N., 74°49'44"W.
(3025) 38°00'00"N., 74°40'14"W. and, bounded on the east and north by a line connecting the following points:
(3026) 39°00'00"N., 74°41'00"W.
(3027) 38°50'29"N., 74°50'18"W.
(3028) 38°48'48"N., 74°55'15"W.
(3029) 38°48'20"N., 74°59'18"W.
(3030) 38°49'06"N., 75°01'39"W.
(3031) 38°51'16"N., 75°02'50"W.

(3032)
### §167.174 Off Delaware Bay: Precautionary area.
(3033) A precautionary area is established as follows: from
(3034) 38°42'48"N., 74°58'54"W.; thence northerly by an arc of eight nautical miles centered at
(3035) 38°48'54"N., 75°05'36"W.; to
(3036) 38°48'19"N., 74°55'18"W.; thence westerly to
(3037) 38°47'30"N., 75°01'48"W.; thence northerly to
(3038) 38°50'45"N., 75°03'24"W.; thence northeasterly to
(3039) 38°51'16"N., 75°02'50"W.; thence northerly to
(3040) 38°54'48"N., 75°01'36"W.; thence westerly by an arc of 6.7 nautical miles centered at
(3041) 38°48'54"N., 75°05'36"W. to
(3042) 38°55'32"N., 75°05'52"W.; thence southwesterly to
(3043) 38°54'00"N., 75°08'00"W.; thence southerly to
(3044) 38°46'36"N., 75°03'33"W.; thence southeasterly to
(3045) 38°42'48"N., 74°58'54"W.

(3046)
### §167.200 In the approaches to Chesapeake Bay Traffic Separation Scheme: General.
(3047) (a) The traffic separation scheme in the approaches to Chesapeake Bay consists of three parts: a Precautionary Area, an Eastern Approach, and a Southern Approach. The Southern Approach consists of inbound and outbound lanes for vessels drawing 12.8 meters (42 feet) of fresh water or less, separated by a deep-water (DW) route for inbound and outbound vessels with drafts exceeding 12.8 meters (42 feet) in fresh water and for naval aircraft carriers. Each part is defined geographically, using North American Datum 1983 (NAD 83), in §§167.201, 167.202, 167.203.
(3048) (b) All vessels approaching the Traffic Separation Scheme in the Approaches to Chesapeake Bay should use the appropriate inbound or outbound traffic lane.

(3049)
### §167.201 In the approaches to Chesapeake Bay: Precautionary area.
(3050) A precautionary area is established bounded by a circle with a two-mile radius, centered on the following geographic position:
(3051) 36°56.13'N., 75°57.45'W.

(3052)
### §167.202 In the approaches to Chesapeake Bay: Eastern approach.

(3053)    (a) A separation line is established connecting the following geographic positions:

(3054)    36°57.50'N., 75°48.21'W.

(3055)    36°56.40'N., 75°52.40'W.

(3056)    36°56.40'N., 75°54.95'W.

(3057)    (b) A traffic lane for westbound traffic is established between the separation line and a line connecting the following geographical positions:

(3058)    36°57.94'N., 75°48.41'W.

(3059)    36°56.90'N., 75°52.40'W.

(3060)    36°56.90'N., 75°55.14'W.

(3061)    (c) A traffic lane for eastbound traffic is established between the separation line and a line connecting the following geographical positions:

(3062)    36°57.04'N., 75°48.01'W.

(3063)    36°55.88'N., 75°52.40'W.

(3064)    36°55.88'N., 75°54.95'W.

(3065)
### §167.203 In the approaches to Chesapeake Bay: Southern approach.

(3066)    (a) A separation line connects the following geographical positions:

(3067)    36°50.33'N., 75°46.29'W.

(3068)    36°52.90'N., 75°51.52'W.

(3069)    36°55.96'N., 75°54.97'W.

(3070)    (b) A separation line connects the following geographical positions:

(3071)    36°55.11'N., 75°55.23'W.

(3072)    36°52.35'N., 75°52.12'W.

(3073)    36°49.70'N., 75°46.80'W.

(3074)    (c) A separation line connects the following geographic positions:

(3075)    36°49.52'N., 75°46.94'W.

(3076)    36°52.18'N., 75°52.29'W.

(3077)    36°54.97'N., 75°55.43'W.

(3078)    (d) A separation line connects the following geographical positions:

(3079)    36°54.44'N., 75°56.09'W.

(3080)    36°51.59'N., 75°52.92'W.

(3081)    36°48.87'N., 75°47.42'W.

(3082)    (e) A traffic lane for inbound traffic is established between the separation lines described in paragraphs (a) and (b) of this section.

(3083)    (f) A traffic lane for outbound traffic is established between the separation lines described in paragraphs (c) and (d) of this section.

(3084)    (g) A deep-water route is established between the separation lines described in paragraphs (b) and (c) of this section. The following vessels should use the deep-water route established in paragraph (g) of this section when bound for Chesapeake Bay from sea or to sea from Chesapeake Bay;

(3085)    (1) Deep draft vessels (drafts greater than 13.5 meters/45 feet in fresh water); and

(3086)    (2) Naval aircraft carriers.

(3087)    (h) It is recommended that a vessel using the deep-water route established in paragraph (g) of this section–

(3088)    (1) Announce its intention on VHF–FM channel 16 as it approaches Chesapeake Bay Southern Approach Lighted Whistle Buoy CB on the south end, or Chesapeake Bay Junction Lighted Buoy CBJ on the north end of the route;

(3089)    (2) Avoid, as far as practicable, overtaking other vessels operating in the deep-water route; and

(3090)    (3) Keep as near to the outer limit of the route which lies on the vessel's starboard side as is safe and practicable.

(3091)    (i) Vessels other than those listed in paragraph (d) of this section should not use the deep-water route.

(3092)
## Part 169–ShipReporting Systems

(3093)
## Subpart A–General

(3094)
### 169.1 What is the purpose of this subpart?

(3095)    This subpart prescribes the requirements for mandatory ship reporting systems. Ship reporting systems are used to provide, gather, or exchange information through radio reports. The information is used to provide data for many purposes including, but not limited to: navigation safety, maritime security and domain awareness, environmental protection, vessel traffic services, search and rescue, weather forecasting and prevention of marine pollution.

(3096)
### §169.5 How are terms used in this part defined?

(3097)    As used in this part–

(3098)    *Administration* means the Government of the State whose flag the ship is entitled to fly.

(3099)    *Cargo ship* means any ship which is not a passenger ship.

(3100)    *Flag Administration* means the Government of a State whose flag the ship is entitled to fly.

(3101)    *Gross tonnage* means tonnage as defined under the International Convention on Tonnage Measurement of Ships, 1969 (Incorporated by reference, see §169.15).

(3102)    *Gross tons* means vessel tonnage measured in accordance with the method utilized by the flag state administration of that vessel.

(3103)    *High speed craft* means a craft that is operable on or above the water and is capable of a maximum speed equal to or exceeding $V=3.7 \times displ.1667$, where "V" is the maximum speed and "displ" is the vessel displacement corresponding to the design waterline in cubic meters.

(3104)    *High speed passenger craft* means a high speed craft carrying more than 12 passengers.

(3105)    *International voyage* means a voyage from a country to which the present International Convention for the

Safety of Life at Sea (SOLAS), 1974 applies to a port outside such country, or conversely. For U.S. ships, such voyages will be considered to originate at a port in the United States, regardless of when the voyage actually began. Such voyages for U.S. ships will continue until the ship returns to the United States from its last foreign port.

(3106)    *Long range identification and tracking (LRIT) information or position report* means a report containing the following information:

(3107)    (1) The identity of the ship;

(3108)    (2) The position of the ship (latitude and longitude); and

(3109)    (3) The date and time of the position provided.

(3110)    *LRIT Data Center* means a center established by a SOLAS Contracting Government or a group of Contracting Governments, or in the case of International Data Center, by IMO, to request, receive, process, and archive LRIT information. An LRIT Data Center may be National, Regional, Co-operative or International.

(3111)    *Mandatory ship reporting system* means a ship reporting system that requires the participation of specified vessels or classes of vessels, and that is established by a government or governments after adoption of a proposed system by the International Maritime Organization (IMO) as complying with all requirements of regulation V/8–1 of the International Convention for the Safety of Life at Sea, 1974, as amended (SOLAS), except paragraph (e) thereof.

(3112)    *Mobile offshore drilling unit* means a self-propelled vessel capable of engaging in drilling operations for the exploration or exploitation of subsea resources.

(3113)    *Passenger ship* means a ship that carries more than 12 passengers.

(3114)    *Self-propelled ships* means ships propelled by mechanical means.

(3115)    *Shore-based authority* means the government appointed office or offices that will receive the reports made by ships entering each of the mandatory ship reporting systems. The office or offices will be responsible for the management and coordination of the system, interaction with participating ships, and the safe and effective operation of the system. Such an authority may or may not be an authority in charge of a vessel traffic service.

(3116)    *United States* means the States of the United States, the District of Columbia, Guam, Puerto Rico, the Virgin Islands, American Samoa, the Northern Mariana Islands, and any other territory or possession of the United States.

(3117)
### §169.10 What geographic coordinates are used?

(3118)    Geographic coordinates expressed in terms of latitude or longitude, or both, are not intended for plotting on maps or charts where the referenced horizontal datum is the North American Datum of 1983 (NAD 83), unless such geographic coordinates are expressly labeled NAD 83. Geographic coordinates without the NAD 83 reference

may be plotted on maps or charts referenced to NAD 83 only after application of the appropriate corrections that are published on the particular map or chart being used.

(3119)
### §169.15 Incorporation by reference: Where can I get a copy of the publications mentioned in this part?

(3120)    (a) Certain material is incorporated by reference into this part with the approval of the Director of the Federal Register under 5 U.S.C. 552(a) and 1 CFR part 51. To enforce any edition other than that specified in this section, the Coast Guard must publish notice of change in the **Federal Register** and the material must be available to the public. All approved material is available for inspection at the National Archives and Records Administration (NARA). For information on the availability of this material at NARA, call 202–741–6030 or go to *http://www.archives.gov/federal_register/ code_of_federal_regulations/ibr_locations.html*. Also, it is available for inspection at the Coast Guard, Office of Navigation Systems (CG–5532), 2100 2nd St. SW., Stop 7580, Washington, DC 20593–7580, and is available from the sources indicated in this section.

(3121)    (b) *International Electrotechnical Commission (IEC) Bureau Central de la Commission Electrotechnique Internationale*, 3 rue de Varembé, P.O. Box 131, 1211 Geneva 20, Switzerland.

(3122)    (1) IEC 60945, Fourth edition 2002–08, Maritime navigation and radiocommunication equipment and systems-General requirements-Methods of testing and required test results, incorporation by reference approved for §169.215.

(3123)    (2) [Reserved]

(3124)    (c) *International Maritime Organization (IMO)*, 4 Albert Embankment, London SE1 7SR, U.K.

(3125)    (1) IMO Resolution MSC.202(81), adopted on May 19, 2006, Adoption of Amendments to the International Convention for the Safety of Life at Sea, 1974, as Amended, incorporation by reference approved for §160.240.

(3126)    (2) IMO Resolution MSC. 210(81), adopted on May 19, 2006, Performance Standards and Functional Requirements for the Long-Range Identification and Tracking of Ships, incorporation by reference approved for §§169.215 and 169.240.

(3127)    (3) IMO Resolution MSC.254(83), adopted on October 12, 2007, Adoption of Amendments to the Performance Standards and Functional Requirements for the Long-Range Identification and Tracking of Ships, incorporation by reference approved for §§169.215 and 169.240.

(3128)    (4) IMO Resolution A.694(17), adopted on November 6, 1991, General Requirements for Shipborne Radio Equipment Forming Part of the Global Maritime Distress and Safety System (GMDSS) and for Electronic Navigational Aids, incorporation by reference approved for §165.215.

(3129)    (5) International Convention on Tonnage Measurement of Ships, 1969, incorporation by reference approved for §169.5.

(3130)

## Subpart B–Establishment of Two Mandatory Ship Reporting Systems for the Protection of North Atlantic Right Whales

(3131)

### §169.100 What mandatory ship reporting systems are established by this subpart?

(3132)    This subpart prescribes requirements for the establishment and maintenance of two mandatory ship reporting systems for the protection of the endangered northern right whale (also known as the North Atlantic right whale). These two systems are designated for certain areas of the East Coast of the United States. One system is located in the northeast and is identified as WHALESNORTH. The other system is located in the southeast and is identified as WHALESSOUTH.

(3133)    **Note** to §169.100: 50 CFR 224.103(c) contains requirements and procedures concerning North Atlantic right whale approach limitations and avoidance procedures.

(3134)

### §169.102 Who is the shore-based authority?

(3135)    The U.S. Coast Guard is the shore-based authority for these mandatory ship reporting systems.

(3136)

### §169.105 Where is the northeastern reporting system located?

(3137)    Geographical boundaries of the northeastern area include the waters of Cape Cod Bay, Massachusetts Bay, and the Great South Channel east and southeast of Massachusetts. The coordinates (NAD 83) of the area are as follows: from a point on Cape Ann, Massachusetts at

(3138)    42°39'N, 70°37'W; then northeast to

(3139)    42°45'N, 70°13'W; then southeast to

(3140)    42°10'N, 68°31'W; then south to

(3141)    41°00'N, 68°31'W; then west to

(3142)    41°00'N, 69°17'W; then northwest to

(3143)    42°05'N, 70°02'W; then west to

(3144)    42°04'N, 70°10'W; and then along the Massachusetts shoreline of Cape Cod Bay and Massachusetts Bay back to the point on Cape Ann at

(3145)    42°39'N, 70°37'W.

(3146)

### 169.110 When is the northeastern reporting system in effect?

(3147)    The mandatory ship reporting system in the northeastern United States operates year-round.

(3148)

### 169.115 Where is the southeastern reporting system located?

(3149)    Geographical boundaries of the southeastern area include coastal waters within about 25 nautical miles (45 kilometers) along a 90–nautical mile (170–kilometer) stretch of the Atlantic seaboard in Florida and Georgia. The area coordinates (NAD 83) extends from the shoreline east to 80°51.6'W. with the southern and northern boundaries at 30°00'N. and 31°27'N., respectively.

(3150)

### §169.120 When is the southeastern reporting system in effect?

(3151)    The mandatory ship reporting system in the southeastern United States operates during the period beginning on November 15 each year through April 16 of the following year.

(3152)

### §169.125 What classes of ships are required to make reports?

(3153)    Each self-propelled ship of 300 gross tons or greater must participate in the reporting systems, except government ships exempted from reporting by regulation V/8–1(c) of SOLAS. However, exempt ships are encouraged to participate in the reporting systems.

(3154)

### §169.130 When are ships required to make reports?

(3155)    Participating ships must report to the shore-based authority upon entering the area covered by a reporting system. Additional reports are not necessary for movements made within a system or for ships exiting a system.

(3156)

### §169.135 How must the reports be made?

(3157)    (a) A ship equipped with INMARSAT C must report in IM0 standard format as provided in §169.140 in table 169.140.

(3158)    (b) A ship not equipped with INMARSAT C must report to the Coast Guard using other means, listed below in order of precedence–

(3159)    (1) By email to rightwhale.msr@noaa.gov;

(3160)    (2) HF voice communication, or

(3161)    (3) VHF voice communications.

(3162)    (c) HF reports made directly to the Coast Guard's Communications Command (COMMCOM) in Chesapeake, VA, or VHF reports made to Coast Guard shore units, should only be made by ships not equipped with INMARSAT C. Ships in this category must provide all the required information to the Coast Guard watchstander.

(3163)

### §169.140 What information must be included in the report?

(3164)    Each ship report made to the shore-based authority must follow the standard reporting and format requirements listed in this section in table 169.140. Current email addresses and telex numbers are published annually in the U.S. Coast Pilot.

(3165)

| TABLE 169.140 – Requirements for Ship Reports | | |
|---|---|---|
| Telegraphy | Function | Information required |
| Name of system | System identifier | Ship reporting system WHALESNORTH or WHALESSOUTH |
| M | INMARSAT Number | Vessel INMARSAT number |
| A | Ship | The name, call sign or ship station identity, IMO number, and flag of the vessel. |
| B | Date and time of event | A 6-digit group giving day of month (first two digits), hours and minutes (last four digits) |
| E | True course | A 3-digit group indicating true course. |
| F | Speed in knots and tenths of knots | A 3-digit group. |
| H | Date, time and point of entry into system | Entry time expressed as in (B) and entry position expressed as–(1) a 4-digit group giving latitude in degrees and minutes suffixed with N (north) or S (south) and a 5-digit group giving longitude in degrees and minutes suffixed with E (east) or W (west); or (2) True bearing (first 3 digits) and distance (state distance) in nautical miles from a clearly identified landmark (state landmark) |
| I | Destination and expected time of arrival | Name of port and date time group expressed as in (B) |
| L | Route information | Intended track. |

(3166)

## Subpart C–Transmission of Long Range Identification and Tracking Information

(3167)

### §169.200 What is the purpose of this subpart?

(3168) This subpart implements Regulation 19–1 of SOLAS chapter V (SOLAS V/19–1) and requires certain ships engaged on an international voyage to transmit vessel identification and position information electronically. This requirement enables the Coast Guard to obtain long range identification and tracking (LRIT) information and thus heightens our overall maritime domain awareness, enhances our search and rescue operations, and increases our ability to detect anomalies and deter transportation security incidents.

(3169)

### §169.205 What types of ships are required to transmit LRIT information (position reports)?

(3170) The following ships, while engaged on an international voyage, are required to transmit position reports:

(3171) (a) A passenger ship, including high speed passenger craft.

(3172) (b) A cargo ship, including high speed craft, of 300 gross tonnage or more.

(3173) (c) A mobile offshore drilling unit while underway and not engaged in drilling operations.

(3174)

### §169.210 Where during its international voyage must a ship transmit position reports?

(3175) The requirements for the transmission of position reports, imposed by the United States, vary depending on the relationship of the United States to a ship identified in §169.205.

(3176) (a) *Flag State relationship.* A U.S. flag ship engaged on an international voyage must transmit position reports wherever they are located.

(3177) (b) *Port State relationship.* A foreign flag ship engaged on an international voyage must transmit position reports after the ship has announced its intention to enter a U.S. port or place under requirements in 33 CFR part 160, subpart C.

(3178) (c) *Coastal State relationship.* A foreign flag ship engaged on an international voyage must transmit position reports when the ship is within 1,000 nautical miles of the baseline of the United States, unless their Flag Administration, under authority of SOLAS V/19–1.9.1, has directed them not to do so.

(3179)

### §169.215 How must a ship transmit position reports?

(3180) A ship must transmit position reports using Long Range Identification and Tracking (LRIT) equipment that has been type-approved by their Administration. To be type-approved by the Coast Guard, LRIT equipment must meet the requirements of IMO Resolutions A.694(17), MSC.210(81), and MSC.254(83), and IEC standard IEC 60945 (Incorporated by reference, see §169.15).

(3181)

### §169.220 When must a ship be fitted with LRIT equipment?

(3182) A ship identified in §169.205 must be equipped with LRIT equipment–

(3183) (a) Before getting underway, if the ship is constructed on or after December 31, 2008.

(3184) (b) By the first survey of the radio installation after December 31, 2008, if the ship is–

(3185) (1) Constructed before December 31, 2008, and

(3186) (2) Operates within–

(3187) (i) One hundred (100) nautical miles of the United States baseline, or

(3188) (ii) Range of an Inmarsat geostationary satellite, or other Application Service Provider recognized by the Administration, with which continuous alerting is available.

(3189) (c) By the first survey of the radio installation after July 1, 2009, if the ship is–

(3190) (1) Constructed before December 31, 2008, and

(3191) (2) Operates within the area or range specified in paragraph (b)(2) of this section as well as outside the range of an Inmarsat geostationary satellite with which continuous alerting is available. While operating in the area or range specified in paragraph (b)(2) of this section, however, a ship must install LRIT equipment by the first survey of the radio installation after December 31, 2008.

(3192)
### §169.225 Which Application Service Providers may a ship use?

(3193)     A ship may use an Application Service Provider (ASP) recognized by its administration. Some Communication Service Providers may also serve as an ASP.

(3194)
### §169.230 How often must a ship transmit position reports?

(3195)     A ship's LRIT equipment must transmit position reports at 6-hour intervals unless a more frequent interval is requested remotely by an LRIT Data Center.

(3196)
### §169.235 What exemptions are there from reporting?

(3197)     A ship is exempt from this subpart if it is–

(3198)     (a) Fitted with an operating automatic identification system (AIS), under 33 CFR 164.46, and operates only within 20 nautical miles of the United States baseline,

(3199)     (b) A warship, naval auxiliaries or other ship owned or operated by a SOLAS Contracting Government and used only on Government non-commercial service, or

(3200)     (c) A ship solely navigating the Great Lakes of North America and their connecting and tributary waters as far east as the lower exit of the St. Lambert Lock at Montreal in the Province of Quebec, Canada.

(3201)
### §169.240 When may LRIT equipment be switched off?

(3202)     A ship engaged on an international voyage may switch off its LRIT equipment only when it is permitted by its Flag Administration, in circumstances detailed in SOLAS V/19–1.7, or in paragraph 4.4.1, of resolution MSC.210(81), as amended by resolution MSC.254(83) (Incorporated by reference, see §169.15).

(3203)
### §169.245 What must a ship master do if LRIT equipment is switched off or fails to operate?

(3204)     (a) If a ship's LRIT equipment is switched off or fails to operate, the ship's master must inform his or her Flag Administration without undue delay.

(3205)     (b) The master must also make an entry in the ship's logbook that states–

(3206)     (1) His or her reason for switching the LRIT equipment off, or an entry that the equipment has failed to operate, and

(3207)     (2) The period during which the LRIT equipment was switched off or non-operational.

(3208)     Note to §169.245: for U.S. vessels, the U.S. Coast Guard serves as the Flag Administration for purposes of this section. All LRIT notifications for the U.S. Flag administration, in addition to requests or questions about LRIT, should be communicated to the U.S. Coast Guard by e-mail addressed to LRIT@uscg.mil.

(3209)
## Part 207–Navigation Regulations

(3210)
### §207.100 Inland Waterway from Delaware River to Chesapeake Bay, Delaware and Maryland (Chesapeake and Delaware Canal); use, administration, and navigation.

(3211)     These regulations are given in the description of the canal in chapter 7 of this Coast Pilot.

(3212)
### §207.800 Collection of navigation statistics.

(3213)     (a) *Definitions*. For the purpose of this regulation the following terms are defined:

(3214)     (1) *Navigable waters of the United States* means those waters of the United States that are subject to the ebb and flow of the tide shoreward to the mean high water mark, and/or are presently used, or have been used in the past, or may be susceptible to use to transport interstate or foreign commerce. (See 33 CFR part 329 for a more complete definition of this term.)

(3215)     (2) *Offenses and Violations* mean:

(3216)     (i) Failure to submit a required report.

(3217)     (ii) Failure to provide a timely, accurate, and complete report.

(3218)     (iii) Failure to submit monthly listings of idle vessels or vessels in transit.

(3219)     (iv) Failure to submit a report required by the lockmaster or canal operator.

(3220)     (3) *Leased or chartered vessel* means a vessel that is leased or chartered when the owner relinquishes control of the vessel through a contractual agreement with a second party for a specified period of time and/or for a specified remuneration from the lessee. Commercial movements on an affreightment basis are not considered a lease or charter of a particular vessel.

(3221)     (4) *Person or entity* means an individual, corporation, partnership, or company.

(3222)     (5) *Timely* means vessel and commodity movement data must be received by the Waterborne Commerce Statistics Center within 30 days after the close of the month in which the vessel movement or nonmovement takes place.

(3223)     (6) *Commercial vessel* means a vessel used in transporting by water, either merchandise or passengers for compensation or hire, or in the course of business of the owner, lessee, or operator of the vessel.

(3224)     (7) *Reporting situation* means a vessel movement by an operator that is required to be reported. Typical examples are listed in the instructions on the various ENG Forms. Five typical movements that are required to be reported by vessel operating companies include the following examples: Company A is the barge owner, and the barge transports corn from Minneapolis, MN to New Orleans, LA, with fleeting at Cairo, IL.

(3225) (i) *Lease/Charter:* If Company A leases or charters the barge to Company B, then Company B is responsible for reporting the movements of the barge until the lease/charter expires.

(3226) (ii) *Interline Movement:* A barge is towed from Minneapolis to Cairo by Company A, and from Cairo to New Orleans by Company B. Since Company A is the barge owner, and the barge is not leased. Company A reports the entire movement of the barge with an origin of Minneapolis and a destination of New Orleans.

(3227) (iii) *Vessel Swap/Trade:* Company A swaps barge with Company B to allow Company B to meet a delivery commitment to New Orleans. Since Company A has not leased/chartered the barge, Company A is responsible for filing the report. Company B is responsible for filing the report on the barge which is traded to Company A. The swap or trade will not affect the primary responsibility for reporting the individual vessel movements.

(3228) (iv) *Re-Consignment:* Barge is reconsigned to Mobile, AL. Company A reports the movements as originating in Minneapolis and terminating in Mobile. The point from which barge is reconsigned is not reported, only points of loading and unloading.

(3229) (v) *Fleeting:* Barge is deposited at a New Orleans fleeting area by Company A and towed by Company B from fleeting area to New Orleans area dock for unloading. Company A, as barge owner, reports entire movements from Minneapolis to the unloading dock in New Orleans. Company B does not report any barge movement.

(3230) (b) Implementation of the waterborne commerce statistics provisions of the River and Harbor Act of 1922, as amended by the Water Resources Development Act of 1986 (Pub. L. 99–662), mandates the following:

(3231) (1) *Filing Requirements.* Except as provided in paragraph (b)(2) of this section, the person or entity receiving remuneration for the movement of vessels or for the transportation of goods or passengers on the navigable waters is responsible for assuring that the activity report of commercial vessels is timely filed.

(3232) (i) For vessels under lease/charter agreements, the lessee or charterer of any commercial vessel engaged in commercial transportation will be responsible for the filing of said reports until the lease/charter expires.

(3233) (ii) The vessel owner, or his designated agent, is always the responsible party for ensuring that all commercial activity of the vessel is timely reported.

(3234) (2) The following Vessel Information Reports are to be filed with the Army Corps of Engineers, at the address specified on the ENG Form, and are to include:

(3235) (i) *Monthly Reports.* These reports shall be made on ENG Forms furnished upon written request of the vessel operating companies to the Army Corps of Engineers. The forms are available at the following address: U.S. Army Corps of Engineers, Waterborne Commerce Statistics Center, Post Office Box 62180, New Orleans, LA 70161–1280.

(3236) (A) All movements of domestic waterborne commercial vessels shall be reported, including but not limited to: Dry cargo ship and tanker moves, loaded and empty barge moves, towboat moves, with or without barges in tow, fishing vessels, movements of crew boats and supply boats to offshore locations, tugboat moves and movements of newly constructed vessels from the shipyard to the point of delivery.

(3237) (B) Vessels idle during the month must also be reported.

(3238) (C) Notwithstanding the above requirements, the following waterborne vessel movements need not be reported:

(3239) (1) Movements of recreational vessels.

(3240) (2) Movements of fire, police, and patrol vessels.

(3241) (3) Movements of vessels exclusively engaged in construction (e.g., piledrivers and crane barges). **Note:** however, that movements of supplies, materials, and crews to or from the construction site must be timely reported.

(3242) (4) Movements of dredges to or from the dredging site. However, vessel movements of dredged material from the dredging site to the disposal site must be reported.

(3243) (5) Specific movements granted exemption in writing by the Waterborne Commerce Statistics Center.

(3244) (D) ENG Forms 3925 and 3925b shall be completed and filed by vessel operating companies each month for all voyages or vessel movements completed during the month. Vessels that did not complete a move during the month shall be reported as idle or in transit.

(3245) (E) The vessel operating company may request a waiver from the Army Corps of Engineers, and upon written approval by the Waterborne Commerce Center, the company may be allowed to provide the requisite information of the above paragraph (D), on computer printouts, magnetic tape, diskettes, or alternate medium approved by the Center.

(3246) (F) Harbor Maintenance Tax information is required on ENG Form 3925 for cargo movements into or out of ports that are subject to the provisions of section 1402 of the Water Resources Development Act of 1986 (Pub. L. 99–662).

(3247) (1) The name of the shipper of the commodity, and the shipper's Internal Revenue Service number or Social Security number, must be reported on the form.

(3248) (2) If a specific exemption applies to the shipper, the shipper should list the appropriate exemption code. The specific exemption codes are listed in the directions for ENG Form 3925.

(3249) (3) Refer to 19 CFR part 24 for detailed information on exemptions and ports subject to the Harbor Maintenance Tax.

(3250) (ii) *Annual Reports.* Annually an inventory of vessels available for commercial carriage of domestic commerce and vessel characteristics must be filed on ENG Forms 3931 and 3932.

(3251)     (iii) *Transaction Reports*. The sale, charter, or lease of vessels to other companies must also be reported to assure that proper decisions are made regarding each company's duty for reporting vessel movements during the year. In the absence of notification of the transaction, the former company of record remains responsible until proper notice is received by the Corps.

(3252)     (iv) Reports to Lockmasters and Canal Operators. Masters of self-propelled non-recreational vessels which pass through locks and canals operated by the Army Corps of Engineers will provide the data specified on ENG Forms 3102b, 3102c, and/or 3102d to the lockmaster, canal operator, or his designated representative in the manner and detail dictated.

(3253)     (c) *Penalties for Noncompliance*. The following penalties for noncompliance can be assessed for offenses and violations.

(3254)     (1) *Criminal Penalties*. Every person or persons violating the provisions of this regulation shall, for each and every offenses, be liable to a fine of not more than $5,000, or imprisonment not exceeding two months, to be enforced in any district court in the United States within whose territorial jurisdiction such offense may have been committed.

(3255)     (2) In addition, any person or entity that fails to provide timely, accurate, and complete statements or reports required to be submitted by the regulation in this section may also be assessed a civil penalty of up to $5,903 per violation under 33 U.S.C. 555, as amended.

(3256)     (3) *Denial of Passage*. In addition to these fines, penalties, and imprisonments, the lockmaster or canal operator can refuse to allow vessel passage.

(3257)     (d) *Enforcement Policy*. Every means at the disposal of the Army Corps of Engineers will be utilized to monitor and enforce these regulations.

(3258)     (1) To identify vessel operating companies that should be reporting waterborne commerce data, The Corps will make use of, but is not limited to, the following sources.

(3259)     (i) Data on purchase and sale of vessels.

(3260)     (ii) U.S. Coast Guard vessel documentation and reports.

(3261)     (iii) Data collected at Locks, Canals, and other facilities operated by the Corps.

(3262)     (iv) Data provided by terminals on ENG Form 3926.

(3263)     (v) Data provided by the other Federal agencies including the Internal Revenue Service, Customs Service, Maritime Administration, Department of Transportation, and Department of Commerce.

(3264)     (vi) Data provided by ports, local facilities, and State or local governments.

(3265)     (vii) Data from trade journals and publications.

(3266)     (viii) Site visits and inspections.

(3267)     (2) *Notice of Violation*. Once a reporting violation is determined to have occurred, the Chief of the Waterborne Commerce Statistics Center will notify the responsible party and allow 30 days for the reports to be filed after the fact. If the reports are not filed within this 30-day notice period, then appropriate civil or criminal actions will be undertaken by the Army Corps of Engineers, including the proposal of civil or criminal penalties for noncompliance. Typical cases for criminal or civil action include, but are not limited to, those violations which are willful, repeated, or have a substantial impact in the opinion of the Chief of the Waterborne Commerce Statistics Center.

(3268)     (3) *Administrative Assessment of Civil Penalties*. Civil penalties may be assessed in the following manner.

(3269)     (i) *Authorization*. If the Chief of the Waterborne Commerce Statistics Center finds that a person or entity has failed to comply with any of the provisions specified herein, he is authorized to assess a civil penalty in accordance with the Class I penalty provisions of 33 CFR part 326. Provided, however, that the procedures in 33 CFR part 326 specifically implementing the Clean Water Act (33 U.S.C. 1319(g)(4)), public notice, comment period, and state coordination, shall not apply.

(3270)     (ii) *Initiation*. The Chief of the Waterborne Commerce Statistics Center will prepare and process a proposed civil penalty order which shall state the amount of the penalty to be assessed, described by reasonable specificity the nature of the violation, and indicate the applicable provisions of 33 CFR part 326.

(3271)     (iii) *Hearing Requests*. Recipients of a proposed civil penalty order may file a written request for a hearing or other proceeding. This request shall be as specified in 33 CFR part 326 and shall be addressed to the Director of the Water Resources Support Center, Casey Building, Fort Belvoir, VA 22060–5586, who will provide the requesting person or entity with a reasonable opportunity to present evidence regarding the issuance, modification, or revocation of the proposed order. Thereafter, the Director of the Water Resources Center shall issue a final order.

(3272)     (4) *Additional Remedies*. Appropriate cases may also be referred to the local U.S. Attorney for prosecution, penalty collection, injunctive, and other relief by the Chief of the Waterborne Commerce Statistics Center.

(3273)

## Part 334–DangerZones and Restricted Area Regulations

(3274)

### §334.1 Purpose.

(3275)     The purpose of this part is to:

(3276)     (a) Prescribe procedures for establishing, amending and disestablishing danger zones and restricted area;

(3277)     (b) List the specific danger zones and restricted areas and their boundaries; and

(3278)     (c) Prescribe specific requirements, access limitations and controlled activities within the danger zones and restricted areas.

(3279)
## §334.2 Definitions.

(3280)　(a) *Danger zone*. A defined water area (or areas) used for target practice, bombing, rocket firing or other especially hazardous operations, normally for the armed forces. The danger zones may be closed to the public on a full-time or intermittent basis, as stated in the regulations.

(3281)　(b) *Restricted area*. A defined water area for the purpose of prohibiting or limiting public access to the area. Restricted areas generally provide security for Government property and/or protection to the public from the risks of damage or injury arising from the Government's use of that area.

(3282)
## §334.3 Special policies.

(3283)　(a) *General*. The general regulatory policies stated in 33 CFR part 320 will be followed as appropriate. In addition, danger zone and restricted area regulations shall provide for public access to the area to the maximum extent practicable.

(3284)　(b) *Food fishing industry*. The authority to prescribe danger zone and restricted area regulations must be exercised so as not to unreasonably interfere with or restrict the food fishing industry. Whenever the proposed establishment of a danger zone or restricted area may affect fishing operations, the District Engineer will consult with the Regional Director, U.S. Fish and Wildlife Service, Department of the Interior and the Regional Director, National Marine Fisheries Service, National Oceanic & Atmospheric Administration (NOAA),

(3285)　(c) *Temporary, occasional or intermittent use*. If the use of the water area is desired for a short period of time, not to exceed thirty days in duration, and that planned operations can be conducted safely without imposing unreasonable restrictions on navigation, and without promulgating restricted area regulations in accordance with the regulations in this section, applicants may be informed that formal regulations are not required. Activities of this type shall not reoccur more often than biennially (every other year), unless danger zone/ restricted area rules are promulgated under this part. Proper notices for mariners requesting that vessels avoid the area will be issued by the Agency requesting such use of the water area, or if appropriate, by the District Engineer, to all known interested persons. Copies will also be sent to appropriate State agencies, the Commandant, U.S. Coast Guard, Washington, DC 20590, and Director, National Geospatial-Intelligence Agency, Washington, DC 20390, ATTN: Code NS 12. Notification to all parties and Agencies shall be made at least two weeks prior to the planned event, or earlier, if required for distribution of Local Notice to Mariners by the Coast Guard.

(3286)
## §334.4 Establishment and amendment procedures.

(3287)　(a) *Application*. Any request for the establishment, amendment or revocation of a danger zone or restricted area must contain sufficient information for the District Engineer to issue a public notice, and as a minimum must contain the following:

(3288)　(1) Name, address and telephone number of requestor including the identity of the command and DoD facility and the identity of a point of contact with phone number.

(3289)　(2) Name of waterway and if a small tributary, the name of a larger connecting waterbody.

(3290)　(3) Name of closest city or town, county/parish and state.

(3291)　(4) Location of proposed or existing danger zone or restricted area with a map showing the location, if possible.

(3292)　(5) A brief statement of the need for the area, its intended use and detailed description of the times, dates and extent of restriction.

(3293)　(b) *Public notice*. (1) The Corps will normally publish public notices and **Federal Register** documents concurrently. Upon receipt of a request for the establishment, amendment or revocation of a danger zone or restricted area, the District Engineer should forward a copy of the request with his/her recommendation, a copy of the draft public notice and a draft **Federal Register** document to the Office of the Chief of Engineers, ATTN: CECW-OR. The Chief of Engineers will publish the proposal in the **Federal Register** concurrent with the public notice issued by the District Engineer.

(3294)　(2) *Content*. The public notice and **Federal Register** documents must include sufficient information to give a clear understanding of the proposed action and should include the following items of information:

(3295)　(i) Applicable statutory authority or authorities; (40 Stat. 266; 33 U.S.C. 1) and (40 Stat. 892; 33 U.S.C. 3).

(3296)　(ii) A reasonable comment period. The public notice should fix a limiting date within which comments will be received, normally a period not less than 30 days after publication of the notice.

(3297)　(iii) The address of the District Engineer as the recipient of any comments received.

(3298)　(iv) The identity of the applicant/proponent;

(3299)　(v) The name or title, address and telephone number of the Corps employee from whom additional information concerning the proposal may be obtained;

(3300)　(vi) The location of the proposed activity accompanied by a map of sufficient detail to show the boundaries of the area(s) and its relationship to the surrounding area.

(3301)　(3) *Distribution*. Public notice will be distributed in accordance with 33 CFR 325.3(d)(1). In addition to this general distribution, public notices will be sent to the following Agencies:

(3302)　(i) The Federal Aviation Administration (FAA) where the use of airspace is involved.

(3303)　(ii) The Commander, Service Force, U.S. Atlantic Fleet, if a proposed action involves a danger zone off the U.S. Atlantic coast.

(3304)　(iii) Proposed danger zones on the U.S. Pacific coast must be coordinated with the applicable commands as follows:

(3305)　Alaska, Oregon and Washington:

(3306)    Commander, Naval Base, Seattle

(3307)    California:

(3308)    Commander, Naval Base, San Diego

(3309)    Hawaii and Trust Territories:

(3310)    Commander, Naval Base, Pearl Harbor

(3311)    (c) *Public hearing.* The District Engineer may conduct a public hearing in accordance with 33 CFR part 327.

(3312)    (d) *Environmental documentation.* The District Engineer shall prepare environmental documentation in accordance with Appendix B to 33 CFR part 325.

(3313)    (e) *District Engineer's recommendation.* After closure of the comment period, and upon completion of the District Engineer's review he/she shall forward the case through channels to the Office of the Chief of Engineers, ATTN: CECW-OR with a recommendation of whether or not the danger zone or restricted area regulation should be promulgated. The District Engineer shall include a copy of environmental documentation prepared in accordance with appendix B to 33 CFR part 325, the record of any public hearings, if held, a summary of any comments received and a response thereto, and a draft of the regulation as it is to appear in the **Federal Register**.

(3314)    (f) *Final decision.* The Chief of Engineers will notify the District Engineer of the final decision to either approve or disapprove the regulations. The District Engineer will notify the applicant/proponent and publish a public notice of the final decision. Concurrent with issuance of the public notice the Office of the Chief of Engineers will publish the final decision in the **Federal Register** and either withdraw the proposed regulation or issue the final regulation as appropriate. The final rule shall become effective no sooner than 30 days after publication in the Federal Register unless the Chief of Engineers finds that sufficient cause exists and publishes that rationale with the regulations.

(3315)

### §334.5 Disestablishment of a danger zone.

(3316)    (a) Upon receipt of a request from any agency for the disestablishment of a danger zone, the District Engineer shall notify that agency of its responsibility for returning the area to a condition suitable for use by the public. The agency must either certify that it has not used the area for a purpose that requires cleanup or that it has removed all hazardous materials and munitions, before the Corps will disestablish the area. The agency will remain responsible for the enforcement of the danger zone regulations to prevent unauthorized entry into the area until the area is deemed safe for use by the public and the area is disestablished by the Corps.

(3317)    (b) Upon receipt of the certification required in paragraph (a) of this section, the District shall forward the request for disestablishment of the danger zone through channels to CECW-OR, with its recommendations. Notice of proposed rulemaking and public procedures

as outlined in §334.4 are not normally required before publication of the final rule revoking a restricted area or danger zone regulation. The disestablishment/revocation of the danger zone or restricted area regulation removes a restriction on a waterway.

(3318)

### §334.6 Datum.

(3319)    (a) Geographic coordinates expressed in terms of latitude or longitude, or both, are not intended for plotting on maps or charts whose reference horizontal datum is the North American Datum of 1983 (NAD 83), unless such geographic coordinates are expressly labeled NAD 83. Geographic coordinates without the NAD 83 reference may be plotted on maps or charts referenced to NAD 83 only after application of the appropriate corrections that are published on the particular map or chart being used.

(3320)    (b) For further information on NAD 83 and National Service nautical charts please contact:

(3321)    Director, Coast Survey (N/CS2)

(3322)    National Ocean Service, NOAA

(3323)    1315 East-West Highway, Station 6147

(3324)    Silver Spring, MD 20910–3282.

(3325)

### §334.100 Atlantic Ocean off Cape May, NJ; Coast Guard Rifle Range.

(3326)    (a) *The danger zone.* The waters of the Atlantic Ocean within an area described as follows: Beginning at Cape May West Jetty Light; thence 180° true, 800 yards; thence 250° true 1,325 yards; and thence 335° true to the shore line.

(3327)    (b) *The regulations.* (1) No person or vessel shall enter or remain in the danger area between sunrise and sunset daily, except as authorized by the enforcing agency.

(3328)    (2) The regulations in this section shall be enforced by the Commander, Third Coast Guard District, or his authorized representative.

(3329)

### §334.110 Delaware Bay off Cape Henlopen, DE; naval restricted area.

(3330)    (a) *The area.* Beginning at a point on the south shore of Delaware Bay at longitude 75°06'12"; thence to latitude 38°47'25", longitude 75°06'20"; thence to latitude 38°47'48", longitude 75°06'00"; thence to latitude 38°50'43", longitude 75°02'11"; thence to latitude 38°49'16", longitude 74°59'35"; thence to a point on the shore at latitude 38°46'09"; thence northwesterly and southwesterly along the shore at Cape Henlopen to the point of beginning.

(3331)    (b) *The regulations.* (1) Anchoring, trawl fishing, crabbing, dragging, grappling, and towing with hawser on bottom are prohibited in the area and no object attached to a vessel shall be placed on or near the bottom.

(3332)    (2) This section does not apply to anchored floating navigational aids or to placement or removal of such aids by the Coast Guard.

(3333)　　(3) This section does not apply to vessels engaged in commercial or pleasure boat fishing provided anchors, trawls, and ground tackle are not used.

(3334)　　(4) The regulations in this section shall be enforced by the Commandant, Fourth Naval District, and such agencies as he may designate.

(3335)

### §334.120 Delaware Bay off Milford Neck; naval aircraft bombing target area.

(3336)　　(a) *The danger zone*. A circular area of one nautical mile radius having its center in Delaware Bay at latitude 38°58'12", longitude 75°17'30".

(3337)　　(b) *The regulations*. (1) Anchoring, trawling, crabbing, fishing and dragging in the danger zone are prohibited during daylight hours.

(3338)　　(2) The regulations in this section shall be enforced by the Commandant, Fourth Naval District, and such agencies as he may designate.

(3339)

### §334.130 Atlantic Ocean off Wallops Island and Chincoteague Inlet, VA; danger zone.

(3340)　　(a) *The area*. An area immediately behind and directly offshore from Wallops Island defined by lines drawn as follows: Beginning at

(3341)　　37°53'00"N, 75°29'48"W; thence to

(3342)　　37°53'03"N, 74°50'52"W; thence to

(3343)　　37°38'28"N, 74°51'48"W; thence to

(3344)　　37°22'00"N, 75°09'35"W; thence to

(3345)　　37°19'11"N, 75°30'00"W; thence to

(3346)　　37°47'57"N, 75°32'19"W; and thence to

(3347)　　37°53'00"N, 75°29'48"W.

(3348)　　(b) *The regulations*. (1) Persons and vessels shall only be prohibited from entering the area when launch operations are being conducted.

(3349)　　(2) In advance of scheduled launch operations which, in the opinion of the enforcing agency, may be dangerous to persons and watercraft, appropriate warnings will be issued to navigation interests through official government and civilian channels or in such other manner as the District Engineer, U.S. Army Corps of Engineers, may direct. Such warnings will specify the location, time, and duration of operations, and give other pertinent information as may be required in the interests of safety. Announcement of area of closure will appear in the weekly "Notice to Mariners."

(3350)　　(3) The intent to conduct rocket-launching operations in the area shall also be indicated by visual signals consisting of a large orange-colored "blimp-shaped" balloon by day and a rotating alternately red and white beacon by night. The balloon shall be flown at 37°50'38"N, 75°28'47"W and the beacon shall be displayed about 200 feet above mean high water at 37°50'16"N, 75°29'07"W. The appropriate signals shall be displayed 30 minutes prior to rocket-launching time and shall remain displayed until the danger no longer exists.

(3351)　　(4) In addition to visual signals and prior to conducting launch operations, the area will be patrolled by aircraft or surface vessels and monitored by radars and cameras to ensure no persons or watercraft are within the danger zone or designated area of interest within the danger zone. Patrol aircraft and surface vessels are equipped with marine band radios and may attempt to hail watercraft and request that they leave the designated area and remain clear of the area at a safe distance until launch operations are complete, and launch will not occur until the designated area is clear. Patrol aircraft may also employ the method of warning known as "buzzing" which consists of low flight by the airplane and repeated opening and closing of the throttle. Surveillance vessels may also come close to watercraft and employ flashing light to establish communications to indicate that the watercraft is entering the designated hazard area.

(3352)　　(5) Any watercraft being so warned shall immediately leave the designated area until the conclusion of launch operations, and shall remain at a distance to ensure that it will be safe from falling debris.

(3353)　　(6) Nothing in this regulation shall be intended to prevent commercial fishing or the lawful use of approved waterfowl hunting blinds along the shorelines of the Wallops Flight Facility at Wallops Island, Virginia, provided that all necessary licenses and permits have been obtained from the Virginia Marine Resources Commission, Virginia Department of Game and Inland Fisheries, and U.S. Fish and Wildlife Service. Commercial fishermen and waterfowl hunters must observe all warnings and range clearances during hazardous range operations.

(3354)　　(c) *Enforcement*. The regulations in this section shall be enforced by the Director, National Aeronautics and Space Administration, Goddard Space Flight Center, Wallops Flight Facility Wallops Island, VA, or such agencies as he or she may designate.

(3355)

### §334.140 Chesapeake Bay; United States Army Proving Ground Reservation, Aberdeen, MD.

(3356)　　(a) *Restricted area defined*. The following indicates the limits of the waters of or adjacent to the Aberdeen Proving Ground, Maryland, and inside of which boundaries will lie the restricted area known as the Aberdeen Proving Ground, Maryland.

(3357)　　(1) Beginning at a point on the westerly side of Chesapeake Bay, at the south side of the mouth of Swan Creek, Harford County, Maryland, the most northerly point of the reservation known as Plum Point; thence southeasterly along the low water mark on the shore of Chesapeake Bay to and across the north entrance of Spesutie Narrows to and thence along the low water mark on the north shore of Spesutie Island to Locust Point; thence along straight line from Locust Point to Turkey Point for a distance of approximately 1,400 yards; thence following a line parallel with and 1,000 yards from the low water mark on the easterly shore of Spesutie Island to a point 1,000 yards due southeast of Sandy Point; thence approximately southwest in a straight line to a point approximately 1,250 yards S. 10°30' W. from Bear

Point; thence approximately 9,275 yards S. 51°04'W. to a point in Chesapeake Bay about 1,700 yards due east from Taylor Island Point; thence southwesterly in a straight course, except such variations as may be necessary to include all of Pooles Island to the southwesterly point of Pooles Island, thence in a northwesterly direction to the most southwesterly point of Spry Island, including all of Spry Island; thence northwesterly in a straight line to extreme southerly island off Lower Island Point; thence northwesterly in a straight line through Brier Point to a point in Seneca Creek where this line intersects a straight line which passes through monuments No. 124 and No. 125 on westerly part of Carroll Island; thence northeasterly in a straight line passing through Marshy Point, at the junction of Dundee Creek and Saltpeter Creek, to the intersection of the center line of Riordan Inlet with Gunpowder River, except such variations as may be necessary to exclude any and all parts of the point of land on the westerly side of Gunpowder River about one mile south of Oliver Point; thence northerly along the center line of Riordan Inlet to its intersection with the southeasterly line of the right of way of the Pennsylvania Railroad; thence northeast along the Pennsylvania Railroad following the reservation boundary line to shore of Bush River, and along its western shore to Fairview Point; thence northeast in a straight line across Bush River to concrete monument No. 64, located on the eastern shore of Bush River, south of Chelsea; thence along the eastern shore of Bush River northerly to the mouth of Sod Run; thence by a broken line along the boundary of the reservation to Swan Creek; and thence in a straight line to Plum Point. (The above description may be traced on National Ocean Survey Chart No. 12273.)

(3358)      (b) *Authority delegated Commanding Officer*. The Commanding Officer, Aberdeen Proving Ground, has been delegated the authority by the Secretary of the Army to designate from time to time by suitably posted bulletins or announcements, the conditions under which the public, including food fishermen and crabbers, may enter restricted waters of the Aberdeen Proving Ground.

(3359)      (c) *Penalty*. All persons who enter the restricted waters, except as authorized in this section, without the authority of the Commanding Officer, Aberdeen Proving Ground MD, are under the terms of the information given above, guilty of a misdemeanor and upon conviction thereon are punishable by a fine not exceeding $500 or by imprisonment not exceeding 6 months.

(3360)      (d) *Entrance into restricted waters by the public*.

(3361)      (1) The following water areas are closed to the public at all times:

(3362)      (i) Spesutie Narrows-all waters north and east of a line between Bear Point and Black Point;

(3363)      (ii) All creeks except Landerick Creek;

(3364)      (iii) The water adjacent to Carroll Island which lies between Brier Point and Lower Island Point also known as Hawthorne Cove;

(3365)      (iv) The waters immediately off the mouth of Romney Creek;

(3366)      (v) The waters adjacent to Abbey Point Recovery Field more accurately described as area number 16; depicted in Aberdeen Proving Ground Regulation 210–10, Appendix A.

(3367)      (vi) The waters on the north side of the Bush River from Pond Point to Chelsea Chimney are closed for fishing purposes.

(3368)      (2) The remainder of the restricted areas will normally be open for authorized use (including navigation and fishing) during the following hours:

(3369)      (i) Monday through Thursday, 5 p.m. to 7:30 a.m.;

(3370)      (ii) Weekends, 5 p.m. Friday to 7:30 a.m. Monday;

(3371)      (iii) National (not State) holidays, 5 p.m. the day preceding the holiday to 7:30 a.m. the day following the holiday.

(3372)      (3) When requirements of tests, as determined by the Commanding Officer, Aberdeen Proving Ground, or his designee, necessitate closing the restricted areas during the aforementioned times and days, the Commanding Officer, Aberdeen Proving Ground, will publish appropriate circulars or cause to be broadcast over local radio stations notices informing the public of the time and days which entrance to the restricted waters of Aberdeen Proving Ground by the general public will be prohibited.

(3373)      (4) A fleet of patrol boats will be positioned at the perimeter of the restricted water zone boundaries (except in extreme weather conditions such as gales or ice) during periods of testing to prevent unauthorized entry. If necessary to attract attention of another vessel about to penetrate the restricted area, the patrol boat may operate a distinctive rotating blue and red light, public address system, and sound a siren, or by radio contact on shipshore FM channel 16 and citizen band channel 12. Buoys will mark the restricted waters along the Chesapeake Bay perimeter during the period, normally 4 June through 1 October annually.

(3374)      (5) *Authorized use*. Authorized use as used in this section is defined as fishing from a vessel, navigation using a vessel to transverse a water area, or anchoring a vessel in a water area. Any person who touches any land, or docks or grounds a vessel, within the boundaries of Aberdeen Proving Ground, Maryland, is not using the area for an authorized use and is in violation of this regulation. Further, water skiing in the water area of Aberdeen Proving Ground is permitted as an authorized use when the water area is open for use by the general public provided that no water skier touches any land either dry land (fast land) or subaqueous land and comes no closer than 200 meters from any shoreline. Further, if any person is in the water area of Aberdeen Proving Ground, Maryland, outside of any vessel (except for the purposes of water skiing as outlined above) including, but not limited to, swimming, scuba diving, or other purpose, that person is not using the water in an authorized manner and is in violation of this regulation.

(3375)      (e) *Entry onto land and limitations of firing over land*. (1) Entry onto any land, either dry land (fast land) or subaqueous land, within the boundaries of the Aberdeen

Proving Ground Reservation as defined in paragraph (a)(1) is prohibited at all times. Provided, the Commander, Aberdeen Proving Ground, is authorized to grant exceptions to this regulation either by written permission or by local regulation. Entry onto the land is punishable as in paragraph (c) of this section.

(3376)     (2) There are no limitations on test firing by Federal testing facilities at Aberdeen Proving Ground over land belonging to Aberdeen Proving Ground.

(3377)     (f) *Permits required from the Commanding Officer to set fixed nets in restricted waters.* (1) Fishermen and crabbers desiring to set fixed nets within the restricted waters of Aberdeen Proving Ground Reservation are required in every instance to have a written permit. A fixed net for the purpose of this paragraph is defined as a pound net, staked gill net, hedge fike net, hoop net, eel pot, crab pot, and all other types of nets fastened by means of poles, stakes, weights, or anchors. Permits to fish and crab within the restricted waters of Aberdeen Proving Ground may be obtained by written application to the Commanding Officer, Department of the Army, Aberdeen Proving Ground, Attention: Provost Marshall Division, Aberdeen Proving Ground, MD. Applicants for permits must state the location at which they desire to set fixed nets and state the period of time for which they desire the permit to cover. Nets placed in the restricted waters are subject to damage by gunfire and bombing, and the risk of such damage will be assumed by the holder of the permit.

(3378)     (2) Holders of permits for setting fixed nets must comply with the provisions of this part and also with 33 CFR 206.50(d), not carried in this Pilot.

(3379)     (g) *Identification signs required at each location of fixed nets.* Fishermen and crabbers who have been granted permits to fish or crab within the restricted waters of Aberdeen Proving Ground Reservation with fixed nets must at each location have a stake securely driven at the outer end of the line of nets on which is mounted a sign board which contains their name and permit number. All stakes set within the restricted area established by this regulation will project at least three (3) feet above the surface of the water at all ordinary high stages of the tide. Nets and other fishing and crabbing structures erected will be marked by stakes set at intervals not greater than fifty (50) feet. Fishing and crabbing structures erected in Aberdeen Proving Ground waters will be plainly marked on both ends, and will be lighted with a white light between sunset and sunrise, by and at the expense of the owner.

(3380)     (h) *Removal of pound net poles and or stakes.* At the end of the fishing and crabbing season, fishermen and crabbers must remove and haul away from the location all pound nets, pots, poles or stakes used in their operation. Pound net poles or stakes must not be cast adrift after removal.

(3381)     (i) *Restrictions on fishermen and crabbers.* It must be distinctly understood that holders of permits to fish or crab are not authorized to enter the restricted waters of Aberdeen Proving Ground Reservation outside the hours as announced by the Commanding Officer, Aberdeen Proving Ground. In addition, the privileges granted in this paragraph include no right to land nor to cut or procure pound nets poles or stakes on the Aberdeen Proving Ground Reservation.

(3382)     (j) Aberdeen Proving Ground Regulations (APGR) 210–10 will govern commercial fishing and crabbing and APGR 210–26 will govern recreational (non-commercial) fishing and crabbing. This section shall be enforced by the Commander, Aberdeen Proving Ground, and such agencies as he/she may designate.

(3383)     (k) *Compliance with Federal, State and county laws required.* The taking of fish and crabs in the waters of Aberdeen Proving Ground Reservation and the setting of and location of nets, in a manner not in compliance with Federal, State, and county laws is prohibited.

(3384)

### §334.145 Curtis Creek and Arundel Cove, U.S. Coast Guard Yard, Baltimore; restricted area.

(3385)     (a) *The area.* All of the navigable waters of Curtis Creek extending approximately 120 meters from the high-water mark of the United States Coast Guard facility, bounded by these coordinates (including the Arundel Cove): Commencing from the shoreline at 39°12′05.8″N., 076°34′28.4″W.; thence to 39°12′04.8″N., 076°34′32″W.; thence to 39°11′59″N., 076°34′28″W.; thence to 39°11′44.8″N., 076°34′25″W.; thence to 39°11′44.5″N., 076°34′07″W.; and thence along the shoreline to the point of origin. The datum for these coordinates is NAD–83.

(3386)     (b) *The regulations.* (1) The restricted area as described in paragraph (a) of this section is only open to government vessels. Government vessels include, but are not limited to, U.S. Coast Guard, U.S. Coast Guard Auxiliary, Department of Defense, National Oceanic and Atmospheric Administration, state and local law enforcement, emergency services and vessels under contract with the U.S. Government. Vessels transiting the restricted area shall proceed across the area by the most direct route and without unnecessary delay. Fishing, crabbing, trawling, net-fishing and other aquatic activities are prohibited without prior approval from the Commanding Officer, U.S. Coast Guard Yard or his/her designated representative. The Coast Guard will install warning signs along the shoreline notifying individuals of the restricted area and prohibiting all unauthorized entry into the area along the property boundary.

(3387)     (2) All persons, vessels and other craft are prohibited from entering, transiting, drifting, dredging or anchoring within the restricted area as described in paragraph (a) of this section without prior approval from the Commanding Officer, U.S. Coast Guard Yard or his/her designated representative.

(3388)     (3) The restrictions described in paragraph (b)(1) of this section are in effect 24 hours a day, seven days a week.

(3389)     (c) *Enforcement.* The regulations in this section shall be enforced by the Commanding Officer, U.S. Coast Guard Yard or such persons or agencies he/she may designate.

(3390)
### §334.150 Severn River at Annapolis, MD; experimental test area, U.S. Navy Marine Engineering Laboratory.

(3391)     (a) *The restricted area.* The waters of Severn River shoreward of a line beginning at the southeasternmost corner of the U.S. Navy Marine Engineering Laboratory sea wall and running thence southwesterly perpendicular to the main Severn River channel, approximately 560 feet, thence northwesterly parallel to and 50 feet shoreward of the edge of the channel, 1,035 feet, and thence northeasterly perpendicular to the channel, approximately 600 feet, to the shore. Spar buoys will mark the corners of the area adjacent to the channel.

(3392)     (b) *The regulations.* (1) No vessel or person other than specifically authorized military and naval vessels and persons shall enter or remain in the area during its use for experimental purposes. At all other times vessels and persons may use the area without restriction.

(3393)     (2) The area will be in use intermittently, and this use will be signified by the presence of white-painted boats or floats, which will be lighted at night.

(3394)     (3) Upon observing the boats or floats referred to in paragraph (b)(2) of this section, or upon being warned, vessels and persons shall immediately vacate the area and remain outside the area during the period of use.

(3395)     (4) The regulations in this section shall be enforced by the Commandant, Severn River Naval Command, and such agencies as he may designate.

(3396)
### §334.155 Severn River, Naval Station Annapolis, Small Boat Basin, Annapolis, MD; naval restricted area.

(3397)     (a) *The area.* The waters within the Naval Station Annapolis small boat basin and adjacent waters of the Severn River enclosed by a line beginning at the southeast corner of the U.S. Navy Marine Engineering Laboratory; thence to 38°58'56.5"N., 76°28'11.5"W.; thence to 38°58'50.5"N., 76°27'52.0"W.; thence to the southeast corner of the Naval Station's seawall.

(3398)     (b) *The regulations.* No person, vessel or other craft shall enter or remain in the restricted area at any time except as authorized by the enforcing agency.

(3399)     (c) *Enforcement.* The regulations in this section shall be enforced by the Superintendent, U.S. Naval Academy, in Annapolis, Maryland, and such agencies as he/she may designate.

(3400)
### §334.160 Severn River, at U.S. Naval Academy Santee Basin, Annapolis, MD; naval restricted area.

(3401)     (a) *The area.* The waters within the U.S. Naval Academy Santee Basin and adjacent waters of Severn River inclosed by a line beginning at the northeast corner of Dewey Field seawall; thence to latitude 38°59'03", longitude 76°28'47.5"; thence to latitude 38°58'58", longitude 76°28'40"; and thence to the northwest corner of Farragut Field seawall.

(3402)     (b) *The regulations.* (1) No person in the water, vessel or other craft shall enter or remain in the restricted area at any time except as authorized by the enforcing agency.

(3403)     (2) The regulations in this section shall be enforced by the Superintendent, U.S. Naval Academy, Annapolis, MD, and such agencies as he may designate.

(3404)
### §334.170 Chesapeake Bay, in the vicinity of Chesapeake Beach, MD; firing range, Naval Research Laboratory.

(3405)     (a) *The danger zone*–(1) *Area A.* A roughly rectangular area bounded on the north by latitude 38°39'55"; on the south by latitude 38°39'09"; on the east by longitude 76°31'03"; and on the west by the shore of Chesapeake Bay.

(3406)     (2) *Area B.* The sector of a circle bounded by radii of 9,600 yards bearing 31° (to Bloody Point Bar Light) and 137°30' (to Choptank River Approach Buoy 2), respectively, from the center at the southeast corner of building No. 3; excluding Area A.

(3407)     (3) *Area C.* The segment of a circle inclosed by the arcs of two circles having radii of 9,600 yards and 13,200 yards, respectively, and bounded by the extended radii marking the north and south limits of Area B.

(3408)     Note: All bearings referred to true meridian.

(3409)     (4) *Area D.* A roughly rectangular area bounded on the north by an east-west line through Chesapeake Beach Light 2 at the entrance channel to Fishing Creek; on the south by an east-west line through Plum Point Shoal Buoy 1 northeast from Breezy Point; on the east by the established fishing structure limit line; and on the west by the shore of Chesapeake Bay.

(3410)     (b) *The regulations.* (1) No person or vessel shall enter or remain in Area A at any time.

(3411)     (2) No person or vessel shall enter or remain in Area B or Area C between the hours of 1:00 p.m. and 5:00 p.m. daily except Sundays, except that through navigation of commercial craft will be permitted in Area C at all times, but such vessels shall proceed on their normal course and shall not delay their progress.

(3412)     (3) No fishing structures, other than those presently in established locations, which may be maintained, will be permitted to be established in Area D without specific permission from the Commanding Officer, Naval Research Laboratory.

(3413)     (4) The areas will be in use throughout the year, and no further notice is contemplated that firing is continuing.

(3414)     (5) Prior to the conduct of each firing practice a patrol vessel will patrol the range to warn navigation. "Baker" will be flown from a conspicuous point on the patrol vessel and from a prominent position on shore.

(3415)  (6) This section shall be enforced by the Commander, Naval Base, Norfolk, Virginia, and such agencies as he/she may designate.

(3416)

### §334.180 Patuxent River, MD; restricted areas, U.S. Naval Air Test Center, Patuxent River, MD.

(3417)  (a) Except in the gut off the tip of Point Patience, no person in the water and no craft shall approach closer than 75 yards to the beaches, shoreline, or piers of the area formerly occupied by the U.S. Naval Mine Warfare Test Station, or of U.S. Naval Air Station property. A person in the water or a civilian craft shall not approach rafts, barges, or platforms closer than 100 yards.

(3418)  (b) Diving tenders will exhibit a square red flag with white X when underwater diving takes place from naval small craft. At such times, persons in the water and civilian craft shall stay at least 200 yards clear of these vessels and the civilian craft shall proceed at a speed not greater than five knots when within 1,000 yards thereof.

(3419)  (c) On occasions, seaplane landings and takeoffs will be practiced in the seadrome area north of the U.S. Naval Air Station, Patuxent River. This area includes those waters of the Patuxent River between Town Point and Hog Point shoreward of a line described as follows: Beginning at a point on the shore just west of Lewis Creek, bearing 161°30' true, 2,000 yards from Patuxent River Light 8; thence to a point bearing 130° true, 1,850 yards from Patuxent River Light 8; thence to a point bearing 247°30' true, 3,650 yards from Drum Point Light 2; thence to a point bearing 235° true, 2,060 yards from Drum Point Light 2; thence to a point bearing 129° true, 700 yards from Drum Point Light 2; thence to a point bearing 137° true, 1,060 yards from Drum Point Light 2; and thence to a point on the shore west of Harper Creek entrance, bearing 158°30' true, 1,900 yards from Drum Point Light 2.

(3420)  (d) The regulations in this section shall be enforced by the Commanding Officer, U.S. Naval Air Station, Patuxent River, MD, and such agencies as he may designate.

(3421)

### § 334.190 Chesapeake Bay, in vicinity of Bloodsworth Island, MD, U.S. Navy.

(3422)  (a) *The areas*–(1) *Prohibited area.* All waters within a circle 0.5 miles in radius with its center at 38°10'00"N., 76°06'00"W.; Bloodsworth Island, Pone Island, Northeast Island, and Adams Island.

(3423)  (2) *The danger zone.* All waters of Chesapeake Bay and Tangier Sound within an area bounded as follows: Beginning at

(3424)  38°08'15"N., 76°10'00"W.; thence to

(3425)  38°12'00"N., 76°10'00"W.; thence to

(3426)  38°12'00"N., 76°07'00"W.; thence to

(3427)  38°13'00"N., 76°06'00"W.; thence to

(3428)  38°13'00"N., 76°04'00"W.; thence to

(3429)  38°12'00"N., 76°02'00"W.; thence to

(3430)  38°12'00"N., 76°00'00"W.; thence to

(3431)  38°08'15"N., 76°00'00"W.; thence to the point of beginning, excluding the prohibited area described in paragraph (a)(1) of this section.

(3432)  (b) *The regulations.* (1) No person, vessel or other craft shall approach closer than 75 yards to the beaches, shoreline, or piers of Bloodsworth Island, Pone Island, Northeast Island, Adams Island, or any Patuxent River Naval Air Station property at any time unless authorized to do so by the enforcing agency. No person, vessel or other craft shall approach rafts, barges, or platforms closer than 100 yards.

(3433)  (2) No person, vessel, or other craft shall enter or remain in the danger zone when notified by the enforcing authority to keep clear. Any watercraft under way or at anchor, upon being so warned, shall immediately vacate the area and shall remain outside the area until conclusion of potentially hazardous test or training events.

(3434)  (3) The area will be in use intermittently throughout the year.

(3435)  (4) Prior to the commencement of any potentially hazardous test or training event that requires clearing of non-participant boats from the danger zone, surface or air search of the entire area will be made for the purpose of locating and warning all craft and persons not connected with the test or training event, and a patrol will be maintained throughout the duration of the event.

(3436)  (5) All persons, vessels, or other craft shall clear the area when warned by patrol vessels.

(3437)  (6) Patrol vessels will provide warning that a potentially hazardous test or training event is in progress or is about to commence; when so warned, fishing or oystering vessels or other craft not directly connected with the event shall not navigate within the danger zone. Deep-draft vessels proceeding in established navigation channels normally will be permitted to traverse the area upon coordination with range patrol vessels. The patrol vessels will ensure safe separation between all non-participant vessels and potentially hazardous operations.

(3438)  (7) When potentially hazardous testing or training is not in progress or is not about to commence, oystering and fishing boats and other craft may operate within the danger zone.

(3439)  (8) All potentially hazardous test or training events will be performed in such a way as to contain the hazard footprint to the established danger zone described in paragraph (a) of this section. Naval authorities will not be responsible for damage to nets, traps, buoys, pots, fish pounds, stakes, or other equipment that may be located within the danger zone.

(3440)  (9) Nothing in this regulation shall be intended to prevent the lawful use of approved waterfowl hunting blinds along the shorelines of Bloodsworth Island range complex, provided that all necessary licenses and permits have been obtained from the Maryland Department of Natural Resources and the completed copy of the permit has been submitted to the Conservation Division Director at NAS Patuxent River. Waterfowl hunters must observe all warnings and range clearances, as noted herein.

(3441)     (10) The regulations in this section shall be enforced by the Commander, Naval Air Station Patuxent River, Maryland, and such agencies as he/she may designate.

(3442)

### §334.200 Chesapeake Bay, Point Lookout to Cedar Point; aerial and surface firing range and target area, U.S. Naval Air Station, Patuxent River, Maryland, danger zones.

(3443)     (a) *Aerial firing range* (1) *The danger zone.* The waters of Chesapeake Bay within an area described as follows: Beginning at the easternmost extremity of Cedar Point; thence easterly to the southern tip of Barren Island; thence southeasterly to

(3444)     38°01'15"N., 76°05'33"W.; thence southwesterly to

(3445)     37°59'25"N., 76°10'54"W.; thence northwesterly to

(3446)     38°02'20"N., 76°17'26"W.; thence northerly to Point No Point Light; thence northwesterly to the shore at 38°15'45"N.; thence northeasterly along the shore to the point of beginning. Aerial and surface firing and dropping of nonexplosive ordnance will be conducted throughout the year.

(3447)     (2) *The regulations.* (i) Through navigation of surface craft outside the target areas will be permitted at all times. Vessels shall proceed on their normal course and shall not delay their progress.

(3448)     (ii) Prior to firing or ordnance drops, the range will be patrolled by naval surface craft or aircraft to warn watercraft likely to be endangered. Surface craft so employed will display a square red flag. Naval aircraft will use a method of warning consisting of repeated shallow dives in the area, following each dive by a sharp pullup.

(3449)     (iii) Any watercraft under way or at anchor, upon being so warned, shall immediately vacate the area and shall remain outside the area until conclusion of firing practice.

(3450)     (iv) Nothing in this section shall prevent the taking of shellfish or the setting of fishing structures within the range outside target areas in accordance with Federal and State regulations; Provided, That no permanent or temporary fishing structures or oyster ground markers shall be placed on the western side of the Chesapeake Bay between Point No Point and Cedar Point without prior written approval of the Commanding Officer, U.S. Naval Air Station, Patuxent River, MD.

(3451)     (v) Naval authorities will not be responsible for damage caused by projectiles, bombs, missiles, or Naval or Coast Guard vessels to fishing structures or fishing equipment which may be located in the aerial firing range immediately adjacent to the target areas.

(3452)     (b) *Target areas*–(1) *Prohibited area.* A circular area with a radius of 1,000 yards having its center at latitude 38°13'00", longitude 76°19'00" identified as Hooper Target.

(3453)     (2) *The area.* A circular area with a radius of 1,000 yards having its center at 38°02'18"N., 76°09'26"W., identified as Hannibal Target.

(3454)     (3) *The regulations.* Nonexplosive projectiles and bombs will be dropped at frequent intervals in the target areas. Hooper and Hannibal target areas shall be closed to navigation at all times, except for vessels engaged in operational and maintenance activities as directed by the Commanding Officer of the U.S. Naval Air Station, Patuxent River, Maryland. No person in the waters, vessel, or other craft shall enter or remain in the closed area or climb on targets except on prior written approval of the Commanding Officer, U.S. Naval Air Station, Patuxent River, Maryland.

(3455)     (c) *Enforcement.* The regulations in this section shall be enforced by the Commanding Officer of the Naval Air Station, Patuxent River, Maryland and such agencies as he or she may designate.

(3456)

### §334.210 Chesapeake Bay, in vicinity of Tangier Island; Naval guided missiles test operations area.

(3457)     (a) *The danger zone*–(1) *Prohibited area.* A circle 1,000 yards in radius with its center at latitude 37°47'54", longitude 76°03'48".

(3458)     (2) *Restricted area.* A circle three nautical miles in radius with its center at latitude 37°47'54", longitude 76°03'48", excluding the prohibited area.

(3459)     (b) *The regulations.* (1) Persons, vessels or other craft shall not enter or remain in the prohibited area at any time unless authorized to do so by the enforcing agency.

(3460)     (2) Except as otherwise provided in paragraph (b) (6) of this section, persons, vessels or other craft shall not enter or remain in the restricted area when firing is or will soon be in progress unless authorized to do so by the enforcing agency.

(3461)     (3) Advance notice will be given of the date on which the first firing is to be conducted and such notice will be published in "Notice to Mariners." Thereafter, the danger zone will be in use intermittently throughout the year and no further notice is contemplated that firing is continuing.

(3462)     (4) Warning that firing is or will soon be in progress will be indicated by a red flag displayed from one of six dolphin platforms on the perimeter of the prohibited area, and by patrol vessels within the danger zone or by aircraft employing the method of warning known as "buzzing" which consists of low flight by the airplane and repeated opening and closing of the throttle. Surface or air search of the entire area will be made prior to the commencement of firing on each scheduled day. During periods of firing a patrol vessel will remain in the approaches to the restricted area and maintain continuous contact with the firing planes to warn when the area is not clear.

(3463)     (5) Upon observing the warning flag or upon receiving a warning by any of the patrol vessels or aircraft, persons, vessels or other craft shall immediately vacate the restricted area and remain outside the area until the conclusion of firing for the day.

(3464)     (6) This section shall not deny traverse of portions of the restricted area by commercial craft proceeding in established steamer lanes, but when firing is or will soon be in progress all such craft shall proceed on their normal course through the area with all practicable speed.

(3465)    (7) All projectiles, bombs and rockets will be fired to land within the prohibited area, and on or in the immediate vicinity of a target in the restricted area located adjacent to the west side of Tangier Island. The Department of the Navy will not be responsible for damages by such projectiles, bombs, or rockets to nets, traps, buoys, pots, fishponds, stakes, or other equipment which may be located within the restricted area.

(3466)    (8) The regulations of this section shall be enforced by the Commander, Naval Air Bases, Fifth Naval District, Norfolk, Virginia, and such agencies as he may designate.

(3467)
### §334.220 Chesapeake Bay, south of Tangier Island, Virginia; naval firing range.

(3468)    (a) *The danger zone*. Beginning at latitude 37°46'39", longitude 75°57'43", thence to latitude 37°43'42", longitude 75°55'30"; thence to latitude 37°27'00", longitude 76°02'48"; thence to latitude 37°27'00", longitude 76°08'00"; thence to latitude 37°45'00", longitude 76°09'48"; thence to latitude 37°45'00", longitude 76°08'51"; and thence along the circumference of a circle of five nautical miles radius whose center is at latitude 37°47'54", longitude 76°03'48", to the point of beginning.

(3469)    (b) *The regulations*. (1) Any vessel propelled by mechanical means or by sail at a speed greater than five knots may proceed through the danger zone to and from points without, but not from one point to another point within, the area, except when especially notified to the contrary.

(3470)    (2) All vessels, other than naval craft, are forbidden to anchor within the danger zone except in cases of great emergency. All vessels anchoring under circumstances of great emergency within the area shall leave the area immediately after the emergency ceases or upon notification by the enforcing agency.

(3471)    (3) Fishing, oystering, clamming, crabbing, and other aquatic activities are forbidden within the limits of the danger zone, except that existing fishing structures licensed by the State of Virginia may be maintained and operated; Provided, The owners thereof obtain written permits from the enforcing agency designated in paragraph (b)(5) of this section.

(3472)    (4) Day and night firing over the range will be conducted intermittently by one or more vessels, depending on weather and operating schedules. When firing is in progress, adequate patrol by naval craft will be conducted to prevent vessels from entering or remaining within the danger zone.

(3473)    (5) This section shall be enforced by the Commandant, Fifth Naval District, U.S. Naval Base, Norfolk, Virginia, and such agencies as he may designate.

(3474)
### §334.230 Potomac River.

(3475)    (a) Naval Surface Warfare Center, Dahlgren, VA–(1) *The areas*. Portions of the Upper Machodoc Creek and Potomac River near Dahlgren, VA as described below:

(3476)    (i) *Lower zone*. The entire portion of the lower Potomac River between a line from Point Lookout, Maryland, to Smith Point, Virginia, and a line from Buoy 14 (abreast of St. Clements Island) to a point near the northeast shore of Hollis Marsh at 38°10'00"N., 76°45'22.4"W. Hazardous operations are conducted in this zone at infrequent intervals.

(3477)    (ii) *Middle zone*. Beginning at the intersection of the Harry W. Nice Bridge with the Virginia shore; thence to Light 33; thence to 38°19'06"N., 76°57'06"W. which point is about 3,300 yards east-southeast of Light 30; thence to Line of Fire Buoy O, about 1,150 yards southwest of Swan Point; thence to Line of Fire Buoy M, about 1,700 yards south of Potomac View; thence to Line of Fire Buoy K, about 1,400 yards southwesterly of the lower end of Cobb Island; thence to Buoy 14, abreast of St. Clements Island, thence southwest to a point near the northeast shore of Hollis Marsh at 38°10'00"N., 76°45'22.4"W.; thence northwest to Line of Fire Buoy J, about 3,000 yards off Popes Creek, Virginia; thence to Line of Fire Buoy L, about 3,600 yards off Church Point; thence to Line of Fire Buoy N, about 900 yards off Colonial Beach; thence to Line of Fire Buoy P, about 1,000 yards off Bluff Point; thence northwest to 38°17'54"N., 77°01'02"W., a point of the Virginia shore on property of the Naval Support Facility Dahlgren, a distance of about 4,080 yards; thence north along the Potomac shore of Naval Surface Warfare Center, Dahlgren to Baber Point; and thence west along the Upper Machodoc Creek shore of Naval Surface Warfare Center, Dahlgren to Howland Point at 38°19'0.5"N., 77°03'23"W.; thence northeast to 38°19'18"N., 77°02'29"W., a point on the Naval Surface Warfare Center, Dahlgren shore about 350 yards southeast of the base of the Navy recreational pier. Hazardous operations are normally conducted in this zone daily except Saturdays, Sundays, and national holidays.

(3478)    (iii) *Upper zone*. Beginning at Mathias Point, VA; thence north to Light 5; thence north-northeast to Light 6; thence east-southeast to Lighted Buoy 2, thence east-southeast to a point on the Maryland shore at approximately 38°23'35.5"N., 76°59'15.5"W.; thence south along the Maryland shore to, and then along, a line passing through Light 1 to the Virginia shore, parallel to the Harry W. Nice Bridge; thence north with the Virginia shore to the point of beginning. Hazardous operations are conducted in this zone at infrequent intervals.

(3479)    (2) *The regulations*. (i) Hazardous operations normally take place between the hours of 8 a.m. and 5 p.m. daily except Saturdays, Sundays and national holidays, with infrequent night firing between 5 p.m. and 10:30 p.m. During a national emergency, hazardous operations will take place between the hours of 6 a.m. and 10:30 p.m. daily except Sundays. Hazardous operations may involve firing large or small caliber guns and projectiles, aerial bombing, use of directed energy, and operating manned or unmanned watercraft.

(3480)    (ii) When hazardous operations are in progress, no person, or fishing or oystering vessels shall operate within the danger zone affected unless so authorized by the Naval Surface Warfare Center, Dahlgren's patrol boats. Oystering and fishing boats or other craft may cross the river in the danger zone only after they have reported to the patrol boat and received instructions as to when and where to cross. Deep-draft vessels using dredged channels and propelled by mechanical power at a speed greater than five miles per hour may proceed directly through the danger zones without restriction except when notified to the contrary by the patrol boat. Unless instructed to the contrary by the patrol boat, small craft navigating up or down the Potomac River during hazardous operations shall proceed outside of the northeastern boundary of the Middle Danger Zone. All craft desiring to enter the Middle Danger Zone when proceeding in or out of Upper Machodoc Creek during hazardous operations will be instructed by the patrol boat; for those craft that desire to proceed in or out of Upper Machodoc Creek on a course between the western shore of the Potomac River and a line from the Main Dock of Naval Surface Warfare Center, Dahlgren to Line of Fire Buoy P, clearance will be granted to proceed upon request directed to the patrol boat.

(3481)    (iii) Due to hazards of unexploded ordnance, no person or craft in the Middle Danger Zone shall approach closer than 100 yards to the shoreline of Naval Surface Warfare Center, Dahlgren, previously known as the Naval Surface Weapons Center.

(3482)    (3) *Enforcement.* The regulations shall be enforced by the Commander, Naval Surface Warfare Center, Dahlgren and such agencies as he/she may designate. Patrol boats, in the execution of their mission assigned herein, shall display a square red flag during daylight hours for purposes of identification; at night time, a 32 point red light shall be displayed at the mast head. Naval Surface Warfare Center, Dahlgren (Range Control) can be contacted by Marine VHF radio (channel 16) or by telephone 540–653–8791.

(3483)    (4) *Exceptions.* Nothing in this regulation shall be intended to prevent commercial fishing or the lawful use of approved waterfowl hunting blinds along the shorelines of Naval Surface Warfare Center, Dahlgren, provided that all necessary licenses and permits have been obtained from the Maryland Department of Natural Resources, the Virginia Department of Game and Inland Fisheries, or the Potomac River Fisheries Commission. Waterfowl hunters shall provide a completed copy of their blind permit to the Natural Resources Manager at Naval Surface Warfare Center, Dahlgren. Commercial fishermen and waterfowl hunters must observe all warnings and range clearances, as noted herein. Federal, State and local law enforcement agencies are exempt from the provisions of paragraph (a) of this section.

(3484)    (b) Accotink Bay, Accotink Creek, and Pohick Bay; United States Military Reservation, Fort Belvoir, VA–(1) *The danger zone.* The waters of Accotink Bay, Accotink Creek, and Pohick Bay, Virginia, within and adjacent to the target ranges of the United States Military Reservation, Fort Belvoir, as follows: All of Accotink Bay; all of Accotink Creek below the bridge which crosses Accotink Creek approximately 400 yards south of U.S. Highway No. 1; and that portion of Pohick Bay bordering its north shore. The mouth of Accotink Bay and that portion of Pohick Bay within the danger zone will be marked by the Post Commander with suitable warning buoys.

(3485)    (2) *The regulations.* (i) When firing affecting the area is in progress, the Post Commander will post guards at such locations that the waters in the danger zone may be observed and arrange signals whereby these guards may stop the firing should any person be seen in the danger zone. When firing is in progress, the Post Commander will cause to be displayed both on the east shore of Accotink Bay at its mouth and near the danger zone boundary on Accotink Creek a red streamer which shall be visible to a person in a boat near those points.

(3486)    (ii) Persons desiring to cross the waters in the danger zone shall first determine whether a red streamer is displayed on the east Shore of Accotink Bay at its mouth or near the danger zone boundary on Accotink Creek. If the red streamer is displayed, it will indicate that firing is in progress and that the waters in the danger zone are covered by rifle fire, and the area shall not be entered until the streamer is lowered.

(3487)    (iii) The Post Commander is hereby authorized by using such agencies and equipment necessary to stop all boats at the boundary of the danger zone and prohibit their crossing the area until convenient to the firing schedule to do so.

(3488)

### §334.235 Potomac River, Marine Corps Base Quantico (MCB Quantico) in vicinity of Marine Corps Air Facility (MCAF), restricted area.

(3489)    (a) *The area.* All of the navigable waters of the Potomac River extending approximately 500 meters from the high-water mark on the Eastern shoreline of the MCAF, bounded by these coordinates (including the Chopawamsic Creek channel, but excluding Chopawamsic Island): Beginning at

(3490)    38°29'34.04"N., 077°18'22.4"W. (Point A); thence to

(3491)    38°29'43.01"N., 077°18'4.1"W. (Point B); thence to

(3492)    38°29'55.1"N., 077°17'51.3"W. (Point C); thence to

(3493)    38°30'10.01"N., 077°17'40.3"W. (Point D); thence to

(3494)    38°30'23.43"N., 077°17'50.30"W. (Point E); then along the western shoreline of Chopawamsic Island to

(3495)    38°30'35.13"N., 077°17'47.45"W. (Point F); thence to

(3496)    38°30'42.1"N., 077°17'37.1"W. (Point G); thence to

(3497)      38°30'50.71"N., 077°17'54.12"W. (Point H); then along the shoreline to

(3498)      38°30'0.58"N., 077°18'39.26"W. (Point I); then across the Chopawamsic Channel to

(3499)      38°29'58.45"N., 077°18'39.97"W. (Point J); thence to

(3500)      38°29'38.2"N., 077°18'38.14"W. (Point K); and thence to the beginning point of origin.

(3501)      (b) *The regulations.* (1) All persons, vessels, or other craft are prohibited from entering, transiting, drifting, dredging, or anchoring within the restricted area without the permission of the Commander, MCB Quantico or his/her designated representatives. The restriction will be in place 24 hours a day, seven days a week.

(3502)      (2) The boundary of the restricted area will be demarcated with marked buoys and warning signs set at 500 foot intervals. In addition, floating small craft intrusion barriers marked with reflective material will be placed across the Chopawamsic Creek channel at the entrance to the channel from the Potomac River and immediately west of the CSX railroad bridge.

(3503)      (c) *Enforcement.* The regulations in this section shall be enforced by the Commander, MCB Quantico or any such agencies he/she designates. The areas identified in paragraph (a) of this section will be monitored 24 hours a day, 7 days a week. Any person or vessel encroaching within the areas identified in paragraph (a) of this section will be directed to immediately leave the restricted area. Failure to do so could result in forceful removal and/or criminal charges.

(3504)      (d) Exceptions. Commercial fisherman will be authorized controlled access to the restricted area (with the exception of Chopawamisc Creek channel) after registering with MCD Quantico officials and following specific access notification procedures.

(3505)

### §334.240 Potomac River, Mattawoman Creek and Chicamuxen Creek; U.S. Naval Surface Weapons Center, Indian Head Division, Indian Head, MD.

(3506)      (a) *The danger zone.* Beginning at a point on the easterly shore of the Potomac River at

(3507)      38°36'00"N., 77°11'00"W.; thence

(3508)      38°34'30"N., 77°13'00"W.; thence

(3509)      38°33'20"N., 77°14'20"W.; thence

(3510)      38°32'20"N., 77°15'10"W.; thence

(3511)      38°32'00"N., 77°15'00"W.; thence

(3512)      38°32'30"N., 77°14'00"W.; thence upstream along the easterly shoreline of Chicamuxen Creek to its head; thence downstream along the westerly shoreline of Chicamuxen Creek to the southernmost point of Stump Neck; thence northeasterly along the shoreline of Stump Neck to the mouth of Mattawoman Creek; thence along the southeasterly shore of Mattawoman Creek to the pilings remaining from the footbridge connecting the left bank of the creek to Naval Surface Warfare Center, Indian Head Division; thence along the northwesterly shore of Mattawoman Creek from the pilings remaining

from the footbridge to the mouth of the creek; thence in a northeasterly direction along the easterly shore of the Potomac River to the point of beginning.

(3513)      (b) *The regulations.* (1) Firings consisting of controlled explosions within the danger zone, and controlled shore operations, or accidental explosions, hazardous to vessel traffic within the limits of the danger zone, may take place at any time of the day or night and on any day of the week.

(3514)      (2) Flashing red lights, horns, and signs established at appropriate points will warn vessels of impending tests or operations considered to be hazardous to vessels within the danger zone.

(3515)      (3) No persons or vessels except vessels of the United States or vessels authorized by the enforcing agency shall enter or remain in the danger zone while lights are flashing, when warning horns are in operation, or when warned or directed by a patrol vessel.

(3516)      (4) Nothing in this section shall prohibit the use of Mattawoman Creek or Chicamuxen Creek as a harbor of refuge because of stress of weather.

(3517)      (5) Except as prescribed in paragraph (b)(3) of this section, persons and vessels may enter and proceed through the danger zone without restriction. However, accidental explosions may occur at any time and persons and vessels entering the area do so at their own risk.

(3518)      (6) Fishermen operating in the danger zone when warning signals are sounded shall evacuate the area immediately.

(3519)      (7) The regulations in this section shall be enforced by the Commanding Officer, U.S. Naval Surface Warfare Center, Indian Head Division, Indian Head, Maryland.

(3520)

### §334.250 Gunston Cove, at Whitestone Point, VA; U.S. Army restricted area.

(3521)      (a) *The area.* The waters within an area beginning at a point on the shoreline at longitude 77°08'36"; thence to latitude 38°40'22", longitude 77°08'39"; thence to latitude 38°40'14", longitude 77°08'22"; thence to a point on the shoreline at longitude 77°08'18" and thence along the shoreline to the point of beginning.

(3522)      (b) *The regulations.* No person, vessel, or other craft shall enter or remain in the area at any time except as authorized by the enforcing agency.

(3523)      (c) The regulations in this section shall be enforced by the District Engineer, U.S. Army Engineer District, Philadelphia, PA and such agencies as he may designate.

(3524)

### §334.260 York River, VA; naval restricted areas.

(3525)      (a) *The areas*—(1) *Naval mine service-testing area (prohibited).* A rectangular area surrounding Piers 1 and 2, Naval Weapons Station, and extending upstream therefrom, beginning at a point on the shore line at

(3526)      37°15'25"N., 76°32'32"W.; thence to

(3527)      37°15'42"N., 76°32'06"W.; thence to

(3528)      37°15'27"N., 76°31'48"W.; thence to

(3529)    37°15'05"N., 76°31'27"W.; thence to a point on the shore line at

(3530)    37°14'51"N., 76°31'50"W.; and thence along the shore line to the point of beginning.

(3531)    (2) *Naval mine service-testing area (restricted)*. A rectangular area adjacent to the northeast boundary of the prohibited area described in paragraph (a)(1) of this section, beginning at

(3532)    37°16'00"N., 76°32'29"W.; thence to

(3533)    37°16'23"N., 76°32'00"W.; thence to

(3534)    37°15'27"N., 76°30'54"W.; thence to

(3535)    37°15'05"N., 76°31'27"W.; thence to

(3536)    37°15'27"N., 76°31'48"W.; thence to

(3537)    37°15'42"N., 76°32'06"W.; thence to

(3538)    37°15'40"N., 76°32'09"W.; and thence to the point of beginning.

(3539)    (3) *Explosives-Handling Berth (Naval)*. A circular area of 600 yards radius with its center at 37°13'56"N, 76°28'48"W.

(3540)    (4) *Felgates Creek (prohibited)*. Navigable waters of the United States as defined at 33 CFR part 329 within Felgates Creek from the boundary fence line at the mouth to the mean high water line of the head and all associated tributaries. The area contains the entirety of Felgates Creek and all associated tributaries south of the line which begins at 37°16'24"N., 76°35'12"W. and extends east to 37°16'21"N., 76°35'00"W.

(3541)    (5) *Indian Field Creek (prohibited)*. Navigable waters of the United States as defined at 33 CFR part 329 within Indian Field Creek from the boundary fence line at the mouth to the mean high water line of the head and all associated tributaries. The area contains the entirety of Indian Field Creek and all associated tributaries south of the line which begins at 37°16'05"N, 76°33'29"W. and extends east to 37°16'01"N., 76°33'22"W.

(3542)    (b) *The regulations*. (1) All persons and all vessels other than naval craft are forbidden to enter the prohibited area described in paragraph (a)(1) of this section.

(3543)    (2) Trawling, dragging, and net-fishing are prohibited, and no permanent obstructions may at any time be placed in the area described in paragraph (a)(2) of this section. Upon official notification, any vessel anchored in the area and any person in the area will be required to vacate the area during the actual mine-laying operation. Persons and vessels entering the area during mine-laying operations by aircraft must proceed directly through the area without delay, except in case of emergency. Naval authorities are required to publish advance notice of mine-laying and/ or retrieving operations scheduled to be carried on in the area, and during such published periods of operation, fishing or other aquatic activities are forbidden in the area. No vessel will be denied passage through the area at any time during either mine-laying or retrieving operations.

(3544)    (3) The Explosives-Handling Berth (Naval) described in paragraph (a)(3) of this section is reserved for the exclusive use of naval vessels and except in cases of emergency no other vessel shall anchor therein without the permission of local naval authorities, obtained through the Captain of the Port, U.S. Coast Guard, Norfolk, Virginia. There shall be no restriction on the movement of vessels through the Explosive-Handling Berth.

(3545)    (4) Vessels shall not be anchored, nor shall persons in the water approach within 300 yards of the perimeter of the Explosives-Handling Berth (Naval) when that berth is occupied by a vessel handling explosives.

(3546)    (5) All persons and all vessels are forbidden to enter the prohibited areas described in paragraphs (a)(4) and (a)(5) of this section without prior permission of the enforcing agency.

(3547)    (6) The regulations of this section shall be enforced by the Commander, Naval Weapons Station Yorktown, Virginia, and such agencies as he/she may designate.

(3548)

### §334.270 York River adjacent to Cheatham Annex Depot, Naval Supply Center, Williamsburg, Virginia; restricted area.

(3549)    (a) *The area*. The waters of York River bounded as follows: Beginning at a point on shore at Cheatham Annex Depot at

(3550)    37°17'14"N., 76°35'38"W.; thence to a point offshore at

(3551)    37°17'52"N., 76°35'20"W.; thence approximately parallel to the shore to a point at

(3552)    37°17'23"N., 76°34'39"W.; thence to the shore at

(3553)    37°16'58"N., 76°35'03"W.; and thence along the shore at Cheatham Annex Depot to the point of beginning.

(3554)    (b) *The regulations*. (1) No loitering will be permitted within the area. Oystermen may work their own leaseholds or public bottom within the area, provided they obtain special permission from the Officer in Charge, Cheatham Annex Depot, Naval Supply Center, Williamsburg, Virginia.

(3555)    (2) The regulations in this section shall be enforced by the Officer in Charge, Cheatham Annex Depot, U.S. Naval Supply Center, Williamsburg, Virginia.

(3556)

### §334.275 North and Southwest Branch, Back River, Hampton, U.S. Air Force Base, Langley, VA; restricted area.

(3557)    (a) *The area*. Beginning at a point on the island at the entrance to Tide Mills Creek in the Southwest Branch of the Back River at 37°03'50"N., 076°22'00"W., thence along the shore of Langley Air Force Base, 35 yards off the ordinary mean high water (MHW) mark, to a point in the Northwest Branch of the Back River at 37°06'40"N., 076°22'55"W.

(3558)    (b) *The regulations*.

(3559)    (1) No persons or vessels, recreational or commercial, may enter this restricted area without the permission of the Commanding Officer, Langley Air Force Base.

(3560)    (2) The Commanding Officer shall not prevent persons from fulfilling their legal obligation to the Commonwealth of Virginia with regard to oyster planting ground leases that lie within the restricted area. The Commanding Officer may, at his/her discretion, require those persons and vessels working those leases to register with the Langley Air Force Base Security Officer on an annual basis. Failure to comply with this request may result in denial to access the oyster grounds until such time as the request has been complied with.

(3561) (3) Persons or vessels contracted with or utilized by the Commonwealth of Virginia to work the oyster grounds shall give verbal notification to the base Security Office prior to entering the restricted area.

(3562) (4) City, State and Federal law enforcement vessels may enter the restricted area at any time they deem necessary for the enforcement of their respective laws.

(3563) (c) *Enforcement.* The regulations in this section shall be enforced by the Commanding Officer of the Langley Air Force Base and such agencies as he/she may designate.

(3564)
### § 334.280 James River, Skiffes Creek and Warwick River surrounding Joint Base Langley-Eustis, Virginia; restricted areas and danger zones.

(3565) (a) *The areas.* The datum for the coordinates for the restricted areas and danger zones described in this section is NAD–83.

(3566) (1) *Army Training and Small Craft Testing Area (restricted area).* Beginning on the shore at 37°09′53″N., 76°36′23″W.; thence westerly to 37°09′53″N., 76°36′59″W.; thence westerly to 37°09′50″N., 76°37′45″W.; thence southerly to 37°09′00″N., 76°38′05″W.; thence southerly to 37°08′22″N., 76°37′55″W.; thence due east to the shore at 37°08′22″N., 76°37′20″W.; thence northerly following the shoreline to the point of beginning.

(3567) (2) *3rd Port Facility (restricted area).* An area surrounding the 3rd Port facility, Fort Eustis, beginning at a point on the shoreline at 37°09′53″N., 76°36′23″W.; thence northerly, following the shoreline to 37°10′03″N., 76°36′25″W.; thence northerly, following the shoreline to 37°10′19″N., 76°36′07″W.; thence northerly, across the mouth of Bailey's Creek to 37°10′24″N., 76°36′02″W.; thence northerly, following the shoreline to 37°10′29″N., 76°36′06″W.; thence westerly, across Skiffes Creek to 37°10′33″N., 76°36′20″W.; thence southerly following the shoreline to 37°10′13″N., 76°36′42″W.; thence southerly to 37°09′53″N., 76°36′59″W.; thence to the point of beginning.

(3568) (3) *Warwick River and any tributaries, creeks, estuaries, tidal areas, to include Butlers Gut and Jail Creek (restricted area).* All navigable waters of the United States as defined in 33 CFR part 329 within the boundaries of Fort Eustis, westerly of a line connecting the following coordinates: Commencing from the shoreline at 37°09′47″N., 76°33′52″W.; thence following the meanders of the installation boundary along the westerly mean low waterline of Warwick River, thence to a point on the installation boundary at 37°04′35″N., 76°33′19″W.

(3569) (4) *James River and any tributaries, creeks, estuaries, tidal areas, to include Nells Creek, Locust Neck Creek, Dudleys Creek, Morrisons Creek, Morleys Gut, Blows Creek, and Milstead Creek (restricted area).* Navigable waters of the United States as defined at 33 CFR part 329 within the boundaries of Fort Eustis, north/northeasterly of a line connecting the following coordinates: Commencing from the shoreline at 37°04′35″N., 76°33′19″W.; thence following the meanders of the installation boundary along the northeasterly mean low waterline of the James River, thence to a point on the installation boundary at 37°10′03″N., 76°36′25″W., at a point at the mouth of Skiffes Creek.

(3570) (5) *Skiffes Creek and any tributaries, creeks, estuaries, tidal areas, to include Baileys Creek (restricted area).* All navigable waters of the United States as defined at 33 CFR part 329 within the boundaries of Fort Eustis, easterly of a line connecting the following coordinates: Commencing from a point on the installation boundary at 37°10′03″N., 76°36′25″W.; thence northerly, following the shoreline to 37°10′19″N., 76°36′07″W.; thence northerly, across the mouth of Bailey's Creek to 37°10′24″N., 76°36′02″W.; thence northerly, following the shoreline to 37°10′29″N., 76°36′06″W.; thence northerly, following the meanders of the installation boundary to a point at the centerline of an unnamed tributary at 37°10′36″N., 76°36′01″W.; thence southeasterly, following the centerline of the unnamed tributary to a point on the installation boundary at 37°10′24″N., 76°35′32″W.

(3571) (6) *Danger Zone Warwick River.* Navigable waters of the United States as defined at 33 CFR part 329 that encroach upon the boundaries of the Danger Zone of Fort Eustis, westerly of a line connecting the following coordinates: Commencing from the installation boundary at 37°06′44″N., 76°34′04″W.; thence to a point at 37°06′44″N., 76°34′02″W.; thence to a point at 37°06′35″N., 76°33′56″W.; thence to a point at 37°06′28″N., 76°33′57″W.; thence to a point at 37°06′15″N., 76°33′30″W.; thence to a point at 37°05′43″N., 76°33′13″W.; thence to a point at 37°05′33″N., 76°33′17″W.; thence to a point at 37°05′13″N., 76°32′53″W.; thence to a point at 37°05′03″N., 76°33′09″W.; thence following the meanders of the installation boundary along the southwesterly mean low waterline of Warwick River, thence to a point at 37°04′52″N., 76°33′13″W.; thence to a point at 37°04′49″N., 76°33′11″W.; thence to a point at 37°04′43″N., 76°33′28″W.; thence following the meanders of the installation boundary along the southwesterly mean low waterline of Warwick River, thence to a point at 37°04′35″N., 76°33′19″W.

(3572) (7) *Danger Zone James River.* Navigable waters of the United States as defined at 33 CFR part 329 that encroach upon the boundaries of the Danger Zone of Fort Eustis, north/northeasterly of a line connecting the following coordinates: Commencing from the installation boundary at 37°04′35″N., 76°33′19″W.; thence following the meanders of the installation boundary along the easterly mean low waterline of James River to a point at 37°04′39″N., 76°33′39″W.; thence to a point at 37°04′33″N., 76°34′15″W.; thence to a point at 37°04′52″N., 76°34′19″W.; thence to a point at 37°04′52″N., 76°34′18″W.; thence to a point at 37°04′60″N., 76°34′20″W.; thence to a point at 37°05′19″N., 76°34′51″W.; thence to a point at 37°05′53″N., 76°35′00″W.; thence to a point at 37°06′03″N., 76°35′08″W.; thence following the meanders of the installation boundary along the easterly mean low waterline of James River, thence to a point at 37°06′40″N., 76°35′52″W.; thence to a point at 37°06′35″N., 76°36′19″W.; thence to a point on the installation boundary at 37°06′50″N., 76°36′21″ W.

(3573)    (b) *The regulations.* (1) For the restricted areas defined in paragraphs (a)(1) and (2) of this section:

(3574)    (i) All vessels will contact the 3rd Port Harbor Master on marine channel 12 or 68 prior to entering or transiting these restricted areas.

(3575)    (ii) The passage of fishing vessels to or from authorized traps, or the transit of commercial vessels, will be coordinated with the 3rd Port Harbor Master on marine channel 12 or 68.

(3576)    (iii) The harvesting and cultivation of oyster beds or the setting of fish traps within these restricted areas will be allowed provided the commercial fisherman coordinate access to these areas with the 3rd Port Harbor Master on marine channel 12 or 68.

(3577)    (iv) The Commander, Joint Base Langley-Eustis will, to the extent possible, give public notice from time to time through local news media and the Coast Guard's Local Notice to Mariners of the schedule of intended Department of Defense use of the restricted areas.

(3578)    (2) For the restricted areas defined in paragraphs (a) (3), (4), and (5) of this section:

(3579)    (i) Entry into these areas is for official government purposes only, or as authorized by the Commander, Joint Base Langley-Eustis.

(3580)    (ii) Entry will be coordinated and conducted in accordance with the policies and procedures established by the Commander, Joint Base Langley-Eustis.

(3581)    (3) For the danger zones defined in paragraphs (a) (6) and (7) of this section:

(3582)    (i) Persons, vessels or other craft shall not enter or remain in the danger zone when firing is or will soon be in progress unless authorized to do so by the enforcing agency.

(3583)    (ii) Advance notice of the schedule of small arms firing will be provided via the Joint Base Langley-Eustis web page.

(3584)    (iii) All projectiles will be fired to land within the impact area on the Fort Eustis peninsula. Neither the Department of the Army nor the Department of the Air Force will be responsible for damages by such projectiles to nets, traps, buoys, pots, fishpounds, stakes, or other equipment which may be located within these danger zones.

(3585)    (c) *Enforcement.* The regulations of this section shall be enforced by the Commander, Joint Base Langley-Eustis, Virginia, and such agencies as the commander may designate.

(3586)

### §334.285 York River and the Naval Weapons Station Yorktown-Cheatham Annex, Yorktown, Virginia; danger zone.

(3587)    (a) *The area.* The waters within an area beginning at mean high water on the shore at the facility located at

(3588)    37°17′33.10″N, 76°36′19.06″W; then northeast to a point in the York River at

(3589)    37°18′36.65″N, 76°34′39.01″W; thence south, southeast to

(3590)    37°17′59.37″N, 76°34′13.65″W; then southwest to a point on the shore located at

(3591)    37°17′26.75″N, 76°36′14.89″W.

(3592)    (b) *The regulations.* (1) Vessels and persons may transit this area at any time. No vessel or persons shall anchor, fish or conduct any waterborne activities within the danger zone established in accordance with this regulation any time live firing exercises are being conducted.

(3593)    (2) Anytime live firing is being conducted, the person or persons in charge shall display a red flag from a conspicuous location along the shore to signify the range is active and post lookouts to ensure the safety of all vessels passing through the area. At night, red lights will be displayed in lieu of flags.

(3594)    (3) No firing activities shall be conducted when the visibility is less than the maximum range of the weapons being used at the facility or while a vessel is within the danger zone.

(3595)    (4) Recreational and commercial activities may be conducted in this area anytime the range is inactive.

(3596)    (c) *Enforcement.* The regulations in this section shall be enforced by the Commander, Naval Weapons Station, Yorktown, or such agencies as he or she may designate.

(3597)

### §334.290 Elizabeth River, Southern Branch, VA, naval restricted areas.

(3598)    (a) *The areas*–(1) *St. Helena Annex Area.* Beginning at a point at St. Helena Annex of the Norfolk Naval Shipyard, on the eastern shore of Southern Branch of Elizabeth River, at latitude 36°49′43″, longitude 76°17′26.5″; thence in a southwesterly direction to a point on the eastern boundary of Norfolk Harbor 40-foot channel at latitude 36°49′42″, longitude 76°17′33″; thence in a southerly direction along the eastern boundary of Norfolk Harbor 40-foot channel to latitude 36°49′28″, longitude 76°17′27″; thence easterly to the shore at latitude 36°49′28″, longitude 76°17′22″; and thence, northerly along the shore to the point of beginning.

(3599)    (2) *Norfolk Naval Shipyard Area.* Beginning at a point on the shore at the northeast corner of the Norfolk Naval Shipyard, at latitude 36°49′43.5″, longitude 76°17′41.5″; thence due east approximately 100 feet to the western boundary of Elizabeth River channel; thence in a southerly direction along the western boundary of the channel to the point where it passes through the draw of the Norfolk and Portsmouth Belt Line Railroad bridge, thence in a southwesterly direction along the northerly side of the bridge to the western shore of Southern Branch of Elizabeth River; and thence along the shore in a northerly direction to the point of beginning.

(3600)      (3) *Southgate Terminal Area.* Beginning at a point at the northeast corner of Southgate Terminal Annex of Norfolk Naval Shipyard, at latitude 36°48'23", longitude 76°17'39"; thence east to latitude 36°48'23", longitude 76°17'29"; thence southerly along the western boundary of Norfolk Harbor 35-foot channel to latitude 36°48'04", longitude 76°17'33"; thence west to latitude 36°48'04", longitude 76°17'41"; and thence along the shore in a northerly direction to the point of beginning.

(3601)      (b) *The regulations.* (1) No vessels other than Naval vessels and other vessels authorized to move to and from piers at the Norfolk Naval Shipyard and its two annexes described in paragraph (a)(1) and (3) of this section, and no person other than persons embarked in such vessels, shall enter the restricted areas.

(3602)      (2) This section shall be enforced by the Commander, Norfolk Naval Shipyard, Portsmouth, VA, and such agencies as he may designate.

(3603)
### §334.293 Elizabeth River, Craney Island Refueling Pier Restricted Area, Portsmouth VA; Naval Restricted Area.

(3604)      (a) *The area.* (1) The waters within an area beginning at a point on the shore at
(3605)      36°53'17.4"N., 76°20'21.0"W.; thence easterly to
(3606)      36°53'16.8"N., 76°20'14.4"W.; thence southwesterly to
(3607)      36°53'00.0"N., 76°20'18.0"W.; thence southeasterly to
(3608)      36°52'55.2"N., 76°20'16.5"W.; thence southwesterly to
(3609)      36°52'52.2"N., 76°20'18.0"W.; thence southwesterly to
(3610)      36°52'49.8"N., 76°20'25.8"W.; thence northwesterly to
(3611)      36°52'58.2"N., 76°20'33.6"W.; thence northeasterly to a point on the shore at
(3612)      36°53'00.0"N., 76°20'30.0"W.; thence northerly along the shoreline to the point of beginning.
(3613)      (b) *The regulation.* No vessel or persons may enter the restricted area unless specific authorization is granted by the Commander, Navy Region, Mid-Atlantic and/or other persons or agencies as he/she may designate.
(3614)      (c) *Enforcement.* The regulation in this section, promulgated by the Corps of Engineers, shall be enforced by the Commander, Navy Region, Mid-Atlantic, and such agencies or persons as he/she may designate.

(3615)
### §334.300 Hampton Roads and Willoughby Bay, Norfolk Naval Base, Naval Restricted Area, Norfolk, Virginia.

(3616)      (a) *The area.* (1) The waters within an area beginning at
(3617)      36°55'55.0"N., 76°20'02.0"W.; thence northwesterly to
(3618)      36°56'00.0"N., 76°20'08.0"W.; thence northerly along the eastern limit of Norfolk Harbor Channel to
(3619)      36°57'52.0"N., 76°20'00.0"W.; thence easterly to
(3620)      36°57'52.0"N., 76°19'35.0"W.; thence to
(3621)      36°57'47.7"N., 76°18'57.0"W.; thence southeasterly to
(3622)      36°57'26.0"N., 76°18'42.0"W.; thence easterly to
(3623)      36°57'26.2"N., 76°17'55.2"W.; thence southerly to
(3624)      36°57'05.0"N., 76°17'52.0"W.; thence southeasterly to
(3625)      36°56'56.2"N., 76°17'27.0"W.; thence northeasterly to
(3626)      36°57'10.0"N., 76°16'29.0"W.; thence to the shoreline at
(3627)      36°57'18.8"N., 76°16'22.0"W. at the Naval Air Station.
(3628)      (2) Beginning at a point on the Naval Station shore at
(3629)      36°56'37.5"N., 76°19'44.0"W.; thence westerly and northerly along the breakwater to its extremity at
(3630)      36°56'41.5"N., 76°19'54.0"W.; thence westerly to a point on the eastern limit of Norfolk Harbor Channel at
(3631)      36°56'41.5"N., 76°20'05.5"W.; thence northerly along the eastern limit of Norfolk Harbor Channel to
(3632)      36°57'52.0"N., 76°20'00.0"W.; thence easterly to
(3633)      36°57'52.0"N., 76°19'35.0"W.; thence to
(3634)      36°57'47.7"N., 76°18'57.0"W.; thence southeasterly to
(3635)      36°57'26.0"N., 76°18'42.0"W.; thence easterly to
(3636)      36°57'26.2"N., 76°17'55.2"W.; thence southerly to
(3637)      36°57'05.0"N., 76°17'52.0"W.; thence southeasterly to
(3638)      36°56'56.2"N., 76°17'27.0"W.; thence northeasterly to
(3639)      36°57'10.0"N., 76°16'29.0"W.; and thence to the shoreline at
(3640)      36°57'18.8"N., 76°16'22.0W., at the Naval Air Station.
(3641)      (b) *The regulation.* No vessel or persons may enter the restricted area unless specific authorization is granted by the Commander, Navy Region, Mid-Atlantic and/or other persons or agencies as he/she may designate.
(3642)      (c) *Enforcement.* The regulation in this section, promulgated by the United States Army Corps of Engineers, shall be enforced by the Commander, Navy Region, Mid-Atlantic and/or such agencies or persons as he/she may designate.

(3643)
### §334.305 Little Creek Harbor, Fisherman's Cove,

### Joint Expeditionary Base Little CreekFort Story, Little Creek, Virginia, Restricted Areas.

(3644)     (a) *The Little Creek Restricted Areas.* The Little Creek Restricted Areas consist of two distinct areas: The Outer Harbor Restricted Area and the Inner Harbor Restricted Area. The datum for the coordinates in this section is NAD–83.

(3645)     (1) *The Outer Harbor Restricted Area.* The waters within an area beginning at 36°55′57.7″N., 76°10′35″W.; thence southwesterly to a point at 36°55′53″N., 76°10′44″W., thence southerly to 36°55′21.2″N., 76°10′42″W.; thence southwesterly to 36°55′18.3″N., 76°10′49″W.; thence northwesterly to a point in Fisherman's Cove at 36°55′22″N., 76°11′15.5″W.; thence southerly to 36°55′19.2″N., 76°11′16″W., thence easterly near the southern shoreline of Fisherman's Cove, to 36°55′15.8″N., 76°10′58.8″W.; and ending at 36°55′18″N., 76°10′30″W.; thence to the point of origin.

(3646)     (2) *The Inner Harbor Restricted Area.* The waters within Little Creek Harbor south of a line beginning at 36°55′15.8″N., 76°10′58.8″W.; and ending at 36°55′18″N., 76°10′30″W.

(3647)     (b) *The regulations*—(1) The Outer Harbor Restricted Area. (i) All privately owned vessels, properly registered and bearing identification in accordance with Federal and/or State laws and regulations, and all Government owned vessels (public vessels) may enter or exit the waters described in paragraph (a)(1) of this section at any time and transit inbound/outbound of the marked dredged channel leading to Little Creek Harbor between jetties 8 miles westward of Cape Henry Light. All vessels transiting inbound/outbound of the channel except for those vessels listed in paragraph (c)(2) of this section shall proceed at speeds commensurate with minimum wake. Any vessel equipped with a marine radio can monitor VHF–FM channel 12 for message traffic from Little Creek Port Control.

(3648)     (ii) When Commanding Officer, Joint Expeditionary Base Little Creek-Fort Story is ordered to implement Force Protection Conditions (FPCONs) Charlie/Delta, or when specific authority is granted by the District Engineer, all vessel traffic movement can be restricted except for those vessels that meet the criteria in paragraph (c)(2) of this section. FPCONs are a system of protective measures used by the Department of Defense (DOD) installations to guard against and deter terrorist attack. Senior commanders assign the FPCONs for their region, and installation commanders may raise FPCONS and tighten security measures based on local conditions. In the event FPCONs Charlie/Delta is implemented by the Commanding Officer, Joint Expeditionary Base Little Creek, which requires the restriction of vessel traffic movement in the Outer Harbor Restricted Area, the installation will coordinate with the U.S. Coast Guard, Fifth District; Army Corps of Engineers, Norfolk District; and state and local law enforcement and governmental authorities. The installation will also disseminate information to the public and local news media outlets.

Information on whether vessel traffic movement has been restricted in the Outer Harbor Restricted Area due to the implementation of FPCONs Charlie/Delta will also be published and disseminated by the U.S. Coast Guard.

(3649)     (2) *The Inner Harbor Restricted Area.* All vessels or persons intending to transit inbound/outbound of the Inner Harbor Restricted Area shall request permission from Little Creek Harbor Port Control using VHF–FM channel 12 prior to transiting and will provide their destination/intentions with the exception of those vessels that meet the criteria in paragraph (c)(2) of this section. The Inner Harbor Restricted Area is limited to those privately owned vessels or persons calling upon the commercial/private piers located within the Inner Harbor and government owned vessels (public vessels) transiting to and from U.S. Navy or U.S. Coast Guard facilities and authorized DOD patrons of the U.S. Navy recreational marina. No other vessels or persons may enter or exit this area unless specific authorization is granted by Commanding Officer, Joint Expeditionary Base Little Creek-Fort Story, and/or other persons or agencies as he/she may designate.

(3650)     (3) All vessels or persons transiting inbound/outbound of the Inner Harbor Restricted Area are subject to all applicable federal and state laws including laws or regulations designed to protect the naval facility and persons or vessels assigned therein. Federal and state law enforcement officials may at any time take action to ensure compliance with their respective laws. In addition, this regulation authorizes Navy security personnel, designated by Commander, Joint Expeditionary Base Little Creek-Fort Story or persons authorized to act in his/her behalf, the authority to ascertain the identity and intent of any vessels and/or persons transiting the restricted area that indicate by way of appearance or action they are a possible threat to government assets. If a determination is made that the vessel and/or persons are a threat to government assets located within the restricted area, Navy security units may take actions as provided by law or regulation that are deemed necessary to protect government personnel and assets located within the restricted area.

(3651)     (c) *Enforcement.* (1) The regulation in this section shall be enforced by the Commanding Officer, Joint Expeditionary Base Little Creek-Fort Story, U.S. Coast Guard, local/state law enforcement, and/or persons or agencies as he/she may designate during emergency situations.

(3652)     (2) Federal and state law enforcement vessels and personnel may enter anywhere in the restricted area at any time in the operation of their statutory missions or to enforce their respective laws.

(3653)     (3) Nothing in this regulation is deemed to preempt 33 CFR 165.501.

(3654)     (4) Vessels or persons calling upon the commercial/private piers located within the Inner Harbor with proper identification and clearance will be allowed entry subject to the same provisions described in paragraph (b) of this section. Commanding Officer, Joint Expeditionary Base Little Creek-Fort Story reserves the right to temporarily deny entry in emergency situations, elevated DOD Force Protection conditions in the Harbor, or other safety of navigation constraints.

(3655)

### §334.310 Chesapeake Bay, Lynnhaven Roads; Navy amphibious training area.

(3656)　(a) *The restricted area.* Beginning at

(3657)　36°55'47.0"N., 76°11'04.5"W.; thence to

(3658)　36°59'04.0"N., 76°10'11.0"W.; thence to

(3659)　36°58'28.5"N., 76°07'54.0"W.; thence to

(3660)　36°55'27.5"N., 76°08'42.0"W.; thence westerly along the shore and across the mouth of Little Creek to the point of beginning.

(3661)　(b) *The regulations.* (1) No fish-pound stakes or structures shall be allowed in the restricted area.

(3662)　(2) No person or vessel shall approach within 300 yards of any naval vessel or within 600 yards of any vessel displaying the red "baker" burgee.

(3663)　(3) This section shall be enforced by the Commandant, Fifth Naval District, and such agencies as he may designate.

(3664)

### §334.320 Chesapeake Bay entrance; naval restricted area.

(3665)　(a) *The area.* Beginning at a point on the south shore of Chesapeake Bay at longitude 76°03'06"W.; thence to

(3666)　37°01'18"N., 76°02'06"W.; thence to

(3667)　37°00'18"N., 75°55'54"W.; thence to

(3668)　36°58'00"N., 75°48'24"W.; thence to

(3669)　36°51'48"N., 75°51'00"W.; thence to the shore at 75°58'48"W., and thence northwesterly and southwesterly along the shore at Cape Henry to the point of beginning.

(3670)　(b) *The regulations.* (1) Anchoring, trawling, crabbing, fishing, and dragging in the area are prohibited, and no object attached to a vessel or otherwise shall be placed on or near the bottom.

(3671)　(2) This section shall be enforced by the Commandant, Fifth Naval District, Norfolk, VA.

(3672)

### §334.330 Atlantic Ocean and connecting waters in vicinity of Myrtle Island, VA; Air Force practice bombing, rocket firing, and gunnery range.

(3673)　(a) *The danger zone.* The waters of the Atlantic Ocean and connecting waters within an area described as follows: Beginning at

(3674)　37°12'18"N., 75°46'00"W.; thence southwesterly to

(3675)　37°08'21"N., 75°50'00"W.; thence northwesterly along the arc of a circle having a radius of three nautical miles and centered at

(3676)　37°11'16"N., 75°49'29"W., to

(3677)　37°10'14"N., 75°52'57"W.; thence northeasterly to

(3678)　37°14'30"N., 75°48'32"W.; thence southeasterly to

(3679)　37°13'38"N., 75°46'18"W.; and thence southeasterly to the point of beginning.

(3680)　(b) *The regulations.* (1) No person or vessel shall enter or remain in the danger zone except during intervals specified and publicized from time to time in local newspapers or by radio announcement.

(3681)　(2) This section shall be enforced by the Commanding General, Tactical Air Command, Langley Air Force Base, Virginia, and such agencies as he may designate.

(3682)

### §334.340 Chesapeake Bay off Plumtree Island, Hampton, va; Air Force precision test area.

(3683)　(a) *The danger zone.* The waters of Chesapeake Bay and connecting waters within an area bounded as follows: Beginning at 37°08'12"N., 76°19'30"W., which is a point on the circumference of a circle of 10,000-foot radius with its center on Plumtree Point at 37°07'30"N., 76°17'36"W.; thence clockwise along the circumference of the circle to 37°09'06"N., 76°18'00"W.; thence southeasterly to 37°08'12"N., 76°17'48"W.; thence clockwise along the circumference of a circle of 4,000-foot radius (with its center at 37°07'30"N., 76°17'36"W. to 37°07'48"N., 76°18'24"W.; thence northwesterly to the point of beginning.

(3684)　(b) *The regulations.* (1) The danger zone will be in use not more than a total of 4 hours per month, which hours shall be during not more than any 2 days per month.

(3685)　(2) No person or vessel shall enter or remain in the danger zone during periods of firing or bombing or when the zone is otherwise in use.

(3686)　(3) The Commander, Tactical Air Command, Langley Air Force Base, VA, shall be responsible for publicizing in advance through the Coast Guard's "Local Notice to Mariners," in the local press, and by radio from time to time the schedule of use of the area, and shall station patrol boats to warn vessels during periods of use.

(3687)　(4) This section shall be enforced by the Commander, Tactical Air Command, Langley Air Force Base, VA, or such agency as he may designate.

(3688)　(c) *Disestablishment of danger zone.* The danger zone will be disestablished not later than December 31, 1967, unless written application for its continuance shall have been made to and approved by the Secretary of the Army prior to that date.

(3689)

### §334.350 Chesapeake Bay off Fort Monroe, VA; firing range danger zone.

(3690)　(a) *The danger zone.* All of the water area lying within a section extending seaward a distance of 4,600 yards between radial lines bearing 83° True and 115° True, respectively, from a point on shore at latitude 37°01'30"N., longitude 76°17'54"W.

(3691)　(b) *The regulations.* (1) No weapon having a greater range than the 30-caliber carbine is to be fired into the firing range danger zone.

(3692)　(2) During periods when firing is in progress, red flags will be displayed at conspicuous locations on the beach. Observers will be on duty and firing will be suspended as long as any vessel is within the danger zone.

(3693)    (3) Passage of vessels through the area will not be prohibited at any time, nor will commercial fishermen be prohibited from working fish nets within the area. No loitering or anchoring for other purposes will be permitted during announced firing periods.

(3694)    (4) No firing will be done during hours of darkness or low visibility.

(3695)    (5) The Commander, Fort Monroe, VA, is responsible for furnishing in advance the firing schedule to the Commander, 5th Coast Guard District, for publication in his "Local Notice to Mariners" and to the local press at Norfolk and Newport News, VA.

(3696)    (c) The regulations in this section shall be enforced by the Commanding Officer, Fort Monroe, VA, and such agencies as he may designate.

(3697)

### §334.360 Chesapeake Bay off Fort Monroe, Virginia; restricted area, U.S. Naval Base and Naval Surface Weapon Center.

(3698)    (a) *The area.* Beginning at

(3699)    37°01'03"N., 76°17'52"W.; thence to

(3700)    37°01'00"N., 76°16'11"W.; thence to

(3701)    36°59'43"N., 76°16'11"W.; thence to

(3702)    36°59'18"N., 76°17'52"W.; thence to

(3703)    37°00'05"N., 76°18'18"W.; thence north along the seawall to the point of beginning.

(3704)    (b) *The regulations.* (1) Anchoring, trawling, fishing and dragging are prohibited in the restricted area, and no object, either attached to a vessel or otherwise, shall be placed on or near the bottom unless authorized by the Facility Manager, Naval Surface Warfare Center, Dahlgren Division Coastal Systems Station Detachment, Fort Monroe, Virginia.

(3705)    (2) This section shall be enforced by the Commander, Naval Base, Norfolk, Virginia, and such agencies as he may designate.

(3706)

### §334.370 Chesapeake Bay, Lynnhaven Roads; danger zones, U.S. Naval Amphibious Base.

(3707)    (a) *Underwater demolitions area (prohibited)–* (1) *The area.* A portion of the restricted area for Navy amphibious training operations described in Sec. 334.310 along the south shore of the Chesapeake Bay, bounded as follows: Beginning at a point at the mean high water line,

(3708)    36°55'26.5"N., 76°08'43"W.; thence 700 yards to

(3709)    36°55'48"N., 76°08'38"W.; thence 500 yards to

(3710)    36°55'46"N., 76°08'57"W.; thence 500 yards to

(3711)    36°55'37"N., 76°09'02"W.; thence 100 yards to

(3712)    36°55'36"N., 76°08'57"W.; thence 200 yards to the mean high water line at

(3713)    36°55'39.5"N., 76°08'59"W.; thence 400 yards along the mean high water line to the point of beginning. The area will be marked by range poles set on shore of the prolongation of the lines forming the eastern and western boundaries.

(3714)    (2) *The regulations.* Persons or vessels, other than those vessels owned and operated by the United States,

shall not enter the prohibited area at any time unless authorized to do so by the enforcing agency.

(3715)    (b) *Small-arms firing range–*(1) *The Area.* Beginning at a point on the shore line at

(3716)    36°55'27"N., 76°08'38"W.; thence to

(3717)    36°55'50"N., 76°08'37"W.; thence to

(3718)    36°57'11"N., 76°08'11"W.; thence to

(3719)    36°56'53"N., 76°07'18"W.; thence to

(3720)    36°55'39"N., 76°07'46"W.; thence to

(3721)    36°55'22"N., 76°08'17"W.; thence along the shore line to the point of beginning.

(3722)    (2) *The regulations.* (i) Passage of vessels through the area will not be prohibited at any time, nor will commercial fishermen be prohibited from working fish nets within the area. No loitering or anchoring for other purposes will be permitted.

(3723)    (ii) A large red warning flag will be flown on shore during periods when firing is in progress. Observers will be on duty and firing will be suspended for the passage of vessels and for the placing and maintenance of fish nets within the area.

(3724)    (c) This section shall be enforced by the Commanding Officer, U.S. Naval Amphibious Base, Little Creek, Norfolk, Virginia.

(3725)

### § 334.390 Atlantic Ocean south of entrance to Chesapeake Bay; firing range.

(3726)    (a) *The danger zone.* (1) A section extending seaward for a distance of 12,000 yards between two radial lines bearing 030° True and 083° True, respectively, from a point on shore at 36°46'48"N., 75°57'24"W.; and an adjacent sector extending seaward for a distance of 15 nautical miles between two radial lines bearing 083° True and 150° True, respectively, from the same shore position. The datum for these coordinates is WGS–1984.

(3727)    (b) *The regulation.* (1) To accommodate ingress and egress within the southern approach to the Chesapeake Bay Federal navigation channels, no live fire exercise will take place within the area northeast of, and defined by a line intersecting points 36°47'59"N., 75°46'05"W., and 36°44'25"N., 75°38'57"W., and this area is open to unrestricted surface navigation.

(3728)    (2) Within the remainder of the danger zone vessels shall proceed through the area with caution and shall remain therein no longer than necessary for the purpose of transit.

(3729)    (3) When firing is in progress during daylight hours, red flags will be displayed at conspicuous locations on the beach. When firing is in progress during periods of darkness, red flashing lights will be displayed from conspicuous locations on the beach which are visible from the water a minimum distance of four (4) nautical miles.

(3730)    (4) Firing on the ranges will be suspended as long as any vessel is within the danger zone.

(3731)    (5) Lookout posts will be manned by the activity or agency operating the firing range at the Naval Air Station

Oceana, Dam Neck Annex, in Virginia Beach, Virginia. After darkness, night vision systems will be utilized by lookouts to aid in locating vessels transiting the area.

(3732)    (6) There shall be no firing on the range during periods of low visibility which would prevent the recognition of a vessel (to a distance of 7,500 yards) which is properly displaying navigation lights, or which would preclude a vessel from observing the red range flags or lights.

(3733)    (7) Throughout the entire danger zone anchoring, dredging, trawling and any bottom disturbing activities should be conducted with caution due to the potential of unexploded ordnance (UXO) and other munitions and explosives of concern (MEC) on the bottom.

(3734)    (c) *Enforcement.* The regulation in this section shall be enforced by the Commander, Naval Air Force Atlantic, U.S. Fleet Forces Command, Norfolk, Virginia, and such agencies as he or she may designate.

(3735)

# TITLE 40–PROTECTION OF ENVIRONMENT

(3736)

## Part 140–MarineSanitation Device Standard

(3737)

### §140.1 Definitions.

(3738)    For the purpose of these standards the following definitions shall apply:

(3739)    (a) *Sewage* means human body wastes and the wastes from toilets and other receptacles intended to receive or retain body wastes;

(3740)    (b) *Discharge* includes, but is not limited to, any spilling, leaking, pumping, pouring, emitting, emptying, or dumping;

(3741)    (c) *Marine sanitation device* includes any equipment for installation onboard a vessel and which is designed to receive, retain, treat, or discharge sewage and any process to treat such sewage;

(3742)    (d) *Vessel* includes every description of watercraft or other artificial contrivance used, or capable of being used, as a means of transportation on waters of the United States;

(3743)    (e) *New vessel* refers to any vessel on which construction was initiated on or after January 30, 1975;

(3744)    (f) *Existing vessel* refers to any vessel on which construction was initiated before January 30, 1975;

(3745)    (g) *Fecal coliform bacteria* are those organisms associated with the intestines of warm-blooded animals that are commonly used to indicate the presence of fecal material and the potential presence of organisms capable of causing human disease.

(3746)

### §140.2 Scope of standard.

(3747)    The standard adopted herein applies only to vessels on which a marine sanitation device has been installed. The standard does not require the installation of a marine sanitation device on any vessel that is not so equipped.

The standard applies to vessels owned and operated by the United States unless the Secretary of Defense finds that compliance would not be in the interest of national security.

(3748)

### §140.3 Standard.

(3749)    (a) (1) In freshwater lakes, freshwater reservoirs or other freshwater impoundments whose inlets or outlets are such as to prevent the ingress or egress by vessel traffic subject to this regulation, or in rivers not capable of navigation by interstate vessel traffic subject to this regulation, marine sanitation devices certified by the U.S. Coast Guard (see 33 CFR part 159, published in 40 FR 4622, January 30, 1975), installed on all vessels shall be designed and operated to prevent the overboard discharge of sewage, treated or untreated, or of any waste derived from sewage. This shall not be construed to prohibit the carriage of Coast Guard-certified flow-through treatment devices which have been secured so as to prevent such discharges.

(3750)    (2) In all other waters, Coast Guard-certified marine sanitation devices installed on all vessels shall be designed and operated to either retain, dispose of, or discharge sewage. If the device has a discharge, subject to paragraph (d) of this section, the effluent shall not have a fecal coliform bacterial count of greater than 1,000 per 100 milliliters nor visible floating solids. Waters where a Coast Guard-certified marine sanitation device permitting discharge is allowed include coastal waters and estuaries, the Great Lakes and inter-connected waterways, freshwater lakes and impoundments accessible through locks, and other flowing waters that are navigable interstate by vessels subject to this regulation.

(3751)    (b) This standard shall become effective on January 30, 1977 for new vessels and on January 30, 1980 for existing vessels (or, in the case of vessels owned and operated by the Department of Defense, two years and five years, for new and existing vessels, respectively, after promulgation of implementing regulations by the Secretary of Defense under section 312(d) of the Act).

(3752)    (c) Any vessel which is equipped as of the date of promulgation of this regulation with a Coast Guard-certified flow-through marine sanitation device meeting the requirements of paragraph (a)(2) of this section, shall not be required to comply with the provisions designed to prevent the overboard discharge of sewage, treated or untreated, in paragraph (a)(1) of this section, for the operable life of that device.

(3753)    (d) After January 30, 1980, subject to paragraphs (e) and (f) of this section, marine sanitation devices on all vessels on waters that are not subject to a prohibition of the overboard discharge of sewage, treated or untreated, as specified in paragraph (a)(1) of this section, shall be designed and operated to either retain, dispose of, or discharge sewage, and shall be certified by the U.S. Coast Guard. If the device has a discharge, the effluent shall not have a fecal coliform bacterial count of greater than 200 per 100 milliliters, nor suspended solids greater than 150 mg/1.

(3754)     (e) Any existing vessel on waters not subject to a prohibition of the overboard discharge of sewage in paragraph (a)(1) of this section, and which is equipped with a certified device on or before January 30, 1978, shall not be required to comply with paragraph (d) of this section, for the operable life of that device.

(3755)     (f) Any new vessel on waters not subject to the prohibition of the overboard discharge of sewage in paragraph (a)(1) of this section, and on which construction is initiated before January 31, 1980, which is equipped with a marine sanitation device before January 31, 1980, certified under paragraph (a)(2) of this section, shall not be required to comply with paragraph (d) of this section, for the operable life of that device.

(3756)     (g) The degrees of treatment described in paragraphs (a) and (d) of this section are "appropriate standards" for purposes of Coast Guard and Department of Defense certification pursuant to section 312(g)(2) of the Act.

(3757)

### §140.4 Complete prohibition.

(3758)     (a) Prohibition pursuant to CWA section 312(f) (3): a State may completely prohibit the discharge from all vessels of any sewage, whether treated or not, into some or all of the waters within such State by making a written application to the Administrator, Environmental Protection Agency, and by receiving the Administrator's affirmative determination pursuant to section 312(f)(3) of the Act. [...]

(3759)     (b) Prohibition pursuant to CWA section 312(f) (4)(A): a State may make a written application to the Administrator, Environmental Protection Agency, under section 312(f)(4)(A) of the Act, for the issuance of a regulation completely prohibiting discharge from a vessel of any sewage, whether treated or not, into particular waters of the United States or specified portions thereof, which waters are located within the boundaries of such State. Such application shall specify with particularly the waters, or portions thereof, for which a complete prohibition is desired. The application shall include identification of water recreational areas, drinking water intakes, aquatic sanctuaries, identifiable fish-spawning and nursery areas, and areas of intensive boating activities. If, on the basis of the State's application and any other information available to him, the Administrator is unable to make a finding that the waters listed in the application require a complete prohibition of any discharge in the waters or portions thereof covered by the application, he shall state the reasons why he cannot make such a finding, and shall deny the application. If the Administrator makes a finding that the waters listed in the application require a complete prohibition of any discharge in all or any part of the waters or portions thereof covered by the State's application, he shall publish notice of such findings together with a notice of proposed rule making, and then shall proceed in accordance with 5 U.S.C. 553. If the

Administrator's finding is that applicable water quality standards require a complete prohibition covering a more restricted or more expanded area than that applied for by the State, he shall state the reasons why his finding differs in scope from that requested in the State's application. [...]

(3760)     (c)(1) Prohibition pursuant to CWA section 312(f) (4)(B): A State may make written application to the Administrator of the Environmental Protection Agency under section 312(f)(4)(B) of the Act for the issuance of a regulation establishing a drinking water intake no discharge zone which completely prohibits discharge from a vessel of any sewage, whether treated or untreated, into that zone in particular waters, or portions thereof, within such State. Such application shall:

(3761)     (i) Identify and describe exactly and in detail the location of the drinking water supply intake(s) and the community served by the intake(s), including average and maximum expected amounts of inflow;

(3762)     (ii) Specify and describe exactly and in detail, the waters, or portions thereof, for which a complete prohibition is desired, and where appropriate, average, maximum and low flows in million gallons per day (MGD) or the metric equivalent;

(3763)     (iii) Include a map, either a USGS topographic quadrant map or a NOAA nautical chart, as applicable, clearly marking by latitude and longitude the waters or portions thereof to be designated a drinking water intake zone; and

(3764)     (iv) Include a statement of basis justifying the size of the requested drinking water intake zone, for example, identifying areas of intensive boating activities.

(3765)     (2) If the Administrator finds that a complete prohibition is appropriate under this paragraph, he or she shall publish notice of such finding together with a notice of proposed rulemaking, and then shall proceed in accordance with 5 U.S.C. 553. If the Administrator's finding is that a complete prohibition covering a more restricted or more expanded area than that applied for by the State is appropriate, he or she shall also include a statement of the reasons why the finding differs in scope from that requested in the State's application.

(3766)     (3) If the Administrator finds that a complete prohibition is inappropriate under this paragraph, he or she shall deny the application and state the reasons for such denial.

(3767)     (4) For the following waters the discharge from a vessel of any sewage, whether treated or not, is completely prohibited pursuant to CWA section 312(f)(4)(B):

(3768)     (i) Two portions of the Hudson River in New York State, the first is bounded by an east-west line through the most northern confluence of the Mohawk River which will be designated by the Troy-Waterford Bridge (126th Street Bridge) on the south and Lock 2 on the north, and the second of which is bounded on the north by the southern end of Houghtaling Island and on the south by a line between the Village of Roseton on the western shore and Low Point on the eastern shore in the vicinity of

Chelsea, as described in Items 2 and 3 of 6 NYCRR Part 858.4.

(3769)    (ii) [Reserved]

(3770)
### §140.5 Analytical procedures.

(3771)    In determining the composition and quality of effluent discharge from marine sanitation devices, the procedures contained in 40 CFR part 136, "Guidelines Establishing Test Procedures for the Analysis of Pollutants," or subsequent revisions or amendments thereto, shall be employed.

(3772)
## TITLE 46–SHIPPING

(3773)
## Part 15–Manning Requirements (in part)

(3774)
## Subpart I–Vessels in Foreign Trade

(3775)
### §15.1001 General.

(3776)    Self-propelled vessels engaged in foreign commerce are required to use a pilot holding a valid MMC or license with appropriate endorsement as a first-class pilot when operating in the navigable waters of the United States specified in this subpart.

(3777)
### §15.1030 New York and New Jersey.

(3778)    The following U.S. navigable waters located within the States of New York and New Jersey when the vessel is making an intra-port transit, to include, but not limited to, a movement from a dock to a dock, from a dock to an anchorage, from an anchorage to a dock, or from an anchorage to an anchorage, within the following listed operating areas:

(3779)    (a) East River from Execution Rocks to New York Harbor, Upper Bay;

(3780)    (b) Hudson River from Yonkers, New York to New York Harbor, Upper Bay;

(3781)    (c) Raritan River from Grossman Dock/Arsenal to New York Harbor, Lower Bay;

(3782)    (d) Arthur Kill Channel;

(3783)    (e) Kill Van Kull Channel;

(3784)    (f) Newark Bay;

(3785)    (g) Passaic River from Point No Point to Newark Bay;

(3786)    (h) Hackensack River from the turning basin to Newark Bay; and

(3787)    (i) New York Harbor, Upper and Lower Bay.

(3788)    Note to §15.1030:

(3789)    "Intra-port transit" as used in this section includes the movement of a foreign-trade vessel inbound from sea from the point where a State-licensed pilot ceases providing pilotage to another point within the identified areas (i.e., a dock or anchorage). Likewise, intra-port transit also includes the movement of a foreign-trade vessel outbound to sea from a point within the identified areas (i.e., a dock or anchorage) to the point where a State licensed pilot begins providing pilotage.

(3790)
### §15.1040 Massachusetts.

(3791)    The following U.S. navigable waters located within the State of Massachusetts when the vessel is in transit, but not bound to or departing from a port within the following listed operating areas:

(3792)    (a) Cape Cod Bay south of 41°48'54"N.;

(3793)    (b) The Cape Cod Canal; and

(3794)    (c) Buzzards Bay east of a line extending from the southernmost point of Wilbur Point (41°34'55"N., 70°51'15"W.) to the easternmost point of Pasque Island (41°26'55"N., 70°50'30"W.).

(3795)
## TITLE 50–WILDLIFE AND FISHERIES

(3796)
## Part 222–General Endangeredand Threatened Marine Species

(3797)
## Subpart A–Introduction and General Provisions

(3798)
### §222.101 Purpose and scope of regulations.

(3799)    (a) The regulations of parts 222, 223, and 224 and this chapter implement the Endangered Species Act (Act), and govern the taking, possession, transportation, sale, purchase, barter, exportation, importation of, and other requirements pertaining to wildlife and plants under the jurisdiction of the Secretary of Commerce and determined to be threatened or endangered pursuant to section 4(a) of the Act. These regulations are implemented by the National Marine Fisheries Service, National Oceanic and Atmospheric Administration, U.S. Department of Commerce. This part pertains to general provisions and definitions. Specifically, parts 223 and 224 pertain to provisions to threatened species and endangered species, respectively. Part 226 enumerates designated critical habitat for endangered and threatened species. Certain of the endangered and threatened marine species enumerated in §§224.102 and 223.102 are included in Appendix I or II to the Convention on International Trade of Endangered Species of Wild Fauna and Flora. The importation, exportation, and re-exportation of such species are subject to additional regulations set forth of 50 CFR part 23, chapter I.

(3800)    (b) For rules and procedures relating to species determined to be threatened or endangered under the jurisdiction of the Secretary of the Interior, see 50 CFR parts 10 through 17. For rules and procedures relating to the general implementation of the Act jointly by the

Departments of the Interior and Commerce and for certain species under the joint jurisdiction of both the Secretaries of the Interior and Commerce, see 50 CFR chapter IV. Marine mammals listed as endangered or threatened and subject to these regulations may also be subject to additional requirements pursuant to the Marine Mammal Protection Act (for regulations implementing that act, see 50 CFR part 216).

(3801)     (c) No statue or regulation of any state shall be construed to relieve a person from the restrictions, conditions, and requirements contained in parts 222, 223, and 224 of this chapter. In addition, nothing in parts 222, 223, and 224 of this chapter, including any permit issued pursuant thereto, shall be construed to relieve a person from any other requirements imposed by a statute or regulation of any state or of the United States, including any applicable health, quarantine, agricultural, or customs laws or regulations or any other National Marine Fisheries Service enforced statutes or regulations.

(3802)
## Part 224-EndangeredMarine and Anadromous Species

(3803)
### §224.103 Special prohibitions for endangered marine mammals.

(3804)     (c) *Approaching right whales.*

(3805)     (1) *Prohibitions.* Except as provided under paragraph (c)(3) of this section, it is unlawful for any person subject to the jurisdiction of the United States to commit, attempt to commit, to solicit another to commit, or cause to be committed any of the following acts:

(3806)     (i) Approach (including by interception) within 500 yards (460 m) of a right whale by vessel, aircraft, or any other means;

(3807)     (ii) Fail to undertake required right whale avoidance measures specified under paragraph (c)(2) of this section.

(3808)     (2) *Right whale avoidance measures.* Except as provided under paragraph (c)(3) of this section, the following avoidance measures must be taken if within 500 yards (460 m) of a right whale:

(3809)     (i) If underway, a vessel must steer a course away from the right whale and immediately leave the area at slow safe speed.

(3810)     (ii) An aircraft must take a course away from the right whale and immediately leave the area at a constant airspeed.

(3811)     (3) *Exceptions.* The following exceptions apply to this section, but any person who claims the applicability of an exception has the burden of proving that the exception applies:

(3812)     (i) Paragraphs (c)(1) and (c)(2) of this section do not apply if a right whale approach is authorized by the National Marine Fisheries Service through a permit issued under part 222, subpart C, of this chapter (General Permit Procedures) or through a similar authorization.

(3813)     (ii) Paragraphs (c)(1) and (c)(2) of this section do not apply where compliance would create an imminent and serious threat to a person, vessel, or aircraft.

(3814)     (iii) Paragraphs (c)(1) and (c)(2)of this section do not apply when approaching to investigate a right whale entanglement or injury, or to assist in the disentanglement or rescue of a right whale, provided that permission is received from the National Marine Fisheries Service or designee prior to the approach.

(3815)     (iv) Paragraphs (c)(1) and (c)(2) of this section do not apply to an aircraft unless the aircraft is conducting whale watch activities.

(3816)     (v) Paragraph (c)(2) of this section does not apply to the extent that a vessel is restricted in her ability to maneuver and, because of the restriction, cannot comply with paragraph (c)(2) of this section.

(3817)
### §224.105 Speed restrictions to protect North Atlantic Right Whales.

(3818)     (a) The following restrictions apply to: All vessels greater than or equal to 65 ft (19.8 m) in overall length and subject to the jurisdiction of the United States, and all other vessels greater than or equal to 65 ft (19.8 m) in overall length entering or departing a port or place subject to the jurisdiction of the United States. These restrictions shall not apply to U.S. vessels owned or operated by, or under contract to, the Federal Government. This exemption extends to foreign sovereign vessels when they are engaging in joint exercises with the U.S. Department of the Navy. In addition, these restrictions do not apply to law enforcement vessels of a State, or political subdivision thereof, when engaged in law enforcement or search and rescue duties.

(3819)     (1) *Southeast U.S. (south of St. Augustine, FL to north of Brunswick, GA):* Vessels shall travel at a speed of 10 knots or less over ground during the period of November 15 to April 15 each year in the area bounded by the following: Beginning at 31°27'00.0"N., 80°51'36.0"W.; thence west to charted mean high water line then south along charted mean high water line and inshore limits of COLREGS limit to a latitude of 29°45'00.0"N., thence east to 29°45'00.0"N., 80°51'36.0"W.; thence back to starting point. (Fig. 1).

(3820)     (2) *Mid-Atlantic U.S. (from north of Brunswick, Georgia to Rhode Island):* Vessels shall travel 10 knots or less over ground in the period November 1 to April 30 each year:

(3821)     (i) In the area bounded by the following: 33°56'42.0"N., 77°31'30.0"W.; thence along a NW bearing of 313.26° True to charted mean high water line then south along mean high water line and inshore limits of COLREGS limit to a latitude of 31°27'00.0"N.; thence east to

(3822)     31°27'00.0"N., 80°51'36.0"W.; thence to

(3823)     31°50'00.0"N., 80°33'12.0"W.; thence to

(3824)     32°59'06.0"N., 78°50'18.0"W.; thence to

(3825)     33°28'24.0"N., 78°32'30.0"W.; thence to

(3858)

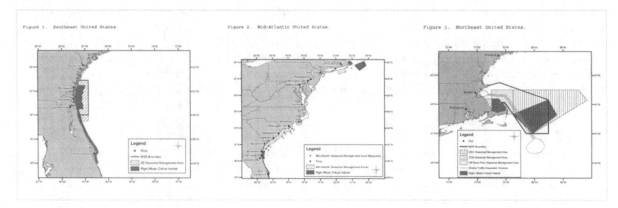

(3826)    33°36'30.0"N., 77°47'06.0"W.; thence back to starting point.;

(3827)    (ii) Within a 20-nm (37 km) radius (as measured seaward from COLRGES delineated coast lines and the center point of the port entrance) (Fig. 2) at the

(3828)    (A) Ports of New York/New Jersey:

(3829)    40°29'42.2"N., 73°55'57.6"W.;

(3830)    (B) Delaware Bay (Ports of Philadelphia and Wilmington): 38°52'27.4"N., 75°01'32.1"W.;

(3831)    (C) Entrance to the Chesapeake Bay (Ports of Hampton Roads and Baltimore): 37°00'36.9"N., 75°57'50.5"W.; and

(3832)    (D) Ports of Morehead City and Beaufort, NC: 34°41'32.0"N., 76°40'08.3"W.; and

(3833)    (iii) In Block Island Sound, in the area bounded by the following coordinates: Beginning at

(3834)    40°51'53.7"N., 70°36'44.9"W.; thence to

(3835)    41°20'14.1"N., 70°49'44.1"W.; thence to

(3836)    41°04'16.7"N., 71°51'21.0"W.; thence to

(3837)    40°35'56.5"N., 71°38'25.1"W.; thence back to starting point. (Fig. 2).

(3838)    (3) *Northeast U.S. (north of Rhode Island):*

(3839)    (i) *In Cape Cod Bay, MA:* Vessels shall travel at a speed of 10 knots or less over ground during the period of January 1 to May 15 in Cape Cod Bay, in an area beginning at 42°04'56.5"N., 70°12'00.0"W.; thence north to 42°12'00.0"N., 70°12'00.0"W.; thence due west to charted mean high water line; thence along charted mean high water within Cape Cod Bay back to beginning point. (Fig. 3).

(3840)    (ii) *Off Race Point:* Vessels shall travel at a speed of 10 knots or less over ground during the period of March 1 to April 30 each year in waters bounded by straight lines connecting the following points in the order stated (Fig. 3):

(3841)    42°30'00.0"N., 69°45'00.0"W.; thence to

(3842)    42°30'00.0"N., 70°30'00.0"W.; thence to

(3843)    42°12'00.0"N., 70°30'00.0"W.; thence to

(3844)    42°12'00.0"N., 70°12'00.0"W.; thence to

(3845)    42°04'56.5"N., 70°12'00.0"W.; thence along charted mean high water line and inshore limits of COLREGS limit to a latitude of 41°40'00.0"N., thence due east to

41°41'00.0"N., 69°45'00.0"W.; thence back to starting point.

(3846)    (iii) *Great South Channel:* Vessels shall travel at a speed of 10 knots or less over ground during the period of April 1 to July 31 each year in all waters bounded by straight lines connecting the following points in the order stated (Fig. 3):

(3847)    42°30'00.0"N., 69°45'00.0"W.

(3848)    41°40'00.0"N., 69°45'00.0"W.

(3849)    41°00'00.0"N., 69°05'00.0"W.

(3850)    42°09'00.0"N., 67°08'24.0"W.

(3851)    42°30'00.0"N., 67°27'00.0"W.

(3852)    42°30'00.0"N., 69°45'00.0"W.

(3853)    (b) Except as noted in paragraph (c) of this section, it is unlawful under this section:

(3854)    (1) For any vessel subject to the jurisdiction of the United States to violate any speed restriction established in paragraph (a) of this section; or

(3855)    (2) For any vessel entering or departing a port or place under the jurisdiction of the United States to violate any speed restriction established in paragraph (a) of this section.

(3856)    (c) A vessel may operate at a speed necessary to maintain safe maneuvering speed instead of the required ten knots only if justified because the vessel is in an area where oceanographic, hydrographic and/or meteorological conditions severely restrict the maneuverability of the vessel and the need to operate at such speed is confirmed by the pilot on board or, when a vessel is not carrying a pilot, the master of the vessel. If a deviation from the ten-knot speed limit is necessary, the reasons for the deviation, the speed at which the vessel is operated, the latitude and longitude of the area, and the time and duration of such deviation shall be entered into the logbook of the vessel. The master of the vessel shall attest to the accuracy of the logbook entry by signing and dating it.

(3857)    (d) No later than January 1, 2019, the National Marine Fisheries Service will publish and seek comment on a report evaluating the conservation value and economic and navigational safety impacts of this section, including any recommendations to minimize burden of such impacts.

(3859)

## Part 226–DesignatedCritical Habitat

(3860)

### §226.101 Purpose and scope.

(3861)     The regulations contained in this part identify those habitats designated by the Secretary of Commerce as critical, under section 4 of the Act, for endangered and threatened species under the jurisdiction of the Secretary of Commerce. Those species are enumerated at §223.102 of this chapter if threatened and at §224.101 of this chapter if endangered. For regulations pertaining to the designation of critical habitat, see part 424 of this title; for regulations pertaining to prohibitions against the adverse modification or destruction of critical habitat, see part 402 of this title. Additional information regarding designated critical habitats that is not provided in this section may be obtained upon request to the Office of Protected Resources (*see* §222.102, definition of "Office of Protected Resources").

(3862)

### § 226.203 Critical habitat for North Atlantic right whales (*Eubalaena glacialis*).

(3863)     Critical habitat is designated for North Atlantic right whales as described in this section. The textual descriptions in paragraph (b) of this section are the definitive source for determining the critical habitat boundaries. The maps of the critical habitat units provided in paragraph (c) of this section are for illustrative purposes only.

(3864)     (a) Physical and biological features essential to the conservation of endangered North Atlantic right whales.

(3865)     (1) *Unit 1.* The physical and biological features essential to the conservation of the North Atlantic right whale, which provide foraging area functions in Unit 1 are: The physical oceanographic conditions and structures of the Gulf of Maine and Georges Bank region that combine to distribute and aggregate *C.finmarchicus* for right whale foraging, namely prevailing currents and circulation patterns, bathymetric features (basins, banks, and channels), oceanic fronts, density gradients, and temperature regimes; low flow velocities in Jordan, Wilkinson, and Georges Basins that allow diapausing *C.finmarchicus* to aggregate passively below the convective layer so that the copepods are retained in the basins; late stage *C.finmarchicus* in dense aggregations in the Gulf of Maine and Georges Bank region; and diapausing *C.finmarchicus* in aggregations in the Gulf of Maine and Georges Bank region.

(3866)     (2) *Unit 2.* The physical features essential to the conservation of the North Atlantic right whale, which provide calving area functions in Unit 2, are:

(3867)     (i) Sea surface conditions associated with Force 4 or less on the Beaufort Scale,

(3868)     (ii) Sea surface temperatures of 7°C to 17°C, and

(3869)     (iii) Water depths of 6 to 28 meters, where these features simultaneously co-occur over contiguous areas of at least 231 nmi2 of ocean waters during the months of November through April. When these features are available, they are selected by right whale cows and calves in dynamic combinations that are suitable for calving, nursing, and rearing, and which vary, within the ranges specified, depending on factors such as weather and age of the calves.

(3870)     (b) *Critical habitat boundaries.* Critical habitat includes two areas (Units) located in the Gulf of Maine and Georges Bank Region (Unit 1) and off the coast of North Carolina, South Carolina, Georgia and Florida (Unit 2).

(3871)     (1) *Unit 1.* The specific area on which are found the physical and biological features essential to the conservation of the North Atlantic right whale include all waters, seaward of the boundary delineated by the line connecting the geographic coordinates and landmarks identified herein:

(3872)     (i) The southern tip of Nauset Beach (Cape Cod) (41°38.39′N., 69°57.32′W.).

(3873)     (ii) From this point, southwesterly to 41°37.19′N., 69°59.11′W.

(3874)     (iii) From this point, southward along the eastern shore of South Monomoy Island to 41°32.76′N., 69°59.73′W.

(3875)     (iv) From this point, southeasterly to 40°50′N., 69°12′W.

(3876)     (v) From this point, east to 40°50′N., 68°50′W.

(3877)     (vi) From this point, northeasterly to 42°00′N., 67°55′W.

(3878)     (vii) From this point, east to 42°00′N., 67°30′W.

(3879)     (viii) From this point, northeast to the intersection of the U.S.-Canada maritime boundary and 42°10′N.

(3880)     (ix) From this point, following the U.S.-Canada maritime boundary north to the intersection of 44°49.727′N., 66°57.952′W.; From this point, moving southwest along the coast of Maine, the specific area is located seaward of the line connecting the following points:

(3881)

| Latitude | Longitude |
|---|---|
| 44°49.727′N. | 66°57.952′W. |
| 44°49.67′N. | 66°57.77′W. |
| 44°48.64′N. | 66°56.43′W. |
| 44°47.36′N. | 66°59.25′W. |
| 44°45.51′N. | 67°02.87′W. |
| 44°37.07′N. | 67°09.75′W. |
| 44°27.77′N. | 67°32.86′W. |
| 44°25.74′N. | 67°38.39′W. |
| 44°21.66′N. | 67°51.78′W. |
| 44°19.08′N. | 68°02.05′W. |
| 44°13.55′N. | 68°10.71′W. |
| 44°08.36′N. | 68°14.75′W. |
| 43°59.36′N. | 68°37.95′W. |
| 43°59.83′N. | 68°50.06′W. |

| Latitude | Longitude |
|---|---|
| 43°56.72'N. | 69°04.89'W. |
| 43°50.28'N. | 69°18.86'W. |
| 43°48.96'N. | 69°31.15'W. |
| 43°43.64'N. | 69°37.58'W. |
| 43°41.44'N. | 69°45.27'W. |
| 43°36.04'N. | 70°03.98'W. |
| 43°31.94'N. | 70°08.68'W. |
| 43°27.63'N. | 70°17.48'W. |
| 43°20.23'N. | 70°23.64'W. |
| 43°04.06'N. | 70°36.70'W. |
| 43°02.93'N. | 70°41.47'W. |
| 43°02.55'N. | 70°43.33'W. |

(3882)     (x) From this point (43°2.55'N., 70°43.33'W.) on the coast of New Hampshire south of Portsmouth, the boundary of the specific area follows the coastline southward along the coasts of New Hampshire and Massachusetts along Cape Cod to Provincetown southward along the eastern edge of Cape Cod to the southern tip of Nauset Beach (Cape Cod) (41°38.39'N., 69°57.32'W.) with the exception of the area landward of the lines drawn by connecting the following points:

(3883)

| Latitude | Longitude | | |
|---|---|---|---|
| 42°59.986'N. | 70°44.654'W. | to | Rye Harbor |
| 42°59.956'N. | 70°44.737'W. | | Rye Harbor |
| 42°53.691'N. | 70°48.516'W. | to | Hampton Harbor |
| 42°53.519'N. | 70°48.748'W. | | Hampton Harbor |
| 42°49.136'N. | 70°48.242'W. | to | Newburyport Harbor |
| 42°48.964'N. | 70°48.282'W. | | Newburyport Harbor |
| 42°42.145'N. | 70°46.995'W. | to | Plum Island Sound |
| 42°41.523'N. | 70°47.356'W. | | Plum Island Sound |
| 42°40.266'N. | 70°43.838'W. | to | Essex Bay |
| 42°39.778'N. | 70°43.142'W. | | Essex Bay |
| 42°39.645'N. | 70°36.715'W. | to | Rockport Harbor |
| 42°39.613'N. | 70°36.60'W. | | Rockport Harbor |
| 42°20.665'N. | 70°57.205'W. | to | Boston Harbor |
| 42°20.009'N. | 70°55.803'W. | | Boston Harbor |
| 42°19.548'N. | 70°55.436'W. | to | Boston Harbor |
| 42°18.599'N. | 70°52.961'W. | | Boston Harbor |
| 42°15.203'N. | 70°46.324'W. | to | Cohasset Harbor |
| 42°15.214'N. | 70°47.352'W. | | Cohasset Harbor |
| 42°12.09'N. | 70°42.98'W. | to | Scituate Harbor |
| 42°12.211'N. | 70°43.002'W. | | Scituate Harbor |
| 42°09.724'N. | 70°42.378'W. | to | New Inlet |
| 42°10.085'N. | 70°42.875'W. | | New Inlet |
| 42°04.64'N. | 70°38.587'W. | to | Green Harbor |
| 42°04.583'N. | 70°38.631'W. | | Green Harbor |
| 41°59.686'N. | 70°37.948'W. | to | Duxbury Bay/ Plymouth Harbor |

| Latitude | Longitude | | |
|---|---|---|---|
| 41°58.75'N. | 70°39.052'W. | | Duxbury Bay/ Plymouth Harbor |
| 41°50.395'N. | 70°31.943'W. | to | Ellisville Harbor |
| 41°50.369'N. | 70°32.145'W. | | Ellisville Harbor |
| 41°45.87'N. | 70°28.62'W. | to | Sandwich Harbor |
| 41°45.75'N. | 70°28.40'W. | | Sandwich Harbor |
| 41°44.93'N. | 70°25.74'W. | to | Scorton Harbor |
| 41°44.90'N. | 70°25.60'W. | | Scorton Harbor |
| 41°44.00'N. | 70°17.50'W. | to | Barnstable Harbor |
| 41°44.00'N. | 70°13.90'W. | | Barnstable Harbor |
| 41°45.53'N. | 70°09.387'W. | to | Sesuit Harbor |
| 41°45.523'N. | 70°09.307'W. | | Sesuit Harbor |
| 41°45.546'N. | 70°07.39'W. | to | Quivett Creek |
| 41°45.551'N. | 70°07.32'W. | | Quivett Creek |
| 41°47.269'N. | 70°01.411'W. | to | Namskaket Creek |
| 41°47.418'N. | 70°01.306'W. | | Namskaket Creek |
| 41°47.961'N. | 70°0.561'W. | to | Rock Harbor Creek |
| 41°48.07'N. | 70°0.514'W. | | Rock Harbor Creek |
| 41°48.432'N. | 70°0.286'W. | to | Boat Meadow River |
| 41°48.483'N. | 70°0.216'W. | | Boat Meadow River |
| 41°48.777'N. | 70°0.317'W. | to | Herring River |
| 41°48.983'N. | 70°0.196'W. | | Herring River |
| 41°55.501'N. | 70°03.51'W. | to | Herring River, inside Wellfleet Harbor |
| 41°55.322'N. | 70°03.191'W. | | Herring River, inside Wellfleet Harbor |
| 41°53.922'N. | 70°01.333'W. | to | Blackfish Creek/ Loagy Bay |
| 41°54.497'N. | 70°01.182'W. | | Blackfish Creek/ Loagy Bay |
| 41°55.503'N. | 70°02.07'W. | to | Duck Creek |
| 41°55.753'N. | 70°02.281'W. | | Duck Creek |
| 41°59.481'N. | 70°04.779'W. | to | Pamet River |
| 41°59.563'N. | 70°04.718'W. | | Pamet River |
| 41°03.601'N. | 70°14.269'W. | to | Hatches Harbor |
| 41°03.601'N. | 70°14.416'W. | | Hatches Harbor |
| 41°48.708'N. | 69°56.319'W. | to | Nauset Harbor |
| 41°48.554'N. | 69°56.238'W. | | Nauset Harbor |
| 41°40.685'N. | 69°56.781'W. | to | Chatham Harbor |
| 41°40.884'N. | 69°56.28'W. | | Chatham Harbor |

(3884)     (xi) In addition, the specific area does not include waters landward of the 72 COLREGS lines (33 CFR part 80) described below.

(3885)     (A) *Portland Head, ME to Cape Ann, MA*.

(3886)     (1) A line drawn from the northernmost extremity of Farm Point to Annisquam Harbor Light.

(3887)     (2) [Reserved]

(3888)     (B) *Cape Ann MA to Marblehead Neck, MA*.

(3889)     (1) A line drawn from Gloucester Harbor Breakwater Light to the twin towers charted at latitude 42°35'06.177"N., longitude 70°41'32.330"W.

(3890)     (2) A line drawn from the westernmost extremity of Gales Point to the easternmost extremity of House Island;

(3897)

## North Atlantic Right Whale Critical Habitat
## Northeastern U.S. Foraging Area

**Unit 1**

Critical Habitat

200m Depth Contour

This map is provided for illustrative purposes only of
North Atlantic right whale critical habitat. For the precise legal
definition of critical habitat, please refer to the narrative description.

(3898)

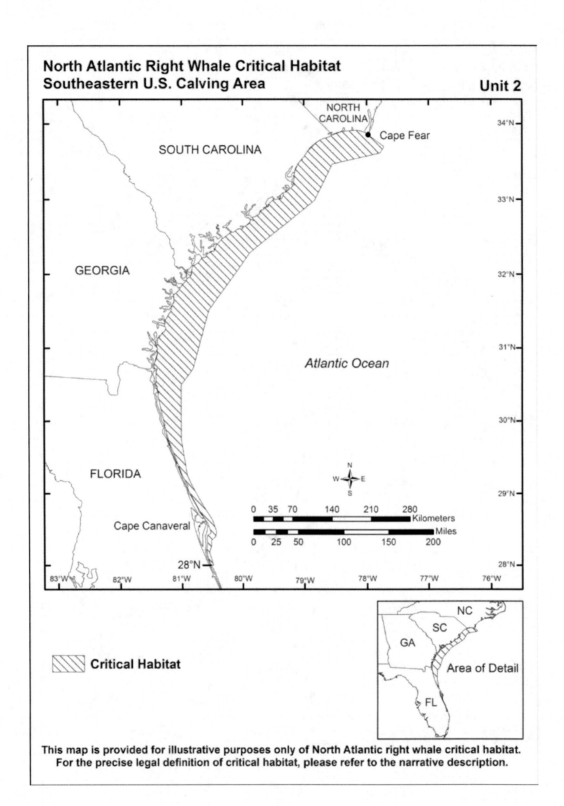

**North Atlantic Right Whale Critical Habitat
Southeastern U.S. Calving Area**

**Unit 2**

This map is provided for illustrative purposes only of North Atlantic right whale critical habitat.
For the precise legal definition of critical habitat, please refer to the narrative description.

thence to Bakers Island Light; thence to Marblehead Light.

(3891)    (C) *Hull, MA to Race Point, MA.*

(3892)    (1) A line drawn from Canal Breakwater Light 4 south to the shoreline.

(3893)    (2) [Reserved]

(3894)    (2) *Unit 2.* Unit 2 includes marine waters from Cape Fear, North Carolina, southward to 28°N latitude (approximately 31 miles south of Cape Canaveral, Florida) within the area bounded on the west by the shoreline and the 72 COLREGS lines, and on the east by rhumb lines connecting the following points in the order stated from north to south.

(3895)

| Latitude | Longitude |
|----------|-----------|
| 33°51'N. | at shoreline |
| 33°42'N. | 77°43'W. |
| 33°37'N. | 77°47'W. |
| 33°28'N. | 78°33'W. |
| 32°59'N. | 78°50'W. |
| 32°17'N. | 79°53'W. |

| Latitude | Longitude |
|----------|-----------|
| 31°31'N. | 80°33'W. |
| 30°43'N. | 80°49'W. |
| 30°30'N. | 81°01'W. |
| 29°45'N. | 81°01'W. |
| 29°15'N. | 80°55'W. |
| 29°08'N. | 80°51'W. |
| 28°50'N. | 80°39'W. |
| 28°38'N. | 80°30'W. |
| 28°28'N. | 80°26'W. |
| 28°24'N. | 80°27'W. |
| 28°21'N. | 80°31'W. |
| 28°16'N. | 80°31'W. |
| 28°11'N. | 80°33'W. |
| 28°00'N. | 80°29'W. |
| 28°00'N. | at shoreline |

(3896)    (c) Overview maps of the designated critical habitat for the North Atlantic right whale follow.

# Sandy Hook to Cape Henry

(1)    Between New York Bay and Delaware Bay is the New Jersey coast with its many resorts, its inlets and its Intracoastal Waterway. Delaware Bay is the approach to Wilmington, Chester, Philadelphia, Camden and Trenton; below Wilmington is the Delaware River entrance to the Chesapeake and Delaware Canal, the deep inside link between Chesapeake and Delaware Bays. The Delaware-Maryland-Virginia coast has relatively few resorts; the numerous inlets are backed by a shallow inside passage that extends all the way from Delaware Bay to Chesapeake Bay. The last seven chapters, nearly half of this book, are required to describe Chesapeake Bay to Norfolk and Newport News, to Washington and Baltimore and to Susquehanna River 170 miles north of the Virginia Capes.

(2)    A vessel approaching this coast from seaward will be made aware of its nearness by the number of vessels passing up and down in the coastal trade. The coast of New Jersey is studded with large hotels, prominent standpipes and elevated tanks. South of Delaware Bay, the principal landmarks are the lighthouses and Coast Guard stations.

(3)    The general tendency along this mostly sandy coast is for the ocean beaches and the points on the north sides of the entrances to wash away and for the points on the south sides of the entrances to build out. Protective works have done much to stabilize the New Jersey coast, but several lighthouses have been abandoned between Delaware Bay and Chesapeake Bay because of erosion.

(4)    The shores of Delaware Bay and Delaware River are mostly low and have few conspicuous marks, other than lights, below the industrial centers along the river. The shores of Chesapeake Bay are low as far north as Patuxent River, then rise to considerable heights at the head of the bay.

(5)
### Disposal Sites and Dumping Grounds

(6)    These areas are rarely mentioned in the Coast Pilot but are shown on the nautical charts. (See Disposal Sites and Dumping Grounds, chapter 1, and charts for limits.)

(7)
### Aids to navigation

(8)    Lights are numerous along the section of the coast covered by this Coast Pilot. Sound signals are at most of the principal light stations. Many coastal and harbor buoys are equipped with radar reflectors, which greatly increase the range at which the buoys may be detected on the radarscope. The critical dangers are marked.

(9)
### Chesapeake Bay Interpretive Buoy System (CBIBS)

(10)    The **Chesapeake Bay Interpretive Buoy System (CBIBS)** is a network of data-sensing buoys along the Captain John Smith Chesapeake National Historic Trail. The buoys broadcast real-time weather/environmental data and voice narration of natural and cultural history of the area. Real-time information from the buoy can be retrieved by phone at 877–BUOY–BAY or at *www.buoybay.noaa.gov*.

(11)
### Radar

(12)    **Radar**, though always a valuable navigational aid, is generally of less assistance in navigation along this coast due to the relatively low relief; the accuracy of radar ranges to the beach cannot be relied upon. Coastal buoys equipped with radar reflectors are of help in this regard. It is sometimes possible to obtain a usable radar return from the larger lighthouses, but positive target identification is usually difficult. Radar is of particular importance in detecting other traffic and in the prevention of collisions during periods of inclement weather and in fog and low visibility.

(13)
### COLREGS Demarcation Lines

(14)    Lines have been established to delineate those waters upon which mariners must comply with the International Regulations for Preventing Collisions at Sea, 1972 (72 COLREGS) and those waters upon which mariners must comply with the Inland Navigational Rules Act of 1980 (Inland Rules). The waters inside of the lines are **Inland Rules Waters**, and the waters outside of the lines are **COLREGS Waters**. (See **33 CFR Part 80**, chapter 2, for specific lines of demarcation.)

(15)
### Ports and waterways safety

(16)    (See **33 CFR Part 160**, chapter 2, for regulations governing vessel operations and requirements for notification of arrivals, departures, hazardous conditions and certain dangerous cargoes to the Captain of the Port.)

(17)
### Regulated Navigation Areas

(18)    **Regulated Navigation Areas** have been established within the navigable waters of the First Coast Guard District to increase operational safety for towing vessels and tank barges. (See **33 CFR 165.100**, chapter 2, for limit and regulations.)

(33)

# North Atlantic right whale

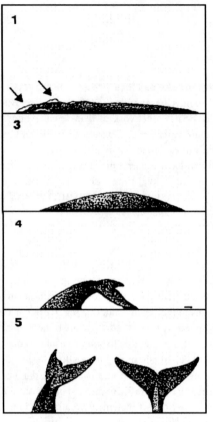

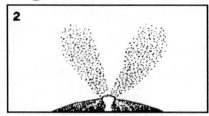

1) Whitish patches of raised and roughened skin (called callosities) on top of the head (see arrows)

2) V-shaped blow easily visible from in front or behind the whale

3) No dorsal fin on the back

4) Tail flukes often lifted vertically when the animal dives

5) All black tail on the top and underside

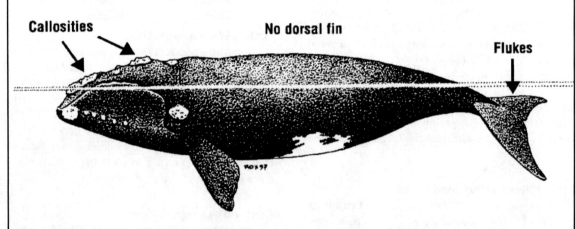

Callosities  No dorsal fin  Flukes

Images courtesy of Center for Coastal Studies

(19)
## Harbor and inlet entrances

(20)      The channels into Delaware and Chesapeake Bays are broad and deep. The entrances to the inlets are comparatively shallow and are more or less obstructed by shifting sandbars. Some of the inlets have been improved by dredging and by the construction of jetties. On many of the bars the buoys are moved from time to time to mark the shifting channels. The best time to enter most of the inlets is on a rising tide with a smooth sea. Strangers should not attempt to enter the inlets without assistance when the seas are breaking on the bars. The tidal currents have considerable velocity in all of the entrances, and their direction is affected by the force and direction of the wind.

(21)
## Traffic Separation Schemes

(22)      **Traffic Separation Schemes (Traffic Lanes)** have been established at the entrances to New York Harbor, Delaware Bay and Chesapeake Bay and in the main channel of Chesapeake Bay off Smith Point just south of the entrance to the Potomac River. (See chapters 4, 6, 9, and 12, respectively, for details.)

(23)
## Anchorages

(24)      The only protected anchorage for deep-draft vessels between New York Bay and Chesapeake Bay is outside the channel limits in Delaware Bay according to draft. Absecon Inlet, Cape May Inlet and some of the others can accommodate light-draft vessels such as trawlers and small yachts, but not medium or deep drafts. Small local craft often seek shelter inside the shallower inlets, but entrance is difficult in heavy weather, and the unimproved inlets are often difficult even in good weather, particularly for strangers.

(25)      A number of anchorage areas have been established by Federal Regulations within the area of this Coast Pilot. (See **33 CFR Part 110**, chapter 2, for limits and regulations.)

(26)
## Dangers

(27)      The principal dangers along this coast are the outlying sand shoals, the fogs and the doubtful direction and velocity of the currents after heavy gales. Depths of 7.5 fathoms are found as far as 20 miles from shore. There are many wrecks along this coast, but most of them have been blasted off or cleared to safe navigational depths; the others are marked by obstruction buoys.

(28)      Gales from northeast to southeast cause heavy breakers on the beaches and outlying shoals; the sea breaks in 4 to 5 fathoms of water, and shoals of that depth or less usually are marked during easterly gales. The bars across the inlets are then impassable and are defined by breakers even in comparatively smooth water with a light swell. The heaviest surf on the beach is on a rising tide near high-water springs; the least surf is encountered on a falling tide near low water. A very heavy surf makes on the beaches after a southeasterly gale followed by a sudden shift of wind to northwest.

(29)
## Danger zones

(30)      **Danger zones** have been established within the area of this Coast Pilot. (See **33 CFR Part 334**, chapter 2, for limits and regulations.)

(31)
## North Atlantic right whales

(32)      The North Atlantic right whale is one of the world's most endangered large whale species. North Atlantic right whales are found primarily in continental shelf waters between Florida and Nova Scotia. They migrate annually along the east coast between the feeding grounds off New England and Canada and the calving grounds off Florida, Georgia and South Carolina. Because right whales mate, rest, feed and nurse their young at the surface, and often do not move out of the way of oncoming ships, they are highly vulnerable to being struck. Pregnant females and females with nursing calves appear to be particularly vulnerable to collisions with ships. Ship strikes and fishing gear entanglements are the two known sources of human-related mortality. Intentionally approaching within 500 yards of right whales is prohibited and is a violation of federal law. (See **50 CFR 224.103**, chapter 2 for limits, regulations and exceptions.)

(34)      **Description of North Atlantic right whale:** Right whales are large baleen whales. Adults are generally 45 to 55 feet in length and can weigh up to 70 tons. The body is mostly black, but irregularly shaped white patches may be present on the ventral surface. The best field identification marks are a broad back with no dorsal fin, irregular bumpy white patches (callosities) on the head and a distinctive two-column V-shaped blow when viewed from directly behind or in front of the whale. The whales have broad, paddle-shaped flippers and a broad, deeply notched tail. (See diagrams and photographs.) Right whales are slow moving and seldom travel faster than 5 or 6 knots. They can stay submerged for 10 to 20 minutes and may appear suddenly when surfacing to breathe. They are often seen alone or in small groups. At times, right whales form large courtship groups of 20 to 30 animals.

(35)      **Seasonal occurrence of North Atlantic right whales:** During seasons and in areas where right whales may occur, vessel operators should maintain a sharp lookout for whales and reduce speeds when consistent with safe navigation. In any given year oceanographic variability may affect the seasonal distribution of right whales. In 1986, right whales were frequently sighted within the Stellwagen Bank National Marine Sanctuary throughout the summer, and in the early spring of 1998 a large number of right whales were documented near the Narragansett/Buzzards Bay Traffic Separation Scheme. Three areas in U.S. waters have been designated as critical habitats for North Atlantic right whales. The northern critical habitats, the Great South Channel

(east of Cape Cod) and Cape Cod Bay extending into Massachusetts Bay, are feeding and nursery grounds. The southern critical habitat, off coastal Florida and Georgia (Sebastian Inlet, Florida to the Altamaha River, Georgia), is a calving area. (See **50 CFR 226.203**, chapter 2 for limits, regulations and exceptions).

(36)

| Seasonal occurrence of North Atlantic right whales | | |
|---|---|---|
| Location | Season | Comments |
| Central Gulf of Maine (Jordan Basin, Cashes Ledge) | April to June October to December | |
| Cape Cod Bay | December to May | |
| Great South Channel, northern edge of Georges Bank | March to July | |
| Bay of Fundy, Scotian Shelf (Browns Bank, Roseway Basin) | July to October | Most of the population can be found in this area during this time. |
| Jeffreys Ledge | October to December | Whales are frequently sighted in this area. |
| Stellwagen Bank National Marine Sanctuary | Year-round | Peak sightings occur in the early spring with infrequent sightings in the summer. |
| New York to North Carolina | November to April | The migration corridor between right whale habitats is within 30 miles of the Atlantic coast. |
| South Carolina, Georgia and Florida calving area | November to April | Calving right whales have been sighted as far north as Cape Fear, NC and as far south as Miami, FL with rare sightings in the Gulf of Mexico. |

(37)     **Mandatory Speed Restrictions:** Vessels 65 feet or greater in length overall (LOA) are subject to mandatory speed restrictions of 10 knots or less in seasonal management areas (SMAs) along the U.S. East Coast during times when right whales are likely to be present (See following map for locations of SMAs). The Northeastern SMA speed restrictions are in place from January 1 through May 15 in Cape Cod Bay, from March 1 through April 30 off Race Point and from April 1 through July 31 in the Great South Channel. Speed restrictions in the mid-Atlantic U.S. SMAs are in place from November 1 to April 30 and include Block Island Sound, entry into the Ports of New York/New Jersey, Delaware Bay, Entrance to Chesapeake Bay and the Ports of Morehead City and Beaufort, NC, and within a continuous boundary approximately 20 nautical miles from shore around the major ports of Wilmington, NC, Charleston, SC, and Savannah, GA. Speed restrictions are in place in the Southeastern U.S. SMA from November 15 to April 15; this area extends from shore approximately 30 nautical

miles eastward and contains the major ports of Brunswick, GA, Fernandina Beach, FL, and Jacksonville, FL. (See **50 CFR 224.105**, chapter 2 for regulations, limitations and exceptions and complete description of the SMAs.) Boundaries of the SMAs are shown on NOAA Electronic Navigational Charts. NOAA Fisheries may also establish voluntary Dynamic Management Areas (DMAs) when right whales are present in areas and times not covered by the SMAs. Information about established DMAs will be announced over NOAA's customary maritime communication media. Mariners are encouraged to avoid or reduce speeds to 10 knots or less while transiting through DMAs.

(38)

**Area to be avoided**

(39)     In order to significantly reduce the risk of ship strikes to the North Atlantic right whale, an area to be avoided was established in the Great South Channel, east of the Boston Harbor traffic lanes. Ships of 300 gross tons and above should avoid the area bounded by lines connecting the following geographical positions:

(40)     41°44'08"N., 69°34'50"W.;

(41)     42°10'00"N., 68°31'00"W.;

(42)     41°24'53"N., 68°31'00"W.; and

(43)     40°50'28"N., 68°58'40"W. between the period of April 1 through July 31.

(44)     **Early Warning and Sighting Advisory Systems:** As weather and conditions permit, dedicated seasonal programs of aerial and vessel surveys are conducted in the northeast and southeast U.S. to provide whale sighting information to mariners. Surveys typically occur in the following locations at the specified times: a) Cape Cod Bay, the Gulf of Maine and the Great South Channel and Rhode Island, Block Island and Long Island Sounds from January through July; b) South Carolina-North Carolina border south to Crescent Beach, FL, from December through March. Survey planes occasionally use VHF-FM channel 16 to contact ships directly if whales have been spotted in close proximity to that vessel. However, many right whales go undetected by surveys. Seasonal right whale advisories and sighting reports are broadcast periodically for these and surrounding areas by Coast Guard Broadcast Notice to Mariners, NAVTEX, NOAA Weather Radio, Cape Cod Canal Vessel Traffic Control and the Bay of Fundy Vessel Traffic Control, and are included in the return message from the Right Whale Mandatory Ship Reporting (MSR) systems. General sighting information may be obtained by sending an email to ne.rw.sightings@noaa.gov (northeast) or se.rw.sightings@noaa.gov (southeast).

(45)     **Precautions when transiting right whale habitat and areas of recently reported right whale sightings:**

(46)     NOAA recommends the following precautionary measures be taken to avoid adverse interactions with North Atlantic right whales:

(47)     Before entering right whale habitat (See "Seasonal Occurrence" table), check Coast Guard Broadcast

Notices to Mariners, NAVTEX, NOAA Weather Radio, Mandatory Ship Reporting (MSR) system, Cape Cod Canal Vessel Traffic Control and the Bay of Fundy Vessel Traffic Control, as well as other sources for recent right whale sighting reports. Local ship pilots also have information on whale sightings and safe local operating procedures.

(48)     Review right whale identification materials and maintain a sharp watch with lookouts familiar with spotting whales. Although right whales are large, their dark color and lack of a dorsal fin can make them difficult to spot.

(49)     Avoid transiting through the right whale habitats and areas where right whales have recently been sighted. If transiting between ports within critical habitats, minimize transit distance. Route around observed or recently reported right whales and anticipate delays due to prudent seamanship in response to whale sightings. Avoid transits at night or during periods of low visibility.

(50)     If a right whale is sighted from the ship or reported along the intended track of the ship, mariners should exercise caution, post a lookout and reduce speed to 10 knots when consistent with safe navigation. If a right whale is sighted, a vessel must steer a course away from the right whale and immediately leave the area at slow safe speed. Do not assume right whales will move out of the way of an approaching vessel. Mariners should keep in mind that it is illegal to approach a right whale closer than 500 yards. (See **50 CFR 224.103**, chapter 2 for limits, regulations and exceptions.)

(51)     Any whale accidentally struck, dead whale carcass and sighting of an injured or entangled whale should be reported immediately to the Coast Guard or NOAA National Marine Fisheries Service noting the precise location, date and time of the accident or sighting. Call 866–755–6622 for reports to NOAA for the area from Virginia to Maine or 877–942–5343 (877–WHALE–HELP) for the area from North Carolina to Florida. In the event of a strike or sighting of a dead, injured or entangled whale, the following information should be provided:

(52)     location, date and time of the accident or sighting of a carcass or an entangled whale,

(53)     speed and course of the vessel,

(54)     vessel specifications such as size and propulsion,

(55)     water depth,

(56)     environmental conditions such as visibility, wind speed and direction,

(57)     description of the impact,

(58)     fate of the animal, and

(59)     species and size, if known.

(60)     **Recommended Two-Way Routes to avoid whales:** To reduce the possibility of vessel strikes with right whales, Two-Way Routes were developed for vessels entering and transiting through Cape Cod Bay and arriving and departing the ports of Brunswick, GA, Fernandina Beach, FL, and Jacksonville, FL. The routes were developed from an analysis of historical right whale sightings and are designed to reduce the likelihood of adverse interactions between large vessels and right whales. The routes are found on the latest NOAA Nautical Charts. In July 2007, the northern leg of the Boston Traffic Separation Scheme (TSS) was shifted to direct ship traffic away from an area of high whale density. Use of the modified TSS is expected to considerably reduce the risk of striking a whale.

(61)
### Mandatory Ship Reporting Systems (MSR) WHALES-NORTH and WHALESSOUTH

(62)     Mandatory Ship Reporting (MSR) systems require all vessels, 300 gross tons or greater, to report to the U.S. Coast Guard upon entering two designated reporting areas off the east coast of the United States. (See **33 CFR 169**, chapter 2, for limits and regulations.) Sovereign immune vessels are exempt from the requirement to report but are encouraged to participate.

(63)     The two reporting systems will operate independently of each other. The system in the northeastern United States will operate year round, and the system in the southeastern United States will operate each year from November 15 through April 15. Reporting ships are only required to make reports when entering a reporting area during a single voyage (that is, a voyage in which a ship is in the area). Ships are not required to report when leaving a port in the reporting area nor when exiting the system.

(64)     Mariners should check all MSR messages carefully before transmittal to ensure the message includes the correct address and format. Additional greeting or comments in the message will preclude message receipt by the MSR system. Failure to receive a timely return message from the MSR system that provides locations of recent right whale sightings and precautionary guidance should be reported to the local Marine Safety Office of the U.S. Coast Guard.

(65)     **Northeastern reporting system/Southeastern reporting system** (See **33 CFR 169.105** and **169.115**, chapter 2, for limits.)

(66)     Vessels shall make reports in accordance with the format in IMO Resolution A.858 (20) in accordance with the International Convention for the Safety of Life at Sea 1974 (SOLAS 74). (See **33 CFR 169.135** and **169.140**, chapter 2, for additional information.) Vessels should report via INMARSAT C or via alternate satellite communications to one of the following addresses:

(67)     Email: RightWhale.MSR@noaa.gov or Telex: 48156090.

(68)     Vessels not equipped with INMARSAT C or Telex should submit reports to the U.S. Coast Guard's Communication Area Master Station Atlantic (CAMSLANT) via HF voice frequencies on 4125 kHz, 6215 kHz, 8291 kHz, 12290 kHz, and 16420 kHz or by calling 800-742-8519x0. Vessels equipped only with VHF-FM voice communications should submit reports to the nearest U.S. Coast Guard activity or group.

(69)     **Fishweirs** are numerous along the outside coast and in Chesapeake Bay and tributaries. The stakes often

become broken off and form a hazard to navigation, especially at night. Regulations limiting the areas within which fishweirs may be established have been prescribed by the Chief of Engineers, U.S. Army. The areas within which fishweirs are permitted are shown on charts of 1: 80,000 scale and larger. The exact locations of the weirs within the designated areas are not shown.

(70)     Along the outer coasts the limits of fishweir areas are not marked. In Chesapeake Bay and tributaries, black and white horizontal-banded buoys mark the turns of the limits. Strangers should proceed with caution when crossing areas of possible fishweirs and should avoid crossing such areas at night.

(71)
### Pipelaying barges
(72)     With the increased number of pipeline-laying operations, operators of all types of vessels should be aware of the dangers of passing close aboard, close ahead or close astern of a jetbarge or pipelaying barge. Pipelaying barges and jetbarges usually move at 0.5 knot or less and have anchors that extend out about 3,500 to 5,000 feet in all directions and that may be marked by lighted anchor buoys. The exposed pipeline behind the pipelaying barge and the area in the vicinity of anchors are hazardous to navigation and should be avoided. The pipeline and anchor cables also represent a submerged hazard to navigation. It is suggested, if safe navigation permits, for all types of vessels to pass well ahead of the pipelaying barge or well astern of the jetbarge. The pipelaying barge, jetbarge and attending vessels may be contacted on VHF-FM channel 16 (156.80 MHz) for passage instructions.

(73)
### Drawbridges
(74)     The general regulations that apply to all drawbridges are given in **33 CFR 117.1** through **117.59**, chapter 2, and the specific regulations that apply only to certain drawbridges are given in **33 CFR Part 117**, Subpart B, chapter 2. Where these regulations apply, references to them are made in the Coast Pilot under the name of the bridge or the waterway over which the bridge crosses.
(75)     The drawbridge opening signals (see **33 CFR 117.15**, chapter 2) have been standardized for most drawbridges within the United States. The opening signals for those few bridges that are nonstandard are given in the specific drawbridge regulations. The specific regulations also address matters such as restricted operating hours and required advance notice for openings.
(76)     The mariner should be acquainted with the general and specific regulations for drawbridges over waterways to be transited.

(77)
### Routes
(78)     Deep-draft vessels should stay outside of Barnegat Lighted Horn Buoy B and Five Fathom Bank Lighted

Buoy F between New York Harbor and Delaware Bay and outside Delaware Lighted Buoy D, Jack Spot Buoy 2JS (38°05.3'N., 74°45.1'W.) and Chesapeake Light between Delaware Bay and Chesapeake Bay. Traffic is heavy along this coast, and a sharp lookout must be kept to avoid collision. Vessels should approach Delaware Bay and Chesapeake Bay through the Traffic Separation Schemes that have been established off the entrances to these bays.

(79)
### Inside navigation
(80)     Navigation on the waterways covered by this volume requires a knowledge of the channel conditions and other factors restricting navigation. General items of interest to the vessel operator are indicated in the paragraphs that follow; details are given in the text.

(81)
### Federal regulations
(82)     (See **33 CFR 207.100**, chapter 7, for the regulations governing the use, administration and navigation of the Chesapeake and Delaware Canal.)

(83)
### Bends and curves
(84)     The New Jersey Intracoastal Waterway and adjoining waterways have many sharp bends that are dangerous to vessels meeting or passing. On approaching a bend a vessel should reduce speed sufficiently to be able to stop within half the distance to a ship coming from the opposite direction. Under no circumstances should a vessel attempt to overtake and pass another at a bend. Even with sufficient view of the channel ahead and after proper exchange and understanding of signals, the overtaken vessel may suddenly sheer from current action. This is even more pronounced with larger vessels and tows.

(85)
### Cross currents
(86)     Where two streams cross, the current will have a greater velocity in the deeper channel. This is noticeable along the New Jersey Intracoastal Waterway where it follows a dredged canal cutting across a winding stream. Cross currents will also be noticed where either an inlet from the ocean or a drainage canal enter the waterway.
(87)     Cross currents are especially strong at Beach Haven Inlet, Absecon Inlet, Townsend Inlet and Tuckerton Creek. Failure to allow for cross currents when passing these and other inlets has resulted in many rescue calls to the Coast Guard.

(88)
### Stumps and sunken logs
(89)     Reports are frequently made that vessels have struck shoals or rocks in rivers that have later proved to be stumps or sunken logs. Mariners are warned against navigating too close to the banks of streams where submerged stumps are known or may be expected to exist.

(90)
### Hurricane moorings

(91)　　On receiving an advisory notice of a tropical disturbance, small boats should seek shelter in a small winding stream whose banks are lined with trees, preferably trees with deep roots. Moor with bow and stern lines fastened to the lower branches; if possible snug up with good chafing gear. The knees of the trees will act as fenders, and the branches, having more give than the trunks, will ease the shocks of the heavy gusts. If the banks are lined only with small trees or large shrubs, use clumps of them within each hawser loop. Keep clear of any tall pines or other shallow-rooted trees, since they generally are more apt to be blown down.

(92)
### Tides

(93)　　The mean range of tide is 3.4 to 4.4 feet along the coast. In passages away from the inlets, the range may be as little as 0.5 foot. In Delaware River the mean range reaches 6.8 feet at Trenton, while in Chesapeake Bay the mean range is only 1.1 feet at Baltimore. Real-time water levels, tide predictions and tidal current predictions are available at *tidesandcurrents.noaa.gov*.

(94)
### Currents

(95)　　Rotary currents and Gulf Stream currents could be discussed at considerable length, but the important currents are those in the inlets and the inside passages; the tidal currents have considerable velocity in all of the entrances, and their direction is affected by the force and direction of the wind. See the Tidal Current prediction service at *tidesandcurrents.noaa.gov* for specific information about times, directions, and velocities of the current at numerous locations throughout the area. Links to a user guide for this service can be found in chapter 1 of this book.

(96)
### Ice

(97)　　The intracoastal passages of New Jersey, Delaware and Maryland usually are closed by ice during ordinary winters; the Virginia passages are closed only during severe winters and then only for short periods. Local vessels use all the inlets and adjacent channels from Sandy Hook to Cape Charles all winter, even when through navigation is blocked.

(98)　　In Delaware River, ice is present in sufficient amounts even in ordinary winters to be of some concern. The Chesapeake and Delaware Canal is kept open as long as possible but may be closed at times. In severe winters, navigation has been interrupted above Chester but tugs and large vessels keep the channels open to Philadelphia. Above Philadelphia, the river may be closed for extended periods in January and February, and navigation is practically suspended during severe winters.

(99)　　Ice seldom interferes with navigation of full-powered vessels in Hampton Roads even in severe winters. Large vessels can always pass up and down Chesapeake Bay,

but ice jams are of frequent occurrence off Baltimore Harbor. The harbor itself sometimes freezes over and navigation may be blocked for small, low-powered vessels for limited periods.

(100)　　Conditions in other Chesapeake Bay tributaries are somewhat similar to those in the same latitudes along the coast. Ice is not much of a problem in the southerly tributaries. The upper part of Potomac River is closed during severe winters, and Patuxent River is closed nearly to the mouth. Severn River, strangely enough, is said to remain open except for short periods in severe winters. Susquehanna River, at the head of the bay, usually is completely closed for about 3 months. Ice conditions in the Eastern Shore tributaries correspond roughly to those across the bay.

(101)　　During some winter months or when threatened by icing conditions, lighted buoys may be removed from station or replaced by unlighted buoys; unlighted buoys, daybeacons and lights on marine sites also may be removed. (See LIGHT LIST.)

(102)　　For icing hazards to vessels see Superstructure icing, following.

(103)
### Weather

(104)　　Weather hazards can plague navigation along this stretch of coast in all seasons, whether sailing the open Atlantic or the more sheltered inland waterway.

(105)　　In this chapter, a brief seasonal overview of weather difficulties is followed by a summary of weather hazards and related problems. Detailed local weather problems are discussed in the appropriate chapters. Climatological summaries for coastal stations and marine areas can be found in the appendix.

(106)　　The area covered in this Coast Pilot is generally low and flat. Long stretches of sandy beaches and tidewater marshes characterize the New Jersey, Delaware and Maryland ocean coasts. The eastern shore of Chesapeake Bay consists of low, flat, almost featureless plains, with numerous irregularities and small islands. The western shore is a gently rolling upland. Tidewater Virginia encompasses numerous flat peninsulas, wide estuaries and many swamps. Topography farther inland rises in an irregular pattern of progressively higher northeast-southwest mountain ranges to the main Appalachian Mountains. Although some distance from the ocean, this mountain barrier exerts an important influence on the winter climatic pattern in the coastal area; it partly blocks the cold continental air from the interior, and this combines with the moderating effect of the ocean to produce a more equable climate than is found in continental locations in the same latitude elsewhere.

(107)　　Winter navigation is restricted by extratropical storms that ravage the mid-Atlantic coast. These low pressure systems, which develop over the interior Gulf of Mexico and off the southeastern coast, usually move northward through east-northeastward, sweeping through the mid-Atlantic coast often accompanied by strong gusty

(113)

## Mean Surface Water Temperatures (°C) and Densities

| | Years | | Jan | Feb | Mar | Apr | May | Jun | Jul | Aug | Sep | Oct | Nov | Dec | Mean |
|---|---|---|---|---|---|---|---|---|---|---|---|---|---|---|---|
| Sandy Hook, NJ | 32 | Temp | 1.6 | 1.4 | 4.1 | 9.1 | 14.6 | 20.1 | 23.5 | 23.5 | 20.8 | 15.0 | 9.3 | 3.8 | 12.2 |
| | | Density | 17.0 | 16.9 | 15.9 | 15.0 | 16.2 | 17.7 | 19.0 | 19.1 | 19.2 | 19.1 | 18.4 | 17.5 | 17.6 |
| Atlantic City, NJ | 56 | Temp | 2.9 | 2.3 | 4.4 | 8.5 | 13.2 | 17.9 | 20.7 | 21.9 | 20.9 | 16.3 | 10.9 | 5.3 | 12.1 |
| | | Density | 23.1 | 23.2 | 23.1 | 23.0 | 23.2 | 23.5 | 23.6 | 23.5 | 23.4 | 23.4 | 23.4 | 23.2 | 23.3 |
| Breakwater Harbor, DE | 25 | Temp | 2.8 | 2.6 | 5.3 | 9.9 | 15.1 | 20.1 | 22.9 | 23.1 | 21.7 | 16.3 | 11.1 | 5.3 | 13.1 |
| | | Density | 20.9 | 21.0 | 20.6 | 20.4 | 20.9 | 21.3 | 22.1 | 22.1 | 22.0 | 23.4 | 21.9 | 21.4 | 21.4 |
| Philadelphia, PA | 39 | Temp | 2.3 | 2.5 | 5.4 | 10.8 | 17.5 | 23.3 | 26.3 | 26.1 | 23.3 | 17.5 | 10.8 | 4.8 | 14.2 |
| | | Density | -0.6 | -0.6 | -0.5 | -0.4 | -0.2 | -0.2 | -0.2 | -0.2 | -0.2 | -0.4 | -0.4 | -0.6 | -0.4 |
| Kiptopeke Beach, VA | 19 | Temp | 3.9 | 3.9 | 6.8 | 11.8 | 17.4 | 22.4 | 25.2 | 25.2 | 23.1 | 17.9 | 11.9 | 6.6 | 14.7 |
| | | Density | 19.7 | 19.4 | 18.6 | 18.0 | 18.2 | 19.0 | 19.4 | 20.3 | 20.5 | 20.4 | 20.0 | 19.7 | 19.4 |
| Cape Charles, VA | 5 | Temp | 5.5 | 5.4 | 7.5 | 12.8 | 18.1 | 23.8 | 26.6 | 26.2 | 24.0 | 18.8 | 12.5 | 6.7 | 15.7 |
| | | Density | 16.0 | 15.6 | 15.2 | 14.8 | 14.6 | 15.7 | 16.9 | 17.4 | 17.8 | 17.7 | 17.6 | 16.8 | 16.3 |
| Virginia Beach, VA | 9 | Temp | 5.3 | 4.4 | 6.3 | 10.7 | 15.7 | 20.6 | 23.0 | 23.7 | 22.4 | 18.6 | 13.7 | 8.3 | 14.4 |
| | | Density | 20.4 | 19.8 | 19.6 | 19.2 | 19.0 | 18.8 | 19.8 | 20.3 | 20.1 | 20.2 | 20.6 | 20.6 | 19.9 |
| Old Point Comfort, VA | 9 | Temp | 5.8 | 5.8 | 9.1 | 14.0 | 19.5 | 23.9 | 26.7 | 26.2 | 23.9 | 18.8 | 12.7 | 7.3 | 16.1 |
| | | Density | 14.0 | 13.2 | 12.0 | 12.3 | 12.8 | 13.7 | 15.1 | 15.7 | 15.8 | 15.8 | 15.9 | 14.9 | 14.3 |
| Little Creek, VA | 6 | Temp | 4.2 | 5.1 | 8.3 | 12.9 | 18.7 | 23.4 | 26.1 | 26.6 | 24.1 | 18.8 | 12.9 | 7.3 | 15.7 |
| | | Density | 15.8 | 15.2 | 14.3 | 14.3 | 15.0 | 16.2 | 17.7 | 17.6 | 17.6 | 17.6 | 17.0 | 16.4 | 16.2 |
| Richmond, VA | 21 | Temp | 4.7 | 5.6 | 8.9 | 14.8 | 20.7 | 25.2 | 28.1 | 27.4 | 24.3 | 18.0 | 11.3 | 5.5 | 16.2 |
| | | Density | -0.7 | -0.7 | -0.7 | -0.6 | -0.5 | -0.4 | -0.4 | -0.5 | -0.5 | -0.6 | -0.7 | -0.6 | -0.6 |
| Gloucester Point, VA | 18 | Temp | 4.3 | 4.6 | 7.7 | 13.1 | 19.2 | 23.8 | 26.5 | 26.6 | 24.2 | 18.8 | 12.7 | 7.7 | 15.7 |
| | | Density | 14.7 | 13.9 | 13.0 | 12.6 | 12.6 | 13.3 | 14.7 | 15.4 | 15.6 | 15.6 | 15.6 | 15.2 | 14.4 |
| Washington, DC | 26 | Temp | 2.8 | 3.5 | 7.7 | 14.1 | 20.2 | 25.3 | 28.3 | 27.6 | 24.6 | 18.3 | 11.4 | 4.8 | 15.7 |
| | | Density | -0.9 | -0.9 | -0.8 | -0.8 | -0.7 | -0.6 | -0.5 | -0.6 | -0.6 | -0.7 | -0.8 | -0.8 | -0.7 |
| Crisfield, MD | 2 | Temp | 2.6 | 4.4 | 7.5 | 15.0 | 21.9 | 26.0 | 27.9 | 28.4 | 24.7 | 18.4 | 10.7 | 4.0 | 16.0 |
| | | Density | 11.9 | 17.3 | 11.1 | 10.9 | 11.6 | 11.6 | 11.7 | 11.6 | 12.2 | 12.8 | 12.4 | 12.0 | 12.3 |
| Solomons, MD | 32 | Temp | 3.3 | 3.1 | 6.0 | 11.5 | 18.2 | 23.6 | 26.7 | 26.7 | 24.2 | 18.6 | 12.4 | 6.3 | 15.0 |
| | | Density | 10.7 | 10.3 | 9.3 | 7.8 | 7.5 | 7.8 | 8.8 | 9.5 | 10.5 | 11.4 | 12.0 | 11.4 | 9.8 |
| Cambridge, MD | 8 | Temp | 4.1 | 4.1 | 7.1 | 13.0 | 19.1 | 24.1 | 27.1 | 26.4 | 23.3 | 17.4 | 11.4 | 4.9 | 15.2 |
| | | Density | 6.6 | 6.1 | 6.1 | 5.6 | 5.2 | 5.3 | 5.6 | 5.7 | 7.0 | 8.0 | 8.4 | 7.6 | 5.9 |
| Annapolis, MD | 23 | Temp | 2.9 | 2.8 | 6.1 | 12.0 | 18.3 | 23.6 | 26.9 | 26.6 | 23.8 | 18.3 | 11.6 | 5.4 | 14.9 |
| | | Density | 7.9 | 7.5 | 6.5 | 4.8 | 4.6 | 5.2 | 6.2 | 7.0 | 8.1 | 9.3 | 9.8 | 8.6 | 7.1 |
| Baltimore, MD | 56 | Temp | 3.0 | 2.8 | 5.9 | 11.7 | 17.9 | 23.4 | 26.4 | 26.4 | 23.9 | 18.6 | 12.2 | 6.1 | 14.9 |
| | | Density | 6.8 | 6.7 | 5.5 | 3.8 | 3.6 | 3.8 | 4.5 | 5.3 | 6.5 | 7.5 | 7.7 | 7.3 | 5.8 |

Temperature (Celsius)
F (Fahrenheit) = 1.8C (Celsius) + 32

Density as used in this table is the specific gravity of the sea water or the ratio between the weight of a sea-water sample and the weight of an equal volume of distilled water at 15°C (59°F).

winds and rain or snow. Highs from the interior usually follow the passage of these lows, producing a pattern of rapidly changing air masses and variable winter weather from about November through March. There are marked temperature fluctuations and alternating periods of brief stormy weather, clear crisp days and relatively mild conditions. A combination of strong winds, rough seas and cold temperatures can result in superstructure icing, where sea spray and sometimes precipitation can freeze to a ship's superstructure. This adds tremendous weight and creates dangerous instability.

(108) In spring a semipermanent fair weather system known as the Bermuda High, although still centered far to the southeast, begins to influence the southeast coast. The mid-Atlantic area is usually outside its circulation and is still subject to the passage of extratropical cyclones, frontal activity and changing air masses. Warm rainy spells alternate with cool dry weather. Fog becomes a problem when warm air flows across still cold water.

(109) By early summer, the Bermuda High has built northward and westward, embracing the entire eastern seaboard with its circulation. It is responsible for the warm humid southerly flow that prevails. When it persists, the Bermuda High can block low pressure systems from the continent, providing a week or two of typical summertime weather, warm temperatures, high humidity, light to moderate southerly and southwesterly winds and showers and thunderstorms. When pressure gradients are

weak an alternating land-sea breeze is common along the coast. Summer is also the start of the hurricane season.

(110)     The threat of tropical storms and hurricanes continues in autumn as the Bermuda High begins to shift southward and eastward and weaken. This leaves the coast under the influence of a weak continental high that gradually gives way to the winter weather pattern of increased frontal activity, winter storms and migratory high pressure systems. While autumn brings a battle for control of the weather, these are mainly periods of dry sunny days and cool clear nights. During these periods there is the possibility of radiation type fog, forming inland at night and drifting out along the coast in the early morning. This fog is more localized than the spring advection fog and usually burns off before noon.

(111)

### Climatological tables

(112)     Climatological tables for coastal localities and meteorological tables for the coastal ocean areas covered in this volume follow the appendix. The meteorological tables were compiled from observations made by ships in passage. Listed in the appendix are National Weather Service offices and radio stations that transmit weather information.

(114)

### Superstructure icing

(115)     In certain weather conditions, ice accumulating on hulls and superstructures can be a serious danger to ships. Ice accumulation may occur from three causes:

(116)     (a) Fog with freezing conditions;

(117)     (b) Freezing rain or drizzle;

(118)     (c) Sea spray or seas breaking over the ship when the air temperature is below the freezing point of seawater (about 28.6°F, -1.89°C).

(119)     Ice accumulation from the first two causes, if appreciable, could induce enough damage to the rigging to cause it to fall. This is minor, however, in comparison with the weight of the ice accumulated in rough weather and low temperatures, when large amounts of spray and often heavy seas break over a vessel. When the air temperature is below the freezing point of sea water and the ship is in heavy seas, considerable amounts of water will freeze to the superstructure and those parts of the hull that are sufficiently above the waterline to escape being frequently washed by the sea. The amounts frozen to surfaces exposed to the air will rapidly increase with falling air and sea temperatures and might in extreme cases lead to capsizing of the vessel. The dangerous conditions are those in which gale-force winds last for several days in association with air temperatures of 28°F (-2.2°C) or lower. These conditions will normally occur when the wind comes from the northern quadrants. Indications of when these conditions are likely to occur can often be obtained by observing the rate of fall of the barometer, at the onset of strengthening winds from a cold quarter, together with observations of air and sea temperatures.

(120)     Superstructure icing at its worst can sink a small vessel. It elevates the center of gravity, decreasing the metacentric height. Icing increases the sail area and the heeling moment due to wind action. Its non-uniform distribution changes the trim; it can hamper steerability and lower ship speed. Icing can also cause hazardous deck conditions.

(121)

### Pressure

(122)     The pressure pattern changes considerably from summer to winter. At individual stations along the coast, however, the differences of mean annual pressure are quite small. The highest monthly mean pressure occurs during the winter and the lowest in late spring and early summer. Large short-term variations of pressure are occasionally experienced during tropical cyclones in the late summer and autumn and during the movement of extratropical cyclones and anticyclones in the winter and spring. The day-to-day changes of pressure in summer are less marked and average lower than in winter.

(123)

### Winds

(124)     Prevailing winds at most stations are from northwest during the cooler months, October through March, and from the southwest, May through September. The average wind speeds during the warmer months are generally lower than during the colder seasons, because of the absence of extratropical cyclones. Highest average speeds occur in March and lowest in August.

(125)     In the winter, the winds over the open ocean are slightly stronger than those over land. Little difference is apparent in summer. In the warmer season, a daily shift in wind direction occurs when the region is not under the influence of cyclonic storms. During the warmer part of the day winds blow onshore, and during the cooler part, offshore. This land-sea breeze seldom penetrates more than a few miles inland.

(126)     Gales (force 8 or higher) are reported in about 6 percent of ships' observations in winter. Gales are generally from the westerly quadrants. Summer gales are rare, but may be encountered during tropical cyclones or local thunderstorms.

(127)

### Temperatures

(128)     Along the mid-Atlantic Coast temperatures are generally moderate. Mean annual temperatures range from 55.1°F (12.8°C) at Philadelphia to 60.1°F (15.6°C) at Norfolk. The lowest mean monthly temperature is 31.1°F (-0.5°C) at Trenton in January; the highest, 79.4°F (26.3°C) at Norfolk in July. January is the coldest month and July the warmest. Over the open water areas, January mean air temperatures may be several degrees warmer than at coastal points, and in July they may be a few degrees cooler. Over land surfaces, the air warms and cools readily, but over water it does so slowly and relatively little. Land surfaces absorb heat in only a thin

surface layer and give it up freely, while water absorbs heat to substantial depths and retains it longer.

(129) The daily temperature range averages from 10° to 20°F (12.2° to 6.7°C) throughout the year and is generally much less over the water. Readings in the coastal areas rarely exceed 100°F (37.8°C), and the 90°F (32.2°C) level is reached on only one-third to one-half of the days during summer. Freezing temperatures (<0°C) are probable on one-half or more of the days from November through March, except from Maryland southward where the average is about one in three. Below-zero readings (< -17.8°C) have been recorded during December, January and February at most stations, except Dover where no reading below 0°F (-17.8°C) has ever been observed.

(130) Sea-surface temperatures are warmer than air temperatures most of the time, ranging from 4° to 7°F (15.6° to 13.9°C) warmer in winter to about the same temperature in the spring.

(131)
### Relative humidity

(132) Throughout the year the relative humidity is high, averaging from 64 to 90 percent at 0700 and from 46 to 62 percent at 1900. Humidities usually are higher with onshore winds (blowing from sea toward land) and lower with offshore winds (blowing from land toward sea).

(133)
### Cargo care

(134) High humidities and temperature extremes can be encountered navigating the East Coast and may cause sweat damage to cargo. This problem is most likely when cargoes are loaded in warm summer air or can occur anytime temperatures fluctuate rapidly.

(135) When free air has a higher dewpoint than the temperature of the surface with which it comes in contact, the air is often cooled sufficiently below its dewpoint to release moisture. When this happens condensation will occur on board ship either on relatively cool cargo or on the ship's structure within the hold, where it drips onto the cargo. If cargo is stowed in a cool climate and the vessel sails into warmer waters, ventilation of the hold with outside air can lead to sweat damage of any moisture-sensitive cargo. Unless the cargo generates internal heat, then as a rule, external ventilation should be shut off. When a vessel is loaded in warm weather and moves into a cooler region, vulnerable cargo should be ventilated.

(136) In general, whenever accurate readings show the outside air has a dewpoint below the dewpoint of the air surrounding the vulnerable cargo, such outside air is capable of removing moisture and ventilation may be started. However, if the outside dewpoint is higher than the dewpoint around the cargo, ventilation will increase moisture and result in sweating. This generality does not take into account the possibility of necessary venting for gases or fumes.

(137)
### Cloudiness and precipitation

(138) At sea in winter, overcast conditions (cloud amount 0.8 or more) are recorded in 45 to 50 percent of observations, while clear conditions (0.2 or less) are recorded in about 30 percent. In summer, some 30 to 35 percent of observations show overcast and an equal percent, clear skies. The least cloudiness occurs when the air is dominated by the Bermuda High in late summer and early autumn, and the greatest cloudiness during the frequent winter cyclones. In the coastal area, from one-third to one-half the days are overcast in winter, and 25 to 35 percent in summer.

(139) Precipitation over the coastal sections is moderately heavy and well distributed. Normal monthly totals vary from minima of about 2.5 to 3.0 inches (64 to 76 mm) in February or October to maxima of 4.5 to 6.0 inches (114 to 152 mm) in August. Annual totals range between 41 and 45 inches (1,041 and 1,143 mm). Summer thunderstorms are most frequent over land and near coastal waters in the afternoon; at night they are more frequent over open water. Thunderstorm rainfall is less intense over the ocean but can severely restrict visibility. Snow may be expected from November through March; maximum fall is in January and February. Snow usually does not remain on the ground for extended periods. On rare occasions, freezing rain, or glaze, is encountered; if prolonged, it can cause damage to rigging. Snow at sea is little more than a severe restriction to visibility.

(140)
### Visibility

(141) Although generally good, visibility can be hampered by fog, precipitation, haze and smoke. Fog is usually the most restrictive. It is most likely over open waters in spring and early summer when warm moist air moves across still cool waters. Off the coast from March through June, this advection fog restricts visibility to less than 0.5 mile (0.80 km), 3 to 8 percent of the time. Visibilities fall below 2 miles (3.2 km) 5 to 12 percent of the time during this period. While advection fog sometimes drifts onshore, radiation fog in autumn and winter is more common just inland. Radiation fog forms on calm, clear nights and may drift over water during the early morning hours. It usually burns off by noon. At coastal locations visibilities fall below 0.25 mile (0.40 km) about 2 to 5 days per month from September through March; some locations suffer through June if they are exposed to sea fog. Smoke and haze by themselves rarely reduce visibilities below 2 miles (3.2 km) but precipitation can briefly, particularly in heavy showers.

(142)
### Thunderstorms

(143) While they can develop in any month, thunderstorms are most likely from May through October. They can occur in squall lines or a single cell, stirring a breeze or creating gusts to 100 knots. Thunderstorms can spring up rapidly or be tracked for several days or bring gentle showers or a

torrential downpour. Thunderstorms can harbor a tornado or waterspout and produce vivid lightning displays. The number of thunderstorms can vary from year to year, but on the average they can be expected on 4 to 10 days per month from May through August.

(144)     Along the coast and over the bays, thunderstorms are most likely from midafternoon through the evening. These are the typical air mass thunderstorms that result from warm moist air being heated and forced to rise. Cold fronts can also generate thunderstorms and often squall lines, which can occur at any time. When thunderstorms coincide with the time of maximum daily heating, they are most violent. In spring and early summer, thunderstorms usually develop to the west and southwest and approach at 20 to 35 knots; they are often severe. As summer progresses air mass thunderstorms are more likely. These form to the west and east of Chesapeake Bay and move eastward at about 10 to 20 knots.

(145)

### Tropical Cyclones

(146)     Tropical storms and hurricanes are an infrequent but dangerous threat to navigation. At sea, winds can reach 175 knots or more and waves of 35 to 40 feet (11 to 12 m) are likely; in an intense storm the waves may exceed 50 feet (15 m). On the coast, storm tides as much as 17 feet (5 m) or more above mean sea level are possible as is rainfall of 15 inches (381 mm) or more. A tropical cyclone is a warm-core, low-pressure system that develops over the warm waters of the tropical oceans and exhibits a rotary, counterclockwise circulation in the Northern Hemisphere (clockwise in the Southern Hemisphere). Tropical cyclones occur almost entirely in six rather distinct regions of the world; one of these, the **North Atlantic Region** (West Indies, Caribbean Sea, Gulf of Mexico and waters off the east coast of the United States), includes the area covered by this Coast Pilot. In this region, tropical cyclones with winds of 34 to 63 knots are called **tropical storms,** while tropical cyclones with winds greater than 63 knots are called hurricanes. **Hurricanes** are infrequent in comparison with middle- and high-latitude storms, but they have a record of destruction far exceeding that of any other type of storm. Because of their fury and the fact that they are predominately oceanic, they merit the special attention of all mariners, whether professional or amateur.

(147)     While tropical cyclones can occur at any time, they are most likely from June through early November. Along this section of the coast their greatest frequency occurs from mid-August through September. They are often in the process of recurving and tend to parallel the coastline. The most dangerous storms are those that move slowly northward and remain just off the coast. Fortunately, tropical cyclones tend to accelerate as they move into higher latitudes; forward speeds of 20 to 30 knots are not uncommon.

(148)     Rarely does the mariner who has experienced a fully developed tropical cyclone (hurricane) at sea wish to encounter a second one, having learned the wisdom of avoiding them if possible. The uninitiated may be misled by the deceptively small size of a tropical cyclone as it appears on a weather map and by the fine weather experienced only a few hundred miles from the reported center of such a storm. The rapidity with which the weather can deteriorate with approach of the storm, and the violence of the hurricane, are difficult to visualize if they have not been experienced.

(149)     As a tropical cyclone moves out of the tropics to higher latitudes, it normally loses energy slowly, expanding in area until it gradually dissipates or acquires the characteristics of extratropical cyclones. At any stage, a tropical cyclone normally loses energy at a much faster rate if it moves over land. As a general rule, tropical cyclones of the North Atlantic Region move with the prevailing winds of the area. In small hurricanes the diameter of the area of destructive winds may not exceed 25 miles (40 km) while in some of the greatest storms the diameter may be as much as 400 to 500 miles (644 to 805 km).

(150)     At the center is a comparative calm known as the **eye** of the storm. The diameter of this eye varies with individual storms and may be as little as 7 miles (11 km), but is rarely more than 30 miles (48 km). The average is 15 to 20 miles (24 to 32 km). This center is the region of low atmospheric pressure around which winds blow in a more or less circular course, spiraling inward in a counterclockwise direction. Winds at the outer edge of the storm area are light to moderate and gusty, and often increase toward the center to speeds too high for instrument recording. Although the air movement near the center of the hurricane is usually light and fitful, the seas in this area are in most cases very heavy and confused, rendered so by the violent shifting winds that surround it. Furthermore, after the center has passed a vessel, she may expect a sharp renewal of the gales, with winds from a more or less opposite direction. The hurricane may affect an area covering tens of thousands of square miles.

(151)     In an average year over the entire North Atlantic (including the Caribbean Sea and the Gulf of Mexico) about nine or ten tropical cyclones come to life and about six of these reach hurricane strength. They usually form over a wide range of ocean between the Cape Verde Islands and the Windward Islands, over the western Caribbean Sea and in the Gulf of Mexico. While some may initially move northward most take a westerly to northwesterly course. Of these, some curve gradually northward either east or north of the larger islands of the West Indies, then finally turn northeastward or eastward off the U.S. Atlantic coast.

(152)     A considerable number, however, remain in low latitudes and do not turn appreciably northward. Freak movements are not uncommon, and there have been storms that described loops, hairpin-curved paths and other irregular patterns. Movement toward the southeast is rare, and in any case of short duration. The entire

Caribbean area, the Gulf of Mexico, the coastal regions bordering these bodies of water and the Atlantic Coast are subject to these storms during the hurricane season.

(153)     Hurricanes develop over the southern portions of the North Atlantic, including the Gulf of Mexico, and Caribbean Sea, **mostly from June through October, infrequently in May and November, and rarely in other months;** the hurricane season reaches its peak in September. An average of nine tropical cyclones form each year (reaching at least tropical storm intensity), and five of these reach hurricane strength. June and July storms tend to develop in the northwestern Caribbean or Gulf of Mexico; during August there is an increase in number and intensity, and the area of formation extends east of the Lesser Antilles. September storms develop between 50° W and the Lesser Antilles, in the southern Gulf of Mexico, the western Caribbean, near the Bahamas and around the Cape Verde Islands. Formation in October shifts primarily to the western Caribbean, and off-season storms are widespread with a slight concentration in the southwestern Caribbean.

(154)     The average speed of movement of tropical cyclones in the tropics is about 10 to 15 knots. This speed, however, varies considerably according to the location of the storm, its development, and attendant meteorological conditions. The highest rates of progression usually occur when the storm is moving northward or northeastward in the middle or higher latitudes.

(155)
### Extratropical cyclones
(156)     These winter-type storms, while abundant all year, are most intense from fall through spring. Along this coast they are often known as "nor'easters." They can generate hurricane-force winds and can vary in size from 100 miles to nearly 1,000 miles (160 to 1,600 km) in diameter. Waves generated by these storms commonly exceed 40 feet (12 m) and have been reported at more than 60 feet (18 m) in the open ocean. Like tropical cyclones, they can devastate the shore, rearrange the coastal topography, and cause extensive flooding.

(157)     These storms generally move into this region from the west or southwest. Those from the Gulf of Mexico area are usually more intense because of their overwater route. They often intensify off Cape Hatteras before sweeping northeastward. Heavy rain or snow before the passage of the storm center may be extensive. After the center passes, northwesterly winds coming from the interior may be strong and cold. The classic "nor'easter" is so called because winds over the coastal area are out of the northeast. They may occur at any time but are most frequent and violent between September and April. They often develop off the mid-Atlantic coast and head northeastward toward New England.

(158)
### Locating and tracking tropical cyclones
(159)     By means of radio, the National Weather Service collects weather observations daily from land stations, ships at sea and aircraft. When a tropical cyclone is located, usually in its early formative stage, it is followed closely. In the North Atlantic, U.S. Navy, Air Force and NOAA aircraft make frequent flights to the vicinity of such storms to provide information needed for tracking the tropical cyclone and determining its intensity. Long-range shore radar stations follow the movement of the storm's precipitation area when it is in range. Bulletins are broadcast to ships several times daily, giving information on each storm's location, intensity and movement. As a further aid, the mariner may obtain weather reports by radio directly from other ships in the vicinity of a tropical cyclone.

(160)
### Signs of approach
(161)     Although radio reports normally prove adequate for locating and avoiding a tropical cyclone, knowledge of the appearance of the sea and sky in the vicinity of such a storm is useful to the mariner. The passage of a hurricane at sea is an experience not soon to be forgotten.

(162)     An early indication of the approach of such a storm is the presence of a long swell. In the absence of a tropical cyclone, the crests of swell in the deep waters of the Atlantic pass at the rate of perhaps eight per minute. Swell generated by a tropical cyclone is about twice as long, the crests passing at the rate of perhaps four per minute. Swell may be observed several days before arrival of the storm.

(163)     When the storm center is 500 to 1,000 miles away, the barometer usually rises a little, and the skies are relatively clear. Cumulus clouds, if present at all, are few in number, and their vertical development appears suppressed. The barometer usually appears restless, pumping up and down a few hundredths of an inch.

(164)     As the tropical cyclone comes nearer, a cloud sequence begins that resembles that associated with the approach of a warm front in middle latitudes. Snow-white, fibrous "mare's tails" (cirrus) appear when the storm is about 300 to 600 miles away. Usually these seem to converge, more or less, in the direction from which the storm is approaching. This convergence is particularly apparent at about the time of sunrise and sunset.

(165)     Shortly after the cirrus appears, but sometimes before, the barometer starts a long, slow fall. At first the fall is so gradual that it only appears to alter somewhat the normal daily cycle (two maximums and two minimums in the tropics). As the rate of fall increases, the daily pattern is completely lost in the more or less steady fall.

(166)     The cirrus becomes more confused and tangled and then gradually gives way to a continuous veil of cirrostratus. Below this veil, altostratus forms, and then stratocumulus. These clouds gradually become more dense, and as they do so, the weather becomes unsettled. A fine, mistlike rain begins to fall, interrupted from time to time by showers. The barometer has fallen perhaps a tenth of an inch.

(167)     As the fall becomes more rapid, the wind increases in gustiness, and its speed becomes greater, reaching a value of perhaps 22 to 40 knots (Beaufort 6-8). On the horizon appears a dark wall of heavy cumulonimbus, the **bar** of the storm. Portions of this heavy cloud become detached from time to time and drift across the sky, accompanied by rain squalls and wind of increasing speed. Between squalls, the cirrostratus can be seen through breaks in the stratocumulus.

(168)     As the bar approaches, the barometer falls more rapidly and wind speed increases. The seas, which have been gradually mounting, become tempestuous and squall lines, one after the other, sweep past in ever increasing number and intensity.

(169)     With the arrival of the bar, the day becomes very dark, squalls become virtually continuous, and the barometer falls precipitously, with a rapid increase in the wind speed. The center may still be 100 to 200 miles away in a hurricane. As the center of the storm comes closer, the ever-stronger wind shrieks through the rigging and about the superstructure of the vessel. As the center approaches, rain falls in torrents. The wind fury increases. The seas become mountainous. The tops of huge waves are blown off to mingle with the rain and fill the air with water. Objects at a short distance are not visible. Even the largest and most seaworthy vessels become virtually unmanageable, and may sustain heavy damage. Less sturdy vessels do not survive. Navigation virtually stops as safety of the vessel becomes the prime consideration. The awesome fury of this condition can only be experienced. Words are inadequate to describe it.

(170)     If the eye of the storm passes over the vessel, the winds suddenly drop to a breeze as the wall of the eye passes. The rain stops, and skies clear sufficiently to permit the sun to shine through holes in the comparatively thin cloud cover. Visibility improves. Mountainous seas approach from all sides, apparently in complete confusion. The barometer reaches its lowest point, which may be 1.5 to 2 inches below normal in hurricanes. As the wall on the opposite side of the eye arrives, the full fury of the wind strikes as suddenly as it ceased, but from the opposite direction. The sequence of conditions that occurred during approach of the storm is reversed and pass more quickly, as the various parts of the storm are not as wide in the rear of a storm as on its forward side.

(171)
**Locating the center of a tropical cyclone**

(172)     If intelligent action is to be taken to avoid the full fury of a tropical cyclone, early determination of its location and direction of travel relative to the vessel is essential. The bulletins and forecasts are an excellent general guide, but they are not infallible and may be sufficiently in error to induce a mariner in a critical position to alter course so as to unwittingly increase the danger of the vessel. Often it is possible, using only those observations made aboard ship, to obtain a sufficiently close approximation to enable the vessel to maneuver to the best advantage.

(173)     As previously stated, the presence of an exceptionally long swell is usually the first visible indication of the existence of a tropical cyclone. In deep water it approaches from the general direction of origin (the position of the storm center when the swell was generated). However, in shoaling water this is a less reliable indication because the direction is changed by refraction, the crests being more nearly parallel to the bottom contours.

(174)     When the cirrus clouds appear, their point of convergence provides an indication of the direction of the storm center. If the storm is to pass well to one side of the observer, the point of convergence shifts slowly in the direction of storm movement. If the storm center will pass near the observer, this point remains steady. When the bar becomes visible, it appears to rest upon the horizon for several hours. The darkest part of this cloud is in the direction of the storm center. If the storm is to pass to one side, the bar appears to drift slowly along the horizon. If the storm is heading directly toward the observer, the position of the bar remains fixed. Once within the area of the dense, low clouds, one should observe their direction of movement, which is almost exactly along the isobars, with the center of the storm being 90° from the direction of cloud movement (left of direction of movement in the Northern Hemisphere).

(175)     The winds are probably the best guide to the direction of the center of a tropical cyclone. The circulation is cyclonic, but because of the steep pressure gradient near the center, the winds there blow with greater violence and are more nearly circular than in extratropical cyclones.

(176)     According to Buys Ballot's law, an observer who faces into the wind has the center of the low pressure on his right (Northern Hemisphere) and somewhat behind him. If the wind followed circular isobars exactly, the center would be exactly eight points, or 90°, from dead ahead when facing into the wind. However, the track of the wind is usually inclined somewhat toward the center, so that the angle dead ahead varies between perhaps 8 and 12 points (90° to 135°). The inclination varies in different parts of the same storm. It is least in front of the storm, and greatest in the rear, since the actual wind is the vector sum of that due to the pressure gradient and the motion of the storm along the track. A good average is perhaps 10 points in front and 11 or 12 points in the rear. These values apply when the storm center is still several hundred miles away. Closer to the center, the wind blows more nearly along the isobars, the inclination being reduced by one or two points at the wall of the eye. Since wind direction usually shifts temporarily during a squall, its direction at this time should not be used for determining the position of the center.

(177)     When the center is within radar range, it might be located by this equipment. However, since the radar return is predominately from the rain, results can be deceptive, and other indications should not be neglected.

(178)     Distance from the storm center is more difficult to determine than direction. Radar is perhaps the best guide. The rate of fall of the barometer is of some help; this is

only a rough indication, however, for the rate of fall may be quite erratic and will vary somewhat with the depth of the low at the center, the speed of the storm center along its track, and the stage in the life cycle of the storm.

(179)
**Maneuvering to avoid the storm center**

(180)     The safest procedure with respect to tropical cyclones is to avoid them. With the aid of ship observations, satellite information and computers, there is ample warning time, usually 24 to 48 hours, to prepare for the approach of a tropical cyclone along this coast. These warnings are given wide distribution by commercial radio and television, Coast Guard and NOAA weather radio and visual displays whenever winds, weather, sea conditions or storm tides are expected to be a hazard to marine operations. If action is taken sufficiently early, this is simply a matter of setting a course that will take the vessel well to one side of the probable track of the storm, and then continuing to plot the position of the storm center, as given in the weather bulletins, revising the course as needed. Detailed information on the vulnerability of North Atlantic ports to hurricanes may be found in the **Hurricane Havens Handbook for the North Atlantic Ocean** published by the Marine Meteorology Division, Naval Research Laboratory, Monterey, CA 93943, and available at *nrlmry.navy.mil/pubs.htm*. Additional local information may be found in the individual chapters of this book.

(181)     However, such action is not always possible. If one finds oneself within the storm area, the proper action to take depends in part upon the vessel's position relative to the storm center and its direction of travel. It is customary to divide the circular area of the storm into two parts. In the Northern Hemisphere, that part to the **right** of the storm track (facing in the direction toward which the storm is moving) is called the **dangerous semicircle.** It is considered dangerous because (1) the actual wind **speed** is greater than that due to the pressure gradient alone, since it is augmented by the forward motion of the storm, and (2) the **direction** of the wind and sea is such as to carry a vessel into the path of the storm (in the forward part of the semicircle). The part to the **left** of the storm track is called the **navigable semicircle.** In this part, the wind is decreased by the forward motion of the storm, and the wind blows vessels away from the storm track (in the forward part). Because of the greater wind speed in the dangerous semicircle, the seas are higher here than in the navigable semicircle.

(182)     A plot of successive positions of the storm center should indicate the semicircle in which a vessel is located. However, if this is based upon weather bulletins, it is not a reliable guide because of the lag between the observations upon which the bulletin is based and the time of reception of the bulletin, with the ever present possibility of a change in the direction of motion of the storm. The use of radar eliminates this lag, but the return is not always a true indication of the center. Perhaps the most reliable guide

is the wind. Within the cyclonic circulation, a **veering wind** (one changing direction to the right in the Northern Hemisphere and to the left in the Southern Hemisphere) indicates a position in the dangerous semicircle, and a **backing wind** (one changing in a direction opposite to a veering wind) indicates a position in the navigable semicircle. However, if a vessel is underway, its motion should be considered. If it is outrunning the storm or pulling rapidly toward one side (which is not difficult during the early stages of a storm, when its speed is low), the opposite effect occurs. This should usually be accompanied by a rise in atmospheric pressure, but if motion of the vessel is nearly along an isobar, this may not be a reliable indication. If in doubt, the safest action is usually to stop long enough to determine definitely the semicircle. The loss in valuable time may be more than offset by the minimizing of the possibility of taking the wrong action and increasing the danger to the vessel. If the wind direction remains steady (for a vessel which has stopped), with increasing speed and falling barometer, the vessel is in or near the path of the storm. If it remains steady with decreasing speed and rising barometer, the vessel is on the storm track, behind the center.

(183)     The first action to take if one finds oneself within the cyclonic circulation, is to determine the position of one's vessel with respect to the storm center. **While the vessel can still make considerable way through the water, a course should be selected to take it as far as possible from the center.** If the vessel can move faster than the storm, it is a relatively simple matter to outrun the storm if sea room permits. But when the storm is faster, the solution is not as simple. In this case, the vessel, if ahead of the storm, will approach nearer to the center. The problem is to select a course that will produce the greatest possible minimum distance. This is best determined by means of a relative movement plot.

(184)     As a very general rule, for a vessel in the Northern Hemisphere, safety lies in placing the wind on the starboard bow in the dangerous semicircle and on the starboard quarter in the navigable semicircle. If on the storm track ahead of the storm, the wind should be put about two points on the starboard quarter until the vessel is well within the navigable semicircle and the rule for that semicircle then followed. With a faster than average vessel, the wind can be brought a little farther aft in each case. However, as the speed of the storm increases along its track, the wind should be brought farther forward. If land interferes with what would otherwise be the best maneuver, the solution should be altered to fit the circumstances. If the speed of the vessel is greater than that of the storm, it is possible for the vessel, if behind the storm, to overtake it. In this case, the only action usually needed is to slow enough to let the storm pull ahead.

(185)     In all cases, one should be alert to changes in the direction of movement of the storm center, particularly in the area where the track normally curves toward the pole. If the storm maintains its direction and speed, the ship's course should be maintained as the wind shifts.

(186)     If it becomes necessary for a vessel to heave to, the characteristics of the vessel should be considered. A power vessel is concerned primarily with damage by direct action of the sea. A good general rule is to heave to with head to the sea in the dangerous semicircle or stern to the sea in the navigable semicircle. This will result in greatest amount of headway away from the storm center, and least amount of leeway toward it. If a vessel handles better with the sea astern or on the quarter, it may be placed in this position in the navigable semicircle or in the rear half of the dangerous semicircle, but never in the forward half of the dangerous semicircle. It has been reported that when the wind reaches hurricane speed and the seas become confused, some ships ride out the storm best if the engines are stopped and the vessel is permitted to seek its own position. In this way, it is said, the ship rides with the storm instead of fighting against it.

(187)     In a sailing vessel, while attempting to avoid a storm center, one should steer courses as near as possible to those prescribed above for power vessels. However, if it becomes necessary for such a vessel to heave to, the wind is of greater concern than the sea. A good general rule always is to heave to on whichever tack permits the shifting wind to draw aft. In the Northern Hemisphere this is the starboard tack in the dangerous semicircle and the port tack in the navigable semicircle.

(188)
### Practical rules
(189)     When there are indications of a hurricane, vessels should remain in port or seek one if possible. Changes in barometer and wind should be carefully observed and recorded, and every precaution should be taken to avert damage by striking light spars, strengthening moorings and if a steamer, preparing steam to assist the moorings. In the ports of the southern States hurricanes are generally accompanied by very high tides, and vessels may be endangered by overriding the wharf where moored if the position is at all exposed.

(190)     Vessels in the Straits of Florida may not have sea room to maneuver so as to avoid the storm track and should try to make a harbor or to stand out of the straits to obtain sea room. Vessels unable to reach a port and having sea room to maneuver usually observe the previously discussed general rules for avoiding the storm center, which, for power-driven vessels, are summarized as follows:

(191)     **Right or dangerous semicircle:** Bring the wind on the starboard bow (045° relative), hold course, and make as much way as possible. If obliged to heave to, do so with head to the sea.

(192)     **Left or navigable semicircle:** Bring the wind on the starboard quarter (135° relative), hold course, and make as much way as possible. If obliged to heave to, do so with stern to the sea.

(193)     **On storm track, ahead of center:** Bring the wind two points on the starboard quarter (157.5° relative), hold course, and make as much way as possible. When well within the navigable semicircle, maneuver as indicated above.

(194)     **On storm track, behind center:** Avoid the center by the best practicable course, keeping in mind the tendency of tropical cyclones to curve northward and eastward.

(195)
### Coastal effects
(196)     Along the coast, water may inflict greater damage than wind. The storm tide is the result of the tropical cyclone's pressure and wind on the normal astronomical tide. When these forces occur simultaneously with a normal high tide the resultant flooding can be devastating. Add to that the unusually high seas generated by the storm and there is the potential for a disaster. Aids to navigation may be blown out of position or destroyed. Craft in harbors, unless properly secured, may drag anchor and/ or be blown against obstructions.

(197)     When proceeding along a shore recently visited by a hurricane, a navigator should remember that time is required to restore aids to navigation that have been blown out of position or destroyed. In some instances the aid may remain, but its light or sound apparatus may be inoperative. Landmarks may have been damaged or destroyed.

(198)
### Dangerous waves along the Gulf Stream
(199)     Winter and spring storms passing over the Gulf Stream along the east coast of the United States may be modified rapidly enough to create dangerous wind and wave situations. This is particularly true in the North Wall, a narrow band of extreme horizontal water temperature change that marks the northern edge of the Gulf Stream. In early winter, cold air outbreaks along this northern edge sometimes result in a doubling of the wind speed of surrounding seas. During February and March the waters north of the Gulf Stream are at their coldest while the Gulf Stream remains relatively warm. Also, from the North Wall to 10 to 20 miles into the Gulf Stream, strong northeasterly currents are encountered. The strong northeasterly winds of intense coastal storms tend to pull cold Arctic air across the slope water to near Cape Hatteras. As this cold air reaches the Gulf Stream it encounters rapidly increasing sea surface temperatures. This sudden warming produces an increase in wind speeds and gustiness. In turn, this causes higher and confused seas. In addition, these northeasterly seas encounter opposing currents of 3 to 5 knots resulting in a sharp increase in wave heights and much steeper wave slopes. Waves may even break. This action causes problems for small craft navigating inlets in waves of only a few feet in height. With 20- to 30-foot seas the result is dangerous to any ship. To avoid this problem it is often best in late winter and spring to cross the Gulf Stream as far east as possible, since the cold air should be modified somewhat, reducing the instability effect.

(200)
## Principal ports

(201)　　The ports within the area of this Coast Pilot that have deep-draft commercial traffic are Delaware City, DE; Wilmington, DE; Marcus Hook, PA; Chester, PA; Philadelphia, PA; Gloucester City, NJ; Atlantic City, NJ; Camden, NJ; Trenton, NJ; Norfolk, VA; Portsmouth, VA; Newport News, VA; Richmond, VA; Piney Point, MD; Alexandria, VA; Cove Point, MD; Cambridge, MD; and Baltimore, MD.

(202)
## Pilotage, general

(203)　　Pilotage is compulsory for all foreign vessels and U.S. vessels under register in the foreign trade. Pilotage is optional for coastwise vessels that have on board a pilot properly licensed by the Federal Government for the waters which the vessel travels.

(204)　　The Maryland Pilots maintain a pilot station at Cape Henry; Virginia State pilots maintain a pilot station at Cape Henry; pilots for Delaware Bay and River maintain a pilot station at Cape Henlopen; Maryland State pilots and pilots for Delaware Bay and River also maintain a joint pilot station at Chesapeake City, MD, on the Chesapeake and Delaware Canal.

(205)　　The Chesapeake and Interstate Pilots Association offers pilotage to U.S. vessels engaged in the coastwise trade. Pilotage is also available to public vessels. The association serves vessels transiting Chesapeake Bay and its tributaries, Chesapeake and Delaware Canal, and Delaware Bay and River. Chesapeake and Interstate Pilots Association has an office in Norfolk (telephone, 757-855-2733).

(206)　　The Interport Pilots Agency, Inc., offers pilotage to public vessels and private vessels in the coastal trade transiting the Delaware Bay and River, Chesapeake and Delaware Canal, Upper Chesapeake Bay, New York Harbor, Long Island Sound and other areas along the northeast coast. Arrangements for their services are made 24 hours in advance through the ship's agents or by contacting Interport Pilots Agency, Inc., 906 Port Monmouth Road, Port Monmouth, NJ 07758-0236, telephone 732-787-5554 (24 hours), or by email at interport@verizon.net. Additional information about Interport Pilots can be obtained at *interportpilots.com*.

(207)　　Pilotage is available for foreign vessels and U.S. vessels under register, for all ports on the New Jersey seacoast from Sandy Hook to and including Atlantic City, from the Sandy Hook Pilot Association, 201 Edgewater Street, Staten Island, NY 10305.

(208)　　Telephone 718-448-3900, fax 718-447-1582;

(209)　　Email: PILOTOFFICE@sandyhookpilots.com. A 24-hour advance notice is required.

(210)　　All pilot associations provide 24-hour service. Arrangements for pilots should be made well in advance through ships' agents.

(211)　　Detailed information on pilotage procedures is given in the text for the ports concerned.

(212)
## Towage

(213)　　Tugs are available at all major ports; they can usually be obtained for the smaller ports on advance notice if none are available locally. Arrangements for tugs should be made in advance through ships' agents or the pilots. (See the text for the ports concerned as to the availability of tugs.)

(214)
## Dead Ship tows

(215)　　The Captain of the Port (COTP) Delaware Bay has determined that a dead ship is a hazardous condition and that special attention needs to be paid to the movement of these vessels. Responsible parties, their surveyors and towing companies maintain ultimate responsibility for conducting a safe tow. The authority to control, approve, and monitor dead ship tows is derived from Title 33, Code of Federal Regulations (CFR), Part 160.111 (c) and Part 160.215. (See Chapter 2 of this Coast Pilot.)

(216)　　**Requirements to ensure a safe dead ship tow** within or transiting through Sector Delaware Bay Regulated Navigation Area, Title 33 CFR, Part 165.510 (See chapter 2 of this Coast Pilot):

(217)　　1. Towing companies (excluding commercial salvage companies) contracted to conduct a dead-ship tow of any commercial, Department of Defense (DOD), ex-commercial or ex-DOD vessel (regardless of length) must submit a proposal to the Coast Guard Sector Delaware Bay Waterways Management Branch. For vessels being towed within the port, the proposal must be submitted at least **48 hours** before the start of the towing operation. If the vessel is to be towed out of port, the proposal must be submitted at least **5 days** in advance. Proposals may be submitted via fax at 215-271-4903 during business hours, or 215-271-4833 after business hours. A follow-up telephone call to 215-271-4889 during business hours or 215-271-4807 after business hours is required to ensure the proposal was received. When received, the Sector will evaluate the proposal and send a return letter by fax. If a tow of more than one dead-ship is planned, a more detailed tow plan must be submitted to the Sector for approval.

(218)　　2. Depending on the particulars of the vessel being towed (age, extended lay up status, vessel condition, etc.), the COTP Delaware Bay may require that additional safety precautions be established before the tow is authorized. This may include requirements such as obtaining a marine surveyor's report attesting to the vessel's seaworthiness for the desired tow or allowing a representative from Sector Delaware Bay to examine the vessel to verify seaworthiness, pollution potential and the adequacy of the towing arrangement. Nothing in this policy relieves the vessel owner or agent from any of the requirements regarding vessel safety and the protection of the environment specified in the applicable sections of 46 CFR "Shipping" and 33 CFR "Navigation and Navigable Waters." (See chapter 2.)

(219)     3. Once the tow begins, the licensed person-in-charge is responsible for the safe execution of the dead ship tow. This includes ensuring adequate under keel clearance over the route and adequate vertical clearance when passing under overhead obstructions. Additionally, the monitoring of the tow's stability and structural adequacy throughout the tow is the responsibility of the person-in-charge.

(220)     4. Approval for a dead ship tow will be voided if any changes are made to the information submitted with the original request.

(221)     5. Sector Delaware Bay will issue a Notice to Mariners that will be broadcast on VHF-FM channel 16 while the dead ship tow is being conducted in the COTP Delaware Bay zone to advise other vessels to use caution when in the vicinity of the tow.

(222)
### Vessel arrival inspections

(223)     Quarantine, customs, immigration and agricultural quarantine officials are stationed in most major U.S. ports. (See Appendix A for addresses.) Vessels subject to such inspections generally make arrangements in advance through ships' agents. Unless otherwise directed, officials usually board vessels at their berths.

(224)     **Harbormasters**, if available, are mentioned in the text. They generally have charge of the anchorage and berthing of vessels.

(225)
### Supplies

(226)     Water, marine supplies, other supplies and services and all grades of heavy bunker oil, lubricants and diesel oil are available to large vessels at Hampton Roads ports, Baltimore and other major ports along the Delaware Bay and River.

(227)     Gasoline, diesel fuel, water and marine supplies and services can also be obtained at most of the smaller ports.

(228)
### Repairs

(229)     Large oceangoing vessels can be drydocked and have major repair work done at Philadelphia, Chester, Baltimore, Newport News, Norfolk and Portsmouth. Repair facilities for smaller vessels are also available at many places in the area covered by this Coast Pilot. (See text.)

(230)     Wrecking and salvage equipment is available at Philadelphia, Baltimore and Norfolk.

(231)
### Small-craft facilities

(232)     Marine supplies, repair facilities and other services for small craft are available at all the major ports, at numerous places on the New Jersey Intracoastal Waterway and on many of the tributaries of the Chesapeake and Delaware Bays. For isolated places and small cities, the Coast Pilot describes the more important of these facilities; for large port areas, where individual facilities are too numerous to mention, the information given is more general. Additional information may be obtained from the series of small-craft charts published for the many places and from various local small-craft guides.

(233)     **A vessel of less than 65.6 feet (20 meters) in length or a sailing vessel shall not impede the passage of a vessel that can safely navigate only within a narrow channel or fairway. (Navigation Rules, International-Inland Rule 9(b).)**

(234)
### Standard time

(235)     The area covered by this Coast Pilot uses eastern standard time (e.s.t.), which is 5 hours slow of Coordinated Universal Time (UTC). For example, when it is 1000 UTC, it is 0500 at Philadelphia, PA.

(236)
### Daylight saving time

(237)     Throughout the area of this Coast Pilot, clocks are advanced 1 hour on the second Sunday of March and are set back to standard time on the first Sunday of November.

(238)
### Legal public holidays

(239)     New Year's Day, January 1; Martin Luther King, Jr.'s Birthday, third Monday in January; Washington's Birthday, third Monday in February; Memorial Day, last Monday in May; Independence Day, July 4; Labor Day, first Monday in September; Columbus Day, second Monday in October; Veterans Day, November 11; Thanksgiving Day, fourth Thursday in November; and Christmas Day, December 25. The national holidays are observed by employees of the Federal Government and the District of Columbia and may not be observed by all the states in every case.

(240)     In the areas covered by this Coast Pilot, other holidays are observed: Lee-Jackson Day, Friday preceding the third Monday in January, in Virginia; Presidential Inauguration Day, January 20, every fourth year in the District of Columbia; Lincoln's Birthday, February 12, in all states except Virginia; Good Friday, in Delaware, New Jersey, Pennsylvania, and Maryland; Maryland Day, March 25, in Maryland; Flag Day, June 14, in Pennsylvania; Defender's Day, September 12, in Maryland; General Election Day, first Tuesday after the first Monday in November, except in the District of Columbia.

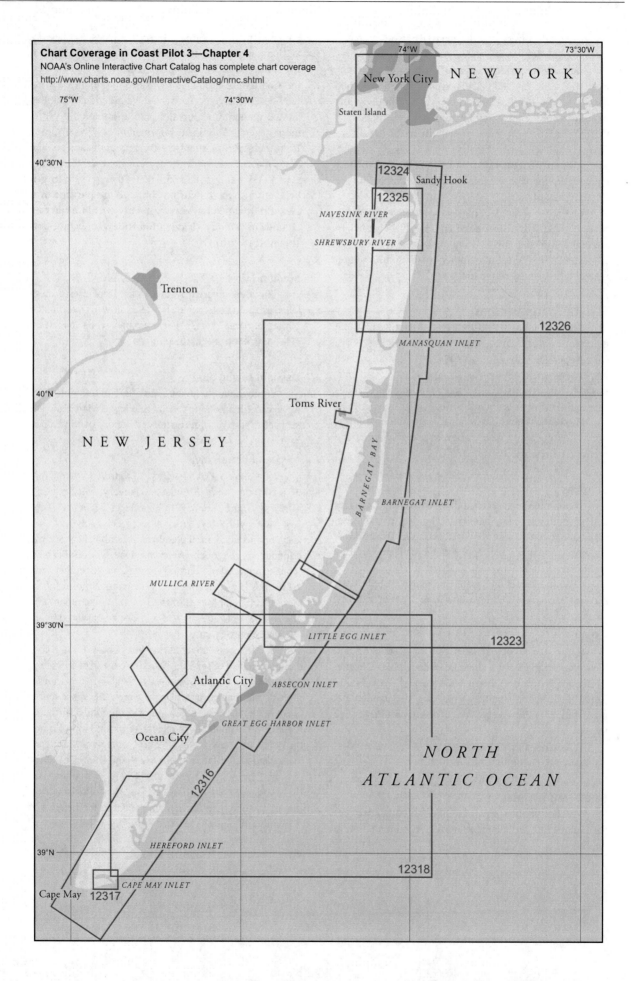

**Chart Coverage in Coast Pilot 3—Chapter 4**
NOAA's Online Interactive Chart Catalog has complete chart coverage
http://www.charts.noaa.gov/InteractiveCatalog/nrnc.shtml

# New Jersey Coast

(1)     This chapter describes the coast of New Jersey from Sandy Hook to Cape May Point and the various inlets that make into it from the Atlantic Ocean. Also discussed are the resort towns of Atlantic City, Ocean City and Cape May.

(2)
**ENCs - US4NY1AM, US4NY1BM, US4NJ23M, US5N-J25M, US4NJ22M, US4DE12M, US4DE11M**
**Charts - 12326, 12323, 12318, 12304, 12214**

(3)     The coast of New Jersey extends in a general southerly direction for 44 miles from Sandy Hook to Barnegat Inlet, then southwesterly for 66 miles to Cape May Point. From Sandy Hook to Atlantic City the 60-foot curve is 5 to 10 miles from shore; off Delaware Bay the distance has increased to 17 miles.

(4)     Deep-draft vessels should stand off the coast in depths of 60 feet or more between New York Bay and Delaware Bay. Light-draft vessels can follow the shore more closely if they pay strict attention to the charts for fishweir areas, shoals, wrecks and other obstructions. Small craft should wait for favorable weather before attempting an outside run along this coast.

(5)     The principal shallow-draft entrances are Shark River Inlet, Manasquan Inlet, Barnegat Inlet, Absecon Inlet and Cape May Inlet. There are several others that are unimproved. The inlets are, or may be, obstructed by shifting bars, and most require local knowledge to carry the best water. The best time to enter is on a rising tide with a smooth sea; passage is hazardous during easterly gales and heavy seas.

(6)     In most cases the aids marking the various inlets are not charted due to the changing conditions.

(7)     The greater part of the New Jersey coast is summer-resort area, and the numerous standpipes and elevated tanks are prominent from seaward. The New Jersey Intracoastal Waterway, an inside passage from Manasquan Inlet to Delaware Bay, is described in chapter 5.

(8)
### North Atlantic Right Whales
(9)     Endangered North Atlantic right whales may occur within 30 nautical miles of the New Jersey coast (peak season: November through April, although right whales have been sighted in the area year round). (See **North Atlantic Right Whales**, indexed as such in chapter 3, for more information on right whales and recommended measures to avoid collisions.)

(10)     All vessels 65 feet or greater in length overall (LOA) and subject to the jurisdiction of the United States are restricted to speeds of 10 knots or less in a Seasonal Management Area existing around the Ports of New York/New Jersey between November 1 and April 30. The area is defined as the waters within a 20-nm radius of 40°29'42.2"N., 73°55'57.6"W. (See **50 CFR 224.105** in chapter 2 for regulations, limitations and exceptions.)

(11)
### COLREGS Demarcation Lines
(12)     The lines established for New York Harbor and the inlets of the New Jersey coast are described **33 CFR 80.165**, **80.170**, and **80.501**, chapter 2.

(13)
### Traffic Separation Scheme
(14)     **Traffic Separation Scheme off New York** has been established in the approaches to New York Harbor from sea. See **Traffic Separation Schemes**, chapter 1, for additional information. See also **33 CFR 167.1** through **167.155**, chapter 2, for limits and regulations.

(15)     **Caution.**—Numerous fishing floats have been reported in the approach to New York Harbor in the Traffic Separation Scheme precautionary area.

(16)     Shipping safety fairways have been established connecting the eastern approach off Ambrose of Traffic Separation Scheme Off New York and the eastern approach off Nantucket of Traffic Separation Scheme Off New York. (See **33 CFR 166.100** through **166.500**, chapter 2, for limits and regulations.)

(17)
### Weather
(18)     Strong winds are most often a problem from November through March. Gales (winds of 34 knots or more) are encountered 3 to 5 percent of the time in these waters; they blow most frequently out of the northwest although northerlies and northeasterlies can also create problems. They are slightly more frequent in the stretch of ocean between Atlantic City and Cape May. In open waters, on the average, extreme winds can be expected to reach 70 to 75 knots compared with 60 to 70 knots in the inland waterway. Summer gales are rare but may be encountered in a thunderstorm or infrequent tropical cyclone. Along the coast strong winds (28 to 40 knots) blow 10 percent of the time in winter compared with less than 1 percent in summer.

(19)     Seas are roughest from September to March. In January waves of 8 feet (2.4 m) or more are encountered about 15 to 25 percent of the time in deep waters. Rough seas are most likely with west and northwest winds of 20 knots or more and have reached 40 feet (12.2 m). While fog, haze, precipitation and smoke can hamper visibility,

(34)

### Structures across Shark River

| Name | Type | Location | Clearances (feet) | | Information |
|------|------|----------|-------------------|---|-------------|
| | | | Horizontal | Vertical* | |
| Ocean Avenue bridge | bascule | 40°11'14"N., 74°00'36"W. | 90 | 15 | Note 2<br>Call sign KMD-281 |
| State Route 71/Main Street bridge | fixed | 40°11'12"N., 74°01'24"W. | 80 | 8 | North channel of Shark River |
| State Route 71/Main Street bridge | bascule | 40°11'07"N., 74°01'25"W. | 50 | 13 | South channel of Shark River<br>Notes 1 and 2<br>Call sign KT-4202 |
| N.Y. and L.B. Company Railroad bridge | fixed | 40°11'12"N., 74°01'30"W. | 20 | 8 | North channel of Shark River |
| N.Y. and L.B. Company Railroad bridge | bascule | 40°11'04"N., 74°04'33"W. | 50 | 8 | South channel of Shark River<br>Notes 1 and 2<br>Call sign KT-4202 |
| Overhead cable | power | 40°11'12"N., 74°01'31"W. | | 32 | North channel of Shark River |
| Overhead cable | power | 40°11'04"N., 74°01'34"W. | | 31 | South channel of Shark River |
| State Route 35 bridge | fixed | 40°11'12"N., 74°01'31"W. | 35 | 8 | North channel of Shark River |
| State Route 35 bridge | fixed | 40°11'04"N., 74°01'34"W. | 50 | 50 | South channel of Shark River |
| Overhead cable | power | 40°11'13"N., 74°01'32"W. | | 32 | North channel of Shark River |
| Overhead cable | power | 40°11'04"N., 74°01'36"W. | | 31 | South channel of Shark River |

\* Clearances are referenced to Mean High Water
Note 1 – See 33 CFR 117.1 through 117.59 and 117.751, chapter 2, for drawbridge regulations.
Note 2 – Bridgetender monitors VHF-FM channel 13.

it is most restricted by advection fog. This occurs most often in late spring and early summer when warm south to southwest winds blow across the cold Labrador Current. May is usually the worst month, when visibilities less than 0.5 mile (0.8 km) are encountered 4 to 9 percent of the time and less than 2 miles (3.2 km) 5 to 15 percent of the time; highest frequencies occur nearest the New York Bight. Along the coast, visibilities less than 0.25 mile (0.4 km) occur on 3 to 6 days per month from October through March. This is a combination of radiation fog, precipitation and smoke.

(20)

### Pilotage, New Jersey Coast

(21)      Pilotage is compulsory for foreign vessels and U.S. vessels under register. Pilotage is available from the Sandy Hook Pilot Association, 201 Edgewater Street, Staten Island, NY 10305, telephone 718-448-3900, fax 718-447-1582, email: pilotoffice@sandyhookpilots.com. Arrangement for pilotage may be made through ship's agents or directly. A 24-hour advance notice is required.

(22)

### ENCs - US4NY1AM, US4NY1BM
### Chart - 12326

(23)      **Sandy Hook** on the south side of the entrance to **New York Harbor,** is the most northerly part of the New Jersey coast. **Sandy Hook Light** (40°27'42"N., 74°00'07"W.), 88 feet above the water, is shown from an 85-foot stone tower 1.2 miles from the north end of the point. The light, established in 1764, is the oldest in continuous use in the United States.

(24)      **Sandy Hook Coast Guard Station**, a standpipe, several towers and two marine lights are prominent on the northern part of the hook.

(25)      Sandy Hook is a government reservation, and landing is prohibited as far south, approximately, as the bridge over the mouth of Shrewsbury River. Vessels awaiting favorable weather for an outside run can anchor in Sandy Hook Bay south of a line bearing due west from Sandy Hook Light.

(26)      **Sandy Hook Bay**, **Navesink River** and **Shrewsbury River** are described in United States Coast Pilot 2, Atlantic Coast, Cape Cod to Sandy Hook.

(27)      On the northwest side of the approach to Navesink River is the highest ground along the open Atlantic Coast between Maine and Florida. The 276-foot wooded ridge is 4 miles south of Sandy Hook Light and 0.5 mile back of the outer beach. Abandoned **Navesink Lighthouse** (40°23'48"N., 73°59'12"W.) is in a cleared space on the easternmost spur at a ground elevation of 180 feet; the two 73-foot brownstone towers, the north one octagonal and the south square, are connected by a dwelling. A privately maintained light, 246 feet above the water, is now shown seasonally from the north tower.

(28)      **Shrewsbury Rocks**, 7.3 miles south of Sandy Hook Light, are 0.4 to 1 mile offshore and have a least depth of 16 feet. A buoy is eastward of the rocks.

(29)      The sea **boundary** between the First and Fifth Coast Guard Districts is on a line **122°** from 40°18'N on the New Jersey coast south of Shrewsbury Rocks.

(30)

### ENC - US5NJ30M
### Chart - 12324

(31)      **Shark River**, which enters Shark Inlet 17 miles south of Sandy Hook Light, is the only small-craft harbor

(39)

Manasquan Inlet, New Jersey
Image courtesy of Waterway Images (2004)

between Sandy Hook and Manasquan Inlet. The town of **Avon** fronts the ocean on the north side of the river, and **Belmar** is on the south side.

(32)　　　**Shark River Inlet** is protected by jetties, each marked by a light near its outer end. A dredged channel leads through the inlet and through Shark River to the Belmar Municipal Boat Basin, 1.2 miles above the jetties. The State of New Jersey maintains and marks several channels through the flats north and west of the boat basin. **Shark River Coast Guard Station** is on the north side of the river, about 0.3 mile above the jetties. An anchorage is just east of State Route 71 highway bridge.

(33)　　　In stormy weather, breakers form along the bar off the inlet, but entrance can be made in moderately rough weather with some local knowledge. When the winds and the tides are opposed, the inlet is difficult to enter. A cross current, strongest on the ebb, may be encountered at Ocean Avenue Bridge at the inner end of the jetties. Vessels for which the closed bridge clearance is insufficient should not attempt entrance until the drawspan is completely open.

(35)　　　There are excellent small-craft and fishing-boat facilities in Shark River inside the inlet. Most of these facilities are on both sides and above the inner bridges and in the Belmar Municipal Boat basin.

(36)
**Pilotage, Shark River Inlet**

(37)　　　Pilotage is compulsory for foreign vessels and U.S. vessels under register. Pilotage is available from the Sandy Hook Pilot Association, 201 Edgewater Street, Staten Island, NY 10305, telephone 718-448-3900, fax 718-876-8055, email: pilotoffice@sandyhookpilots.com. Arrangements for pilotage may be made through ship's agents or directly. A 24-hour advance notice is required.

(38)　　　**Manasquan Inlet**, 22 miles southward of Sandy Hook Light, is the Atlantic entrance to Manasquan River and the northern terminus of the New Jersey Intracoastal Waterway, as described in chapter 5. **Manasquan Inlet Coast Guard Station** is on the south side of the inlet.

(40)　　　A marked dredged channel leads through Manasquan Inlet between two jetties and extends about 5 miles up **Manasquan River**. The jetties are marked by lights; a sound signal is at the south jetty light. Traffic conditions in Manasquan Inlet can be hazardous due to the large volume of commercial and pleasure boat traffic. Mariners are advised to exercise caution and control speed and wake while transiting the inlet. The Coast Guard monitors traffic in the inlet, and safe boating is enforced.

(41)　　　The current velocity in Manasquan Inlet is about 1.8 knots in the inlet.

(48)

Barnegat Inlet, New Jersey
Image courtesy of Waterway Images (2004)

—N→

(42)    Mariners should exercise caution when entering Manasquan Inlet when the winds and tides are opposed; local knowledge is advised.

(43)

**Pilotage, Manasquan Inlet**

(44)    Pilotage is compulsory for foreign vessels and U.S. vessels under register. Pilotage is available from the Sandy Hook Pilot Association, 201 Edgewater Street, Staten Island, NY 10305, telephone 718-448-3900, fax 718-876-8055, e-mail: pilotoffice@sandyhookpilots. com. Arrangements for pilotage may be made through ship's agents or directly. A 24-hour advance notice is required.

(45)

**ENCs - US4NJ23M, US5NJ30M**
**Charts - 12323, 12324**

(46)    **Bay Head**, 2 miles south of Manasquan Inlet, is marked by a prominent elevated water tank. From Bay Head south, the resorts are more widely spaced on the low, narrow barrier beach which separates the inside waters from the ocean.

(47)    **Barnegat Inlet**, 21 miles southward of Manasquan Inlet, forms a passage from the Atlantic Ocean through **Oyster Creek Channel** to the New Jersey Intracoastal Waterway and Barnegat Bay. The approach to the inlet is marked by a lighted whistle buoy about 1.7 miles southeast of the north jetty. The inlet is protected by two jetties marked by lights. A sound signal is at the south jetty light. Two orange and white danger buoys are northeast of the north jetty to mark the submerged jetty between Light 6 and the exposed jetty. Buoys inside the channel are moved frequently and not charted. **Barnegat Light** (39°45'51"N., 74°06'22"W.), on the south side of the inlet, is the most prominent landmark in the area; it is a 163-foot-high brick tower, dark red on its upper half and white on its lower half. The lighted tower is maintained by the State of New Jersey as a historical monument. Also prominent from seaward is a 391-foot-high powerplant stack at the head of Oyster Creek, on the west side of Barnegat Bay.

(49)    Barnegat Inlet Channel and Oyster Creek Channel are subject to continual change due to severe shoaling. The buoys marking these channels are shifted frequently to mark the best water and therefore are not charted. Mariners are advised to use caution and local knowledge. It was reported that various aids marking Oyster Creek Channel may be submerged because of strong tidal currents. Breakers make across the inlet with an ebb tide and an easterly wind. Strangers should not attempt to transit the inlet under any but ideal conditions. Boatmen needing assistance should lay outside the inlet and contact the local Coast Guard station.

(59)

Absecon Inlet, New Jersey
Image courtesy of Waterway Images (2004)

(50)　　　The current velocity in Barnegat Inlet is about 2.5 knots in the inlet, although currents as high as 7 knots have been reported.

(51)　　　**Barnegat Light** is a resort town on the south side of Barnegat Inlet. The channel to the small-craft and fishing-boat facilities on the bay side of the town is marked by privately maintained seasonal buoys or markers; these aids are not charted.

(52)

**ENCs - US4NJ23M, US5NJ24M, US5NJ20M**
**Charts - 12323, 12316**

(53)　　　**Beach Haven Inlet** (39°30.0'N., 74°15.1'W.), 17 miles south-southwestward of Barnegat Inlet, is unmarked. Numerous wrecks and shoal spots are at the entrance. Due to changing conditions of the channel, boatmen are advised to seek local knowledge prior to entering.

(54)　　　The entrance to Beach Haven Inlet should not be mistaken for Little Egg Inlet, which is close southward. **Beach Haven Coast Guard Station** is inside the barrier beach, 3.2 miles north of Beach Haven Inlet.

(55)

**ENCs - US5NJ25M, US4NJ22M, US5NJ24M, US5N-**
**J20M**
**Charts - 12318, 12316**

(56)　　　**Little Egg Inlet** (39°29'00"N., 74°17'30"W.), 19 miles south-southwestward of Barnegat Inlet and close southward of Beach Haven Inlet, is used considerably by local pleasure and fishing boats. Depth over the bar is ample for any vessel that can navigate the inside waters, but in very heavy weather breakers form all the way across the bar. The inlet channels and shoreline are constantly changing; the entrance is well marked, but the buoys are not charted because they are frequently shifted in position. In 2007, an unmarked partially submerged wreck was reported at about 39°29'09"N., 74°17'31"W.; caution is advised.

(57)　　　**Brigantine Inlet**, 2.6 miles south-southwestward of Little Egg Inlet, has shoaled to such an extent that it is unsafe for even the shallowest drafts. **Brigantine Shoal,** 3 miles south of the inlet, has a least depth of 18 feet.

(58)　　　**Absecon Inlet**, 8.7 miles southwestward of Little Egg Inlet, is on the northeast side of **Atlantic City,** the largest resort on the New Jersey coast. The inlet is protected at the entrance by jetties; a revetment extends along the Atlantic City side of the inlet. Small-craft facilities are available at a hotel marina on the southwest side of the inlet.

(60)　　　The entrance channel is subject to continual change and the buoys are frequently shifted to mark the best water.

(74)

Great Egg Harbor Inlet, New Jersey
Image courtesy of Waterway Images (2004)

—N→

The channel through the inlet intersects the New Jersey Intracoastal Waterway 1.9 miles above the inlet entrance south jetty. *The New Jersey Intracoastal Waterway is described in chapter 5.* Current velocities up to 6 knots have been reported in the channel.

(61)

### Weather

(62)     The climate of Atlantic City is principally continental in character; however, the moderating influence of the Atlantic Ocean is apparent throughout the year. As a result, the summers are relatively cooler and winters milder than elsewhere at the same latitude. Land and sea breezes often prevail. Temperatures of 90°F (32.2°C) or higher are recorded about three times per year, which is considerably less frequent than locations further inland. The weather tends to remain comparatively mild late into the fall, but on the other hand, warming is retarded in the spring.

(63)     January is the coldest month and July the warmest. The average annual temperature for Atlantic City is 53.7°F (12.1°C). The average January temperature is 31.7°F (-0.2°C) and the average July temperature is 75.3°F (24.1°C). Temperatures in excess of 100°F (37.8°C) have occurred in each month, June through August, and temperatures in excess of 90°F (32.2°C) have occurred in each month, April through October. Each month has recorded below-freezing temperatures except June, July and August, and each month, December through February, has recorded temperatures below 0°F (-17.8°C). The warmest temperature on record for Atlantic City is 106°F (41.1°C), recorded in June 1969, while the coldest temperature on record is -11°F (-23.9°C), recorded in February 1979.

(64)     Precipitation, on the average, is moderate and well distributed throughout the year, with June the driest month and August the wettest. The average annual precipitation for Atlantic City is 41 inches (1,041 mm). Thunderstorms are mostly a warm season phenomena. The bulk of winter precipitation results from storms that move northeasterly along or close to the coast. Snowfall, at about 17 inches (432 mm) per year, is considerably less than elsewhere at the same latitude and does not remain long on the ground. Snow has fallen in each month, October through May. The greatest 24-hour snowfall was 16.6 (421.6 mm) recorded in February 1979. Ice storms are relatively infrequent.

(65)     **Atlantic City**, on the south side of Absecon Inlet, is a base for a large fleet of fishing vessels and pleasure craft. The city has highway, rail and air connections with the mainland; highways lead to the coastal towns northward and southward.

(66)

### Pilotage, Atlantic City

(67)     Pilotage is compulsory for foreign vessels and U.S. vessels under register. Pilotage is available from the Sandy Hook Pilot Association, 201 Edgewater Street, Staten Island, NY 10305, telephone 718-448-3900, fax

(87)

Cape May Inlet, New Jersey
Image courtesy of Waterway Images (2004)

718-876-8055, e-mail: pilotoffice@sandyhookpilots. com. Arrangements for pilotage may be made through ship's agents or directly. A 24-hour advance notice is required.

(68)

**Coast Guard**

(69)     **Atlantic City Coast Guard Station** is on the north side of the entrance to Clam Creek.

(70)     **Clam Creek**, on the south side of Absecon Inlet, has its marked entrance 1 mile northwestward of the south jetty light. The creek includes **Gardner Basin, Snug Harbor** and **Delta Basin** on its southerly side, and the small-boat basin of the State marina on its northerly side. The municipal wharf is on the east side of the entrance to the small-boat basin.

(71)     Gasoline, diesel fuel, water, ice and marine supplies can be obtained at the several small-craft facilities in the creek and in the small-boat basin. Hull and engine repairs can be made at the facilities in Gardner Basin and Snug Harbor; maximum haul-out capacities are: marine railway, 65 feet; lift, 20 tons. The **harbormaster** at the State marina assigns slips in the small-boat basin; a fuel float is on the west side of the basin, and the harbormaster's office is on the east side.

(72)     The highway bridge, 1.5 miles above Absecon Inlet entrance, has a fixed span with a clearance of 60 feet. Two fishing piers, the remains of a former bascule bridge, are about 50 yards northward of the bridge. Care must

be exercised when passing through this bridge because of the strong currents; velocities of 2.5 knots have been reported.

(73)     **Great Egg Harbor Inlet**, 7 miles southwest of Absecon Inlet, is subject to continual change due to severe shoaling. The buoys marking the inlet are not charted because they are shifted frequently to mark the best water. The inlet is used by many local fishing and pleasure boats with drafts up to 5 feet. Breakers extend along the bar even in moderate weather and are hazardous to small boats. Local knowledge is advised at all times in entering the inlet. The bridges, just inside Great Egg Harbor Inlet, are described in chapter 5 in connection with the New Jersey Intracoastal Waterway.

(75)     **Ocean City**, a large summer resort on the southwest side of Great Egg Harbor Inlet, has highway connections with the mainland. Supplies and facilities are described in connection with the New Jersey Intracoastal Waterway. **Great Egg Coast Guard Station** is in a basin on the inner side of the city.

(76)     **Corson Inlet**, 14 miles southwest of Absecon Inlet, is subject to constant change in depth and should not be used.

(77)     A shoal, covered 16 feet and marked by a buoy, is 3.8 miles east of Townsends Inlet. **Avalon Shoal**, covered 27 feet and marked by a lighted bell buoy, is 7 miles east-southeast of Townsends Inlet.

(78)        **Townsends Inlet**, 20 miles southwest of Absecon Inlet, is subject to considerable changes in position and depth and is used principally by pleasure craft. Channel buoys are not charted, because they are shifted frequently to mark the best water. The depth over the bar is about 4 feet. Numerous wrecks and obstructions are in the approaches to the inlet from seaward.

(79)        **Townsends Inlet** is a small resort on the northeast side of the inlet. A seasonal Coast Guard station is on the northeast side of the resort.

(80)        The highway bridge over Townsends Inlet has a bascule span with a clearance of 23 feet. (See **33 CFR 117.1** through **117.59** and **117.757**, chapter 2, for drawbridge regulations.) The route of the New Jersey Intracoastal Waterway is just west of the bridge. In 1987, it was reported that a sandbar in a north-south direction across the east approach to the channel at the center of the drawspan causes hazardous conditions for mariners, especially during south winds and flood tidal currents that create a loss of steering and dangerous clockwise currents at the base of the bridge; extreme caution is advised in this area.

(81)        **Hereford Inlet**, 28 miles southwest of Absecon Inlet, is subject to rapid change. Breakers form at all times on the shoals and in moderate weather on the bar. The approach to the inlet is extremely dangerous with a following sea. The depth over the bar is about 4 feet, but passage should not be attempted without local knowledge.

(82)        **Hereford Inlet Light** (39°00'24"N., 74°47'28"W.), 57 feet above the water, is shown from a white square tower with cupola on a white dwelling on the south side of the inlet.

(83)        **Nummy Island** is on the inner side of Hereford Inlet; the Intracoastal Waterway passes west of the island. Ocean Drive highway crosses Nummy Island and has drawbridges over **Great Channel**, which leads northward from the inlet, and **Grassy Sound Channel**, which leads westward; both bascule spans have a clearance of 15 feet. (See **33 CFR 117.1** through **117.59**, **117.721** and **117.733**, chapter 2, for drawbridge regulations.)

(84)        Supplies and facilities at Stone Harbor and Wildwood are described with the New Jersey Intracoastal Waterway, chapter 5.

(85)
**ENCs - US5NJ21M, US5NJ24M, US5NJ20M, US-4DE11M**
**Charts - 12317, 12316, 12214**

(86)        **Cape May Inlet** (38°56.2'N., 74°51.8'W.), 34 miles southwest of Absecon Inlet, is protected by jetties whose lights are inshore of the submerged ends. A **327°** lighted range marks the channel between the jetties. Buoys mark the channel inside the harbor. At night the lights on the towers on the east side and from the U.S. Coast Guard rescue tower on the west of the inlet are visible from well offshore.

(88)        The danger area of a Coast Guard rifle range extends from **Sewell Point** westward from Cape May Inlet. (See **33 CFR 334.100**, chapter 2, for limits and regulations.)

(89)

**Pilotage, Cape May Harbor**

(90)        Pilotage is compulsory for all foreign vessels of 100 gross tons or more and all U.S. vessels under register engaged in foreign trade or commerce of 100 gross tons or more. Pilotage is optional for all U.S. Government vessels and for all U.S. vessels under enrollment in a coastwise trade if they have on board a pilot licensed by the Federal Government to operate in these waters. Pilotage service is available from the Pilots' Association for Bay and River Delaware on a limited 24-hour basis. Arrangements for pilotage can be made through ships' agents or directly. A 24-hour advance notice is requested with updated 6-hour ETA. Pilots will board just southwestward of Lighted Bell Buoy 2CM off Cape May Inlet. (See Pilotage, Bay and River Delaware, chapter 6.)

(91)        **Cape May Harbor** is used by fishing fleets, pleasure craft and the Coast Guard. The fishing vessels operate from wharves below and above the bridge at the northeast end of the harbor and from wharves in **Schellenger Creek**, at the west end of the harbor. Pleasure-craft facilities are on the north and west sides of the harbor. **Cape May Coast Guard Training Center** and its attendant facilities are on the south side of the harbor.

(92)        The resort town of **Cape May** fronts the ocean 2 miles west of Cape May Inlet. Depths between 11 and 30 feet can be carried through the inlet to the end of the inner jetties. From the inner jetties a channel marked by lights and daybeacons leads west through Cape May Harbor then divides north to the mouth of Cape May Canal and south to the mouth of Schellenger Creek. A side channel leads through Schellenger Creek and Spicer Creek Canal to a connection with the Cape May Canal. Traffic through Schellenger Creek is restricted by the 38-foot-wide fixed span highway bridge with a clearance of 4 feet that remains in the closed position. (See **33 CFR 117.1** through **117.59** and **117.750**, chapter 2, for drawbridge regulations.)

(93)

**Current**

(94)        The current velocity is about 2 knots in Cape May Inlet.

(95)

**Quarantine, customs, immigration, and agricultural quarantine**

(96)        (See chapter 3, Vessel Arrival Inspections, and appendix for addresses.)

(97)        **Quarantine** is enforced in accordance with regulations of the U.S. Public Health Service. (See Public Health Service, chapter 1.)

(98)
**Small-craft facilities**

(99)    Most of the fishing and small-craft facilities are along the northern and western sides of Cape May Harbor and in Schellenger Creek.

(100)    The Coast Guard piers on the inner side of Sewell Point are the largest in the harbor and have depths of 15 feet to 10 feet alongside.

(101)    The waterway to **Jarvis Sound**, at the northeast end of Cape May Harbor, and through Cape May Canal at the west end, is described with the New Jersey Intracoastal Waterway, chapter 5.

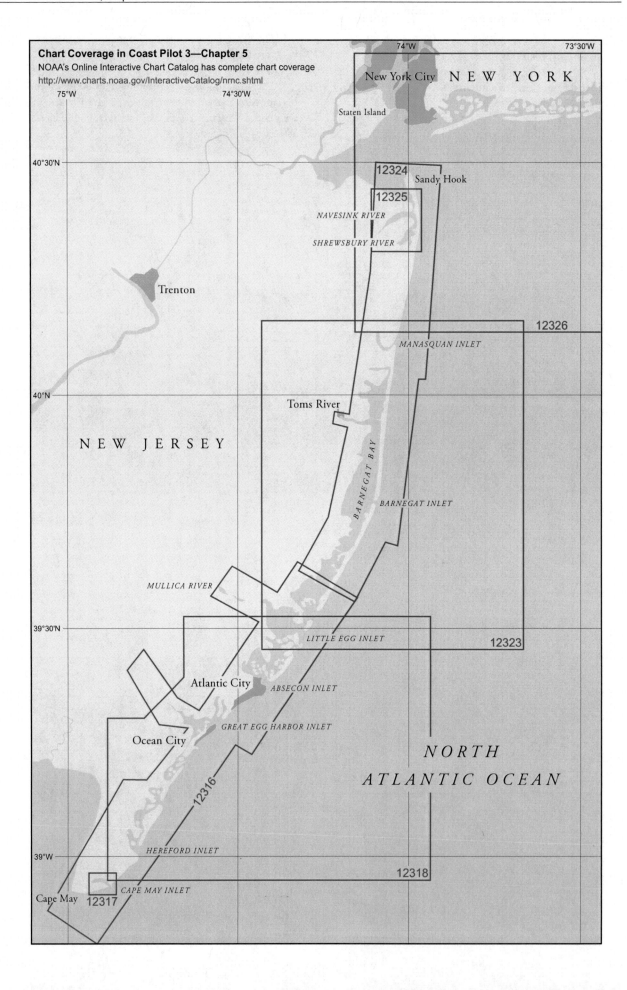

**Chart Coverage in Coast Pilot 3—Chapter 5**
NOAA's Online Interactive Chart Catalog has complete chart coverage
http://www.charts.noaa.gov/InteractiveCatalog/nrnc.shtml

# Intracoastal Waterway

(1)	The **Intracoastal Waterway** is a toll-free passage that roughly parallels the Atlantic Coast and extends 118 statute miles through bays, lagoons, thorofares and land cuts from Manasquan Inlet to Delaware Bay at a point 2 miles north of Cape May Light.

(2)	In addition to the Intracoastal Waterway and the waters through which it passes, this chapter also describes the several rivers and tributaries that empty into these waters, as well as some of the more important towns and landings along these waterways.

(3)	The Intracoastal Waterway is used mainly by pleasure craft and commercial and sport fishing vessels. The U.S. Army Corps of Engineers, Philadelphia Engineer District, has supervision of the waterway's construction, maintenance and operation. (See Appendix A for address.)

(4)
## Mileage
(5)	The Intracoastal Waterway mileage is zeroed in 40°06'03"N., 74°01'55"W., off the outer ends of the Manasquan Inlet jetties, which are 40 nautical miles by outside run from The Battery, NY.

(6)	Distances along the Intracoastal Waterway are in statute miles to facilitate reference to the charts; all other distances are in nautical miles—mileage conversion tables are at the end of chapter 1.

(7)
## Channels
(8)	The channel of the Intracoastal Waterway is generally 100 feet wide and has dredged depths of 6 feet from Manasquan Inlet to Cape May Harbor, thence 12 feet through Cape May Canal to Delaware Bay.

(9)	Effort is made to maintain a 6-foot controlling depth for the waterway, but due to continuous shoaling, 3 feet or less may be found in places, particularly inside the ocean inlets. For detailed channel information and minimum depths as reported by the U.S. Army Corps of Engineers (USACE), use NOAA Electronic Navigational Charts. Surveys and channel condition reports are available through a USACE hydrographic survey website listed in Appendix A.

(11)
## Aids to navigation
(12)	The U.S. Coast Guard maintains the standard aids that mark the inlets and the special aids that mark the Intracoastal Waterway. The special aids have characteristic yellow markings that distinguish them from aids to navigation marking other waters. (See U.S. Coast Guard Light Lists or Chart 1 (Nautical Chart Symbols and Abbreviations) for illustrations of special markings.)

(13)	The Department of Environmental Protection, State of New Jersey, maintains the aids to navigation on the rivers and creeks that empty into the New Jersey Intracoastal Waterway.

(14)	Lights and daybeacons should not be passed close aboard because those marking dredged channels are usually placed back from the bottom edge of the channel and others may have riprap mounds around them to protect the structures.

(15)	The buoys marking the waterways are frequently shifted with changing channel conditions.

(16)
## Tides
(17)	In the inland waters, the tides are greatly affected by the winds both in time and height, westerly winds producing low water and easterly winds high water. In Barnegat Bay, northerly and southerly winds drive the water to the ends of the bay. While the normal range of tide is only about 0.5 foot in sections of the waterway removed from the inlets, strong winds of long duration may cause variations in level of as much as 3 feet below mean low water or 3 feet above mean high water. Near the inlets, the wind has less effect and the normal range of tide is 3 to 4 feet.

(18)
## Currents
(19)	Current velocities may reach 3 knots in the inlets and in the narrow channels that connect the inlets with the inside waters.

(20)
## Ice
(21)	The inside waters are completely closed to navigation by ice during extreme winters. In ordinary winters, some of the channels, especially near the inlets where the currents are strong, remain open most of the time, though ice always forms on the flats. The inlets themselves are rarely closed, but passage is often difficult because of running ice. All the principal inlets and adjacent channels are used in winter by local fishing boats, but through navigation is usually blocked.

(22)
## Weather
(23)	While the waterway is more protected than the open waters weather is critical since navigation is more confined. Winds diminish over land due to surface friction. However, winds and currents may be intensified

(10)

### Structures across the Intracoastal Waterway—Manasquan Inlet to Delaware Bay (Statute Mile 0 to 118)

| Name | Type | Mile | Waterway Location | Clearances (feet) Horizontal | Clearances (feet) Vertical* | Information |
|------|------|------|-------------------|------------|----------|-------------|
| Railroad bridge | bascule | 0.9 | Manasquan River | 48 | 3 | Note 2 (call sign KT-4203) |
| State Route 35 bridge | bascule | 1.1 | Manasquan River | 90 | 30 | Note 1 |
| Overhead cable | power | 1.1 | Manasquan River | | 107 | |
| Overhead cable | power | 2.7 | Point Pleasant Canal | | 86 | |
| State Route 88 bridge | vertical lift | 3.0 | Point Pleasant Canal | 134 | 31 (down) 66 (up) | |
| Overhead cables | power and television | 3.0 | Point Pleasant Canal | | 72 | |
| State Route 13 bridge | vertical lift | 3.9 | Point Pleasant Canal | 80 | 30 (down) 65 (up) | |
| County Road 528 bridge | bascule | 6.3 | Barnegat Bay | 80 | 30 | Note 1 |
| State Route 37 bridge | bascule and fixed | 14.1 | Barnegat Bay | 80 | 30 (bascule) 60 (fixed) | Note 1 |
| State Route 72 bridge | fixed | 37.4 | Manahawkin Bay | 100 | 56 | |
| Absecon Boulevard/U.S. 30 bridge | bascule | 67.2 | Beach Thorofare | 60 | 20 | Note 1 |
| Overhead power cable | power | 67.2 | Beach Thorofare | | 60 | |
| AMTRAK New Jersey Transit Rail Operations Railroad bridge | swing | 68.9 | Beach Thorofare | 50 | 5 | Note 1 |
| Atlantic City Expressway | fixed | 68.9 | Beach Thorofare | 80 | 35 | |
| Albany Avenue bridge | bascule | 70.0 | Inside Thorofare | 50 | 10 | Note 1 |
| Dorset Avenue bridge | bascule | 72.1 | Inside Thorofare | 50 | 9 | Note 1 |
| Margate City bridge | bascule | 73.0 | Beach Thorofare | 60 | 14 | |
| Route 152 bridge | fixed | 77.8 | Beach Thorofare | 140 | 56 | |
| 9th Street bridge | fixed | 80.7 | Beach Thorofare | 100 | 55 | |
| Roosevelt Boulevard bridge | fixed | 84.3 | Crooked Horn Thorofare | 80 | 35 | |
| Overhead cable | power | 84.3 | Crooked Horn Thorofare | | 42 | |
| Overhead cable | television | 84.3 | Crooked Horn Thorofare | | 35 | |
| Railroad bridge | swing | 86.6 | Crooked Horn Thorofare | 59 | 2 | Bridge is reported to be removed |
| 41st Street/Sea Isle City bridge | fixed | 93.6 | Ludlam Thorofare | 80 | 35 | |
| Overhead cables | power | 93.8 | Ludlam Thorofare | | 52 | |
| Avalon Boulevard bridge | fixed | 98.2 | Ingram Thorofare | 80 | 35 | |
| Overhead cable | power | 98.2 | Ingram Thorofare | | 60 | |
| Stone Harbor Boulevard bridge | bascule | 102.0 | Great Channel | 51 | 10 | Note 1 |
| Route 147 bridge | fixed | 105.2 | Grassy Sound Channel | 100 | 55 | |
| Overhead cable | power | 107.5 | Grassy Sound Channel | | 100 | |
| Overhead cable | power | 108.7 | Grassy Sound Channel | | 100 | |
| Rio Grande bridge | bascule | 108.9 | Grassy Sound Channel | 57 | 25 | |
| Two-Mile bridge | bascule | 112.2 | Middle Thorofare | 50 | 23 | Notes 1 and 2 (call sign WQZ-342) |
| Route 109 bridge | fixed | 114.3 | Cape May Canal | 80 | 55 | |
| Overhead cable | power | 114.3 | Cape May Canal | | 75 | |
| Cape May Canal Railroad bridge | swing | 115.1 | Cape May Canal | 50 | 4 | Note 1 |
| Route 162 bridge | fixed | 115.5 | Cape May Canal | 80 | 55 | |
| Overhead cable | television | 115.9 | Cape May Canal | | 60 | |

\* Clearances are referenced to Mean High Water
Note 1 – See 33 CFR 117.1 through 117.59 and 117.733, chapter 2, for drawbridge regulations.
Note 2 – Bridgetender monitors VHF-FM channel 13.

in restricted channels and inlets. November through April      is the windiest time of the year. Gales are encountered

(24) about 1 to 2 percent of the time while speeds greater than 16 knots occur about 10 to 17 percent of the time. Fog is also a problem particularly in restricted waterways. Visibilities drop below 0.5 mile (0.8 km) on about 2 to 5 days per month; they are best from mid to late summer. During the fall and early winter radiation fog often reduces morning visibilities but usually burns off by afternoon. At times in spring, advection fog from the open water may be carried ashore by winds with an easterly component. Smoke and precipitation also add to the problem in all seasons.

(24) Seas can be a problem at ocean entrances such as Manasquan Inlet, Barnegat Inlet and Little Egg Inlet. This is true with strong winds between northeast and south, particularly on an ebb tide.

(25)
### Facilities

(26) At communities along or adjacent to the waterway are numerous piers, wharves and docks, many of which are open to general public use. Fuel, water and other supplies are readily available. Public and privately owned boat basins are located in many streams entering the bays and thorofares through which the waterway passes. Boat-repair and storage yards with marine railways are also scattered along the waterway. Facilities for icing, storing and shipping seafood are available at most of the larger communities.

(27)
### No-Discharge Zone

(28) The State of New Jersey, with the approval of the Environmental Protection Agency, has established a No-Discharge Zone (NDZ) in Barnegat Bay Complex and its navigable tributaries. The boundary lines have been defined for the Point Pleasant Canal, Barnegat Inlet and Egg Harbor Inlet as lines between the following points: Point Pleasant Canal 40°04.0'N., 74°03.3'W. to 40°04.1'N., 74°03.3'W.; and Barnegat Inlet – a line between the North and South Buoys; and Little Egg Inlet 39°30.5'N., 74°18.3'W. to 39°30.5'N., 74°17.3'W.

(29) Within the NDZ, discharge of sewage, whether treated or untreated, from all vessels is prohibited. Outside the NDZ, discharge of sewage is regulated by **40 CFR 140** (see chapter 2).

(30)
### COLREGS Demarcation Lines

(31) The lines established for New York Harbor, the inlets of the New Jersey coast and Delaware Bay are described in **33 CFR 80.165**, **80.170**, **80.501** and **80.503**, chapter 2.

(32)
### ENC - US5NJ30M
### Chart - 12324

(33) **Manasquan Inlet**, 22 miles southward of Sandy Hook Light, is the northern terminus of the New Jersey Intracoastal Waterway and the Atlantic entrance to shallow **Manasquan River**, which flows into the inlet from the westward. The inlet is used by many commercial fishing craft and pleasure craft. Mariners should exercise caution when entering Manasquan Inlet when the wind and tide are opposed; local knowledge is advised. **Manasquan Inlet Coast Guard Station** is on the south side of the inlet.

(34) Traffic conditions in Manasquan Inlet can be hazardous due to the large volume of commercial and pleasure boat traffic. Mariners are advised to exercise caution and control speed and wake while transiting the inlet. The Coast Guard monitors traffic in the inlet and safe boating is enforced.

(35)
### Pilotage, Manasquan Inlet

(36) Pilotage is compulsory for foreign vessels and U.S. vessels under register. Pilotage is available from the Sandy Hook Pilot Association, 201 Edgewater Street, Staten Island, NY 10305, telephone 718-448-3900, fax 718-876-8055, email: pilotoffice@sandyhookpilots.com. Arrangements for pilotage may be made through ship's agents or directly. A 24-hour advance notice is required.

(37) A marked dredged channel, protected at the inlet entrance by two jetties, leads through Manasquan Inlet to the first bridge.

(38) The north jetty is marked by a light on its outer end. The south jetty is marked by a light near the outer end; a sound signal is at the south jetty light. Give the jetties a good berth to avoid any loose rocks.

(39)
### Current

(40) The current velocity in Manasquan Inlet is about 1.8 knots in the inlet and 2.2 knots at the State Route 35 bridge.

(41) The resort towns of **Manasquan** and **Point Pleasant Beach** are on the north and south sides of Manasquan Inlet, respectively, while the towns of **Brielle (Mile 1.3)**, **Point Pleasant (Mile 2.6)** and **Riviera Beach** (3.5 miles above the inlet jetties) are on Manasquan River.

(42) **Cooks Creek**, **Mile 0.4**, is an outlet for **Lake Louise** on the south side of Manasquan River. The fixed highway bridge over the creek has a 28-foot channel span with a clearance of 10 feet. Depths are about 8.5 feet below the bridge decreasing to 2 feet above it.

(43) **Crabtown Creek**, **Mile 0.9**, enters Manasquan River on the north side. The staked channel has a controlling depth of about 5 feet for 0.7 mile into the northwest fork. The highway bridge over the creek has a 31-foot bascule span with a clearance of 9 feet. (See **33 CFR 117.1** through **117.49** and **117.719**, chapter 2, for drawbridge regulations.)

(44) The State Route 70 highway bridge over Manasquan River at Riviera Beach has a fixed span with a clearance of 25 feet.

(45)
### Small-craft facilities

(46) Small-craft facilities are along Cooks Creek, Crabtown Creek and tributaries; up Manasquan River near the two bridges a mile inside Manasquan Inlet; and near Point Pleasant and Riviera Beach. Commercial fishing wharves, a 300-ton railway and other small-craft facilities are along **Wills Hole Thoroughfare**, westward of Cooks Creek. In 2004, depths of 1.1 to 7.0 feet were available. Mariners should favor the south side of the waterway for deepest water.

(47) From Manasquan Inlet, the New Jersey Intracoastal Waterway follows the dredged channel in Manasquan River to **Mile 2.7** where it turns south into the **Point Pleasant Canal**. The 1.9-mile narrow land cut has bulkheaded sides; vessels are required to pass through at a safe speed to avoid damage to structures and boats.

(48) Local sources, including both bridge tenders and the marine police, verified present data that indicate that the tides are greatly affected by winds, therefore diminishing any regularity in the tidal cycle.

(49)
### Mariners should consider the following precautionary measures before transiting the canal:

(50) 1. The time differential of the tidal cycle between the Mansaquan reference station, located at the railroad bridge crossing the Manasquan River, and Point Pleasant Canal is reported to be about 3 hours.

(51) 2. The safest time to transit the canal is at slack high water.

(52) 3. Existing wind conditions, in relation to tides, are extremely important factors to be considered when picking the time to transit.

(53) 4. Navigators should be especially cautious of two-way traffic and of following too close, particularly at the bridges.

(54) A small marina on the east side of the canal, at **Mile 4.1**, has some marine supplies, and two travel lifts to 30 tons are available for hull and engine repairs.

(55) At **Mile 4.6**, the waterway route leaves the canal and passes through **Barnegat Bay**, which has a north-south length of about 25 miles. The western half of the bay has depths of 5 to 10 feet; the eastern half is mostly extensive flats.

(56) Supplies, repairs and berthing facilities are available in **Bay Head Harbor** at the north end of Barnegat Bay; maximum haul-out capacities: railway, 80 feet; lift, 35 tons.

(57) **Beaverdam Creek** enters the west side of Barnegat Bay opposite **Mile 4.8**. The marked channel into the creek has a controlling depth of about 3 feet. The Beaverdam Road bridge, 0.4 mile from the mouth, has a bascule span with a vertical clearance of 14 feet. (See **33 CFR 117.1** through **117.59** and **117.705**, chapter 2, for drawbridge regulations.) The Midstreams Road/Jordan Road bridge, 1.5 miles above the mouth, has a 31-foot fixed span with a vertical clearance of 12 feet.

(58) **Metedeconk River**, separated from Beaverdam Creek by **Wardells Neck**, flows eastward into Barnegat Bay. The northern approach to the river is the same as for Beaverdam Creek; the southern approach is a marked passage between **Herring Island** and **Metedeconk Neck**. The controlling depth into the river is about 4 feet; depths above the entrances are 5 to 8 feet for about 3 miles.

(59) **Laurelton**, 4 miles up Metedeconk River from the Intracoastal Waterway, has facilities for small craft. Under average conditions, boats drawing as much as 3 feet can maneuver the shallow channel to Laurelton; the mean range of tide is almost negligible, and the wind has much more effect than the tide.

(60) There are facilities on the west side of the waterway on both sides of the County Road 528 bridge at **Mile 6.3**. These can provide fuel, marine supplies, transient berths, electricity, water, ice, pump-out and repairs. Maximum haul-out capacities are lifts to 50 tons and marine railway to 75 feet.

(61) **Caution:** In 1983, numerous stakes were reported on the west side of the waterway in the vicinity of **Mile 7.3**, in about 40°01'55"N., 74°03'50"W.

(62) **Kettle Creek** flows southeastward into Barnegat Bay opposite **Mile 9.6**. The creek has depths of 4 feet to the forks, 1.4 miles above the mouth. Gasoline and some supplies are available.

(63) **Shelter Cove**, on the west side of Barnegat Bay at the entrance to **Goose Creek**, opposite **Mile 12.8**, has some supplies and slips. Repairs can be made; travel lift, 15 tons. The controlling depth into the cove is about 5 feet.

(64) A marked 6-foot channel follows the inner barrier beach from **Lavallette**, east of **Mile 10.7**, to **Seaside Heights**, east of **Mile 14.1**. The bridge with a 33-foot fixed span to **West Point Island**, east of **Mile 12.6**, has a clearance of 10 feet, but with local knowledge, the bridge can be bypassed through the narrow channel west of the island. The fixed span of the State Route 37 bridge between Pelican Island and Seaside Heights has a vertical clearance of 15 feet.

(65) There are many facilities along the inner barrier beach from **Mile 9.5** to **Mile 16.0**.

(66) The municipal dock, 0.2 mile south of the bridge on the inner side of Seaside Heights, has depths of about 7 feet at the face.

(67) **Toms River**, which empties into the west side of Barnegat Bay at **Mile 14.6**, has midchannel depths of 3.5 to 5 feet. The channel is well marked. In 1982, shoaling to an unknown extent was reported about 0.25 mile south of Long Point in about 39°56'00"N., 74°08'19"W.

(68) **Island Heights**, on the high wooded point on the north side of Toms River, 1.7 miles above Barnegat Bay, has a public pier with about 5 feet alongside. Gasoline, diesel fuel, marine supplies, ice, water, a pump-out station and berthing with electricity are available at one of several facilities. Repairs can be made; largest haul-out capacities: lifts to 25 tons.

(69)      The town of **Toms River**, 4 miles upriver from Barnegat Bay, is the head of navigation; controlling depth to the town is about 5 feet. There are complete fuel, supply, repair and slip facilities; maximum haul-out capacities; railway, 60 feet; lift, 60 tons.

(70)      Gasoline, diesel fuel, ice, water, a pump-out station, launching ramp, some marine supplies and slips are available at a marina on **Goodluck Point** at **Mile 16.2**. Minor engine and hull repairs can be made; largest lift, 25 tons.

(71)      **Cedar Creek**, which empties into the west side of Barnegat Bay at **Mile 20.2**, has depths of 3 to 4 feet. There is a light on the south side of the entrance to the creek.

(72)

## Small-craft facilities

(73)      Small-craft facilities along the 1.4-mile navigable length of Cedar Creek have gasoline, diesel fuel, marine supplies, berthing with electricity, ice, water, storage and a pump-out station and hull and engine repairs can be made; lift capacity, 40 tons.

(74)      **Forked River**, on the west side of Barnegat Bay opposite **Mile 23.8,** is entered by a marked channel that leads to the head of navigation at the town of **Forked River,** about 1.8 miles above the bay. In 1997, the controlling depth was reported to be 4 feet. The river forks into three branches about halfway up; the town is on the north side of **North Branch**. Forked River is reported to afford excellent hurricane shelter. There are several marinas and boatyards on both sides of North Branch.

(75)      A State marina is at the head of North Branch. The **harbormaster** at this facility assigns transient berths. The New Jersey Bureau of Coastal Engineering, Aids to Navigation Section, is based at the marina and can provide mariners with the latest information of conditions on the Intracoastal Waterway and on other waters marked by the State of New Jersey.

(76)      **Oyster Creek**, on the west side of Barnegat Bay opposite **Mile 24.7,** has a navigable length of over 1 mile to the highway bridge.

(77)      At **Mile 25.9,** Oyster Creek Channel leads eastward to Barnegat Inlet. The channel and the inlet were described in chapter 4.

(78)      **Waretown**, west of **Mile 26.3** on the bay shore, has many small-craft facilities along its easterly shore, and in **Waretown Creek,** on the north side of town, and in the small-boat basin, known as **Sanborn Anchorage,** on the south side of town. Controlling depths are about 4 feet in Waretown Creek and about 5 feet in Sanborn Anchorage.

(79)      **Double Creek**, southwest of **Mile 28.0**, is protected on the north side of its entrance by a jetty that has a light on its outer end. The channel is navigable to just above the fixed highway bridge 0.7 mile above Barnegat Bay. In 2021, shoaling to less than 1 foot was reported in the channel at 39°46'34"N., 74°08'04"W.; caution is advised.

(80)      At **Mile 37.4,**the State Route 72 bridge with a clearance of 56 feet over the intracoastal route crosses **Manahawkin Bay** connecting the westerly shore of the bay with the barrier beach. The bridge also crosses three minor channels, one close to the westerly shore of the bay, one between the two marshy islands on the east side of the bay, and the other between the more easterly island and the barrier beach, all under construction (2017). An overhead power and digital media cable runs along the spans to the barrier beach and has a minimum clearance of 18 feet.

(81)

## Small-craft facilities

(82)      There are many small-craft facilities along the bay shore of **Long Beach** between Barnegat Inlet and Beach Haven Inlet. Most of these are near the bridge at **Mile 37.4**; at **Ship Bottom**, **Mile 39.0**; and at **Beach Haven**, **Mile 45.7**.

(83)      **Westecunk Creek**, 2 miles northwest of **Mile 42.5**, is marked at the entrance by a light. A marked channel leads from Little Egg Harbor to a public landing 2.5 miles above the mouth of the creek. In 1999, the channel had a reported controlling depth of 6 feet. The town of **West Creek** is 0.3 mile west of the landing. Small-craft facilities are on the southwesterly side of the creek.

(84)
## ENCs - US5NJ24M, US5NJ20M
## Chart - 12316

(85)      **Little Egg Harbor** has general depths of 4 to 6 feet in its northwestern part; in the southern part is a large group of marshy islands surrounded by a shallow area with depths of 1 to 3 feet. Buoys mark a race course in the harbor. Between some of these islands are narrow unmarked channels which begin and end abruptly in the shallow areas. The Intracoastal Waterway continues southward along the inner side of the barrier beach.

(86)      **Parker Cove** is on the north side of Little Egg Harbor about 3 miles northwest of **Mile 44.3**. **Parker Run**, marked by a light on the south side of the entrance, empties into the northwest corner of the cove. Depths of about 4 feet can be carried to a public dock on the north side of Parker Run, 0.3 mile above the entrance. There are numerous small-craft facilities along Parker Run.

(87)      **Tuckerton Creek** empties into the west side of Little Egg Harbor about 4 miles northwest of **Mile 49.4**. A dredged channel, marked by lights, extends 1.6 miles from the north end of **Story Island Channel** to the mouth of the creek. Overhead power cables, about 0.6 mile above the mouth, have a clearance of 60 feet.

(88)

## Current

(89)      Cross currents may be experienced in the approach channel to Tuckerton Creek. A **speed limit** of 8 miles per hour is prescribed for the channel. (See **33 CFR 162.30,** chapter 2.)

(90)
## Small-craft facilities

(91)      There are numerous small-craft facilities along the creek and on the north side of the approach channel below the entrance to the creek.

(92)      At **Mile 50.2, Marshelder Channel,** with depths of 7 feet or more, makes northward and around the southwest side of **Story Island** for 2.5 miles to Little Egg Harbor and the dredged approach to Tuckerton Creek.

(93)      There are several thorofares through the marsh area south and west of Marshelder Channel, but **Little Sheepshead Creek** is the only one of any importance. This 2-mile winding passage from **Mile 50.7** of the Intracoastal Waterway to the eastern side of Great Bay is used extensively. In 1973, shoaling to 1 foot was reported in the creek in about 39°31'20"N., 74°19'16"W. The fixed highway bridge over Little Sheepshead Creek has an 18-foot channel span with a clearance of 14 feet; overhead power cables have a least clearance of 36 feet.

(94)      The waterway route skirts the inner ends of the shoals in **Beach Haven Inlet** and **Little Egg Inlet**, both mentioned in chapter 4, and continues westward through **Shooting Thorofare** and along the south side of **Great Bay**, which has general depths of 4 to 7 feet.

(95)      **Big Creek**, marked by a light at the entrance, empties into the north side of Great Bay opposite **Mile 55.0**. Depths of about 5 feet can be carried to a large marina 2 miles above the mouth. The marina can provide gasoline, transient berths, limited marine supplies, full repairs and a 10-ton lift. The highway bridge crossing the creek 1.2 miles above the mouth has a 42-foot fixed span with a vertical clearance of 12 feet.

(96)      **Mullica River,** which empties into the northwestern part of Great Bay, is navigable to a milldam 20 miles above the bay. In 1998, it was reported a depth of about 5 feet can be carried across the Great Bay flats to the mouth of the river. Once inside the river, the water is deep and the midchannel is clear for a long distance.

(97)      In 1998, it was reported that depths of 8 to 4 feet can be carried from the mouth of Mullica River to the bridge 16 miles above the entrance, and thence 2.5 feet to within a mile of the milldam. A lighted cutoff, 3 miles above the mouth, has ample depth and reduces distances to points on the upper river by about 2 miles.

(98)      The navigation of Mullica River is fairly easy in the lower reaches, but the chart should be followed closely to avoid the unmarked 3-foot shoals in the entrance. The last few miles to the milldam are shallow, difficult and full of stumps. The river is marked by lights and stake daybeacons as far as the first bridge; stake daybeacons mark the reaches above the bridge.

(99)      In 2012, the fixed highway bridge 6.5 miles above the mouth of Mullica River was under construction; overhead power cables, 500 feet above the bridge, have a clearance of 50 feet. A boatyard, 0.5 mile below the bridge, has a 20-ton lift; hull and engine repairs can be made, and berths, gasoline, diesel fuel and marine supplies are available.

(100)
## Small-craft facilities

(101)      Gasoline, diesel fuel, some supplies and slips are available at small-craft facilities at **Green Bank** and **Sweetwater**, about 16 and 17 miles above the mouth, respectively. Minor repairs can be made; largest lift, 15 tons.

(102)      **Nacote Creek** empties into the southwest side of Mullica River 4 miles above the mouth. Controlling depths are about 5 feet to the U.S. Route 9 highway bridge, 1.5 miles above the mouth of the creek, and thence 3 feet to **Port Republic**, at the head of navigation 3.6 miles from the mouth. The U.S. Route 9 bridge has a fixed span with a clearance of 25 feet. The overhead power cables just upstream of the bridge have a clearance of 57 feet.

(103)      A boatyard is on the north side of the creek just below the U.S. Route 9 bridge. Berths and gasoline are available; lifts to 10 tons can handle hull and motor repairs.

(104)      **Bass River**, which empties into the north side of Mullica River 5 miles above the mouth, has depths of about 4 feet to **New Gretna**, 2.4 miles above Mullica River. The U.S. Route 9 fixed highway bridge at New Gretna was under construction in 2012. The overhead power cable just below the bridge has a clearance of 42 feet. The fixed highway bridge just upstream has a clearance of 20 feet.

(105)
## Small-craft facilities

(106)      Two small-craft facilities just below the bascule bridge, on both sides of the river, have berths with electricity, gasoline, diesel fuel, water, ice, a pump-out station, dry storage and marine supplies. A 12-ton lift is available; hull, engine and electronic repairs can be made.

(107)      **Wading River**, which empties into the north side of Mullica River 7.5 miles above the mouth, has depths of about 4 feet to State Route 542 highway bridge 4 miles upstream (bridge not shown on chart).

(108)      **Mott Creek**, on the west side of Great Bay, is marked by a light and has depths of about 4 feet to a bulkhead landing 1.5 miles above the mouth; gasoline and some supplies are available. The 2-mile thorofare that winds northward through the marshes from the Mott Creek landing to the mouth of Nacote Creek has a controlling depth of about 3 feet.

(109)      **Oyster Creek**, on the west side of Great Bay 0.7 mile south of Mott Creek, is marked by a light and has depths of 4 feet in the entrance channel thence 2 feet to the small fishing village of **Oyster Creek**, 0.3 mile from the mouth, and 0.2 mile beyond to a public landing.

(110)      The Intracoastal Waterway leaves Great Bay at **Mile 56.8** and follows **Main Marsh Thorofare** to **Little Bay**, thence along the western side of Little Bay across the mouths of **Hammock Cove**, and **Perch Cove** and westward of **Shad Island.**

(111)     At **Mile 60.3**, an alternate route swings eastward in **Brigantine Channel**, which leads to **Brigantine Inlet**, mentioned in chapter 4. About 1.3 miles along the channel, the alternate route turns southward and follows **Obes Thorofare** along the inner side of Brigantine. The overhead power cable that crosses Obes Thorofare, 1.3 miles from Brigantine Channel, has a clearance of 47 feet.

(112)
### Small-craft facilities
(113)     There are many small-craft facilities along the bay side of **Brigantine**. **Baremore Quarters**, a cove on the inner side of Brigantine 2.3 miles along Obes Thorofare from Brigantine Channel, is a good harbor of refuge.

(114)     From Baremore Quarters, the alternate route follows **Bonita Tideway** along the city waterfront, then swings westward through **Golden Hammock Thorofare** and rejoins the main route at **Mile 64.2**. The total length of the alternate route is 7 miles. Depths of 5 feet or more are on the alternate route along the inner side of Brigantine, but the channel shoals as it nears the main Intracoastal Waterway route and can be navigated only by shallow drafts.

(115)     The main route of the waterway leaves Little Bay at **Mile 60.3** and continues along the northwestern side of **Grassy Bay**, a shoal area mostly bare at low water, to **Meadow Cut**. From this short land cut, the route follows the southeastern side of **Reed Bay** to and through **Gull Island Thorofare**, across the mouth of **Broad Creek**, through **Middle Thorofare**, where it is rejoined by the alternate route from Brigantine, and into Absecon Channel at **Mile 64.5**, which leads to Absecon Inlet and the marine facilities in Clam Creek at **Atlantic City**. (See chapter 4.)

(116)     **Absecon Channel**, the marked approach to Absecon Creek through Absecon Bay, can be entered at **Mile 64.5** or through **Point Bar Thorofare** at **Mile 65.6**. **Absecon Bay** is shallow and bares in some places at low water.

(117)     **Absecon Creek**, which flows into the northwest side of the bay, is crossed by three fixed bridges, about 1.5 miles above the mouth, at **Absecon;** least clearance is 3 feet. A marked channel with reported depths of about 5 feet leads across Absecon Bay to the mouth of the creek. In 1999, the reported midchannel controlling depth in the creek was 5 feet from the mouth to the bridges; the creek is reported navigable by small outboards for about 2 miles above the bridges.

(118)
### Small-craft facilities
(119)     A small-craft facility is on the north side of the creek, about 0.5 mile below the bridges. A 7-ton lift and a 30-foot marine railway are available; engine, hull and electronic repairs can be made. Gasoline, dry storage, water, ice and marine supplies are also available.

(120)     From Absecon Channel, the Intracoastal Waterway follows **Beach Thorofare** along the northwest side of Atlantic City.

(121)     The route of the Intracoastal Waterway leaves Beach Thorofare at **Mile 69.5** and continues along the inner side of Atlantic City by way of **Inside Thorofare**.

(122)     The waterway turns sharply northwestward at **Mile 71.4** and follows **West Canal** along the southwest side of Ventnor Heights to **Mile 72.3**, where it rejoins Beach Thorofare and continues southwestward.

(123)
### Small-craft facilities
(124)     A small-craft facility southwest of the turn has water, ice, wet and dry storage, marine supplies, launching ramp, hull, engine and electronic repairs available.

(125)     From **Mile 73.3** southwest of **Shelter Island**, a marked channel with a controlling depth of about 3 feet leads northward along the eastern shores of **Shelter Island Bay** and **Lakes Bay** to **West Atlantic City**, 2.2 miles from the waterway. The channel continues along the north shore of Lakes Bay to a yacht club at **Pleasantville**, 3.4 miles from the waterway.

(126)     At **Mile 75.4, Risley Channel** and **Dock Thorofare** lead northward for 2.2 miles to a marine basin near **Northfield.**

(127)
### Small-craft facilities
(128)     Small-craft facilities, on the northwesterly side of Dock Thorofare, can provide gasoline, diesel fuel, water, ice and marine supplies. Hull and engine repairs can be made; largest lift, 50 tons.

(129)     At **Mile 75.4** there is a choice of two routes to the inner side of Ocean City. The exposed route west of the **Longport** waterfront and across **Great Egg Harbor Inlet** has deeper water but is restricted by the 25-foot clearance of the fixed highway bridge, 0.2 mile south-southwestward of **Mile 75.4**. Care is necessary when passing through the bridge to avoid the shoal making out into the channel from the west side. Currents are strong at the inlet crossing, and the route is exposed to heavy easterly seas. The highway bridge over the inlet, 1.5 miles eastward of **Mile 80.0** has a fixed span with an authorized clearance of 65 feet. A portion of the old bridge has been retained as a fishing pier, extending north 490 feet into the inlet, adjacent to the existing bridge.

(130)     The protected route is through Risley Channel and **Broad Thorofare**, but the channel is subject to continuous shoaling. State Route 152 fixed highway bridge over Broad Thorofare at **Mile 78.0** has a vertical clearance of 56 feet.

(131)     **Ship Channel** extends northwestward from **Mile 79.1** to Great Egg Harbor Bay. **Bass Harbor**, a narrow channel leading northward from Ship Channel 1.7 miles from the inlet bridge, has depths of about 10 feet in the entrance; State Route 152 fixed highway bridge, 0.3 mile north of the entrance, has a 14-foot span with an authorized vertical clearance of 6 feet. An overhead power cable just south of the bridge has an authorized clearance of 38 feet.

(132)   **Somers Point**, on the north side of Ship Channel 2 miles from the inlet bridge, is a summer resort with wharves that have depths of 2 to 5 feet at their outer ends.

(133)   There are many marinas and boatyards in Bass Harbor and along Somers Point.

(134)   At **Mile 80.4,** a 2-mile combination of causeways and highway bridges with a clearance of 55 feet extends southeastward over the Intracoastal Waterway, channels and islands in **Great Egg Harbor Bay** from Somers Point to Ocean City.

(135)
## Small-craft facilities

(136)   A marina, south of the bridge, has gasoline, diesel fuel, berths, launching ramp, dry storage, water and ice available.

(137)   The Garden State Parkway bridges, crossing Great Egg Harbor Bay between **Drag Island** and **Beesleys Point**, have a central-span vertical clearance of 50 feet. The bridges are currently under construction (2016). The Beesleys Point Bridge, a highway bridge 0.2 mile west of the Garden State Parkway bridges, has a bascule span with a vertical clearance of 14 feet. An overhead power cable, with a clearance of 76 feet over the channel and 50 feet outside the channel, crosses near the head of the bay.

(138)   **Patcong Creek**, marked on the westerly side of the entrance by a light, empties into the north side of Great Egg Harbor Bay, 2.6 miles northwestward of the bridge at **Mile 80.4.** The depth over the bar at the entrance is about 3 feet. A fixed highway bridge, 0.5 mile above the mouth of the creek, has a clearance of 15 feet. Near the bridge gasoline, marine supplies, a 10-ton lift and transient berths are available; some repairs can be made.

(139)   **Tuckahoe River**, marked at the entrance by a light, empties into the south side of Great Egg Harbor 2.7 miles westward of the bridge at **Mile 80.4.** Controlling depths are about 2 feet across the flats at the entrance, thence 3 feet for 7 miles to the town of **Tuckahoe**. The overhead power cable, 1 mile below Tuckahoe, has a clearance of 41 feet. The State Route 50 highway bridge at the town has a 30-foot bascule span with a clearance of 9 feet. (See **33 CFR 117.1** through **117.59** and **117.758**, chapter 2, for drawbridge regulations.)

(140)   A boatyard is just below the bridge. Gasoline and some marine supplies can be obtained. Complete repairs can be made; a 120-foot marine railway and a 60-ton mobile hoist are available.

(141)   **Cedar Swamp Creek** empties into the south side of Tuckahoe River 4.3 miles above the river mouth. The creek has depths of about 4 feet to a highway culvert 2.5 miles from the river where a marine railway can haul out boats up to 25 feet for repairs.

(142)   **Great Egg Harbor River** is a northwestward continuation of Great Egg Harbor Bay. The controlling depth is about 4 feet from Great Egg Harbor Bay to Mays Landing, at the head of navigation. The overhead power cables between the bay and Mays Landing have clearances of 65 feet or more.

(143)   **Middle River** empties into the southwest side of Great Egg Harbor River 0.5 mile above the bay. Depths of 4 feet can be carried up Middle River for 2 miles.

(144)   **Powell Creek** empties into the east side of Great Egg Harbor River 5 miles above the bay.

(145)   **Mays Landing**, at the head of navigation on Great Egg Harbor River, is 12 miles from Great Egg Harbor Bay. The river water is nearly fresh at the town. The town bulkhead has depths of about 5 feet alongside. A marina here can provide gasoline, berths, water, ice and some marine supplies. Minor hull and engine repairs can be made; marine railway, 50 feet; lift, 3 tons.

(146)   The Intracoastal Waterway continues southerly along the inner side of **Ocean City**; lagoons here accommodate craft drawing up to 5 feet.

(147)   The waterway follows **Beach Thorofare** to **Peck Bay**; the mudflats bordering the channel through the bay are visible in some places at low water. A marina, just north of the Roosevelt Boulevard bridge and on the west side of the waterway, can provide gasoline, diesel fuel, transient berths, electricity, water, ice, pump-out, marine supplies, 35-ton lift and full repairs. In 2002, 4 feet was reported in the approach to the marina.

(148)   The waterway enters **Middle Thorofare** at **Mile 88.0,** thence continues through **Ben Hands Thorofare** to **Mile 89.8** in **Main Channel**, which leads eastward and northward for 1.5 miles to the inner side of **Strathmere**, just south of Corson Inlet. The Ocean Drive bridge over Middle Thorofare, just north of Coroson Inlet, has a 10-foot fixed span with a clearance of 6 feet. The highway bridge over the waterfront channel at Strathmere has a bascule span with a clearance of 15 feet. The bridgetender monitors VHF-FM channel 13; call sign WQZ-342. (See **33 CFR 117.1** through **117.59** and **117.714**, chapter 2, for drawbridge regulations.)

(149)
## Small-craft facilities

(150)   There are several small-craft facilities at Strathmere. These facilities can provide gasoline, transient berths, water, ice, limited marine supplies and engine repairs; a 14-foot marine railway is available.

(151)   The waterway follows Main Channel southwestward, passing into shallow **Ludlam Bay** at **Mile 91.3** and enters **Ludlam Thorofare** at **Mile 92.5.**

(152)   **Sea Isle City**, on the barrier beach has several basins at **Mile 93.8** with depths of 3 to 6.5 feet in the entrances and slightly more inside.

(153)   The Intracoastal Waterway enters **Townsend Channel** at **Mile 95.3** and follows the inner side of the resort known as **Townsends Inlet.**

(154)
## Small-craft facilities

(155)   Gasoline, diesel fuel, water, ice, berths and marine supplies are available at the small-craft facilities at Townsends Inlet. Engine repairs can be made; marine railway, 35 feet.

(172)

Cape May Canal (west approach), New Jersey
Image courtesy of Air Station Atlantic City (2002)

—N—

(156)    At **Mile 96.4**, the waterway is 300 yards west of the highway bridge over **Townsends Inlet**, described in chapter 4. **Avalon**, on the southwest side of the inlet, is separated from the waterway's **Ingram Thorofare** by a wide marsh area.

(157)    **Cornell Harbor**, leads southeastward through the marsh from **Mile 96.8** to Avalon thence along the inner side of the resort.

(158)    **Pennsylvania Harbor**, 0.5-mile southwestward of Cornell Harbor, had a reported controlling depth of 2.7 feet (4.5 feet at midchannel) in 2000. **Princeton Harbor**, 0.2-mile southwestward of Pennsylvania Harbor, had a reported controlling depth of 2.3 feet (deeper water is available with local knowledge) in 1999–2000. Both waterways lead to the Avalon waterfront. The fixed bridges over the Avalon channel at the inner ends of the two harbors restrict passage between them or to the southwest to an overhead clearance of 4 feet.

(159)    Gasoline, diesel fuel, water, ice, berths, some marine supplies and a 4-ton forklift are available at Avalon; hull and engine repairs can be done.

(160)    The waterway follows Ingram Thorofare westward to **Paddy Thorofare**, thence into shallow **Great Sound** at **Mile 98.0.** At **Mile 100.0**, the route leaves Great Sound and follows **Gull Island Thorofare** southward to the Stone Harbor waterfront.

(161)    **Stone Harbor** is a resort on the northeast side of Hereford Inlet. Several basins are along the waterfront.

(162)    The waterway follows **Great Channel** southwestward along the Stone Harbor waterfront, then turns sharply westward at **Mile 103.3** and follows the northwestern shore of **Nummy Island**. The bridge over the channel that leads along the east side of Nummy Island to Hereford Inlet was described in chapter 4.

(163)    At **Mile 104.6,** the waterway route through **Grassy Sound Channel** is joined by the main channel from Hereford Inlet. The bascule bridge over the inlet channel was described in chapter 4.

(164)    **Beach Creek,** on the inner side of North Wildwood just south of Hereford Inlet, has depths of about 2 feet in the entrance, but deeper water inside. The fixed bridge, 0.4 mile above the entrance, has a 40-foot span with a vertical clearance of 14 feet.

(165)    The route enters **Grassy Sound** at **Mile 106.1** and follows a well-marked channel.

(166)    At **Mile 107.5,** a 5-foot channel leads along the northeast side of West Wildwood for 0.8 mile to the inner waterfront of **Wildwood**. Passage is limited by the 5-foot clearances of the fixed bridges that connect the two communities.

(167)    At **Mile 108.7, Post Creek** extends eastward from the waterway and widens into a small bay between Wildwood and West Wildwood. **Ottens Harbor**, a dredged slip with depths of about 10 feet, extends 0.5 mile southeastward from the mouth of Post Creek. Commercial wharves

along the waterway can accommodate vessels up to 150 feet.

(168) **Sunset Lake**, a comparatively deep basin on the inner side of **Wildwood Crest**, can be entered from either **Mile 109.3** or **Mile 110.2** of the Intracoastal route. The controlling depth is about 7 feet in the entrances.

(169) The waterway continues southward through **Jarvis Sound** and **Middle Thorofare**. Just north of the bridge over Middle Thorofare, **Lower Thorofare** leads eastward from the waterway for 0.3 mile, then turns northward. There is a long marginal fish wharf on the east side of Lower Thorofare; fuel and supplies are available.

(170) The waterway route crosses the inner end of **Cape May Inlet** at **Mile 12.6** and continues westward through Cape May Harbor; the inlet and harbor were described in chapter 4.

(171) **Cape May Canal** is entered at **Mile 114.1.** Vessels transiting the canal should limit their speed to 5 knots and should proceed with special care in the vicinity of the bridges. A federal project provides for a depth of 12 feet through the canal to Delaware Bay. (See Notice to Mariners and latest editions of charts for controlling depths.) Two submerged dolphins, hazardous to navigation, are on the southern edge of the channel on the west side of the State Route 162 bridge.

(173)

### Current

(174) In Cape May Canal, the current velocity is 1.9 knots at the east end and 0.9 knot at the west end; passage of barge tows may be delayed because of tide and current conditions.

(175) The Cape May terminal of the **Cape May-Lewes Ferry** is on the north side of Cape May Canal at **Mile 117.3.** Significant shoaling is reported opposite the ferry berths along the southern bank of the canal, and mariners are advised to stand clear of the area.

(176) The ferry basin contains six ferry slips with the main operating pier located at the extreme western end of the basin. Mariners are advised not to impede the passage of ferries as they proceed in and out of Cape May Canal West End jetties and maneuver into and out of their berths. A private sound signal is located on the main operating pier. Private vessels are prohibited from docking at the ferry terminal. The ferries are AIS equipped and monitor VHF-FM channels 13 and 16 while operating. More information about the ferry can be obtained at *capemaylewesferry. com*.

(177) At **Mile 117.7,** Cape May Canal enters Delaware Bay between stone jetties that are 2 miles north of Cape May Light. The outer ends of the jetties are marked by lights; a sound signal is on the north jetty. The project channel is offset to the north of the centerline between the jetties. Vessels should avoid overtaking or meeting ferries while they are transiting the entrance to the canal or the canal to their berths. Also, mariners should avoid anchoring within the jetties or outside the entrance to the canal.

(178) Choppy seas are reported to form on Delaware Bay when the wind and tidal currents are contrary; it is especially hazardous at the entrance to Cape May Canal. Large waves may form within the canal during periods of strong northwesterly winds.

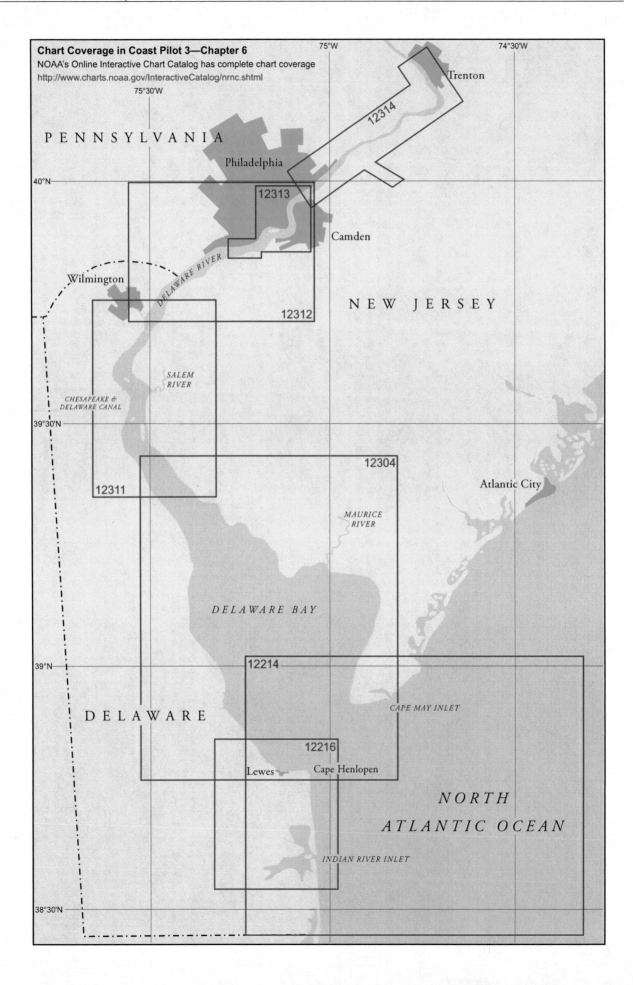

**Chart Coverage in Coast Pilot 3—Chapter 6**
NOAA's Online Interactive Chart Catalog has complete chart coverage
http://www.charts.noaa.gov/InteractiveCatalog/nrnc.shtml

# Delaware Bay

(1)     This chapter describes Delaware Bay and River and their navigable tributaries and includes an explanation of the Traffic Separation Scheme at the entrance to the bay. Major ports covered are Wilmington, Chester, Philadelphia, Camden and Trenton, with major facilities at Delaware City, Deepwater Point and Marcus Hook. Also described are Christina River, Salem River, and Schuylkill River, the principal tributaries of Delaware River and other minor waterways, including Mispillion, Maurice and Cohansey Rivers.

(3)

## North Atlantic Right Whales

(4)     Endangered North Atlantic right whales may occur within 30 miles of the Delaware coast in the approaches to Delaware Bay and ports of Philadelphia (peak season: November through April, although right whales have been sighted in the area year-round). (See **North Atlantic Right Whales**, indexed as such in chapter 3, for more information on right whales and recommended measures to avoid collisions.)

(5)     All vessels 65 feet or greater in length overall (LOA) and subject to the jurisdiction of the United States are restricted to speeds of 10 knots or less in a Seasonal Management Area existing around Delaware Bay between November 1 and April 30. The area is defined as the waters within a 20-nm radius of 38°52'27.4"N., 75°01'32.1"W. (See **50 CFR 224.105** in chapter 2 for regulations, limitations and exceptions.)

(6)

## COLREGS Demarcation Lines

(7)     The lines established for Delaware Bay are described in **33 CFR 80.503**, chapter 2.

(8)
**ENC - US4DE11M**
**Chart - 12214**

(9)     **Delaware Bay** and Delaware River form the boundary between the state of New Jersey on the east and the states of Delaware and Pennsylvania on the west. The bay is an expansion of the lower part of Delaware River; the arbitrary dividing line, 42 miles above the Delaware Capes, extends from Liston Point, DE, to Hope Creek, NJ. Deep-draft vessels use the Atlantic entrance, which is about 10 miles wide between Cape May on the northeast and Cape Henlopen on the southwest. Vessels with drafts less than 33 feet can enter Delaware River from Chesapeake Bay through the Chesapeake and Delaware Canal, which is described in chapter 7.

(10)     **Mileages** shown in this chapter, such as Mile 0.9E and Mile 12W, are the nautical miles above the **Delaware Capes** (or "the Capes"), referring to a line from Cape May Light to the tip of Cape Henlopen. The letters N, S, E, or W, following the numbers, denote by compass points the side of the river where each feature is located.

(11)     The approaches to Delaware Bay have few off-lying dangers.

(12)     The 100-fathom curve is 50 to 75 miles off Delaware Bay, and the 20-fathom curve is about 25 miles off. Depths inside the 20-fathom curve are irregular, and in thick weather a deep-draft vessel should not approach the coast closer than depths of 12 fathoms until sure of its position; the safest approach or passing courses would be outside Five Fathom Bank Lighted Buoy F (38°46'49"N., 74°34'32"W.) and Delaware Lighted Buoy D (38°27'18"N., 74°41'47"W.).

(13)     **Cape May** is the extensive peninsula on the northeast side of the entrance to Delaware Bay. **Cape May Light** (38°55'59"N., 74°57'37"W.), 165 feet above the water, is shown from a white tower with a red cupola and two white dwellings nearby on Cape May Point.

(14)     The shoals off Cape May are mixed clay and sand and have the consistency of hardpan; the ridges run in approximately the same directions as the currents. **Cape May Channel**, 1 mile southwest of the cape, is an unmarked passage between shoals, with depths from 2 to 4 feet on either side. The channel is seldom used, and then only by fishing vessels and pleasure craft; local knowledge is required for safe passage.

(15)     The channels have strong currents, and many tide rips form near **Prissy Wicks Shoal,** which has depths as little as 2 feet about 2 miles south of Cape May Light. In Cape May Channel, the current velocity is 1.5 knots on the flood and 2.3 knots on the ebb.

(16)     **Overfalls Shoal** has a depth of 8 feet about 4 miles southwestward of Cape May Light. The 30-foot curve extends 3 miles farther in the general direction of Cape Henlopen and has a depth of 17 feet just inside its outermost limit.

(17)     **McCrie Shoal**, 7 miles southeast of Cape May Light, has a least charted depth of 19 feet; a lighted buoy is on the southeast side of the shoal.

(18)     **Five Fathom Bank** has a least charted depth of 19 feet about 15 miles eastward of Cape May Light. The area, enclosed by the 30-foot curve, is about 9 miles long, north to south, and about 2 miles wide. The greater part of Five Fathom Bank is within authorized fishtrap limits. Several buoys are moored around the bank.

(2)

## Navigation Guidelines for Delaware Bay and River

The U.S. Coast Guard Captain of the Port, Sector Delaware Bay and the Mariner's Advisory Committee for the Bay and River Delaware jointly recommend the following precautionary measures be taken while transiting the Delaware Bay and River.

### Non-commercial Vessels

The Delaware Bay and River is the port of call for large commercial ships and tug/barge units that can only transit in the main ship channel. All non-commercial shallow draft vessels are strongly encouraged to transit the Delaware Bay and River outside of the main shipping channel and maintain a listening watch on VHF-FM channel 13 and 16.

The Delaware Bay is a large, open bay that is subject to confusing, and sometimes dangerous, sea and swell conditions due to a large fetch, strong currents and numerous shoals. Also, it has very few harbors of refuge between the entrance and the Chesapeake and Delaware Canal. Vessels transiting the area are strongly encouraged to navigate as appropriate by monitoring current weather conditions and forecast, and filing a float plan. Commercial vessels transiting the main channel will be using VHF-FM channel 13. Non-commercial vessels should maintain a listening watch on this VHF-FM channel and answer when called.

All foreign registered vessels, including non-commercial vessels, 100 tons and over, are required by Title 23 of the Delaware State Code and Title 55 of the Pennsylvania State Code to employ a Delaware or Pennsylvania state licensed pilot. Information about making arrangement for a pilot is described in this chapter, **Pilotage, Delaware Bay and River**.

Mariners should be especially vigilant while navigating in the Delaware Bay entrance area between Delaware Bay Approach Lighted Whistle Buoy CH and Brown Shoal Light. This highly congested area includes a pilotage transfer area, ferries crossing between Cape May and the Harbor of Refuge, and commercial vessels proceeding inbound and outbound to the main ship channel. Also, large deep-draft tankers will be proceeding out of the Big Stone Beach anchorage area and turning into the main navigational channel starting at Brown Shoal Light.

The Salem Power Plant is located at the extreme northwesterly portion of Delaware Bay where Delaware Bay turns into the Delaware River. The area in the vicinity of this prominent power plant is designated as a Security Zone. (See **33 CFR 165.553**, chapter 2, for limits and regulations.)

Vessels proceeding to or from the Chesapeake and Delaware Canal should be aware that information about this waterway, along with appropriate regulations, is contained in chapter 7 of this Coast Pilot. Vessels approaching the junction area of the Chesapeake and Delaware Canal and the Delaware River off Reedy Point should use particular caution. Ships and tug/barge units will be proceeding in and out of the main ship channel and in and out of the Bulkhead Shoal Channel that goes to the oil refinery inside of Pea Patch Island, and in and out of the Salem River Channel, as well as making the sharp turn into and out of the Chesapeake and Delaware Canal. As ships and tug/barge units that are entering and exiting the Chesapeake and Delaware Canal are subject to strong cross currents, all vessels including non-commercial vessels, should avoid meeting at this location. It is also strongly advised that recreational vessels transiting this area proceed outside the main channels when possible.

Vessels bound for Cape May should refer to chapter 5 of this volume for a detailed description of this area. Vessels bound for the Harbor of Refuge, Breakwater Harbor and Lewes, Delaware should refer to the detailed description of this area in chapter six.

### Commercial Vessels

#### Delaware Bay Approaches and Entrance

• Vessels arriving at the Delaware Bay entrance are advised to use the Delaware sea-lane or the Five-fathom sea-lane. It is recommended that vessels with a draft exceeding 34 feet use the Delaware sea-lane from the southeast. Towing traffic transiting off the southeastern New Jersey coast is requested to use the inshore traffic route.

• Vessels arriving at the Delaware Bay entrance are advised to contact the voluntary vessel traffic information service through the Delaware Pilot traffic tower on VHF-FM channel 14. Contact should be made upon a vessel's entrance into the appropriate sea-lane. Inbound towing traffic using the inshore route should contact the tower when off of McCrie Shoal Lighted Buoy 2MS.

• Vessels outbound are requested to contact the traffic tower when they are passing the Brown Shoal or Tanker Anchorage Approach Lighted Buoy A if exiting Big Stone Beach anchorage. Additionally, outbound towing traffic should report out of the entrance area while passing Delaware Bay Entrance Channel Lighted Buoy 8.

### Anchorage Recommendations

• Vessels using anchorage #12 off of Kaighn Point, in Philadelphia Harbor are recommended not to exceed 600 feet in length (LOA) or to exceed 34 feet in draft. Vessels over 30 feet in draft should anchor between Pier 78 and the Walt Whitman Bridge.

• Vessels using anchorage #9 off of Mantua Creek, New Jersey are recommended not to exceed 700 feet in length (LOA) or to exceed 37 feet in draft. Vessels are requested to anchor in sections A or C, whenever there is sufficient room. Anchorage areas within sections B and D are used for maneuvering when docking and undocking vessels at adjacent piers. Vessels are requested to only anchor in sections B and D when there is insufficient space in sections A and C. It is also recommended that vessels with a LOA less than 350 feet to use the northern 0.5 mile of the anchorage which is off the Army Corps of Engineers dock or as close as practical.

• Vessels using anchorage #6 off of Wilmington, Delaware are recommended not to exceed 700 feet in length (LOA) or to exceed 35 feet in draft. It is also recommended that vessels with a LOA less than 350 feet to use the southern end of the anchorage.

• Vessels in excess of 700 feet in length (LOA) may anchor at anchorage #7 off of Marcus Hook, Pennsylvania with a maximum draft of 40 feet. Vessels under 700 feet are requested to anchor in section A whenever there is sufficient room. Section B is needed for vessels over 700 feet in length. It is also recommended that vessels with a LOA less than 350 feet to use the northern 0.5 mile of the anchorage which is above lighted buoy 9M or as close as practical.

• In the event that anchorage #3 (Reedy Point) is full, it is recommended that vessels waiting for clearance to use the Chesapeake and Delaware Canal use anchorage #3 (Artificial Island) or the upper end of Bombay Hook anchorage on Liston Range.

### Lower River and Bay

• The maximum fresh water draft for river transit from sea to Delair, New Jersey is 40 feet.

• All vessels arriving with a fresh water draft in excess of 37 feet are to transit during flood current only.

• All vessels over Panamax size beam (106 ft) having a fresh water draft in excess of 35 feet, 6 inches shall only transit during flood current.

• Vessels outbound from Paulsboro, New Jersey and above, having a fresh water draft of 37 feet and up to 40 feet should arrange to sail two hours after low water. Due to the extended time of transit for these particular deep draft vessels, two river pilots will be arranged for transit to sea.

### Navigation Guidelines for Delaware Bay and River

• The maximum salt-water draft for entrance into Delaware Bay and Big Stone Beach anchorage is 55 feet, as per federal regulation. Qualified offshore advisors with portable DGPS units are available upon request from the Pilots' Association for the Bay and River Delaware.

• Safe Under-Keel Clearance (UKC) should be assured for all transits, taking into consideration the vessel's squat and variations of actual tidal levels due to high winds, barometric pressure, and other atmospheric conditions. Actual tidal heights for many points in the Delaware Bay and River can be determined on the NOAA PORTS site at *co-ops.nos.noaa.gov/map*, or by calling 866–307–6787 (866–30–PORTS).

• Actual tidal levels and currents will vary from predicted heights due to high winds, barometric pressure, and other atmospheric conditions. Actual tidal heights, currents, bridge air gaps and other data can be determined for many points in the Delaware Bay and River on the NOAA PORTS web site at *co-ops.nos.noaa.gov/map*, or by calling 866–307–6787 (866–30–PORTS).

• The U.S. Army Corps of Engineers periodically surveys the bottom conditions of the Delaware Bay and River main channel and anchorages, publishing the results of these surveys at *nap.usace.army.mil*.

### Vessel Reporting

It is recommended that vessels report their position and status to the Maritime Exchange over VHF-FM channel 14 in the following situations:
1) When anchoring
2) When getting underway
3) When passing through Marcus Hook
4) When entering or exiting the Chesapeake and Delaware Canal
5) When making fast to the dock
Tugs operating without a barge are exempt from this recommendation. Tugs with barges are requested to report to the Philadelphia Maritime Exchange when anchoring and leaving all anchorages.
It is important to stand by on VHF-FM channels 14 and 16 at all times. AIS should always be on if the vessel is equipped with it.

### Delaware Bay and River Checkpoints

1) Inbound and outbound at Cape Henlopen
2) Entering or exiting the Chesapeake and Delaware Canal at Reedy Point
3) Inbound or outbound at Marcus Hook
4) First line or last line at any berth
5) Anchor up or anchor down at any anchorage
For checkpoints 2 through 5, all vessels need to call the Maritime Exchange on VHF-FM channel 14.

### Chesapeake and Delaware Canal

• There is no recommended length limitation for vessels using the Chesapeake and Delaware Canal, however the maximum draft limitation is 33 feet.

• Vessels in excess of 760 feet are required to have an operational bow thruster for transit. Vessels in excess of 886 feet are required to have an operational bow and stern thruster for transit. These oversized vessels may use a tug assist instead of a working thruster.

• The maximum combined beam of vessels transiting the Chesapeake and Delaware Canal at the same time is 190 feet.

### Upper Delaware River

The Upper Delaware River pertains to the area of navigation from Delair, New Jersey to the head of navigation on the Delaware River at Trenton, New Jersey. The maximum drafts referred to in these advisories pertain to navigation within the Federal maintained 40-foot channel which ends off Newbold Island, New Jersey.

**Vessel Particulars**
• Any vessel whose beam exceeds 128 feet should transit through the Tacony-Palmyra Bridge during daylight only. Vessels of greater beam and vessels known to be difficult to maneuver should be scheduled on a case by case basis after consultation between the pilots and the operators prior to arrival and departure.
• Maximum air draft should not exceed 132 feet.
• Vessels of combined beam greater than 185 feet should not meet between the Delair Railroad Bridge and the Burlington Bristol Bridge.
• Shipping traffic should avoid meeting above the Burlington Bristol Bridge.

**Vessel Draft Inbound**
• Vessels less than 32 feet, 6 inches FW (fresh water) may transit on any stage of the tide or current.
• Vessels 32 feet, 6 inches FW or greater up to 35 feet FW in draft should arrive in Philadelphia harbor no later than 9 hours and 15 minutes, or earlier than 5 hours and 45 minutes from slack flood current at Cape Henlopen.
• Vessels 35 feet, 1 inch FW or greater up to 38 feet, 6 inches FW in draft should arrive in Philadelphia harbor no later than 8 hours and 15 minutes, or earlier than 5 hours and 45 minutes from slack flood current at Cape Henlopen.
• Vessels 32 feet, 6 inches FW or greater up to 38 feet, 6 inches FW in draft shall avoid meeting outbound shipping traffic above the Delair Railroad Bridge.

**Vessel Draft Outbound**
• Vessel less than 32 feet, 6 inches FW may transit on any stage of the tide or current.
• Vessels 32 feet, 6 inches FW or greater up to 38 feet, 6 inches FW in draft, should sail from terminals above the Delair Railroad Bridge between 1 hour before high water and 3 hours after high water at the dock at which it is sailing.
• Vessels 32 feet, 6 inches FW or greater up to 38 feet, 6 inches FW in draft, shall avoid meeting inbound shipping traffic above the Delair Railroad Bridge.

**Tug Attendance**
Vessels in excess of 375 feet should have a tug in attendance during upper river transits.

(19)     **Five Fathom Bank Lighted Buoy F** (38°46'49"N., 74°34'32"W.) is about 20 miles east-southeast of Cape May Light. The buoy is yellow, shows a flashing yellow light and is equipped with AIS.

(20)     **Cape Henlopen**, on the southwest side of the entrance to Delaware Bay, is marked by a number of towers and buildings. About 0.5 mile southward from

(21) the tip of the cape is a visual **reporting station** and radio control point for the Philadelphia Maritime Exchange.

(21) Cape Henlopen is building out from the northeastward to the northwestward; mariners are advised to exercise extreme caution in this area.

(22) A **naval restricted area** extends northeastward from Cape Henlopen to Overfalls Shoal. (See **33 CFR 334.110**, chapter 2, for limits and regulations.)

(23) **Hen and Chickens Shoal** extends southeastward from the tip of Cape Henlopen and has depths of 9 to 14 feet.

(24) The Cape May-Lewes Ferry crosses the main channel in Delaware Bay about 4 miles northward of Cape Henlopen. The ferry usually departs Lewes from the southern entrance to Harbor of Refuge and enters Lewes from the northern entrance to Harbor of Refuge.

(25) **Delaware Lighted Buoy D** (38°27'18"N., 74°41'47"W.) is about 28 miles southeastward of Cape Henlopen. The buoy is yellow, shows a flashing yellow light and is equipped with AIS.

(27)

**Traffic Separation Scheme**

(28) A **Traffic Separation Scheme (Delaware Bay)** has been established off the entrance to Delaware Bay.

(29) The scheme is composed basically of **directed traffic areas** each with one-way inbound and outbound **traffic lanes** separated by defined **separation zones, a precautionary area** and a **pilot boarding area.** The scheme is recommended for use by vessels approaching or departing Delaware Bay but is not necessarily intended for tugs, tows or other small vessels that traditionally operate outside of the primary traffic lanes or close inshore.

(30) The **Traffic Separation Scheme** has been designed to aid in the prevention of collisions at the approaches to major harbors but is not intended in any way to supersede or alter the applicable Navigation Rules. Separation zones are intended to separate inbound and outbound traffic lanes and to be free of ship traffic and should not be used except for crossing purposes. Mariners should use extreme caution when crossing traffic lanes and separation zones. (See Traffic Separation Schemes, chapter 1, for additional information.)

(31) The **Precautionary Area** for Delaware Bay entrance is inscribed by part of a circle with a radius of 8 miles centered on Harbor of Refuge Light (38°48'52"N., 75°05'33"W.) and extending from off Cape May Point to the shore south of Cape Henlopen with the traffic lanes fanning out from the circumference of the circle.

(32) The outer part of the northeast quadrant of the area is full of shoals, and there are shoal spots covered from 28 to 30 feet in the western extension of the Five Fathom Bank-Cape Henlopen Traffic Lane, about 1 mile west-northwest of Delaware Bay North Approach Lighted Buoy 4. In the southeast quadrant, the eastern limit of Hen and Chickens Shoal is marked by lighted buoys and the red sector of Harbor of Refuge Light. A wreck, covered

59 feet, is about 1 mile north of Delaware Traffic Lane Lighted Buoy DC.

(33) The usable part of the precautionary area has depths of 31 to over 100 feet. Several wrecks and obstructions, covered 48 to 61 feet, are about 1 to 1.7 miles east and southeast of Harbor of Refuge Light. Tugs and tows entering Delaware Bay from the north and northbound upon leaving the Bay often pass between Delaware Bay South Shoal Lump Lighted Buoy 8A and Delaware Bay Entrance Channel Lighted Buoy 6 and between Delaware Bay South Shoal Lump Buoy 8B and Delaware Bay Entrance Channel Lighted Buoy 8. This track allows tugs and tows to keep clear of large vessels entering the Bay through the pilot boarding area southward of Lighted Buoy 6. Since the precautionary area is used by both incoming and outgoing vessels, making the transition between Delaware Bay and the traffic lanes, extreme care is advised in navigating within the area.

(34) The **pilot boarding area** is about 2.5 miles southeastward of Cape Henlopen. (See pilotage later in this chapter.)

(35) **Eastern Directed Traffic Area, Five Fathom Bank to Cape Henlopen Traffic Lane (inbound)**—The eastward approach to Delaware Bay is north of Five Fathom Bank Lighted Buoy F (38°46'49"N., 74°34'32"W.) in the traffic lane, which tapers from 2 miles to 1 mile wide in its 16.4-mile length. By entering the traffic lane 1.5 miles north of Five Fathom Bank Lighted Buoy F, a course of **268°** follows the centerline of the traffic lane to the precautionary area, thence west-southwesterly courses for about 5 miles passing southward of Delaware Bay North Approach Lighted Buoy 4, to the pilot boarding area. Reported depths in the traffic lane are 39 feet or greater.

(36) **Eastern Directed Traffic Area, Cape Henlopen to Five Fathom Bank Traffic Lane (outbound)**—The eastward exit by outbound vessels is south of Five Fathom Bank Traffic Lane Buoy FB (38°46'51"N., 74°55'35"W.) in the traffic lane that expands from 1 mile to 2 miles wide. By entering the traffic lane 1 mile southward of Lighted Buoy FB, a course of **091.5°** follows the centerline of the outbound traffic lane. When seaward of Five Fathom Bank Lighted Buoy F steer usual courses to destination. Depths in the traffic lane are 40 feet or more.

(37) **Separation Zone**—The eastern separation zone between the inbound and outbound traffic lanes is 1 mile wide centered on a line through Five Fathom Bank Lighted Buoy F and two lighted buoys 7.5 miles and 16.4 miles, respectively, westward from the Five Fathom Bank Lighted Buoy F.

(38) **Southeastern Directed Traffic Area, Delaware to Cape Henlopen Traffic Lane (inbound)**—The southeastward approach to Delaware Bay is north of Delaware Lighted Buoy D (38°27'18"N., 74°41'47"W.) in the traffic lane, which tapers from 2 miles to 1 mile wide in its 21-mile length. By entering the traffic lane 1.5 miles northeastward of Delaware Lighted Buoy D, a course of **322°** follows the centerline of the traffic lane to

(26)

### Centerline Channel Control Coordinates (U.S. Army Corps of Engineers)

**Philadelphia, PA to Trenton, NJ**

| Point | Centerline Latitude/Longitude | Point | Centerline Latitude/Longitude |
|---|---|---|---|
| 1 | 39°58'35.897"N., 75°04'48.292"W. | 19 | 40°07'25.194"N., 74°49'29.492"W. |
| 2 | 39°58'42.398"N., 75°04'25.889"W. | 20 | 40°07'34.219"N., 74°49'29.059"W. |
| 3 | 39°59'16.004"N., 75°03'47.772"W. | 21 | 40°07'41.347"N., 74°48'59.440"W. |
| 4 | 40°00'12.150"N., 75°03'24.372"W. | 22 | 40°07'12.259"N., 74°47'21.368"W. |
| 5 | 40°00'26.532"N., 75°03'09.475"W. | 23 | 40°07'15.960"N., 74°46'54.944"W. |
| 6 | 40°00'57.290"N., 75°01'57.601"W. | 24 | 40°08'00.092"N., 74°45'46.044"W. |
| 7 | 40°01'21.713"N., 75°00'31.759"W. | 25 | 40°08'07.123"N., 74°45'20.516"W. |
| 8 | 40°02'23.723N., 74°59'19.180"W. | 26 | 40°08'04.268"N., 74°44'39.876"W. |
| 9 | 40°03'25.117"N., 74°57'35.737"W. | 27 | 40°08'07.019"N., 74°44'27.290"W. |
| 10 | 40°04'13.742"N., 74°55'38.945"W. | 28 | 40°08'46.918"N., 74°43'25.705"W. |
| 11 | 40°04'14.614"N., 74°55'38.723"W. | 29 | 40°09'00.479"N., 74°43'18.242"W. |
| 12 | 40°04'42.395"N., 74°53'07.505"W. | 30 | 40°09'39.424"N., 74°43'19.247"W. |
| 13 | 40°04'55.186"N., 74°51'48.902"W. | 31 | 40°10'40.796"N., 74°44'16.307"W. |
| 14 | 40°05'29.897"N., 74°51'24.408"W. | 32 | 40°10'49.501"N., 74°44'31.189"W. |
| 15 | 40°05'37.691"N., 74°51'13.518"W. | 33 | 40°10'56.968"N., 74°44'59.374"W. |
| 16 | 40°05'56.281"N., 74°50'29.738"W. | 34 | 40°11'09.568"N., 74°45'17.399"W. |
| 17 | 40°06'15.872"N., 74°50'09.103"W. | 35 | 40°11'19.824"N., 74°45'23.753"W. |
| 18 | 40°07'25.194"N., 74°49'39.799"W. | 36 | 40°11'31.650"N., 74°45'26.993"W. |

the precautionary area, thence a northwesterly course for an additional 4.5 miles leads to the pilot boarding area. Depths in the traffic lane are 58 feet or more.

(39) **Southeastern Directed Traffic Area, Cape Henlopen to Delaware Traffic Lane (outbound)**—The southeastward exit by outbound vessels is southwestward of Delaware Traffic Lane Lighted Buoy DC (38°43'47"N., 74°57'33"W.) in the traffic lane that expands from 1 mile to 2 miles wide. By entering the traffic lane 1 mile southwestward of Lighted Whistle Buoy DC, a course of **145°** follows the centerline of the outbound traffic lane. When seaward of Delaware Lighted Horn Buoy D, steer usual courses to destination. Depths in the traffic lane are 48 feet or more.

(40) **Separation Zone**—The southeastern separation zone between the inbound and outbound traffic lanes is 1 mile wide centered on a line through Delaware Lighted Buoy D and three lighted buoys 6.7, 13.6 and 20.6 miles, respectively, on a bearing of **323°** from Delaware Lighted Buoy D.

(41) An additional Traffic Separation Scheme has been established to better separate large inbound vessels from tug and barge traffic transiting easterly and northerly along New Jersey coastal route just northward of Five Fathom Bank to Cape Henlopen Traffic Lane. The scheme consists of a two-way traffic lane. The lane has a 0.5 mile width and a least known depth of 30 feet. For purposes of INTERNATIONAL RULE 10, this additional scheme has been adopted by the IMO. (See **Traffic Separation Scheme**, chapter 1, and **33 CFR 167**, chapter 2, for additional information.)

(42) A **Regulated Navigation Area** has been established in Delaware Bay and River. (See **33 CFR 165.1** through **165.13**, and **165.510**, chapter 2, for limits and regulations.)

(43)

### Channels

(44) Delaware Bay is shallow along its northeastern and southwestern sides, and there are extensive shoal areas close to the main channel. The bay has natural depths of 50 feet or more for a distance of 5 miles above the Capes; thence Federal project depths of 40 feet to the upper end of Newbold Island, 110 miles above the Capes, thence 25 feet to the Trenton Marine Terminal, 115 miles above the Capes, and thence 12 feet to the railroad bridge at Trenton. For detailed channel information and minimum depths as reported by the U.S. Army Corps of Engineers (USACE), use NOAA Electronic Navigational Charts. Surveys and channel condition reports are available through a USACE hydrographic survey website listed in Appendix A.

(45)

### Anchorages

(46) In 1993, the NOAA ship WHITING reported vessels waiting offshore before taking on pilots and proceeding into Delaware Bay often anchor in the area between the Eastern Directed Traffic Area and Southeastern Directed Traffic Area. The area has a mostly sand bottom and offers good holding ground in depths of 31 to over 100 feet.

(47) Deep-draft vessels sometimes anchor in various places along the dredged channel through the lower bay but usually continue to more sheltered areas in the upper

(55)

**METEOROLOGICAL TABLE – COASTAL AREA OFF DELAWARE BAY**
Between 38°N to 40°N and 70°W to 76°W

| WEATHER ELEMENTS | JAN | FEB | MAR | APR | MAY | JUN | JUL | AUG | SEP | OCT | NOV | DEC | YEARS OF RECORD |
|---|---|---|---|---|---|---|---|---|---|---|---|---|---|
| Wind > 33 knots [1] | 6.9 | 6.6 | 5.9 | 2.4 | 0.7 | 0.3 | 0.2 | 0.5 | 1.1 | 2.6 | 4.7 | 6.5 | 3.1 |
| Wave Height > 9 feet [1] | 14.2 | 14.6 | 11.4 | 7.0 | 2.7 | 1.3 | 0.9 | 2.6 | 3.6 | 7.3 | 9.8 | 12.7 | 7.3 |
| Visibility < 2 nautical miles [1] | 4.0 | 5.7 | 5.7 | 7.3 | 10.9 | 9.1 | 5.1 | 2.7 | 2.2 | 2.3 | 2.1 | 2.8 | 5.0 |
| Precipitation [1] | 12.1 | 11.8 | 8.6 | 6.4 | 5.7 | 4.3 | 4.0 | 4.4 | 5.1 | 5.7 | 7.6 | 9.9 | 7.0 |
| Temperature > 69° F | 0.1 | 0.2 | 0.3 | 0.6 | 3.1 | 29.2 | 84.0 | 87.8 | 54.8 | 12.8 | 1.7 | 0.3 | 24.0 |
| Mean Temperature (°F) | 42.8 | 41.9 | 45.6 | 50.3 | 57.7 | 67.3 | 74.3 | 75.3 | 70.8 | 62.7 | 55.0 | 47.1 | 58.0 |
| Temperature < 33° F [1] | 14.0 | 14.8 | 3.5 | 0.2 | 0.0 | 0.0 | 0.0 | 0.0 | 0.0 | 0.0 | 0.2 | 4.9 | 3.0 |
| Mean RH (%) | 78 | 78 | 78 | 80 | 84 | 85 | 84 | 82 | 79 | 77 | 77 | 76 | 80 |
| Overcast or Obscured [1] | 43.7 | 41.0 | 36.7 | 32.4 | 31.8 | 28.4 | 24.4 | 21.3 | 23.2 | 25.0 | 31.2 | 38.9 | 31.2 |
| Mean Cloud Cover (8ths) | 5.6 | 5.4 | 4.9 | 4.4 | 4.5 | 4.4 | 4.4 | 4.3 | 4.2 | 4.4 | 4.9 | 5.4 | 4.7 |
| Mean SLP (mbs) | 1017 | 1017 | 1016 | 1016 | 1016 | 1016 | 1016 | 1017 | 1018 | 1018 | 1018 | 1018 | 1017 |
| Ext. Max. SLP (mbs) | 1047 | 1047 | 1039 | 1040 | 1039 | 1036 | 1034 | 1035 | 1037 | 1043 | 1043 | 1046 | 1047 |
| Ext. Min. SLP (mbs) | 982 | 978 | 978 | 984 | 988 | 991 | 996 | 995 | 994 | 989 | 986 | 986 | 978 |
| Prevailing Wind Direction | NW | NW | NW | SW | SW | SW | SW | SW | NE | N | NW | NW | SW |
| Thunder and Lightning [1] | 0.5 | 0.4 | 0.7 | 0.5 | 0.9 | 1.2 | 1.9 | 2.0 | 1.4 | 0.8 | 0.7 | 0.6 | 1.0 |

[1] Percentage Frequency

bay and river. General, explosives, quarantine and naval anchorages are in Delaware Bay and Delaware River. (See **33 CFR 110.1** and **110.157**, chapter 2, for limits and regulations.)

(48) Mariners are warned that submarine cables are in the north corner of the anchorage on the northeast side of New Castle Range. Furthermore, submerged pipelines are in the southwest part of the anchorage on the southeast side of Marcus Hook Range and in the middle of the anchorage southeast of Mifflin Range.

(49) In bad weather tows and small craft sometimes anchor behind the breakwaters north and west of Cape Henlopen.

(50)
**Current**

(51) The current velocity is 1.8 knots in Delaware Bay entrance. See the Tidal Current prediction service at *tidesandcurrents.noaa.gov* for specific information about times, directions, and velocities of the current at numerous locations throughout the area. Links to a user guide for this service can be found in chapter 1 of this book. The tables also list current differences and other constants for about 55 other places in Delaware Bay and River.

(52)
**Weather**

(53) Strong northwesterlies are prevalent from November through March; gales are encountered about 1 to 3 percent of the time. It has been reported that with sustained northwesterlies over an extended period of time, lower than predicted low tides may occur in Delaware Bay and River and its tributaries. Seas build to 10 feet (3 m) or more about 1 percent of the time from November through March. High seas are most likely with northwest or southeast winds. Average seas run 3 feet (0.9 m) from October through March. During the summer, prevailing

southerlies are often reinforced by the sea breeze and afternoon windspeeds may reach 15 to 25 knots. Strong easterly or southeasterly winds sometimes cause high tides in the Delaware Bay and River, resulting in the flooding of lowlands and damage to bay and river front properties.

(54) Visibility is generally good although sometimes hampered by fog, precipitation, smoke and haze. During the spring and early summer advection fog is carried into the bay on east and southeast winds; they can occur when a front stalls to the south or the Bermuda High is displaced northward. These fogs can be tenacious; they often lift somewhat during the day, particularly near the shore. Visibilities are worst from December through June. Fog is most frequent during April, May and June when visibilities drop below 0.2 mile (0.4 km) and about 3 percent of the time. Visibility of 2 miles (4 km) or less is most likely in January and February due to the greater frequency of precipitation, particularly snow. Fog is less likely in July, August and September.

(56)
**Ice**

(57) In ordinary winters there is usually sufficient ice in Delaware Bay and River to be of some concern to navigation. Thin ice has been known to form early in December between Chester and Philadelphia, but the heavier ice usually does not begin to run before January. The tidal currents keep the ice in motion, except where it packs in the narrower parts of the river; tugs and larger vessels from Philadelphia keep these parts of the river open. The ice usually packs heavier than elsewhere at Ship John Shoal, at Pea Patch Island, at Deepwater Point and below Gloucester City. Ice is rarely encountered after the early part of March.

(58) In severe winters, navigation has occasionally been interrupted above Chester, but the powerful vessels

employed in the foreign and coasting trade keep the channel fairly open.

<sup>(59)</sup>
### Freshets

<sup>(60)</sup>
Freshets are of rare occurrence, except in the vicinity of Trenton, and do not interfere with navigation unless accompanied by ice. Freshets and ice above Philadelphia are discussed further in the latter part of this chapter.

<sup>(61)</sup>
### Pilotage, Delaware Bay and River

<sup>(62)</sup>
Pilotage on Delaware Bay, Delaware River and tributaries thereof is compulsory for all foreign vessels of 100 gross tons or more and all U.S. vessels under register engaged in the foreign trade or commerce of 100 gross tons or more. Pilotage is optional for all U.S. Government vessels and for all U.S. vessels in the coastwise trade that have on board a pilot licensed by the Federal Government for these waters.

<sup>(63)</sup>
Pilot services are provided on a 24-hour basis by the Pilots' Association for the Bay and River Delaware, Chesapeake and Interstate Pilots Association (Federal Pilots) and Interport Pilots Agency, Inc. (Federal Pilots).

<sup>(64)</sup>
The Pilots' Association for the Bay and River Delaware maintains its office in Philadelphia, PA, a pilot station in Lewes, DE, and a pilot watch tower on Cape Henlopen. The office address is 800 South Columbus Blvd., Philadelphia, PA 19147; telephone, 215–465–8340; fax, 215–465–3970; cable, DELPILOTS in Philadelphia; and email address: dispatch@delpilots.com. The pilot station address is 41 Cape Henlopen Drive, Lewes, DE 19958; telephone, 302–645–2228; fax, 302–645–7822. The pilot watch tower at Cape Henlopen's telephone number is 302–645–8538; fax, 302–645–1728. Pilots are generally arranged for in advance through ships' agents and board incoming vessels from the pilot boat in the pilot boarding area off Cape Henlopen. Vessels are requested to contact pilots when inbound at either Delaware Lighted Buoy D or Five Fathom Bank Lighted Buoy F; both buoys are equipped with AIS. Vessels not requiring pilots are requested to contact "Cape Henlopen Tower" one hour prior to entering or departing Delaware Bay.

<sup>(65)</sup>
The pilot boats are 50 feet long with black hulls and white houses with the word "PILOT" in large letters on each side. The pilot station and pilot boats may be contacted on VHF-FM channels 14 and 16. The pilots carry portable radiotelephones for bridge-to-bridge communications on VHF-FM channel 13.

<sup>(66)</sup>
The Pilots' Association for the Bay and River Delaware also provides qualified offshore "advisors" for the deepest draft vessels between Lighted Buoy "D" and the anchorage areas in Delaware Bay. A notice of 24 hours before estimated arrival is requested for this service.

<sup>(67)</sup>
The Chesapeake and Interstate Pilots Association offers pilot services to U.S. vessels engaged in the coastwise trade and to public vessels between Cape Henlopen, Philadelphia and Delair. Arrangements for pilots are made through ships' agents or the pilot office in Norfolk (telephone, 757–855–2733). Pilots use commercial launch services and will meet vessels in the Pilotage Area off Cape Henlopen. Pilots arrive at the launch one hour prior to arrival and monitor VHF-FM channel 16 one hour prior to last ETA. Cellular telephone confirmation with the pilot office in Norfolk or the launch service can be made at 302–422–7604 if radio contact is unsuccessful. Advance pilot ordering with a 6-hour ETA update and any subsequent changes is requested.

<sup>(68)</sup>
The Interport Pilots Agency, Inc. offers pilotage to public vessels and private vessels in the coastal trade transiting the Delaware Bay and River, Chesapeake and Delaware Canal, Upper Chesapeake Bay, New York Harbor, Long Island Sound and other areas along the northeast coast. Arrangements for their services are made 24 hours in advance through the ship's agents or by contacting Interport Pilots Agency, Inc., 906 Port Monmouth Road, Port Monmouth, NJ 17758–0236, telephone 732–787–5554 (24 hours), or by e-mail at interport@verizon.net. Additional information about Interport Pilots can be obtained at *interportpilots.com*.

<sup>(69)</sup>
Pilots meet vessels at the pilot boarding area off Cape Henlopen using Delaware Bay Launch Service, which monitors VHF-FM channels 16 and 9. Their (24 hour) phone number is: 302–422–7604. Additional information about Delaware Bay Launch Service may be found at *delawarebaylaunch.com*.

<sup>(70)</sup>
Vessels entering Delaware Bay with drafts of 35 feet or more should use the **Delaware to Cape Henlopen Traffic Lane**.

<sup>(71)</sup>
**The Ports of Philadelphia Maritime Exchange**, in cooperation with the **Pilots Association for the Bay and River Delaware**, has established a communication and information system for vessels operating in the Delaware Bay and rivers. The lower bay area is monitored by "Cape Henlopen Tower" and the upper bay and rivers are handled by Ports of Philadelphia Maritime Exchange. Ship reporting services are provided through these two stations on VHF-FM channel 14. VHF-FM channels 20 and 74 are also used for port operations. Vessels are requested to pass information related to position, ETA, docking instructions, arriving/departing piers or anchorages in the upper bay and river to the Ports of Philadelphia Maritime Exchange.

<sup>(72)</sup>
To obtain the maximum benefits of this service, ships are requested to monitor VHF channels 14 and 16 while transiting Delaware Bay and River.

<sup>(73)</sup>
### Towage

<sup>(74)</sup>
A large fleet of tugs operating out of Philadelphia is available at any time of the day or night for any type service required. Most of the tugboat companies will dispatch their vessels to any place in Delaware Bay or its tributaries. Some of the companies also have tugs available for deep-sea towing.

(75)

### Quarantine, customs, immigration and agricultural quarantine

(76)      (See chapter 3, Vessel Arrival Inspections, and appendix for addresses.)

(77)      **Quarantine** is enforced in accordance with regulations of the U.S. Public Health Service. (See Public Health Service, chapter 1.) Vessels subject to boarding for quarantine inspection and destined to points above Marcus Hook are required to anchor off the Marcus Hook boarding station. Detention cases are taken to Philadelphia General Hospital. (See **33 CFR 110.1 and 110.157**, chapter 2, for quarantine anchorage regulations and limits.)

(78)      Philadelphia is a **customs port of entry**.

(79)

### Supplies

(80)      Bunker oil is available in quantity at Philadelphia and at several other places. Most large vessels are bunkered from barges alongside. Fresh water is unlimited in the larger ports. Small craft can obtain fuel and supplies not only in the larger ports, but at many of the smaller cities and towns along the river and bay.

(81)

### Repairs

(82)      The largest shipyard along Delaware River is at Chester. Many of the other cities and towns have boatyards for small craft.

(83)

## ENC - US5DE10M
## Chart - 12216

(84)      Delaware Breakwater is the popular name for the anchorage areas behind the outer and inner breakwaters north and west of Cape Henlopen. Harbor of Refuge is the outer and deeper of the two areas; Breakwater Harbor is the inner area.

(85)      **Harbor of Refuge** is behind the breakwater that begins 0.7 mile north of Cape Henlopen and extends 1.3 miles in a north-northwestward direction. A line of ice breakers, marked by lights at the outer ends, extends 0.4 mile in a west-southwest direction onto **The Shears** from a position 0.4 mile northwestward of the north end of the breakwater. **Harbor of Refuge Light** (38°48'52"N., 75°05'33"W.), 72 feet above the water, is shown from a white conical tower on a cylindrical substructure near the south end of the breakwater; the station has a sound signal. A light marks the breakwater near its northern end.

(86)      The harbor has depths of 17 to 70 feet between the breakwater and a shoal ridge, 8 to 12 feet deep, 1 mile to the southwestward. The deepest water is behind the Harbor of Refuge Light. The entrance from southeastward is deep and clear, while that from northwestward across The Shears has depths of 10 feet or less. Harbor of Refuge affords good protection during easterly gales. A strong set into Harbor of Refuge reportedly occurs across the southern entrance during tidal floods.

(87)      **Breakwater Harbor**, between the inner breakwater and the shore, is excellent for light-draft vessels in all weather except heavy northwesterly gales and even then affords considerable protection. A **naval restricted area** is in the eastern part of the harbor. (See **33 CFR 334.110**, chapter 2, for limits and regulations.)

(88)      The inner breakwater begins 0.3 mile southwest of the tip of Cape Henlopen and extends 0.8 mile in a west-northwest direction. A light is shown from a skeleton tower on the west end of the breakwater. A dangerous sunken wreck, covered 15 feet, is about 0.3 mile 300° from this light.

(89)      The Lewes terminal of the **Cape May-Lewes Ferry** is in the basin at the southwest end of Breakwater Harbor, 1.3 miles southwest of Delaware Breakwater Light. The basin is protected on its west side by a breakwater marked by private lights. Mariners are advised that the ferry maintains daily service between Lewes, DE, and Cape May, NJ. Mariners are also advised not to impede the ferries while they are maneuvering near the ferry terminal or proceeding inbound and outbound via the Breakwater Harbor and the Harbor of Refuge. A private sound signal is located on the main operating pier and private vessels are prohibited from docking at the ferry terminal. All ferries are equipped with AIS and monitor VHF-FM channels 13 and 16 while operating. More information about the ferry may be obtained at *capemaylewesferry. com*.

(90)

## ENC - US4DE12M
## Chart - 12304

(91)      The low, marshy southwestern shore of Delaware Bay has few prominent marks above Cape Henlopen. There are scattered groups of houses, a few observation towers and the lights and ranges of the tributaries.

(92)      The tributaries are narrow and crooked, and vessels have difficulty making some of the turns. These streams are little used except by local fishing boats and by vessels carrying petroleum products to the towns along the banks. Strangers seldom attempt to enter. When entering or leaving these tributaries, allowance should be made for the bay currents that set across the entrances and have considerable velocity at times.

(93)      There are many shoal spots with depths as shallow as 2 to 6 feet between Cape Henlopen and Bombay Hook Point (39°18.7'N., 75°26.5'W.). Most of the spots are unmarked and are subject to some change, both in depth and position. Strangers should proceed with caution in any of the passages southwest of the ship channel.

(94)      Buoys mark a passage along the southwestern side of Delaware Bay from a point about 7.7 miles northwestward of Cape Henlopen and about 3 miles offshore to the entrance to Murderkill River. The many fish and oyster

stakes in the area are to be avoided. The passage should not be attempted at night.

(95)      Vessels entering the southwestern passage from northward usually leave the main ship channel about 2.5 miles below Ship John Shoal Light and head in a southerly direction for a position (39°04.0'N., 75°20.8'W.) about 1.4 miles east of Murderkill River Entrance Approach Light 1. A depth of about 7 feet can be carried through this passage, but care must be taken to avoid the 4 to 6 feet shoal spots about 3 miles off Port Mahon and the 5-foot shoal 3.3 miles off Little River.

(96)      Roosevelt Inlet, 3 miles west of Cape Henlopen, is described in chapter 8.

(97)      **Mispillion River**, protected at the entrance by jetties, empties from the westward into Delaware Bay 13 miles northwest of Cape Henlopen. The jetties, about 200 feet apart, extend about 1 mile southeastward from shore and are marked at the seaward ends by lights. The river is used by pleasure and fishing craft and oil barges bound for **Milford.**

(98)
### Current
(99)      The current velocity is 1.5 knots on the flood and 1.0 knot on the ebb. In 1980, it was reported that current velocities up to 3 knots on the flood and 4 knots on the ebb may be encountered in the river. Occasional periods of lower than normal low water levels were encountered.

(100)
### Small-craft facilities
(101)      Small-craft facilities on Mispillion River, just above the fixed bridges about 1 mile below Milford, can provide gasoline, diesel fuel and water. The oil terminal about 1 mile below Milford has about 5 feet alongside, and the wharves at Milford have 5 to 7 feet alongside, mud bottom. A boatyard with a 25-ton mobile lift is just east of the bascule bridge at Milford. A marine railway just below the fixed highway bridge at Milford can haul out craft up to 55 feet for repairs.

(102)      Just inside the jetties, a dredged channel known as **Cedar Creek** extends southward for about 1 mile to a point just beyond the State Route 36 highway bridge. There are small-craft facilities and marinas on both sides of the bridge.

(103)

**Structures across Mispillion River**

| Name | Type | Location | Clearances (feet) Horizontal | Clearances (feet) Vertical* |
|---|---|---|---|---|
| Overhead cable | power | 38°57'21"N., 75°23'37"W. | | 57 |
| Coastal Highway bridges | fixed | 38°55'02"N., 75°24'11"W. | 124 | 25 |
| North Rehobeth Boulevard bridge **See Note 1** | bascule | 38°55'03"N., 75°25'58"W. | 45 | 5 |
| Overhead cable | power | 38°55'02"N., 75°25'05"W. | | 45 |
| Pedestrian bridge | fixed | 38°54'48"N., 75°25'30"W. | 59 | 8 |

**Structures across Mispillion River**

| Name | Type | Location | Clearances (feet) Horizontal | Clearances (feet) Vertical* |
|---|---|---|---|---|

*Clearances are referenced to Mean High Water
**Note 1** – See **33 CFR 117.1** through **117.59** and **117.237**, chapter 2, for drawbridge regulations.

(104)
### Danger zone
(105)      A **danger zone** of a naval aircraft bombing area is within a circular area offshore of **Milford Neck**, just north of the entrance to Mispillion River. (See **33 CFR 334.120**, chapter 2, for limits and regulations.)

(106)      **Murderkill River**, 21 miles northwestward of Cape Henlopen, is used by fishing vessels and a few pleasure craft. A piling, which uncovers 3 feet, is on the northwest edge of the entrance channel at about 39°03'40"N., 75°23'22"W.

(107)      A **247.7°** lighted range, a light and buoys mark the entrance to Murderkill River.

(108)      **Bowers Beach**, a summer resort on the north side of the entrance to Murderkill River, is prominent from offshore. Gasoline and some marine supplies are available. The wharves along Murderkill River are used extensively by fishing and oyster boats. The overhead cables crossing the river at Bowers Beach have a clearance of 50 feet, and the overhead power cable crossing about 4.3 miles above the mouth has a clearance of 62 feet. The fixed highway bridge, 6 miles above the mouth, has a clearance of 15 feet.

(109)      **St. Jones River**, 0.5 mile north of Murderkill River, leads to the city of **Dover**, about 9.5 miles above the mouth, the capital of Delaware.

(110)
### Current
(111)      The current velocity off the entrance is about 0.7 knot.

(112)

**Structures across St. Jones River**

| Name | Type | Location | Clearances (feet) Horizontal | Clearances (feet) Vertical* |
|---|---|---|---|---|
| Overhead cable | power | 39°03'58"N., 75°24'12"W. | | 60 |
| Overhead cable | power | 39°04'47"N., 75°26'29"W. | | 56 |
| U.S. 113 bridge | fixed | 39°05'08"N., 75°27'30"W. | 50 | 24 |
| Old Lebanon Road Pedestrian bridge | fixed | 39°06'45"N., 75°30'00"W. | 29 | 6 |
| Overhead cable | power | 39°06'50"N., 75°29'58"W. | | 50 |
| St. Jones River bridge | fixed | 39°08'58"N., 75°30'06"W. | 78 | 11 |

*Clearances are referenced to Mean High Water

(113)      **Little River** (39°09.6'N., 75°24.5'W.) is 26 miles northwest of Cape Henlopen. In 1974, the controlling depth was 2 feet in the entrance channel and 1.5 feet to the fixed highway bridge at the town of **Little Creek**, 2

miles above the river mouth. An overhead power cable with a clearance of 52 feet crosses the river 0.2 mile below the fixed highway bridge.

(114)     **Mahon River** empties into Delaware Bay at **Port Mahon**, 27 miles northwest of Cape Henlopen. The river is used by commercial fishing boats and small fuel barges. The controlling depth is about 8 feet in the marked entrance channel with deeper water inside. The Dover Air Force Base fuel pier, about 200 feet long with reported depths of 10 feet along the east side, is on the west side of the entrance. Some marine supplies can be obtained at the landing 0.4 mile above the mouth. A State-maintained boat launching facility with floating piers is on the west side of the river 0.8 mile above the mouth.

(115)     **Leipsic River**, 30 miles northwestward of Cape Henlopen, is used occasionally by fishermen. In 1980, the reported depths were 5 feet in the entrance and deeper water inside to Leipsic, 7 miles above the mouth. The entrance is marked by a light. The wharves at **Leipsic** have depths of 5 to 8 feet alongside. The fixed highway bridge at Leipsic has a clearance of 13 feet.

(116)     **Smyrna River** (39°22.0'N., 75°30.7'W.), 39 miles northwest of Cape Henlopen, is navigable to **Smyrna Landing**, about 8 miles above the mouth and 1 mile from the town of **Smyrna**. In 1986, the entrance bar had a reported centerline controlling depth of 4 feet; thence in 1971, the reported centerline controlling depth was 8 feet to Flemings Landing, thence in 1964, 3 feet to Smyrna Landing.

(117)     The entrance to the Smyrna River is protected by jetties. A daybeacon marks the outer end of the south jetty; ruins of the former south jetty light may be in the vicinity of the outer end of the jetty. In 1983, it was reported that the south jetty had collapsed; caution is advised. Within the river, the best water generally follows a midchannel course or favors the ebbtide bends.

(118)     The current velocity is about 1.5 knots in the entrance to Smyrna River. State Route 9 highway bridge at **Flemings Landing,** 3 miles above the mouth, has a fixed span with a clearance of 8 feet. Overhead power cables with a least clearance of 48 feet cross the river about 0.8 mile above the bridge.

(119)
**Local magnetic disturbance**
(120)     Differences of as much as 5° from the normal variation have been observed near the mouth of Smyrna River.

(121)     The New Jersey side of Delaware Bay is low, with few prominent marks. The principal tributaries are Maurice and Cohansey Rivers, which can be used as harbors of refuge by small boats going between Cape May Canal and the Chesapeake and Delaware Canal; there are also many small creeks used mostly by fishing boats. General depths along this side of the bay are 7 to 15 feet, but there are many spots with depths of less than 6 feet. The shoals generally are not marked, and some local knowledge is needed to avoid them. Most of the creeks have bars across their mouths.

(122)
**Tides and currents**
(123)     The channels have strong currents, and many tide rips form near Prissy Wicks Shoal. In unmarked Cape May Channel, the current velocity is 1.5 knots on the flood and 2.3 knots on the ebb. In the channel immediately northwestward of Overfalls Shoal, the velocity is 2 knots on the flood and 1.9 knots on the ebb.

(124)     **Cape May Canal**, 2 miles northward of Cape May Light, is described in chapter 5 in connection with the Intracoastal Waterway. Farther north are several creeks. The first of any importance to navigation is **Bidwell Creek** (39°07.7'N., 74°53.4'W.), a drainage canal 12 miles north-northeastward of Cape May Light; a light marks the jetties at the entrance. Strong currents may be encountered at and inside the entrance jetties, and entry at night during bad weather is extremely hazardous.

(125)     **Deadman Shoal**, 9 miles north-northwestward of Cape May Light, has a minimum depth of 5 feet; the shoal is marked by a lighted buoy.

(126)     **Dennis Creek**, 14 miles north-northeastward of Cape May Light, has depths of about 2 feet over the flats at the mouth and much deeper water inside. The creek is navigable for a considerable distance but has no commerce and is little used.

(127)     **Maurice River** flows into the northeast corner of **Maurice River Cove** 17 miles north-northwestward of Cape May Light. **East Point,** on the east side of the entrance, is marked by a light. Large shellfish plants are along the lower part of the river; shipbuilding facilities are at Dorchester.

(128)     Maurice River is entered through a partially dredged crooked channel that passes east of **Fowler Island**, which is in about the middle of the river's mouth. The northernmost section passing east of the island has natural depths.

(129)     When approaching Maurice River, mariners should use care and not confuse the structure of East Point Light with a private house with a tower about 1.3 miles to the east; both landmarks are similar in appearance.

(130)     The entrance channel is marked by lighted and unlighted buoys. The river channel above Mauricetown to Millville is marked by seasonal buoys.

(131)     For about 15 miles above the mouth of Maurice River, the channel is easily followed, but a sharp lookout is necessary to avoid stakes and dolphins extending into the river, many of which are broken off and covered at high water. Without local knowledge, it is safer to navigate this part of the river on a rising tide and proceed with caution. The upper part is narrow but not difficult to navigate when the buoys are on station.

(132)
**Current**
(133)     The current velocity is about 1 knot in the entrance and about 2.3 knots at Mauricetown; at Millville, the

flood is very weak and the ebb velocity is 0.4 knot. Owing to dereliction of the dikes along the river, greater current velocities have been reported; extreme care is required in docking.

(134)
### Ice

(135)    Ice may be encountered on Maurice River from the latter part of December through the early part of March.

(136)    The shellfish industry is concentrated along the lower part of Maurice River with plants at the towns of **Bivalve**, **Port Norris** and **Shell Pile**, about 3 miles above the mouth. The wharves have depths greater than 7 feet alongside. Gasoline is available.

(137)    A marina on the west side of the river about 3.5 miles above the mouth has berthing with water and electricity, a 20-foot boat ramp, gasoline, diesel fuel, ice and marine supplies. Hull and engine repairs can be made. A 50-foot marine railway and a 12-ton mobile hoist are available.

(138)
### Small-craft facilities

(139)    There is a small-craft facility at Bivalve, on the east side of the river about 3 miles above the mouth, and several other facilities on the east side of the river from about 4.5 miles to 6 miles above the mouth. Most of these facilities can provide gasoline, diesel fuel, berths and marine supplies.

(140)    The shipyard at **Dorchester**, 9 miles above the mouth of Maurice River, has a 165-foot railway. A marina at Dorchester has gasoline, slips, a 60-foot marine railway and a 20-ton mobile hoist. Hull and engine repairs can be made at all of the facilities.

(141)    At **Mauricetown**, 10 miles above the mouth of Maurice River, there is a fixed highway bridge with a clearance of 25 feet. The overhead power cable 300 yards southward has a clearance of 60 feet.

(142)    **Port Elizabeth** is 1 mile up **Manumuskin River** and about 12 miles above the mouth of Maurice River. About 1.5 miles above Port Elizabeth on Maurice River is a boatyard with a 40-foot marine railway; hull and engine repairs can be made.

(143)    **Millville**, 20 miles above the mouth of Maurice River, has several factories but no municipal docks. An overhead power cable about 1 mile south of Millville has a clearance of 67 feet. The fixed highway bridge at Millville has a clearance of 4 feet and is the head of navigation.

(144)    **Egg Island Point** (39°10.8'N., 75°08.2'W.), 17 miles north-northwest of Cape May Light, is marked by a light. Southward of the point are **Egg Island Flats**, which have depths of 5 to 9 feet. The flats are thick with oyster-bed stakes. Between Egg Island Point and the inner end of the flats is a natural channel, with depths of 7 feet, used by local boats.

(145)    **Fortescue Creek** is 4 miles north-northwestward of Egg Island Point. The entrance channel is marked by a lighted buoy, and an unlighted buoy marks the end of a jetty at the mouth. **Fortescue**, a small summer settlement on the south side of the highway bridge, 0.4 mile above the entrance, offers gasoline, diesel fuel and some supplies. Near the bridge are two marine railways that can haul out boats up to 45 feet.

(146)    **Nantuxent Point**, 8 miles northwestward of Egg Island Point, is on the southeast side of the entrance of **Nantuxent Cove**. The point is marked by a light.

(147)    **Nantuxent Creek**, on the north side of Nantuxent Point, has depths of about 5 feet in the mouth and is navigable at high water by local fishing boats for about 5 miles.

(148)    A small-craft facility is at **Money Island**, a town about 1.2 miles above the mouth. Gasoline, berths and limited marine supplies are available here.

(149)    **Back Creek**, 27 miles northwest of Cape May Light and 2 miles northwestward of Nantuxent Point, is used by local boats as an anchorage. The creek has depths of about 5 feet over the flats at the entrance and good depths for several miles above; however, local knowledge is advised. Berths, gasoline and marine supplies are available at a landing 5 miles above the mouth. Hull and engine repairs can be made; lift, 6 tons.

(150)    **Ben Davis Point** is on the northwest side of the entrance to Nantuxent Cove. **Ben Davis Point Shoal**, 2.5 miles south-southwest of the point and within 0.4 mile of the main channel through the bay has depths of 7 to 10 feet.

(151)    **Cohansey River**, which empties into the northeast side of Delaware Bay 31 miles northwestward of Cape May Light, is used mostly by pleasure craft, although some petroleum is transported to Bridgeton. **Cohansey Light** (39°20'30"N., 75°21'41"W.), 42 feet above the water, is shown from a black skeleton tower with a black and white daymark on the south side near the natural entrance. A dredged cut through the narrow neck of land on which the light stands gives a more direct approach to the river; the cut, 0.3 mile northwest of Cohansey Light, is marked on its west side by a light. The river is unmarked above the dredged cut.

(152)    The usual approach to Cohansey River is along the axis of the dredged cut, but the natural channel eastward of Cohansey Light is sometimes used; the latter has a controlling depth of about 7 feet, and unmarked shoals with depths of 4 to 6 feet must be avoided on either side. Local knowledge is advised when using this approach and in the dredged channel in the upper part of the river off Bridgeton.

(153)
### Current

(154)    High water at Bridgeton is about 2 hours later than at the entrance. The current velocity is about 1.3 knots half a mile above the entrance and less than 0.5 knot at Bridgeton.

(155)
### Small-craft facilities

(156)    There are small-craft facilities near **Greenwich Pier**, 4 miles above the mouth, and at **Fairton**, 14 miles above

(161)

Delaware River (Delaware Memorial Bridge)
Image courtesy of Waterway Images (2006)

the mouth. Gasoline, diesel fuel and marine supplies are available; lift of 30 tons can handle hull and engine repairs.

(157)    **Bridgeton**, about 17 miles above the mouth, is an important manufacturing town and rail center but has no municipal piers or marinas. Broad Street bridge at Bridgeton has a 40-foot bascule span and a clearance of 6 feet but is kept in a closed position. (See **33 CFR 117.711**, chapter 2, for drawbridge regulations.) The overhead power cable 0.2 mile below the bridge has a clearance of 44 feet.

(158)
**ENC - US5DE13M**
**Chart - 12311**

(159)    **Bay Side** (39°22.8'N., 75°24.2'W.) is a fishing resort on the east side of the entrance to **Stow Creek**. The creek has very little traffic.

(160)    The dividing line between **Delaware River** and Delaware Bay is 42 miles above the Delaware Capes. The line, defined arbitrarily by the legislatures of Delaware and New Jersey, extends from a monument on **Liston Point**, DE, to a similar monument on the south side of the entrance to **Hope Creek**, NJ.

(162)
**Bridges**

(163)    For regulations affecting drawbridges crossing the Delaware River see **33 CFR 117.1** through **117.59**, **117.716**, and **117.904**, chapter 2.

(164)    **Artificial Island**, Mile 44E, is the name given to the peninsula formed by the filled area covering most of **Baker Shoal**. The domes of the Salem Nuclear Power Plant, at the south end of the island, are prominent from upstream and downstream. An unmarked channel leads to a basin south of the powerplant. In 1980, 18 feet was reported in the channel and basin.

(165)
**Local magnetic disturbance**

(166)    Differences of as much as 2° to 5° from normal variation have been observed along the channel from Artificial Island to Marcus Hook.

(167)    **Alloway Creek**, Mile 47.5E, has a controlling depth of about 3 feet to Quinton. The approach to Alloway Creek is unmarked. The shoals on either side of the mouth must be avoided. Above the mouth, the best water is not always in midstream, and some local knowledge is needed to find it. The current velocity is 2.1 knots 0.2 mile above the entrance and about 1.4 knots at New Bridge.

(168)

**Structures across Alloway Creek**

| Name | Type | Location | Clearances (feet) Horizontal | Clearances (feet) Vertical* |
|---|---|---|---|---|
| Overhead cable | power | 39°29'50"N., 75°31'03"W. | | 80 |
| Overhead cable | power | 39°30'32"N., 75°27'38"W. | | 50 |
| Hancocks bridge*** | swing | 39°30'32"N., 75°27'39"W. | 40** | 4 |
| Upper Hancocks bridge*** | swing | 39°31'40"N., 75°27'04"W. | 35 | 3 |
| Overhead cable | power | 39°32'54"N., 75°24'54"W. | | 50 |
| State Route 49 bridge*** | swing | 39°32'53"N., 75°24'54"W. | 30 | 3 |

\* Clearances are referenced to Mean High Water
\*\* Clearance is for the north draw
\*\*\* See **33 CFR 117.1** through **117.59** and **117.701**, chapter 2, for regulations.

(169)     **Salem River** is entered through **Salem Cove** at Mile 50E, across the Delaware River from the entrance to the Chesapeake and Delaware Canal. The approach channel follows the southeast side of Salem Cove for about 2 miles to the mouth of the river; it is marked by a lighted buoy, lights and a directional light. Within the river, the channel enters a land cut 0.8 mile above the mouth, thence leads to a basin at **Salem**, thence to the fixed highway bridge in Salem. The channel and basin have a Federal project depth of 16 feet. (See Notice to Mariners and latest edition of charts for controlling depths.)

(170)
**Tides and currents**

(171)     The tides at Salem are about 35 minutes later than at Reedy Island. The current velocity is about 1.6 knots in the entrance. The maximum expected current in the land cut is 3 knots.

(172)     An overhead power cable near the mouth of the river has a clearance of 66 feet. State Route 49 highway bridge, crossing the river near Salem, has a fixed span with a clearance of 10 feet. (See **33 CFR 117.1** through **117.59** and **117.749**, chapter 2, for drawbridge regulations.) An overhead power cable just above the bridge has a clearance of 59 feet.

(173)     Several marinas and boatyards are along the north bend of Salem River and at Salem; slips, gasoline and some marine supplies are available; hull and engine repairs can be made. Mobile lifts up to 25 tons are available along Salem River.

(174)     **Appoquinimink River** (39°26.9'N., 75°34.7'W.), Mile 44W, has no commerce and is little used except by pleasure craft and a few fishing boats. The current velocity in the entrance is about 1.1 knots. The fixed highway bridge, 3 miles above the mouth, has a width of 37 feet and a clearance of 6 feet. The fixed highway bridge at **Odessa**, 5.5 miles above the mouth, has a width of 38 feet and a clearance of 4 feet. Overhead power cables across the river have a minimum clearance of 45 feet.

(175)     **Reedy Island**, Mile 48W, is the site of a former Federal quarantine and detention station. The pier on the channel side of the island has a depth of 10 feet at the outer end; the current velocity is about 2.5 knots off the pier. A submerged dike extends 3 miles southward from Reedy Island and roughly parallels the western shore; the dike is marked by lights and unlighted seasonal warning buoys.

(176)     **Port Penn** is a village on the western shore opposite Reedy Island. The best approach to the village is through a gap in the Reedy Island dike. The gap, 0.2 mile south of the island, is 5 feet deep and 150 feet wide and marked on the north side by a light and a daybeacon on the south side. Approaches to the village from north of Reedy Island or from south of the dike are over flats with depths of 2 feet. Anchorage depths off Port Penn are 15 feet or more, but in 1980, none of the landings at the village were usable.

(177)     The **Chesapeake and Delaware Canal**, Mile 51W, is described in chapter 7.

(178)     **Pea Patch Island**, Mile 53W, is the site of **Fort Delaware State Park**. The wharf, on the main channel, is marked by a light. In 1983, the wharf was in ruins. In 2002, shoaling to 7 feet was reported at the channel entrance. A dike, mostly submerged at high water, extends northward along **Bulkhead Shoal** for about 3 miles from Pea Patch Island; the dike is marked by lights and daymarkers. A private sound signal and racon are located on an overhead power cable tower about 0.8 mile north of Pea Patch Island. The current velocity is 2.3 knots in the main channel east of the island. A ferry runs between Delaware City and Pea Patch Island on weekends, April through October.

(179)     **Delaware City** is on the southwest side of Delaware River opposite Pea Patch Island. **Delaware City Branch Channel**, marked by a light at the Delaware River entrance, extends southward from the riverfront to the Chesapeake and Delaware Canal. In 2000, the entrance channel at the Chesapeake and Delaware Canal end of the branch channel was reported to have a depth of 7 feet; a submerged pile was also reported on the west side of the channel. Mariners are cautioned to stay well inside the north and south entrance channels.

(180)     A highway bascule bridge with a clearance of 6 feet crosses the channel about 0.6 mile above the entrance; the bridge is maintained in the closed position. An overhead power cable 500 feet north of the bridge has a clearance of 64 feet; overhead power and telephone cables just south of the bridge have a clearance of 30 feet.

(181)     Berths, gasoline, diesel fuel, ice and some marine supplies are available on the west side of Delaware City Branch Channel at a marina 0.3 mile southwest of the northeast entrance. Hull and engine repairs can be made; a 25-ton mobile hoist is available.

(182)     **Bulkhead Shoal Channel**, privately maintained, extends northwestward from the Delaware River to a refinery terminal on the northwest side of Delaware City. The channel is marked, a private **306°** lighted range and private buoys. The three offshore wharves at the terminal

(192)

**Structures across Christina River**

| Name | Type | Location | Mile | Clearances (feet) Horizontal | Clearances (feet) Vertical* | Information |
|---|---|---|---|---|---|---|
| Overhead cable | power | 39°43'31"N., 75°31'58"W. | 1.3 | | 82 | |
| Interstate 495 Highway bridge | fixed | 39°43'33"N., 75°31'58"W. | 1.3 | 259 | 60 | |
| Norfolk Southern Railroad bridge | swing | 39°43'43"N., 75°32'01"W. | 1.4 | 84 | 6 | |
| Overhead cables | power | 39°43'48"N., 75°32'01"W. | 1.5 | | 80 | |
| Third Street bridge | bascule | 39°44'07"N., 75°32'27"W. | 2.3 | 145 | 20 | Note 1 |
| Walnut Street bridge | bascule | 39°44'07"N., 75°33'04"W. | 2.8 | 175 | 13 | Note 1 |
| Market Street bridge | bascule | 39°44'11"N., 75°33'14"W. | 3.0 | 175 | 8 | Note 1 |
| Overhead cable | telephone | 39°44'12"N., 75°33'20"W. | 3.1 | | 23 | |
| Norfolk Southern Railroad bridge | swing | 39°43'26"N., 75°33'37"W. | 4.1 | 62 | 6 | |
| Overhead cables | power | 39°43'26"N., 75°33'37"W. | 4.1 | | 70 | |
| Norfolk Southern Railroad bridge | swing | 39°43'23"N., 75°33'37"W. | 4.2 | 57 | 3 | |
| Overhead cable | power | 39°43'05"N., 75°34'38"W. | 5.3 | | 80 | |
| Industrial Trail Pedestrian bridge | fixed | 39°43'05"N., 75°34'40"W. | 5.4 | | | Bridge under construction |
| Interstate 95 Highway bridge | fixed | 39°43'07"N., 75°34'48"W. | 5.5 | 50 | 22 | |
| Route 141 bridge | fixed | 39°42'38"N., 75°36'29"W. | 7.5 | 93 | 28 | |
| Overhead cables | power | 39°42'38"N., 75°36'30"W. | 7.5 | | 42 | |
| James Street bridge | bascule | 39°42'38"N., 75°36'32"W. | 7.5 | 49 | 4 | |
| Overhead pipeline | | 39°42'33"N., 75°36'41"W. | 7.6 | 291 | 29 | |

*Clearances are referenced to Mean High Water
Note 1 – See 33 CFR 117.1 through 117.59 and 117.237, chapter 2, for drawbridge regulations.

(182) have a combined berthing area of 2,850 feet with dolphins. In 1984 depths of 28 to 38 feet were reported alongside with a deck height of 15 feet. The terminal has a storage capacity of 8.8 million barrels. Water is available at the wharves.

(183) The current velocity is 2.1 knots between Pea Patch Island and Delaware City.

(184) An overhead power cable with a clearance of 223 feet crosses the river about 1.5 miles above Fort Delaware. The power cable support tower, on the west side of the channel, has a private sound signal and a racon.

(185) **New Castle**, Mile 57W, has little waterborne commerce. The principal public wharf was in ruins in 1983. Several stone fenders that stand about 5 feet above high water protect the wharves from drifting ice. A 40-foot marine railway, 0.4 mile north-northeast of the public wharf, can handle boats for emergency repairs at high water.

(186) **Pennsville**, Mile 58E, has a small marina with an 8-ton mobile hoist; minor repairs can be made.

(187) A partially submerged jetty, marked by seasonal buoys, is in **Travis Cove** at about Mile 58.7E. In 2009, debris was reported spilling westward; caution is advised.

(188) **Delaware Memorial Bridge**, Mile 60, has twin suspension spans over the main channel with a clearance of 188 feet for the middle 800 feet.

(189) **Salem Canal**, at the east end of the bridges, once gave access to the upper part of Salem River. The route is now blocked in several places, the first being at a dam about 300 yards above the mouth.

(190) **Deepwater Point**, 0.6 mile above the New Jersey end of the Memorial Bridge, is the site of DuPont Chambers Works. A 550-foot offshore wharf provides 715 feet of berthing space with depths of 33 feet reported alongside and a deck height of 10.5 feet. Acids and organic chemicals are handled at the wharf.

(191) **Christina River**, Mile 61.5W, is the approach to the city of Wilmington and to the towns of Newport and Christiana.

(193)

**Channels**

(194) A Federal project provides for a 38- and 35-foot channel from Delaware River to Lobdell Canal and 38 feet in a turning basin opposite the Wilmington Marine Terminal, thence 21 feet for 2.4 miles to 39°43'38"N., 75°33'40"W, thence 10 feet to the head of the project, 3.9 miles above the mouth. The channel is subject to frequent shoaling. For detailed channel information and minimum depths as reported by the U.S. Army Corps of Engineers (USACE), use NOAA Electronic Navigational Charts. Surveys and channel condition reports are available through a USACE hydrographic survey website listed in Appendix A. A steel sheet-pile jetty, marked at its outer end by a light, is on the south side of the entrance. The entrance channel is marked by a **293°** lighted range and by a lighted buoy on the north side of the entrance.

(195) **Brandywine Creek**, on the northeast side of Christina River 1.6 miles above the mouth, has depths of about 4 feet to the railroad bridge 1 mile above its mouth. The channel is rocky above the railroad bridge,

(198)

Wilmington, Delaware
Image courtesy of Waterway Images (2006)

but depths of 1 to 2 feet can be carried 0.7 mile to Market Street bridge, above which there are rapids. The river is used mostly for anchorage and storage of pleasure boats.

(196)     An overhead power cable about 0.1 mile above the mouth has a clearance of 59 feet. The railroad bridge about 1 mile above the mouth of the creek and the highway bridges above it have fixed spans with a minimum width of 40 feet and a clearance of 10 feet. The overhead power cable 300 yards above the railroad bridge has a clearance of 34 feet.

(197)     **Wilmington**, on the north side of Christina River 2.5 miles above the mouth, has large manufacturing interests. Both sides of the river at the city are lined with wharves that support a large amount of barge traffic. The deepwater facilities, which were described earlier, are on the south side of the river just inside the entrance.

(199)     **Newport**, on the north side 6.8 miles above the mouth, is at the head of practical navigation.

(200)

### Anchorages

(201)     Vessels must not anchor in Christina River channel within the city limits of Wilmington or tie up at any wharf more than two abreast without permission of the harbor commissioners. A general anchorage is off Deepwater Point, south of the river entrance. (See **33 CFR 110.1** and **110.157**, chapter 2, for limits and regulations.)

(202)

### Weather

(203)     Wilmington is in a region about midway between the rigorous climates of the North and the mild climates of the South and located at the head of the Delaware Bay.

(204)     Rainfall distribution throughout the year is rather uniform with the spread between the wettest month (July) and the driest month (February) being only 1.42 inches (36.1 mm). The average annual precipitation for Wilmington is 41.48 inches (1,054 mm). The greatest 24-hour rainfall occurred in July 1989 when 6.63 inches (168.4 mm) fell.

(205)     Snowfall occurs on about 30 days per year on the average; however, an average of only 4 days annually produce snowfalls greater than 1.5 inches (38.1 mm). The average annual snowfall is 20.7 inches (525.8 mm). January is the snowiest month but it is trailed closely by February. The greatest 24-hour snowfall occurred in January 1996 when 22.0 inches (558.8 mm) fell.

(206)     Glaze or freezing rain occurs on an average of only once per year, generally in January or February. However, some occurrences have been noted in November and December. Some years pass without the occurrence of freezing rain, while in others it occurs on as many as 8 to 10 days.

(207)     Since 1950, eight tropical storms have influenced the Wilmington area, and the direction of approach has always been from the south through southwest.

Fortunately, all have been in the dissipation stage and no hurricane damage has been noted.

(208)     In summer, the area is under the influence of the large semipermanent high-pressure system commonly known as the Bermuda High. Based on climatology, it is usually centered over the Atlantic Ocean near latitude 30°N. This high-pressure system brings a circulation of warm, humid air masses over the area from the deep South. The proximity of large water areas and the inflow of southerly winds contribute to high relative humidities during much of the year.

(209)     January is the coldest month, and July, the warmest. The average annual temperature at Wilmington is 54.5°F (12.5°C) with an average high of 63.8°F (17.7°C) and an average low of 44.8°F (7.1°C). The warmest temperature on record at Wilmington is 102°F (38.9°C), last recorded on July 3rd and 4th, 1966. The coldest temperature on record is -14°F (-25.6°C), last recorded in January 1985. Each month, October through May, has recorded temperatures below freezing (0°C), while each month, June through September, has seen temperatures in excess of 100°F (37.8°C).

(210)
### Current
(211)     The current velocity is about 0.8 knot at Wilmington.

(212)
### Quarantine, customs, immigration and agricultural quarantine
(213)     (See chapter 3, Vessel Arrival Inspections, and appendix for addresses.)

(214)     **Quarantine** is enforced in accordance with regulations of the U.S. Public Health Service. (See Public Health Service, chapter 1.) Vessels subject to boarding for quarantine inspection are required to anchor off Marcus Hook boarding station, 7 miles up the Delaware River from Wilmington.

(215)     Wilmington is a **customs port of entry.**

(216)
### Harbor regulations
(217)     Navigation regulations state that the speed of certain vessels in Christina River is limited to 8 miles per hour. (See **33 CFR 162.35**, chapter 2, for regulations.)

(218)
### Supplies
(219)     Water can be supplied at the Wilmington Marine Terminal from the city mains. The nearest facilities for supplying deep-draft vessels with bunker oil are at Marcus Hook. Light-draft vessels can obtain fuel at a wharf on the south side of Christina River just above the second bridge; the depth at the wharf is about 8 feet. Small craft can obtain gasoline and supplies at Wilmington near the second bridge over Christina River.

(220)
### Repairs
(221)     **Repairs** can be made to light-draft vessels and small craft at the boatyards near the second bridge on Christina River; largest marine railway, 110 feet. Small-craft repairs can also be made at a boatyard above the second bridge on Brandywine Creek.

(222)
### Communications
(223)     Railroad passenger service (Amtrak) is available at the Wilmington station 5 miles from the port. The local airport is the New Castle County Airport (formerly the Greater Wilmington Airport), 5 miles southwest of Wilmington; no regular scheduled passenger service is available. The nearest airport with regular scheduled passenger service is Philadelphia International Airport, 22 miles northeast of Wilmington.

(224)
## ENC - US5PA11M
## Chart - 12312

(225)     **Carneys Point** (39°42.9'N., 75°29.1'W.), Mile 61.8E, is across the Delaware River from Christina River.

(226)
### Speed
(227)     The Corps of Engineers has requested that masters limit the speed of their vessel when passing wharves and piers so as to avoid damage by suction or wave wash to property or persons.

(228)     **Edgemoor** is at Mile 63 W. The wharves at Delmarva Power have depths of 20 feet reported at their outer ends.

(229)     A submerged groin extends 0.3 mile offshore from **Oldmans Point**. About 0.3 mile southward of the groin are the ruins of a long pier.

(230)
### Local magnetic disturbance
(231)     Differences of 2° to 5° from normal variation have been observed astride the Delaware River Channel from Oldmans Point to the mouth of Oldmans Creek.

(232)     **Oldmans Creek**, Mile 66E, has an unmarked channel leading from the Delaware River to the mouth of the creek. Due to shoaling, mariners should exercise extreme caution when transiting this area. Three fixed bridges cross the creek between the mouth and **Pedricktown,** about 3.6 miles above the mouth.

(233)     **Marcus Hook**, Mile 69N, is an important petroleum center where large quantities of crude oil are received and refined petroleum products are shipped. Vessels can be bunkered at the rate of 1,500 to 5,000 barrels per hour, and the companies also operate barges for bunkering in the stream or alongside other wharves.

(234)     On the southeast side of the main ship channel opposite Marcus Hook is a **general anchorage** with a preferential area for vessels awaiting quarantine inspection. (See **33 CFR 110.1** and **110.157**, Chapter 2, for limits and regulations.)

(235)
### Current
(236)     The current velocity is about 1.7 knots at Marcus Hook.

(245)

Delaware River (Commodore John Barry Bridge)
Image courtesy of Waterway Images (2006)

N

(237)
### Quarantine, customs, immigration, and agricultural quarantine.

(238) (See chapter 3, Vessel Arrival Inspections, and appendix for addresses.)

(239) **Quarantine** is enforced in accordance with regulations of the U.S. Public Health Service. (See Public Health Service, chapter 1.)

(240) **Raccoon Creek**, Mile 70S, is the approach to the towns of Bridgeport and Swedesboro. The creek carries some traffic in fertilizer and fertilizer materials. The approach to Raccoon Creek is a dredged channel that extends west-southwestward through the shallow flats for 1.1 miles from the mouth. A light marks the outer end of a breakwater on the south side of the entrance.

(241) The U.S. Route 130 highway bridge at **Bridgeport**, 1.5 miles above the mouth, has a vertical-lift span with clearance of 4 feet down and 64 feet up. The ConRail bridge, 0.3 mile above the highway bridge, has a swing span with a width of 38 feet and a clearance of 7 feet. (See **33 CFR 117.1** through **117.59** and **117.741**, chapter 2, for drawbridge regulations.) Gasoline and minor repairs are available at a small marina on the north bank 1 mile below the highway bridge.

(242) Between Bridgeport and **Swedesboro,** 7.1 miles above the mouth, the least bridge clearances are: swing bridge, 50 feet horizontal, 6 feet vertical; fixed bridges, 33 feet horizontal, 8 feet vertical. Overhead power cables crossing the creek between the mouth and Swedesboro have a least clearance of 64 feet.

(243) An overhead power cable across Delaware River at Mile 70.5, near the northeast end of Marcus Hook Range, has a clearance of 210 feet.

(244) The **Commodore John Barry Bridge**, a fixed highway bridge with a clearance of 181 feet for a width of 1,600 feet over the main channel and a clearance of 190 feet for the middle 822 feet of the span, crosses the Delaware River between Chester and Bridgeport at Mile 71.

(246) **Chester**, Mile 72N, is an important manufacturing center, and many of its industries use the wharf facilities along the 3-mile waterfront. The nearest designated anchorage is off Marcus Hook.

(247)
### Quarantine, customs, immigration and agricultural quarantine

(248) (See chapter 3, Vessel Arrival Inspections, and appendix for addresses.)

(249) **Quarantine** is enforced in accordance with regulations of the U.S. Public Health Service. (See Public Health Service, chapter 1.)

(250) Chester is a **customs port of entry.**

(251) Waterborne traffic to the wharves and piers in Chester consists mainly of barge traffic and light-draft vessels. The wharves have depths of 15 to 20 feet alongside, and some have as little as 5 feet. There are

storage facilities and mechanical transfer equipment, and most have rail and highway connections. Water is piped to most facilities.

(252) **Chester Creek** empties into Delaware River about at the midpoint of the city waterfront. The railroad bridge just above the mouth has a swing span with a clearance of 1.5 feet. (See **33 CFR 117.1** through **117.59** and **117.901**, chapter 2, for drawbridge regulations.)

(253) Above that point, navigation is restricted by the 6-foot minimum clearance of the fixed bridges. Navigation is suitable only for very shallow-draft boats to the second bridge, about 0.2 mile above the entrance.

(254)
### Current
(255) The current velocity is 1.7 knots on the flood and 2.2 knots on the ebb off **Eddystone,** Mile 73N.

(256) **Essington**, Mile 75N, has several boatyards that can provide berths, fuel and supplies. Major hull and minor engine repairs to small craft can be made. Maximum haul-out capacities: marine railways, 50 feet; mobile lifts, 20 tons. Between Essington and Delaware River main channel is marshy **Little Tinicum Island**, which is about 2 miles long. Local vessels usually pass around the west end of the island where the controlling depth is about 9 feet.

(257)
### Anchorages
(258) A **special anchorage** is between the Essington waterfront and Little Tinicum Island. (See **33 CFR 110.1** and **110.67**, chapter 2, for limits and regulations.) The current velocity is about 1.3 knots.

(259) Gasoline, diesel fuel, water, ice, berths and marine supplies are available along the Essington waterfront eastward of Darby Creek. Maximum haul-out capacities are: railway, 125 feet; lift, 15 tons.

(260) A **general anchorage** is between Thompson Point and Crab Point and the south side of the main channel. (See **33 CFR 110.1** and **110.157**, chapter 2, for limits and regulations.)

(261)
### Current
(262) The current velocity is about 2 knots a half-mile east of Crab Point.

(263) There are several large petroleum facilities at **Paulsboro**, Mile 77S.

(264) **Mantua Creek**, Mile 78S, passes on the east side of Paulsboro and meanders southeastward to the vicinity of **Mantua**, 7.6 miles above the mouth. There is waterborne traffic in chemicals and paper to the first bridge, above which the creek is used only by small boats. A jetty on the east side of the entrance is marked on the outer end by a light and a buoy is just inside the mouth of the creek.

(265) The fixed highway bridge about 0.8 mile above the mouth was under construction (2014). The railroad bridge 1.3 miles above the mouth has a 45-foot-wide vertical-lift span with a clearance of 1 foot down and 25 feet up. State

Route 44 highway bridge, 1.5 miles above the mouth, has a vertical-lift span with clearance of 3 feet down and 53 feet up. (See **33 CFR 117.1** through **117.59** and **117.729**, chapter 2, for drawbridge regulations.) Above this point, the fixed bridges and overhead cables have minimum clearances of 10 feet and 50 feet, respectively.

(266) The wharves below the first bridge on Mantua Creek have depths of 20 to 14 feet alongside.

(267)
### Anchorages
(268) A **general anchorage** is on the southeasterly side of the main channel above the entrance to Mantua Creek. (See **33 CFR 110.1** and **110.157**, chapter 2, for limits and regulations.)

(269)
### Current
(270) The current velocity is about 2 knots in the channel opposite the anchorage.

(271) On the northeast side of the Delaware River at Mile 78N, there are two petroleum terminals, both of which have railroad and highway connections and water.

(272) **Sun Refining and Marketing Co., Hog Island Wharf** (39°51'38"N., 75°14'19"W.) provides 2,754 feet of berthing space; 30 to 31 feet reported alongside; deck height, 16 feet; 2¾ million-barrel storage capacity; receipt of crude oil and methyl tertiary butyl; owned by the City of Philadelphia and operated by Sun Refining and Marketing Co., a subsidiary of Sun Oil Co., Inc.

(273) **Citgo Asphalt Refining Co., Paulsboro Terminal Main Wharf** (39°51'15"N., 75°13'42"W.): 40-foot face providing 1,000 feet of berthing space with mooring dolphins, 40 feet alongside; deck height, 10 feet; pipelines extend from wharf to six steel storage tanks with a capacity of 1 1/3 million barrels; receipt of crude oil and shipment of asphalt; owned and operated by Citgo Asphalt Refining Co.

(274) **Sun Pipe Line Co., Fort Mifflin Terminal Wharf, Berth A** (39°52'08"N., 75°13'07"W.) **and Berth B** (39°52'13"N., 75°13'01"W.): 1,845 feet of berthing space; 37 to 40 feet alongside; deck height, 15 feet; 440,000-barrel storage capacity; receipt of petroleum products and crude oil; bunkering of vessels; owned and operated by Sun Pipe Line Co., a subsidiary of Sun Oil Co. Inc.

(275) **Fort Mifflin**, Mile 79.5N, is the site of the United States Army Corps of Engineers wharves, with depths of 10 to 40 feet at their outer ends.

(276) **Woodbury Creek**, Mile 79.5S, is used only by small craft; local knowledge is needed. The approach must be made from the west-southwest because of the 2-foot shoal directly off the creek. At low water the channel within the creek is well defined. The highway bridge 0.8 mile above the mouth has a fixed span with a clearance of 15 feet. An overhead power cable close westward of the bridge has a clearance of 35 feet. Above this point, fixed bridges and overhead cables have a minimum clearance of 4 feet and 45 feet, respectively.

(288)

Delaware River (Benjamin Franklin Bridge)
Image courtesy of Waterway Images (2006)

(277)
## ENC - US5PA12M
## Chart - 12313

(278)     **Philadelphia**, one of the chief ports of the United States, is at the junction of Delaware and Schuylkill Rivers. The midharbor point along Delaware River is at Chestnut Street, Mile 86.5W.

(279)     The Port of Philadelphia, as defined for Customs purposes, comprises such waters of the Delaware and Schuylkill Rivers bordering on the municipality as are navigable; the municipal limits on Delaware River extend from Fort Mifflin on the south to Poquessing Creek on the north, a distance of about 20 miles.

(280)     Large quantities of general cargo are handled at the port in both foreign and domestic trade. In addition, crude petroleum and petroleum products, sugar and ore are imported, while coal, grain and refined petroleum products are exported. Coastwise receipts are mostly crude petroleum and petroleum products, and shipments consist chiefly of refined petroleum products.

(281)
### Channels
(282)     A Federal project provides for a channel 40 feet deep from the sea through the main channel in Delaware Bay and River to Newbold Island, Mile 110, thence dredging depths of 25 feet to the Trenton Marine Terminal, Mile

115. For detailed channel information and minimum depths as reported by the U.S. Army Corps of Engineers (USACE), use NOAA Electronic Navigational Charts. Surveys and channel condition reports are available through a USACE hydrographic survey website listed in Appendix A.

(283)     In the section of the river between Philadelphia and Trenton, masters are especially requested to limit speed of their vessels when passing wharves and piers so as to avoid damage by suction or wave wash to property or persons.

(284)
### Anchorages
(285)     General and naval anchorages are at Philadelphia. (See **33 CFR 110.1** and **110.157**, chapter 2, for limits and regulations.)

(286)
### Bridges
(287)     **Walt Whitman Bridge**, Mile 84, a highway suspension bridge connecting Philadelphia with Gloucester City, has a clearance of 150 feet at the center of the main span and minimum clearance of 139 feet under the full width of the main span. **Benjamin Franklin Bridge**, Mile 86.8, 0.3 mile above Chestnut Street, has a suspension span with a clearance of 135 feet for the middle 800 feet of the span and 128 feet under the rest of the span. However, Benjamin Franklin Bridge has

movable maintenance walkways when in use, the vertical clearances are reduced to 121 feet under the middle 800 feet of the span and 114 feet under the rest of the river channel span. The Benjamin Franklin Bridge is under construction (2020); caution is advised.

### Towage

(290)     A large fleet of tugs up to 3,300 hp is available at Philadelphia, day and night, for any type service required. As a general rule, tugs are not required for vessels moving between Philadelphia and the sea; most vessels traverse this distance under their own power.

(291)

### Weather

(292)     The proximity of Philadelphia to Delaware Bay probably has some effects on temperature conditions locally. Periods of extended cold weather are relatively rare, with below zero readings reported only 24 times since official records began. Sustained periods of very high or low temperatures seldom last more than 3 or 4 days as conditions change fairly rapidly. Due to the prevalence of maritime air during the summer months, the humidity adds to the discomfort of the high temperatures. Fog can be expected during the autumn and winter.

(293)     The average annual temperature at Philadelphia is 55.1°F (12.8°C). The average annual extremes are 63.9°F (17.7°C) and 45.7°F (7.6°C). July is the warmest month, with an average temperature of 77.4°F (25.2°C), while January is the coldest month with an average temperature of 32.1°F (0°C). The warmest temperature on record is 104°F (40°C), recorded in July 1966, and the coldest temperature on record is -7°F (-21.7°C), last recorded in January 1984. Each month June through September has recorded temperatures at or above 100°F (37.8°C), while each month October through May has recorded temperatures below freezing (0°C).

(294)     Precipitation is fairly evenly distributed throughout the year with maximum amounts during mid-summer. Much of the summer rainfall is in connection with local thunderstorms. July is the wettest month averaging 4.77 inches (121 mm), and October is the driest month averaging 2.69 inches (68 mmm). The greatest 24-hour rainfall occurred in August 1971: 4.77 inches (121 mm). The average annual snowfall for Philadelphia is 20.7 inches (526 mm), and snow has fallen in each month October through May. Single snow storms of 10 inches (254 mm) or more occur about every 5 years. The greatest 24-hour snowfall occurred in February 1983: 21.1 inches (536 mm).

(295)     The prevailing wind direction for the summer is from the southwest, while northwesterly winds prevail during the winter. The annual prevailing direction is from the west-southwest. Destructive velocities are comparatively rare and occur mostly in gusts during summer thunderstorms. High winds in the winter, as a rule, come with the advance of cold air after the passage of a deep low-pressure area. Only rarely have hurricanes

in the vicinity caused widespread damage, then primarily through flooding. Since 1950, seven storms have come within 57.8 miles (93 km) of Philadelphia, all from the south or southwest.

(296)     Flood stages in the Schuylkill River normally occur about twice a year. Flood stages seldom last over 12 hours and usually occur after excessive falls of precipitation during summer thunderstorms. Flood stages in the Delaware River are caused by abnormally high tides due to the water "backing up" under the influence of strong south or southeast winds.

(297)     The office of the National Weather Service is at the Philadelphia International Airport at the southwestern end of the city. **Barometers** may be compared there or checked by telephone/internet.

(298)

### Quarantine, customs, immigration and agricultural quarantine

(299)     (See chapter 3, Vessel Arrival Inspections, and appendix for addresses.)

(300)     **Quarantine** is enforced in accordance with regulations of the U.S. Public Health Service. (See Public Health Service, chapter 1.) Vessels subject to boarding for quarantine inspection are required to anchor off Marcus Hook boarding station. (See **33 CFR 110.1** and **110.157**, chapter 2, for quarantine anchorage regulations and limits.)

(301)     Philadelphia is a **customs port of entry**.

(302)

### Coast Guard

(303)     A **Marine Safety Office** is in Philadelphia. (See appendix for address.)

(304)

### Harbor regulations

(305)     Local rules and regulations are enforced by the Navigation Commission for the Delaware River (Pennsylvania). The authority of the Commission extends from the Pennsylvania-Delaware boundary line on the south to the head of the navigable waters of Delaware River on the north. Copies of the regulations may be obtained from the Navigation Commission for the Delaware River (Pennsylvania), 1400 W. Spring Garden Street, Philadelphia, PA 19130.

(306)

### Wharves

(307)     Philadelphia has more than 45 deep-water piers and wharves along its Delaware River waterfront and along Schuylkill River. Most of the piers and wharves have highway and railroad connections. The port is served by multiple rail lines. Each of these carriers connect with tracks of the Philadelphia Belt Line Railroad which extends along the main part of the port's Delaware River waterfront. Freshwater is piped to most piers and wharves; electrical shore-power connections, if available, are mentioned under the particular facility.

(308)     The Schuylkill River wharves and piers are mostly used to handle bulk petroleum products. Most of the

general cargo piers and wharves are between the Walt Whitman Bridge and Port Richmond, 2 miles above the Benjamin Franklin Bridge, and at Ten Mile Point, 7 miles above the Benjamin Franklin Bridge.

(309)      Coal, fertilizer, and ore are handled at the facilities south of Greenwich Point, just below the Walt Whitman Bridge.

(310)      Cargo is generally handled by ships' tackle; special handling equipment, if available, is mentioned in the description of the particular facility. A barge crane with an 800-ton capacity is available by special arrangement; a 375-ton crane is also available.

(311)      The alongside depths for each facility are reported. For information on the latest depths contact the Port of Philadelphia or the private operator. Only the major deep-draft facilities are described.

(312)
### Facilities in Schuylkill River, East Bank:

(313)      **Creedon Tug and Barge Works, Girard Point, Pier No. 1** (39°53'38"N., 75°11'49"W.): upper side 1,092 feet long; 31 feet alongside; deck height, 11 feet; two 35-ton gantry cranes; 3 acres of open storage; mooring barges for cleaning, and vessels for repair; owned by Harry Hays Tug and Towing Service, Inc., and operated by Creedon Tug and Barge Works and Creedon's Terminal.

(314)      **Sun Refining and Marketing Co., Philadelphia Refinery, Girard Point Plant, Wharves 1, 2 and 3**: about 0.2 mile above Interstate 95 bridge; 2,075 feet of berthing space; 32 feet alongside; deck height, 12 feet; pipelines extend from wharf to steel storage tanks with a capacity of 1.6 million barrels; receipt and shipment of petroleum products, cumene and benzene; owned and operated by Sun Refining and Marketing Co., a subsidiary of Sun Oil Co., Inc.

(315)
### Facilities in Schuylkill River, West Bank:

(316)      **Louis Dreyfus Energy, North America, Philadelphia Wharf** (39°55'38"N., 75°12'46"W.): 206-foot face; 16 feet alongside; deck height, 9 feet; pipelines extend from wharf to steel storage tanks with a capacity of 850,000 barrels; receipt and shipment of petroleum products; owned and operated by Louis Dreyfus Energy, North America.

(317)      **C.R. Wamer, Yankee Point Terminal Mooring** 39°54'41"N., 75°12'37"W.): 195-foot face; 24 to 26 feet alongside, deck height, 6 feet; pipelines extend from barge to steel storage tanks with a capacity of 135,000 barrels; receipt and occasional shipment of petroleum products; owned and operated by C.R. Wamer, Inc.

(318)      **Maritank Philadelphia Wharf** (39°54'36"N., 75°12'58"W.): 750-foot face; 33 feet alongside; deck height, 12 feet; pipelines extend from berth to steel storage tanks with a capacity of 947,300 barrels; receipt and shipment of petroleum products; owned and operated by Maritank Philadelphia, Inc.

(319)
### Facilities in Delaware River, south of Benjamin Franklin Bridge (39°57'10"N., 75°08'07"W.):

(320)      **Greenwich Ore Pier 122S, South Wharves** (39°53'47"N., 75°08'16"W.): south side 850 feet long, 40 feet alongside; north side 850 feet long, 20 feet alongside; deck height, 12 feet; four cranes, unloading rate 1,200 tons per hour; electric conveyor and hopper system; 2-million-ton iron ore open storage; receipt of ore; owned by ConRail and operated by Pennsylvania Tidewater Dock Co.

(321)      **Packer Ave. Marine Terminal Wharf** (39°54'08"N., 75°08'03"W.): 3,101-foot face with 3,150 feet of berthing space; 40 feet alongside; deck height, 13 feet; 100,000 square feet heated covered storage and 90,000 square feet covered cold-storage; one 375-ton crane; lift capacity; forklift trucks; receipt and shipment of conventional, containerized and roll-on/roll-off general cargo including fruit and steel; electrical shore-power connections; owned by Philadelphia Regional Port Authority and operated by Holt Cargo Systems, Inc.

(322)      **Pier 96S, South Wharves** (39°54'45"N., 75°07'56"W.): south side 1,320 feet long, north side 1,220 feet long, 30 feet alongside; deck height, 14 feet; 3 acres open storage; electric and water connections; receipt and shipment of automobiles; owned by Philadelphia Regional Port Authority and operated by Pasha Auto Warehousing and Pasha Terminal Co.

(323)      **Pier 82S, South Wharves** (39°55'03"N., 75°08'03"W.): 45-foot face; deck height 11.7 feet; south side 852 feet long, deck height, 7.7 feet; north side 1,155 feet long, deck height, 11.7 feet; 30 feet alongside; 75,000 square feet covered storage; receipt of fruit, vegetables and other perishable commodities; shipment of paper products; owned by Philadelphia Regional Port Authority and operated by Horizon Stevedoring.

(324)      **Pier 80S, South Wharves** (39°55'10"N., 75°08'12"W.): 358-foot face; south side 1,150 feet long; north side 1,063 feet long; 30 feet alongside; deck height, 11 feet; 254,024 square feet covered storage; 3 acres open storage; electric and water connections; receipt and shipment of newsprint, coated paper, wood pulp, lumber and other forest products; owned by Philadelphia Regional Port Authority and operated by Penn Warehousing and Distribution Services, Inc., and J.H. Stevedoring.

(325)
### Facilities at Port Richmond:

(326)      **Tioga II Marine Terminal Wharf** (39°58'37"N., 75°05'40"W.): 736-foot face, 28 feet alongside; southwest side 626 feet long, (depth alongside unknown); northeast side 620 feet long, 32 feet alongside; deck height, 10.6 feet; two 1.5-ton electric cranes; electric and water connections; 130,000 square feet covered storage; 10 acres of open storage; pipelines extend from wharf to steel storage tanks with 1.2-million-barrel capacity; receipt and shipment of petroleum products, petrochemicals and miscellaneous bulk liquids; owned

(339)

## Structures across Schuylkill River

| Name | Type | Location | Mile | Clearances (feet) | | Information |
|------|------|----------|------|-------------------|--|-------------|
| | | | | Horizontal | Vertical* | |
| Interstate 95 bridge | fixed | 39°53'34"N., 75°11'49"W. | 0.6 | 400 | 135 | |
| George C. Platt Memorial bridge | fixed | 39°53'52"N., 75°12'42"W. | 1.5 | 339 | 135 | |
| Overhead cable | power | 39°53'53"N., 75°12'43"W. | 1.5 | | 156 | |
| Overhead cable | power | 39°55'03"N., 75°12'10"W. | 3.4 | | 150 | |
| Passyunk Avenue bridge | bas-cule | 39°55'11"N., 75°12'06"W. | 3.5 | 200 | 50 | Note 1 |
| Railroad bridge | swing | 39°56'07"N., 75°12'21"W. | 5.1 | 57 | 15 | Notes 1 and 2 |
| Overhead cable | power | 39°56'08"N., 75°12'22"W. | 5.1 | | 97 | |
| Conrail bridge | swing | 39°56'26"N., 75°12'18"W. | 5.5 | 75 west draw 65 east draw | 22 | Bridge is abandoned |
| Grays Ferry Avenue bridge | fixed | 39°56'28"N., 75°12'18"W. | 5.6 | 75 west channel 65 east channel | 50 22 | Bridge under construction |
| Overhead cable | power | 39°56'31"N., 75°12'19"W. | 5.7 | | 75 | |
| Overhead cable | power | 39°56'33"N., 75°12'05"W. | 5.9 | | 75 | |
| University Avenue bridge | bacule | 39°56'34"N., 75°11'49"W. | 6.2 | 100 | 32 | Note 1 |
| Overhead cable | power | 39°56'33"N., 75°11'48"W. | 6.2 | | 70 | |
| Schuylkill Expressway | fixed | 39°56'31"N., 75°11'40"W. | 6.3 | 140 | 50 | |
| Overhead cable | power | 39°56'35"N., 75°11'31"W. | 6.4 | | 79 | |
| CSX Railroad bridge | swing | 39°56'35"N., 75°11'32"W. | 6.4 | 67 | 26 | Note 1 |
| South Street bridge | fixed | 39°56'49"N., 75°11'13"W. | 6.7 | 105 | 35 | |
| Walnut Street bridge | fixed | 39°57'06"N., 75°10'54"W. | 7.2 | 115 | 34 | |
| Chestnut Street bridge | fixed | 39°57'11"N., 75°10'51"W. | 7.3 | 159 | 27 | |
| Market Street bridge | fixed | 39°57'16"N., 75°10'51"W. | 7.4 | 164 | 27 | |
| Pennsylvania Boulevard bridge | fixed | 39°57'20"N., 75°10'48"W. | 7.5 | 178 | 16 | |
| Pennsylvania Railroad bridge | fixed | 39°57'22"N., 75°10'47"W. | 7.5 | 172 | 38 | |
| Vine Street bridge | fixed | 39°57'36"N., 75°10'47"W. | 7.8 | 136 | 20 | |
| Spring Garden Street bridges | fixed | 39°57'52"N., 75°11'00"W. | 8.1 | 140 | 19 | |

* Clearances are referenced to Mean High Water
Note 1 – See 33 CFR 117.1 through 117.59 and 117.905, chapter 2, for drawbridge regulations.
Note 2 – Bridgetender monitors VHF–FM channel 13; call sign KXS-238.

by Philadelphia Regional Port Authority and operated by GATX Terminals Corp.

(327) **Tioga I Fruit Terminal Wharf** (39°58'42"N., 75°05'10"W.): 1,753-foot face, 670-foot lower side with roll-on/roll-off berth; 40 feet alongside; deck height, 12 feet; 397,500 square feet covered storage; forklift trucks to 10 tons, container lift trucks to 35 tons, one top-lift container truck to 40 tons; receipt and shipment of conventional, containerized and roll-on/roll-off general cargo including fruit; owned and operated by Philadelphia Regional Port Authority.

(328)

### Supplies

(329) All types of marine supplies and services are available in the Philadelphia area. Bunker oil and diesel oil can be obtained at terminals along the Schuylkill River. Other bunkering terminals are at Marcus Hook, Paulsboro and Eagle Point. Most larger vessels receive fuel from barges alongside.

(330)

### Repairs

(331) There are several shore-based firms engaged in the field of general ship repairs; work is done on the vessel or in the company shops. Repairs to small vessels can be made at shipyards on Cooper Point in Camden. Small-craft repair facilities are at Dredge Harbor, NJ, and Essington, PA, described earlier in this chapter.

(332)

### Communications

(333) Philadelphia is served by three major railroad systems. More than 100 steamship lines operate to and from the port. Several major airlines provide frequent scheduled service between Philadelphia International Airport, 5.5 miles southwest of City Hall, and domestic and overseas points.

(334) **Schuylkill River**, Mile 80N, is navigable for 7.3 miles to **Fairmount Dam** and is an important outlet for a part of the commerce of Philadelphia.

(335)     The Federal project provides for a channel 33 feet deep to Passyunk Avenue bridge, 3.1 miles above the mouth, thence 26 feet deep to Gibson Point, 4 miles above the mouth, and thence 22 feet deep to University Avenue bridge, 5.3 miles above the mouth. Above that point most of the wharves have depths of about 12 feet at their faces. (See Notice to Mariners and latest edition of the chart for controlling depths.)

(336)     A light marks the outer end of a sunken jetty on the east side of the entrance to Schuylkill River. A **021.5°** lighted range marks the entrance, and buoys mark the channel within the river as far as Yankee Point, 2.1 miles above the mouth.

(337)     A **safety zone** is on the east side of the Schuylkill River, opposite Point Breeze. The safety zone surrounds a barge dock and is only enforced at specific times. See **33 CFR 165.1** through **165.40** and **165.784**, chapter 2, for limits and regulations.

(338)     A **Security zone** has been established in portions of the Delaware and Schuykill Rivers in the waters surrounding the Philadelphia International Airport extending north into the Schuykill River to approximately 500 yards northwest and parallel with the George C. Platt Memorial–Penrose Avenue fixed bridge. This zone is not active at all times but during VIP transits to and from the airport. (See **33 CFR 165.1** through **165.40** and **165.558**, chapter 2, for limits and regulations.)

(340)
### Current

(341)     In Schuylkill River, the current velocity is about 0.5 knot at the entrance.

(342)     The confluence of Schuylkill and Delaware Rivers is the center of the petroleum industry in the city of Philadelphia. The deep-draft piers and wharves along the river were described previously in this chapter under Wharves. Most of the other wharves and piers along the river have depths of 9 to 12 feet at their faces.

(343)     **League Island**, now a part of the mainland at the junction of Delaware and Schuylkill Rivers, is the site of the **Philadelphia Naval Shipyard**. The yard has a frontage of 0.6 mile on the east side of Schuylkill River and 2 miles on the north side of Delaware River. **Reserve Basin**, in the northwest part of the yard, is used to store vessels of the reserve fleet.

(344)     **Coastal Eagle Point Oil Co., Berths 1A, 2, and 3** (centered at 39°52'43"N., 75°09'20"W.), east of **Eagle Point**, Mile 81.8S: offshore wharves with up to 1,937 feet of berthing space; 32 to 40 feet alongside; deck height, 16 feet; railroad and highway connections; receipt of crude oil; receipt and shipment of petroleum products; bunkering of vessels; pipelines extending from wharves to storage tanks with a capacity of 8.6-million barrels; owned and operated by Coastal Eagle Point Oil Co.

(345)     **Big Timber Creek**, Mile 82.9S, has an authorized entrance channel, which is no longer maintained, and local knowledge is needed to navigate the channel. The minimum clearance of the fixed bridges at **Westville**,

about 1 mile above the mouth, is 14 feet. Above Westville, the fixed bridges have a least vertical clearance of 8 feet. The overhead cables crossing the creek have a least clearance of 30 feet.

(346)     The creek is used mainly by pleasure craft. Several marinas are along the creek; slips, gasoline, limited marine supplies and hull and engine repairs are available. Maximum haul-out capacities are 48 feet (marine railway) and lifts to 10 tons.

(347)     **Gloucester City**, Mile 83.5, is the site of large manufacturing plants. The three deep-draft facilities along the waterfront, which are described below, have railroad and highway connections.

(348)     **Koch Refining Co., Gloucester City Wharf** (39°53'41"N., 75°07'51"W.), about 0.7 mile below Walt Whitman Bridge: 50-foot face with 850 feet of berthing space; 35 feet alongside; deck height, 12 feet; pipelines from wharf to storage tanks with 800,400-barrel capacity; receipt and shipment of petroleum products; owned and operated by Koch Refining Co. L.P.

(349)     **Holt Hauling and Warehousing Systems, Gloucester City Marine Terminal, Berths 9 and 9A** (39°54'04"N., 75°07'42"W.), about 1,000 feet south of Walt Whitman Bridge provide 1,530 feet of berthing space with 35 to 45 feet alongside; deck height, 12 feet; 125,000 square feet covered dry and refrigerated storage; 40 acres open storage; receipt and shipment of containerized general cargo; owned by Holt Cargo Systems, Inc,. and operated by Holt Hauling and Warehousing Systems Inc., Gloucester City Refrigerated Warehousing and Gloucester City Terminals.

(350)     **Holt Hauling and Warehousing Systems, Gloucester City Marine Terminal, Berth North 8A** (39°54'16"N., 75°07'38"W.), about 500 feet south of Walt Whitman Bridge, provides 610 feet of berthing space with 40 feet alongside; deck height, 12 feet; 101,000 square feet covered dry storage and 20,000 square feet covered refrigerated storage; 40 acres open storage; receipt and shipment of conventional general cargo; owned by Holt Cargo Systems, Inc., and operated by Holt Hauling and Warehousing Systems, Inc., Gloucester City Refrigerated Warehousing and Gloucester City Terminals.

(351)     **Holt Cargo Systems, Pier 7**, is about 300 yards north of Walt Whitman Bridge on the south side of Newton Creek; 2,130 feet of berthing space with 24 to 40 feet alongside; deck height, 12 feet; two 150-ton cranes and forklift trucks with lifting capacity to 25 tons; about 250,000 square feet of covered storage and about 90 acres of open storage; receipt and shipment of general cargo; owned and operated by Holt Cargo Systems, Inc.

(352)     The current velocity is about 2.1 knots off Gloucester City.

(353)     **Newton Creek**, Mile 84.2E, forms the boundary between Gloucester City and Camden. Navigation is blocked 500 yards above the mouth by low fixed bridges.

(354)     **Camden**, NJ, is an important manufacturing center directly opposite Philadelphia, with which its industrial and shipping activities are closely allied. The South

Jersey Port Corporation, with headquarters at Camden, has jurisdiction over the New Jersey ports bordering Delaware River and Bay from Trenton to the ocean.

(355)
### Quarantine, customs, immigration and agricultural quarantine
(356)  (See chapter 3, Vessel Arrival Inspections, and appendix for addresses.)

(357)  **Quarantine** is enforced in accordance with regulations of the U.S. Public Health Service. (See Public Health Service, chapter 1.)

(358)
### Wharves
(359)  The Camden city waterfront extends about 3.4 miles from Newton Creek to Cooper River; also included are the petroleum terminals at Pettys Island and Fisher Point Dike. All of the wharves have highway and some have railroad connections. Camden is served by ConRail. Beckett Street and Broadway Terminals have fresh water and electrical shore-power connections. MAFCO Worldwide Corp. Pier has water connections.

(360)  Cargo is generally handled by ships' tackle; special handling equipment, if available, is mentioned in the description of the particular facility. An 800-ton floating crane is available at Philadelphia by special arrangement; a 375-ton heavy lift crane is also available at Philadelphia.

(361)  The alongside depths for each facility are reported. For information on the latest depths contact the South Jersey Port Corp. or the private operator. Only the major deep-draft facilities are described.

(362)  **Broadway Terminal, Berth No. 5** (39°54'31"N., 75°07'24"W.): 1,100-foot face; 35 feet alongside; deck height, 12 feet; 129,000 square feet of covered storage; 30 acres of open storage; one 80-ton crane; receipt and shipment of conventional and containerized general cargo including fruit; owned by South Jersey Port Corp., and operated by Del Monte Fresh Food, Inc.

(363)  **Broadway Terminal, Pier No. 2** (39°54'54"N., 75°07'29"W.): 62-foot face, 1,005-foot lower side, 809-foot upper side; 35 feet alongside; deck height, 10 to 12 feet; vessel mooring and repair; owned by South Jersey Port Corp. and operated by South Jersey Port Corp. and McAllister Brothers, Inc.

(364)  **Broadway Terminal, Berths 1 and 1A** (39°54'56"N., 75°07'32"W.): 443-foot face (Berth 1A), 35 feet alongside; south side (Berth 1), 856 feet long, 35 to 40 feet alongside; deck height, 11 feet; 59,600 square feet covered storage; 22 acres of open storage; one 40-ton gantry crane; receipt and shipment of conventional general cargo, coal and petroleum coke; owned and operated by South Jersey Port Corp.

(365)  **MAFCO Worldwide Corp. Pier** (39°55'09"N., 75°07'38"W.): 252-foot face, 30 feet alongside; south side, 427 feet long, 22 to 30 feet alongside; north side, 388 feet long; deck height, 12 feet; receipt of fuel oil for plant consumption; owned and operated by MAFCO Worldwide Corp.

(366)  **GP Gypsum Corp. Wharf** (39°55'51"N., 75°07'57"W.): offshore wharf, 410 feet long, 30 feet alongside; deck height, 11 feet; open storage for 200,000 tons of gypsum rock; receipt of gypsum rock; owned and operated by GP Gypsum Corp.

(367)  **Beckett Street Terminal Wharf** (39°56'13"N., 75°07'55"W.): 2,655-foot face, 40 feet alongside; deck height, 11 feet; 149,930 square feet of covered storage; 15 acres of open storage; cranes to 85 tons, and forklift trucks are available; receipt and shipment of general and containerized cargo and steel; receipt of lumber, ores, coal, salt and dry bulk commodities; shipment of scrap metal; owned and operated by South Jersey Port Corporation.

(368)  **Citgo Petroleum Corp., Petty's Island Terminal Dock** (39°58'14"N., 75°05'58"W.): 800 feet of berthing space; 26 feet alongside; deck height, 11 feet; 1-million barrel storage capacity for petroleum products; 165,000-barrel storage capacity for asphalt; receipt and shipment of petroleum products; receipt of asphalt; owned by Citgo Petroleum Corp., and operated by Citgo Petroleum Corp. and Koch Oil, Inc.

(369)  **Amerada Hess Corp., Pennsauken Dock 1 and Lower Dock** (39°58'43"N., 75°04'09"W.): 285 to 300 feet of berthing space; 39 to 40 feet alongside; deck heights, 12 to 13.5 feet; 2.3-million barrel storage capacity; receipt and shipment of petroleum products; owned and operated by Amerada Hess Corp.

(370)  There are no major repair facilities at Camden for large vessels.

(371)  A ferry operates across Delaware River from Penns Landing to the Camden waterfront.

(372)  There are several shipyards at **Cooper Point,** above the Benjamin Franklin Bridge, that can make all kinds of above and below water repairs to small vessels. The largest floating drydock has a capacity of 850 tons, 182 feet long and 66.5 feet wide, and has a depth of 12 feet over the keel blocks. The largest marine railway has a haul-out capacity of 750 tons.

(373)  **Back Channel** between **Petty Island** and the New Jersey shore has a controlling depth of about 10 feet. The entrance to Back Channel south of Petty Island is marked by a buoy. Care is necessary to avoid shallow areas extending from both the island and the mainland. The railroad-highway bridge over the northeastern end of Back Channel has a fixed span with a clearance of 15 feet. Most of the boatyards along the New Jersey shore southward of Petty Island are inactive.

(374)  **Cooper River** empties into the south side of Back Channel, 0.6 mile above the southwest entrance. In 1980, the centerline controlling depth was 6 feet to the end of the dredged channel. The drawbridges over this section of the river have a minimum width of 20 feet and a clearance of 3 feet. (See **33 CFR 117.1** through **117.59** and **117.713**, chapter 2, for drawbridge regulations.)

(380)

### Structures across Delaware River above Philadelphia

| Name | Type | Location | Clearances (feet) | | Information |
|------|------|----------|-----------|---------|-------------|
| | | | Horizontal | Vertical* | |
| Delair Railroad bridge | vertical lift | 39°58'58"N., 75°04'08"W. | 500 | 49 (down) 135 (up) | Notes 1 and 2. Bridgetender monitors VHF-FM channel 13 (call sign KS-9970) |
| Overhead cable | power | 39°58'54"N., 75°04'05"W. | | 140 | |
| Betsy Ross bridge | fixed | 39°59'06"N., 75°03'59"W. | 400 | 140 | |
| Tacony-Palmyra bridge | bascule | 40°00'42"N., 75°02'33"W. | 240 | 50 | Notes 1 and 2. Bridgetender monitors VHF-FM channel 13 (call sign KBA-328) |
| Overhead cable | power | 40°04'47"N., 74°52'44"W. | | 140 | |
| Burlington/Bristol bridge | vertical lift | 40°04'52"N., 74°52'10"W. | 500 | 61 (down) 133 (up) | Notes 1 and 2. Bridgetender monitors VHF-FM channel 13 (call sign KBA-339) |
| Overhead cable | power | 40°05'32"N., 74°50'13"W. | | 45 | Crosses auxiliary channel south of Burlington Island |
| Delaware River Turnpike | fixed | 40°07'01"N., 74°49'50"W. | 550 | 135 | |
| Overhead cables | power | 40°11'02"N., 74°45'08"W. | | 166 | |
| West Railroad bridge | fixed | 40°12'29"N., 74°46'02"W. | 58 | 20 | |

\* Above Mean High Water
Note 1 – See **33 CFR 117.1** through **117.59** and **117.904**, chapter 2, for drawbridge regulations.
Note 2 – See **33 CFR 117.1** through **117.59** and **117.716**, chapter 2, for drawbridge regulations.

(375)

## ENC - US5PA13M
## Chart - 12314

(376)    Above Philadelphia, the 40-foot dredged channel continues to Newbold Island, Mile 110, thence the project depths are 25 feet to the Trenton Marine Terminal and 12 feet to the railroad bridge at Trenton. Depths above Newbold Island may be considerably below project depths. For detailed channel information and minimum depths as reported by the U.S. Army Corps of Engineers (USACE), use NOAA Electronic Navigational Charts. Surveys and channel condition reports are available through a USACE hydrographic survey website listed in Appendix A.

(377)

### Ice

(378)    Above Philadelphia the river usually is closed by ice for extended periods during January and February, and in severe winters navigation is practically suspended during these months; ice seldom forms before January.

(379)    During March and April, **freshets** 10 to 20 feet in height above mean low water may be expected at Trenton. The highest level is reached during the ice breakup in the spring; heavy rains do not ordinarily raise the level to more than 9 feet above mean low water. Freshets usually are not dangerous to shipping unless accompanied by ice. The 1903 freshet, highest on record, reached heights above low water of 21.5 feet at Trenton, 19.5 feet at Bordentown and 13 feet at Bristol.

(381)    Gasoline and some supplies are available at a small boatyard on the west side of the bridge at Tacony; minor engine repairs can be made.

(382)    **Dredge Harbor**, Mile 96S, has several marinas and boatyards. The entrance has depths of about 10 feet, thence up to 15 feet inside. The channel through the harbor is marked by lighted bouys. The marinas can provide berths, gasoline, diesel fuel, marine supplies and hull and engine repairs; maximum haul-out capacity is 30 tons.

(383)    **Rancocas Creek**, Mile 96S, is used mainly by pleasure boats. Depths are about 5 feet to **Centerton** 6 miles above the mouth. The channel is narrow and crooked above Bridgeboro and in general follows ebb-tide bends back and forth between shoals; navigation is difficult without local knowledge. The current velocity is about 1 knot in the entrance.

(384)

### Small-craft facilities

(385)    There are small-craft facilities near the first bridge and at **Bridgeboro.** Berths, gasoline and marine supplies are available. A small-craft facility at Bridgeboro can make hull and engine repairs to trailerable craft.

(386)

### Structures across Rancocas Creek

| Name | Type | Location | Clearances (feet) | |
|------|------|----------|-----------|---------|
| | | | Horizontal | Vertical* |
| County Route 543 bridge **See Note 1** | swing | 40°02'40"N., 74°57'30"W. | 50** | 4 |
| New Jersey Transit Railroad bridge | fixed | 40°02'40"N., 74°57'12"W. | 160 | 20 |
| U.S. Route 130 bridge **See Note 1** | fixed | 40°01'44"N., 74°55'56"W. | 201 | 19 |
| Overhead cables | power/ television | 40°01'42"N., 74°55'55"W. | | 46 |
| Overhead cables | power | 40°00'50"N., 74°54'20"W. | | 83 |
| County Route 635 bridge **See Note 1** | swing | 39°59'51"N., 74°52'20"W. | 48 | 6 |
| U.S. 295 bridges | fixed | 39°59'45"N., 74°52'03"W. | 60 | 20 |
| New Jersey Turnpike bridge | fixed | 39°59'46"N., 74°51'53"W. | 60 | 20 |

| Structures across Rancocas Creek | | | | |
|---|---|---|---|---|
| | | | Clearances (feet) | |
| Name | Type | Location | Horizontal | Vertical* |
| Overhead cable | power | 39°59'43"N., 74°51'52"W. | | 50 |

\* Clearances are referenced to Mean High Water
\*\* Clearance is for both the north and south draws
**Note 1** – See **33 CFR 117.1** through **117.59** and **117.745**, chapter 2, for drawbridge regulations.

(387)   **Poquessing Creek**, Mile 97N, forms the upper boundary of the city of Philadelphia. A yacht club at **Torresdale**, a part of the city on the lower side of the creek, has a float landing. In 1998, reported depths at the float were 9 to 12 feet.

(388)   **Mud Island Shoal**, just above Poquessing Creek, is a flat that is partly submerged at high water and is covered with marsh grass in the summer. The channel between Mud Island Shoal and the Pennsylvania mainland has a controlling depth of about 7 feet. The lower part of the channel is used considerably as a small-boat anchorage.

(389)   **Andalusia**, Mile 97.5N, is a suburban residential community with few industries along the waterfront. A yacht club at **Cornwells Heights**, 1 mile eastward of Andalusia, has a float landing with about 10 feet alongside; gasoline, berths and water are available on weekends only.

(390)   **Neshaminy Creek**, Mile 100N, has depths of about 5 feet to the fixed highway bridge 0.7 mile above the mouth, thence about 3 feet for another 0.3 mile to where the creek has shoaled to bare. The fixed highway bridge has a clearance of 9 feet. There are several boatyards and marinas along the creek which can provide transient berths, gasoline, diesel fuel, water, limited marine supplies and hull and engine repairs. Maximum haul-out capacities are 60 feet (marine railway) and lifts to 20 tons.

(391)   At Mile 100.1N, a dredged channel leads to a small-craft basin at **Neshaminy State Park**. Transient berths, ice, water and electricity are available. In 1974, the controlling depth was 9 feet in the basin. In 1978, shoaling was reported in the basin in about 40°04.6'N., 74°54.4'W. The mouth of the entrance channel is marked by a light.

(392)   **Burlington**, Mile 102.5S, fronts in part on the main channel of Delaware River and part on the auxiliary channel southeast of Burlington Island. Several industries are located at Burlington and its suburb, **East Burlington**, which is centered a mile along the auxiliary channel.

(393)   The Delaware River main channel continues along the northwest side of Burlington Island, and the auxiliary channel extends along the southeast side for 1.2 miles to a turning basin. (See Notice to Mariners and the latest edition of the chart for controlling depths.) Eastward of the turning basin, the back channel has natural depths of about 6 to 11 feet through the northeast entrance.

(394)
**Current**

(395)   The current velocity is 1.3 knots on the flood and 1.6 knots on the ebb in the main channel west of Burlington Island. In the back channel east of the island, the velocity is 0.9 knot on the flood and 1.8 knots on the ebb.

(396)   The town wharf, about 0.4 mile east of Assiscunk Creek, has depths of 12 feet reported alongside. A marina at the entrance to **Assiscunk Creek** has berths, gasoline, diesel fuel, ice and some marine supplies. A 7-ton mobile hoist is available for hauling out vessels for hull and engine repairs.

(397)   **Bristol**, Mile 103.5N, has a public wharf at the lower end of the town with depths of about 3.5 feet reported at the face. A yacht club near the upper end of Bristol has float landings with 8 feet reported alongside; water is available; members or guests may use the club railway to haul out boats up to 38 feet but must make their own repairs.

(398)   At about Mile 105.9N, an oil company operates a wharf that has 875 feet of berthing space with dolphins. A depth of 37 feet is alongside; deck height, 15 feet. There are highway connections near the wharf. The facility is used for receipt of petroleum products.

(399)   **Florence**, Mile 107W, is a manufacturing community with no waterborne commerce.

(400)   **Newbold Island**, just above the Roebling main wharf, is 1.5 miles long, with a greatest width of 0.7 mile. The main channel of Delaware River is along the north side of Newbold Island.

(401)   In 1982, a section of the channel south of Newbold Island was reported to have shoaled to bare.

(402)   At Mile 109N is a basin where sand and gravel are handled. The wharves have depths of about 10 feet at their faces.

(403)   **Fieldsboro**, Mile 110.5S, is a residential community with no waterborne commerce.

(404)
**Current**

(405)   The current velocity in Whitehill Range off Fieldsboro is 1.4 knots on the ebb; the flood current is weak and of short duration.

(406)   **Crosswicks Creek**, Mile 111.1S, is used extensively by pleasure craft. Berths and gasoline can be obtained at one of the yacht clubs at Bordentown, near the mouth of the creek. A fixed highway bridge (I-295) crosses Crosswicks Creek at Mile 0.0 and has a clearance of 35 feet.

(407)   **Bordentown** is on the high bank on the southeast side of the entrance to Crosswicks Creek.

(408)   Mariners are advised to stay in the dredged channel when navigating between Bordentown and Trenton because of the rocky ledges and shoals bordering the channel.

(409)   On **Duck Island**, Mile 113E, there are two oil-receiving piers with 16 feet reported alongside and a public utility coal pier with 25 feet reported alongside.

Vessels stay in the main channel until north of the coal pier before heading toward shore and southward to the oil terminals to avoid the shoal area between the main channel and the terminals.

(410)
**Small-craft facilities**

(411)      On the New Jersey shore between Duck Island and Trenton are small-craft facilities where gasoline, berths, water and some marine supplies are available. Minor hull and engine repairs can be made.

(412)      **Trenton**, the capital of New Jersey, is at the railroad bridge crossing the river at Mile 116. The railroad bridge is the head of powerboat navigation. The city is an important manufacturing center.

(413)
**Weather**

(414)      Trenton is in a region about midway between the rigorous climates of the North and the mild climates of the South and located at on the Delaware River, upstream from Philadelphia.

(415)      Rainfall distribution throughout the year is rather uniform with the spread between the wettest month (July) and the driest month (February) being only 1.82 inches (46.2 mm). The average annual precipitation for Trenton is 41.97 inches (1,066 mm). The greatest 24-hour rainfall occurred in July 1975 when 5.75 inches (146 mm) fell.

(416)      Snowfall occurs on about 20 days per year on the average; however, an average of only 6 days annually produce snowfalls greater than 1.5 inches (38.1 mm). The average annual snowfall is 24.7 inches (627.4 mm). February is the snowiest month but it is trailed closely by January. The greatest 24-hour snowfall occurred in February 1978 when 13.4 inches (340.4 mm) fell.

(417)      In summer, the area is under the influence of the large semipermanent high-pressure system commonly known as the Bermuda High. Based on climatology, it is usually centered over the Atlantic Ocean near latitude 30°N. This high-pressure system brings a circulation of warm, humid air masses over the area from the deep South. The proximity of large water areas and the inflow of southerly winds contribute to high relative humidities much of the year.

(418)      January is the coldest month, and July, the warmest. The average annual temperature at Trenton is 54.3°F (12.4°C) with an average high of 62.2°F (16.8°C) and an average low of 45.9°F (7.7°C). The warmest temperature on record at Trenton is 102°F (38.9°C), last recorded in July 1966. The coldest temperature on record is -4°F (-20°C), last recorded in January 1978. Each month October through April has recorded temperatures below freezing (0°C), while only July has seen temperatures in excess of 100°F (37.8°C).

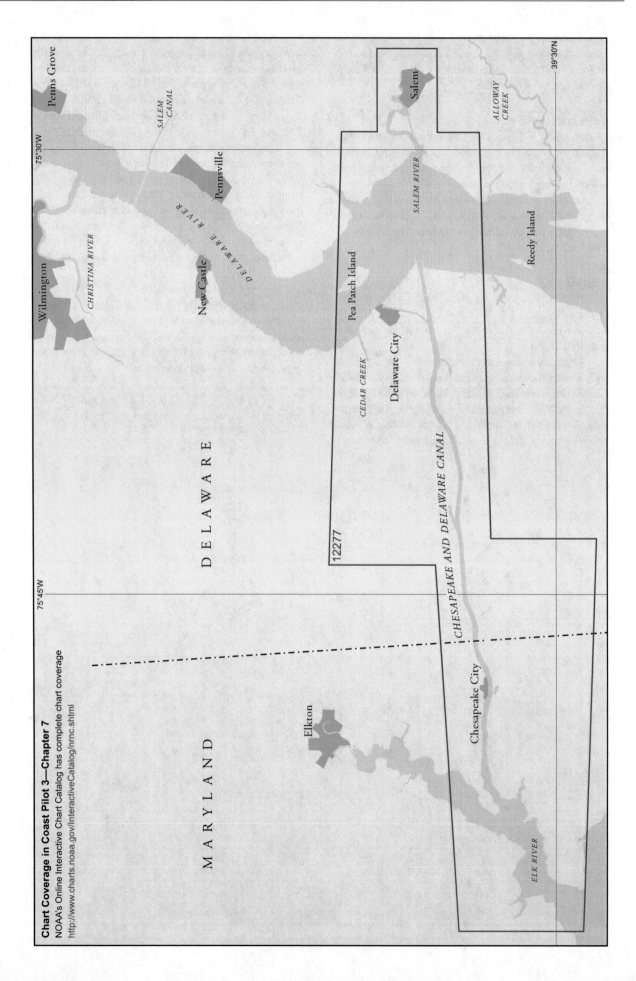

**Chart Coverage in Coast Pilot 3—Chapter 7**
NOAA's Online Interactive Chart Catalog has complete chart coverage
http://www.charts.noaa.gov/InteractiveCatalog/nrnc.shtml

# Chesapeake and Delaware Canal

(1)

**ENC - US5MD15M**

**Chart - 12277**

(2)     The **Chesapeake and Delaware Canal** is a sea-level waterway that extends from Delaware River at Reedy Point, DE, to **Back Creek** at Chesapeake City, MD, thence down Back Creek to Elk River and Chesapeake Bay. The Reedy Point entrance is 51 miles above the Delaware Capes, 35.5 miles below Philadelphia, 62 miles from Baltimore and 187.5 miles from the Virginia Capes. **Miles** in the following text are the distances in nautical miles along the canal from the middle of Delaware River. **Reedy Point**, at Mile 0.7 on the north side of the Delaware entrance, is jettied and is marked by a light; the jetty on the south side is similarly marked.

(3)     **Note**–The system of marking the channel with buoys and lights is from each entrance and reverses at Chesapeake City. Even numbers and flashing red lights are on the north side and odd numbers and flashing green lights are on the south side between the Delaware Bay entrance and Chesapeake City. Even numbers and flashing red lights are on the south side and odd numbers and flashing green lights are on the north side from Chesapeake City to the west end of the canal. Each bend along the canal is marked by an amber light.

(4)     In addition to the navigational aids, the north and south banks of the Chesapeake and Delaware Canal are lighted by mercury vapor luminaries spaced 500 feet apart on poles at a height of 25 feet mean high water. They are designed to illuminate the banks at the waters edge to assist ships navigating the canal at night. The U.S. Army Corps of Engineers maintained poles are 250 feet apart with a light on every other pole.

(5)

**COLREGS Demarcation Lines**

(6)     The lines established for Delaware Bay and Chesapeake Bay are described in **33 CFR 80.503** and **80.510**, chapter 2.

(7)

**Navigation regulations**

(8)     The following regulations are from **33 CFR 162** and **33 CFR 207**:

(9)

**§162.40 Inland waterway from Delaware River**

**to Chesapeake Bay, DE and MD (Chesapeake and Delaware Canal).**

(10)     (a) Applicability. The regulations in this section are applicable to that part of the inland waterway from Delaware River to Chesapeake Bay, DE and MD, between Reedy Point, Delaware River, and Old Town Point Wharf, Elk River.

(11)     (b) Speed. No vessel in the waterway shall be raced or crowded alongside another vessel. Vessels of all types, including pleasure craft, are required to travel at all times at a safe speed throughout the canal and its approaches so as to avoid damage by suction or wave wash to wharves, landings, riprap protection, or other boats, or injury to persons. Pilots and vessel operators transiting the canal and its approaches are warned that violation of this rule may result in having their privilege to transit the canal suspended. Passages of vessels through the canal will be monitored and specific cases will be investigated where damage by suction or wave wash does occur. Owners and operators of yachts, motorboats, rowboats, and other craft are cautioned that large deep-draft ocean-going vessels and other large commercial vessels ply the canal, and such owners and operators should be particularly careful to moor or anchor well away from the main ship channels, with moorings and lines which are sufficient and proper.

(12)     (c) Right-of-way. All vessels proceeding with the current shall have the right-of-way over those proceeding against the current. Large vessels or tows must not overtake and attempt to pass other large vessels or tows in the waterway. All small pleasure craft shall relinquish the right-of-way to deeper draft vessels, which have a limited maneuvering ability due to their draft and size.

(13)     (d) Stopping in waterway. Vessels will not be permitted to stop or anchor in the ship channel.

(14)     (e) Water skiing. Water skiing in the waterway is prohibited between Reedy Point and Welch Point.

(15)     (f) Sailboats. Transiting the canal by vessels under sail is not permitted between Reedy Point and Welch Point.

(16)

**§ 207.100 Inland waterway from Delaware River to Chesapeake Bay, DE and MD (Chesapeake and Delaware Canal); use, administration, and navigation.**

(17)     (a) *Applicability*. The regulations in this section are applicable to that part of the inland waterway from Delaware River to Chesapeake Bay, DE and MD, between Reedy Point, Delaware River, and Old Town Point Wharf, Elk River.

(18)　(b) *Supervision.* The District Engineer, Corps of Engineers, Philadelphia, PA, has administrative supervision over the waterway and is charged with the enforcement of these regulations. The District Engineer from time to time will prescribe rules governing the dimensions of vessels which may transit the waterway, and other special conditions and requirements which will govern the movement of vessels using the waterway. The District Engineer's representative is the Chesapeake City Resident Engineer. The Chesapeake City Resident Engineer through the dispatcher on duty will enforce these regulations and monitor traffic through the canal.

(19)　(c) *Safe navigation required.* Clearance for any vessel to enter or pass through any part of the waterway will be contingent on the vessel's having adequate personnel, machinery, and operative devices for safe navigation. In the event of question as to the ability of any vessel to navigate the waterway safely, a ruling will be made by the dispatcher. The owner, agent, master, pilot, or other person in charge of the vessel concerned may appeal the dispatcher's ruling to the District Engineer whose decision shall be final. A clearance by the dispatcher for a vessel's passage through the waterway shall not relieve the owners, agents, and operators of the vessel of full responsibility for its safe passage.

(20)　(d) *Radio equipment.* Requirements for radio equipment on vessels transiting the waterway are as described in rules governing traffic through the waterway issued by the District Engineer. Vessels not having the mandatory radio equipment will not be permitted to transit the canal.

(21)　(e) *Anchorage and wharfage facilities.* The anchorage basin at Chesapeake City and free wharfage facilities on the west side of the anchorage basin are available for small vessels only. These facilities are of limited capacity, and permission to occupy them for periods exceeding 24 hours must be obtained in advance from the dispatcher at Chesapeake City.

(22)　(f) *Projections from vessels.* No vessel carrying a deck load which overhangs or projects beyond the sides of the vessel will be permitted to enter or pass through the waterway. Vessels carrying rods, poles, or other gear extending above the top of the vessel's mast will be required to lower such equipment to a level with the top of the mast before entering the waterway.

(23)　(g) (Reserved)

(24)　(h) Tows–(1) *Integrated pusher-type tows.* The maximum overall length and extreme breadth of this type of tow which may transit the canal are as described in rules governing traffic through the waterway issued by the District Engineer.

(25)　(2) *All other types of tows.* All ships or tugs engaged in towing vessels not equipped with a rudder, whether light or loaded, shall use two towlines or a bridle on one towline. If the vessel in tow is equipped with a rudder, one towline without a bridle may be used. All towlines must be hauled as short as practicable for safe handling of the tows. No towboat will be permitted to enter the waterway with more than two loaded, or three light barges. Two or more barges or other vessels, not self-propelled, shall be towed abreast and not in tandem, using two towlines unless the towboat is made fast alongside the tow.

(26)　(i) (Reserved)

(27)　(j) *Traffic lights.* Traffic lights are located at Reedy Point and Old Town Point Wharf. These traffic lights are described in the rules governing traffic through the waterway issued by the District Engineer.

(28)　(k) *Drawbridges.* Operation of the Penn Central vertical lift bridge across the canal will be in accordance with regulations promulgated by the U.S. Coast Guard. (See **33 CFR 117.1** through **117.59** and **117.235**, chapter 2, for drawbridge regulations.)

(29)　(l) (Reserved)

(30)　(m) *Refuse and oil.* The depositing of trash, refuse, debris, oil, or other material in the waterway or upon the banks or right-of-way is prohibited. Violators are subject to penalties as prescribed by Federal law.

(31)　(n) *Damage to waterway property.* Damage to the waterway, lands, banks, bridges, jetties, piers, fences, buildings, trees, telephone lines, lighting structures, or any other property of the United States pertaining to the waterway is prohibited.

(32)　(o) *Fish and game.* The fish and game laws of the United States and of the States of Delaware and Maryland, within their respective bounds, will be enforced upon the waters and lands pertaining to the waterway owned by the United States.

(33)　(p) *Grounded, wrecked,* or damaged vessels. In the event a vessel is grounded or wrecked in the waterway or is damaged by accident or successive mechanical breakdown, the owner, agent, or operator shall take prompt action to prevent the vessel from becoming or remaining an obstruction to navigation, and such persons shall also respond to such instructions as may be issued by the District Engineer to prevent the vessel from becoming or remaining a menace to navigation. The lack of reasonable response from owner, agent, or operator may be deemed sufficient cause for the District Engineer to undertake repair or removal of the vessel as he may determine to be in the best interest to the Government.

(34)　(q) (Reserved)

(35)　(r) (Reserved)

(36)　(s) (Reserved)

(37)　(t) *Pilotage.* Any pilot who pilots in the canal shall comply with State laws or Coast Guard regulations and must be licensed for this waterway by the U.S. Coast Guard.

(38)　(u) *Vessels difficult to handle.* Vessels which are observed by the pilot or master in charge, to be difficult to handle, or which are known to have handled badly on previous trips, must transit the canal during daylight hours and must have tug assistance. Such vessels must obtain permission from the dispatcher to enter the canal and must be provided with the number of tugs sufficient to afford safe passage. Agents must make their own arrangements for tug assistance. Such eastbound vessels must clear Reedy Point Bridge, and such westbound vessels the Chesapeake City Bridge, before dark.

(39)

**Local Regulations**

(40)     1. The following rules governing traffic through the Chesapeake and Delaware Canal are issued to supplement the rules and regulations governing the use, administration and navigation of the waterway that are prescribed by the Secretary of the Army. These rules were effective 8 August 1975 and were amended effective 1 April 1985 and 2 May 1988. Copies of the approved rules and regulations may be obtained from the District Engineer.

(41)     2. Traffic through the canal is monitored by the dispatcher at Chesapeake City. Vessels transiting the canal are subject to the following rules:

(42)     a. Vessels exceeding 800 feet are required to have bow thrusters.

(43)     b. The maximum combined extreme breadth of vessels, tugs and tows meeting and overtaking each other anywhere between Reedy Point and Town Point is 190 feet.

(44)     c. Vessels, tugs and tows, or any combination thereof, are required to have radiotelephone equipment as specified by the Vessel Bridge-to-Bridge Radiotelephone Act (Public Law 92–63). The radio requirement applies to the following:

(45)     (1) Every power-driven vessel of three hundred gross tons and upward.

(46)     (2) Every vessel of one hundred gross tons and upward carrying one or more passengers for hire.

(47)     (3) Every towing vessel of twenty six feet or over in length.

(48)     d. Vessels listed in 2.c. above will not enter the canal until radio communications are established with the dispatcher in Chesapeake City. Communications shall be established on channel 13 two hours prior to entering the canal. (Dispatcher Call Sign is WB–33 and Dispatcher Phone Number is 410–885–5621). The dispatcher also monitors channel 16 for the purpose of responding to transmissions of an emergency nature. Pilots and shipmasters shall acknowledge receipt of 2-hour clearance and conform with supplemental information listed in 3.e. below. All communications with the dispatcher on these frequencies shall be confined to that necessary to transit the Chesapeake and Delaware Canal.

(49)     e. A westbound vessel must be able to pass either Pea Patch Island or Reedy Island within 1 hour after receipt of clearance. An eastbound vessel must be able to pass Arnold Point within 1 hour of receipt of clearance. A clearance to enter the canal becomes invalid and a new one must be solicited whenever the pilot or shipmaster determines that the passage at these check points will not be made within 1 hour after the dispatcher has given a clearance to enter the Canal. The dispatcher will be furnished the actual time of passing these check points, along with the estimated time of arrival at Town Point

or Reedy Point. A vessel entering or departing the Canal must also report to the dispatcher the time of passing the outer end of the jetties at Reedy Point and Old Town Point Wharf.

(50)     f. A clearance by the dispatcher for a vessel's passage through the waterway shall not relieve the owners, agents and operators of the vessel of full responsibility of its safe passage.

(51)     3. The traffic controls located at Reedy Point and Old Town Point Wharf consist of a flashing green light when the Canal is open and a flashing red light when it is closed.

(52)     4. Vessel monitoring is performed by TV cameras, located at Reedy Point, Old Town Point Wharf and the SRNJ Railroad Bridge. These cameras are remotely controlled and monitored by the dispatcher at Chesapeake City.

(53)     5. Owners, designated agents or pilots of vessels transiting the Canal will furnish statistical data on cargo and passengers by completing Waterway Traffic Report, ENG 3102–R, which will be mailed or delivered to the Philadelphia District Engineer. This form may be obtained from the District Engineer or the Superintendent of Operations and Maintenance, Chesapeake and Delaware Canal, at Chesapeake City.

(54)     6. Vessel operators are warned that failure to comply with the rules and regulations governing traffic through the Canal will result in referral of violations to the U.S. Coast Guard.

(55)

**Supplemental local regulations**

(56)     The following rules regarding transit of dead ships or other structures not normally under tow through the Chesapeake and Delaware Canal are issued to supplement the rules and regulations governing the use, administration and navigation of the waterway that are prescribed by the Secretary of the Army.

(57)     These regulations appeared in a Notice to Mariners issued by District Engineer, Philadelphia District, dated August 14, 1986, and were effective immediately.

(58)     All dead and disabled ships, drydocks and all other structures not normally under tow must obtain specific advance approval to transit the waterway in accordance with this notice.

(59)     Minimum requirements for these transits are as follows:

(60)     (1) First class pilot or towing vessel operator, licensed by U.S. Coast Guard, with minimum experience of 10 previous trips through the Chesapeake & Delaware Canal, including one trip within the past year, will be on board to supervise transit.

(61)     (2) Tugboat Assistance.

(62)     (a) Vessels (structures) up to 350 feet in length: minimum 1 tug with at least 1,500 hp.

(63)     (b) Vessels (structures) between 350 feet and 550 feet in length: minimum 2 tugs with at least 3,000 total hp.

(74)

Chesapeake and Delaware Canal (east entrance), Delaware
Image courtesy of Waterway Images (2006)

—N⟶

(64)    (c) Vessels (structures) between 550 feet and 760 feet in length: minimum 3 tugs with at least 6,000 total hp.

(65)    Request for transit approval must be received by Chief, Operations Division, at least 72 hours prior to desired transit time. Initial requests may be written or verbal. Verbal requests will be confirmed in writing. All requests will provide the following information:

(66)    (1) The name and type of dead ship or structure and its length, width, height and draft.

(67)    (2) The number, horsepower and configuration of towing vessel(s), including the length of any towing lines (hawsers) to be used.

(68)    (3) Specific details regarding any characteristic(s) of the subject ship/structure that may impact on handling during transit through the Canal.

(69)    (4) Name and telephone number of point of contact.

(70)    Approval, if granted, will be given for one transit on a specific date, during daylight hours, with no vessels overtaking or passing in opposite direction. All other rules and regulations governing transit of the Canal will remain in effect.

(71)
### Channels

(72)    The Federal project for the canal provides for a channel 35 feet deep and 400 feet wide. For detailed channel information and minimum depths as reported by the U.S. Army Corps of Engineers (USACE), use NOAA Electronic Navigational Charts. Surveys and channel condition reports are available through a USACE hydrographic survey website listed in Appendix A.

(73)    **Delaware City** and the **Delaware City Branch Channel** are described in chapter 6.

(75)
### Anchorages

(76)    An anchorage basin is provided on the south side of the canal at Mile 12.8, opposite Chesapeake City. The entrance to the basin is subject to periodic shoaling. Regulations for the use of the anchorage and mooring basin are given in **33 CFR 207.100(e)** provided previously in this chapter. Also see **33 CFR 165.1** through **165.13** and **165.556**, chapter 2, for **regulated navigation area** regulations.

(77)
### Local magnetic disturbance

(78)    Differences of as much as 6° from the normal variation have been observed in Elk River Channel from Courthouse Point to Old Town Point.

(80)
### Tides

(81)    High and low waters in Delaware River are about 2 hours later than in Elk River. The heights of high and low waters are greatly affected by the winds; northeast storms raise the level and westerly storms lower it.

(79)

**Structures across the Chesapeake and Delaware Canal**

| Name | Type | Location | Clearances (feet) Horizontal | Clearances (feet) Vertical* | Information |
|------|------|----------|-----------|----------|-------------|
| Reedy Point bridge | fixed | 39°33'29"N., 75°34'57"W. | 450 | 133 (136 at center) | |
| Overhead cables | power | 39°33'11"N., 75°37'19"W. | | 161 | |
| St. Georges East bridge | fixed | 39°33'09"N., 75°39'03"W. | 450 | 132 (137 at center) | |
| St. Georges West bridge | fixed | 39°33'00"N., 75°39'22"W. | 450 | 142 | |
| Conrail bridge | vertical lift | 39°32'35"N., 75°42'11"W. | 450 | 45 (down) 129 (up) | Notes 1 and 2 |
| Overhead pipeline | | 39°32'32"N., 75°43'26"W. | | 141 | |
| Overhead cable | power | 39°32'32"N., 75°43'31"W. | | 159 | |
| Summit bridge | fixed | 39°32'29"N., 75°44'19"W. | 450 | 131 (138 at center) | |
| Overhead cable | power | 39°32'25"N., 75°45'14"W. | | 157 | |
| Overhead cable | power | 39°32'07"N., 75°46'31"W. | | 161 | |
| Overhead cable | power | 39°32'08"N., 75°46'36"W. | | 161 | |
| Chesapeake City bridge | fixed | 39°31'45"N., 75°48'51"W. | 450 | 134 (140 at center) | |

* Clearances are referenced to Mean High Water
Note 1 – See **33 CFR 117.1** through **117.59** and **117.235**, chapter 2, for drawbridge regulations.
Note 2 – Vertical clearance shown is the normal low limit stop for the raised position. A limit override allows an additional 8 feet of vertical clearance.

(82)  **Staff gages**, with zeros set at **canal datum**, are at numerous places along the canal and at both ends. The datum is 2 feet below local mean low water at the mouth of Back Creek and about less than 1 foot below at Delaware River.

(83)
### Current
(84)  The current velocity is 2.6 knots on the flood and 2.1 knots on the ebb at the Reedy Point bridge and about 2 knots at the Chesapeake City bridge. The flood sets eastward and the ebb westward. Storms may increase these velocities to 3.0 knots or more; at such times, tows usually have difficulty in making headway against the current. See the Tidal Current prediction service at *tidesandcurrents.noaa.gov* for specific information about times, directions, and velocities of the current at numerous locations throughout the area. Links to a user guide for this service can be found in chapter 1 of this book.

(85)
### Ice
(86)  Ice sufficient to interfere with the navigation of small craft may be expected at any time between December and April and is worst during January and February. The canal is kept open as long as possible. During mild winters, local vessels use the canal throughout most of the season, but strangers should make inquiries before attempting passage. Wooden vessels passing through thin ice are liable to be cut through at the waterline. Vessels with low horsepower are cautioned against transiting the canal in heavy ice.

(87)
### Pilotage, Chesapeake and Delaware Canal
(88)  Pilotage through the canal from Delaware River to Chesapeake City is provided by the Pilots' Association for the Delaware Bay and River. (See Pilotage, Bay and River Delaware, indexed as such, chapter 6.) Pilotage from Chesapeake City to Maryland ports and to Washington, D.C., is provided by the Association of Maryland Pilots. (See chapter 15.) Both pilots associations maintain a common station on the north bank of the canal at Chesapeake City. A white motor launch is used for exchanging pilots in the general vicinity of Chesapeake City. Vessels proceeding from Chesapeake City to Washington, D.C., or the lower part of Chesapeake Bay, when using Maryland pilots, sometimes transfer pilots at a designated transfer area in Chesapeake Bay off the entrance to Patuxent River or on the Potomac River off Piney Point, depending on the port of call.

(89)  The Maryland pilots are replaced by Virginia pilots off the entrance of the Patuxent River or on the Potomac River off Piney Point, depending on the port of call.

(90)  The Interport Pilots Agency, Inc., offers pilotage to public vessels and private vessels in the coastal trade transiting the Chesapeake and Delaware Canal and continuing to ports in the Delaware Bay and River, Upper Chesapeake Bay, New York Harbor and Long Island Sound. They board vessels at any Delaware River or Upper Chesapeake Bay port, the pilot boarding area off Cape Henlopen as described in chapter 6, or at the Reedy Point Anchorage near the east end of the Chesapeake and Delaware Canal. Arrangements for pilot services are made 24 hours in advance with a 6-hour ETA update through the ships agent or with Interport Pilots Agency,

Inc., 906 Port Monmouth Road, Port Monmouth, NJ 07758-0236, telephone 732–787–5554 (24 hours), or email at interport@verizon.net. Additional information about Interport Pilots can be obtained at: interportpilots. com.

(91)     The Chesapeake and Interstate Pilots Association offers pilot services to U.S. vessels engaged in the coastwise trade and to public vessels transiting the Chesapeake and Delaware Canal. Pilots will meet vessels between Cape Henlopen, any port or place on the Delaware Bay and River, or any port or place on the Chesapeake Bay and its tributaries and provide all pilot services required when vessels use the canal. Arrangements for pilots are made through ships' agents or the pilot office in Norfolk (telephone, 757–855–2733). The pilots use commercial launch services. Advance pilot orders requested with 6-hour ETA update and any subsequent changes requested. Pilots will get underway generally 30 minutes prior to the time they have been ordered.

(92)     All pilots carry radiotelephones for bridge-to-bridge communications and for communications with the canal traffic dispatcher at Chesapeake City. Delaware Bay and River pilots use VHF-FM channel 14, and the Maryland pilots use VHF–FM channel 11; all associations use VHF-FM channel 13.

(93)     The traffic dispatcher at Chesapeake City also monitors VHF–FM channel 16 and channel 13 on a 24-hour basis.

(94)
**Supplies and repairs**

(95)     At Mile 7.5, on the north side of the canal, is a private marina. In 1991, the entrance channel and basin had reported depths of 10 feet. The marina can provide transient berths, gasoline, diesel fuel, electricity, water, marine supplies, pump-out facility, dry storage, a 50-ton travel lift and hull and engine repairs. The harbormaster is available 24 hours a day and monitors VHF-FM channel 16.

(96)     At Chesapeake City, berths, gasoline, diesel fuel and some marine supplies are available. The principal wharves and slips have reported depths of 7 to 17 feet at their faces.

(97)     At Mile 16.2, 0.4 mile eastward of **Courthouse Point**, a privately marked channel leads to a marina. In 2000, the channel had a reported controlling depth of 4 feet. Berths, gasoline and marine supplies are available. Hull and engine repairs can be made; a 20-ton mobile hoist is available. A boatyard on Courthouse Point has gasoline and a 6-ton lift; minor hull and engine repairs can be made.

(98)     (For discussion of Elk River and the upper part of Chesapeake Bay, see chapter 15.)

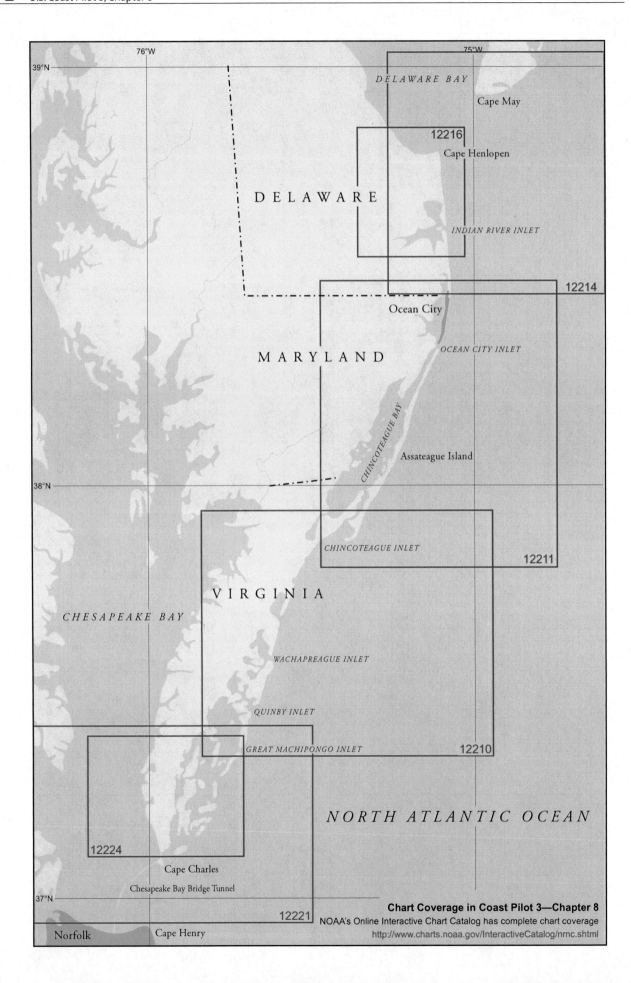

**Chart Coverage in Coast Pilot 3—Chapter 8**
NOAA's Online Interactive Chart Catalog has complete chart coverage
http://www.charts.noaa.gov/InteractiveCatalog/nrnc.shtml

# Delaware-Maryland-Virginia Coast

(1)　　　This chapter describes that section of the Delaware, Maryland and Virginia coastline extending from Cape Henlopen to Cape Charles and the Virginia Inside Passage. Included in the discussion are Roosevelt Inlet, the Delaware Bay entrance to the Lewes and Rehoboth Canal, Indian River Inlet, Assawoman Canal and Bay, Isle of Wight Bay, Ocean City Inlet, Chincoteague Bay and Inlet and the various inlets that lead through the barrier beach to the Virginia Inside Passage.

(2)　　　Also described are the cities of Lewes, Rehoboth, Ocean City and Chincoteague and several of the smaller communities on these waterways.

(3)
### North Atlantic Right Whales
(4)　　　Endangered North Atlantic right whales may occur within 30 miles of the Delaware, Maryland and Virginia coasts (peak season: October through November and February through May). (See **North Atlantic Right Whales**, indexed as such in chapter 3, for more information on right whales and recommended measures to avoid collisions.)

(5)　　　All vessels 65 feet or greater in length overall (LOA.) and subject to the jurisdiction of the United States are restricted to speeds of 10 knots or less in a Seasonal Management Area existing around the Delaware Bay and the entrance to the Chesapeake Bay between November 1 and April 30. The areas are defined as the waters within a 20-nm radius of 38°52'27.4"N., 75°01'32.1"W. (Delaware Bay) and 37°00'36.9"N., 75°57'50.5"W. (Chesapeake Bay). (See **50 CFR 224.105** in chapter 2 for regulations, limitations and exceptions.)

(6)
### COLREGS Demarcation Lines
(7)　　　The lines established for Delaware Bay and the inlets of the Delaware-Maryland-Virginia coast are described in **33 CFR 80.503** and **80.505**, chapter 2.

(8)
### ENCs - US5VA71M, US4VA70M, US4VA50M, US5MD50M, US4DE11M, US4VA12M, US4VA1AM
### Charts - 12210, 12211, 12214, 12221

(9)　　　The coast extends southward for 21 miles from Cape Henlopen to the Delaware-Maryland boundary line, thence south-southwestward for 27 miles to the Maryland-Virginia boundary, and thence 63 miles to Cape Charles. The low sand beaches are backed by bays, rivers and creeks that are bordered by marsh and woodland. Broken ground fringes the coast, and depths of 36 feet or less are found as far as 12 miles from shore.

(10)　　　Visible from seaward are the summer resorts of Rehoboth Beach, Bethany Beach, Dewey Beach and Ocean City, all within 30 miles of Cape Henlopen. The most prominent marks south of Ocean City are the light structures and the Coast Guard stations.

(11)　　　The bays and connecting channels back of the barrier beaches form a continuous inside passage from Delaware Bay to Chesapeake Bay, but Assawoman Canal and Little Assawoman Bay are now navigable only for rowboats and outboards.

(12)　　　There are no harbors of refuge for deep-draft vessels along this coast. The inlets are subject to frequent change, and their navigation requires local knowledge.

(13)
### Fishtrap
(14)　　　**Fishtrap** areas along the coast from Cape Henlopen to Cape Charles have been established under Federal authority and are shown on the charts. Numerous pile remains of former traps are said to menace inshore navigation.

(15)
### Navigational aids
(16)　　　Most of the navigable inlets are marked by buoys, but the channels shift and the buoys cannot always be depended upon to mark the best water. Breakers form on the shoals even in ordinary weather and are good marks. Some of the interior channels are marked by daybeacons and lights, but others are marked only by bush stakes. The channels through the flats can be followed best at low water when the flats are visible.

(17)
### Tides
(18)　　　High and low waters occur at about the same time as at Sandy Hook. Levels in the inside waters are greatly affected by winds, westerly winds producing low water and easterly winds high water. In Assawoman, Isle of Wight, Sinepuxent and Chincoteague Bays, northerly and southerly winds drive the water to the ends of the bays. With strong winds of long duration, depths may be as much as 3 feet above or below the normal level.

(19)
### Current
(20)　　　The currents have considerable velocity in the inlets and in the narrow channels connecting the inlets with adjacent bays and sounds. Velocities of as much as 3 knots may be encountered at times in places where the currents are strongest.

### Weather

(22)　　From Cape Henlopen to Cape Charles this coast is exposed to the rigors of the North Atlantic. Winter gales can be expected about 5 percent of the time while winds of 28 knots or more are twice as frequent. Strongest and most prevalent are those out of the northwest through north, averaging 18 to 20 knots. Wave heights of 10 feet (3 m) or more are encountered 8 to 12 percent of the time from December through March. Winter visibilities suffer from precipitation and fog; visibilities fall below 2 miles (3.2 km) about 3 percent of the time and below 0.5 mile (0.8 km) 1 to 2 percent of the time. Precipitation occurs about 8 percent of the time.

(23)　　Spring brings milder conditions. Gales and wind speeds of 28 knots or more occur about one-half as frequently as they did in winter. Directions are variable, but south and southwest winds are most frequent by April. Waves of 10 feet (3 m) or more become increasingly less frequent; by May they are encountered less than 3 percent of the time. However, warm air blowing over still cold water brings fog. Visibilities of less than 0.5 mile (0.8 km) occur about 3 percent of the time; about one-half that for visibilities less than 2 miles (3.2 km). Precipitation occurs about 6 percent of the time.

(24)　　Summer, except for the threat of thunderstorms and a rare tropical cyclone, brings good sailing weather. Winds are out of the south and southwest about one-half of the time; westerlies and northeasterlies are also common. Strong winds are unlikely outside of thunderstorms, tropical cyclones and an occasional frontal passage. Poor visibilities are also uncommon, and waves of 10 feet (3 m) or more occur 1 to 2 percent of the time. Precipitation is encountered about 4 percent of the time and about one-half of the time is in the form of thunderstorms. Thunderstorms are most likely from May through September and often occur during the late night and early morning hours at sea. In squall lines winds can reach hurricane force in gusts.

(25)　　With autumn comes more of a threat of both tropical and extratropical storms, variable, strong winds and rough seas. Tropical cyclones are a threat throughout the fall, but particularly in September and October when recurving storms tend to brush this coast on occasion. Extra tropical storms pick up in October and are partially responsible for the increase in northerlies and northwesterlies. Winds out of the east, southwest and northwest are also common. In October, gales occur about 2 percent of the time compared to winds of 28 knots or more, which are encountered about 6 percent of the time. Wave heights of 10 feet (3 m) or more are generated 7 to 8 percent of the time during autumn. At sea visibilities remain good; less than 0.5 mile (0.8 km) less than 1 percent of the time, while less than 2 miles (3.2 km) about 2 percent of the time. Precipitation falls about 5 percent of the time.

### Ice

(27)　　The inside waters north of Chincoteague Bay occasionally are closed by ice during ordinary winters. The tributary waters south of the bay are closed during severe winters but remain so only for short periods. The principal inlets are rarely closed and are used by local boats throughout the winter.

(28)　　During the ice navigation season, the inside waters of Maryland, described in this chapter, are a **regulated navigation area**. (See **33 CFR 165.10**, **165.33** and **165.503**, chapter 2, for limits and regulations.)

### ENC - US5DE10M
### Chart - 12216

(30)　　**Cape Henlopen**, on the southwest side of the entrance to Delaware Bay, is described in chapter 6.

(31)　　**Roosevelt Inlet**, 3 miles west of Cape Henlopen, is the Delaware Bay entrance to the Lewes and Rehoboth Canal and to Broadkill River. The inlet is protected by jetties that are awash at low water; each jetty is marked by a light on its outer end. The channel is marked by the jetty lights and a **213°** lighted range. In Roosevelt Inlet, the current velocity is about 0.9 knot. (See Notice to Mariners and latest edition of charts for controlling depths.) Gasoline and diesel fuel can be obtained at a yacht club on the northeast side of the inlet.

(32)　　**Broadkill River** is entered by way of an inside passage that extends northwestward for 2 miles from the Roosevelt Inlet jetties to the old mouth of the river; the river then extends 9 miles westward to the town of **Milton**. (See the latest chart and notice to mariners for the controlling depth in the river.)

(33)　　Overhead power cables at the entrance to the Broadkill River, just north of the Coast Guard station, have a clearance of 50 feet. Twin fixed highway bridges over Broadkill River have a clearance of 18 feet. The overhead power cable just northwestward of the bridges has a clearance of 64 feet. Above the bridges, the river has numerous snags and much floating debris.

(34)　　The **Lewes and Rehoboth Canal** is a tidal waterway that extends southeastward and southward for 8 miles from Roosevelt Inlet to Rehoboth Bay. The canal passes northeastward of Lewes and westward of Rehoboth Beach; the entrance to Rehoboth Bay is between marked, submerged, stone jetties a mile southwest of Dewey Beach. The posted **speed limit** is 4 miles per hour in the canal.

(35)　　**Lewes**, 1.7 miles inside Roosevelt Inlet, has rail connections and is the southern terminal for the Cape May-Lewes ferry.

(36)　　Several small-craft facilities are in the vicinity of the first and second bridges at Lewes. Gasoline, diesel fuel, berths, and marine supplies can be obtained, and hull and engine repairs can be made. A 70-foot marine railway and a 25-ton mobile hoist are available.

(37)

**Structures across the Lewes and Rehoboth Canal**

| Name | Type | Location | Horizontal | Vertical* | Information |
|------|------|----------|------------|-----------|-------------|
| | | | Clearances (feet) | | |
| Overhead cable | power | 38°46'33"N., 75°08'18"W. | | 68 | |
| Savannah Road bridge | bascule | 38°46'32"N., 75°08'16"W. | 70 | 15 | Note 1 |
| Overhead cable | power | 38°46'25"N., 75°08'04"W. | | 68 | |
| Railroad bridge | swing | 38°46'25"N., 75°08'01"W. | 46 | 10 | Span is kept in the open position |
| U.S. Route 9 bridge | fixed | 38°46'23"N., 75°07'58"W. | 46 | 35 | |
| State Route 1 Alternate bridge | bascule | 38°42'52"N., 75°05'35"W. | 49 | 16 | Note 1 |
| Overhead cables | power | 38°42'50"N., 75°05'36"W. | | 55 | |
| Overhead cables | power | 38°42'33"N., 75°05'37"W. | | 55 | |
| State Route 1 bridge | fixed | 38°42'32"N., 75°05'35"W. | 100 | 35 | |
| Overhead cables | power | 38°42'29"N., 75°05'38"W. | | 55 | |

* Clearances are referenced to Mean High Water
Note 1 – See **33 CFR 117.1** through **117.59** and **117.239**, chapter 2, for drawbridge regulations.
The bridges over the canal restrict the normal flow of water and produce very strong currents—small craft should transit these areas with caution.

(38)    A yacht club at which slips, gasoline and some marine supplies are available is in a basin on the east side of the canal 4 miles southeastward of Lewes.

(39)    **Rehoboth Bay** has depths of 1 to 7 feet. The 5-mile route down Rehoboth Bay from the Lewes and Rehoboth Canal to Indian River Bay is marked by lighted and unlighted buoys. Gasoline, some supplies and slips are available at the northeast end of Rehoboth Bay at **Dewey Beach**.

(40)    **Love Creek**, at the northwest corner of Rehoboth Bay, is navigable for small craft to a milldam about 4 miles above the mouth. An unmarked, privately dredged channel leads from Rehoboth Bay 3 miles above the mouth of the creek. In 2000, the channel had a reported centerline controlling depth of 2 feet. The fixed highway bridge 2.3 miles above the mouth has an 18-foot channel span with a clearance of 7 feet. Above the bridge are berthing facilities in depths of 1 to 2 feet.

(41)    **Herring Creek**, at the southwest corner of Rehoboth Bay, has depths of 3 to 5 feet to the forks 2 miles above the mouth, thence 1 to 3 feet for 0.5 mile in Burton Prong and 3 to 5 feet for 1 mile in Hopkins Prong. The creek, partially marked by private daybeacons, is little used except by local residents.

(42)    **Indian River Inlet**, 12 miles south of Cape Henlopen, is the first opening in the barrier beach south of Delaware Bay. The entrance is marked by buoys, and a light is on the end of the south jetty. **Indian River Inlet Coast Guard Station** is on the north side 0.5 mile inside the inlet. The fixed highway bridge over the inlet has a clearance of 45 feet. An overhead power cable with a clearance of 66 feet crosses the inlet about 100 yards westward of the bridge.

(43)    A channel leads from Indian River Inlet through Indian River Bay and up Indian River to Millsboro, 12 miles above the inlet. The channel from the entrance to Buoy 20 in Indian River Bay is subject to continual change due to severe shoaling. The channel is marked by uncharted buoys that are frequently shifted to mark the best water. The channel to Millsboro is marked by daybeacons and seasonal buoys.

(44)

**Current**

(45)    The current velocity is about 2 knots; caution is necessary, because the buoys sometimes tow under.

(46)

**Supplies**

(47)    Gasoline, diesel fuel, slips and some marine supplies are available in the small-boat basin on the north side, 0.8 mile inside Indian River Inlet, and at a marina on the south side 0.9 mile inside the inlet. Hull and engine repairs can be made at both facilities. The boat basin has a 10-ton lift and the marina a 25-ton lift.

(48)

**Anchorages**

(49)    **Indian River Bay**, a shallow lagoon with depths of 1 to 6 feet, extends for about 5 miles west of Indian River Inlet, then becomes **Indian River**, which is navigable for an additional 7 miles to Millsboro. Overhead power cables with a least clearance of 61 feet crosses Indian River about 2.9 miles above the mouth of the river. The 5-mile route down the bay from Rehoboth Bay to Assawoman Canal is marked by seasonal buoys and daybeacons; the controlling depth is about 2 feet.

(50)    **Millsboro**, on the south side of Indian River at the head of navigation, has a town bulkhead; gasoline and some supplies are available. About 100 yards below the causeway at Millsboro, there is an overhead power cable with a clearance of 43 feet. The town has railroad-freight service.

(51)    The State of Delaware has established State-leased clam and oyster grounds, which extend westward from a line connecting Lingo Point (38°36'24"N., 75°09'24"W.) and Ellis Point (38°35'36"N., 75°08'06"W.) to the mouth of Indian River and just inside the mouth of Pepper Creek.

Mariners are advised to use caution when navigating outside the marked channel in this area because of numerous unlighted stakes, wood spar buoys and other dangerous markers.

(52)    **Pepper Creek**, on the south side of Indian River Bay near its western end, has a dredged channel marked by daybeacons extending for 3 miles above the entrance. A clam plant is at the upper end of the creek. Gasoline and slips are available 2 miles above the entrance.

(53)    Most of the piers and facilities on the north side of Indian River are private.

(54)    **White Creek** is on the south side of Indian River Bay 1.5 miles back of the outer beach. A channel, marked by daybeacons, passes through the bay and creek to Assawoman Canal and **Ocean View**. Gasoline and some supplies are available at Ocean View.

(55)    **Assawoman Canal** is a 3-mile land cut that connects White Creek with the north end of Little Assawoman Bay. Logs were reported to obstruct the channel at several points. Three fixed highway bridges over the canal have a minimum width of 14 feet and clearance of 4 feet. The power cables over the canal have a minimum clearance of 28 feet.

(56)
## ENCs - US4VA50M, US5MD50M
## Chart - 12211

(57)    **Little Assawoman Bay**, behind the barrier beach of **Fenwick Island** is 3 miles long. The bay, marked by private daybeacons, has depths of 2 to 4 feet but in some areas shoals to bare.

(58)    **Fenwick Island Light** (38°27'06"N., 75°03'18"W.), 83 feet above the water, is shown from a white tower, about 0.3 mile back of the beach. The tower, just north of the Delaware-Maryland boundary line, is 9 miles south of Indian River Inlet and 21 miles south of Cape Henlopen.

(59)    **Fenwick Shoal**, about 5.5 miles eastward of the northern end of Fenwick Island, has a least depth of 16 feet; however, two wrecks on the shoal have a least depth of 11 feet. A lighted buoy marks the southwest end of the shoal.

(60)    **Isle of Wight Shoal**, about 8.5 miles northeastward of Ocean City Inlet, has a depth of 19 feet. A 26-foot shoal is about midway between Isle of Wight Shoal and Fenwick Shoal.

(61)    A narrow thoroughfare links the southern end of Little Assawoman Bay with Assawoman Bay; the controlling depth is about 2 feet. It is navigable by small boats with local knowledge. The fixed highway bridge near the north end of the thorofare has a width of 37 feet and a clearance of 11 feet.

(62)    **Assawoman Bay** and **Isle of Wight Bay** form a continuous lagoon that extends from close southward of Little Assawoman Bay to Ocean City. The bays have depths of 4 to 6 feet along their western sides and are frequented by boats from Ocean City.

(63)    The State Route 90 fixed highway bridge with a clearance of 35 feet crosses Isle of Wight Bay between Isle of Wight and Fenwick Island.

(64)    **Ocean City Inlet** (38°19.4'N., 75°05.2'W.), between Fenwick Island and Assateague Island, is 29 miles south of Cape Henlopen and is the only break in the barrier beach between Indian River Inlet and Chincoteague Inlet. The entrance is between stone jetties, but the north jetty and the outer end of the south jetty are covered at high water. A 200-foot-long fishing pier is 0.2 mile north of the north jetty.

(65)

## No-discharge Zone

(66)    The State of Maryland, with the approval of the Environmental Protection Agency, has established a No-Discharge Zone (NDZ) in the northern Coastal Bays. The NDZ includes the waters of the Ocean City Inlet, Ocean City commercial fish harbor (Swordfish Basin), Isle of Wight Bay and Assawoman Bay. The area covered is defined as follows: Ocean City Inlet – west of a line beginning at a point at or near the east end of the north Ocean City Inlet jetty at 38°19'27.0"N., 75°05'05.5"W., then running approximately 248° to a point at or near the east end of the south Ocean City Inlet jetty at 38°19'20.7"N., 75°05'24.9"W.; and Sinepuxent Bay – north of a line beginning at a point at or near the shore of the southeast entrance of the Ocean City commercial fish harbor (Swordfish Basin) at 38°19'37.0"N., 75°06'06.0"W., then running approximately 110° to a point at or near the shore at the northwest tip of Assateague Island at 38°19'32.0"N., 75°05'49.0"W.; and Maryland-Delaware line – south of the Maryland-Delaware line beginning at a point at or near the east side of Assawoman Bay at 38°27'04.5"N., 75°04'11.2"W., then running approximately 270° to a point at or near the west side of Assawoman Bay at 38°27'04.4"N., 75°05'09.3"W.

(67)    Within the NDZ, discharge of sewage, whether treated or untreated, from all vessels is prohibited. Outside the NDZ, discharge of sewage is regulated by **40 CFR 140** (see chapter 2).

(68)

## Coast Guard

(69)    **Ocean City Coast Guard Station** is 0.6 mile inside the inlet on the southwest side of Ocean City.

(70)    **Little Gull Bank**, 2.5 miles southeastward of Ocean City Inlet, has a least depth of 18 feet. **Great Gull Bank**, 5 miles southeastward of the inlet, has a least depth of 19 feet.

(71)    **Ocean City**, that part of Fenwick Island barrier beach in Maryland, is a large summer resort visited by many small boats and is a shipping point for a large amount of seafood. Numerous water tanks and numerous high-rise condominiums are prominent along the beach of this resort. A large, cylindrical water tank, about 1.5 miles west of Ocean City Inlet, is prominent and is a good landmark while entering the inlet.

(72)    Ocean City Inlet is subject to continual change. The north jetty at the entrance is marked by a light and a mariner radio activated sound signal, initiated by keying the microphone five times on VHF-FM channel 83A. The channel through the inlet is marked by lighted buoys. During the summer months fishing vessels anchor at the entrance to the inlet near the north and south jetties. Within the inlet a strong ebb current exists. Caution is advised when entering and transiting the inlet.

(73)    The channel to Isle of Wight Bay is marked by lights, daybeacons, lighted and unlighted buoys.

(74)    The U.S. Route 50 highway bridge over Isle of Wight Bay from the mainland to Ocean City, 0.9 mile above the entrance jetties, has a bascule span with a clearance of 18 feet. The bridgetender monitors VHF–FM channel 16 and works on channels 13 and 68; call sign KYU–698. (See **33 CFR 117.1** through **117.59** and **117.559**, chapter 2, for drawbridge regulations.) Pile remains of an abandoned highway bridge are 0.2 mile south of the bridge.

(75)    There are numerous privately owned pile and timber piers and bulkhead wharves on the inner side of Ocean City. The **Commercial Fish Harbor**, on the mainland side 1 mile directly back of the inlet, has a 1,000-foot public bulkhead landing and several private bulkhead wharves open to the public for transaction of business with the owners.

(76)
### Small-craft facilities

(77)    There are several small-craft facilities at Ocean City and in Commercial Fish Harbor. Gasoline, diesel fuel, water, berths and marine supplies can be obtained at most of the facilities, and hull and engine repairs can be made at some.

(78)    **Sinepuxent Bay**, narrow and mostly shoal, and **Chincoteague Bay**, with depths of 4 to 7 feet along its western side but shoal along its eastern side, are behind **Assateague Island** and provide a 30-mile inside route for small boats from Ocean City to Chincoteague. The bays are used by fishing and pleasure boats. The Maryland-Virginia boundary line is marked by white and orange buoys worded *MD/VA*.

(79)    A dredged channel extends 12 miles south through Sinepuxent Bay to open water in Chincoteague Bay. The route here continues through a natural channel in Chincoteague Bay to Chincoteague, Virginia. The channels are well marked by lights, daybeacons and lighted and unlighted buoys. Sinepuxent Bay channel is subject to frequent shoaling and lesser than charted depths may be encountered. A submerged rock is at the entrance to Sinepuxent Bay in about 38°19'34"N., 75°05'54"W.

(80)    The State Route 611 fixed highway and pedestrian bridge across Sinepuxent Bay has a clearance of 35 feet. Submerged pilings from a former overhead cable cross the bay in the vicinity of Sinepuxent Bay Channel Buoys 27A and 28.

(81)    **Public Landing** (38°08'54"N., 75°17'12"W.), on the mainland side of Chincoteague Bay 15 miles from Ocean City Inlet, has a public wharf, private landings and fish piers; all have depths of about 4 feet alongside. A highway leads westward from the landing to **Snow Hill** on Pocomoke River. A small-boat basin with depths of 3 feet and a launching ramp is entered just north of the piers.

(82)    A marina at the entrance to **Tanhouse Creek**, 1 mile south of Public Landing, has gasoline, diesel fuel, and an 8-ton mobile hoist for hauling out boats for minor hull and engine repairs. The entrance to the creek is marked by a light.

(83)    **George Island Landing** is a small town on the mainland 0.8 mile northward of **Purnell Point** (38°01'42"N., 75°21'36"W.). The public wharf at the town is reached from the southward from Chincoteague Bay through a private channel marked by lights and daybeacons.

(84)    **Greenbackville**, 1.5 miles southwestward of Purnell Point, is a village on the mainland side of Chincoteague Bay just south of the Maryland-Virginia boundary line and 4 miles north of Chincoteague. Jetties at the entrance to the harbor are marked by lights; lighted buoys here mark wrecks near the entrance channel.

(85)    A dredged channel, marked by lighted and unlighted buoys and a light, 4.5 miles south of Purnell Point, is usually used to reach Chincoteague from Chincoteague Bay. Other passages between Chincoteague Bay and Chincoteague Inlet through marshy islands west of Chincoteague Island are used only by small boats with local knowledge. Depths through these passages range from 1 to 6 feet.

(86)

### Structures across Chincoteague Channels

| Name | Type | Location | Clearances (feet) Horizontal | Vertical* |
|---|---|---|---|---|
| Route 175 bridge | fixed | Mosquito Creek | 33 | 10 |
| Overhead cable | power | Mosquito Creek | | 31 |
| Route 175 bridge | fixed | Cockle Creek | 33 | 13 |
| Overhead cable | power | Cockle Creek | | 33 |
| Route 175 bridge | fixed | Queen Sound | 33 | 13 |
| Overhead cable | power | Queen Sound | | 33 |
| Route 175 bridge | fixed | Wire Narrows | 40 | 10 |
| Overhead cable | power | Wire Narrows | | 25 |
| Route 175 bridge | fixed | Black Narrows | 33 | 6 |
| Overhead cable | power | Black Narrows | | 27** |
| Route 175 bridge **Note 1** | bascule | Chincoteague Channel | 60 | 15 |

\* Clearances are referenced to Mean High Water
\*\* Reported clearance
**Note 1** – See **33 CFR 117.1** through **117.49** and **117.1005**, chapter 2, for drawbridge regulations.

(87)  **Assateague Light** (37°54'40"N., 75°21'22"W.), 154 feet above the water, is shown from a 142-foot red and white horizontally banded conical tower 3 miles from the south end of Assateague Island. The light stands well above the surrounding trees.

(88)  **Winter Quarter Shoal**, 11 miles east-northeast of Assateague Light has a least depth of 13 feet with obstructions to 12 feet. During periods of high winds and seas, breakers have been observed over the shoal.

(89)  **Blackfish Bank**, about 6 miles eastward of the south end of Assateague Island, has depths of 15 to 21 feet along its 5-mile length. A 26-foot shoal is 2.5 miles east of the bank. Coasting vessels seeking protection from westerly weather pass westward of Blackfish Bank.

(90)  **Chincoteague Shoals**, extending about 3 miles east and south of the lower end of Assateague Island, has a least depth of 8 feet near **Turners Lump**. A lighted buoy marks the south end of the shoals. Breakers have been observed over the shoaler areas when winds are southerly.

(91)  **Chincoteague Inlet**, between Assateague Island and Wallops Island, is 30 miles south-southwestward from Ocean City Inlet. The marked channel through the inlet to **Chincoteague Channel** is subject to frequent change; the buoys are shifted with changing conditions. Breakers are evident on either side of the channel. A sunken wreck is about 0.4 mile southwest of Fishing Point in 37°51'54"N., 75°24'04"W. Caution is advised when navigating the inlet.

(92)  Assateague Light and the lookout tower on the southern tip of Assateague Island are good marks for approaching Chincoteague Inlet.

(93)  **Fishing Point**, the hook-shaped sandspit forming the south side of **Toms Cove**, is continually making out to the westward, requiring caution when in the vicinity.

(94)  **Chincoteague**, occupying most of **Chincoteague Island**, is between the mainland and the south end of Assateague Island. The town is principally a shellfish and fishing center, but pleasure craft operate from here during the summer. The wharves and piers along the waterfront have depths of 3 to 10 feet alongside. There are small-craft facilities at Chincoteague that can provide gasoline, diesel fuel, water, berths and limited marine supplies. Hull and engine repairs can be made; a 40-ton marine railway at Chincoteague can handle craft up to 80 feet. A boat basin is at the extreme southwest end of Chincoteague Island.

(95)  **Coast Guard**

(96)  **Chincoteague Coast Guard Station** is on the east side of Chincoteague Channel, 0.3 mile south of the highway bridge.

(97)  **ENCs - US5VA71M, US4VA70M**
**Chart - 12210**

(98)  The 35-mile stretch of coast between Chincoteague Inlet and Great Machipongo Inlet is formed by six islands

of about equal length. The islands are separated from each other by narrow inlets and from the mainland by marsh and flats through which are numerous sloughs and channels. **Wallops Island**, northernmost of the six, is on the southwest side of Chincoteague Inlet.

(99)

**Danger zone**

(100)  A **danger zone** extends for about 5 miles off the coast of Wallops Island and covers the area just southwest of the entrance to Chincoteague Inlet. (See **33 CFR 334.130**, chapter 2, for limits and regulations.)

(101)  **Assawoman Inlet**, the ocean entrance between **Wallops Island** and **Assawoman Island**, is very shallow and is not used. **Gargathy Inlet**, the ocean inlet separating Assawoman Island and **Metompkin Islands**, is not used.

(102)  **Metompkin Inlet**, the ocean entrance between Metompkin Islands and **Cedar Island**, is used by some small local fishing and oyster boats. The changeable entrance channel is unmarked and should not be entered without local knowledge.

(103)  **Porpoise Banks**, 10 miles offshore from Metompkin Inlet, have irregular bottom with depths of 34 to 40 feet.

(104)  **Wachapreague Inlet**, between Cedar Island and **Parramore Island**, is 20 miles south-southwestward of Chincoteague Inlet. The entrance is marked by a lighted whistle buoy and the channel by a lights and daybeacons that are shifted in position with changing channel conditions. The inlet is used by many fishing boats and by some boats seeking shelter but should only be entered with local knowledge.

(105)

**Anchorages**

(106)  The best anchorage is in **Horseshoe Lead**, southwest of the entrance, where there are depths of 20 to 30 feet west of the middle ground.

(107)

**Coast Guard Station**

(108)  **Wachapreague Coast Guard Station** is about 4.0 miles west-northwest of Wachapreague Inlet in the town of Wachapreague.

(109)  **Parramore Banks** extend about 8 miles offshore from Wachapreague Inlet. The area has an irregular bottom with depths ranging from 22 to 40 feet. A large fish haven, with a minimum depth of 15 feet, is on the banks 2.6 miles east-southeast of Wachapreague Inlet. Another fish haven, with a minimum depth of 30 feet, is east of the banks.

(110)  **Wachapreague**, a town on the mainland about 4 miles west-northwest of Wachapreague Inlet, is an oystering and fishing center and a base for some pleasure boats during the summer. The town can be reached through **Hummock Channel** and **Wachapreague Channel**, which are both well marked by lights and daybeacons. Gasoline, diesel fuel, transient berths and some marine supplies are available at the waterfront. Hull and engine

repairs can be made, with the largest marine railway being 50 feet.

(111)    **Quinby Inlet**, the ocean entrance between Parramore Island and Hog Island, has a fan of breakers across the bar at the entrance. Buoys marking the channel through the inlet are frequently shifted in position and not charted. The inlet should not be used without local knowledge.

(112)    **Quinby** is a village on the mainland about 6 miles north-northwest of Quinby Inlet. A channel to the village follows **Sandy Island Channel** to **Upshur Bay**, thence through a slough in the mudflats to a dredged channel leading to a basin that has a public landing with a pump-out station available. The channel is well marked with lights, buoys and daybeacons. A no-wake **speed limit** is enforced.

(113)    **Great Machipongo Inlet** leads between Hog Island and **Cobb Island** to Great Machipongo Channel. Shoals on either side of the entrance are marked by breakers at all times; the bar breaks only in heavy weather. The inlet is marked by buoys that are shifted in position with changing channel conditions.

(114)    **Great Machipongo Channel** extends northwestward through Hog Island Bay from the inlet to the mainland where it continues as **Machipongo River**. **Willis Wharf**, on the west bank of **Parting Creek** 1 mile above the junction with Machipongo River, is a base for shellfish and fishing boats. A public launching ramp is available and a marine railway can handle craft up to 60 feet.

(115)    A state-owned boat harbor is just below Willis Wharf on the west side of Parting Creek. An area with about 41 slips available for commercial fishing boats. The harbor has electricity, water and a launching ramp.

(116)
## ENC - US5VA14M
## Chart - 12224

(117)    **Sand Shoal Inlet**, the ocean entrance between Cobb Island and **Wreck Island**, may be entered through three channels. **Northeast Channel** leads along the south end of Cobb Island, **Southeast Channel** and **South Channel** just east of Wreck Island. The bar over Southeast Channel breaks in heavy weather. These channels are subject to continual change and stangers should seek local knowledge before transiting through the inlet.

(118)
### Anchorages
(119)    A good fair-weather anchorage is in **Loon Channel** just east of **Little Cobb Island** for boats able to cross the 3-foot entrance bar.

(120)    **Sand Shoal Channel**, marked by lights and daybeacons, extends westward from Sand Shoal Inlet for 6 miles where it joins a marked dredged channel leading to the wharves and public bulkhead at **Oyster** on the mainland. Public piers and a launching ramp are on the northern side of the basin. Numerous wrecks are reported near these facilities; caution is advised. Oyster is the shipping point for large amounts of clams and oysters.

(121)    **Ship Shoal Inlet**, the ocean entrance between Ship Shoal Island and **Myrtle Island**, is shallow and unmarked; it is used only by local oyster boats. There is deep water back of the inlet, but the channels to the inside passages are shallow and tortuous.

(122)
### Danger zone
(123)    The **danger zone** of a bombing and gunnery range is centered on Myrtle Island, 6 miles northeastward of Cape Charles Light. (See **33 CFR 334.330**, chapter 2, for limits and regulations.)

(124)    **Little Inlet**, between Myrtle Island and Smith Island, is shallow and is little used. Small boats can connect with the inside passage at high water.

(125)    **Cape Charles** and the islands on the north side of the entrance to Chesapeake Bay are described in chapter 9.

(126)    **Smith Island Inlet**, between Smith Island and Fishermans Island, is fairly wide, but the narrow, changeable channel lies between sandbars and breakers. The inlet is used by many local boats with drafts of 3 to 4 feet, but it is unmarked and should not be used by strangers. The controlling depth over the bar is said to be 1.5 feet.

(127)
## ENCs - US4VA50M, US5MD50M, US5VA71M, US-4VA70M, US4VA12M, US4VA1AM
## Charts - 12211, 12210, 12221

(128)    **Virginia Inside Passage** is between the barrier beach along the Atlantic Ocean on the east and the Virginia portion of the mainland peninsula on the west. The passage extends 74 miles from the south end of Chincoteague Bay through creeks, thorofares, marshy cuts and bays to enter Chesapeake Bay at Cape Charles. The route is marked with lights and daybeacons that have daymarks with white reflector borders to distinguish them from aids to navigation marking other waterways. Buoys are temporarily established from time to time to mark destroyed aids or critical places.

(129)    The Federal project depth is 6 feet for the waterway. Maintenance dredging is performed to provide a 6-foot controlling depth, but due to continuous shoaling 3 feet or less may be found in places, particularly inside the ocean inlets. The overhead clearance is limited only by the 40-foot fixed bridge across Cat Creek, 8 miles southward of Chincoteague; the 50-foot clearance of the power cable over Longboat Creek inshore from Metompkin Inlet, 22 miles southward of Chincoteague; and the 40-foot fixed bridge at Cape Charles.

(130)
### Tides
(131)    The mean range of tide varies in the inlets along the Virginia coast; greater fluctuations in the water level in the inside waters are caused by high winds and storms.

(132)

### Supplies

(133)     Gasoline, diesel fuel and some marine supplies are available at Wachapreague, 29 miles south of Chincoteague; at Quinby, 33 miles south of Chincoteague; at Willis Wharf, 37 miles south of Chincoteague; and at Oyster, 60 miles south of Chincoteague and 12 miles north of Cape Charles. Hull and engine repairs can be made at Wachapreague.

(134)     From Chincoteague, the Virginia Inside Passage follows Chincoteague Channel across Chincoteague Inlet to **Walker Point**, thence through **Ballast Narrows**, **Island Hole Narrows**, the dredged cut in **Bogues Bay** and **Cat Creek** to the sloughs marked by lights and daybeacons back of Assawoman Inlet, 10 miles southwestward of Chincoteague. The fixed highway bridge over Cat Creek has a clearance of 40 feet. The overhead power cable just north of the bridge has a clearance of 60 feet.

(135)     From 1 mile back of Assawoman Inlet, the inside passage continues through **Northam Narrows**, thence through dredged cuts in **Kegotank Bay** and back of Gargathy Inlet to **Wire Passage**, 15 miles southwestward of Chincoteague.

(136)     From Gargathy Inlet, the inside passage goes through Wire Passage into a dredged cut in **Metompkin Bay** and enters Folly Creek westward of Metompkin Inlet. A dredged channel with a controlling depth of 1.5 feet in 2006 extends about 0.8 mile up **Parkers Creek** from Virginia Inside Passage Light 80. The channel is marked by a lights and daybeacons. **Folly Creek**, which leads westward from the south end of Metompkin Bay, has a depth of 1 foot to the landing at its head, 3 miles above the mouth. A launching ramp and a pier are on the south side of Folly Creek about 1 mile west of Light 87.

(137)     The passage continues through a dredged cut from Folly Creek into **Longboat Creek**, which has a power cable over its northern part with a clearance of 50 feet, thence through cuts in **Cedar Island Bay**, **Teagles Ditch** and **Burtons Bay** into Wachapreague Channel, which leads to Wachapreague, 29 miles southward of Chincoteague. Supplies and repair facilities are available at Wachapreague. (Refer to previous description in this chapter.)

(138)     From Wachapreague Channel, the passage continues through a cut in **Bradford Bay**, a part of **Millstone Creek**, a cut in **Swash Bay**, a part of **The Swash**, and **Little Sloop Channel** to Sandy Island Channel, 3 miles inside Quinby Inlet and 36 miles southward of Chincoteague.

(139)     The passage southward of Quinby Inlet follows **Sloop Channel** and a dredged cut into **Cunjer Channel**, thence westward in **North Channel** at the north end of **Hog Island Bay** to Great Machipongo Channel, 43 miles southward of Chincoteague.

(140)     After passing through Great Machipongo Channel to a point 2 miles inside Great Machipongo Inlet, the route goes westward through **Gull Marsh Channel**, thence southwestward through a natural channel and cut in **Outlet Bay** and **Spidercrab Bay** to **Eckichy Channel**, thence southeastward to Sand Shoal Channel, 1.5 miles inside Sand Shoal Inlet, 56 miles southward of Chincoteague.

(141)     From inside of Sand Shoal Inlet, the passage continues westward through Sand Shoal Channel and southward through **Mockhorn Channel** to Magothy Bay.

(142)     **Magothy Bay**, which extends southward from Mockhorn Channel to Smith Island Inlet, is shallow except in the well-marked inside passage that passes through the bay to Cape Charles. **Magotha** is a village on the west side of the bay 3.5 miles northwestward of Cape Charles Light.

(143)     From the southern part of Magothy Bay, the passage continues southwestward through a dredged cut across Cape Charles into the deep water in Chesapeake Bay. The fixed highway bridge over the passage from Cape Charles to Fishermans Island has a clearance of 40 feet.

**Chart Coverage in Coast Pilot 3—Chapter 9**
NOAA's Online Interactive Chart Catalog has complete chart coverage
http://www.charts.noaa.gov/InteractiveCatalog/nrnc.shtml

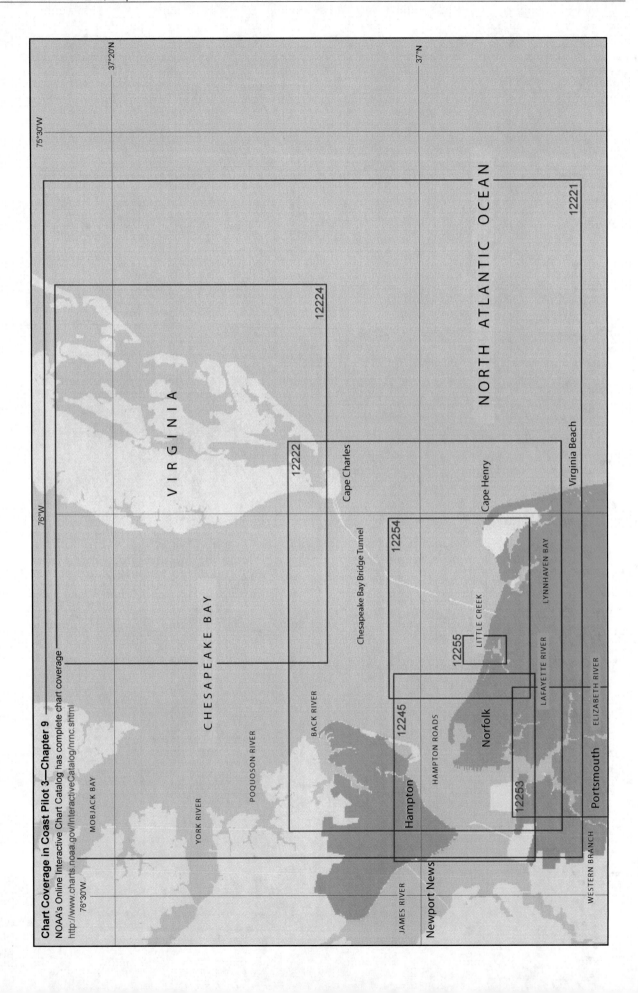

# Chesapeake Bay Entrance

(10)

## METEOROLOGICAL TABLE – COASTAL AREA OFF NORFOLK, VIRGINIA
Between 36°N to 38°N and 72°W to 76°W

| WEATHER ELEMENTS | JAN | FEB | MAR | APR | MAY | JUN | JUL | AUG | SEP | OCT | NOV | DEC | YEARS OF RECORD |
|---|---|---|---|---|---|---|---|---|---|---|---|---|---|
| Wind > 33 knots [1] | 4.9 | 5.5 | 4.7 | 2.3 | 0.5 | 0.4 | 0.2 | 0.3 | 1.1 | 2.1 | 3.6 | 5.0 | 2.5 |
| Wave Height > 9 feet [1] | 9.2 | 9.6 | 8.0 | 4.7 | 2.1 | 1.5 | 0.9 | 1.3 | 2.8 | 5.5 | 6.5 | 9.8 | 4.9 |
| Visibility < 2 nautical miles [1] | 3.1 | 4.4 | 4.8 | 4.7 | 5.2 | 3.6 | 1.6 | 1.3 | 1.3 | 1.7 | 1.7 | 1.9 | 2.9 |
| Precipitation [1] | 9.3 | 8.3 | 6.9 | 5.5 | 4.9 | 4.3 | 4.2 | 4.1 | 4.7 | 5.6 | 6.3 | 7.7 | 5.9 |
| Temperature > 69° F | 1.0 | 0.9 | 1.3 | 4.3 | 16.1 | 61.5 | 96.3 | 96.9 | 76.8 | 25.9 | 6.6 | 1.7 | 33.7 |
| Mean Temperature (°F) | 47.6 | 47.6 | 50.4 | 56.2 | 63.3 | 71.9 | 77.6 | 77.9 | 73.9 | 66.1 | 58.6 | 51.6 | 62.3 |
| Temperature < 33° F [1] | 6.2 | 5.5 | 1.1 | 0.0 | 0.0 | 0.0 | 0.0 | 0.0 | 0.0 | 0.0 | 0.1 | 1.8 | 1.2 |
| Mean RH (%) | 76 | 76 | 76 | 78 | 81 | 82 | 82 | 81 | 79 | 76 | 74 | 75 | 78 |
| Overcast or Obscured [1] | 38.3 | 36.7 | 33.9 | 27.9 | 26.0 | 22.7 | 21.0 | 19.8 | 20.7 | 22.7 | 26.3 | 34.2 | 27.3 |
| Mean Cloud Cover (8ths) | 5.2 | 5.1 | 4.8 | 4.3 | 4.4 | 4.4 | 4.4 | 4.4 | 4.2 | 4.2 | 4.5 | 5.1 | 4.6 |
| Mean SLP (mbs) | 1019 | 1017 | 1017 | 1016 | 1016 | 1016 | 1017 | 1017 | 1018 | 1018 | 1018 | 1019 | 1017 |
| Ext. Max. SLP (mbs) | 1047 | 1047 | 1039 | 1040 | 1038 | 1036 | 1035 | 1037 | 1036 | 1044 | 1044 | 1045 | 1047 |
| Ext. Min. SLP (mbs) | 982 | 978 | 978 | 987 | 990 | 991 | 996 | 995 | 993 | 990 | 986 | 986 | 978 |
| Prevailing Wind Direction | N | NW | N | SW | S | SW | SW | SW | NE | N | N | NW | N |
| Thunder and Lightning [1] | 0.6 | 0.7 | 0.9 | 1.0 | 1.7 | 1.8 | 2.7 | 2.7 | 1.4 | 1.0 | 0.7 | 0.6 | 1.3 |

[1] Percentage Frequency

(1)      This chapter describes the deep-draft southerly entrance to Chesapeake Bay from the Atlantic Ocean; the waters of Lynnhaven Roads, Lynnhaven Inlet, Little Creek, Hampton Roads, Willoughby Bay, Lafayette River and Elizabeth River, including Western, Eastern and Southern Branches; and the ports of Hampton, Newport News, Norfolk, Berkley, Portsmouth and Chesapeake.

(2)

## COLREGS Demarcation Lines

(3)      The lines established for Chesapeake Bay are described in **33 CFR 80.510**, chapter 2.

(4)

## Weather

(5)      This summary provides climatological information applicable to the entire Chesapeake Bay. From November through April, Chesapeake Bay, particularly the southern portion, is rough sailing. Storms moving up the Atlantic coast generate winds out of the northeast quadrant ahead of their centers; speeds often reach 30 to 50 knots. Several days of strong and gusty northwest winds may follow. Strong cold fronts from the west can generate 25- to 45-knot gusts over open water. Waves associated with strong winds can be rough and bad chop develops when these winds oppose strong tidal currents. Northerlies of 25 knots or more, over a long fetch of the bay, can easily build 8- to 10-foot seas in the central portion and 5- to 7-foot seas in the south. Seas of 8 feet or more occur about 2 to 4 percent of the time from fall through early spring, in the bay. Gales can occur from September through March.

(6)      Another problem during this period is poor visibilities. Fog forms most often when warm, moist air moves across the bay's cold waters from the southeast through south. Most of the 30 to 40 dense fog days each year develop from January through April. Dense fog is more common offshore and should be expected on unusually warm, humid winter and spring days. Fog over particularly cold waters with winds less than 10 knots may drop visibilities to near zero. Precipitation, particularly snow, may also hamper visibilities.

(7)      When temperatures drop below about 28°F (-2.2°C) and winds are blowing at 13 knots or more, there exists a potential for moderate superstructure icing. This potential exists in the bay from November through March; January and February are the worst months when the potential exists about 3 percent of the time.

(8)      During March and April, cold fronts often trigger fast-moving narrow bands of thunderstorms. Preceding the cold front these bands move eastward at 10 to 30 knots generating lightning and gusty winds of gale force. Thunderstorms are also a bay-wide threat during spring and summer when they develop about 6 to 9 days each month. They may develop over land during the afternoon as warm, humid air is forced aloft by surface heating. The thunderstorm may precede a cold front. When a cold front passes during a period of maximum afternoon heating thunderstorms may be severe. In spring and early

(11)

**METEOROLOGICAL TABLE – COASTAL AREA OFF CHESAPEAKE BAY**
Between 36°N to 40°N and 76°W to 77°W

| WEATHER ELEMENTS | JAN | FEB | MAR | APR | MAY | JUN | JUL | AUG | SEP | OCT | NOV | DEC | YEARS OF RECORD |
|---|---|---|---|---|---|---|---|---|---|---|---|---|---|
| Wind > 33 knots [1] | 0.4 | 1.0 | 1.0 | 0.2 | 0.2 | 0.0 | 0.1 | 0.3 | 1.2 | 1.3 | 1.3 | 0.8 | 0.6 |
| Wave Height > 9 feet [1] | 0.8 | 0.4 | 0.8 | 1.0 | 0.5 | 0.4 | 0.3 | 0.2 | 0.5 | 0.4 | 0.8 | 0.7 | 0.5 |
| Visibility < 2 nautical miles [1] | 9.1 | 8.1 | 5.9 | 6.9 | 5.7 | 3.0 | 2.1 | 2.8 | 4.0 | 4.4 | 9.6 | 11.0 | 5.9 |
| Precipitation [1] | 9.3 | 10.9 | 9.0 | 7.0 | 6.2 | 4.2 | 5.8 | 6.6 | 8.4 | 6.1 | 7.6 | 10.7 | 7.6 |
| Temperature > 69° F | 0.0 | 0.2 | 1.9 | 6.8 | 30.2 | 77.4 | 96.5 | 93.1 | 72.4 | 18.2 | 3.9 | 0.4 | 35.6 |
| Mean Temperature (°F) | 41.8 | 42.9 | 49.2 | 57.1 | 66.9 | 75.5 | 79.1 | 77.9 | 74.1 | 64.4 | 53.9 | 44.0 | 61.6 |
| Temperature < 33° F [1] | 17.3 | 12.7 | 2.6 | 0.1 | 0.0 | 0.0 | 0.0 | 0.0 | 0.0 | 0.0 | 0.6 | 9.1 | 3.2 |
| Mean RH (%) | 74 | 72 | 72 | 70 | 75 | 75 | 77 | 77 | 76 | 75 | 73 | 73 | 74 |
| Overcast or Obscured [1] | 33.5 | 35.2 | 28.8 | 26.0 | 23.4 | 19.8 | 20.3 | 20.9 | 24.1 | 22.6 | 26.3 | 32.8 | 25.9 |
| Mean Cloud Cover (8ths) | 4.5 | 4.6 | 4.2 | 4.1 | 4.2 | 4.3 | 4.6 | 4.6 | 4.4 | 3.7 | 4.2 | 4.6 | 4.3 |
| Mean SLP (mbs) | 1020 | 1018 | 1018 | 1017 | 1016 | 1016 | 1016 | 1017 | 1017 | 1018 | 1019 | 1019 | 1017 |
| Ext. Max. SLP (mbs) | 1046 | 1046 | 1039 | 1040 | 1037 | 1032 | 1031 | 1032 | 1033 | 1039 | 1041 | 1041 | 1046 |
| Ext. Min. SLP (mbs) | 988 | 985 | 987 | 991 | 991 | 994 | 998 | 997 | 994 | 992 | 990 | 987 | 985 |
| Prevailing Wind Direction | N | N | N | N | SW | SW | SW | SW | NE | N | N | N | SW |
| Thunder and Lightning [1] | 0.0 | 0.1 | 0.2 | 0.4 | 0.6 | 0.6 | 1.0 | 0.9 | 0.2 | 0.2 | 0.2 | 0.0 | 0.4 |

[1] Percentage Frequency

summer they usually develop to the west of the bay and move toward the northeast at speeds of 25 to 35 knots. Occasionally thunderstorms will approach from the northwest; these are often severe, tend to move very fast, and can pack winds reaching 70 to 90 knots. Severe squall lines can also generate tornadoes that may move over the bay developing waterspouts; winds can exceed 200 knots in these systems. By midsummer, fronts become weaker and less frequent, and thunderstorms are mainly the air mass type that move at 10 to 20 knots and usually do not organize into a squall line. Thunderstorms are likely to occur on 8 to 9 days in July compared to 6 to 7 days in August.

(9) Good weather in late summer and fall is compromised mainly by the threat of a tropical cyclone, particularly from mid-August through the first week in October. A hurricane affects the Chesapeake Bay about once every 10 years on the average. Thunderstorms occur on 1 to 3 days per month in September and October and are usually associated with increasingly frequent and rigorous cold fronts. Fog becomes more of a problem, particularly north of Annapolis. This is a morning fog that forms on 1 to 4 days per month during September and October over the upper reaches of the bay; it usually lifts by noon. In late summer and autumn waterspouts may be sighted. These are short lived and less severe than those associated with thunderstorms; maximum winds climb to about 50 knots. They are caused by cooler air overriding a body of warm moist air in association with a cloud build up over the bay; they usually occur in fair weather.

(12)

**ENCs - US4VA12M, US4VA1AM**

**Chart - 12221**

(13) **Chesapeake Bay**, the largest inland body of water along the Atlantic coast of the United States, is 168 miles long with a greatest width of 23 miles. The bay is the approach to Norfolk, Newport News, Baltimore and many lesser ports. Deep-draft vessels use the Atlantic entrance, which is about 10 miles wide between Fishermans Island on the north and Cape Henry on the south. Medium-draft vessels can enter from Delaware Bay on the north via Chesapeake and Delaware Canal, and light-draft vessels can enter from Albemarle Sound on the south via the Intracoastal Waterway.

(14) **Safety/Security Zones** have been established surrounding vessels carrying certain dangerous cargo within the Chesapeake Bay and its tributaries. (See **33 CFR 165.500**, chapter 2, for limits and regulations.)

(15)

**North Atlantic Right Whales**

(16) Endangered North Atlantic right whales may occur within 30 miles of the Virginia coasts in the approaches to the Chesapeake Bay (peak season: November through April, although right whales have been sighted in the area year round). (See **North Atlantic Right Whales**, indexed as such in chapter 3, for more information on right whales and recommended measures to avoid collisions.)

(17) All vessels 65 feet or greater in length overall (LOA) and subject to the jurisdiction of the United States are restricted to speeds of 10 knots or less in a Seasonal Management Area existing around the entrance to the Chesapeake Bay between November 1 and April 30. The area is defined as the waters within a 20-nm radius of 37°00'36.9"N., 75°57'50.5"W. (See **50 CFR 224.105** in chapter 2 for regulations, limitations and exceptions.)

(18)

**Mileages**

(19) Many of the distances in this and later Chesapeake Bay chapters are given in nautical miles above the **Virginia Capes**, or "the **Capes**," which is a short way

of referring to a line from Cape Charles Light to Cape Henry Light.

(20)     **Cape Charles**, on the north side of the entrance, is low and bare, but the land back of it is high and wooded. **Wise Point** is the most southerly mainland tip of the cape. Low **Fishermans Island**, a National Wildlife Refuge, is 1 mile south of Wise Point.

(21)     The southwest end of **Smith Island** is 2.4 miles eastward of Wise Point; the island is 6 miles long, low and sparsely wooded and awash at half tide midway along its length.

(22)     **Smith Island Shoal** is 7.5 miles east-southeast of Smith Island and breaks in heavy weather. The area has general depths between 25 and 30 feet.

(23)     **Nautilus Shoal**, which extends 4 miles southeastward from Fishermans Island, has patches with depths of 7 to 11 feet. A buoyed channel leads along the southwest side of Nautilus Shoal, thence northward between Fishermans Island and **Inner Middle Ground**. The channel is used by local vessels drawing up to 12 feet. This channel is not recommended for strangers because of shifting shoals.

(24)     Breakers frequently occur along the axis of Inner Middle Ground, starting on the seaward side of the Chesapeake Bay Bridge-Tunnel and continuing the entire length of the shoal. This phenomenon appears to be associated with large swells rolling in from sea from the south-southeast to southeast.

(25)
## ENCs - US5VA13M, US4VA12M, US4VA1AM, US-4VA40M
## Charts - 12222, 12221, 12225

(26)     **Cape Henry**, on the south side of the entrance, has a range of sand hills about 80 feet high.

(27)     **Cape Henry Light** (36°55'35"N., 76°00'26"W.), 164 feet above the water, is shown from an octagonal, pyramidal tower, upper and lower half of each face alternately black and white, on the beach near the turn of the cape.

(28)     The gray octagonal, pyramidal tower 110 yards southwest of Cape Henry Light is the abandoned 1791 lighthouse.

(29)
### Local magnetic disturbance
(30)     Differences of as much as 6° from the normal variation have been observed 3 to 17 miles offshore from Cape Henry to Currituck Beach Light.

(31)     A **naval restricted area** extends northward and eastward from Cape Henry. (See **33 CFR 334.320**, chapter 2, for limits and regulations.)

(32)     The summer resort of **Virginia Beach** is about 5 miles southward of Cape Henry Light. Many high-rise buildings, two water tanks, and an aerobeacon 2.8 miles inland are prominent. A hotel cupola, 3.4 miles south of Cape Henry Light, is distinctive.

(33)     The **Chesapeake Bay Bridge-Tunnel** extends from Cape Charles across the bay entrance to a point 6 miles westward of Cape Henry. The 15-mile crossing has vehicular tunnels under Chesapeake Channel and Thimble Shoal Channel with fixed bridges over Fishermans Inlet and secondary channels. The openings at Chesapeake and Thimble Shoal Channels are marked by lights, sound signals and lighted buoys. At night the floodlighted tunnel houses are more prominent than the privately maintained lights marking the channels.

(34)     **Caution**—The Chesapeake Bay Bridge-Tunnel complex has on several occasions suffered damage from vessels. In every case, adverse weather prevailed with accompanying strong winds from the northwest quadrant generally related to a frontal system. Weather deterioration in the lower bay is quite often sudden and violent and constitutes an extreme hazard to vessels operating or anchoring in this area. The proximity of the bridge-tunnel complex to main shipping channels and anchorages adds to the danger. Currents in excess of 3.0 knots can be expected in the area.

(35)     Normal precautions dictated by prudent seamanship are expected of all vessels. Mariners transiting this area are, however, urged to be particularly alert in regards to the weather. To assist in this respect, the National Weather Service provides 24-hour weather broadcasting on 162.55 MHz. The local Marine Operator also transmits weather information at 0000, 0600, 1200 and 1800 local time on 2450 kHz and 2538 kHz. Information of a pending weather frontal passage should be met with advance preparations. Engines readied for short-notice maneuvering and anchor details alerted are considered minimum prudent precautions. Maneuvering in close proximity of the bridge-tunnel complex is also discouraged.

(36)     A **regulated navigation area** has been established in the waters of the Atlantic Ocean and in Chesapeake Bay. (See **33 CFR 165.1** through **165.13**, and **165.501**, chapter 2, for limits and regulations.)

(37)     All vessels 300 gross tons and over, including tug and barge combined, are required to obtain permission prior to entering, departing and/or moving within the Regulation Navigation Area. To obtain permission, vessels shall contact the Joint Harbor Operations Center (JHOC) at least 30 minutes prior to entry or movement via channel 12, alternate 13/16 VHF-FM, and relay vessel documentation number, IMO number or VIN for verification. This includes entries from offshore, James River, Chesapeake Bay or Intracoastal Waterway. Alternate JHOC phone numbers are 757-638-6635/6633. If the JHOC cannot be reached, the Captain of the Port (COTP) Command Duty Officer may be reached at 757-668-5555.

(38)
### Traffic Separation Schemes
(39)     Traffic Separation Schemes for the Chesapeake Bay entrance and in the vicinity of Smith Point (37°52'47"N., 76°11'01"W.) have been established to aid navigation and to prevent collisions. The schemes are not intended in any way to supersede or alter the applicable Navigation

Rules (See **33 CFR 167.1** through **167.15** and **167.200** through **167.203**, chapter 2, for limits and regulations and Traffic Separation Schemes, chapter 1, for additional information.)

(40) **Traffic Separation Scheme (Chesapeake Bay Entrance)** provides for inbound-outbound traffic lanes to enter or depart Chesapeake Bay from the northeastward and from the southeastward.

(41) A precautionary area with a radius of 2 miles is centered on Chesapeake Bay Entrance Lighted Whistle Buoy CH (36°56'08"N., 75°57'27"W.). A racon is at the buoy.

(42) The northeasterly inbound-outbound traffic lanes are separated by a line of lighted bell and gong buoys on bearing 250°/070°. The outermost buoy in the line is 6.4 miles 313° from Chesapeake Light and the innermost buoy is 4.5 miles 074° from Cape Henry Light.

(43) The southeasterly approach is marked by Chesapeake Bay Southern Approach Lighted Whistle Buoy CB (36°49'00"N., 75°45'36"W.); a racon is at the buoy. The inbound/outbound traffic lanes are separated by a **deep-water route** marked by lighted buoys on bearings 302°/122° and 317°/137°. The deep-water route is intended for deep-draft vessels and naval aircraft carriers entering or departing Chesapeake Bay. A vessel using the deep-water route is advised to announce its intentions on VHF-FM channel 16 as it approaches Lighted Whistle Buoy CB on the south end and Lighted Whistle Buoy CH on the north end of the route. All other vessels approaching the Chesapeake Bay Traffic Separation Scheme should use the appropriate inbound/outbound lanes of the northeasterly or southeasterly approaches.

(44) The Coast Guard advises that upon entering the traffic lanes, all inbound vessels are encouraged to make a security broadcast on VHF-FM channel 13, announcing the vessel's name, location and intentions.

(45) **Exercise extreme caution where the two routes converge off Cape Henry**. Mariners are also warned that vessels may be maneuvering in the pilotage area that extends into the western part of the precautionary area.

(46) **Traffic Separation Scheme (Smith Point)** is in the main channel in the Chesapeake Bay off Smith Point. A fairway buoy, 1.5 miles east of Smith Point Light, marks the single turn in the scheme. Northbound traffic will pass eastward of the buoy and southbound traffic will pass westward of the buoy.

(47)
### Channels

(48) The deepest route to and from Chesapeake Bay is south of Chesapeake Light through the buoyed Deep-Water Route in the southeasterly approach. Federal project main channel depths are 50 feet from the Virginia Capes to Baltimore and 55 feet from the Capes to Hampton Roads. For detailed channel information and minimum depths as reported by the U.S. Army Corps of Engineers (USACE), use NOAA Electronic Navigational Charts. Surveys and channel condition reports are available through a USACE hydrographic survey website listed in Appendix A.

(49) The well-marked channel to Baltimore is discussed further in chapters 11 to 15.

(50)
### Current

(51) The current velocity is often 1.0 knot on the flood and 1.5 knots on the ebb in Chesapeake Bay Entrance. See the Tidal Current prediction service at *tidesandcurrents. noaa.gov* for specific information about times, directions, and velocities of the current at numerous locations throughout the area. Links to a user guide for this service can be found in chapter 1 of this book.

(52)
### Pilotage, Chesapeake Bay

(53) Pilotage is compulsory for all foreign vessels and for U.S. vessels under register in the foreign trade. Pilotage is optional for U.S. vessels under enrollment in the coastwise trade if they have on board a pilot licensed by the Federal Government to operate in these waters.

(54) The Association of Maryland Pilots has an office in Baltimore (email: dispatch@mdpilots.com, telephone: 410-342-6013). They provide service to any port in Maryland and service between Cape Henry, VA, to Baltimore and between Baltimore and the Head of the Chesapeake Bay including to Chesapeake City in the C&D Canal. Transmit ETA 72 hours with confirmation/updates 24, 12 and 6 hours before arrival pilot station. Email ETA, transit speed, and draft to: dispatch@mdpilots.com. The Virginia Pilot Association has an office in Virginia Beach (telephone: 757-496-0995) and provides service to any port in Virginia. Vessels bound for Washington, DC, may take a pilot from either association.

(55) The Maryland pilots maintain a Pilot Tower with the Virginia pilots at Cape Henry, just north of Cape Henry Light. The pilots monitor VHF-FM channels 11, 13 and 16. The pilot boats are stationed in Lynnhaven Inlet. They are 52 feet long with a black hull and white house displaying the "PILOT" on each side.

(56) The Virginia Pilot Association maintains a pilot station at Cape Henry, just north of Cape Henry Light. The pilots monitor VHF-FM channels 11, 16 and 74. Other channels are used on request. Email address: dispatch@vapilotassn.com. Four pilot boats are stationed in Lynnhaven Inlet; two are in use at any given time. The pilot boats are 50 feet long with orange hulls and white houses with the word "PILOT" on each side.

(57) The Chesapeake and Interstate Pilots Association offers pilot services to vessels engaged in the coastwise trade and public vessels between Cape Henry and various ports and places on the Chesapeake Bay and its tributaries. Arrangements for pilots are made through ships' agents or the pilot office in Norfolk (telephone: 757-855-2733). The pilots board from a commercial launch. Pilot ladders are recommended to be rigged 4 feet above the water on the leeward side. The pilot vessel monitors VHF-FM channels 13 and 16, 90 minutes prior

(57) to the last ETA received. Cellular confirmation of arrival is recommended if radio contact is not successful.

(58)　　Vessels are boarded in the Pilot boarding area off Cape Henry.

(59)　　It has been noted that sometimes considerable differences occur between a vessel's ETA and her actual arrival due to conditions encountered between Cape Hatteras and Cape Henry. Revisions to the ETA of 1 hour or greater should be passed to the pilots especially if the vessel's arrival will be sooner than previously advised.

(60)
## ENCs - US5VA19M, US5VA13M, US5VA20M
## Charts - 12254, 12222, 12256

(61)　　**Thimble Shoal Channel**, the improved approach to Hampton Roads, begins 2.3 miles northwest of Cape Henry Light and extends 9.5 miles west-northwestward; a Federal project provides for a 55-foot-deep channel with a 32-foot-deep auxiliary channel on each side of the main channel. For detailed channel information and minimum depths as reported by the U.S. Army Corps of Engineers (USACE), use NOAA Electronic Navigational Charts. Surveys and channel condition reports are available through a USACE hydrographic survey website listed in Appendix A.

(62)　　**Naval** and **general anchorages** are west of Cape Henry between Thimble Shoal Channel and Lynnhaven Roads. (See **33 CFR 110.1** and **110.168**, chapter 2, for limits and regulations.)

(63)　　Thimble Shoal Channel is a **regulated navigation area** and draft limitations apply. A vessel drawing less than 25 feet may not enter the channel, unless the vessel is crossing the channel. (See **33 CFR 165.501**, chapter 2, for limits and regulations.)

(64)　　**Lynnhaven Roads**, an open bight westward of Cape Henry, is protected from southerly winds and is sometimes used as an anchorage. The former dumping-ground area in the western part of the bight has shoals and obstructions with depths as little as 11 feet; elsewhere, general depths are 20 to 28 feet. Eastward of Lynnhaven Inlet, the 18-foot curve is no more than 0.3 mile from shore; westward of the inlet, the shoaling is gradual and depths of 18 feet can be found 0.8 mile from shore.

(65)　　There are two small-craft openings in the Chesapeake Bay Bridge-Tunnel south of Thimble Shoal Channel. Each fixed span has a clearance of 21 feet.

(66)　　**Lynnhaven Inlet**, 4 miles westward of Cape Henry Light, is subject to continual change. The entrance channel through the inlet is marked by lights and lighted and unlighted buoys. **Lynnhaven Bay**, south of the inlet, has a large turning area just south of the highway bridge over the inlet.

(67)

### Structures across Lynnhaven Inlet and Tributaries

| Name | Type | Location | Clearances (feet) Horizontal | Vertical* |
|---|---|---|---|---|
| **Lynnhaven Inlet** | | | | |
| Lesner/ Shore Drive (Bridge is under construction) | fixed | 36°54'27"N., 76°05'32"W. | 84 | 35 |
| Overhead cable | power | 36°54'22"N., 76°05'32"W. | | 68 |
| **Broad Bay Canal** | | | | |
| Overhead cables | power | 36°54'10"N., 76°04'08"W. | | 55 |
| West Great Neck Road | fixed | 36°54'11"N., 76°04'06"W. | 60 | 35 |
| North Great Neck Road | fixed | 36°54'10"N., 76°04'01"W. | 160 | 36 |
| **Long Creek** | | | | |
| Overhead cables | power | 36°54'13"N., 76°04'10"W. | | 37 |
| West Great Neck Road | fixed | 36°54'15"N., 76°04'09"W. | 40 | 20 |
| North Great Neck Road | fixed | 36°54'16"N., 76°04'02"W. | 160 | 36 |

\* Clearances are Referenced to Mean High Water

(68)　　The entrance to **Broad Bay** is through a dredged channel leading eastward from the north end of Lynnhaven Bay. The channel is marked by daybeacons and a light at each end. The channel has extremely heavy boat traffic and is especially congested on summer weekends; caution is advised.

(69)　　An alternate route to Broad Bay is through **Long Creek**, which branches northeastward from the dredged channel just west of West Great Neck Road Bridge.

(70)　　Depths in Broad Bay are about 6 to 7 feet. A marked dredged channel leads southeastward through The Narrows to the southern end of **Linkhorn Bay** near Virginia Beach.

(71)　　Small-craft facilities are along the dredged channel from Lynnhaven inlet to Broad Bay, in Long Creek and the east fork of Linkhorn Bay.

(72)　　**Little Creek** is entered between jetties 8 miles westward of Cape Henry Light. The **U.S. Naval Amphibious Base** occupies much of the creek; small craft use the west arm.

(73)　　A dredged channel in Little Creek leads to a basin off the railroad terminal, 1.2 miles south of the jetties. The channel is marked by a **177.7°** lighted entrance range and by lights. **Little Creek Coast Guard Station** is eastward of the railroad terminal.

(74)　　**Fishermans Cove**, on the west side of Little Creek, has fuel and berthing facilities for small craft. A **speed limit** of 5 knots is prescribed for Fishermans Cove. (See **33 CFR 165.501**, chapter 2, for limits and regulations.)

(75)　　Naval **danger zones** and **restricted areas** extend northward from the vicinity of Little Creek to the edge

(84)

---

### Newport News to Craney Island Pipeline

The Newport News to Craney Island pipeline is a 24-inch diameter submerged pipeline carrying natural gas. The method of construction involved directional drilling from five locations along the length of the pipeline termed *Stitch Points*, labeled A through E on the charts. At each stitch point the pipeline is 10 feet below the seabed. The depth of the pipeline is 20 feet below the seabed at Newport News Channel and 65 feet below the seabed between Stitch Points C through E.

From the shoreline in Newport News, the initial section of pipeline runs to:

**Stitch Point A** (36°58'23.9"N., 76°23'42.1"W.), thence to

**Stitch Point B** (36°57'34.7"N., 76°23'28.8"W.), thence to

**Stitch Point C** (36°57'04.0"N., 76°23'20.4"W.); thence to

**Stitch Point D** (36°56'33.1"N., 76°23'12.0"W.); thence to

**Stitch Point E** (36°55'55.7"N., 76°23'09.4"W.); thence to the shoreline at Craney Island.

---

of Thimble Shoal Channel. (See **33 CFR 334.310** and **334.370**, chapter 2, for limits and regulations.)

(76)

## ENC - US5VA15M
## Chart - 12245

(77)     **Hampton Roads**, at the southwest corner of Chesapeake Bay, is entered 16 miles westward of the Virginia Capes. It includes the Port of Norfolk, encompassing the cities of Norfolk, Portsmouth and Chesapeake and the Port of Newport News, which takes in the cities of Newport News and Hampton.

(78)     Hampton Roads is the world's foremost bulk cargo harbor. Coal, petroleum products, grain, sand and gravel, tobacco and fertilizer constitute more than 90 percent of the heavy traffic movement by water, although an increasing amount of general cargo is handled by the Hampton Roads ports.

(79)

### Channels

(80)     The approach to Hampton Roads is through Thimble Shoal Channel. There are natural depths of 80 to 20 feet in the main part of Hampton Roads, but the harbor shoals to less than 10 feet toward the shores. Dredged channels lead to the principal ports.

(81)     Two main Federal project channels, marked by buoys, lead through Hampton Roads. One channel leads southward along the waterfronts of Norfolk, Portsmouth and Chesapeake to the first bridge across the Southern Branch of Elizabeth River; project depths are 50 feet through Norfolk Harbor Entrance Reach, thence 50 feet through Craney Island Reach at Lamberts Point, thence 40 feet to the bridge. Newport News Channel, with a 55-foot project depth, leads westward to the waterfront at Newport News at the entrance to James River. For detailed channel information and minimum depths as reported by the U.S. Army Corps of Engineers (USACE), use NOAA Electronic Navigational Charts. Surveys and channel condition reports are available through a USACE hydrographic survey website listed in Appendix A.

(82)

### Anchorages

(83)     Numerous general, explosives, naval and small-craft anchorages are in Hampton Roads and Elizabeth River.

(See **33 CFR 110.1** and **110.168**, chapter 2, for limits and regulations.)

(85)

### Current

(86)     Information for several places in Hampton Roads and Elizabeth River is available from the Tidal Current prediction service at *tidesandcurrents.noaa.gov*. The currents are influenced considerably by the winds and at times attain velocities in excess of the tabulated values. The current velocity is about 1.0 knot in Hampton Roads and about 0.6 knot in Elizabeth River. Links to a user guide for the tidal prediciton service can be found in chapter 1 of this book.

(87)

### Ice

(88)     Hampton Roads is free of ice. In severe winters the upper part of Southern Branch, Elizabeth River, is sometimes closed for short periods.

(89)

### Pilotage

(90)     **Pilotage** for Hampton Roads ports. (See Pilotage at the beginning of this chapter and chapter 3.)

(91)

### Towage

(92)     Vessels usually proceed from Cape Henry to points in the Hampton Roads port area under their own power and without assistance. A large fleet of tugs is available at Norfolk and Newport News to assist in docking or undocking and in shifting within the harbor.

(93)

### Quarantine, customs, immigration and agricultural quarantine

(94)     (See chapter 3, Vessel Arrival Inspections, and appendix for addresses.)

(95)     **Quarantine** is enforced in accordance with regulations of the U.S. Public Health Service. (See Public Health Service, chapter 1.) The **quarantine anchorage** is in the Chesapeake Bay, about 6 miles southwest of Fishermans Island, Virginia.

(96)     Hampton Roads is a **customs port of entry**.

(97)

### Coast Guard

(98)     A **Sector Office** is in Portsmouth—see Appendix A for address.

(99)

## Harbor regulations

(100)      Port regulations are principally concerned with grain, coal handling, port charges and pilotage and stevedoring rates. Copies of these regulations may be obtained from the Virginia Maritime Association, 236 East Plume Street, Norfolk, VA 23514.

(101)      **Anchorage regulations** are given in **33 CFR 110.1** and **110.168**, chapter 2.

(102)

## Wharves

(103)      The Hampton Roads area has more than 200 piers and wharves along more than 30 miles of improved waterfront; only the major deepwater facilities are described. Included: are coal piers, containerized-cargo berths, oil storage and bunkering facilities, general-cargo, grain and ore piers, marine railways and drydocks. Available depths are 22 to 42 feet at the general-cargo, ore and grain piers, 36 to 45 feet at the coal piers and 20 to 42 feet at the oil-storage and bunkering facilities. A 350-ton floating crane is available.

(104)

## Supplies

(105)      The principal coal-handling and bunkering piers are those of the Norfolk Southern Railway at Lamberts Point, Norfolk, and of the Chesapeake and Ohio Railway at Newport News. Bunker oil is available at Sewells Point, in Southern Branch of Elizabeth River and at Newport News, or it can be delivered from barges in the stream. Fresh water is available on the principal piers and can be supplied from barges. The area also has numerous ship chandlers and marine suppliers.

(106)

## Repairs

(107)      Hampton Roads has extensive facilities for drydocking and making major repairs to large deep-draft vessels. The largest floating drydock at Norfolk has a capacity of 54,000 tons, and the largest marine railway can handle 6,000 tons. The shipyard at Newport News is one of the largest and best equipped in the United States; the principal graving dock has a length of 1,600 feet on the keel blocks. There are many other yards that are especially equipped to handle medium-sized and small vessels. More details on these repair facilities are given with the discussion of the waterway or port in which they are located.

(108)

## Small-craft facilities

(109)      Complete services and repairs are available at Hampton Roads ports. There are marine railways up to 11 tons and mobile hoists up to 80 tons for repairs.

(110)

## Communications

(111)      Hampton Roads ports are served by a terminal beltline and several large railroads and by more than 50 motor carriers. In addition, over 90 ocean carrier lines connect Hampton Roads with the principal U.S. and foreign ports; most of the lines have regular sailings, and others maintain frequent but irregular service. Airlines offer prompt airfreight, express and passenger service from Norfolk and Newport News to major U.S. cities with connecting service overseas.

(112)      **Thimble Shoal Light** (37°00'52"N., 76°14'23"W.) is on the eastern edge of the shoal. Thimble Shoal is the southern edge of **Horseshoe**, described in chapter 11.

(113)      The entrance to Hampton Roads is between Willoughby Spit and Old Point Comfort, 2 miles to the northward. A **bridge-tunnel complex** crosses Chesapeake Bay from Willoughby Spit to Hampton.

(114)      Mariners are advised that the northern and southern approach bridges of the **Hampton Roads Bridge-Tunnel (HRBT)** are under construction (2021). Construction activities are planned from March 15, 2021 through November, 2025. Detailed project information will be provided via updated local notice to mariners, broadcast notice to mariners and marine safety information bulletins. Mariners should use caution when transiting the area and are advised to maintain a safe distance of at least 300 feet from all HRBT bridge structures/work trestles, HRBT North Island, and HRBT South Island.

(115)      **Old Point Comfort** is the site of historic **Fort Monroe**. The Chamberlin Hotel is an excellent landmark. **Old Point Comfort Light** (37°00'06"N., 76°18'23"W.), 54 feet above the water, is shown from a white tower. Only Government craft can tie up at the wharf on the south waterfront of Old Point Comfort.

(116)      A naval **restricted area** extends eastward and southward of Old Point Comfort, and a **danger zone** of an army firing range extends to seaward from a point 1.5 miles northward of the point. (See **33 CFR 334.360** and **334.350**, chapter 2, respectively, for limits and regulations.)

(117)      **Hampton Bar** begins about 200 yards southwestward of Old Point Comfort and extends 2 miles southwestward; depths on the bar are 2 to 6 feet. The bar is marked along its southern edge by a light, a buoy and daybeacons. These aids to navigation, together with one on Hampton Flats, aid vessels in mooring in the naval and other anchorages northward of the main channel.

(118)      A dredged channel, marked by a light and daybeacons, leads along the west side of Old Point Comfort to the fish wharves at **Phoebus** and has a federal project depth of 12 feet. (See Notice to Mariners and latest edition of the charts for controlling depths.) The wharves have depths of 8 to 12 feet at their outer ends but are in poor condition. Small craft can anchor in depths of 8 to 20 feet along the sides of the channel. The Fort Monroe yacht piers are on the east side of the channel 0.4 mile above Old Point Comfort.

(119)      **Hampton River**, 1.5 miles westward of Old Point Comfort, is entered by a marked channel through Hampton Bar and Flats to a point just below the highway bridge at Hampton. Federal project depths are 12 feet. (See Notice to Mariners and latest edition of the charts for controlling

(132)

### Facilities in Newport News

| Name | Location | Dimensions (feet) | | | Storage, Handling and Purpose | Owned/ Operated by: |
|---|---|---|---|---|---|---|
| | | Space | Depth* | Deck | | |
| Newport News Marine Terminal (Pier B) | 36°58'19"N., 76°26'02"W. | 1,974 | 36-40 | 15 | • Open storage (60 acres)<br>• Covered storage (267,900 square feet)<br>Reciept and shipment of conventional, containerized general cargo | Virginia Port Authority/ Virginia International Terminals, Inc. |
| Newport News Marine Terminal (Pier C) | 36°58'09"N., 76°25'58"W. | 2,422 | 40 | 14 | • Covered storage (123,000 square feet)<br>• Four container cranes (up to 182 tons)<br>Reciept and shipment of conventional, containerized and roll-on/roll-off general cargo and heavy lift items | Virginia Port Authority/ Virginia International Terminals, Inc. |
| Kinder Morgan Bulk Terminals (Pier IX) | 36°58'02"N., 76°25'47"W. | 1,750 | 43-50 | 11.8 | • Open storage (1.4 million tons of coal)<br>• Silo storage (30,000 tons of cement)<br>• Electric belt-conveyor system<br>• Shipment of coal and receipt of cement | Kinder Morgan Energy Partners, LP |
| Dominion Terminal Associates (Pier 11) | 36°57'45"N., 76°25'26"W. | 2,000 | 50 | 13 | • Open storage (1.4 million tons of coal)<br>• Silo storage (6,800 tons)<br>• Electric belt-conveyor system<br>• Shipment of coal | Dominion Terminal Associates |
| Jerry O. Talton (Pier 14) | 36°57'41"N., 76°25'12"W. | 2,180 | 40-45 | 11.5 | Open storage (43 acres)<br>Reciept and shipment of containerized general cargo and military equipment | CSX Real Property, Inc./Jerry O. Talton, Inc. |
| Jerry O. Talton (Pier 15) | 36°57'40"N., 76°25'04"W. | 2,000 | 35-42 | 9.5 | Open storage (43 acres)<br>Reciept and shipment of containerized general cargo and military equipment | CSX Real Property, Inc./Jerry O. Talton, Inc. |
| Koch Materials Newport News Tanker and Barge Dock | 36°57'42"N., 76°24'58"W. | 1,300 | 26-35 | 16-27 | • Tank storage (435,000 barrels)<br>• Hose handling hoists<br>Receipt and shipment of asphalt | Koch Materials Co. |

\* The depths given above are reported. For information on the latest depths contact the port authorities or the private operators.

depths.) Some small craft also enter west of Hampton Bar. **Hampton**, on the west side of the river 2 miles above the channel entrance, is an important seafood center. Traffic on the river consists of seafood and petroleum products, sand and gravel and building materials. The residential and commercial areas of Hampton are on the west side of Hampton River; Hampton University and a Veterans Hospital are on the east side.

(120) **Sunset Creek**, on the west side just above the Hampton River mouth, is entered by a marked dredged channel leading westward from the channel in the river and has a federal project of 12 feet. (See Notice to Mariners and latest editions of the charts for controlling depths.)

(121) The principal commercial wharves at Hampton, just below the bridge, have depths of 7 to 12 feet at their faces. The public landing 500 yards below the bridge has depths of 8 feet at the face; small boats anchor between the public landing and the bridge. The wharves along Sunset Creek have depths of 4 to 9 feet at their outer ends.

(122) Marine supplies, gasoline, diesel fuel and a pump-out station are available at Hampton. A yacht club and several marinas here have berthing space—repairs can be made. The largest marine railway is 120 feet and lifts up to 35 tons.

(123) **Jones Creek**, on the east side of Hampton River 300 yards above the mouth, has depths of 8 to 11 feet. The bulkheads have depths of 3 to 10 feet alongside and

are controlled by the Veterans Hospital on the south and Hampton University on the north.

(124) The 55-foot project channel to Newport News was discussed earlier. Depths along the edges of the dredged section are 19 to 25 feet. The currents do not always set fair with the channel, especially with strong winds, and deep-draft vessels sometimes find it difficult to stay in the channel.

(125) **Newport News Middle Ground Light** (36°56'43"N., 76°23'29"W.), 52 feet above the water, is shown from a red conical tower on a red cylindrical pier near the western end of the shoal.

(126) **Newport News Point** (36°57.8'N., 76°24.7'W.) on the north side of the entrance to James River, is 21.5 miles from the Virginia Capes. The city of **Newport News** extends several miles along the northeast bank of James River.

(127) **Newport News Creek**, just west of Newport News Point, is a city-owned small-boat harbor used by fishing boats, pleasure craft and petroleum barges. Vessels entering the creek should not cut between Buoy 1 and the bridge-tunnel interchange as the bridge-tunnel interchange is surrounded by shoal riprap. In 2007, a rocky bottom with a depth of 6 feet was reported just south-southeast of Newport News Point at 36°57'30"N., 76°24'37"W.; caution is advised. Fuel, supplies and slips are available, and repairs can be made. A 75-ton marine railway and a 40-ton mobile hoist are available.

(128)     Newport News Shipbuilding and Drydock Company is just below the James River Bridge on the east side of the river. A security zone is along the waterfront of the company property. (See **33 CFR 165.1** through **165.33** and **165.504**, chapter 2, for limits and regulations.)

(129)
## Wharves

(130)     The deepwater piers and wharves at Newport News extend from Newport News Point for 2.5 miles up James River. Only the major facilities are listed in the facility table for Newport News. All have access to highways and railroads, freshwater connections and electric shore-power connections. Unless otherwise indicated, these facilities are owned by the Virginia Ports Authority. The alongside depths given for each facility listed are reported—for information on the latest depths, contact the operator.

(131)     The facilities of the Newport News Shipbuilding and Drydock Co. begin 1.7 miles northwest of Newport News Point and extend 2 miles upriver. The company operates four outfitting piers equipped with cranes, largest capacity 80 tons; 2 drydocks, largest 640 feet long, 30 feet alongside; three graving docks, largest 1,670 feet long, 40 feet alongside with cranes of 990- and 310-ton capacity; two inclining shipways with lengths to 60 feet; floating cranes up to 67-ton capacity available.

(133)     **Willoughby Spit**, on the south side of the entrance to Hampton Roads, is a narrow barrier beach 1.3 miles long in an east-west direction. About midway between the spit and Old Point Comfort, on the opposite side of the entrance, is **Fort Wool**, which is on the south edge of the main ship channel.

(134)     **Willoughby Bank**, with depths of 4 to 7 feet, extends east-northeastward along the edge of the main channel for about 2.5 miles from Fort Wool.

(135)     **Willoughby Bay**, on the inner side of Willoughby Spit, has general depths of 7 to 12 feet. On the south side of the bay are the prominent buildings of the Norfolk Naval Base and the Naval Air Station. A marked channel with a Federal project depth of 10 feet, 0.4 mile westward of Fort Wool, leads to a small-boat harbor behind the hook of Willoughby Spit. (See Notice to Mariners and latest editions of the charts for controlling depths.) Some supplies, fuel and berthing are available—repairs can be made. The largest marine railway is 40 feet.

(136)     The western and southern part of Willoughby Bay is a **restricted area**. (See **33 CFR 334.300**, chapter 2, for limits and regulations.)

(137)     Mariners are advised that the bridge across Willoughby Bay, commonly called the **Willoughby Bay Bridge** is under construction (2021). Construction activities are planned from March 15, 2021 through November, 2025. Detailed project information will be provided via updated local notice to mariners, broadcast notice to mariners and marine safety information bulletins. Mariners should use caution when transiting the area and are advised to maintain a safe distance of at least 300 feet from all HRBT bridge structures/work trestles. This area contains a straight row of mooring pilings, referred to as the **Willoughby Mooring and Safe Harbor Area**, for the exclusive use of vessels involved in the HRBT Expansion project. Two end pilings are marked with a solid red light and each interior piling is marked with a solid yellow light. The perimeter of the mooring and safe harbor area is marked with yellow buoys with flashing yellow lights. Mariners are advised to keep clear of the Mooring and Safe Harbor Area.

(138)
## ENCs - US5VA15M, US5VA17M
## Charts - 12245, 12253

(139)     **Norfolk Harbor** comprises a portion of the southern and eastern shores of Hampton Roads and both shores of **Elizabeth River** and its Eastern, Southern and Western Branches, on which the cities of Norfolk, Portsmouth and Chesapeake are located.

(140)     The harbor extends from off Sewells Point south in Elizabeth River to the seventh bridge over Southern Branch, a distance of 15 miles; it extends 1.5 miles up Western Branch to a point 0.5 mile above the West Norfolk highway bridge and up Eastern Branch for 2.5 miles to the Norfolk Southern Railway bridge.

(141)     The main part of Norfolk is on the east side of Elizabeth River north of Eastern Branch, with Berkley, a subdivision, to the southward between Eastern and Southern Branches. South of Berkley is the city of Chesapeake. Portsmouth is opposite Norfolk, and its waterfront extends along the west shore of Southern Branch and the south shore of Western Branch. These cities form practically a single community, united by the same commercial interests and served by the same ship channel.

(142)     **Naval restricted areas** are along both sides of the Elizabeth River (Southern Branch). (See **33 CFR 334.290**, chapter 2, for limits and regulations.)

(143)
## Weather

(144)     Norfolk, located in extreme southeastern Virginia, has an average elevation of 13 feet (3.96 m) above sea level and, almost surrounded by water, has a modified marine climate. The city's geographic position with respect to the principal storm tracks is especially favorable, being south of the average path of storms originating in the higher latitudes and north of the usual track of hurricanes and other tropical storms. These features combine to place Norfolk in one of the favored climatic regions of the United States. Temperatures of 100°F (37°C) or higher are infrequent and cold waves are uncommon.

(145)     The average temperature at Norfolk is 60.1°F (15.6°C). The average daily extremes are 68.5°F (20.3°C) and 51.2°F (10.7°C). January is the coolest month with an average temperature of 40.5°F (4.7°C) while July is the warmest month with an average temperature of 79.4°F (26.3°C). The warmest temperature on record is

(154)

## Facilities in Norfolk

| Name | Location | Dimensions (feet) | | | Storage, Handling and Purpose | Owned/ Operated by: |
|---|---|---|---|---|---|---|
| | | Space | Depth* | Deck | | |
| **South of Sewells Point between the Naval Base and Tanner Point** | | | | | | |
| Norfolk International Terminals (Pier 3) | 36°55'53"N., 76°20'01"W. | 2,902 | 36 | 9.5 | Open storage (3 acres)<br>Covered storage (115,000 square feet)<br>Cold storage (100,000 cubic feet)<br>Occasional receipt of conventional general cargo<br>Occasional shipment of frozen food products | Virginia Port Authority/ Norfolk International Terminals, Inc. |
| Lehigh Cement Company Norfolk Terminal Pier | 36°55'48"N., 76°19'49"W. | 700 | 29 | 11 | Silo storage (32,900 tons of cement)<br>Occasional receipt of bulk cement | Lehigh Cement Company |
| Norfolk International Terminals (North Berth No. 1) | 36°55'32"N., 76°19'46"W. | 1,527 | 40 | 10 | Open storage (200 acres)<br>Three 50-long-ton container cranes<br>Receipt and shipment of containerized general cargo | Virginia Port Authority/ Norfolk International Terminals, Inc. |
| Norfolk International Terminals (RO/RO Berth) | 36°55'10"N., 76°19'42"W. | 900 | 32 | 9.8 | Open storage (1.4 acres)<br>Covered storage (67,000 square feet)<br>One 350-ton floating derrick<br>Receipt and shipment of roll-on/roll-off cargo | Virginia Port Authority/ Norfolk International Terminals, Inc. |
| Norfolk International Terminals (Pier 2) | 36°55'03"N., 76°19'57"W. | 2,656 | 30-32 | 9.8 | Covered storage (275,000 square feet)<br>Receipt and shipment of conventional general cargo | Virginia Port Authority/ Norfolk International Terminals, Inc. |
| Norfolk International Terminals (Pier 1) | 36°54'55"N., 76°19'56"W. | 2,640 | 30-32 | 9.8 | Covered storage (238,000 square feet)<br>Receipt and shipment of conventional general cargo | Virginia Port Authority/ Norfolk International Terminals, Inc. |
| Norfolk International Terminals (Container Berth No. 1) | 36°54'53"N., 76°19'39"W. | 750 | 36 | 9.8 | Open storage area<br>Three 50-long-ton container cranes<br>Receipt and shipment of conventional general cargo | Virginia Port Authority/ Norfolk International Terminals, Inc. |
| Norfolk International Terminals (Container Berth No. 2) | 36°54'45"N., 76°19'38"W. | 830 | 41 | 9.8 | Open storage area<br>Three 50-long-ton container cranes<br>Receipt and shipment of conventional general cargo | Virginia Port Authority/ Norfolk International Terminals, Inc. |
| Norfolk International Terminals (Container Berth No. 3) | 36°54'35"N., 76°19'36"W. | 1,100 | 41 | 9.8 | Open storage area<br>Three 48-long-ton container cranes<br>Receipt and shipment of conventional general cargo | Virginia Port Authority/ Norfolk International Terminals, Inc. |
| Norfolk International Terminals (Container Berth No. 4) | 36°54'22"N., 76°19'34"W. | 1,550 | 41 | 9.8 | Open storage area<br>Three 48-long-ton container cranes<br>Receipt and shipment of conventional general cargo | Virginia Port Authority/ Norfolk International Terminals, Inc. |
| **Facilities at Lamberts Point** | | | | | | |
| Norfolk Southern Railway Company Lambert's Point Coal Pier No. 6 | 36°52'47"N., 76°19'56"W. | 1,850 | 53 | 11 | Silo storage (10,000 tons of coal)<br>Two electric traveling coal loading towers<br>Shipment of coal | Norfolk Southern Corp./ Norfolk Southern Railway Corp. |
| Lambert's Point Docks Pier N | 36°51'57"N., 76°19'11"W. | 2,590 | 24-32 | 10.8 | Open storage (0.5 acre)<br>Tank storage (3.2 million gallons)<br>Covered storage (320,000 square feet)<br>Receipt and shipment of conventional general cargo<br>Receipt of animal and vegetable oils | Norfolk Southern Corp./ Lambert's Point Docks, Inc. and Norfolk Oil Transit, Inc. |
| Lambert's Point Docks Pier P | 36°51'45"N., 76°18'56"W. | 2,790 | 32 | 11 | Open storage (7.5 acres)<br>Covered storage (326,000 square feet)<br>Four cranes to 50 tons<br>Receipt and shipment of conventional and containerized general cargo and roll-on/roll-off cargo | Norfolk Southern Corp./ Lambert's Point Docks, Inc. |
| **Pinner Point** | | | | | | |
| Portsmouth Marine Terminal Wharf | 36°51'26"N., 76°19'33"W. | 3,535 | 40 | 12 | Open storage (55 acres)<br>Covered storage (130,000 square feet)<br>Six container cranes to 60 tons<br>One 110-ton gantry crane<br>Receipt and shipment of conventional, containerized and roll-on/roll-off general cargo<br>Receipt of automobiles and shipment of tobacco | Virginia Port Authority/ Virginia International Terminals, Inc. |
| APM Terminals Portsmouth Wharf | 36°51'29"N., 76°19'06"W. | 1,000 | 40 | 12 | Open storage<br>Three container cranes to 35 long tons<br>Four 50-ton gantry cranes<br>Receipt and shipment of containerized general cargo | Virginia Port Authority/ Universal Maritime Service Corp. |
| **Elizabeth River (Eastern Branch)** | | | | | | |
| Allied Terminals Norfolk Terminal Wharf | 36°50'20"N., 76°16'20"W. | 625 | 25 | 9 | Tank storage (17.6 million gallons)<br>Receipt of liquid fertilizer, mathanol and caustic soda | Allied Terminals Inc. |
| **Elizabeth River (Southern Branch)** | | | | | | |
| United States Gypsum Co. Norfolk Wharf | 36°49'18"N., 76°17'22"W. | 645 | 32 | 10 | Open storage<br>Covered storage<br>Electric belt-conveyor system<br>Receipt of gypsum rock | United States Gypsum Company |

## Facilities in Norfolk

| Name | Location | Dimensions (feet) | | | Storage, Handling and Purpose | Owned/ Operated by: |
|---|---|---|---|---|---|---|
| | | Space | Depth* | Deck | | |
| Crown Central Petroleum Corporation Chesapeake Barge Dock | 36°49'15"N., 76°17'22"W. | 300 | 31-35 | 40-43 | Tank storage (214,300 barrels) Shipment and occasional receipt of diesel fuel | Crown Cenral Petroleum Corp. |
| ExxonMobile Refining and Supply Company Chesepeake Terminal Barge Wharf | 36°49'13"N., 76°17'20"W. | 335 | 21 | 10 | Tank storage (762,000 barrels) Shipment and occasional receipt of petroleum products by barge | ExxonMobile Oil Corp. |
| ExxonMobile Refining and Supply Company Chesepeake Terminal Tanker Wharf | 36°49'08"N., 76°17'23"W. | 810 | 35 | 10 | Tank storage (1.1 million barrels) Receipt and shipment of bulk and packaged petroleum products | ExxonMobile Oil Corp. |
| Mid-Atlantic Terminals Chesapeake Wharf | 36°48'59"N., 76°17'22"W. | 735 | 40 | 12 | Open storage (40 acres) One ship loader and electric belt-conveyor system Shipment and occasional receipt of wood chips and other dry bulk materials | Mid-Atlantic Terminals, LLC. |
| Roanoke Cement Co. Ohio Street Terminal Wharf | 36°48'52"N., 76°17'22"W. | 500 | 35 | 10 | Silo storage (18,500 tons of cement) Covered storage (25,000 tons of cement clinker) Receipt of bulk cement and cement clinker | Titan America, Inc./ Roanoke Cement Co. and Lafarge Calcium Aluminates |
| Roanoke Cement Co. Chesapeake Plant Wharf | 36°48'47"N., 76°17'21"W. | 450 | 25 | 9 | Covered storage (70,000 tons of fertilizer) Occasional shipment of dry bulk fertilizer | Titan America, Inc./ Roanoke Cement Co. |
| Apex Oil Company Chesapeake Terminal Lower Barge Wharf | 36°48'22"N., 76°17'23"W. | 290 | 19 | 11 | Tank storage (250,000 barrels) shared with adjoining upper barge wharf Receipt and shipment of petroleum products by barge | Center Point Terminal Group, Inc./ Apex Oil Co. |
| Apex Oil Company Chesapeake Terminal Upper Barge Wharf | 36°48'16"N., 76°17'24"W. | 390 | 27 | 11 | Tank storage (250,000 barrels) Receipt and shipment of petroleum products Receipt of asphalt | Center Point Terminal Group, Inc./ Apex Oil Co. |
| Perdue Farms Chesapeake Grain Elevator Barge Wharf | 36°48'10"N., 76°17'25"W. | 416 | 38 | 10 | Tank storage (9.2 million gallons) Marine leg and belt conveyor Receipt of grain and soybeans Shipment of soybeans | Perdue Farms, Inc. |
| Perdue Farms Chesapeake Elevator Ship Wharf | 36°48'06"N., 76°17'20"W. | 800 | 39 | 10 | Grain elevator (6.8 million bushels) Covered storage (18,000 tons) Shipment of grain and soybean meal | Perdue Farms, Inc. |
| Allied Terminals Chesapeake Marine Terminal Wharf | 36°47'45"N., 76°17'32"W. | 650 | 31 | 10 | Tank storage (54 million gallons) Receipt and shipment of gasoline, kerosine, liquid fertilizer and edible oils | Allied Terminals, Inc. |
| Southern Aggregates Money Point Barge Dock | 36°47'26"N., 76°17'46"W. | 300 | 15-35 | 7 | Open storage area shared     Shipment of pumice with adjoining ship dock | Southern Aggregates, LLC |
| Southern Aggregates Money Point Plant Pier | 36°47'29"N., 76°17'49"W. | 954 | 16-35 | 12 | Open storage (150,000 tons) Covered storage (20,000 tons) One 65-ton gantry crane Electric belt-conveyor system Receipt of pumice, ulexite and gypsum by vessel and sand/gravel by barge | Southern Aggregates, LLC |
| ExxonMobil Chesapeake Terminal Wharf | 36°47'21"N., 76°18'06"W. | 300 | 28 | 8 | Tank storage (363,000 barrels) Receipt of gasoline by barge | Shotmeyer Oil Co./ ExxonMobile Refining and Supply Co. |
| Amerada Hess Corporation Money Point Barge Wharf | 36°47'14"N., 76°18'09"W. | 300 | 18 | 12 | Tank storage (476,000 barrels) Receipt and shipment of petroleum products | Amerada Hess Corp. |
| Amerada Hess Corporation Money Point Tanker Wharf | 36°47'05"N., 76°18'10"W. | 700 | 35 | 13.5 | Tank storage (540,100 barrels) Receipt and shipment of petroleum products | Amerada Hess Corp. |
| Lafarge North America Cement Company Chesapeake Terminal Wharf | 36°46'42"N., 76°18'22"W. | 650 | 25-35 | 10.5 | Silo storage (30,000 tons of cement) Receipt of bulk cement | Lafarge North America Cement Company |
| Elizabeth River Terminals Pier 1 Wharf | 36°46'41"N., 76°18'08"W. | 1,425 | 12-35 | 8.5 | Covered storage (156,000 tons) One 50-ton gantry crane Electric belt-conveyor systems Receipt of fertilizers, ores, minerals, scrap metal, feeds and grains | Elizabeth River Terminals, LLC |
| Elizabeth River Terminals Pier 2 Wharf | 36°46'42"N., 76°17'56"W. | 750 | 35 | 11 | Covered storage (40,000 tons and 63,000 square feet) Open storage (8 acres) Two crawler cranes to 250 tons Receipt of fertilizers, ores, minerals, scrap metal, feeds and grains | Elizabeth River Terminals, LLC |
| Southern States Cooperative Chesapeake Wharf | 36°46'35"N., 76°17'41"W. | 500 | 37 | 10 | Silo storage (20,000 tons) One 100-ton receiving hopper Electric belt-conveyor Receipt of potash by vessel | Southern States Cooperative, Inc. |
| Tri-Port Terminals Wharf | 36°46'20"N., 76°17'42"W. | 650 | 32 | 8 | Tank storage: 10.9 million gallons (chemicals) and 8.3 million gallons (fertilizer) Reciept of nitrogenous liquid fertilizer and miscellaneous bulk liquid commodities | Tri-Port Terminals, Inc. |

104°F (40°C), recorded in August 1980, and the coolest temperature on record is -3°F (-19.4°C), recorded in January 1985. Each month, October through April, has recorded temperatures below freezing (0°C), while each month, May through August, has seen temperatures in excess of 100°F (37.8°C). The average date of the last freezing temperature in the spring is March 23, while the average date of the first in autumn is November 18.

(146)  The average annual precipitation of Norfolk is 44.83 inches (113.9 mm). Precipitation is uniformly distributed throughout the year except for a noticeable peak in July and August. November is the driest month, averaging only 3 inches (76.2 mm), while, thanks to convective activity, August is the wettest month, averaging 5.27 inches (133.9 mm). The greatest 24-hour precipitation was 7.41 inches (188.2 mm), which fell in August 1964.

(147)  Occasional winters pass without a measurable amount of snowfall, and when snow does occur, it generally occurs in light falls, which usually melt and disappear within 24 hours. Overall, snowfall is light and averages only 8 inches (203.2 mm) each year and has occurred in each month, November through April. The biggest 24-hour snowfall occurred when 13.6 inches (345.4 mm) fell in February 1989.

(148)  Fourteen hurricanes have come within 50 miles (80.5 km) of Norfolk since records have been kept going back to 1878. In contrast, many more hurricanes have passed just south of Norfolk with Cape Hatteras, NC recording fifty-four hurricanes tracking within 50 miles since 1878. Tropical systems do frequent the Norfolk area though and since 1950, thirty-two tropical systems (tropical storms and hurricanes combined) have passed within 50 miles of Norfolk. Most storms approach from the southeast, south and southwest. The area's strongest storms, including the record hurricane of 1933 and Hurricane Isabel both approached Norfolk from the southeast.

(149)  **Sewells Point** (36°57.8'N., 76°19.6'W.), on the east side of the entrance to Elizabeth River, is 18 miles from the Virginia Capes. A breakwater, marked by a light on its outer end, extends about 0.3 mile westward from the point. The piers of the **Norfolk Naval Base** and its annex extend southward from the breakwater along the east bank of the river. General depths at the naval piers are 30 to 50 feet.

(149.001)  A **speed limit** in Norfolk Harbor Reach is prescribed for non public vessels of 300 gross tons or more not to proceed over 10 knots. (See **33 CFR 165.501**, chapter 2, for limits and regulations.)

(150)  **Sewells Point Spit**, covered 3 to 6 feet, extends north-northeastward from the point for 1.4 miles to the outer end of Willoughby Channel. A channel, marked by lights and daybeacons, extends eastward and southward through Sewells Point Spit for about 1.2 miles to an enclosed boat basin used by small navy boats.

(151)  The approach to the naval piers is a **restricted area**. (See **33 CFR 334.300**, chapter 2, for limits and regulations.)

(152)

## Wharves

(153)  Norfolk Harbor has numerous wharves and piers of all types, the majority of which are privately owned and operated. Only the major deepwater facilities are listed in the table. These facilities are southward of Sewells Point, between the Norfolk Naval Base and Tanner Point; on Lamberts Point; on Pinner Point; and on Eastern Branch and Southern Branch of Elizabeth River. All have freshwater connections and access to highways and railroads, and most have electrical shore-power connections. Cargo is generally handled by ship's tackle; special cargo-handling equipment, if available, is mentioned in the description of the particular facility. The alongside depths given for each facility described are reported depths. (For information on the latest depths, contact the operator.)

(155)  **Lafayette River** empties into the east side of Elizabeth River 4 miles south of Sewells Point and 22 miles from the Virginia Capes. The river, used exclusively by pleasure and recreational craft, is entered by a marked dredged channel between **Tanner Point** and **Lamberts Point**, 1.5 miles to the southward. A light, 0.6 mile south of Tanner Point, marks the channel entrance. The dredged channel leads for 1.1 miles to a point about 0.3 mile westward of the Hampton Boulevard Bridge. From this point, a marked natural channel leads for about 2.4 miles to where the river divides into two forks. The dredged channel turns sharply at the light off **Lawless Point**, a mile above the entrance, and vessels must be on the alert to avoid grounding. A yacht club is just below the north end of the Hampton Boulevard Bridge.

(156)

### Structures across Lafayette River

| Name | Type | Location | Clearances (feet) Horizontal | Vertical* |
|---|---|---|---|---|
| Hampton Boulevard | fixed | 36°54'22"N., 76°18'18"W. | 50 | 24 |
| Granby Street | fixed | 36°53'20"N., 76°16'49"W. | 40 | 22 |
| Willow Wood Drive | fixed | 36°53'21"N., 76°16'36"W. | 60 | 18 |
| E 26th Street | fixed | 36°52'25"N., 76°16'22"W. | 27 | 9 |
| Tidewater Drive | fixed | 36°52'07"N., 76°16'06"W. | 23 | 4 |

* Clearances are referenced to Mean High Water

(157)  **Knitting Mill Creek** is on the south side of Lafayette River about 3 miles above the mouth. A dredged channel, marked by daybeacons, leads to a basin near the head of the creek. Gasoline, berths, repairs and some supplies are available within the creek. The largest marine railway is 40 feet and a lift to 10 tons is available.

(158)  **East Haven**, on the south side of Lafayette River about 3.5 miles above the mouth, has a dredged channel that leads to a settling basin and boat ramp.

## Facilities in Norfolk

| Name | Location | Dimensions (feet) | | | Storage, Handling and Purpose | Owned/ Operated by: |
|------|----------|-------|--------|------|-------------------------------|---------------------|
| | | Space | Depth* | Deck | | |
| Nova Chemicals Chesapeake Wharf | 36°45'18"N., 76°17'35"W. | 330 | 22 | 10 | Tank storage (5 million gallons) Receipt of styrene monomer by barge | Nova Chemicals, Inc. |
| Dominion Generation Chesapeake Energy Center Wharf | 36°46'11"N., 76°17'55"W. | 800 | 36 | 10 | Tank storage (45,000 barrels) Receipt of fuel oil for plant consumption | Dominion Virginia Power/Dominion Energy |
| IMTT Chesapeake Terminal Wharf | 36°46'36"N., 76°18'23"W. | 650 | 34 | 12 | Tank storage (810,500 barrels) Receipt of petroleum products and liquid fertilizer | IMTT-Chesapeake |
| Atlantic Energy Wharf | 36°46'43"N., 76°18'39"W. | 800 | 35 | 10 | Tank storage (480,000 barrels) Receipt and shipment of liquified propane and butane | Atlantic Energy, Inc./ Amerigas Propane, Inc. |
| Giant Cement of Virginia Paradise Point Pier | 36°47'55"N., 76°17'38"W. | 750 | 38 | 15 | Silo storage (65,000 tons) One unloading tower Receiving hopper and electric belt-conveyor Receipt of bulk cement | Giant Cement of Virginia/ Paradise Point Marine, Inc. |

\* The depths given above are reported. For information on the latest depths contact the port authorities or the private operators.

(159)

## ENC - US5VA17M
## Chart - 12253

(160)     **Craney Island**, now a part of the mainland, is on the west side of Elizabeth River 4.5 miles south of Sewells Point. The low and thinly wooded area is the site of a navy fuel depot, and the offshore wharf and piers, all on the eastern side, are used only by Government vessels. Two daybeacons close off the northeast end of Craney Island mark submerged rocks. The offshore wharf and piers have depths of 22 to 47 feet alongside. A submerged water main crosses from Craney Island to the north side of Lamberts Point; vessels are cautioned not to anchor in the vicinity of the lighted range that marks the crossing. **Portsmouth Coast Guard Station** is on the west side of the entrance to Craney Island Creek.

(161)     A **naval restricted area** is along the south sides of Craney Island. (See **33 CFR 334.293**, chapter 2, for limits and regulations.)

(162)     **Lamberts Point**, on the east side of Elizabeth River 5.3 miles south of Sewells Point, is the site of several deepwater piers. These facilities are listed in the table *Facilities in Norfolk Harbor*, earlier in this chapter.

(163)     **Western Branch** (36°52.0'N., 76°19.7'W.) empties into the southwest side of Elizabeth River 5.8 miles south of Sewells Point and 23.8 miles from the capes. A marked channel leads from the main channel in Elizabeth River for 4.5 miles upstream to the head of the project about 0.25 mile above the first bridge. A 540-foot pier about 1 mile above the entrance to Western Branch extends to the northern edge of the marked channel; mariners are advised to use caution in the area.

(164)

## Structures across Western Branch

| Name | Type | Location | Clearances (feet) | |
|------|------|----------|-------------------|---|
| | | | Horizontal | Vertical* |
| Route 164 | fixed | 36°51'26"N., 76°20'51"W. | 100 | 45 |
| Churchland bridges (under constr 2020) | fixed | 36°50'33"N., 76°21'44"W. | 100 | 38 |

## Structures across Western Branch

| Name | Type | Location | Clearances (feet) | |
|------|------|----------|-------------------|---|
| | | | Horizontal | Vertical* |
| Overhead cable | power | 36°50'30"N., 76°21'44"W. | | 45 |
| Overhead cable | power | 36°49'59"N., 76°23'20"W. | | 47 |
| Hodges Ferry bridge | fixed | 36°49'24"N., 76°23'54"W. | 60 | 18 |
| Overhead cable | power | 36°49'23"N., 76°23'54"W. | | 37 |

\* Clearances are referenced to Mean High Water

(165)     **West Norfolk**, on the north side of the entrance to Western Branch, has a shipyard and small-craft facilities that can provide fuel, transient berths, marine supplies and a 220-foot marine railway; repairs can be made.

(166)     **Pinner Point** (36°51.3'N., 76°19.1'W.) is on the southwest side of Elizabeth River, 6.8 miles from Sewells Point. Much of the point is occupied by Portsmouth Marine Terminals. A marked dredged channel leads from the main channel in Elizabeth River to the wharves along the north side of the point. The facilities here are listed in the table *Facilities at Norfolk*, earlier in this chapter.

(167)     **Scott Creek** (36°51.1'N., 76°18.5'W.), on the southwest side of Elizabeth River, 7.3 miles from Sewells Point, is entered through a channel marked by daybeacons. A marina with a 60-ton lift is on the south side of the creek about 0.4 mile above channel entrance. A marina is on the point on the south side of the creek, about 0.9 mile above the channel entrance, and had a reported depth of 4 feet in the approach and alongside the piers. Transient berths, electricity, water, ice, towing, launching ramp, a 40-foot marine railway and a 30-ton lift are available; hull, engine and electrical repairs can be made.

(168)     **Hospital Point**, on the southwest side of Elizabeth River 7.5 miles from Sewells Point, is the site of a U.S. Naval Hospital. The main hospital building, the largest structure along the southwest side of Elizabeth River, is visible for many miles. The hospital landing has depths of about 18 feet at the face. A **general anchorage** is off

Hospital Point, extending north and south. (See **33 CFR 110.1** and **110.168**, chapter 2, for limits and regulations.)

(169)     **Norfolk**, or parts of it, has been described at some length in the preceding text. The midpoint of the downtown section can be taken as the **City Wharf** (36°50.9'N., 76°17.8'W.) at the foot of West Main Street and near the moored USS Wisconsin, which is on the northwest side of Elizabeth River 7.7 miles from Sewells Point and 25.7 miles from the Virginia Capes. City Wharf has depths of 15 feet at the face. The wharves northwest and southwest of West Main Street have depths of 14 to 20 feet alongside.

(170)     **Smith Creek**, opposite Hospital Point 7.5 miles from Sewells Point, has entrance depths of about 3 feet with deeper water inside, but the entrance is restricted by a 48-foot-wide fixed highway bridge with a clearance of 13 feet. An **anchorage** for recreational craft is in Smith Creek. (See **33 CFR 110.1** and **110.168**, chapter 2, for limits and regulations.)

(171)     The **Atlantic Marine Operations Center**, the Atlantic shipbase of the National Oceanic and Atmospheric Administration, is on the east side of the entrance to Smith Creek. There are 243-, 251- and 312-foot berths along the bulkhead wharf, which has depths of 20 feet alongside.

(172)     Mariners transiting the area near Town Point Reach are advised that the City of Norfolk has established a **"Slow no-wake" zone** from Scott Creek to the entrance to Eastern Branch.

(173)     **Waterside** is in the downtown area of **Town Point**, on Norfolk, the north side of the intersection between Elizabeth River and Eastern Branch. A municipal marina at this popular tourist stop has reported depths of about 16 feet at the entrance, inside the marina, and alongside the berths. Transient berths are available year-round. A sewage pump-out station is at the marina. Electricity is at the berths; ice and provisions are available nearby. The marina staff monitors VHF-FM channels 16 and 68.

(174)     A local passenger ferry operates between the Portsmouth and Norfolk waterfronts in the vicinity of Town Point Reach. The ferry boats are distinguished by a high-intensity flashing green masthead light which is visible all around the horizon. Mariners are advised to use caution while transiting the area.

(175)     **Eastern Branch** (36°50.5'N., 76°17.6'W.) empties into the east side of Elizabeth River 8 miles from Sewells Point and 26 miles from the Virginia Capes.

(176)     A Federal project provides for a channel 25 feet deep to the Norfolk Southern Railway Bridge, 2.5 miles above the entrance. Above the Norfolk Southern Railway Bridge, the natural channel has depths of 10 to 18 feet to the forks 3.3 miles from the entrance and usually is marked by bush stakes.

(177)     Downtown Norfolk is on the north side of Eastern Branch, and **Berkley**, a subdivision, is on the south side. Traffic is fairly heavy as far as Campostella Bridge. Depths at most of the piers on both sides of the branch range from 14 to 25 feet.

(178)

**Structures across Eastern Branch**

| Name | Type | Location | Clearances (feet) | |
|---|---|---|---|---|
| | | | Horizontal | Vertical* |
| Norfolk-Berkley bridge **Note 1** | bascule | 36°50'28"N., 76°17'11"W. | 150 | 48 |
| Norfolk Southern Railway bridge **Note 1** | bascule | 36°50'21"N., 76°16'31"W. | 140 | 4 |
| Overhead cable | power | 36°50'21"N., 76°16'23"W. | | 150 |
| Campostella Highway bridge | fixed | 36°50'25"N., 76°15'55"W. | 140 | 65 |
| Norfolk Southern Railway bridge **Note 1** | swing | 36°50'10"N., 76°14'40"W. | 60 | 6 |

* Clearances are referenced to Mean High Water
**Note 1** – See **33 CFR 117.1** through **117.59** and **117.1007**, chapter 2.

(179)     There are several shipyards along Eastern Branch: the largest floating drydock has a 3,200-ton capacity and handles vessels up to 316 feet; the largest marine railway has a 5,500-ton capacity and can handle vessels to 380 feet.

(180)     **Southern Branch**, the continuation of Elizabeth River south of the junction with Eastern Branch, is a part of the **Intracoastal Waterway** route southward to Albemarle Sound. The waterway is described at length in **United States Coast Pilot 4, Atlantic Coast, Cape Henry to Key West**.

(181)     The Federal project for Southern Branch provides for a channel 45 feet deep to the third bridge, thence 35 feet deep to the seventh bridge. The channel is maintained at or near project dimensions and is well marked. For detailed channel information and minimum depths as reported by the U.S. Army Corps of Engineers (USACE), use NOAA Electronic Navigational Charts. Surveys and channel condition reports are available through a USACE hydrographic survey website listed in Appendix A.

(182)     A **speed limit** of 6 knots is prescribed for that part of Southern Branch between Eastern Branch and the first bridge. (See **33 CFR 165.501**, chapter 2, for limits and regulations.)

(183)

**Structures across Southern Branch**

| Name | Type | Location | Clearances (feet) | |
|---|---|---|---|---|
| | | | Horizontal | Vertical* |
| Norfolk and Portsmouth Beltline bridge **Note 1** | vertical lift | 36°48'41"N., 76°17'26"W. | 300 | 6 (down) 142 (up) |
| Jordan/Route 337 bridge | fixed | 36°48'30"N., 76°17'24"W. | 270 | 145 |
| Norfolk Southern Railway bridge **Note 1** | vertical lift | 36°47'48"N., 76°17'36"W. | 220 | 10 (down) 135 (up) |
| Glimerton/Route 13 bridge **Note 2** | | 36°46'31"N., 76°17'42"W. | 124 | 36 (down) 136 (up) |
| Norfolk Southern Railway bridge **Notes 1 and 2** | bascule | 36°46'30"N., 76°17'42"W. | 125 | 7 |

* Clearances are referenced to Mean High Water
**Note 1** – See **33 CFR 117.1** through **117.59** and **117.997**, chapter 2, for drawbridge regulations.
**Note 2** – Large vessels must exercise caution when making the turns to these bridges because of the current.

(184)     The facilities on the east side of Southern Branch are mostly shipyards, oil terminals and bulk-cargo piers, while Government installations front most of the west side.

(185)     The port facilities on the Berkley side of Southern Branch are listed in the table *Facilities in Norfolk* given earlier in this chapter.

(186)     The shipyard at Berkley has six piers that can accommodate vessels up to 1,200 feet. The largest floating drydock at the yard is 850 feet long over the keel blocks, 192 feet wide, 36 feet deep over the keel blocks and has a lifting capacity of 54,250 tons. A marine railway with a capacity of 1,000 tons is available at the shipyard;

cranes up to 67 tons are also available. The largest shaft the shipyard is able to produce is 100 feet by 30 inches.

(187)     The **Norfolk Naval Shipyard** is on the **Portsmouth** side of Southern Branch, 3.5 miles from Lamberts Point, and occupies about 2 miles of waterfront. There are naval **restricted** areas along this reach. (See **33 CFR 334.1** through **334.6** and **334.290**, chapter 2, for limits and regulations.)

(188)     Most of the oil terminals are at **Chesapeake**, on the east side of Southern Branch, 10 miles from Sewells Point and 28 miles from the Capes. These facilities, as well as the deep-draft bulk cargo, grain, chemical, and fertilizer piers and wharves, were described earlier in this chapter under Wharves, Norfolk Harbor.

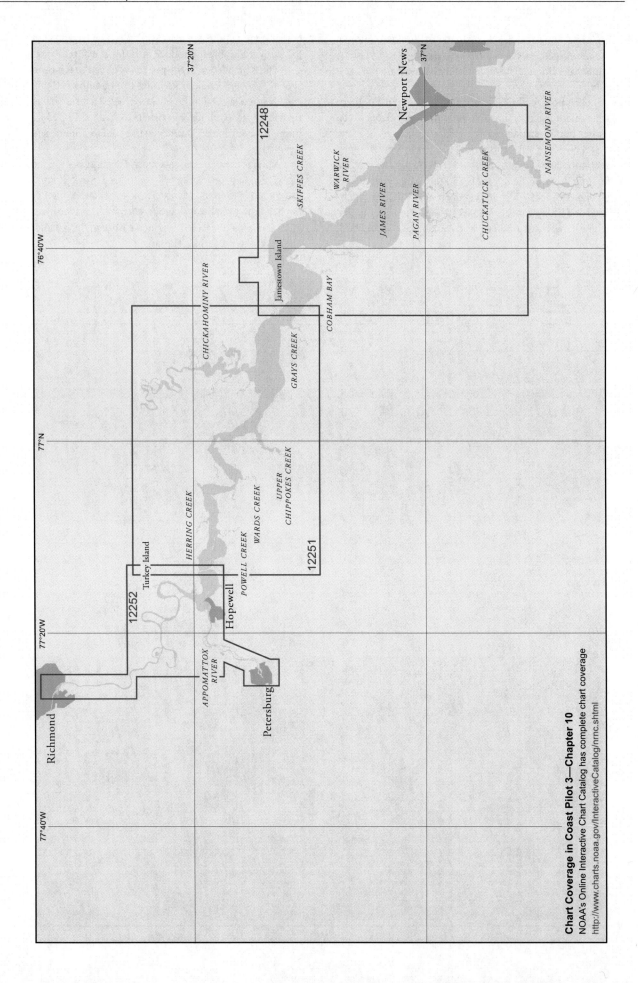

**Chart Coverage in Coast Pilot 3—Chapter 10**
NOAA's Online Interactive Chart Catalog has complete chart coverage
http://www.charts.noaa.gov/InteractiveCatalog/nrnc.shtml

# Chesapeake Bay, James River

(1)       This chapter describes the James River and several of its tributaries of which the Nansemond, Chickahominy and Appomattox Rivers are the more important. Also discussed are the ports of Richmond and Hopewell, as well as several of the minor ports and landings on these waterways.

(2)

### COLREGS Demarcation Lines

(3)       The lines established for Chesapeake Bay are described in **33 CFR 80.510**, chapter 2.

(4)

## ENCs - US5VA25M, US5VA51M
## Charts - 12248, 12251

(5)       **James River** rises in the Allegheny Mountains near Clifton Forge, VA, and flows 295 miles southeastward to Hampton Roads at Newport News, 21.5 miles by main channel from the Virginia Capes. The head of commercial navigation is at Richmond, 78 miles above the mouth. The river varies in width from 1,000 feet at Richmond to 4.3 miles at the mouth. Traffic consists chiefly of general cargo, chemicals, livestock, tobacco and paper products. Drafts of vessels using the river above Newport News generally do not exceed 15 feet, but vessels drawing 24 feet or more navigate it occasionally.

(6)       **Mileages** shown in this chapter as Mile 0.9N, Mile 12W, etc., are the nautical miles above the mouth of James River; the letters N, S, E, and W denote by compass points the side of the river where each feature is located. Mile 0.0 is a point in the main channel on a line between Pig Point and Newport News Point; the midchannel point is 21.5 miles from the Virginia Capes.

(7)       It is to be understood that the mileages given are approximations. The values are not intended to be finite. The intended degree of accuracy is only supposed to be enough to put the user of the chart into the general vicinity of the cited object.

(8)

### Channels

(9)       The Federal project for James River provides for depths from the Richmond Deepwater Terminal and in the Richmond Deepwater Terminal Turning Basin, 74 miles above the mouth, thence to the Richmond Harbor Turning Basin, 77 miles above the mouth, and thence to the Richmond Lock at Richmond, 78 miles above the mouth. The river is well marked. For detailed channel information and minimum depths as reported by the U.S. Army Corps of Engineers (USACE), use NOAA Electronic Navigational Charts. Surveys and channel condition reports are available through a USACE hydrographic survey website listed in Appendix A.

(10)

### Anchorages

(11)       **General anchorages** are just inside the mouth of the James River, south of Newport News Point. (See **33 CFR 110.1** and **110.168**, chapter 2, for limits and regulations.)

(12)

### Dangers

(13)       Numerous stakes, piling, wrecks and other obstructions are on both sides of the main channel in James River.

(14)

### Current

(15)       The currents in James River follow the general direction of the channel, except between Hog Island and Jamestown Island, 25 miles above the mouth, where they set across Goose Hill Flats. In the lower reaches, the velocity of flood is about equal to that of ebb. Near Richmond, the drainage flow predominates and the current seldom, if ever, sets upstream. These normal conditions are subject to change by wind and freshets.

(16)       During severe winters some drift ice appears, and at times the river freezes over, but navigation to Richmond hardly ever is suspended because the ice is broken up by a tug.

(17)       **Freshets** occur irregularly in the fall, winter and spring; their height at Richmond ranges from 6 to 32 feet, though the latter is exceptional. The maximum freshet heights usually occur between the middle of March and the middle of April; the freshets occurring at other times usually reach heights not greater than about 6 feet above the normal high water. The number of freshets that cause the water to rise above the level of the wharves along the main channel at Richmond averages about one per year; the water seldom rises above the level of the city wharf. The flood heights diminish rapidly below Richmond; the extreme is about 11 feet less at Dutch Gap, and the rise is not felt at Hopewell. The cutoffs have reduced the freshet height at Richmond about 1 foot.

(18)

### Pilotage, James River

(19)       Pilotage on the James River is compulsory for all foreign vessels and for U.S. vessels under register in the foreign trade. Pilotage is optional for U.S. vessels in the coastwise trade that have on board a pilot licensed by the Federal Government to operate in these waters.

(20)　The Chesapeake and Interstate Pilots Association offers pilot services to vessels engaged in the coastwise trade and public vessels to any port or place on the James River. Chesapeake and Interstate Pilots Association offers some pilot service in the upper James River at night. Arrangements for pilots may be made through ships' agents or the pilot office in Norfolk (telephone, 757–855–2733). Vessels requesting a river pilot only are boarded off Sewells Point. Pilots from sea are boarded at Cape Henry. Pilots use commercial launch services. Pilots begin radio watches at the launch service on VHF-FM channel 16, 30 minutes prior to last ETA. Advance pilot orders requested with 3-hour ETA update and any subsequent changes requested.

(21)　The Virginia Pilots Association offers pilotage to all vessels. Pilot service for the upper 38 miles of the river is available only during daylight. (See Pilotage, chapters 3 and 9.)

(22)
**Supplies and Repairs**

(23)　The principal places for supplies above Newport News are Hopewell and Richmond. Repair facilities are limited; small marine railways operate in Chuckatuck Creek, Pagan River and Appomattox River and at Falling Creek.

(24)
**ENC - US5VA25M**
**Chart - 12248**

(25)　The entrance to James River is between Pig Point (36°54.3'N., 76°26.5'W.) and **Newport News Point**, 3.6 miles to the north-northeastward; the midchannel point is 21.5 miles from the Virginia Capes and is close to the Newport News Wharves, listed in the table in chapter 9.

(26)　The **Monitor-Merrimac Memorial Bridge Tunnel** crosses Hampton Roads and connects Newport News with Suffolk. The fixed bridge crosses a small boat channel in the south section of the complex and has a clearance of 30 feet.

(27)　**Nansemond River** empties into the mouth of James River between Pig Point and **Barrel Point**, 2 miles to the west-northwest. Traffic on Nansemond River consists chiefly of pleasure craft. The river is used considerably by vessels with drafts of 9 feet and has been navigated with drafts of as much as 11 feet.

(28)　A narrow channel leads to Suffolk, 15 miles above the mouth of Nansemond River. The channel is well marked to Western Branch, 10 miles above the mouth. Local knowledge is necessary to navigate the narrow unmarked channel above Western Branch. A dam is 0.5 mile above the bridge in Suffolk.

(29)
**Current**

(30)　In Nansemond River, the current velocity is about 0.9 knot and follows the general direction of the channel.

(31)　**Pig Point** is on the south side of the entrance to James River and the east side of the entrance to Nansemond River. The submerged pilings of an old pier, 0.4 mile east of Pig Point, extend 0.7 mile into the river and are marked at the outer end by a daybeacon.

(32)　About 2.2 miles southwestward of Pig Point, a narrow, dredged channel marked by a light, buoy and daybeacons leads southward from Nansemond River channel into **Bennett Creek**. Gasoline, diesel fuel and pump-out are available at a small-boat basin near the bridge across the creek.

(33)　From Pig Point to Hollidays Point, 6.5 miles upstream, Nansemond River is wide, but the channel is crooked and leads between extensive shoals that are almost bare at low water in some places. There are many fish stakes on the shoals near the mouth. Above Hollidays Point, the river is narrow and crooked, but the midchannel is clear to Suffolk.

(34)　The highway bridge over Nansemond River at **Town Point**, on the south side 2.4 miles above the mouth, has a fixed span with a clearance of 65 feet. An overhead power cable with a clearance of 96 feet over the main channel crosses the river about 0.8 mile above the bridge.

(35)　**Great Shoal**, just southwest of the overhead power cable and on the northwest side of the channel, is an oyster bar with a least depth of 2 feet; it is marked by bush stakes.

(36)　An overhead power cable with a clearance of 40 feet crosses the river about 2.5 miles south of **Hollidays Point**.

(37)　**Western Branch** empties into the west side of Nansemond River, about 10 miles above the mouth. The channel entrance is marked by daybeacons for about 700 feet above the junction with the Nansemond River. A seasonal marina, 0.7 mile from the main Nansemond channel, has a pier with a depth of about 10 feet at the face. Gasoline, diesel fuel, a 45-foot marine railway and a 4-ton lift are available; minor repairs can be made.

(38)　Twin fixed highway bridges, both with a clearance of 35 feet, cross the Nansemond River about 12.5 miles above its mouth.

(39)　**Suffolk** is an important rail center on the south side of Nansemond River, 15 miles above the mouth. The highway bridge at Suffolk has a 45-foot fixed span and a clearance of 3 feet. The overhead power and telephone cables at the bridge have a clearance of 40 feet.

(40)　**Batten Bay**, on the west side of James River just north of Nansemond River, has general depths of 2 to 6 feet. **Ragged Island Creek**, at the north side of the bay, is shallow and little used.

(41)　**Chuckatuck Creek**, which empties into Batten Bay from southwestward, has depths of about 4 feet in the approach through the bay and deeper water inside for about 1.7 miles. The channel over the bar and through the bay is marked by lights and daybeacons; the channel edges usually are marked by bush stakes.

(42)　The highway bridge over Chuckatuck Creek, 0.8 mile above the mouth, has a fixed span with a clearance of 35 feet. A small shipyard is at **Crittenden**, on the south side of the creek just eastward of the bridge; berths, gasoline, diesel fuel, ice and some marine supplies are available. All types of repairs can be made; a marine railway there can handle craft up to 75 feet long.

(43)     **James River Bridge**, Mile 4, extends 4 miles from shore to shore in a northeast-southwest direction. The main channel vertical-lift span, 1 mile from the northeast shore, has a clearance of 60 feet down and 145 feet up. The bridgetender monitors VHF-FM channel 13; call sign KQ-7169. (See **33 CFR 117.1** through **117.59**, chapter 2, for drawbridge regulations.) A fixed span midway between the two shores has a clearance of 25 feet. The overhead power cable crossing the river close northward of the bridge has a clearance of 172 feet at the lift span and 100 feet at the fixed span. Both of the piers that protect the two cable suspension towers just north of the lift span are marked by three fixed red lights.

(44)     **White Shoal**, on the southwest side of the main channel at Mile 7, is marked near its southeast end by the tower of an abandoned lighthouse. A secondary channel on the opposite side of the shoal also is marked.

(45)     **Pagan River** empties into James River at Mile 7W. Traffic on this river consists chiefly of shellfish, sand and gravel. The approach to Pagan River through the dredged channel southeast of White Shoal is well marked; the river inside is also marked to within 1 mile of Smithfield.

(46)     **Jones Creek**, on the south side of Pagan River 0.7 mile above the mouth is marked by a light and daybeacons at the entrance. A fixed highway bridge 0.5 mile above the mouth has a clearance of 17 feet. An overhead power cable close southward of the bridge has a clearance of 32 feet. A marina and fish pier are at **Rescue**, just below the bridge; some supplies, repairs, fuel and a 30-ton mobile hoist are available. A 45-foot marine railway is 100 yards above the bridge. The fixed highway bridge, 2.5 miles above the mouth, has a width of 40 feet and a clearance of 7 feet.

(47)     **Battery Park** is on the south side of Pagan River 1 mile above the mouth. Hull and engine repairs can be made at the town, in a boatyard 150 yards above the oyster plant.

(48)     **Cypress Creek**, on the south side of Pagan River 4 miles above the mouth, has depths of 4 feet or more for 2 miles. The fixed highway bridge over the entrance has a clearance of 12 feet. An overhead power cable with a clearance of 36 feet crosses the creek about 0.8 mile above the bridge. A fixed highway bridge, with a clearance of 16 feet for a width of 46 feet, crosses the river about 1.1 miles above the mouth.

(49)     **Smithfield**, on the southwest side of Pagan River 4.5 miles above the mouth, is famous for its hams. The fixed highway bridge just above the town has a width of 30 feet and a clearance of 15 feet. An overhead power cable at the bridge and one 0.4 mile west of the bridge have clearances of 30 feet. A fixed highway bridge, with a clearance of 16 feet for a width of 48 feet, crosses the river about 0.6 mile above the fixed highway at Smithfield.

(50)     **Deep Creek**, Mile 8E, is used as an overnight anchorage by many oyster boats. A dredged marked channel leads from James River to a turning basin opposite Menchville. Traffic consists of some shellfish, sand and gravel.

(51)     **Menchville** is on the northwest side of the entrance to Deep Creek. The landings at the town have depths of about 5 feet alongside; gasoline and diesel fuel are available. Numerous pleasure craft use Deep Creek during the summer. Gasoline, supplies and a 12-ton lift are available on the east side about 0.5 mile above the mouth.

(52)     **Warwick River**, marked by daybeacons to a point about 3 miles above the mouth, is entered just north of Deep Creek; depths of 4 feet or more can be carried to **Fort Eustis**, 7 miles above the mouth. The mouth of the river is sometimes used as an anchorage by small oyster boats.

(53)     **Point of Shoals**, Mile 12W, is an extensive shallow area in **Burwell Bay**. There are also wide areas of unmarked shoals between the channel and the northeastern shore. The main channel formerly circled around Point of Shoals but is now through the dredged cut known as **Rocklanding Shoal Channel**. The old channel has shoaled but is still marked by daybeacons; the current velocity is 0.9 knot. The several small landings along the shore of Burwell Bay have depths of about 4 feet at their outer ends.

(54)     A small-craft harbor of refuge is on the west side of Burwell Bay at **Tylers Beach** (37°04.9'N., 76°40.0'W.). A dredged channel, marked by daybeacons and a light, leads from James River to the harbor basin.

(55)     Along the west side of the river between Burwell Bay and **Lawnes Creek** is an anchorage for the **Maritime Administration Reserve Fleet**. (See **33 CFR 162.270**, chapter 2, for regulations restricting navigation in the vicinity of the decommissioned ships.)

(56)     At Mile 16.2E, a dredged channel marked by lights, daybeacons and a lighted range, leads from James River to a boat basin of the U.S. Maritime Administration reservation at **Fort Eustis**. In 1992, the controlling depths were 3 feet (10 feet on centerline) to the basin with 3 to 9 feet in the basin. The ruins of an army pier are visible close northward of the channel. Decommissioned ships are moored on either side of the channel.

(57)     **Deep Water Shoals Warning Light** (37°08'55"N., 76°38'13"W.), Mile 16.9E, 15 feet above the water, is shown from a pile with a white and orange diamond-shaped daymark worded DANGER, in depths of 2 feet.

(58)     **Skiffes Creek**, Mile 17.8E, has a private channel at the entrance leading to an army pier, turning basin and to a small-boat basin proceeding northwards. The channel is marked by lights, daybeacons and lighted and unlighted buoys.

(59)     North of Skiffes Creek is an overhead power cable crossing the river on towers to Gravel Neck. The authorized clearance is 60 feet with 201 feet over the main channel and 188 feet over the secondary channel.

(60)     A **restricted area** is just south of the entrance to the Skiffes Creek. (See **33 CFR 334.280**, chapter 2, for limits and regulations.)

(61)     **College Creek**, Mile 22.5N, has depths of 1 foot across the flats at the mouth. The creek is difficult to navigate without local knowledge. Fixed bridges across the creek at the mouth and about 4 miles above the mouth have clearances of 10 and 12 feet, respectively. Private aids mark the creek.

(62)     **Cobham Bay**, a wide bight at Mile 25.6S, has general depths of 5 to 7 feet.

(63)     **Jamestown Island**, at Mile 26N, is the site of historic **Jamestown**, which was settled by Capt. John Smith and his 105 cavaliers in 1607. The town is on **Church Point**, Mile 28N, the northwest end of the island. The Jamestown white monument is prominent; the ruins of the old church are hidden by trees.

(64)     **The Thorofare**, **Back River** and **Sandy Bay** separate Jamestown Island from the mainland and forms a small-craft passage that connects at each end with James River. The Thorofare is a shallow bay on the northeast side of the island. Back River is a narrow, winding channel that extends from the head of The Thorofare along the north side of the island to Sandy Bay, which opens into the James River. A narrow channel marked by daybeacons leads through the extensive mudflats in the upper part of The Thorofare. The highway bridge across the mouth of Sandy Bay has a 48-foot fixed span with a clearance of 12 feet.

(65)     **Mill Creek**, which empties into The Thorofare from the northward, has a depth of 1 foot at the entrance and 2 or more feet to a landing 1.5 miles above the mouth. Above the landing, the creek is foul with snags and obstructions. The fixed highway bridge across the mouth of the creek has a clearance of 10 feet.

(66)     **Powhatan Creek**, used by fishermen and small pleasure craft during the summer, empties from the northward into Sandy Bay. A fixed bridge, 0.4 mile above the mouth, has a width of 25 feet and a clearance of 12 feet. A noticeable current is reported at the bridge. A marina near the bridge can provide gasoline, water, some marine supplies and a 17-ton lift; minor hull and engine repairs can be made. The numerous snags along the banks of the creek can be avoided by staying in midstream.

(67)     The approach to Powhatan Creek through Sandy Bay is marked with uncharted stakes—local knowledge is required to carry the best water. In 1984, severe shoaling was reported in the channel through the basin.

(68)

**ENC - US5VA51M**
**Chart - 12251**

(69)     **Scotland** (37°11.0'N., 76°47.2'W.), Mile 27.5S, is the mainland terminus of the Jamestown Ferry, which operates to **Glass House Point**, 1 mile northwest of the monument at Jamestown, across the river. Ferry slip depths are about 18 feet on the Scotland side and about 20 feet on the Jamestown side. The piers at Scotland and Glass House Point extend channelward over 700 feet and about 1,600 feet, respectively; the slips are marked by lights and a sound signal. The partly submerged remains of the old Scotland wharf are about 100 yards southeast of the slips.

(70)     **Grays Creek**, Mile 28.2S, is entered through a shallow bay. A 3-foot channel leads to deeper water inside. There are many snags and obstructions in the creek. A marina is 1 mile above the mouth.

(71)     **Chickahominy River**, Mile 33N, is navigable to Walkers Dam, 19 miles above the mouth. The lock in the dam has a length of 60 feet, a width of 15 feet and a depth of 4 feet over the sill. The lock gates are hand operated; there is no tender. It is recommended that at least two strong persons be on board before attempting to use the lock. Obstruction lights mark the dam spillway.

(72)     The channel through the broad flats at the entrance to Chickahominy River is entered 0.7 mile westward of Glass House Point. The channel is marked consistently by buoys and daybeacons to the bridge near the mouth, thence buoys sporadically mark critical points inside. The river is used by fishermen and pleasure boatmen.

(73)     Wharf ruins extend out about 200 yards from shore 0.5 mile above **Barrets Point**, on the east side of the entrance. A sunken barge lies on the eastern edge of the channel 0.8 mile above the point.

(74)     **Judith Stewart Dresser Memorial Bridge**, 1.3 miles above the mouth, has a fixed span with a clearance of 52 feet. A pier with a depth of 7 feet at the face extends 100 yards into the river from the east bank just north of the bridge.

(75)     The Thorofare is an unmarked cut leading through the bend of the river 10 miles above the mouth; the controlling depth is 5 feet. Small boats able to pass through the cut can save 1.2 miles.

(76)     A marina on the west side 11 miles above the mouth, just north of **Mt. Airy**, can provide gasoline, diesel fuel, transient berths, electricity, water, pumpout facility, marine supplies and surfaced ramp.

(77)     **Lanexa**, on the east side 15 miles above the mouth, has a marina with reported depths of 10 feet alongside. Gasoline and supplies are available. Hull and engine repairs can be made; a 70-foot marine railway and a 10-ton mobile lift are at the marina.

(78)     The former ferry slip and piers at **Claremont**, Mile 37.5S, are in ruins, and the bottom area to the southeastward near **Sloop Point** (37°13.8'N., 76°57.0'W.) is foul. The former ferry slip across the river at **Sandy Point** is also in ruins.

(79)     **Upper Chippokes Creek**, Mile 38.5S, has depths of about 5 feet for 3 miles, thence 2 feet for 1 mile to the head of navigation. The channel into the creek is close along the south bank. An overhead power cable about 3.5 miles above the mouth has a clearance of 56 feet. A wreck, marked by a lighted buoy, is off the creek entrance close to the southwest side of James River main channel; the wreck extends about 2 feet above high water.

(80)　　**Wards Creek** empties into James River at Mile 46S. A depth of 2 feet can be carried across the mudflats at the entrance by following the east bank at a distance of about 75 yards. Above the mouth, depths are 4 to 10 feet for 1.7 miles. The creek is an excellent storm anchorage for any boat able to enter.

(81)　　An overhead power cable, with a clearance of 180 feet at the main channel, crosses the river at **Windmill Point**, Mile 49.9S.

(82)　　**Powell Creek**, Mile 53S, has depths of 7 feet through a narrow channel across the mudflats at the entrance and for 2 miles upstream. The creek is a good storm anchorage.

(83)　　A highway lift bridge with a clearance of 50 feet down and 145 feet up crosses the James River at **Jordan Point**, Mile 56.4S. The bridgetender monitors VHF-FM channel 13; call sign KQ-7167. (See **33 CFR 117.1** through **117.49**, chapter 2, for drawbridge regulations.)

(84)　　**Jordan Point Marina**, on the east side of Jordan Point at the south end of the bridge, may be reached through a channel marked by private piles. Berths, gasoline, diesel fuel, water, electricity and some marine supplies are available.

(85)
**ENC - US5VA32M**
**Chart - 12252**

(86)　　**Hopewell**, Mile 59W, is the site of several industries and the terminus of a branch railroad to Petersburg. Allied-Signal, Hopewell Plant Pier (37°18'28"N., 77°15'55"W.), about 0.8 mile southeastward of **City Point**, is 622 feet long with berthing on both north and south sides and has 25 feet reported alongside. The pier is used for receipt of phenol, sulphur, oleum and fuel oil for plant consumption and shipment of dry bulk ammonium sulfate.

(87)　　**Regional Enterprises, Hopewell Wharf** (37°18'46"N., 77°16'11"W.) has a 90-foot face with 300 feet of berthing space and 23 feet alongside. The wharf receives crude oil, petroleum products and fertilizer.

(88)　　**Tidewater Materials, Hopewell Concrete Plant Wharf** (37°18'49"N., 77°16'16"W.) has a 400-foot face with 400 feet of berthing space and 10–18 feet alongside. The wharf receives sand and gravel.

(89)　　The **Appomattox River** has its entrance at Mile 59.5W. The channel through the flats at the mouth is marked by lights, daybeacons and a buoy. A dredged channel in the river starts about 3 miles above the entrance, and continues upstream to just below **Petersburg**.

(90)

**Structures across Appomattox River**

| Name | Type | Location | Clearances (feet) Horizontal | Vertical* |
|---|---|---|---|---|
| Route 10 bridges | fixed | 37°18'43"N., 77°17'48"W. | 102 | 40 |
| CSX Railroad bridge **See Note 1** | swing | 37°18'28"N., 77°19'18"W. | 80 | 10 |

**Structures across Appomattox River**

| Name | Type | Location | Clearances (feet) Horizontal | Vertical* |
|---|---|---|---|---|
| I-295 bridges | fixed | 37°18'50"N., 77°20'07"W. | 80 | 40 |
| Overhead cables | power | 37°18'50"N., 77°20'14"W. | | 113 |
| Overhead cable | power | 37°15'20"N., 77°22'40"W. | | 45 |
| Overhead cables | power | 37°15'10"N., 77°22'42"W. | | 46 |
| Temple Avenue bridges | fixed | 37°15'09"N., 77°22'42"W. | 97 | 40 |

\* Clearances are referenced to Mean High Water
**Note 1** – See 33 CFR **117.1** through **117.59** and **117.995**, chapter 2, for drawbridge regulations.

(91)　　The Hopewell City Marina, on the south side of the river just above the Route 10 bridges, can provide transient berths, open and covered slips, launching ramp, ice and some marine supplies. There are depths of about 6 feet off the T-pier. On the same side of the river, farther upstream just past the CSX Railroad bridge, another marina can provide gasoline, diesel fuel, pump-out station, marine supplies and marine repairs. A small-boat harbor, on the east side of the river, about 7 miles above the mouth has a launching ramp, transient slips, water, electricity, some marine supplies, a 100-foot marine railway and covered storage and repairs can be made; gasoline and diesel fuel can be obtained by truck.

(92)　　Above its junction with Appomattox River, James River becomes narrow and winding. The bends are often referred to as the Curles of the River, and the 14-mile section from Hopewell to Warwick/Richmond Deepwater Terminal is known as The Corkscrew. There is no contemporary hydrography for the Curles of the James River. Several shoal spots have been reported within the Curles; mariners are advised to use extreme caution and local knowledge.

(93)　　**Turkey Island Bend**, 2 miles north of Hopewell, has depths of 10 to 30 feet around its 6-mile length but is seldom used except by pleasure boats because the main channel now leads northwestward through Turkey Island Cutoff; most of the landings along the bend are in ruins. In 2009, severe shoaling was reported throughout the bend; extreme caution is advised. The north and west sections of the bend afford excellent anchorages, because the river current has been greatly diminished by the cutoff and winds from any direction have little effect; the bottom is mostly soft mud.

(94)　　**Turkey Island Cutoff**, Mile 61, is 1 mile long and well marked by lights.

(95)
**Cable ferry**

(96)　　A cable ferry crosses the lower part of Turkey Island Cutoff at Mile 61.1, providing vehicular access to Turkey Island, which is a National Wildlife Refuge. The single cable is moored ashore at both sides; when the self-propelled barge is underway, the cable is picked up to the deck level of the barge, which is about 3 feet above the water, and then dropped astern. **DO NOT ATTEMPT TO PASS A MOVING CABLE FERRY**.

(97)  An overhead power cable with a reported clearance of 171 feet crosses the river at Mile 62.3.

(98)  **Jones Neck Cutoff**, Mile 64, extends about 1 mile northward and westward; the cutoff is well marked by lights. The old river bend around **Jones Neck** has depths of 13 to 44 feet along its 4.5-mile length but is now little used; most of the landings are in ruins. Shoaling has been reported throughout the river bend; caution is advised.

(99)  A fixed highway bridge with a clearance of 145 feet crosses the James River about 0.6 mile below Dutch Gap.

(100)  **Dutch Gap**, Mile 66.5, the first canal dug in the United States, was cut through in 1611. The main channel extends west-northwestward through **Dutch Gap Cutoff** (**Aiken Swamp-Dutch Gap Cutoff**), which is about a mile long and is marked by lights at both ends. There is a gravel basin in **Hatcher Island**, on the north side of the cutoff.

(101)  The old river bend around Hatcher Island has depths of 7 to 25 feet along its 2-mile length. **Richmond Yacht Basin**, north of Hatcher Island, has piers with depths of about 12 feet at their outer ends; gasoline is available. The preferred passage is east of Hatcher Island. In 2009, it was reported that the passage around Hatcher Island had significant shoaling—extreme caution and local knowledge are advised. A small marine railway at the yacht club can handle boats up to 40 feet for repairs. A fixed highway bridge over the western entrance to the bend has a width of 40 feet and a clearance of 21 feet.

(102)  The old channel southward from Dutch Gap has depths of 9 feet or more for over 1 mile to the gravel basin in **Farrar Island**.

(103)  A concrete-and-steel wharf of the Virginia Electric and Power Co. (37°22'57"N., 77°22'44"W.), at Mile 67.5S, has main channel depths at the face. A privately maintained light is shown from the end of the wharf. The overhead cable just above the wharf has a clearance of 165 feet. About 300 yards westward is another cable with a clearance of 166 feet.

(104)  The oil wharf at **Drewrys Bluff**, Mile 71.7W, has 350 feet of berthing space with dolphins and main channel depths at the face. Vessels are requested to reduce speed when passing the wharf.

(105)  **Falling Creek** (37°26'31'"N., 77°25'22"W.) enters James River at Mile 72.4W. A fixed highway bridge with a clearance of 146 feet spans the river about 0.35 mile northeast of Falling Creek.

(106)  **Richmond**, the capital of Virginia, is at Mile 78E. Traffic to and from the city consists chiefly of petroleum products, sand and gravel, general cargo and tobacco. Commercial navigation in the river proper ends at the city wharves, but small boats can go 1 mile farther. The turnpike fixed highway bridge just below **Mayos Island** has a clearance of 40 feet.

(107)

### Weather

(108)  Richmond's climate might be classified as modified continental. Summers are warm and humid and winters generally mild. The mountains to the west act as a partial barrier to outbreaks of cold, continental air in winter, the coldest air being delayed long enough to be modified, then further warmed as it subsides in its approach to Richmond. The open waters of the Chesapeake Bay and Atlantic Ocean contribute to the humid summers and mild winters. The coldest weather normally occurs in late December and in January, when low temperatures usually average in the upper twenties (-2.7° to 1.5°C) and the high temperatures in the upper forties (8.3° to 9.5°C). Temperatures seldom lower to zero (-17.8°C). The average annual temperature for Richmond is 58.5°F (14.7°C), with an average high of 68.8°F (20.4°C) and an average low of 47.6°F (8.7°C). July is the warmest month, with an average temperature of 78.4°F (25.8°C) and January is the coolest month with an average temperature of 38°F (3.3°C). The warmest temperature on record at Richmond is 105°F (40.6°C), recorded last in July 1977, while the coldest temperature is -8°F (-22.2°C), recorded in February 1979. Each month, June through September, has recorded temperatures in excess of 100°F (37.8°C), while each month, October through May, has seen temperatures below freezing (0°C).

(109)  Precipitation is rather uniformly distributed throughout the year with a slight maximum during July and August. However, dry periods lasting several weeks do occur, especially in autumn when long periods of pleasant, mild weather are most common. There is considerable variability in total monthly amounts from year to year so that no one month can be depended upon to be normal. The average annual precipitation totals 42.8 inches (1087 mm). July is the wettest month, averaging 5.16 inches (131.1 mm), and February the driest, averaging just under 3 inches (76.2 mm). Snow has been recorded during 7 of the 12 months, October through April. Snowfalls of 4 inches (101.6 mm) or more occur on an average of once a year. Snow usually remains on the ground only 1 or 2 days at a time. Average annual snowfall is 13 inches (330.2 mm). The greatest 24-hour snowfall, 13.3 inches (337.8 mm), occurred on two occasions; January 1980 and February 1983. Ice storms (freezing rain or glaze) are not uncommon in winter, but they are seldom severe enough to do any considerable damage. The James River reaches tidewater at Richmond where flooding has occurred in every month of the year, most frequently in March and only twice in July. Hurricanes and less severe storms of tropical origin have been responsible for most of the flooding during the summer and early fall. Damaging storms occur mainly from snow and freezing rain in winter and from hurricanes, tornadoes and severe thunderstorms at other seasons. Damage may be from wind, flooding, or rain, or from any combination of these.

(110)  Since 1950, nine tropical storms have directly influenced the Richmond area. The most noteworthy

was the remnants of hurricane Hazel in 1954. Hazel quickly became a destructive cold-core low after coming ashore north of Myrtle Beach, South Carolina, and was still packing winds of greater than 70 miles per hour (61 knots) by the time it approached Richmond. At this time it was moving northward at speeds greater than 50 miles per hour (43 knots).

(111)     The National Weather Service maintains sensors at Byrd Field; **barometers** can be checked by telephone.

(112)
### Towage
(113)     Tug service is available at Richmond to assist in docking and undocking, if desired.

(114)
### Quarantine, customs, immigration and agricultural quarantine
(115)     (See chapter 3, Vessel Arrival Inspections, and appendix for addresses.)
(116)     **Quarantine** is enforced in accordance with regulations of the U.S. Public Health Service. (See Public Health Service, chapter 1.)
(117)     Richmond-Petersburg is a **customs port of entry**.
(118)     The Port of Richmond's **harbormaster** maintains an office at the Department of Public Works, City of Richmond, 800 E. Broad Street, Richmond, VA 23219. He is responsible within the port for the assignment of berths and anchorages.

(119)
### Wharves
(120)     City-owned facilities at the Port of Richmond have turning basins and are served by railway tracks and highways; water is available. The alongside depths given are reported. (For the latest controlling depths, contact the operator.)

(121)     **Port of Richmond, Deepwater Terminal** (37°27'22"N., 77°25'14"W.): 1,584-foot face, 19 feet alongside; deck height, 24.5 feet; livestock loading facility; 300,000 square feet covered storage; 39 acres open storage; three crawler cranes to 350-ton capacity; receipt and shipment of conventional and containerized general cargo including tobacco, forest, paper products, chemicals and cocoa; shipment of scrap iron and livestock; operated by Federal Marine Terminals, Inc. In 1996, a submerged obstruction was reported close to James River Light 168 in about 37°29.4'N., 77°25.3'W., just below the bend in the river at Goode Creek.

(122)     There are eight oil barge wharves and two barge wharves that handle gravel and construction material at Richmond. Most are on the west bank between Falling Creek and across from Richmond Upper Marine Terminal.

(123)
### Supplies
(124)     Gasoline and diesel fuel are available by tank truck. Some marine supplies may be obtained in Richmond, but major supplies must be obtained in the Hampton Roads area.

(125)
### Repairs
(126)     There are no drydocking or major repair facilities in the Port of Richmond; the nearest such facilities are in the Hampton Roads area.

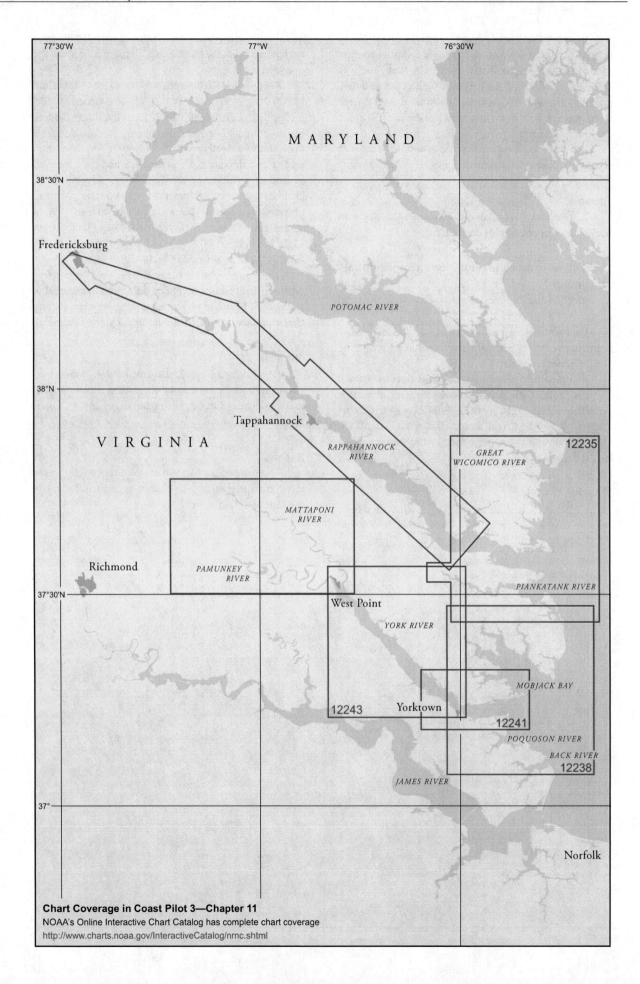

**Chart Coverage in Coast Pilot 3—Chapter 11**
NOAA's Online Interactive Chart Catalog has complete chart coverage
http://www.charts.noaa.gov/InteractiveCatalog/nrnc.shtml

# Chesapeake Bay, York and Rappahannock Rivers

(1)     This chapter describes the western shore of Chesapeake Bay from Old Point Comfort to the Potomac River including its principal tributaries Back, Poquoson, York, Piankatank, Rappahannock and Great Wicomico Rivers and Mobjack Bay. Also discussed are the ports of Yorktown, Fredericksburg, West Point, Tappahannock, Kilmarnock and Reedville, as well as several of the smaller ports and landings on these waterways.

(2)     **COLREGS Demarcation Lines**

(3)     The lines established for Chesapeake Bay are described in **33 CFR 80.510**, chapter 2.

(4)     **ENCs - US4VA12M, US4VA1AM, US4VA40M**
**Charts - 12221, 12225**

(5)     The western shore of Chesapeake Bay from Old Point Comfort to the Potomac River is mostly low. York and Rappahannock Rivers are broad and deep at their entrances and are navigable for long distances.

(6)     **Fishtraps** are thicker in this area than in any other part of the bay.

(7)     **Ice**

(8)     Ice is seldom encountered this far south in the bay but may be found in the upper parts of some of the tributaries.

(9)     **Channels**

(10)     The Federal project for Chesapeake Bay provides for depths of 50 feet in the main channel between the Virginia Capes and Fort McHenry, Baltimore. There are three dredged sections in the lower Chesapeake Bay: the first off Cape Henry, just above the Virginia Capes; the second off York Spit, 11 to 22 miles above the Capes; and the third off Rappahannock Spit, 40 to 46 miles above the Capes; they are well marked. For detailed channel information and minimum depths as reported by the U.S. Army Corps of Engineers (USACE), use NOAA Electronic Navigational Charts. Surveys and channel condition reports are available through a USACE hydrographic survey website listed in Appendix A.

(11)     **York Spit Channel** begins 11 miles above the Capes and extends northward another 11 miles. The current velocity is about 1.0 knot in the channel.

(12)     **Quarantine, customs, immigration and agricultural quarantine**

(13)     (See chapter 3, Vessel Arrival Inspections, and Appendix A for addresses.)

(14)     Quarantine is enforced in accordance with regulations of the U.S. Public Health Service. (See Public Health Service, chapter 1.)

(15)     **ENC - US5VA13M**
**Chart - 12222**

(16)     **Horseshoe** is a shoal that extends several miles out from the shore between Old Point Comfort and Back River, 6.5 miles to the northward. The southern edge of the shoal lies along the north side of the main channel into Hampton Roads; the eastern half has depths of 13 to 18 feet, and the western half, 6 to 11 feet. Local vessels drawing 7 feet or less use the lanes through the fishtraps on the Horseshoe when navigating between Hampton Roads and York River or Mobjack Bay. The tidal current velocity is 0.5 knot over the Horseshoe and is rotary, turning clockwise. See the Tidal Current prediction service at *tidesandcurrents.noaa.gov* for specific information about times, directions, and velocities of the current at numerous locations throughout the area. Links to a user guide for this service can be found in chapter 1 of this book.

(17)     A naval **restricted area** extends eastward and southward of Old Point Comfort, and a **danger zone** of the **Fort Monroe** firing range extends to seaward from a point 1.5 miles northward of the point. (See **33 CFR 334.350** and **334.360**, chapter 2, for limits and regulations, respectively.)

(18)     **Salt Ponds** is entered through a privately dredged inlet on the west side of Chesapeake Bay about 4 miles north of Old Point Comfort. The entrance is marked by private aids.

(19)     **Back River** empties into the west side of Chesapeake Bay 7 miles northward of Old Point Comfort between **Northend Point** and **Plumtree Island**, 1 mile to the northward. A firing and bombing **danger zone** is north of the entrance to Back River. (See **33 CFR 334.340**, chapter 2, for limits and regulations.) The approach to Back River, from southeastward through a lane in the fishtraps, is well marked.

(20)     About 2 miles above the mouth, Back River divides into **Northwest Branch** and **Southwest Branch**, which have general depths of 2 to 5 feet. The **Langley Field**

hangars, water tanks and wind tunnel back of Willoughby Point, between the branches, can be seen for many miles. A channel, marked by lights and daybeacons, extends 3 miles from the mouth of the river to the Langley Field fuel pier on the west side of Southwest Branch. In 1982, shoaling to 3 feet was reported on the south side of the channel about 150 yards east-northeastward of Light 9 at the river entrance. The Langley Yacht Club, just south of the fuel pier, has gasoline and supplies; the depth in the basin is about 4 feet.

(21)     A **restricted area** extends along the shoreline of Langley Air Force Base on the west shore of southwest Branch and Northwest Branch. (See **33 CFR 334.275**, chapter 2, for limits and regulations.)

(22)     A marina on the south side of Back River, just east of **Windmill Point** 1 mile above the mouth, has gasoline, diesel fuel and supplies; marine railways can handle boats up to 40 feet. The reported depth to the marina is about 6.5 feet.

(23)     **Harris River**, on the south side of Back River west of **Windmill Point**, has depths of 6 feet in a marked channel that leads to a marina inside **Stony Point**. Some supplies, gasoline, diesel fuel and berths are available. Repairs can be made; mobile lift, 20 tons.

(24)     **Messick Point** is on the north side of Back River, 1.5 miles above the mouth. A dredged channel leads northward of Back River Channel Daybeacon 16 to a small-craft facility and turning basin on the east side of Messick Point.

(25)     The highway bridge over Southwest Branch, 1.5 miles above Willoughby Point, has a fixed span with a horizontal clearance of 20 feet and a vertical clearance of 6 feet.

(26)     Between Back River and Poquoson River are shoals that extend 1 to 3 miles from shore; on the shoals are scattered oyster rocks that bare, or nearly bare, at low water. Strangers should stay outside the 6-foot curve. A channel about 0.6 mile outside the 6-foot curve extends northwestward through a fishtrap area from about 2.4 miles east-southeast of Northend Point to about 1.6 miles west-southwest of York Spit Light; the channel is marked by daybeacons. In 1980, poles were reported in the lane in about 37°09'54"N., 76°16'21"W., 37°10'45"N., 76°16'42"W., and 37°10'51"N., 76°16'48"W.

(27)
**ENCs - US5VA24M, US5VA26M**
**Chart - 12238**

(28)     **Poquoson River**, which empties into Chesapeake Bay 5 miles northwest of Back River, has depths of 7 feet to the village of **Yorkville**, on the west side 2.5 miles above the mouth. The marked approach to the river is from northeastward and is clear of fishtraps for a width of 400 yards. There is a light on either side of the entrance.

(29)     **Bennett Creek**, on the southeast side of the Poquoson River mouth, has depths of 6 feet or more for 1.3 miles to **Easton Cove,** which makes off to the eastward. The

channel is marked as far as White House Cove, on the west side of Bennett Creek 0.8 mile above the mouth; the channel in White House Cove is marked by daybeacons and has depths of 8 to 2 feet for 0.7 mile above the mouth. A 50-ton mobile hoist at the basin on the north side of the cove entrance can handle boats for hull repairs. Gasoline and diesel fuel are available at a marina near the south end of the cove. A "no wake"**speed limit** is in effect in White House Cove.

(30)     **Chisman Creek**, on the north side of the Poquoson River mouth, has depths of 9 feet or more in a narrow channel for 1.3 miles above its entrance. There are boatyards on the south side, 1 mile above the entrance, gasoline is available and the largest marine railway can handle boats up to 100 feet for hull repairs. The creek is marked by daybeacons and a buoy—a junction light marks the intersection of Chisman Creek and **Goose Creek**.

(31)     **Back Creek**, 1.5 miles south of York River, has depths of 7 feet for 2 miles. The entrance is marked by lights and daybeacons. The creek is used by oystering and fishing boats. A State-owned wharf on the south side, 1.4 miles above the mouth, has a depth of about 9 feet at the face. Gasoline, diesel fuel, limited berthing and some supplies are available at a marina on the south side, 1.8 miles above the mouth; repairs can be made.

(32)     The **Thorofare** is a shallow channel that leads between Back Creek and York River. It is marked a series of warning daybeacons and is not recommended.

(33)
**ENCs - US5VA24M, US5VA26M, US5VA60M, US-5VA61M**
**Charts - 12238, 12241, 12243**

(34)     **York River** formed by the junction of Mattaponi and Pamunkey Rivers 29 miles above the mouth, is 15 miles northward of Old Point Comfort and 26 miles by the main channel from Cape Henry. Traffic on York River consists chiefly of pulpwood, petroleum products, military supplies and shellfish.

(35)     York River has a broad and fairly straight channel and is well marked and easily followed. Drafts of vessels using the river are mostly 18 feet or less, but deep-draft vessels navigate the lower reaches. With the exception of the naval areas described later, vessels can anchor in the wider parts of York River channel.

(36)     The currents in York River follow the general direction of the channel except in the narrowest parts where there is a tendency to set a vessel onto the shoals. The velocity varies throughout the river; the times of slack water and strengths of current are later going up the river. The normal conditions are subject to change by winds and freshets.

(37)

**Ice**

(38)     **Ice** sometimes interferes with navigation of York River for short periods during severe winters, but in

ordinary winters there is no interruption below West Point.

(39)     **Caution**–Mariners transiting the York River are advised to use caution in the vicinity of the Goodwin Islands. The Virginia Pilots periodically anchor large tankers in about 37°14'06"N., 076°25'25"W. These vessels may be as large as 900 feet in length. The Virginia Pilot Tower may be contacted on VHF-FM channel 11 for further information. Ships and craft underway in York River are to proceed at reduced speed and exercise extreme caution in order to reduce generated water motion and to prevent damage to the Virginia Institute of Marine Science equipment and facilities located downstream from the Coleman Memorial Bridge, near Gloucester Point; ships and craft loading volatile fuels at the Giant Industries refinery pier; and other craft and property close to the shores of the river. In no instance should the **speed** of ships underway upriver from Tue Point exceed 12 knots.

(40)
### Pilotage, York River

(41)     Pilotage on the York River is compulsory for all foreign vessels and for U.S. vessels under register in the foreign trade. Pilotage is optional for U.S. vessels in the coastwise trade that have on board a pilot licensed by the Federal Government to operate in these waters.

(42)     The Chesapeake and Interstate Pilots Association offers pilot services to U.S. vessels, engaged in the coastwise trade, and public vessels to Yorktown. Arrangements for pilots may be made through ships' agents or the pilot office in Norfolk (telephone, 757–855–2733). Pilots will meet vessels entering from sea at Cape Henry (discussed in chapter 9) and will meet a vessel at its port if it is on the Chesapeake Bay and its tributaries or Delaware Bay and River and provide pilot services directly to the York River. The Virginia Pilots Association offers pilotage to all vessels. Pilot service above Cheatham Annex is available only during daylight. (See Pilotage, chapters 3 and 9.)

(43)
### Supplies

(44)     **Supplies** are available at Yorktown, West Point and at other places described in this chapter.

(45)
### Repairs

(46)     Repairs can be made to small vessels in Perrin River, Sarah Creek, Wormley Creek and at other places.

(47)
### ENCs - US5VA24M, US5VA26M
### Chart - 12238

(48)     **York Spit** extends outward along the northeast side of the York River approach channel for 7 miles from Guinea Marshes; the inner half of the spit has depths of 1 to 6 feet, and the outer half 10 to 20 feet.

(49)     **York Spit Light** (37°12'35"N., 76°15'15"W.), 30 feet above the water, is shown from a multi-pile structure with a red and white diamond-shaped daymark, in depths of 11 feet near the outer end of the spit. The light is 19.8 miles above Cape Charles.

(50)     The York River entrance channel is well marked and extends from about 7 miles southeast of York Spit Light to about 3 miles northwest of the light. A Federal project provides for a depth of 37 feet in the entrance channel. (See Notice to Mariners and latest editions of the charts for controlling depths). There are natural depths in excess of 37 feet from the north end of the dredged section to the naval installation 5 miles above Yorktown bridge.

(51)     About 1.5 miles northwest of York Spit Light, a channel marked by buoys and daybeacons extends northeastward through an area where submerged fishtraps are commonly found. The channel has depths of 15 feet or more and can be used by medium-draft vessels approaching York River from northward.

(52)     The Swash Channel, which bisects York Spit about 5 miles northwest of York Spit Light, has a controlling depth of about 5 feet; it is marked by a light and daybeacons. The channel shows up well on a bright day.

(53)
### ENC - US5VA60M
### Chart - 12241

(54)     The entrance to York River is between **Tue Point** and **Guinea Marshes**, 25.9 miles above the Virginia Capes.

(55)     **Perrin River**, on the north side of York River 2 miles above the mouth, has depths of 6 feet or more in the approach and through a narrow marked channel to the wharf at **Perrin**, on the north side 0.3 mile above the entrance. A marina on the east side has gasoline, diesel fuel, some supplies and a 20-ton mobile hoist; hull and engine repairs can be made. Gasoline and diesel fuel can be obtained at several of the oysterhouse wharves, on the east side of the river entrance; depths of 4 to 7 feet are alongside the wharves.

(56)     The Amoco offshore pier, on the south side of York River 3.3 miles above the mouth, has reported depths of 36 feet along the 1,240-foot outer face. The pier, connected to shore by a 0.5-mile-long catwalk, is marked by private lights on the east and west ends.

(57)     The intake for an electric powerplant, on the south side of the river 4.2 miles above the mouth, is marked by three lights.

(58)     **Wormley Creek** and **West Branch** have a common entrance on the south side of York River, 4.5 miles above the mouth; a light marks the entrance. A privately dredged channel leads through the entrance to the Coast Guard Reserve Training Center basin and pier on the north side of West Branch 0.8 mile above the entrance light. Local knowledge is advised. Gasoline, diesel fuel, berths, water, electricity, a 37-ton mobile lift and marine supplies can be obtained at a marina on the east side of Wormley

Creek just above the entrance; hull and engine repairs can be made.

(59)   The Coast Guard T-pier (37°13.6'N., 76°28.7'W.), on the south side of York River 5 miles above the mouth, has depths of 30 feet reported at the eastern outer end.

(60)   A **naval explosives handling berth** is northward of the Coast Guard pier. (See **33 CFR 334.260**, chapter 2, for limits and regulations).

(61)   **Sarah Creek**, on the north side of York River 6 miles above the mouth, has depths of 7 feet through the marked entrance channel and for about 0.8 mile up both its branches. A large yacht haven, on the west side 0.3 mile above the entrance, has supplies, gasoline, diesel fuel, a 35-ton and 60-ton travel lift, a pumpout station and numerous berths. Repairs can be made at a boatyard 0.3 mile up Northwest Branch; marine railway, 76 feet; largest lift, 60 tons.

(62)   A fixed highway bridge with a clearance of 6 feet and channel width of 47 feet crosses Northwest Branch about 0.8 mile above its mouth.

(63)   **Yorktown**, the historic Revolutionary War town, is on the southwest side of York River 6.7 miles above the mouth. High on the bluff in the southerly part is the **Yorktown Monument**, and a group of buildings is prominent on the shore behind the wharves. The main part of the town is not visible from the river. **George P. Coleman Memorial Bridge**, from Yorktown to Gloucester Point, has twin spans with clearance of 60 feet; the two spans open clockwise simultaneously. The bridgetender monitors VHF-FM channel 13; call sign KQ-7166. (See **33 CFR 117.1** through **117.49** and **117.1025**, chapter 2, for drawbridge regulations.)

(64)   The waterfront in Yorktown was completely rebuilt in 2005. It has two floating dock piers that can handle vessels up to 53 feet in length. Depths of 50 feet are reported to be alongside outside portion of the dock piers. A pumpout station is available. There is no fuel available with a pumpout facility available. The dockmaster can be contacted on VHF-FM channel 16 or by writing; Dockmaster, 425 Waterstreet, P.O. Box 219, Yorktown, VA 23690.

(65)   **Gloucester Point** is a village at the northeast end of Coleman Bridge. There are several piers and buildings on the low point, and the red brick building of the Virginia Institute of Marine Science is about 500 yards northeastward. The long T-head pier (37°14'46"N., 76°30'02"W.), owned by the Institute, has reported depths of 8 feet at the face. A shorter pier of the Institute is about 150 yards to the northward; depths of 6 feet are reported at the face.

(66)   The **Yorktown Naval Weapons Station** piers on the southwest side of York River, 8 miles above the mouth, have depths of about 29 to 39 feet at their outer ends. A **prohibited area** and a **restricted area** for mine service testing are off the piers. (See **33 CFR 334.260**, chapter 2, for limits and regulations.) The southeastern end of a **naval anchorage** begins off the Naval Weapons Station

piers and extends upriver about 4 miles. (See **33 CFR 110.166**, chapter 2, for limits and regulations.)

(67)   The **Naval Supply Center** pier at **Cheatham Annex Depot**, is on the southwest side of York River 11.5 miles above the mouth. The pier is within a **restricted area.** A small arms live fire **danger zone** is just northwest of the pier. (See **33 CFR 334.1** through **334.6**, **334.270** and **334.285**, chapter 2, for limits and regulations.)

(68)
## ENC - US5VA61M
## Chart - 12243

(69)   **Queen Creek** (37°18.1'N., 76°36.9'W.), on the southwest side of York River 13 miles above the mouth, has depths of about 5 feet with local knowledge through a marked channel across the flats at the entrance and deeper water through a narrow channel inside for 2.7 miles to **Hawtree Landing**. The channel inside is marked by buoys and daybeacons to a point about 0.6 mile below Hawtree Landing. Stakes on either side of the entrance mark the limits of the State's experimental oyster beds.

(70)   **Aberdeen Creek**, on the northeast side of York River, 14 miles above the mouth, has a dredged channel leading to a turning basin and public landing 0.4 mile above the entrance. In 2004, the midchannel controlling depth was 1.3 feet, thence depths of 1 to 2 feet in the basin. Gasoline and diesel fuel are available at a seafood company wharf just north of the public landing.

(71)   The ruins of a long T-head pier are at **Clay Bank,** on the northeast side of York River 15 miles above the mouth.

(72)   **Poropotank Bay**, on the northeast side of York River 22 miles above the mouth, has depths of 5 feet at the entrance; the best water favors the eastern side, which is marked by bush stakes. From the entrance, depths of about 5 feet can be carried 4 miles through **Morris Bay** and **Poropotank River** to **Miller Landing**. There are several other landings along the river. The channel is usually marked by bush stakes but is crooked and narrow in places and difficult to navigate without local knowledge.

(73)   **West Point**, at the junction of Mattaponi and Pamunkey Rivers 29 miles above the mouth of York River, has waterborne commerce in pulpwood, paper products and petroleum. The town is the terminus of a Southern Railway branch line. The pulp, paper and paperboard wharves just above the Eltham Bridge have reported depths of 16 feet alongside.

(74)   At West Point, the maximum current velocity is 0.8 knots on the flood in Mattaponi River and 0.9 knots on the ebb in Pamunkey River. Broken-off piling extends off the south side of West Point.

(75)   A public pier is at the southeast end of West Point, at the mouth of Mattaponi River. Gasoline is available at an oil wharf with depths of 5 to 15 feet alongside 0.4 mile south of the Lord Delaware Bridge; diesel fuel can be delivered by truck. An oil pier 0.2 mile above the bridge

has depths of 18 feet alongside. Supplies can be obtained in town.

(76)

## Mattaponi River to Retreat

(77)    **Mattaponi River**, which empties into York River eastward of West Point (37°31.7'N., 76°47.7'W.), is one of two tributaries that combine to form York River. Traffic on Mattaponi River consists chiefly of pulpwood. Drafts of vessels using the river above West Point usually do not exceed 10 feet.

(78)    Controlling depths in Mattaponi River are as follows: 12 feet to **Courthouse Landing**, 13 miles above the mouth; thence 9 feet for 10 miles to **Locust Grove**; and thence 2 feet to **Aylett**, 32 miles above the mouth.

(79)    The channel in Mattaponi River is unmarked and is difficult to navigate without local knowledge. Freshets occur at irregular intervals, being more severe in March and April, and have reached a height of 17 feet above low water at Aylett, though this is exceptional; the freshet rise is negligible at and below West Point.

(80)    The Lord Delaware Bridge over Mattaponi River at West Point has a fixed span with a clearance of 55 feet. Overhead power cables about 1.8 and 13 miles above the mouth have clearances of 62 feet and 90 feet, respectively.

(81)    The **Walkerton** highway bridge, 24.5 miles above the mouth of Mattaponi River, has a fixed span with a clearance of 20 feet. Two fixed bridges cross the river at Aylett, 32 miles above the mouth; minimum clearance is 20 feet. The minimum clearance of the overhead power cables between the bridges at Walkerton and Aylett is 42 feet.

(82)    **Pamunkey River**, the westerly of the two tributaries that form York River, has many landings along its banks. Traffic on the river consists chiefly of pulpwood; there is a grain elevator platform at **Port Richmond**, 2 miles above the mouth. Vessels with drafts up to 12 feet navigate the river to Port Richmond.

(83)    Controlling depths in Pamunkey River are about 12 feet from the mouth to **Cumberland Landing,** 20 miles above the mouth, thence 8 feet to **White House,** 28 miles above the mouth, and 4 feet to the Newcastle Bridges 46 miles above the mouth. Freshets occur at irregular intervals, being more severe in March and April.

(84)    Pamunkey River is easy to navigate as far as **Brickhouse Landing,** 16 miles above the mouth; farther up, navigation is difficult without local knowledge. Freshwater is available at some of the landings, and the river water is fresh above Cumberland Landing. Several narrow cutoffs have depths enough for small boats, but their use requires local knowledge. Above **Retreat,** 36 miles above the mouth, the river is covered with floating debris and snags.

(85)    The Eltham Bridge over Pamunkey River at West Point has a bascule span with a vertical clearance of 56 feet. The bridgetender monitors VHF-FM channel 13; call sign KQ-7168. (See **33 CFR 117.1** through **117.59** and **117.1023**, chapter 2, for drawbridge regulations.) Power cables crossing the river about 1.7 and 14.6 miles above the mouth have clearances of 66 and 90 feet, respectively. The railroad bridge at White House has a swing span with a clearance of 4 feet; the easterly opening is used.

(86)

## ENCs - US5VA24M, US5VA26M
## Chart - 12238

(87)    **Mobjack Bay**, which is entered between Guinea Marshes at the shore end of York Spit, and New Point Comfort, 4 miles east-northeastward, includes several tributaries, the most important being East, North, Ware and Severn Rivers. The bay is obstructed by extensive shoals but has depths of 22 feet in the entrance and 15 feet for considerable distances into the tributaries. Many of the shoals are marked by lights and buoys.

(88)    The only prominent marks in the approach to Mobjack Bay are York Spit Light on the south and the white tower of the abandoned lighthouse on New Point Comfort on the north. The approach channel extends between fishtrap buoys; numerous crab pots exist shoreward of these buoys. Good anchorage, sheltered from all but southerly and southeasterly winds, can be found in the bay. Small craft find safe anchorage in the bight westward of New Point Comfort and in the rivers and creeks.

(89)    **New Point Comfort**, marked by a light, is the south end of a low, partly wooded island that is separated from the mainland by **Deep Creek,** a crooked and unmarked natural channel. The pile remains of **Bayside Wharf**, viisible at high water 1.5 miles northwest of New Point Comfort, extend about 0.4 mile channelward.

(90)    **Davis Creek**, 1.6 miles northwest of New Point Comfort, has a channel leading to a public landing in the western arm about 0.8 mile above the entrance. The channel is shoal in several places and is marked by warning daybeacons. Several wharves are on the shore in the upper part of the creek; gasoline and diesel fuel are available.

(91)    **Pepper Creek**, 3 miles northwest of New Point Comfort, has depths of 4 feet for about 0.7 mile above the entrance. The approach is marked by daybeacons.

(92)    **East River**, 5 miles northwest of New Point Comfort, has a marked narrow channel with depths of 10 feet for 3.5 miles above the entrance, and thence 4 feet for another 2 miles to the head. Shoals, sometimes marked by bush stakes, extend for some distance off many of the points above the entrance, but the midchannel is clear.

(93)    **Diggs Wharf**, on the east side of East River just inside the entrance, is in ruins. There are no commercial facilities at **Mobjack** opposite Diggs Wharf.

(94)    **Williams Wharf**, on the northeast side of East River about 2.5 miles above the entrance, has reported depths of 10 feet alongside the abandoned oysterhouse bulkhead. A boatyard on the western shore opposite Williams Wharf has a 50-foot marine railway; repairs can be made.

(95) **North River**, which empties into the head of Mobjack Bay from northward, is wide but has long shoals making off from many of the points. The channel has depths of 12 feet for 4 miles and is well marked; depths of 7 feet can be carried 2 miles farther. **Blackwater Creek** empties into North River 3 miles above the mouth. The entrance is marked by a light, and depths of 7 feet can be carried for 0.5 mile to a boatyard and a marina just inside the entrance of **Greenmansion Cove**; gasoline, diesel fuel and some supplies are available. The depth at the face of the dock is 4.5 feet. Hull and engine repairs can be made; marine railway, 42 feet; lift capacity, 5 tons.

(96) **Ware River**, which flows into the head of Mobjack Bay from northwestward, has depths of 15 feet to the mouth of **Wilson Creek**, on the west side 3 miles above the entrance, and 7 feet for another 2 miles. Long shoals, some of which are marked by lights and daybeacons, extend off many of the points. The only commercial landing on Ware River is the J. C. Brown Co. wharf, on the east side about 4 miles above the entrance, which has a depth of about 5 feet off the end; gasoline is available. **Schley**, 0.5 mile inland from the wharf, has a store.

(97) **Severn River**, on the west side of Mobjack Bay, has depths of 18 feet to the junction with **Northwest Branch** and **Southwest Branch,** 8 feet for 1.3 miles in Southwest Branch, and 8 feet for 1.8 miles in Northwest Branch. The most prominent shoals are marked by lights or daybeacons.

(98) A wharf at **Glass**, on the north side of Southwest Branch 1.1 miles above the fork, has depths of about 7 feet to the outer end. Mariners are advised to stay within the marked channel to avoid the 1-foot shoal extending from the point 0.4 mile eastward of the wharf. Gasoline, diesel fuel and marine supplies are available. Hull and engine repairs can be made; marine railway, 60 feet. A marina on the west side of **Rowes Creek**, 0.5 mile southeast of the Glass Wharf, has gasoline, diesel fuel, marine supplies and a 10-ton mobile hoist.

(99) **Browns Bay**, 1 mile south of Severn River, is marked by lights at the entrance and by bush stakes inside. Gasoline and diesel fuel are available at a wharf, with a depth of 4 feet at the end, at the head of the bay. A store is at **Severn**, about 1 mile westward of the wharf.

(100) **Dyer Creek**, which empties into Chesapeake Bay 2 miles north of New Point Comfort, has depths of 3 feet in the entrance and 4 to 5 feet inside. The creek is bush-staked, but local knowledge is essential. Overhead power cables across the creek have a least clearance of 17 feet.

(101) **Horn Harbor** is entered through a dredged channel, 2.4 miles northward of New Point Comfort. The dredged channel is marked by lights, daybeacons and lighted buoys. Lights and daybeacons mark the channel in the upper part of the harbor. A cluster of submerged pilings from a former fishhouse is on the east side of the channel about 1 mile above the entrance. Traffic consists chiefly of fish, shellfish and pleasure craft.

(102) The ruins of a fish wharf are at **New Point,** 0.7 mile above the Horn Harbor entrance. A marina, 3.5 miles above the entrance, has berths with electricity, gasoline, diesel fuel, water, ice, a pump-out station, a 15-ton lift, and some supplies. A 50-foot marine railway can haul out boats for repairs.

(103) **Winter Harbor** is entered through a dredged channel that leads to a turning basin and public landing, 1.5 miles above the entrance. In 2016, the channel was obstructed by a shoal encroaching from the north side of the harbor mouth. Commerce in the harbor consists chiefly of fish and shellfish.

(104) **Wolf Trap**, the area of broken ground 6 miles northward of New Point Comfort, has numerous shoal spots 5 to 10 feet deep that extend as much as 3 miles from the western shore of Chesapeake Bay. The entire shoal area lies within the fishtrap limits.

(105)
## ENC - US4VA40M
## Chart - 12225

(106) The southern limit of a large naval firing range **danger zone** is at latitude 37°27' and extends northward to latitude 37°47'. (See **33 CFR 331.1** through **334.6** and **334.220**, chapter 2, for limits and regulations.) The danger zone also contains a designated hurricane anchorage for shallow and deep-draft naval vessels. During hurricane warnings, naval ships may be anchored in the fairway; caution is advised.

(107)
## ENC - US5VA41M
## Chart - 12235

(108) The entrance to **Piankatank River** is between **Cherry Point** (37°31.0'N., 76°17.8'W.), at the north end of **Gwynn Island**, and **Stingray Point**, 2.5 miles to the northward. The entrance point is 45.3 miles above the Virginia Capes. **Stingray Point Light** (37°33'41"N., 76°16'12"W.), 34 feet above the water, is shown from a skeleton tower on monopile with a green and white diamond-shaped daymark. The light is 1.3 miles east of Stingray Point and is surrounded by depths of 4 to 6 feet.

(109) Traffic on Piankatank River consists of fish, shellfish and shells. Drafts of vessels using the river are mostly 6 feet, but drafts up to 11 feet are on record. The river has depths of about 18 feet in the approach from northeastward through a buoyed lane in the fishtraps. A wreck covered 16 feet lies in the middle of this lane, about 1.3 miles east-southeast of Stingray Point Light. Depths of 16 feet or more are available to the fixed bridge 9 miles above the mouth and 7 feet to Freeport, 13.5 miles above the mouth. Lights and daybeacons mark the lower 6 miles of the river channel.

(110) During severe winters, the Piankatank River is sometimes closed by ice for short periods. Hull repairs can be made to medium-size vessels in Fishing Bay; gasoline and diesel fuel are available.

(111)     **Jackson Creek** is on the north side of Piankatank River, 1 mile above the mouth. A dredged entrance channel leads north from Jackson Creek Channel Light 1 and then turns west-southwest. Above Daybeacon 10, natural depths of about 8 to 9 feet are available in the middle of the creek channel. the channel is marked by a light, buoys and daybeacons. Stakes usually define the channel edges.

(112)     There is a marina along Jackson Creek where fuel, supplies and berths can be obtained. The largest lift can handle boats to 50 tons for hull and engine repairs.

(113)     **Hills Bay**, on the south side of Piankatank River 2 miles above the mouth, has general depths of 14 to 20 feet and is the approach to Queens Creek and Milford Haven.

(114)     **Queens Creek**, at the head of Hills Bay, is entered by a dredged channel that leads across the bar at the entrance and thence to a turning basin about 0.6 mile above the entrance. The channel across the bar and to the turning basin is marked by a light, daybeacons and lighted and unlighted buoys. A few broken piles that remain of the wooden jetty are on the north side of the entrance.

(115)     The channel through the strait between Gwynn Island and the mainland that leads to **Milford Haven** is marked by a light, daybeacons and lighted and unlighted buoys. Traffic on the waterway consists chiefly of fish and shellfish carried in vessels drawing up to 7 feet. A highway bridge crossing the strait has a swing span with a vertical clearance of 12 feet in the north draw. (See **33 CFR 117.1** through **117.49**, chapter 2, for drawbridge regulations.)

(116)     A marina on Gwynn Island just west of the bridge has gasoline, diesel fuel, supplies and berths; hull and engine repairs can be made; lift, 40 tons, railway, 60-foot long. A public landing pier is on Gwynn Island just east of the bridge. **Milford Haven Coast Guard Station** is 0.2 mile east of the south end of the bridge.

(117)     **Callis Wharf** at **Grimstead**, on the Gwynn Island side of Milford Haven 0.7 mile from the jetty, has depths of 9 feet at the face. Gasoline, diesel fuel and some other supplies are available. A marine railway on the southeast side of the entrance to **Edwards Creek**, 0.5 mile eastward of Callis Wharf, can handle boats up to 35 feet for hull repairs.

(118)     A wharf at **Cricket Hill**, on the west side of **Lanes Creek**, opposite Edwards Creek, has gasoline, diesel fuel and ice; depths of 8 feet are reported at the face.

(119)     Milford Haven can also be entered from Chesapeake Bay at the south end of Gwynn Island. This passage, known as**The Hole in the Wall**has a reported controlling depth of about 4 feet and is used by small local boats but is exposed to heavy seas. The passage is marked at the entrance by a lighted buoy, thence by buoys and daybeacons across **Milford Spit** into the harbor. There are also several warning daybeacons along this route—local knowledge is recommended when transiting the passage.

(120)     A fish haven, marked by a private buoy, is about 1.3 miles northeast of the entrance to Hole in the Wall.

(121)     **Stutts Creek** enters the southern part of Milford Haven from the southwestward. There are depths of 6 feet or more from Milford Haven to a yacht club on the north side of Stutts Creek, 1.8 miles above the mouth; gasoline and some supplies can be obtained.

(122)     **Fishing Bay**, on the north side of Piankatank River 4 miles above the mouth, has depths of 12 to 30 feet and provides good protection from north and east winds. On the east side of the bay is narrow 1-mile-long **Stove Point Neck**. A private 700-foot-long pier with a depth of 8 feet at the outer end extends westward from the middle of the neck. Repairs can be made at boatyards at the north end of the bay; largest marine railway, 150 feet; lift 50 tons. Gasoline, diesel fuel and supplies are available.

(123)     **Moore Creek**, just westward of Fishing Bay, is entered through a channel protected by jetties on either side. In 2002, the controlling depth was reported to be 6.5 feet.

(124)     **Cobbs Creek** is on the south side of Piankatank River, 7 miles above the mouth. A channel marked with daybeacons at the entrance and with reported depths of about 6 feet leads to a marina 0.2 mile inside on the west side of the creek. Gasoline, diesel fuel, supplies and berths are available; repairs can be made; 40-foot marine railway. An overhead power cable with a clearance of 50 feet crosses the creek about 0.4 mile above the mouth.

(125)     **Dixie**, a village on the south side of Piankatank River, is 9 miles above the mouth; gasoline is available in the town. The former oil wharf has depths of about 10 feet off its outer end. The fixed highway bridge just west of the village has a clearance of 43 feet; an overhead power cable close westward of the bridge has a clearance of 68 feet.

(126)     About 5.7 miles above the fixed highway bridge, an overhead power cable with a clearance of 64 feet crosses the river.

(127)
## Rappahannock River to Whiting Creek

(128)     **Rappahannock River** flows into the west side of Chesapeake Bay 45.7 miles by channel from the Virginia Capes. Fredericksburg, 93 miles above the mouth, is the head of practical navigation.

(129)     Traffic on the river consists chiefly of pulpwood, shellfish and shells, chemicals and some sand and gravel. Drafts of vessels using the river seldom exceed 11 feet and are mostly 6 feet or less.

(130)     **Mileages** on Rappahannock River, such as Mile 15N and Mile 32W, are the nautical miles above the midchannel point on a line drawn from Stingray Point to Windmill Point. The letters N, S, E, or W following the numbers denote by compass points the side of the river where each feature is located.

(131)     The river has natural depths of 15 feet or more to the bridge at Tappahannock, 37.4 miles above the mouth. Above this point, a Federal project provides for

dredging of the bars to provide a channel 12 feet deep to Fredericksburg.

(132)     In general, vessels can anchor anywhere near the channel of Rappahannock River where the bottom is soft and the depth suitable. Deep-draft vessels will find good anchorage 3 to 5 miles from the mouth. Carter and Urbanna Creeks are used extensively as harbors by small craft.

(133)     The channel from the mouth of Rappahannock River to Tappahannock is comparatively straight, but gradually decreases in width and leads between shoals that make out from both banks. The principal dangers are marked. Strangers can take a draft of 10 feet to Tappahannock by day with the aid of the chart, but navigation of the narrow, crooked channel farther up requires local knowledge. There are rocks in places on both sides of the channel for 4 miles below Fredericksburg, and the shores should be given a good berth. Strangers can safely carry a draft of 5 feet to Fredericksburg with the aid of the chart.

(134)
### Current
(135)     The **currents** follow the general direction of the channel. The velocities throughout the river are usually weak, averaging less than 1 knot at the entrance to 1.4 knots at Tappahannock. Times of slack water and strength of current become later going upriver. These normal conditions are subject to change by winds and changes in drainage flow.

(136)
### Ice
(137)     During severe winters, **ice** closes the river nearly to Tappahannock, but in ordinary winters the channels are usually kept open by the river traffic. Ice sufficient to interfere with navigation of small craft will usually be encountered in January and February, particularly above Port Royal.

(138)
### Freshets
(139)     **Freshets** occur during the spring and fall but are of short duration and ordinarily are not dangerous to shipping. The highest level on record was 33 feet above low water at Fredericksburg, but the usual height due to freshets is not more than 9 to 12 feet and only occasionally rises above the wharves. The freshet effect on the water level decreases rapidly below Fredericksburg and is ordinarily negligible 11 miles downriver.

(140)
### Supplies and repairs
(141)     The principal places along Rappahannock River for supplies and small-vessel **repairs** are Broad Creek, Carter Creek and Urbanna Creek.

(142)     The entrance to Rappahannock River is between Stingray Point and **Windmill Point,** 45.7 miles above the Capes. This is the **Mile 0.0** for distances on the Rappahannock. The shores on both sides of the entrance are wooded; the two lights, off Stingray and Windmill Points, are the most prominent landmarks.

(143)     **Rappahannock Spit** extends southeastward from Windmill Point for about 4.5 miles and has depths of 4 to 18 feet. **Windmill Point Light** (37°35'49"N., 76°14'10"W.), 34 feet above the water, is shown from a platform with a red and white diamond-shaped daymark, in depths of 12 feet on the spit 2.3 miles from the point.

(144)     Depths of 10 feet can be carried across Rappahannock Spit anywhere outside Windmill Point Light. About 0.4 mile outside the light, a lane that extends southwestward through the fishtraps is a shortcut for lightdraft vessels approaching the river from northward.

(145)     A 6-foot marked channel leads to a marina basin on the south side of **Fleets Island** west of Windmill Point. Gasoline, diesel fuel, berths, electricity, sewage pump-out and a launching ramp are available.

(146)     **Broad Creek**, Mile 0.7S, is used by oystermen, fishing boats and yachts. A dredged entrance channel, marked by a light, buoys and daybeacons, leads from Rappahannock River to natural depths of 7 to 5 feet inside the creek. There are several boatyards and marinas and a machine shop on the creek; berths, gasoline, diesel fuel, water, ice, a sewage pump-out station and marine supplies are available. Hull and engine repairs can be made. Maximum haul-out capacities are: marine railway, 100 feet; lift, 50 tons.

(147)     **Locklies Creek**, Mile 6.0S, has depths of about 5 feet through a marked entrance with depths decreasing to about 2 feet inside. An overhead power cable near the head has a clearance of 34 feet. There are marinas on the north and south sides near the entrance. The largest marine railway on the south side of the creek can handle craft up to 45 feet for repairs. Some marine supplies, water, ice, gasoline, diesel fuel, wet and dry storage, berthing with electricity, launching ramp and a pump-out station are available.

(148)     A dredged channel westward of Parrott Island forms an inside passage between Mill Creek and Locklies Creek.

(149)     An inactive fish factory and wharf with depths of 18 feet at the face are on **Cherry Point,** Mile 6.3N.

(150)     A fixed highway bridge crosses the river at Mile 7.0; the channel span has a clearance of 110 feet. An overhead power cable at the bridge has a clearance of 122 feet.

(151)     **Carter Creek**, Mile 8.3N, is the approach to the villages of **Weems** on the west side and **Irvington** on the east side. Traffic on the creek consists chiefly of recreational boats. Drafts using the creek seldom exceed 11 feet and are mostly 6 feet or less.

(152)     Depths of about 6 feet have been reported in Carter Cove. The entrance is marked by lights and daybeacons.

(153)     There are several oysterhouses and yacht facilities in Carter Creek. Most vessels go alongside the wharves with depths of about 8 feet, but the creek also is used as an anchorage.

(154)     **Corrotoman River**, Mile 10.0N, has depths of 14 feet or more for 4 miles to the junction of Eastern and Western Branches. The river channel is obstructed by shoal spits and middle grounds, but the principal shoals as

far as the fork, and for 0.5 mile above in Western Branch, are marked.

(155)     **Whitehouse Creek**, on the west side of Corrotoman River 0.8 mile above the mouth, has depths of 7 feet to the landing at **Bertrand,** on the north side 0.5 mile from the entrance. **Town Creek**, on the west side of Corrotoman River 2 miles above the mouth, has depths of 2 to 4 feet. Gasoline is available near the head. **Taylor Creek**, on the east side of Corrotoman River 2.5 miles above the mouth, has depths of 2 to 5 feet in the entrance and 4 to 8 feet inside the creek.

(156)     **Eastern Branch** of Corrotoman River has depths of 13 feet for 1.4 miles, thence 8 feet for 1.5 miles. **Western Branch** has depths of 12 feet or more for 2.5 miles, thence 5 feet for 2 miles.

(157)
### Cable ferry

(158)     A cable ferry crosses Western Branch from **Ottoman Wharf**, on the southwest side about 1.3 miles above the fork, to **Merry Point**, on the opposite side. The ferry carries passengers and vehicles. The ferry operates between the hours of 0700 and 1900, Monday through Saturday, and 0700 to dark during the winter months. When the ferry is underway, the unmarked cable is suspended about 3 feet above the water's surface and is dropped to the bottom when not underway. **DO NOT ATTEMPT TO PASS A MOVING CABLE FERRY.**

(159)     **Whiting Creek**, Mile 10.5S, is entered from Rappahanock River through a dredged channel. In 2019, the controlling depth was 0.8 foot in the channel.

(160)
## Urbanna Creek to Fredericksburg

(161)     **Urbanna Creek**, Mile 13.8W, is used by many pleasure craft. The town of **Urbanna** is on the west bank, near the entrance.

(162)     A dredged channel leads from Rappahannock River to a turning basin and wharves just below the bridge. The marked entrance is protected by a riprap jetty on the north side. Above the turning basin, depths of 6 feet or more can be carried for about 0.7 mile, and small craft can go another mile upstream. In 1981, shoaling to 4 feet was reported about 0.4 mile above the fixed highway bridge in about 37°37'34"N., 76°34'34"W.

(163)     The wharves at Urbanna have reported depths of 4 to 12 feet alongside. Marine supplies, gasoline, diesel fuels, ice, water and berths with electricity are available. Engine, hull and electronic repairs are available. The largest mobile lift is 40 tons.

(164)     The fixed highway bridge over Urbanna Creek 0.7 mile above the entrance has a 40-foot channel span with a clearance of 21 feet. A "no wake"**speed limit** is in effect in Urbanna Creek.

(165)     **Robinson Creek**, Mile 14.1W, has depths of 5 feet through the entrance to the head. **Urbanna Wharf**, on the south side of the entrance, is about 900 feet long with depths of 6 feet at the outer end. A marina on the

south side of the creek about a mile above the mouth has gas, diesel fuel, pump-out facility, a few berths with electricity, water, ice, a launching ramp and wet and dry storage; electronic repairs can be made.

(166)     **Lagrange Creek**, Mile 14.8W, has depths of 7 feet in the marked entrance and 4 feet for 1 mile to a boatyard on the southwest side. A 42-foot marine railway, a machine shop, gasoline, diesel fuel, water, ice, a pump-out station berthing, some with electric and hull and engine repairs, are available. The lift capacity is 40 tons. The wharf has depths of 4 feet at the outer end.

(167)     **Greenvale Creek**, Mile 16.9E, is used mostly by local fishermen. A dredged channel, marked by a light and daybeacons, leads from Rappahannock River to a landing about 0.3 mile above of the creek. In 2014, a marina in the creek had a reported alongside depth of 5 feet. Gasoline, ice, water, electricity, pump-out station, wet and dry storage, supplies and berthing, some with hull, engine and electronic repairs, are available; lift to 18 tons.

(168)     **Parrotts Creek**, Mile 20.0W, has a dredged channel marked by lights and daybeacons from the entrance to the public landing at **Water View**, 0.5 mile above the mouth. An overhead power cable across the creek just above the mouth has a clearance of 50 feet. Oyster wharves near the entrance have depths of 5 to 8 feet at their faces.

(169)     **Deep Creek**, Mile 21.0E, has depths of 2 feet across the flats at the entrance and 3 to 5 feet in the several branches. The creek usually is bush-staked. The overhead power cables at **Boer** have a minimum clearance of 30 feet.

(170)     **Mulberry Creek**, Mile 22.4N, in 1974, had reported depths of 4 feet in the dredged cut at the entrance. Above the dredged cut there are depths of about 4 feet for 1 mile upstream. A light marks the west side of the entrance, and a shell islet awash at high water is at the inner end of the channel cut. A submerged shell pile is 0.3 mile southwestward of the light. A privately dredged channel passes immediately to the west of the shell pile and had a depth of 3 feet in 1974. Gasoline and some supplies are obtainable at **Morattico**, on the northwest side of the entrance.

(171)     **Lancaster Creek**, Mile 23.5N, has depths of 5 feet in the marked entrance, and thence from 4 to 2 feet for 4 miles to **Woodhouse Landing**. About 2 miles above the entrance, the creek is crossed by an overhead power cable with a clearance of 27 feet. A marina on the west side of the entrance has about 3 feet in its basin; some supplies are available and mechanical repairs can be made.

(172)     **Morattico Creek** enters Rappahannock River just westward of Lancaster Creek. Oysterhouses are on both sides of the entrance. In 1980, the controlling depth was reported to be 6 feet through the entrance and alongside the wharves.

(173)     At **Butylo**, Mile 24.2W, a jetty extends 0.4 mile into the river; depths of 4 feet are reported alongside. An oysterhouse is on the jetty.

(174)    A small-boat harbor is at **Wildwood Beach**, Mile 28.3W. The entrance to the harbor is protected on the north side by a 300-foot-long jetty and on the south side by a point of land extending to seaward about the same distance; a light is off the jetty. The marina can provide gasoline, diesel fuel, transient berths, electricity, water, ice, marine supplies, wet and dry storage, launch ramp and an 8-ton lift; full repairs can be made.

(175)    **Rappahannock River Light 19** (37°49'28"N., 76°43'58"W.), 23 feet above the water, is shown from a cylindrical base, with a square green daymark, in depths of 6 feet at Mile 28.5. **Bowlers Rock**, covered 7 feet and buoyed, is on the east side of the channel about 500 yards eastward of the light. A submerged wreck is on the southwest edge of the channel 100 yards north-northeastward of the light, and foul ground extends upriver along the southwest edge of the channel for 1.3 miles from the light.

(176)    **Totuskey Creek**, Mile 30.8N, is entered by a marked dredged channel that leads to a turning basin below the Totuskey Bridge, 4 miles above the mouth. In 2001, the midchannel controlling depth in the entrance channel and in the creek channel to the bridge was 4.2 feet. The channel is narrow in places and difficult to follow; deeper water is available with local knowledge. A timber-and-bush dike on the northeast side, 2.5 miles above the entrance, is barely visible. An overhead power cable about 3.2 miles above the entrance has a clearance of 75 feet. **Totuskey Bridge** is a fixed concrete span with a clearance of 10 feet. A wharf on the southeast bank, just below the bridge, has depths of 10 feet at the face and is used by grain barges. Barges load pulpwood at a landing on the opposite shore, about 0.2 mile below the bridge.

(177)    An overhead power cable over the Rappahannock River at Mile 32.1 has a clearance of 80 feet over the main channel and 50 feet elsewhere.

(178)    **Piscataway Creek**, Mile 35.0W, has depths of 4 feet in the entrance with greater depths for 5 miles upstream. A highway bridge, 4 miles above the entrance, has a fixed span with a clearance of 7 feet. Overhead power cables between the entrance and the bridge have a minimum clearance of 16 feet.

(179)    **Hoskins Creek** is at Mile 36.8W. A marked dredged channel extends from the entrance to a turning basin about 0.4 mile above the mouth, thence to the highway bridge about 0.6 mile above the mouth. A grain depot is near the bridge, and there is a public wharf about 0.3 mile below the bridge. The fixed highway bridge has a 34-foot channel span with a clearance of 8 feet; the nearby overhead power cable has a clearance of 43 feet. A small marina is near the first bend. A "no wake"**speed limit** is enforced.

(180)    **Tappahannock** is at Mile 37.4W. The highway bridge over the river at Tappahannock has a fixed span with a clearance of 50 feet. A wharf just below the bridge is in ruins.

(181)    A privately marked channel with a depth of about 4 feet leads to a small-boat basin at Tappahannock, 0.2 mile above the bridge. A marina in the basin can provide gasoline, water, ice, launching ramp and a 6-ton lift, and some supplies are available; engine repairs can be made.

(182)    **Mount Landing Creek**, Mile 38.4W, has depths of 3 feet across the flats at the entrance and deeper water inside for 3.5 miles. Twin fixed highway bridges cross the creek near its entrance; minimum width is 34 feet and clearance is 9 feet. The overhead power cable just north of the bridges has a clearance of 18 feet. The creek is used by fishermen.

(183)    **Cat Point Creek**, Mile 39.5E, has depths of about 4 feet across the bar at the entrance. In 2000, shoaling to bare was reported in the section of the creek beginning at a point about 1.5 miles above the mouth. Depths of about 3 feet can be carried to **Menokin Landing**, about 7 miles above the mouth, by using the cutoff in 37°59'16"N., 76°50'19"W., about 1.7 miles above the mouth; local knowledge is advised. A fixed highway bridge over the entrance has a width of 41 feet and a clearance of 10 feet. An overhead power cable 200 yards above the bridge has a clearance of 21 feet. The highway bridge 6 miles above the entrance has a 31-foot fixed span with a clearance of 4 feet.

(184)    **Occupacia Creek**, Mile 44.2W, has depths of 3 feet across the bar at the entrance and 4 feet for 6 miles up the middle branch; an overhead cable 2.5 miles above the entrance has a clearance of 35 feet, and the overhead cable 6 miles above the entrance has a clearance of about 30 feet. **Bridge Creek**, the eastern branch, has depths of 2 feet to a fixed bridge 1 mile above the entrance.

(185)    **Layton** is at Mile 50.5W. In 1980, the lower pier was in poor condition and the upper pier was in ruins. Pulpwood is shipped by barge from **Leedstown**, Mile 52.4N.

(186)    **Port Royal** is at Mile 68.5S. The highway bridge from Port Royal to **Port Conway**has a fixed span with a clearance of 50 feet.

(187)    **Newton Rock**, Mile 91.2S, is 50 feet from shore and almost awash at high tide; the best water is 100 feet off the rock.

(188)    A fixed highway bridge with a clearance of 37 feet is at Mile 92.9N.

(189)    **Fredericksburg**, Mile 93.5W, the historic colonial city, has little trade by water but can accommodate motor vessels and barges drawing up to 10 feet. Practical navigation terminates at the Old City Dock at the southern end of the city, but small boats can go about 1 mile farther upriver. Anchorage space is limited. The fixed highway bridge about 0.5 mile below the dock and the fixed railroad bridge just above the dock have clearances of 37 feet. The fixed highway bridge, 700 yards farther up, has a clearance of 50 feet.

(190)
## ENC - US5VA41M
## Chart - 12235

(191)    **Fleets Bay**, just northward of Rappahannock River entrance, is the approach to Little Bay and Antipoison, Tabbs, Dyme and Indian Creeks.

(192)    Depths of 8 feet can be taken through **Little Bay**, on the south side of Fleets Bay, westward in a narrow channel into **Antipoison Creek** and upstream for over 1 mile. The bay and creek are used by boats with drafts up to 6 feet. Two herring processing plants on the south side of Antipoison Creek 0.6 mile above the entrance have wharves with depths of 6 feet reported at the faces; another plant directly across the creek has a wharf with depths of 6 feet at the face.

(193)    **Tabbs Creek** is on the west side of Fleets Bay 1.5 miles northward of Antipoison Creek. The creek is reported to be periodically dredged to maintain a minimum depth of 6 feet. The entrance to the creek is also reported to be marked by private aids to navigation.

(194)    **Dymer Creek**, on the west side of Fleets Bay about 2 miles northward of Antipoison Creek, had a reported depth of 4.2 feet in 2005 for 2 miles. The approach through Fleets Bay is well marked. An inactive fish factory is on the south side of the creek 1 mile above the entrance; the wharf is in ruins. The boatyard in **Poplar Neck Creek**, just below the fish factory, makes hull and minor engine repairs; marine railway, 65 feet.

(195)    **Indian Creek** is located in the northwest corner of Fleets Bay about 3 miles northward of Antipoison Creek. Traffic on the creek consists chiefly of pulpwood, shellfish, shells and grain. Drafts of vessels using the creek seldom exceed 13 feet and are mostly 6 feet or less. The approach through Fleets Bay and the channel in the creek are well marked.

(196)    A country club pier is about 1 mile above the mouth of Indian Creek, on the northeast side in a cove. The pier has depths of about 6 feet at the face. **Kilmarnock Wharf**, on the west side 2 miles above the entrance, is at the foot of a paved road that leads 1.5 miles inland to the town of **Kilmarnock**. A marina at the wharf has gasoline, diesel fuel, pumpout, electricity, water, ice and nautical supplies. In 2005, an alongside depth of 10 feet was reported. General engine repairs can be made. Depths of 6 feet can be carried for 0.5 mile up the western branch above Kilmarnock Wharf to a marine railway that can handle boats up to 40 feet for repairs.

(197)    **Dividing Creek** is 8.7 miles north-northwestward of Windmill Point Light. The creek has reported depths of 13 feet in the approach and 6.5 feet for 1.6 miles above the entrance, then shoaling to about 3 feet 0.7 mile farther up. The creek is used by boats with drafts of 5 feet or less. The approach between the shoals off the entrance is well marked by lights and daybeacons.

(198)
## ENC - US4VA40M
## Chart - 12225

(199)    In addition to the previously described danger zone of a naval firing range that extends from latitude 37°27' to latitude 37°47', several danger areas are in Chesapeake Bay between Windmill Point Light and Smith Point Light.

(200)    **San Marcos Wreck**, 10.5 miles northeast of Windmill Point Light, is covered by about 20 feet of water, but the depth over it is subject to change, due to the shifting steel.

(201)    **Restricted** and **prohibited areas** are centered about 3.5 miles west-southwest of **Tangier Island**. (See **33 CFR 334.210**, chapter 2, for limits and regulations.) These areas surround naval guided missile test operations–sunken ships and other obstructions are in the areas.

(202)
## ENC - US5VA41M
## Chart - 12235

(203)    **Great Wicomico River**, on the west side of Chesapeake Bay 13 miles northward of Windmill Point Light, is entered between **Dameron Marsh** and **Bull Neck**, 1.7 miles to the northward. The principal mark at the entrance are the buildings at Fleeton, on Bull Neck.

(204)    Great Wicomico River has depths of 17 feet or more for 5.5 miles above the entrance, and thence 9 feet or more for 3 miles. The river is navigable for small craft for another 2 miles. Vessels seeking shelter usually anchor in depths of 15 to 20 feet off and in the entrance to Cockrell Creek or in the large bay just west of Sandy Point. Fishtraps usually will be found on the shoals at the entrance; the approach can be made on a due west course between the buoys marking the trap areas.

(205)    The channel in Great Wicomico River is marked by lights for 4 miles from the entrance.

(206)

### Ice

(207)    Ice does not close the river to navigation except in severe winters, and then only for brief periods; Cockrell Creek is considered a secure harbor from ice.

(208)    **Cockrell Creek**, on the northeast side of Great Wicomico River 1 mile above the mouth, is entered between **Fleeton (Fleet) Point** on the south and Cockrell Point on the north; a light marks the entrance. There are depths of 15 feet for 1.5 miles above the entrance, thence gradual shoaling to 6 feet 1 mile farther up. Traffic consists chiefly of fish, shellfish, construction material and petroleum products. Several fish factories operate along its shores. Drafts of vessels are mostly 12 feet and under, but drafts up to 14 feet use the creek. There are depths of 8 to 15 feet at the faces of the wharves.

(209)    A menhaden fleet is based on each side of Cockrell Creek, about 1 mile above Fleeton Point.

(210)    **Reedville** is on the east side of Cockrell Creek 1.5 miles above the entrance. A petroleum pier and a barge wharf with depths of about 8 feet alongside are on the east side of the peninsula at Reedville. Gasoline, diesel fuel and some marine supplies are available.

(211)    Reedville is a **customs port of entry.**

(212)    The boatyards along Cockrell Creek can handle vessels up to 70 feet for hull, engine and electronic repairs.

(213)    **Mill Creek**, on the southwest side of the river 1.5 miles above the entrance, has reported depths of 7 feet or more through a crooked channel across the flats to the entrance and 5 feet to about 0.4 mile above the entrance. An abandoned grain wharf is 1.5 miles above the mouth.

(214)    **Towles Creek** is entered through a channel privately marked by daybeacons. In 2009, the reported controlling depth was 8.3 feet through the entrance, thence 6.5 feet in the creek. A marina on the south shore has gasoline, diesel fuel and limited supplies.

(215)    **Cranes Creek** is on the west side of Great Wicomico River 1.5 miles above the mouth. The entrance channel, marked by daybeacons, in 2016, had a controlling depth of 6 feet. Greater depths are inside. Several small privately owned wharves along the banks of the creek are used by boats drawing up to 3 feet. Overhead power and telephone cables with a least reported clearance of 25 feet cross the creek near its head.

(216)    **Mila**, on the west side of Great Wicomico River 3.5 miles above the mouth, has a landing with a depth of 5 feet at the outer end.

(217)    The highway bridge over Great Wicomico River 6 miles above the mouth has a fixed span with a clearance of 55 feet. The overhead power cable about 50 yards above the bridge has a clearance of 54 feet at midchannel and 40 feet elsewhere. A marina on the east side of **Glebe Point** at the north end of the bridge can provide gasoline, diesel fuel and supplies; hull and engine repairs can be made. A marine railway here can handle boats up to 65 feet. Gasoline may be obtained at a wharf on Ferry Point, 0.7 mile east of the bridge.

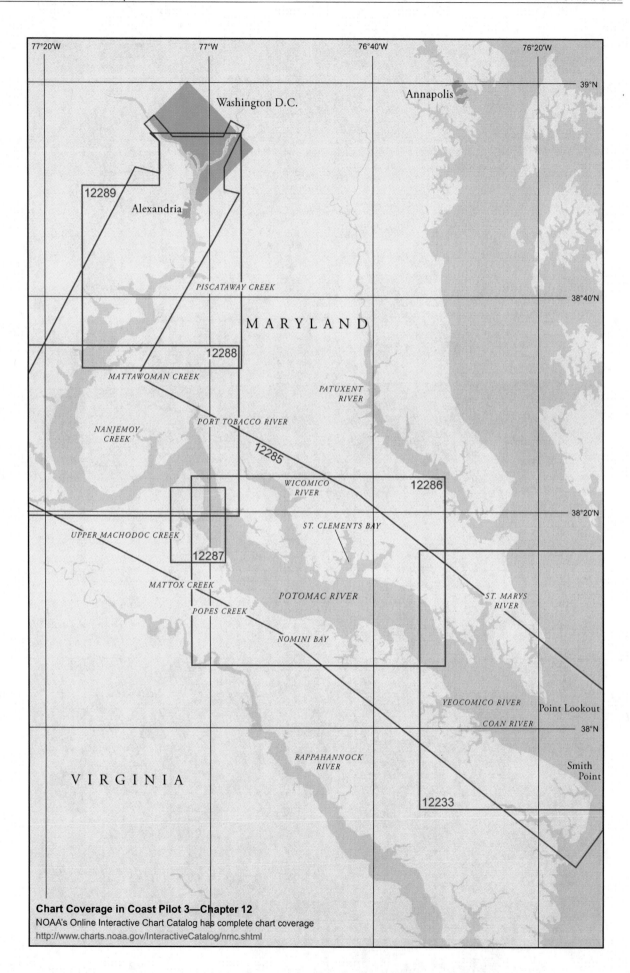

**Chart Coverage in Coast Pilot 3—Chapter 12**
NOAA's Online Interactive Chart Catalog has complete chart coverage
http://www.charts.noaa.gov/InteractiveCatalog/nrnc.shtml

# Chesapeake Bay, Potomac River

(1) This chapter describes the Potomac River and the numerous tributaries that empty into it; included are Coan, St. Marys, Yeocomico, Wicomico and Anacostia Rivers. Also described are the ports of Washington, DC, and Alexandria and several smaller ports and landings on these waterways.

(2) **COLREGS Demarcation Lines**

(3) The lines established for Chesapeake Bay are described in **33 CFR 80.510**, chapter 2.

(4) **ENCs - US5VA22M, US5VA27M, US5MD41M, US5MD43M, US5MD44M, US4MD40M, US5MD40M Charts - 12233, 12286, 12288, 12289, 12285**

(5) **Potomac River** flows into the west side of Chesapeake Bay 68.4 miles above the Virginia Capes. The west bank of the river, generally, is the boundary between Virginia on the west and Maryland on the east, and at the head of tidewater on the east bank is the city of Washington, D.C., the nation's capital.

(6) Hains Point at the junction of Anacostia River and the Washington and Georgetown Channels is 94.6 miles above the mouth of the Potomac. The head of tidewater navigation is at Chain Bridge, Washington, 101 miles above the mouth. The widest point of the river, 6.4 miles, is 11 miles above its mouth.

(7) **Mileages** on Potomac River in this chapter, such as Mile 13W, Mile 41W, and Mile 51N, are the nautical miles above the midchannel entrance point, which is 4.8 miles northwest of Smith Point on a line between Smith Point and Point Lookout; that point is 68.4 miles above the Capes. The letters N, S, E or W following the mileage numbers denote by compass points the side of the river where each feature is located.

(8) It is to be understood that the mileages given are approximations. The intended degree of accuracy is only supposed to be enough to put the user of the chart in the general vicinity of the cited object, for the purpose of locating the object.

(9) Traffic on the river consists chiefly of petroleum products; sand, gravel and crushed rock and some newsprint and fertilizers. Drafts of vessels navigating the river usually do not exceed 20 feet.

(10) **Channels**

(11) The Federal project depth is 24 feet for Potomac River from the mouth to Hains Point. Channel depths of 38 feet or more are available to Ragged Point, 20 miles above the mouth; thence the controlling depth through the dredged cuts is about 18 feet to Hains Point. The channels are maintained at or near project depths. For detailed channel information and minimum depths as reported by the U.S. Army Corps of Engineers (USACE), use NOAA Electronic Navigational Charts. Surveys and channel condition reports are available through a USACE hydrographic survey website listed in Appendix A.

(12) **Anchorages**

(13) Vessels bound up or down the river anchor anywhere near the channel where the bottom is soft; vessels sometimes anchor in Cornfield Harbor or St. Marys River. Above Alexandria, vessels usually go to the wharves; there is little or no anchorage for anything but small craft. Near the mouth of the river, small craft can find secure anchorage in most of the tributaries; Smith Creek is said to have best protection from all winds.

(14) **Fishtrap areas** extend upriver from the mouth to St. Clements Island. Limits of the areas are shown on the chart. Mariners are warned that numerous uncharted duck blinds and fishing structures, some submerged, may exist in the fishtrap areas; such structures are not charted unless known to be permanent.

(15) Numerous markers, established and maintained by the Potomac River Fisheries Commission, mark the Maryland and Virginia jurisdictional fishing boundaries on both sides of the Potomac River from Chesapeake Bay to Mattawoman Creek at Mile 71.5E in Maryland and Occoquan Bay at Mile 73.8W in Virginia and at the entrances to many of the bays and rivers.

(16) The markers are pile structures with white square daymarks with orange borders and identifying black letters "PRM,""PRV" and numbers.

(17) **Danger zones and restricted area**

(18) The Potomac River and its tributaries are used extensively by the military establishments for testing operations and gunnery practice. (Limits and regulations for these areas are given in **33 CFR 334.230, 334.240** and **334.250**, chapter 2.)

(19) **Tides**

(20) Above Washington, the river is tidal as far as Chain Bridge. The tides are influenced by the force and direction of the wind and by freshet conditions and may at times vary considerably. Daily predictions for Washington, DC, are available from the Tide prediction service at

(21) *tidesandcurrents.noaa.gov*. Links to a user guide for this service can be found in chapter 1 of this book..

### Current

(22)     The current in Chesapeake Bay off the mouth of Potomac River can be hazardous to smaller vessels and pleasure boats at ebb tide, when wind and current are opposed and with northwest winds. These conditions are more pronounced off Smith Point. The currents in the Potomac River follow the general direction of the channel. The velocities vary throughout the river and are influenced by wind and freshets. There may be little or no flood current during freshets.

(23)     The current velocity is weak in the lower part of the river between the entrance and Piney Point, averaging less than 1.0 knot. See the Tidal Current prediction service at *tidesandcurrents.noaa.gov* for specific information about times, directions, and velocities of the current at numerous locations throughout the area. Links to a user guide for this service can be found in chapter 1 of this book.

### Ice

(25)     During severe winters the tributaries of the Potomac are closed by ice and the river is frozen over to Cedar Point; the upper part is then closed to navigation. During ordinary winters the powered vessels plying the river keep the channel open.

(26)     When threatened by icing conditions, certain lighted buoys may be replaced by lighted ice buoys with reduced candlepower or by unlighted buoys, and certain unlighted buoys may be discontinued.

### Freshets

(28)     **Freshets** occur at irregular intervals but usually do not interfere with navigation below Alexandria unless accompanied by floating ice.

### Pilotage, Potomac River

(30)     Pilotage is compulsory on the Potomac River for foreign vessels and U.S. vessels under register in the foreign trade. Pilotage is optional for U.S. vessels in the coastwise trade who have on board a pilot licensed by the Federal Government for these waters.

(31)     The Chesapeake and Interstate Pilots Association offers pilot services to U.S. vessels engaged in the coastwise trade and public vessels to Piney Point. Arrangements for pilots may be made through ships' agents or the pilot office in Norfolk (telephone, 757-855-2733). Pilots will meet vessels entering from sea at Cape Henry (discussed in chapter 9) and will meet a vessel at its port if it is on the Chesapeake Bay and its tributaries or Delaware Bay and River and provide all pilot services directly to the Potomac River. Pilots may meet vessels off the Patuxent River or off the mouth of the Potomac River with sufficient coordination. Contact the pilot office for information.

(32)     The Virginia Pilots Association offers pilotage to any vessel bound for a port in Virginia or Washington, DC. The Association of Maryland Pilots offers pilotage to any vessel bound for a port in Maryland or Washington, DC. (See Pilotage, chapters 3 and 9.)

(33)
### ENCs - US5VA22M, US5VA27M, US4MD40M, US5MD40M
### Charts - 12233, 12285

(34)     **Potomac River** is entered between Smith Point and Point Lookout; the width of the entrance, normal to the channel, is about 5 miles.

(35)     The **fishtrap** areas in the lower river are shown on the charts.

### Danger zones

(37)     **Danger zones** for military testing operations extend from the mouth of the river to about 4 miles above the Potomac River Bridge, Mile 43.4. (See **33 CFR 334.230**, chapter 2, for limits and regulations.) When military firing operations are in progress in the danger zones, range patrol boats with white hulls and international orange superstructures and shoreline spotters are stationed near the firing areas. The range patrol boats display a square red flag during daylight hours and an all-round red light from the mast at night. Surface traffic on the range is controlled by the range patrol boats and the shoreline spotters on VHF-FM channel 16.

(38)     **Smith Point**, the southerly entrance point, is low and inconspicuous. A shoal area that extends eastward from the point has depths as little as 8 feet 2 miles from shore; a buoy marks the northeast edge of the shoal.

(39)     **Smith Point Light** (37°52'47"N., 76°11'01"W.), 52 feet above the water, is shown from a white square brick tower and octagonal dwelling on a brown cylindrical pier about 2.5 miles east-southeast of the point. A lighted bell buoy 1.5 miles from the light marks the separation lane of the **Traffic Separation Scheme (Smith Point)** for the bay ship channel. The Scheme discussed in chapter 9.

(40)     **Little Wicomico River**, used by local fishermen and pleasure craft, empties into the Potomac River and Chesapeake Bay at Smith Point. The approach to the river is marked by a light. A marked dredged channel leads from the Potomac River and Chesapeake Bay junction through a jettied entrance to a marked natural channel in the river. Lights mark the outer ends of the jetties. The entrance is subject to shoaling due to the strong current between the jetties; mariners are advised to exercise caution. Daybeacons mark the upper reaches of the river to a point about 3 miles above the entrance; a depth of about 6 feet can be carried for 4 miles upriver with local knowledge.

(41)     **Slough Creek**, marked by daybeacons, empties into the south side of Little Wicomico River about 0.6 mile above the entrance. A small-craft facility on the east side of the creek can provide gasoline, diesel fuel,

water, ice, berths with electricity, a pump-out station, a launching ramp, wet and dry storage and marine supplies. The reported approach depth was 4.5 feet in 2010. Hull, engine and electronic repairs can be made; lift to 12 tons.

(42)

### Cable Ferry

(43)    A cable ferry crosses Little Wicomico River at **Sunnybank**, 1.5 miles above the entrance. The ferry carries passengers and vehicles. The ferry operates between the hours of 0700 and 1900, Monday through Saturday, and 0700 to dark during the winter months. When the ferry is underway, the unmarked cable is suspended about 3 feet above the water surface and is dropped to the bottom when not underway. **DO NOT ATTEMPT TO PASS A MOVING CABLE FERRY.**

(44)

### Small-craft facility

(45)    A small-craft facility on the north side of the river about 3.6 miles above the entrance has berths with electricity. Gasoline, diesel fuel, water, ice, some marine supplies, a pump-out station, a launching ramp and wet and dry storage are available. In 2010, 6 feet was reported in the approach. A marine railway at the facility can handle craft up to 80 feet for hull, electronic and engine repairs; lift to 25 tons.

(46)    **Point Lookout**, the northerly entrance point of Potomac River, is low but well marked by a 195-foot lighted communications tower and several buildings. The shoal that extends about 1 mile southward from the point is marked by **Point Lookout Light** (38°01'30"N., 76°19'25"W.), 39 feet above the water, shown from a skeleton tower with a black and white diamond-shaped daymark on a pile structure.

(47)    **Cornfield Harbor**, just inside Point Lookout, is sheltered from northerly and northeasterly winds; vessels bound up and down the bay frequently use it as an anchorage for the night. The shoaling is gradual, except off **Cornfield Point** and at the south end of the shoal that extends southward from Point Lookout; at these places the hard sand bottom drops off abruptly. An 18-foot spot, and rocks covered 16 and 17 feet, are about 0.7 mile westward from Point Lookout, and a 10-foot spot lies between them and the Point Lookout shore.

(48)    **Lake Conoy** is 0.8 mile north-northwest of Point Lookout. The lake is entered from Cornfield Harbor through a private channel marked by a light and daybeacons; in 1976, the reported controlling depths were 8 feet in the entrance and 6 feet in the basin and alongside the piers. The east side of the lake is the site of **Point Lookout State Park**. The state boating facility on the east shore of the lake has gasoline, water, ice, limited marine supplies and a sewage pump-out station. No overnight berthing is permitted; anchorage in the basin is allowed in an emergency.

(49)    **Coan River** (38°00'00"N., 76°27'00"W.), Mile 7.8S, has depths of 13 to 7 feet for 4.5 miles to within 0.5 mile of the head. The river is used mostly by local oyster and fish boats. A 500-yard lane in the approach is kept clear of fishtraps; the initial course through the lane is **230°**. The entrance to Coan River is marked by buoys and lights and is easy to navigate; the channel inside is marked at the critical points by daybeacons and bush stakes. A warning daybeacon at about 37°59'07"N., 76°27'58"W., marks a shoal area that reduces the channel width to about 30 feet. Shoaling to an unknown extent was reported in the channel about 200 yards eastward of Daybeacon 10 and about 200 yards eastward of the small point about midway between Daybeacons 14 and 16.

(50)    **Kingscote Creek**, on the north side of Coan River 0.6 mile above the mouth, has depths of 8 feet for most of its 1-mile length. A shoal extends halfway across the entrance from the point on the west side. Gasoline, diesel fuel, water, ice, berths, pump-out station, launching ramp, wet and dry storage and marine supplies are available at the small-craft facilities on the east side of the creek at **Lewisetta**. In 2010, 8 feet was reported alongside. Hull, engine and electronic repairs can be made; lift to 25 tons.

(51)    **The Glebe**, on the west side of Coan River 0.7 mile above the mouth, has depths of 9 to 13 feet to the forks 1.5 miles above the entrance. The channel in The Glebe is clear except for a shoal that extends well off from the point on the south side 0.6 mile above the entrance.

(52)    **Stevens Point** is on the west side of Coan River 1 mile above the mouth. The boatyard on the south side makes hull, engine and electronic repairs; lift capacity, 25 tons. Gasoline, diesel fuel, ice, water, berthing with electricity, a pumpout station, some supplies, a launching ramp and wet and dry storage are available. In 2010, 10 feet was reported alongside.

(53)    The grain wharf at **Bundick**, on the west side of Coan River 3.4 miles above the mouth, has depths of 9 feet at the outer end. **Coan** wharf, directly across the river from Bundick, is in ruins. The overhead power cable from Coan to Bundick has a clearance of 60 feet.

(54)    **Smith Creek**, Mile 8.5N, is used by many small fishing and pleasure boats and has the best protection along this part of the river from all winds. A depth of about 8 feet is available over the bar to the junction of the two main branches, 1.5 miles above the entrance light. The entrance is well marked. The lane through the fishtraps can be navigated on a course of **355°**.

(55)    **Wynne**, on the east side of the entrance to Smith Creek, has fish wharves with depths of 5 to 10 feet at their outer ends. Small-craft facilities on the east side of the creek, just above the entrance, can provide gasoline, diesel fuel, water, ice, berths and marine supplies. Hull and engine repairs can be made. Largest haul-out capacities; marine railway, 200 feet; lift, 35 tons.

(56)    **St. Marys River**, Mile 9.7N, is 2 miles wide at the entrance and about 600 yards wide at St. Marys City, 5.5 miles up. The channel has depths of 20 feet or more to St. Marys City, then shoals gradually to 12 feet at **Martin Point** and to 8 feet at **Tippity Wichity Island**, 8 miles above the mouth. St. Marys River is sometimes used as an anchorage by the deeper draft vessels seeking shelter

from heavy gales, but small boats prefer Smith Creek. The river has very little traffic other than local fishing craft. The course through the fishtraps off the entrance is **345°**.

(57)     **St. George Island**, on the west side of the entrance to St. Marys River, is long, low and sparsely wooded. The island is thickly settled, mostly by oystermen and fishermen, and is used to some extent as a summer resort. **St. George Bar** extends 1.3 miles southeastward from the island; a lighted buoy is about 1 mile southeastward of the outer end of the bar.

(58)     **Island Creek**, on the southeast end of St. George Island, is entered by a marked dredged channel that leads to fishing piers and a turning basin inside. In 2010, the controlling depth in the channel and basin was 5 feet.

(59)     **St. George Creek**, which joins St. Marys River along the northeast side of St. George Island, has a narrow, crooked channel with depths of about 9 feet for 3.5 miles; the channel is marked for about 2.8 miles. The creek is used extensively by oystering and fishing boats and by pleasure craft.

(60)     A marked channel enters St. George Creek at the fixed bridge on the north side of St George Island. The bridge has a width of 35 feet and a vertical clearance of 17 feet. Overhead power cables on both sides of the bridge have a clearance of 29 feet.

(61)     The town of **Piney Point**, on the west side of St. George Creek 2.5 miles above the mouth, has several private wharves with depths of 5 to 8 feet.

(62)     At **Morgan Point**, on the west side of St. George Creek 3.5 miles above the mouth, is a boatyard where hull repairs can be made; marine railway, 40 feet. Gasoline, water and berths are available.

(63)     **Carthagena Creek** enters the west side of St. Marys River about 3 miles above the mouth. The creek, marked by daybeacons and a light, is used chiefly by pleasure craft. A marina at **Dennis Point**, on the east shore of the creek about 1.1 miles above the mouth can provide berthing with electricity, gasoline, diesel fuel, ice, water, a pump-out station, wet and dry storage and marine supplies. In 2010, the reported alongside depth was 6 feet. Hull, electronic and engine repairs can be made; lift capacity, 75 tons.

(64)     **St. Inigoes Creek** enters the east side of St. Marys River about 3.5 miles above the mouth. Depths of 11 feet can be carried to the junction of St. Inigoes Creek and **Church Cove,** 1.3 miles above the mouth. The creek is unmarked.

(65)     **Molls Cove** is on the east side of the creek, 0.6 mile above the mouth. **St. Inigoes Coast Guard Station** is on the west side of its entrance.

(66)     **St. Marys City**, at **Church Point**, on the east side of St. Marys River 5.5 miles above the mouth, was the original capital of Maryland. Few traces of the original town remain, but the statehouse was reconstructed in 1934 from the ruins of several other buildings nearby. A landing on the south side of the point has a depth of about 9 feet at the outer end.

(67)     **Yeocomico River**, Mile 10.2S, has depths of 19 to 12 feet to the forks 1.4 miles above the entrance. Lights mark the channel to the forks and bush stakes mark the edges of the tributary channels. The initial course through the fish stakes off the entrance is **244°**.

(68)     There are small-craft facilities on the north fork of Yeocomico River, and on the south side of **White Point Creek**, the westerly arm of **Shannon Branch**. Gasoline, diesel fuel, water, ice, berthing with electricity, some marine supplies and a pump-out station are available. Hull, engine and electronic repairs can be made. In 2010, a depth of 8 feet in the approach and alongside was reported. A 65-foot marine railway and lift to 50 tons are available in White Point Creek.

(69)     **West Yeocomico River**, the west fork, has depths of 13 to 7 feet to **Kinsale**, on the southwest side 1.7 miles above the entrance. The fixed highway bridge at Kinsale has a width of 29 feet and a clearance of 8 feet. The bulkhead wharf has depths of 10 feet alongside; the grain elevators on the wharf are prominent. Small-craft facilities are on the north side of the river and at Kinsale. Gasoline, diesel fuel, berthing with electricity, pump-out, water, ice, marine supplies, wet storage and a launching ramp are available.

(70)     **South Yeocomico River**, the south fork, has depths of 13 to 7 feet to **Lodge**, on the west side of **Lodge Creek** 2 miles above the entrance of the south branch. An overhead power cable with a clearance of 50 feet crosses Lodge Creek about 2.4 miles above the entrance. The fish wharf at **Mundy Point**, on the west side of the entrance, has depths of 6 feet at the wharf. Several small landings on the south side of the point have depths of 9 feet at their outer ends.

(71)     **Harryhogan Point** is on the west side of South Yeocomico River 1 mile south of the entrance. The marine railways at the settlement can handle vessels up to 80 feet. The north landing at the cannery has depths of 9 feet alongside, and the south landing has depths of 5 feet. The lumber-mill landing 0.2 mile southwestward has depths of 7 feet alongside.

(72)

**Small-craft facilities**

(73)     Small-craft facilities are on the south side of Harryhogan Point and on the east side of Lodge Creek. Gasoline, diesel fuel, berths, electricity, water, ice, pump-out station, storage, launching ramp and marine supplies are available. Hull and engine repairs can be made. The largest marine railway in the area can handle craft up to 80 feet; a 50-ton lift is available.

(74)     **Piney Point** (38°08.1'N., 76°31.8'W.) is at Mile 15.9N. An abandoned lighthouse tower and a former Coast Guard station are on the point. The former Coast Guard wharf and the small private landings east of Piney Point have depths of about 5 feet at their outer ends. Gasoline and some supplies are available at a dock about 1 mile northeast of the point.

(75)   A prominent T-head pier of an oil company extends 1,000 feet southwestward from Piney Point. The pier, marked by private lights, has depths of about 35 feet along its 684-foot outer face. The pier is owned and operated by L. P. Steuart Co.

(76)   **Immigration, quarantine** and **customs** officials come from Baltimore upon notification by the maritime exchange that tankers are due at Piney Point; vessels are boarded at the pier.

(77)
**ENCs - US5MD41M, US4MD40M, US5MD40M**
**Charts - 12286, 12285**

(78)   Limits of the **fishtrap** areas that extend upriver as far as St. Clements Island are shown on the charts.

(79)
**Danger zones**

(80)   **Danger zones** for military testing operations extend upriver to about 4 miles above the Harry W. Nice (Potomac River Bridge) Bridge (U.S. Route 301), Mile 43.4. (See **33 CFR 334.230**, chapter 2, for limits and regulations.)

(81)   **Bonum Creek** (38°05'42"N., 76°34'54"W.), Mile 16.0S, is entered from the Potomac River by a dredged channel that leads through jetties to an anchorage basin 0.4 mile inside. A light and daybeacons mark the channel to the basin. The creek is used chiefly by fishing craft.

(82)   **Herring Creek**, Mile 18.7E, is entered by a marked dredged channel protected on both sides of the entrance by jetties; lights mark the outer ends of the jetties. A marina on the south side of the entrance has gasoline, diesel fuel, berths, electricity, water, ice, launching ramp, storage and some marine supplies. Hull and engine repairs can be made with a 30-ton lift. A fish pier with 6 feet at the outer end is just east of the marina fuel pier. Another marina is on the south side of the creek 1.2 miles above the entrance; depths of 5 feet are reported alongside the piers. Gasoline, berths, electricity, water, ice, pump-out station, storage, launching ramp and limited supplies are available. Hull, engine and electronic repairs can be made with a 25-ton lift.

(83)   A shoal extends 0.5 mile offshore from **Ragged Point**, at Mile 19.1S. A light is near the outer edge of the shoal. A marina, south of Ragged Point, can provide gasoline, diesel fuel, berths with electricity, water, ice, a pumpout station, a launching ramp, dry and wet storage and limited marine supplies. In 2009, 7 feet alongside was reported. Hull, engine and electronic repairs are available; lift capacity, 30 tons.

(84)   **Lower Machodoc Creek**, Mile 21.7S, has depths of 15 to 11 feet for 2 miles, thence the depths decrease to 4 feet at a point 4 miles above the entrance. The critical points are marked as far as the narrows 2.2 miles from the entrance; the shoals are usually bush-staked.

(85)   **Branson Cove**, on the east side of Lower Machodoc Creek 1 mile above the entrance, is entered by a marked dredged channel that leads to a boat basin inside. **Coles Point**, the village along the north shore of the cove,

has piers with depths of about 6 feet at the outer ends. A large oyster-packing plant is on the north side of the entrance to the cove. Small-craft facilities in the cove can provide gasoline, diesel fuel, water, ice, berths and marine supplies. Hull and engine repairs can be made.

(86)   **Nomini Bay**, Mile 25S, has depths of 20 to 15 feet in the middle, and is the approach to Nomini Creek and Currioman Bay. The shoaling is abrupt on the east side of the bay and gradual on the west side.

(87)   **Nomini Creek** is entered through a dredged channel that extends about 1.2 miles above the entrance to Hickory Point. The channel is well marked by lights and daybeacons. There is a long jetty on the east side of the entrance to the creek. In 2011, the length of the project had a midchannel controlling depth of 5 feet, with depths to 7 feet in the left outside quarter, and shoaling to bare in the right outside quarter. Depths of about 5 feet may be carried to the second bridge, 5 miles above the entrance, thence 3 feet for 0.5 mile. Traffic on the creek consists chiefly of seafood and fertilizer.

(88)   Mariners should be alert for unmarked fishtrap structures in Nomini Creek.

(89)   The highway bridge at **Nomini**, about 3.5 miles above the entrance, has a 45-foot fixed span with a clearance of 18 feet. The fixed highway bridge at **Prospect Hill**, 5 miles above the entrance, has a 30-foot span with a clearance of 10 feet.

(90)   **Currioman Bay** is separated from the west side of Nomini Bay by **Hollis Marsh**, a narrow 2-mile-long spit that is wooded in the middle. Currioman Bay has depths of 7 to 10 feet in the entrance from the head of Nomini Bay and in most of the area back of Hollis Marsh; the entrance from Potomac River at the northwest end of Hollis Marsh has depths of only 2 to 3 feet.

(91)   **Breton Bay**, Mile 25.2N, is a favorite anchoring ground for yachts. Commercial traffic consists chiefly of petroleum products. Drafts using the bay are mostly 6 feet or less, but occasionally vessels drawing up to 11 feet come inside.

(92)   The bay has depths of 15 to 11 feet for 4.5 miles, thence about 5 feet to Leonardtown, 5 miles above the entrance.

(93)   A 1,000-yard lane extends through the fishtraps off the entrance to Breton Bay; the initial course through the lane is **352°**. The shoal that extends eastward from Heron Island Bar to the Breton Bay approach is marked by an obstruction buoy, and another shoal that extends southwestward from **Huggins Point**, on the east side of the entrance, is marked by a light near its outer end. Daybeacons and lights mark the bay channel to within 0.5 mile of Leonardtown.

(94)   **Combs Creek**, on the north side and 1.6 miles above the mouth of Breton Bay, had a reported controlling depth of 5 feet along the middle of the creek in 1980. The narrow entrance is between shoal spits marked by daybeacons and stakes. Ice, water, a pump-out station, some marine supplies and berthing with electricity are available. The marine railways on the west side of the

creek can handle boats up to 60 feet for hull and engine repairs; lift capacity, 20 tons.

(95)    A channel with a controlling depth of 6 feet, marked by piles, leads into the bight just southwestward of the entrance to Combs Creek. Gasoline, berths and some supplies can be obtained.

(96)    **Lovers Point** is on the east side of Breton Bay 3 miles above the mouth. A bar with depths of less than 1 foot extends 500 yards northwestward from the point and is marked at its outer end by a light.

(97)    **Buzzard Point** is on the west side of Breton Bay 4.5 miles above the mouth. A daybeacon marks the outer end of a bar that extends off the point.

(98)    **Leonardtown** is on the north side of Breton Bay 5 miles above the mouth.

(99)    **St. Clements Island** is at Mile 27.0N. Near the south end of the thinly wooded island is a prominent cross that commemorates the first Catholic mass by English settlers in America on March 25, 1634. Shoals extend from the island in all directions. The long pier on the northeast side of the island has a depth of about 16 feet at the outer end; supply and fishing boats use the pier.

(100)   **Heron Island Bar**, about 1 mile eastward of St. Clements Island, is an extensive shoal area mostly covered at low water; the bar is marked at the eastern and western ends by buoys.

(101)   **St. Clements Bay**, north-northeastward of St. Clements Island, has three entrances. The eastern entrance, between Heron Island Bar and the mainland, is by the way of the Breton Bay lane through the fishtraps; this entrance has depths of 20 to 16 feet and is easily followed in the daytime. The middle entrance, between Heron Island Bar and St. Clements Island, has depths of 15 feet or more and is approached through a 500-yard lane in the fishtraps on an initial course of **352°**; this entrance is narrow and crooked but is marked by a light and buoys and is easily followed in the daytime.

(102)   **Dukeharts Channel**, the western entrance, leads from the Potomac River to St. Clements Bay between St. Clements Island and the mainland 0.5 mile to the north-northwestward; the controlling depth is 5 feet. In 1993, depths of 2 to 3 feet were reported 100 yards northeast of Daybeacon 7 in about 38°13'07.3"N., 76°44'46.2"W. Aids to navigation in Dukeharts Channel are placed for a passage from east to west.

(103)   St. Clements Bay has channel depths of 14 feet for 3 miles then shoals gradually to 8 feet 5 miles above the entrance. The mean range of tide is 1.8 feet.

(104)   **St. Patrick Creek**, on the west side of St. Clements Bay 0.5 mile above the mouth, is entered through a marked dredged channel. In 2009, the midchannel controlling depth in the dredged channel was 1.5 feet. The creek is much frequented by fishermen, oystermen and pleasure craft. There are several small-craft facilities along the creek above **Palmers**, on the south side 0.4 mile above the entrance. The **speed limit** is 6 miles per hour in the creek.

(105)   **Canoe Neck Creek** is on the west side of St. Clements Bay about 1.5 miles above the mouth. The entrance to the creek has a depth of 11 feet, except for a shoal reported encroaching the channel from the north entrance point. The creek shoals gradually from 11 feet at the entrance to 3 feet near the head. The landings at **Morris Point**, on the south side just above the entrance, have depths of 4 to 7 feet at the outer ends. A small-craft facility on Morris Point can provide gasoline.

(106)   **St. Catherine Sound**, Mile 29.0N, has depths of 5 to 9 feet behind **St. Catherine Island.** Two marked dredged channels lead into the sound; one at the northwesterly end and the other at the southeasterly end. Partially submerged pilings were reported in the sound near the southeasterly channel north and east of St. Catherine Island in about 38°14'12"N., 76°47'20"W. and 38°14'35"N., 76°47'45"W. The wharves along the shore of the sound are privately owned.

(107)   **Whites Neck Creek**, on the north side of St. Catherine Sound, has depths of 4 feet in the entrance and 6 to 2 feet inside. A state pier on the west side just inside the entrance has depths of 4 feet at the outer end. The marine railway just upstream can handle boats up to 45 feet for hull and engine repairs.

(108)   **Wicomico River** (38°15.0'N., 76°49.6'W.) is at Mile 31.0N. Its commercial traffic consists chiefly of shellfish vessels. Drafts of vessels using the river are mostly 6 feet or less.

(109)   The river is characterized by long spits, with little depth and abrupt outer ends that extend to the edges of the channel in several places. The entrance is 1.3 miles wide between **St. Margaret Island** on the east and **Cobb Island** on the west. **Cobb Point Bar,** which extends 1 mile southeastward from the island, is marked at the outer end by a light; the shoal extending 0.6 mile westward from St. Margaret Island is marked by a daybeacon.

(110)   The Wicomico River channel has depths of 40 to 12 feet for 5 miles, thence 6 feet with local knowledge for 3 miles, and then decreasing to 3 feet to the head, 11 miles above the mouth. The channel is marked at the most critical points for about 8 miles.

(111)   An overhead power cable with a clearance of 38 feet crosses the river about 10 miles above the mouth. Three suspension towers in the river support the cable.

(112)   **Neale Sound** is on the west side of the entrance of Wicomico River between Cobb Island and the mainland and affords secure anchorage for small boats. An east cut entrance is also available from the Wicomico River. Both entrances are marked by lights, and the critical part of the channel at the northwest end is marked by daybeacons. A fixed highway bridge with a vertical clearance of 20 feet crosses Neale Sound.

(113)   Several small-craft facilities are on both sides of Neale Sound at the bridge.

(114)   **Bushwood Wharf** is on the east side of Wicomico River 1.5 miles above the mouth. A state pier and a gasoline pier have alongside reported depths of 8 and

4 feet, respectively. Gasoline and some supplies are obtainable.

(115)     **Charleston Creek**, on the west side of Wicomico River 3 miles above the mouth, is used by oyster boats as an anchorage.

(116)     From Nomini Bay to within 2 miles of Popes Creek (38°11.6'N., 76°54.2'W.) the Virginia shore of Potomac River is backed by high ground. Along this stretch are **Nomini Cliffs, Stratford Cliffs and Horsehead Cliff** and the valleys between them.

(117)     **Popes Creek**, Mile 33.5S, leads to **Wakefield** and the **George Washington Birthplace National Monument**. The controlling depth is about 1.5 feet in the entrance, and a stone jetty 2 feet high extends 200 feet offshore from the point on the north side. Current velocity up to 4.5 knots has been reported in the entrance.

(118)     **Mattox Creek**, Mile 36.1S, has depths of 7 to 5 feet in a marked narrow channel for 2 miles to **Fox Point**, then the depths decrease to 3 feet at the fixed concrete highway bridge, 4 miles above the entrance. A marina, on the south side of the creek, can provide gasoline, berths with electricity, water, ice, a pumpout station, a launching ramp, dry and wet storage, and some marine supplies. In 2010, a depth of 6 feet was reported in the approach and alongside. Hull, engine and electronic repairs are available; lift capacity, 40 tons.

(119)     **Colonial Beach**, Mile 36.5S, is a summer resort just north of Mattox Creek. The largest of the piers on the river side of the town is the municipal 450-foot T-head pier 1.2 miles above the south end. The pier has reported depths of 6 feet at the outer end.

(120)     **Monroe Creek**, back of Colonial Beach, is entered between **Gum Bar Point**, at the south end of the town, and **Sebastian Point**, 150 yards westward. The creek is used extensively as an anchorage. The dredged channel, marked by lights and daybeacons, leads from the entrance of the creek to a basin at **Robins Grove Point** at Colonial Beach. In 2009, the controlling depths were 6.8 feet in the entrance channel to the basin, thence 5.8 feet in the basin. The entrance is narrow and mariners are requested to transit at low speed to avoid wash damage to vessels moored in the creek.

(121)     There are numerous small-craft facilities along the east side of the creek below and above Robins Grove Point, and a yacht club is on the eastern side of the entrance to the creek.

(122)
**ENCs - US5MD42M, US4MD40M, US5MD40M**
**Charts - 12287, 12285**

(123)     **Potomac Beach** is at Mile 38.8W. A private pier is the only usable landing. In 1982, a reported depth of 2 feet was available to the landing.

(124)     **Rosier Creek**, entered just westward of Potomac Beach, has depths of 2 feet in the entrance and 5 to 2 feet for 1 mile upstream. The creek has no wharves and is little used.

(125)     **Upper Machodoc Creek** is at Mile 40.2W. The **Naval Surface Warfare Center** is at **Dahlgren**, on the north side of the entrance to the creek, but also occupies land for a considerable distance along the south shore; the center monitors VHF-FM channel 16. (See **33 CFR 334.230**, chapter 2, for the limits and regulations governing the danger zones.) River currents may have transported unexploded ordnance outside the charted danger zone limits; extreme caution is advised. The tanks and radio masts at Dahlgren are prominent.

(126)     Two well-marked, Navy-maintained channels lead from the Potomac River to the basin and wharves at Dahlgren. Above Dahlgren, only small piers are found along the banks of Upper Machodoc Creek. A fixed highway bridge with a 47-foot span and a clearance of 10 feet crosses the creek 3.7 miles above the entrance.

(127)     **Williams Creek**, on the north side of Upper Machodoc Creek 1 mile above the mouth, has depths of 4 to 2 feet to the highway bridge 1.1 miles above the entrance. An overhead power cable 0.6 mile above the entrance has a clearance of 28 feet.

(128)     A marina is on the north side of the entrance to Williams Creek. Gasoline, diesel fuel, berthing with electricity, a pump-out station, a launching ramp, wet and dry storage and marine supplies are available. In 2010, a depth of 6 feet alongside was reported. Hull, engine and electronic repairs can be made; lift capacity, 12 tons.

(129)     **Lower Cedar Point** is at Mile 42.1E. A light is shown from a white skeleton tower on piles in depths of 3 feet on the west edge of the main channel 0.7 mile westward of the point.

(130)     **Morgantown** is on the south side of Lower Cedar Point. There are strong cross currents south of the point. The landings that remain intact are suitable only for small boats.

(131)
**ENCs - US5MD43M, US4MD40M, US5MD40M**
**Charts - 12288, 12285**

(132)     The **Harry W. Nice (Potomac River) Bridge**, (U.S. Route 301), Mile 43.4, has a fixed channel span (under construction 2020). The centerline of the main span has a sound signal and is marked by a flashing red aviation obstruction light and by a fixed green light surmounted by three fixed white lights vertically 15 feet apart. The bridge is also marked by fixed red lights on the main trusses and approaches.

(133)     There is a small-boat basin and marina just above the Harry W. Nice Bridge on the Maryland side. The entrance channel and basin have depths of about 6 feet. Gasoline, diesel fuel, berths and marine supplies are available. Hull and engine repairs can be made; lift, 20 tons.

(134)
**Danger zone**

(135)     A **danger zone** for military testing operations extends 4 miles upriver from the Harry W. Nice Bridge. (See **33 CFR 334.230**, chapter 2, for limits and regulations.)

Unexploded ordnance may exist in the vicinity of Mathias Point Neck, Cedar Point Neck, Tayloe Neck and Nanjemoy Creek.

(136)     **Persimmon Point** is at Mile 44.5W. A 3-foot shoal is 0.6 mile southeastward of the point on the west edge of the channel.

(137)     **Popes Creek**, Mile 45.4E, is not navigable. The village of **Popes Creek**, 0.2 mile northward, has overnight docking available at a crabhouse pier. The former railroad wharf is in ruins.

(138)     Between Popes Creek and Upper Cedar Point, 4.5 miles upriver, the Maryland shore of Potomac River bends northward about 2 miles to form **Port Tobacco River Flats**, which have shoal spots of 3 to 5 feet but generally navigable depths of 7 to 10 feet. **Port Tobacco River**, at the head of the bight, has depths of 7 feet for 1.6 miles and thence 5 to 3 feet for another 1.3 miles. A light and daybeacons mark the channel.

(139)     **Chapel Point**, on the east side of Port Tobacco River 1.2 miles above the mouth, is a summer resort. **Port Tobacco**, 4.4 miles above the entrance, is now the head of practical navigation. Marinas at the town have gasoline, berths and some supplies. Hull and engine repairs can be made; lift, 15 tons.

(140)     **Mathias Point** is at Mile 47.7S. A light is shown from a skeleton tower on piles in depths of 3 feet on the south edge of the main channel 0.3 mile northward of the point.

(141)     **Upper Cedar Point**, at Mile 50.0N, is marked by a light shown from a skeleton tower on piles in depths of 3 feet on the north edge of the channel 0.5 mile southeastward of the point. Give the light a berth of at least 200 yards.

(142)     **Nanjemoy Creek**, Mile 51.0N, has a controlling depth of about 4 feet in a privately marked channel to a small-craft launching ramp about 4 miles above the entrance.

(143)     **Metomkin Point** is at Mile 53.1S. A light, shown from a pile structure in depths of 1 foot 0.5 mile off the point, marks the shallowest part of a shoal area along the southeast edge of the channel.

(144)     **Maryland Point Light** (38°20'59"N., 77°11'51"W.), Mile 55.8S, 42 feet above the water, is shown from a skeleton tower with a black and white diamond-shaped daymark on piles in depths of 9 feet on the south edge of the Potomac River channel 0.7 mile southeastward of **Maryland Point.** Other shoals east and west of the light are marked by buoys.

(145)     Two white dish-shaped antennas 1.4 miles northwest of Maryland Point are conspicuous.

(146)     Gasoline, ice, water, a pump-out station and limited berthing with electricity can be obtained at **Fairview Beach**, Mile 57.4S. Depths to the pier are about 4 feet. Hull and engine repairs can be made; lift capacity, 25 tons.

(147)     **Potomac Creek**, Mile 58.5S, is used only by small motorboats. **Bull Bluff,** on the south side of the entrance, is high and wooded. The creek has depths of 7 feet in the entrance, thence 3 feet for 2 miles. The best water favors the south side of the entrance. Gasoline and water are available at small-craft facilities on the south side of the creek 1 mile and 2 miles above the entrance. Hull and engine repairs can be made at the more easterly facility.

(148)     **Aquia Creek**, Mile 60.4W, has depths of 4 to 5 feet to the railroad bridge, and thence 2 feet to **Coals Landing**, 5 miles above the mouth. The entrance to the creek is marked by lights and daybeacons. A fixed railroad bridge, 3 miles above the entrance, has a width of 46 feet and a clearance of 26 feet. An overhead power cable just south of the bridge has a clearance of 36 feet. Small-craft facilities are on the south side of the creek close above and below the bridge.

(149)     **Smith Point**, Mile 61.5E, is marked by a light. **Clifton Beach** is on the point. The broken piling of a former landing 300 yards south of the light is nearly awash at high water.

(150)     There is danger of striking submerged hulks in the mile-wide former restricted anchorage area that extended 2.5 miles upriver along the Virginia shore from directly opposite Smith Point.

(151)     **Liverpool Point** is at Mile 64.4E. **Mallows Bay** is on the north side of Liverpool Point. There are several sunken vessels in the middle and north part of the bay. The western danger limit is a line from Liverpool Point to Sandy Point. A buoy marks the inner edge of the river channel off the bay. The **Mallows Bay-Potomac River National Marine Sanctuary** consists of an area of approximately 18 square miles of waters of the state of Maryland and the submerged lands thereunder, over, around, and under the underwater cultural resources in the Potomac River—see **15 CFR 922.1** through **922.50** and **922.200** through **922.206**, chapter 2, for limits and regulations.

(152)     A **restricted area** has been established on the Potomac River around Chopawamsic Creek and Chopawamsic Island. (See **33 CFR 334.235**, chapter 2, for limits and regulations.)

(153)     **Quantico**, Mile 67.7W, is a training site of the **U.S. Marine Corps**. The T-head pier has depths of 25 to 30 feet at the face, and the launch harbor immediately south of the pier has depths of about 10 feet. Except in emergencies, the pier and harbor are restricted to government vessels.

(154)     **Quantico Creek**, Mile 68.2W, has depths of 7 feet in a narrow, crooked entrance channel, and about 2 feet for 2 miles upstream. The fixed railroad bridges over the entrance have 30-foot spans with a clearance of 12 feet. An overhead power cable along the west side of the bridge, and another one 1.3 miles above the bridge, have clearances of 8 feet and 41 feet, respectively. A small landing on the south side of the entrance is used by local pleasure boats.

(155)     **Possum Point** is at Mile 68.5W. A private light marks the powerplant wharf 0.2 mile northward of the point. An overhead power cable 0.8 mile above Possum Point has a clearance of 170 feet for a midwidth of 1,440 feet over the main channel and 124 to 70 feet elsewhere.

The six support structures for the cable are marked by lights.

(156)    **Chicamuxen Creek**, Mile 69.2E, has depths of 5 feet in the entrance but shoals rapidly farther up. The creek is little used.

(157)
### Danger zone

(158)    A **danger zone** of a Navy explosion test area includes part of Chicamuxen Creek and extends northeastward in Potomac River up to 0.5 mile off the Maryland shore for about 5 miles to Indian Head. (See **33 CFR 334.240**, chapter 2, for limits and regulations.)

(159)    An oil and asphalt terminal is at **Cockpit Point**, Mile 70.3W.

(160)    The Government wharf at the north end of **Stump Neck,** Mile 70.6E, has depths of 15 feet at the outer end and is marked by a light. Lights also mark the ends of the breakwater on the north side. Landing is permitted only in case of emergency.

(161)    **Mattawoman Creek**, Mile 71.5E, has easily navigated depths of 7 to 5 feet for 1 mile to the marsh that extends southeastward from **Deep Point** to the edge of the channel. The channel is marked by a daybeacon and lights. Above this marsh, the creek channel has greater depths for 3 miles, but meanders back and forth between the flats and is almost impossible to follow without a guide. A pier and launching ramp for a public picnic facility is at **Sweden Point**, 2 miles inside the entrance. In 1979, depths of about 3 feet were reported available to the dock.

(162)    **Powells Creek**, Mile 71.1W, has depths of 4 to 5 feet in the approach and 1 to 2 feet through the railroad bridge and for a short distance upstream. The fixed railroad bridge 0.3 mile above the entrance has a width of 40 feet and a clearance of 26 feet. An overhead power cable at the bridge has a clearance of 45 feet.

(163)
### ENCs - US5MD44M, US4MD40M, US5MD40M
### Charts - 12289, 12285

(164)    **Occoquan Bay**, Mile 73.8W, has general depths of 5 to 7 feet. The entrance is 2.5 miles wide between **Freestone Point** on the southwest and **High Point** on the northeast; the channel is 0.3 mile off High Point. A manmade rocky islet, 5 feet high, is near the center of the bay, 1 mile westward of High Point. The bay has little commerce; it and its tributaries are used as an ice harbor when the river channel is closed above.

(165)    **Neabsco Creek**, at the southwest side of Occoquan Bay north of Freestone Point, has depths of 4 to 2 feet. The fixed railroad bridge over the mouth has a 30-foot span with clearance of 33 feet. The overhead cables just west of the bridge have a clearance of 36 feet. Gasoline, diesel fuel, ice, water, a pump-out station, berthing with electricity and marine supplies can be obtained at the small-craft facilities on the south side of the creek above

the bridge. Hull, engine and electronic repairs can be made; lifts up to 20 tons.

(166)    **Belmont Bay**, the northeastern arm of Occoquan Bay, has general depths of 3 to 4 feet. Belmont Bay is said to be rocky throughout; the rocks are covered at low water except during northwest winds.

(167)    **Occoquan River** empties into the head of Occoquan Bay along the west side of Belmont Bay. A marked channel with dredged sections leads through the bay and river to Occoquan. In 2013, the controlling depth was 7 feet from the entrance in Occoquan Bay to Light 14. The channel is marked through Occoquan Bay to the first bridge over Occoquan River.

(168)    Three fixed bridges, the Richmond, Fredericksburg and Potomac Railroad bridge, and the two U.S. Route 1 highway bridges, with a least clearance of 44 feet cross Occoquan River 3.6 miles above the bay entrance. Piles extend out into the channel on both sides of the first bridge. An obstruction, covered 1 foot, is on the north side of the third bridge, in about the center of the river. The twin I-95 fixed highway bridges, 4 miles above the entrance, have a clearance of 44 feet. The State Route 123 fixed highway bridge, 5 miles above the entrance, has a clearance of 42 feet. A rock awash is on the north side of the bridge in the center of the river. A power cable just northwestward of the bridge has a clearance of 44 feet.

(169)    **Occoquan**, on the southwest side of Occoquan River 5 miles above the bay entrance, is the head of navigation. Channel depths off the Occoquan bulkheads are 7 feet in the east half and 5.5 feet in the west half of the channel in 1991. Small-craft facilities, on the southwest side of the river above the first bridge, can provide gasoline, water, berths and marine supplies. Hull and engine repairs can be made; lift capacity to 25 tons.

(170)    Indian Head, Mile 75.3S, is a high wooded bluff. The town of **Indian Head** is back of the bluff. The lower wharf has depths of 12 feet off its northern face, and the small-boat basin on the lower side has depths of 4 feet. The upper wharf has depths of 12 to 15 feet at the face. Landing is permitted at either wharf only in case of emergency. Mariners are advised to use caution in the vicinity of the upper wharf because divers may be training in the area.

(171)    **Craney Island**, Mile 77.3W, is a tiny islet marked by a clump of trees and surrounded by an extensive shoal. Between the islet and the Virginia shore is a narrow unmarked channel with depths of 7 feet.

(172)    **Pomonkey Creek**, Mile 78.0E, has depths of 7 to 3 feet in the entrance but little water inside.

(173)    **Gunston Cove**, Mile 80.0W, has depths of 3 to 5 feet in the entrance and 5 to 7 feet inside. The peninsula between Gunston Cove and Dogue Creek, 2 miles to the northeastward, is a part of the U. S. Army reservation of **Fort Belvoir.**

(174)    The small-boat basin and facilities at **Whitestone Point**, on the north side of the Gunston Cove entrance, are part of Fort Belvoir and are not for public use. A

**restricted area** is off Whitestone Point. (See **33 CFR 334.250**, chapter 2, for limits and regulations.)

(175)     **Pohick Bay** and **Accotink Bay**, which joins at the head of Gunston Cove 2 miles from the entrance, have depths of 2 to 3 feet for about 0.5 mile from the junction. Pohick Bay is foul with submerged duckblind and fish stakes. Parts of both bays are within the **danger zone** of a target range. (See **33 CFR 334.230**, chapter 2, for limits and regulations.)

(176)     **Dogue Creek**, Mile 81.9W, is used by small craft. A privately marked channel leads from the river across the northwest part of the estuary to the mouth of the creek. In 1980, reported depths in the channel were 3 feet, with 1 to 5 feet in the creek. The extreme north corner of the estuary is foul with grass and submerged duckblind stakes.

(177)     **Marshall Hall**, Mile 82.3S, formerly an amusement park, has a wharf with about 10 feet reported alongside. The wharf is in poor condition; landing is not permitted.

(178)     **Mount Vernon**, the home of George Washington, is at Mile 83.2N. The custom of tolling the ship's bell while passing Mount Vernon is said to have originated the night of Washington's death, December 14, 1799. The buildings are open to the public daily from 0900 to 1700 during the summer and 0900 to 1600 during the winter. Excursion boats operate between Mount Vernon and the city of Washington, DC. The buoyed dredged channel leading to Mount Vernon wharf had a controlling depth of 5.6 feet (7.0 feet at midchannel) to the wharf and a depth at 5.0 feet shoaling to 2.8 feet at the wharf in 2008.

(179)     **Little Hunting Creek**, Mile 83.9N, has depths of 2 feet in the approach and about 4.5 feet in a narrow channel, sometimes marked by private buoys, for about 0.6 mile above the entrance. A stone-arch bridge over the entrance has a clearance of 22 feet for a center width of 25 feet.

(180)     **Piscataway Creek**, Mile 85.4S, has depths of 1 to 3 feet. Some marine supplies, gasoline, diesel fuel, berthing with electricity, water, ice and a pump-out station are available at a marina on the north side of the creek 0.5 mile inside the entrance. Approach and alongside depths were reported at 5.5 feet. Hull and engine repairs can be made; lift capacity, 30 tons.

(181)     **Fort Washington**, Mile 85.8E, was built early in the 19th century for the protection of the then new nation's capital; the fort is now a unit of National Capital Parks. There is a light on shore at the fort.

(182)     **Broad Creek**, Mile 88.0E, has depths of 2 to 4 feet. **Indian Queen Bluff** is on the north side of the entrance. The creek is little used.

(183)     **Rosier Bluff**, Mile 89.4E, is wooded and prominent. Only piles remain of the wharf just below the bluff. A light is shown from a pile in depths of 6 feet, below the bluff.

(184)     **Hunting Creek**, Mile 90.0W, has depths of 1 to 4 feet. Fixed highway bridges cross the creek 0.6 and 0.9 mile above the entrance. The lower bridge is a three-arch structure with a width of 44 feet and a clearance of 9 feet for a width of 20 feet; the upper bridge has a clearance of 3 feet. Piles marking an abandoned channel are in the north part of Hunting Creek entrance. Numerous tree trunks, logs, wrecks, mudflats and other obstructions are in the entrance to the creek.

(185)     On the Maryland shore, opposite Hunting Creek, is the large building complex of **National Harbor**. A channel leads to a basin and marina at the harbor from the main channel in Potomac River in the vicinity of **Rosier Bluff**. The channel is marked by lights and daybeacons. The marina can provide gasoline, transient berths, electricity, water, ice and pump-out facility.

(186)     **Jones Point**, Mile 90.5W, is on the north side of the entrance to Hunting Creek and at the lower end of the Alexandria waterfront. **Woodrow Wilson Memorial Bridge**, Mile 90.7, which connects Jones Point with the Maryland shore, has a bascule span with a clearance of 76 feet; a sound signal is at the channel span of the bridge. (See **33 CFR 117.1** through **117.59** and **117.255**, chapter 2, for drawbridge regulations.) Rocks are on the western edge of the channel just southward of the bridge in 38°47'24"N., 77°02'23"W.

(187)     **Alexandria**, Mile 91.4W, has some waterborne traffic. Foreign vessels drawing as much as 23 feet unload newsprint and some general cargo.

(188)     **Pilotage** to Alexandria was discussed at the beginning of the chapter.

(189)

### Regulated Navigation Area

(190)     **Security zones** have been established in sections of the Potomac River, north of the Woodrow Wilson Bridge, continuing north to the Francis Scott Key Bridge and in the Anacostia River. These zones are not active at all times but are enforced during special events. (See **33 CFR 165.1** through **165.40** and **165.508**, chapter 2, for limits and regulations.)

(191)

### Towage

(192)     Tugs are not normally required for docking and undocking.

(193)

### Quarantine, customs, immigration and agricultural quarantine

(194)     (See chapter 3, Vessel Arrival Inspections, and appendix for addresses.)

(195)     **Quarantine** is enforced in accordance with regulations of the U.S. Public Health Service. (See Public Health Service, chapter 1.)

(196)     Alexandria is a **customs port of entry.**

(197)

### Harbor regulations

(198)     Jurisdiction of the District of Columbia harbormaster extends upriver from Jones Point. Harbor regulations provide a **speed limit** of 10 mph when passing the wharf area of Alexandria, except in emergencies.

(199)     The Alexandria waterfront extends about 1.5 miles north of the Woodrow Wilson Memorial Bridge. Some of the wharves are owned by the Government; several

of the privately owned wharves are open to the public by special arrangement. Depths of 20 to 25 feet are at the outer ends of the wharves; in places old piling is a hazard to approaching vessels. Robinson south and north terminals are 0.45 mile and 0.9 mile above the bridge, respectively; each has a 300-foot face with depths of 25 feet alongside. (For information on the latest depths alongside the facilities at Alexandria, contact the individual operators.) Water is available at most of the facilities; cargo is handled by ship's tackle. There are no major repair facilities for oceangoing vessels at Alexandria; the nearest such facilities are at Baltimore, MD, and in the Hampton Roads area.

(200)
**Small-craft facilities**
(201)    Small-craft facilities along the Alexandria waterfront can provide gasoline, diesel fuel, water, berths and marine supplies. Hull and engine repairs can be made; largest marine railway, 35 feet; lift, 16 tons.

(202)    **Oxon Creek**, Mile 91.6E, has bare flats in the approaches and general depths of 1 to 3 feet inside. Sand dredges have cut channels through the flats and made holes inside, but local knowledge is needed to find the deeper water. The fixed highway bridge over the creek has a clearance of 19 feet.

(203)    **Marbury Point** is at Mile 92.1E. A privately buoyed channel with reported depths of about 12 feet leads to the point. Just northward is the Blue Plains sewage-disposal plant. The Government pier 0.4 mile above Marbury Point extends to deep water; use of the pier is restricted to Government vessels.

(204)    **Fourmile Run**, Mile 93.0 W is used only by very small boats and skiffs at high water. The outer basin is navigable for small boats, using care, local knowledge and the chart as guides. Airport landing lights extend 0.5 mile into the basin from the north side. The Washington Sailing Marina is in the cove on the south side of the basin just above the entrance. In 2000, the controlling depths were 5.8 feet (7.3 feet at midchannel) in the marina entrance channel, thence depths of 7.7 feet to 11.1 feet were in the cove, with much lesser depths along the sides.

(205)    **Ronald Reagan Washington National Airport** occupies the extensive fill area on **Gravelly Point** at Mile 94.1W. Many domestic airlines use the airport day and night.

(206)    **Giesboro Point** is at Mile 94.0E. Submerged pile remains of former wharves extend out about 150 feet from shore in the vicinity of the point.

(207)    **Washington, DC**, on the east side of Potomac River 96 miles above the mouth, is the **Capital of the United States**. Prominent from the river are the Capitol Dome, the Washington Monument, and the Lincoln and Jefferson Memorials.

(208)    Commercial traffic in Washington Harbor consists chiefly of petroleum products, sand and gravel.

(209)
**Tides and currents**
(210)    Daily predictions for Washington are available from the Tidal Current prediction service at *tidesandcurrents. noaa.gov.* Currents are variable, but the set is usually in the directions of the channels, and there is little or no flood current during freshets; see the Tidal Current prediction service for specific information about times, directions, and velocities of the current for several places in Washington Harbor. Links to a user guide for this service can be found in chapter 1 of this book.

(211)
**Ice**
(212)    **Ice** closes the river at Washington during severe winters, but power vessels keep the channels open during ordinary winters. During the highest freshet in recent years, the river rose about 11.5 feet above mean low water in Washington Channel.

(213)
**Weather**
(214)    Washington summers are warm and humid, and winters are mild; generally, pleasant weather prevails in the spring and autumn. The coldest weather occurs in late January and early February. The warmest weather occurs late in July. There are no well-pronounced wet and dry seasons. Thunderstorms, during the summer, often bring sudden and heavy rain showers and may be attended by damaging winds, hail or lightning.

(215)    The average annual temperature in Washington is 58.0°F (14.4°C). The average maximum temperature is 66.7°F (19.3°C) while the average minimum is 48.9°F (9.4°C). The warmest temperature on record at Washington is 105°F (40.6°C) recorded in August 1997 and the coolest temperature on record is -5°F (-20.6°C) recorded in January 1982. Each month, October through April, has recorded temperatures below freezing (0°C) and each month, June through September, has recorded maximums in excess of 100°F (37.8°C). Records of the past 20 years show the average date of the last freezing temperature in the spring to be March 29 and the latest, April 16. The average date of the first freezing temperature in the fall is November 10 and the earliest, October 21.

(216)    The average annual precipitation at Washington totals 39.39 inches (1,001 mm). Precipitation is evenly distributed, with the spread between the wettest month (August) and the driest month (February) being only 1.48 inches (37.6 mm). The greatest 24-hour precipitation total is 6.11 inches (155.2 mm) recorded in June 1972.

(217)    Snowfall is moderate and averages 17.1 inches (434.3 mm) each year. Snow has fallen in each month October through April. The greatest 24-hour snowfall occurred in February 1983 when 16.4 inches (416.6 mm) accumulated.

(218)    Tropical disturbances occasionally, during their northward passage, influence Washington's weather mainly with high winds and heavy rainfall, but extensive damage from this cause is rare. Six tropical storms have

(231)

### Structures across Anacostia River

| Name | Type | Location | Clearances (feet) | | Information |
|------|------|----------|-------------------|---|-------------|
| | | | Horizontal | Vertical* | |
| Frederick Douglass Memorial bridge | swing | 38°52'07"N., 77°00'21"W. | 149 | 40 | **Note 1**<br>Bridge under construction (2018)<br>24-hour notice is required for openings (202–727–5522). |
| Eleventh Street bridge | fixed | 38°52'17"N., 76°59'25"W. | 200 | 28 | Bridge under construction (2011) |
| Twelfth Street bridge | fixed | 38°52'19"N., 76°59'21"W. | 200 | 28 | |
| John Phillip Sousa bridge | fixed | 38°52'36"N., 76°58'36"W. | 114 | 35 | |
| CSX Railroad | vertical lift | 38°52'49"N., 76°58'16"W. | 33 | 5 (down)<br>29 (up) | **Note 1** |
| East Capital Street | fixed | 38°53'24"N., 76°57'49"W. | 90 | 23 | |
| East Capital Street | fixed | 38°53'23"N., 76°58'00"W. | 90 | 14 | Bridge crosses Kingman Lake |
| Benning Road | fixed | 38°53'48"N., 76°57'43"W. | 40 | 16 | |
| Benning Road | fixed | 38°53'50"N., 76°57'58"W. | 31 | 8 | Bridge crosses Kingman Lake |
| METRO Railroad | fixed | 38°53'48"N., 76°57'43"W. | 40 | 16 | |
| Overhead cables | power | 38°55'01"N., 76°56'38"W. | | N/A | Clearance data not available |
| CSX Railroad | fixed | 38°55'01"N., 76°56'38"W. | 69 | 12 | |
| New York Avenue | fixed | 38°55'05"N., 76°56'34"W. | 76 | 16 | |

\* Clearances are referenced to Mean High Water
Note 1 – See **33 CFR 117.1** through **117.59** and **117.253**, chapter 2, for drawbridge regulations.

had a direct impact upon Washington since 1950. Perhaps the most noteworthy was hurricane Hazel in 1954. Hazel passed to the west of the District while transitioning from a warm-core to a cold-core system. The storm provided sustained winds of 68 knots with gusts to 85 knots over a three-hour period.

(219) Occasional overflows from the Potomac River result from heavy rain over the basin, at times augmented by melting snow. In a few cases during cold winters, ice forms on the river, and, in spring, flooding is caused by ice gorges when the ice breaks up. The river is in tidewater, and above-normal tides associated with hurricane or severe storms along the coast cause flooding at times. Local flooding in the area is also caused by locally heavy rain. Some flooding occurs from one or the other of these causes every year on the average.

(220) In using the Climatological Tables for the area note that recent observations have been taken at the National Airport, which is in a warmer part of the area. Minimum and maximum temperatures in nearby areas may be 8° and 5° lower, respectively, and rain and snowfall amount may be slightly higher away from the airport.

(221) **Pilotage to Washington, DC**, was discussed at the beginning of the chapter.

(222)

### Quarantine, customs, immigration and agricultural quarantine

(223) (See chapter 3, Vessel Arrival Inspections, and appendix for addresses.)

(224) **Quarantine** is enforced in accordance with regulations of the U.S. Public Health Service. (See Public Health Service, chapter 1.)

(225) Washington, DC, is a **customs port of entry.**

### Harbor regulations

(227) The District of Columbia Harbormaster, who is the officer commanding the Harbor Precinct of the Metropolitan Police Department, regulates the operation, navigation, mooring and anchoring of all vessels within the waters of the District of Columbia and enforces all laws and regulations relating thereto. The person in charge of any vessel 26 feet or more long entering the harbor, shall, if he intends to remain over 24 hours, report the date and time of arrival without delay and shall also report immediately before finally departing to the harbormaster at the Harbor Precinct wharf, Maine Avenue and M Street, SW. or to any police officer under his command. Permission to anchor in the District of Columbia must be obtained from the harbormaster. Both the harbormaster and the police boat monitor VHF-FM channel 16; call sign KUF-703.

(228) At Mile 94.2 is the junction of Potomac River with **Anacostia River** to the eastward, Washington Channel to the northward and Georgetown Channel of the Potomac River to the westward. The lighted junction buoy also marks the outer end of the shoal making southerly from **Hains Point**, 0.4 mile north of the junction. **Washington Harbor** comprises the navigable waters upstream from this junction.

(229) A dredged channel leads from the Potomac River off Hains Point into the Anacostia River to a basin off Washington Navy Yard, through the 11th and 12th street bridges, and to a turning basin about 2.0 miles above the Hains Point Junction Lighted Buoy (38°51'06"N., 77°01'20"W.). (See Notice to Mariners and latest editions of the charts for controlling depths.)

(230)     Harbor regulations prescribe a **speed limit** of 6 mph between the entrance to Anacostia River and the Benning Road Bridge, a distance of 4.4 miles.

(232)     The waterfront of Anacostia River extends along the north side for about 3 miles above the entrance. The Washington Navy Yard Annex occupies the area just above the first bridge to the second bridge; depths at the easternmost pier (which is normally used for visiting vessels) range from 15 to 17 feet. Most of the other piers and bulkhead wharves are privately owned.

(233)

### Small-craft facilities

(234)     There are small-craft facilities on the north side of Anacostia River just above the mouth, between the third and fifth bridges and at **Bladensburg,** 7 miles above the mouth.

(235)     **Washington Channel** extends northward along the east side of Hains Point for 2 miles to the Fourteenth Street causeway. (See Notice to Mariners and latest editions of the charts for controlling depths.) The channel is unmarked above Hains Point. A fixed highway bridge at the upper end of the channel has a clearance of 37 feet.

(236)     Harbor regulations prescribe a **speed limit** of 6 mph upstream from Hains Point.

(237)     The waterfront facilities are on the eastern side of Washington Channel. Pier 5, 1 mile above Hains Point, has depths of about 23 feet at the outer end. The pier is the headquarters of the harbormaster and is used by the police and fire department. Pier 4, just northward, has depths of about 23 feet at the outer end; it is used by excursion boats. The municipal fish and fresh oyster wharves are just below the highway bridge, 1.5 miles above Hains Point.

(238)     Slips and minor repair facilities for pleasure craft are at the north end of Washington Channel. Hull and engine repairs can be made: lift capacity, 20 tons. Water, berthing with electricity and marine supplies are available.

(239)     **Georgetown Channel** is that part of the Potomac River between Hains Point and just above Chain Bridge. In 2007, the midchannel controlling depth was 8.6 feet to the George Mason Memorial Bridge, thence 11.2 feet at midchannel to the Arlington Memorial Bridge, thence 13.9 feet at midchannel to the Francis Scott Key Bridge at Georgetown. The channel from Key Bridge to Chain Bridge, about 2.7 miles above, has unpredictable currents and numerous shoals and rocks. This part of the channel is used by small craft with local knowledge; mariners are advised to exercise caution.

(240)     Georgetown Channel is crossed by eight bridges between Hains Point and Chain Bridge, Mile 101. All bridges have either fixed spans or drawspans fixed in the closed position. (See **33 CFR 117.255**, chapter 2, for drawbridge regulations.) The minimum horizontal clearance of the bridges is 104 feet and the minimum vertical clearance is 18 feet.

(241)     The **Tidal Basin** is on the northeast side of Potomac River 1.6 miles above Hains Point. A fixed bridge with a horizontal clearance of 12 feet and vertical clearance of 11 feet crosses the entrance; tide gates obstruct the entrance.

(242)     Directly across the river from the Tidal Basin is the **Pentagon Lagoon**. Depths of about 2 to 7 feet are available in the lagoon. A marina on the north side of the lagoon has depths of 5 to 8 feet. The fixed bridge over the entrance has a vertical clearance of 18 feet and a horizontal clearance of 46 feet. Complete berthing facilities, gasoline and some supplies are available at the marina. Hull and engine repairs can be made; marine railway, 30 feet. **Boundary Channel**, which extends northward from the lagoon between **Columbia Island** and the Virginia shore, is shallow and is crossed by several fixed bridges.

(243)     **Arlington Memorial Bridge**, under construction (2018), is 2.3 miles above Hains Point and 97 miles above the mouth of Potomac River. Harbor regulations prescribe a speed limit of 6 mph above the bridge.

(244)     **Theodore Roosevelt Island**, Mile 97.5W, is a park area. Boats should not attempt to pass between the island and the Virginia shore.

(245)     **Francis Scott Key Bridge** is at Mile 98.3. The stone piers of the former Aqueduct Bridge, just above Key Bridge, have been removed to a depth of 10 feet except for the one nearest the Virginia shore, which is 9 feet above water.

(246)     **Chain Bridge**, Mile 101, is the head of tidewater navigation on the Potomac River.

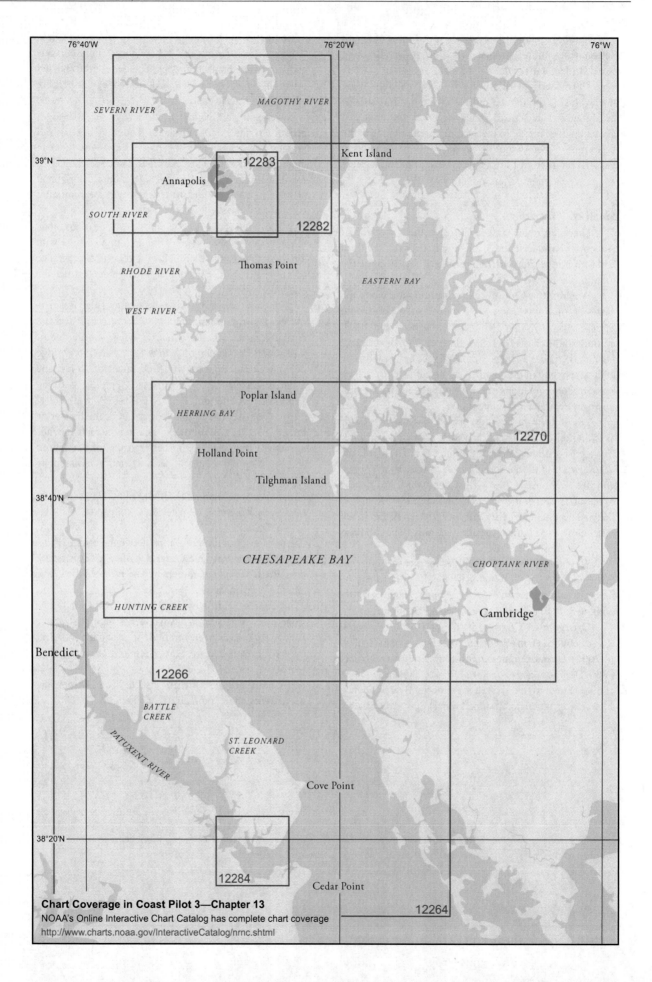

**Chart Coverage in Coast Pilot 3—Chapter 13**
NOAA's Online Interactive Chart Catalog has complete chart coverage
http://www.charts.noaa.gov/InteractiveCatalog/nrnc.shtml

# Chesapeake Bay, Patuxent and Severn Rivers

(1)    This chapter describes the western shore of Chesapeake Bay from Point Lookout, on the north side of the entrance to Potomac River, to Mountain Point, the northern entrance point to Magothy River. Also described are Patuxent River, Herring Bay, West River, South River, Severn River, and Magothy River, the bay's principal tributaries; the ports of Solomons Island, Benedict, Chesapeake Beach, Shady Side, Galesville and Annapolis; and several of the smaller ports and landings on these waterways.

(2)    **COLREGS Demarcation Lines**
(3)    The lines established for Chesapeake Bay are described in **33 CFR 80.510**, chapter 2.

(4)    **ENCs - US4MD20M, US4MD80M, US4MD81M, US4MD82M**
**Charts - 12230, 12263, 12273**

(5)    From Potomac River to Patuxent River, the western shore of Chesapeake Bay is mostly low, although the 100-foot elevation does come within 1 mile of the water midway between the two rivers. Above Patuxent River, the ground rises and 100-foot elevations are found close back of the shore along the unbroken stretch northward to Herring Bay. Above Herring Bay, the 100-foot contour is pushed back by the tributaries. Except for the developed areas, the shore is mostly wooded.

(6)    The bay channel has depths of 50 feet or more and is well marked by lights and buoys.

(7)    The **fishtrap areas** that extend along this entire section of the western shore are marked at their outer limits and are shown on the charts.

(8)    **Ice**
(9)    Ice is encountered in the tributaries, particularly during severe winters. When threatened by icing conditions, certain lighted buoys may be replaced by lighted ice buoys having reduced candlepower or by unlighted buoys, and certain unlighted buoys may be discontinued.

(10)    **ENC - US4MD20M**
**Chart - 12230**

(11)    The **danger zone** of an aerial firing range and target area begins off Point Lookout and extends northward to Cedar Point. (See **33 CFR 334.200**, chapter 2, for limits and regulations.) The target areas in the danger zone are marked by lighted buoys.

(12)    A middle ground with depths of 10 to 18 feet is about 8 miles eastward of Point Lookout; the area is about 7 miles long in a north-south direction and 2 miles wide. The stranded wreck near the middle of the shoal is marked by a light.

(13)    A **fish haven** is about 4.4 miles north-northeast of Point Lookout in about 38°06'28"N., 76°17'57"W.

(14)    **ENCs - US5VA22M, US5VA27M**
**Chart - 12233**

(15)    **St. Jerome Creek**, 5 miles north of Point Lookout, is entered through a channel marked by lights, a daybeacon, buoys, and bush stakes to a basin about 0.5 mile above the entrance, thence northward into the creek. In 2018, the controlling depths were 1.7 feet in the entrance channel and 4.0 feet in the basin, thence 5.6 feet in the channel above the basin. In 1998, severe shoaling was reported in the vicinity of St. Jerome Creek Daybeacon 3. The creek is used principally as an anchorage for oyster and fishing boats.

(16)    There are several small wharves along St. Jerome Creek. A landing is at **Airedele**, on the south side of the creek just above the entrance; gasoline is available. A dredged channel leads south from St. Jerome Creek into **Southern Prong**. Private daybeacons mark the channel to a marina in Southern Prong. Berths with electricity, gasoline, water, ice, a launching ramp, a 40-foot marine railway and partial hull repairs are available.

(17)    **Point No Point**, on the west side of Chesapeake Bay 6 miles north of Point Lookout, has no prominent natural marks. **Point No Point Light** (38°07'41"N., 76°17'25"W.), 52 feet above the water, is shown from a white octagonal brick dwelling on a brown cylinder, in depths of about 22 feet, 1.6 miles southeastward of the point. The light is 1.7 miles due west of a point on the bay ship channel 76.4 miles above the Capes.

(18)    **Hooper Island Light** (38°15'23"N., 76°14'59"W.), 63 feet above the water, is shown from a white conical tower on a brown cylindrical base, in depths of 18 feet near the outer edge of the shoals, 3 miles westward from Hooper Islands. The light is 2.8 miles due east of a point on the bay ship channel 84.4 miles above the Capes.

(19)

## ENC - US5MD21M
## Chart - 12264

(20)     The enclosed naval seaplane basin 8.5 miles north-northwestward of Point No Point and 2 miles southwestward of Cedar Point has depths of about 10 feet. The entrance to the basin is between two breakwaters, each marked at their outer ends by a light.

(21)     **Cedar Point** (38°17.9'N., 76°22.5'W.) is 10 miles north-northwest of Point No Point. The ruins of an abandoned lighthouse are on the tiny islet 0.3 mile off the point. The shoal extending 0.5 mile eastward from the islet is marked at its outer end by a lighted bell buoy. A **fish haven** is 0.6 mile northwestward of Cedar Point.

(22)

## ENCs - US5MD21M, US5MD31M
## Charts - 12264, 12284

(23)     **Patuxent River** empties into the west side of Chesapeake Bay 89.3 miles above the Virginia Capes. Commercial traffic consists chiefly of shellfish and shells and petroleum products. Drafts of vessels using the river are mostly 7 feet or less and seldom exceed 12 feet.

(24)     The river has natural depths of 25 to 30 feet in the approach, 30 to over 100 feet for 16 miles upstream, thence 23 feet to the Benedict highway bridge 19 miles above the mouth, thence 10 feet for 12 miles to within 2 miles of Nottingham, thence 6 feet for 5 miles, and thence 3 feet to Hills Bridge, 40 miles above the mouth. The channel is not difficult to follow as far as the Benedict bridge, and the principal shoals are marked by lights and daybeacons; the channel above the bridge is narrow in places and is marked for about another 2.5 miles.

(25)     Anchorage can be had off the mouth of Patuxent River; shelter from westerly winds is found in depths of 20 to 30 feet close to shore on the north side of the approach. Shelter from easterly winds is found in depths of 30 to 50 feet in the channel about 1.5 miles above the entrance.

(26)     Bottom in Patuxent River channel is mostly soft as far as the Benedict highway bridge, and vessels can anchor where convenient. Small vessels anchor in the creeks back of Solomons Island, but there is little swinging room. St. Leonard Creek is a good small-vessel anchorage in any weather.

(27)     The current velocity is 0.4 knot in the entrance to Patuxent River off Drum Point. Ice closes the river to near the mouth in severe winters.

(28)     Marine supplies and complete hull and machinery repairs are available along the Patuxent River. Principal locations are in the creeks behind Solomons Island, i.e., Back Creek and Mill Creek. Facilities are also available in Town Creek, Cuckold Creek and Island Creek and at Benedict.

(29)     Patuxent River empties into the head of the bight between Cedar Point and **Cove Point**, 5 miles to the northward. **Cove Point Light** (38°23'11"N., 76°22'54"W.), 45 feet above the water, is shown from a white tower on the point. The light is 1 mile west of a point on the bay ship channel 92.6 miles above the Capes. The high bluffs on **Little Cove Point**, 1.5 miles to the southward, are prominent.

(30)     The entrance to Patuxent River is between **Drum Point** and **Fishing Point**, 0.9 mile to the southward. The shoals that extend off Fishing Point and **Hog Point**, 1 mile to the east-northeastward, are marked at their outer ends by lights. A fish haven is about 1 mile east-southeastward of Patuxent River Light 3. A light is just off Drum Point.

(31)     **Mileages** on Patuxent River, shown as Mile 8W, 11E, etc., are the nautical miles above the midchannel point on a line drawn between Drum and Fishing Points. The letters N, S, E and W following the numerals denote by compass points the side of the river where each feature is located.

(32)     The **Patuxent River Naval Air Station** is along the south side of the entrance. The inclosed seaplane basins, East Patuxent Basin at Mile 0.8S and West Patuxent Basin at Mile 1.35S, have depths of 12 feet and 11 to 15 feet, respectively. Lights mark the entrance points to West Patuxent Basin. A **restricted area** off the air station begins about 2.4 miles south of Cedar Point and extends north to the mouth of Patuxent River, thence upstream for about 2.5 miles. (See **33 CFR 334.180**, chapter 2, for limits and regulations.)

(33)     **Solomons Island**, Mile 1.8N, is joined to the mainland on the northwest by a causeway. The shoal that extends 500 yards southward from **Sandy Point**, at the south end of the island, is marked at its outer end by a light. **Solomons** is the village on the island. The pier of the **Chesapeake Biological Laboratory** on the east side of the island has depths of 8 feet at the outer end and is marked by a private light.

(34)     **Back Creek** and **Mill Creek** have a common entrance between Solomons Island and the mainland 200 yards to the north-northeastward. The marked main approach, between the island and the shallow middle ground to the eastward, has depths of 20 to 25 feet. The second marked approach, between the middle ground and the mainland to the northward, has depths of 12 feet.

(35)     The two creeks separate just above the entrance. Mill Creek goes eastward of a shallow spit with a small islet at the southern end, and Back Creek goes westward; the spit and the islet are marked by lights.

(36)     There are many small-craft facilities in Back Creek and Mill Creek and along the northern side of Solomons Island. Lifts to 75 tons are available for complete repairs. Complete hull and machinery services, gasoline, diesel fuel and pump-out station services are available.

(37)     The Back Creek cove between the islet and the inner side of Solomons has general depths of 15 feet and is used as an anchorage by many yachts and fishing boats.

(38)     Back Creek has depths of 12 feet for 0.7 mile above the cove, thence 10 to 6 feet for another 0.5 mile.

(39)     **Mill Creek** has depths of 16 to 12 feet for 1.2 miles, thence 10 to 4 feet for another mile. Two submerged wrecks, reported covered 9 feet, are along the east side of the channel, about 0.5 mile above the mouth. Midchannel courses will safely pass the wrecks.

(40)     **Town Point** is at Mile 2.9S. A shoal with a daybeacon at its outer end extends about 175 yards east of Town Point. **Town Creek**, on the southwest side of the low point, is used by fishing and oyster boats and recreational craft. The creek, marked at the entrance by a light, is entered about 0.5 mile south-southwestward of Town Point. The entrance light also marks the outer end of a shoal that extends southward from the northern entrance point. Submerged wrecks are reported in the southwestern arm of the creek. Several small-craft facilities are on Town Creek.

(41)     State Route 4 fixed highway bridge with a clearance of 30 feet at the west span and 35 feet at the east span crosses Town Creek about 0.3 mile above the entrance light. An overhead power cable with a clearance of 55 feet crosses the north arm of the creek about 0.45 mile above the entrance light.

(42)     Thomas Johnson Memorial (State Route 4) Bridge has a fixed span with a vertical clearance of 140 feet and crosses the Patuxent River between Town Point and the north shore. The area in the immediate vicinity of the bridge is subject to unpredictable and sudden changes in wind conditions. Mariners under sail should exercise caution while navigating in the area.

(43)     **Point Patience** at Mile 3.9N is marked at the outer end by a lighted buoy. The current is reported to be especially strong within 25 yards of the light. The long piers used by the Government on the east and west sides of the point are within a **restricted area**. (See **33 CFR 334.180**, chapter 2, for limits and regulations.)

(44)     **Cuckold Creek** and **Mill Creek** have a common entrance at Mile 4.7W. Lights and daybeacons mark the entrance channel. Gasoline and some supplies are available at **Clarks Landing**, on the peninsula between the two creeks. Depths at the fuel pier are about 6 feet.

(45)     Cuckold Creek, which extends northwestward from the entrance, has depths of 15 to 11 feet for 1 mile, thence 10 to 4 feet into the several arms. Three marinas are on the south side of the creek 0.6 mile, 0.8 mile and 0.9 mile above the entrance, respectively. Gasoline, diesel fuel and some supplies are available. Hull and engine repairs can be made; marine railway, 60 feet; lift, 10 tons.

(46)     **Hellen Creek** enters Patuxent River at Mile 5.3E. In 1990, the reported controlling depth was 7 feet across the bar at the entrance; thence in 1980, depths of 5 feet were reported available for 1 mile into the creek; the deeper water favors the east side of the entrance. The creek is used principally as a small-boat harbor.

(47)     **St. Leonard Creek**, Mile 7E, has depths of 15 to 10 feet for 2 miles, then shoals gradually to 1 foot at the head, 3.5 miles above the entrance. Safe anchorage is available in depths of 15 to 21 feet, 0.5 mile above the entrance. An overhead power cable with a reported clearance of 50 feet crosses the creek about 3.4 miles above the mouth. Gasoline and diesel fuel are available at a marina on the east side, 2 miles above the mouth. The shoal that extends 0.4 mile southward from **Petersons Point**, on the northwest side of the entrance, is marked at its outer end.

(48)     **Broomes Island,** which is not an island but a mainland peninsula, is at Mile 9.5N. A light marks the limit of the shoal area that extends 0.2 mile southward of the peninsula.

(49)     **Island Creek**, which empties into Patuxent River along the east side of Broomes Island, has depths of 8 to 10 feet for 1 mile, but there are unmarked shoals, particularly along the west side of the entrance; a light marks the east side of the entrance.

(50)     The village of **Broomes Island** is on the west side of Island Creek about 1 mile from the outer end of the peninsula. Gasoline and some supplies are available at the crab and oyster piers.

(51)     **Nan Cove**, on the west side of Broomes Island, is entered by a unmarked dredged channel which leads to a turning basin in the upper end of the east arm.

(52)     A private channel, marked by private buoys, leads to a marina at the entrance of **Cat Creek** at Mile 12.6 W. In 1997, the channel had a reported depth of 5 feet. Gasoline, diesel fuel, some supplies, berths, a sewage pump-out station and a 10-ton lift are available; minor repairs can be made.

(53)     **Battle Creek**, Mile 13.2E, has depths of 10 to 7 feet for 1.5 miles. Private daybeacons mark the channel through the shoals just above the entrance. A shoal that extends 0.3 mile southwestward from the point on the east side of the entrance is marked at its outer end by a warning daybeacon.

(54)     The highway bridge over Patuxent River at Mile 18.8, from **Town Point** on the west side to **Hallowing Point** on the east side, has a 49-foot swing span with a clearance of 16 feet. (See **33 CFR 117.1** through **117.59** and **117.567**, chapter 2, for drawbridge regulations.)

(55)     **Benedict**, a village just below the west end of the highway bridge, is the head of commercial navigation on Patuxent River. A marina at the south end of Benedict can provide gasoline, berths and some supplies. Minor repairs can be made; marine railway, 32 feet.

(56)     Navigation on Patuxent River above Benedict is difficult because of the numerous fishtraps and stakes.

(57)     Overhead power cables with a clearance of 60 feet over the main channel cross Patuxent River at Mile 20.9. The supporting towers are marked by private lights.

(58)     An overhead power cable across Patuxent River at Mile 25.5, a mile above **Holland Cliff**, has a clearance of 53 feet.

(59)     **Lower Marlboro** is a village at Mile 28.3E. The state landing has depths of 12 feet at the face.

(60)     **Nottingham**, a village at Mile 32.8W, has a landing with depths of 13 feet at the face. In 1980, a draft of 5 feet could be carried with local knowledge to the Maryland

(71)

Herring Bay and Rockhold Creek, Maryland
Image courtesy of Waterway Images (2004)

Route 4 fixed highway bridge at Upper Marlboro, about 10 miles above Nottingham.

(61)　　On the west side of Chesapeake Bay north of Cove Point is a liquefied natural gas unloading terminal of the Dominion Cove Point LNG, LP., The offshore unloading platform, 2,470 feet long with dolphins, has reported depths of 40 feet alongside. The platform has a deck height of 40 feet and provides berthing space for two LNG tank vessels. The northern berth has depths of 40 feet, but shoaling to 34 feet has been noted at the southern berth. The platform marked by private lights and sound signals, is connected to shoreside facilities by a submerged tunnel. A **safety** and **security zone** surrounds the terminal. (See **33 CFR 165.1** through **165.7**, **165.20** through **165.25**, and **165.502**, chapter 2, for limits and regulations.)

(62)　　**Flag Harbor**, on the west side of Chesapeake Bay 6.3 miles northwest of Cove Point, had a reported depth of 4 feet in the entrance channel in 2008; thence in 1998–2004, 7 feet in the small-boat basin. The 600-foot stone jetties on either side of the entrance are almost covered at high water and marked at their ends by private lights.

(63)

**ENCs - US5MD1AM, US5MD16M**
**Chart - 12266**

(64)　　**Plum Point Creek** (38°36.9'N., 76°30.7'W.) empties into the west side of Chesapeake Bay 15 miles north-northwest of Cove Point. In 1997, depths of 4.5 feet were reported in the entrance to the creek and in the small-boat basin. A marina on the north side of the creek can provide some berths, gasoline, some supplies and a sewage pump-out station.

(65)　　Overhead telephone and power cables with a clearance of 52 feet cross the creek 0.1 mile above the mouth.

(66)　　The **Naval Research Laboratory** firing range fans out from a point near **Randle Cliff Beach** (38°38.5'N., 76°31.7'W.), 18 miles northward of Cove Point. (See **33 CFR 334.170**, chapter 2, for limits and regulations.) The laboratory towers are prominent.

(67)　　**Chesapeake Beach** (38°41'48"N., 76°32'00"W.) is a resort and fishing center on the western shore of Chesapeake Bay 19.6 miles northward of Cove Point. **Fishing Creek**, on the north side of the resort, is entered by a dredged channel which leads from the bay through jetties to an anchorage basin in the creek. The channel is marked by lights and a daybeacon. The fixed highway

(68) bridge 0.3 mile above the jetties has a width of 36 feet and a clearance of 10 feet.

Small-craft facilities on the south side of the creek at Chesapeake Beach have gasoline, diesel fuel, a pump-out station, water, ice, berths and marine supplies. Hull and engine repairs can be made; marine railway, 50 feet; lift, 40 tons.

(69) **Holland Point** (38°43.6'N., 76°31.7'W.), on the western shore of Chesapeake Bay 21.6 miles above Cove Point, has shoal areas extending in all directions; depths of 11 feet are 1.3 miles to the eastward and northeastward. A fish haven is about 2.2 miles east-northeast of Holland Point.

(70) **Herring Bay**, between Holland Point and the marsh 3 miles to the northward, has general depths of 14 to 7 feet. **Long Bar**, with depths of 2 to 5 feet, extends from the north side of the bay to within 1 mile of Holland Point and is marked at its south end by a light.

(72) **Herrington Harbour**, 0.6 mile westward of Holland Point, is entered through a jettied private channel from the south side of Herring Bay. The channel is marked by a **198°** lighted range and other private aids. In 2008, the channel had a reported controlling depth of 7 feet. The channel is very narrow and must be followed closely to carry the best water. A small-craft facility is on the east side of the harbor just inside the entrance. Gasoline, diesel fuel, water, berths with electricity and repairs are available.

(73) **Rockhold Creek**, at the northwest corner of Herring Bay, has good shelter for small boats. A dredged channel leads from the bay to a turning basin just below the fixed highway bridge at **Deale**. Above the bridge, depths of 2 to 3 feet can be carried for about 0.4 mile. The dredged channel is marked with lights, buoys and daybeacons midway to the bridge. A light marks the outer end of two breakwaters at the entrance. The fixed highway bridge 1 mile above the entrance has a horizontal clearance of 47 feet and a vertical clearance of 14 feet. The fixed highway bridge 1.8 miles above the entrance has a horizontal clearance of 41 feet with a vertical clearance of 10 feet.

(74) **Tracys Creek**, branching west from Rockhold Creek at Deale, is crossed by a fixed bridge with a horizontal clearance of 46 feet and a vertical clearance of 11 feet. An overhead power cable at the bridge has a clearance of 37 feet.

(75) A 6 mph **speed limit** is enforced in Rockhold Creek.

(76) There are extensive small-craft facilities on both sides of Rockhold Creek below the first bridge and on the east side of the creek between the first and second bridges.

(77)

### No-Discharge Zone

The State of Maryland, with the approval of the Environmental Protection Agency, has established a No-Discharge Zone (NDZ) in Herring Bay. The area covered includes tidal waters west of a line connecting Holland Point and the north shore of Parkers Creek. Within the NDZ, discharge of sewage, whether treated or untreated, from all vessels is prohibited. Outside the NDZ, discharge of sewage is regulated by **40 CFR 140** (See chapter 2).

(78)

## ENCs - US5MD13M, US5MD17M
## Chart - 12270

(79) **West River**, 8.5 miles above Holland Point, empties into the west side of Chesapeake Bay north of **Curtis Point** (38°51.1'N., 76°29.9'W.). A fish haven is off the entrance. The river has depths of 14 to 7 feet for about 4 miles, then shoals gradually to less than 3 feet in the tributaries. The river channel approach is marked by lighted buoys and by lights and daybeacons to **Galesville**, on the west side of the river 2.5 miles above the entrance light. A yacht club is on the east side of the river at **Avalon Shores**, opposite Galesville. Several small-craft facilities are at Galesville.

(80) **Parish Creek**, on the south side of West River 0.5 mile westward of Curtis Point, is entered by a marked dredged channel that leads to an anchorage basin, and thence to **Shady Side** at the head of the south fork. A 6 mph **speed limit** is enforced.

(81) Small-craft facilities on the north side of Parish Creek and at Shady Side can provide gasoline, diesel fuel, water, electricity, a pump-out facility, berths and marine supplies. Hull and engine repairs can be made. Largest haul-out capabilities: marine railway, 35 feet; lift, 25 tons.

(82) **Rhode River** empties into the north side of West River 1.1 miles westward of West River Entrance Light 2. The river, marked at the entrance by a light, has depths of 11 to 9 feet for 2 miles. The critical shoals extending off the points are marked.

(83) **Cadle Creek**, on the east side of Rhode River 1 mile above the entrance light, has depths of 4 to 7 feet. The entrance to the creek is marked by daybeacons. **Mayo** is a town on the east side of the creek.

(84) **Bear Neck Creek**, on the north side of Rhode River 1.5 miles above the entrance light, has depths of 9 to 5 feet for 1 mile. The entrance is marked by daybeacons.

(85) Small-craft facilities are on Cadle Creek and Bear Neck Creek.

(86) **South River**, just north of West River, has channel depths of 14 feet or more to the second bridge, 6 miles above the mouth, then shoals gradually to 2 feet at the bridge near the head, 8.5 miles above the mouth. The river channel is marked to a point about 0.3 mile below the second bridge. Several of the creeks that flow into the

(87)

South River, Maryland
Image courtesy of Waterway Images (2004)

—N→

river have good depths and are used extensively by local yachts and motorboats. Most of these tributaries are reported to provide good anchorage. There are commercial facilities above and below the first bridge.

(88)　　**Minimum wake areas** and a 6-knot **speed limit** are enforced in many parts of the river and in most of the coves and creeks that flow into the river. These areas are marked by regulatory markers.

(89)　　The entrance to South River is between **Saunders Point** and **Thomas Point**, 1.8 miles to the northeastward. **Thomas Point Shoal Light** (38°53'56"N., 76°26'09"W.), 43 feet above the water, is shown from a white hexagonal tower on piles, in depths of 5 feet near the outer end of the shoal 1.2 miles east-southeastward of the point. The light is 1.5 miles due west of a point on the bay ship channel 124.2 miles above the Capes.

(90)　　**Selby Bay**, on the southwest side of South River 1.7 miles above the mouth, has general depths of 8 to 11 feet. The south end of the bay is shallow. The channel to **Selby Beach**, on the northwest side of the bay, is marked by lights and a daybeacon. **Ramsay Lake** has a narrow entrance from the south end of Selby Bay; in 1998, a depth of 5.5 feet was reported in the entrance, thence 7 to 8 feet in the lake. The fixed highway bridge over the Selby Bay entrance to the lake has a width of 22 feet and a clearance of 14 feet.

(91)　　Small-craft facilities are on the south and west sides of Selby Bay and in Ramsey Lake.

(92)　　**Brewer Creek**, on the southwest side of South River 3 miles above the mouth, has depths of 12 feet in the entrance and 4.5 feet reported through the narrows 0.2 mile above the entrance. The narrows connect Brewer Creek with **Pocahontas Creek** to the southward. Gasoline, water, berths and limited marine supplies are available in Pocahontas Creek; hull and engine repairs can be made.

(93)　　**Glebe Bay**, on the southwest side of South River 3.5 miles above the mouth, has general depths of 13 to 15 feet. Care should be taken to avoid the 2-foot shoal near midbay and the 2-foot shoals along the northwest and southeast sides of the bay. **Glebe Creek**, with depths of 11 to 7 feet for about 0.4 mile, empties into the southwest side of the bay. Gasoline, water and berths are available in the cove on the north side of the bay just inside the entrance.

(94)　　State Route 2 fixed highway bridge at **Edgewater**, 5 miles above the mouth of South River, has a clearance of 53 feet.

(95)　　**Gingerville Creek**, on the north side of South River, extends along the westerly side of Edgewater. The creek has depths of 6 feet for 0.7 mile, nearly to the head.

(96)　　There are small-craft facilities at Edgewater, and in Warehouse Creek, on the south side of the river opposite Edgewater.

(97)　　**Beards Creek**, on the south side of South River 5.7 miles above the mouth, has depths of 15 to 8 feet for 1 mile; a shallow spit extends halfway across the entrance from the point on the northwest side. In 1978, a submerged piling was reported in Beards Creek in about 38°56.6'N., 76°34.6'W. The highway bridge at **Riva,** 6 miles above the mouth of South River, has a fixed span with a clearance of 25 feet.

(98)     **Fishing Creek,** immediately northward of the entrance to South River, has depths of 7 to 4 feet. A privately dredged channel leads from the Chesapeake Bay to the **Annapolis Coast Guard Station** wharf on the northwest side of the creek.

(99)
**ENC - US5MD22M**
**Chart - 12282**

(100)     **Severn River,** the approach to Annapolis, empties into Chesapeake Bay 127 miles above the Virginia Capes. Commercial traffic consists of tour boats, fishing and shell fishing craft. Naval craft and many pleasure craft use the river.

(101)     The river has main channel depths of 17 feet or more from the entrance to Annapolis, thence 15 feet or more for 8 miles, thence 11 to 7 feet for 2 miles to within 1 mile of the head. The channel is well marked as far as Annapolis, above which it is marked at the critical points and is easy to follow.

(102)
**Tides and currents**

(103)     The tide is greatly influenced by winds. The current velocity seldom exceeds 0.5 knot. Ice rarely interferes with navigation except in severe winters, and then only for a short time.

(104)     The Severn River Comprehensive Vessel Management Plan regulations established maximum speed limits for day and night operation of boats and minimum wake speed limits for the Severn River and its tributaries. These speed limits vary and are marked by white and orange regulatory markers. For more information contact Maryland Department of Natural Resources, Marine Police, Tawes State Office Building, Annapolis, MD 21401; telephone 410-260-8880.

(105)
**ENC - US5MD32M**
**Chart - 12283**

(106)     The entrance to Severn River is between **Tolly Point** and Greenbury Point, 2 miles to the northward. **Tolly Point Shoal,** with depths of 4 to 5 feet, extends 1 mile east-southeastward from the point; it is marked at its outer end by a light.

(107)     The entrance to **Lake Ogleton** is on the southwest side of Severn River 0.8 mile above Tolly Point. A dredged entrance channel leads to the lake from the river and has a reported controlling depth of 6 feet on the centerline (1998). The lake has depths of 5 to 9 feet. The entrance channel is marked by lights and daybeacons. The small

private wharves along the shore of the lake are used mostly for mooring pleasure craft.

(108)     **Greenbury Point** is on the north side of the entrance to Severn River. Three towers on the point are prominent up and down the bay; each tower has a flashing red light on top and fixed red lights on the sides. A light marks the shoal extending 0.4 mile south of the point.

(109)     A **naval deep-draft anchorage** is southeast of Greenbury Point, and several smaller **naval anchorages** and **prohibited anchorages** are west and northwest of the point. (See **33 CFR 110.1** and **110.159,** chapter 2, for limits and regulations.) Proper advanced application must be made at least twenty-four (24) hours prior to the planned anchoring. Submit application to the Chairman, Department of Seamanship and Navigation (SEANAV) via email: usna-port-ops-group@usna.edu. Applications should include the following information:

(110)     a. Name and type of vessel, call sign or official number, and registry;

(111)     b. Position (both GPS coordinates and precise anchor circle depicted on the chart);

(112)     c. Dates and times (estimated arrival and departure); and

(113)     d. Name and 24-hour contact information for the person in charge of the anchored vessel. The application will normally be considered on a case-by-case basis. Of particular note, applicants should refrain from requesting to anchor within the circle designated on the chart as Anchorage A.

(114)     The entrance to **Carr Creek** is northwest of Greenbury Point. The creek has depths of 9 feet over the unmarked entrance bar and deeper water through a narrow channel inside. In 1998, shoaling was reported in about 38°58'59"N., 76°27'27"W. A naval rifle range is on the west side of the entrance to the creek. Mariners are warned to keep out of the creek when the red flag is flying from **Carr Point** or the next point southward. Floating breakwaters are in the entrance to Carr Creek, south of Carr Point.

(115)     **Back Creek,** on the southwest side of Severn River 0.7 mile above the mouth, has depths of 7 to 9 feet for most of its 1-mile length. A light marks the outer end of the breakwater on the south side of the entrance, and lights and daybeacons mark the narrow entrance channel. The creek is used by fishing boats and pleasure craft. Berthing and repair facilities are located on the north side of the creek at **Eastport** and on the south side of the creek. Diesel fuel and gasoline are available on the south side of the creek.

(116)     **Spa Creek** is on the southwest side of the Severn River, 1.4 miles above the mouth. Vessels using the creek have drafts of 10 feet or less. The Spa Creek highway bridge, about 0.4 mile above the entrance, has a 40-foot bascule span with a clearance of 15 feet. The bridgetender monitors VHF-FM channel 16 (156.80 MHz) and works on channels 13 and 68; contact by phone at 410–974–3840. (See **33 CFR 117.1** through **117.59** and **117.571,** chapter 2, for drawbridge regulations.) Gasoline, diesel

(118)

Annapolis, Maryland
Image courtesy of Waterway Images (2004)

—N→

fuel, berths, electricity, pump-out station, water and ice are available on the north side of the creek just east of the bridge.

(117)     **Annapolis**, the capital of Maryland, is on the north side of Spa Creek. The **U.S. Naval Academy** occupies the entire northeastern part of the city between Spa Creek and College Creek, 0.7 mile to the northwestward.

(120)

### Quarantine, customs, immigration and agricultural quarantine

(121)     (See chapter 3, Vessel Arrival Inspections, and appendix for addresses.)

(122)     **Quarantine** is enforced in accordance with regulations of the U.S. Public Health Service. (See Public Health Service, chapter 1.)

(123)     Annapolis is a **customs port of entry.**

(124)

### Harbor Regulations

(125)     The **harbormaster** has an office on the north side of Market Slip and enforces city regulations for the harbor. The harbormaster also controls municipal rental berths and mooring available in the harbor. A **speed limit** of 6 mph is enforced.

(126)     The Naval Academy **Santee Basin** on the Severn River side of Annapolis has reported depths of 15 feet.

The basin and seawall are within a **restricted area.** (See **33 CFR 334.160**, chapter 2, for limits and regulations.)

(127)     Spa Creek waterfront has depths of 4 to 10 feet reported alongside the bulkhead and wharves almost to **Market Slip**, 250 yards below the north end of the Spa Creek highway bridge. Market Slip is 250 yards long and 40 yards wide, with depths of 8 to 10 feet; the slip is open to the public and is used extensively by small craft.

(128)     Extensive marine facilities are on both sides of Spa Creek above and below the bridge. Most of the boatyards are on the south, or Eastport, side of Spa Creek.

(129)     The **U.S. Navy Marine Engineering Laboratory** extends from Carr Creek along the eastern shore of Severn River for about 1 mile to **Ferry Point**. **Naval restricted areas** surround the small boat basin, 0.4 mile westward of Carr Creek, and **Dungan** and **Worthington Basins** just to the west. (See **33 CFR 334.150** and **334.155**, chapter 2, for limits and regulations.)

(130)     **College (Dorseys) Creek**, on the southwest side of Severn River 2.1 miles above the mouth, has depths of 11 to 8 feet for most of its 1-mile length; the best water in the entrance is along the south side. A footbridge, two bascule bridges, an overhead pipeline and a fixed bridge cross the creek from Annapolis on the southeast bank to **West Annapolis** on the northwest bank. The drawspans of the bascule bridges are secured in a fixed position. (See **33 CFR 117.555**, chapter 2, for drawbridge regulations.)

(119)

Annapolis, Maryland
Image courtesy of Waterway Images (2004)

The bridges and overhead pipeline have a minimum width of 40 feet and clearance of 5 feet.

(131)  The highway bridge, 2.4 miles above the mouth of Severn River has a fixed span with a clearance of 75 feet. A large fishing pier is above and adjacent to the highway bridge on the east of the Severn River.

(132)
## ENC - US5MD22M
## Chart - 12282

(133)  **Weems Creek** (39°00.0'N., 76°30.1'W.), on the southwest side of Severn River 3.2 miles above the mouth, has depths of 13 feet for 0.8 mile, thence 11 to 7 feet for 0.3 mile to near the head. A shoal extends 300 yards eastward from the point on the north side of the entrance and is marked by a daybeacon. The highway bridge 0.5 mile above the entrance has a swing span with a width of 28 feet and a clearance of 8 feet. (See **33 CFR 117.1** through **117.59** and **117.577**, chapter 2, for drawbridge regulations.) The fixed highway bridge about 500 feet above the drawbridge has a clearance of 28 feet. A private special purpose buoy at the mouth of Weems Creek marks a **speed** controlled area.

(134)  U.S. Route 50/301 fixed highway bridge over Severn River, 3.5 miles above the mouth, has a clearance of 80 feet at the center span.

(135)  **Round Bay**, an expansion of Severn River beginning 6 miles above the mouth and continuing for 2 miles, has depths of 17 to 23 feet and is traveled extensively by motorboats. **Little Round Bay**, west of Round Bay, has depths of 17 to 19 feet and is marked by daybeacons. Depths of 4 feet can be carried to a boatyard in **Browns Cove**, behind **St. Helena Island.** Berths, electricity, gasoline, diesel fuel, water, ice, launching ramp, pump-out station, storage and some marine supplies can be obtained. A 35-ton lift is available for hull and engine repairs.

(136)  **Forked Creek**, on the north side of Severn River 9 miles above the mouth, has depths of 16 to 10 feet for most of its 0.4 mile length. Marine services are on the creek with 4 to 6 feet available alongside. Berths, electricity, water, ice and a launching ramp are available. A marine railway can handle crafts to 50 feet; lift to 9 tons for hull and engine repairs.

(137)  There is a small-boat basin on the east side of Severn River, 11 miles above the mouth. The controlling depth to the basin is about 3 feet.

(138)
## ENCs - US5MD32M, US5MD22M
## Charts - 12283, 12282

(139)  **Whitehall Bay**, on the west side of Chesapeake Bay, is between Greenbury Point (38°58.5'N., 76°27.3'W.) and

(145)

William P. Lane, Jr. Memorial (Chesapeake Bay) Bridge, Maryland
Image courtesy of Waterway Images (2006)

**Hackett Point,** 1.5 miles to the northeastward. The bay has general depths of 13 to 6 feet. The entrance channel is about 300 yards wide between **Whitehall Flats** on the west and **North Shoal** on the east, both with depths of 3 to 4 feet; a light marks the western limit of North Shoal. A lighthouse is on **Sharps Point**, on the west side of the entrance to Whitehall Creek.

(140)     **Mill Creek**, which empties into the northwest corner of Whitehall Bay, is entered through a privately dredged entrance channel marked by a light and daybeacons; in 1998, the reported controlling depth was 7 feet. The depths above the dredged channel are 7 to 14 feet for 1.5 miles to near the head of the creek. Gasoline is available at a pier 0.7 mile above the entrance. A marine railway, 1.3 miles above the entrance, can handle boats up to 40 feet. Gasoline and water are available just west of the railway.

(141)     **Whitehall Creek**, which empties into the northeast corner of Whitehall Bay, has depths of 9 to 13 feet for 1.5 miles, then shoals gradually to 1-foot at the head 0.5 mile farther up. The narrow, crooked entrance channel is marked by daybeacons. In 1998, shoaling to 6 feet was reported in the channel between daybeacons 4 and 5. A 35-ton lift is available on the east side of the creek, 1 mile above the mouth.

(142)     **Meredith Creek**, in the northeast corner of Whitehall Bay just eastward of Whitehall Creek, has depths of about 2 feet in a very narrow entrance, thence 10 to 7 feet for

0.7 mile, then shoals gradually to 1 foot at the head, 0.6 mile farther up. Local knowledge is necessary to carry more than 2 feet through the entrance.

(143)     A fish haven, marked by a buoy, is about 1 mile eastward of Hackett Point.

(144)     The two spans of the **William P. Lane Jr. Memorial Bridge (Chesapeake Bay Bridge)** are 3.7 miles long from shore to shore and 130 miles above the Virginia Capes. The western end is 0.5 mile southwestward of Sandy Point and the eastern end is 4 miles south-southwestward of Love Point. There are two main channel spans along the length of the bridge, **Chesapeake Channel** and **Eastern Channel**.

(146)     The suspension spans over **Chesapeake Channel** 1.4 miles from the western end of the bridge have a horizontal clearance of 1,500 feet and a vertical clearance of 182 feet. Flashing red aerolights are mounted on top of the two suspension towers. Three fixed white lights are mounted vertically over fixed green range lights, at the center of Chesapeake Channel spans. Sound signals are mounted on the south and north sides of the bridge at the center of Chesapeake Channel spans. Lighted buoys mark Chesapeake Channel on either side of the bridge.

(147)     The fixed spans over **Eastern Channel** 1.2 miles from the eastern end of the bridge have a horizontal clearance of 690 feet and a vertical clearance of 58 feet. The center of the spans are marked by a range of two green lights. A sound signal is at the span center.

(148)      A privately marked channel leads to a marina and yacht club at the eastern end of the bridge. In 2004, the reported approach depth was 6 feet. Gasoline, diesel fuel, a pump-out station, electricity, water, ice, marine supplies, dry storage, a launching ramp and hull, engine, and electronic repairs are available; lift to 70 tons.

(149)      **Sandy Point State Park** is just north of the west end of the bridges. In 1998, the reported controlling depth was 5.5 feet in the state-maintained entrance channel and basin at **Mezick Ponds**. The channel and basin are marked by private daybeacons. **Slow no-wake signs** are posted in the entrance channel and in the basin. Gasoline, diesel fuel, water, ice, a pump-out station and some marine supplies are available; overnight mooring is prohibited except in an emergency.

(150)      **Sandy Point Shoal Light** (39°00'57"N., 76°23'04"W.), is extinguished. The red brick house with a white roof, on a brown cylindrical pier structure still remains 51 feet above the water about 0.4 mile northeastward of Sandy Point. The light house structiure is about 0.5 mile west of a point on the bay ship channel 131.5 miles above the Capes.

(151)      **Baltimore Light** (39°03'33"N., 76°23'56"W.), 52 feet above the water, is shown from a white, octagonal house on a brown cylindrical pier, in depths of 22 feet, 2.5 miles north of Sandy Point.

(152)      **Magothy River**, on the west side of Chesapeake Bay 1.7 miles westward of Baltimore Light, has depths of 10 feet or more for 6 miles, thence 4 feet for 0.5 mile to within 0.2 mile of a fixed highway bridge. There are many excellent anchorages in the numerous tributaries, and the area is a favorite cruising ground for pleasure craft. The critical points along the lower half of the channel in Magothy River are marked.

(153)      **Minimum wake areas** and a 6-knot **speed limit** are enforced in many parts of the river and in most of the coves and creeks that flow into the river. These areas are marked by regulatory markers.

(154)      The entrance to Magothy River is between **Persimmon Point** and Mountain Point, 0.4 mile to the north-northeastward. **Mountain Point**, the southernmost extremity of **Gibson Island**, is a sandy spit making out from a high wooded bluff. The current velocity is 0.6 knot on the flood and 0.3 knot on the ebb in the entrance to Magothy River.

(155)      **Deep Creek**, marked through the entrance, is on the south side of Magothy River 0.5 mile above the mouth. The creek has depths of 7 to 5 feet for 0.6 mile to near the head. Gasoline, diesel fuel, water, berths and some marine supplies are available at marinas in the creek. Hull and engine repairs can be made; lift, 25 tons.

(156)      **Sillery Bay**, on the north side of Magothy River along the west side of Gibson Island, has general depths of 8 to 13 feet. The bay is the approach to Magothy Narrows and the harbor on the north side of Gibson Island; the eastern shore of the island is connected with the mainland on the north by a causeway.

(157)      The marked channel through **Magothy Narrows** has depths of about 10 feet, and there are depths of 9 to 10 feet in Inner Harbor. The Gibson Island Yacht Club has facilities in Inner Harbor.

(158)      A marine service pier on the east side of the entrance to **Redhouse Cove**, at the west end of Inner Harbor, has reported depths of 7 feet at the outer end. The boatyard can haul out craft up to 50 feet for repairs.

(159)      **Cornfield Creek,** which flows into the eastern end of Magothy Narrows, has depths of 7 feet nearly to its head. Gasoline, diesel fuel, water, berths and some marine supplies are available just above the mouth.

(160)      **Grays Creek**, in the northwest side of Sillery Bay, has depths of about 3 feet over the entrance bar through a narrow, marked channel that leads to deeper water inside the creek. A marina just inside the north prong has berths with electricity, gasoline, diesel fuel, water, ice, a pump-out station, a 30-ton travel lift and some marine supplies. Hull and engine repairs can be made.

(161)      **Broad Creek**, marked by daybeacons off the entrance, is on the north side of Magothy River 2.5 miles above the mouth. The creek has depths of 9 feet or more to a marina at the upper end of the creek.

(162)      **Blackhole Creek**, on the north side of Magothy River 3.5 miles above the mouth, has depths of 7 feet in a narrow, marked entrance channel and 5 or more feet almost to the head. A **special anchorage** is in the cove on the west side of Blackhole Creek 0.2 mile above the entrance. (See **33 CFR 110.1** and **110.72**, chapter 2, for limits and regulations.)

(163)      **Mill Creek** and **Dividing Creek** have a common entrance on the south side of Magothy River, 3.8 miles above the mouth. Depths of 8 to 12 feet can be carried in both creeks for about 0.3 mile. A small-craft facility just inside Mill Creek has gasoline, water, berths and marine supplies. Hull and engine repairs can be made; lift, 20 tons. An overhead power cable just inside the creek has a clearance of 54 feet.

(164)      **Cypress Creek** is on the southwest side of Magothy River 4 miles above the mouth. The creek is entered by a narrow, marked dredged channel. In 2015, the channel had a controlling depth of 6 feet. Depths of 9 feet are inside the creek, with gradual shoaling to the flats at the head. Hull and engine repairs can be made at a boatyard on the east side of the creek just inside the entrance. A 25-ton lift is available.

(165)      Gasoline, water and marine supplies are available on the southwest side of Magothy River, 5 miles above the mouth. Repairs can be made; lift, 25 tons.

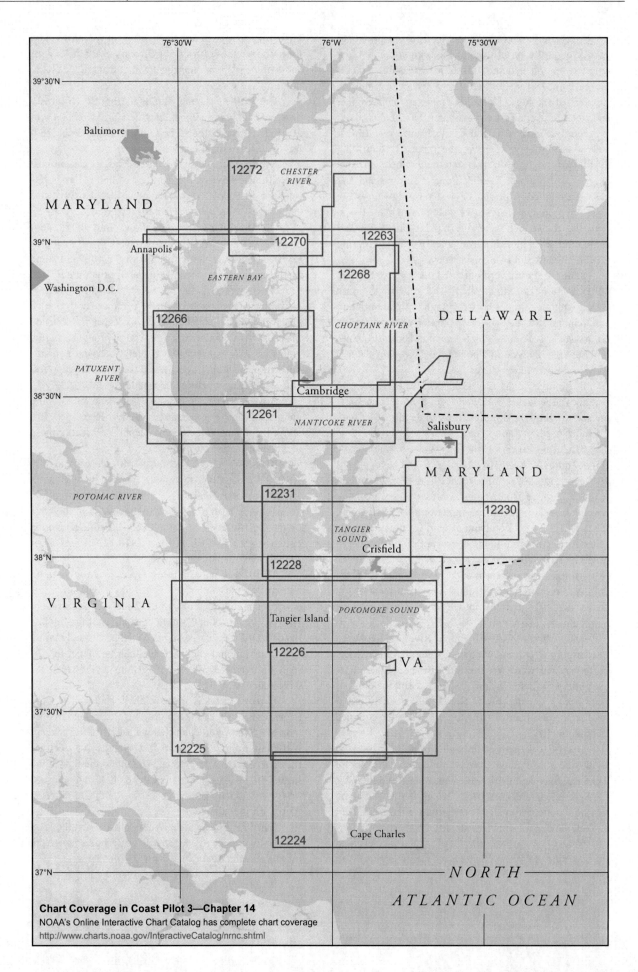

**Chart Coverage in Coast Pilot 3—Chapter 14**
NOAA's Online Interactive Chart Catalog has complete chart coverage
http://www.charts.noaa.gov/InteractiveCatalog/nrnc.shtml

# Chesapeake Bay, Eastern Shore

(1)　　This chapter describes the Eastern Shore of Chesapeake Bay from Cape Charles to Swan Point, about 6 miles northward of the entrance to Chester River, and several bodies of water and their tributaries that empty into this part of the bay. Included are Pocomoke Sound, Pocomoke River, Tangier Sound, Wicomico River, Nanticoke River, Little Choptank River, Choptank River, Eastern Bay and Chester River and the off-lying islands of Tangier, Smith, Hooper and Tilghman.

(2)　　Also described are the ports of Cape Charles, Pocomoke City, Tangier, Crisfield, Salisbury, Easton, Cambridge, St. Michaels and several smaller ports and landings.

(3)
**COLREGS Demarcation Lines**

(4)　　The lines established for Chesapeake Bay are described in **33 CFR 80.510**, chapter 2.

(5)
**ENCs - US4VA12M, US4VA1AM, US4VA40M, US4MD20M, US4MD80M, US4MD81M, US4MD82M**
**Charts - 12221, 12225, 12230, 12263, 12273**

(6)　　The Eastern Shore of Chesapeake Bay, from Cape Charles to Chester River, is mostly low and has few prominent natural features. The mainland and the islands are subject to erosion, and many of the islands and points have completely washed away. **Fishtrap** limits are shown on the charts and usually are marked by black and white horizontal-banded buoys. Mariners should use caution and be aware some traps are temporary and not charted and may be submerged or awash. In the tributaries of Pocomoke Sound, **ice** sufficient to interfere with the navigation of small vessels may be encountered at any time from January through March. The ice from Pocomoke Sound does not interfere with the larger vessels in the bay, but the smaller oyster and fishing boats frequently are held up and sometimes require assistance, especially in Kedges and Hooper Straits.

(7)
**ENC - US5VA14M**
**Charts - 12224**

(8)　　**Wise Point** (37°07.0'N., 75°58.3'W.), the mainland tip of Cape Charles, is included in chapter 9, which also describes Fishermans Island, Cape Charles Light on Smith Island and the Atlantic entrance to Chesapeake Bay.

(9)　　**Kiptopeke Beach**, 3.2 miles northward of Wise Point, is the site of a former ferry terminal. The offshore breakwaters are obsolete ships filled with sand and sunk end-to-end. The Virginia State Park at Kiptopeke Beach includes a public fishing pear, launching ramp and supplies. **Butlers Bluff**, which has steep bare faces conspicuous from the bay.

(10)　　**Old Plantation Creek**, 7 miles northward of Wise Point, has depths of about a foot. Many of the bars and middle grounds are marked by discolored water, and the channel usually is marked by bush stakes, but it is narrow and difficult to navigate without local knowledge. The opening in the thick woods at the mouth is visible from outside. No supplies are available along the creek.

(11)　　**Cape Charles Harbor**, 9 miles northward of Wise Point, is a dredged basin on the south side of the town of **Cape Charles**. A well-marked dredged channel leads to the harbor between sand flats on the south and a stone jetty on the north. Two small dredged basins are eastward of the main harbor basin. The northerly basin is known as the Harbor of Refuge and the southerly basin as Mud Creek Basin. (See Notice to Mariners and latest edition of charts for controlling depths.)

(12)　　**Cape Charles Coast Guard Station** is on the spit between Mud Creek and the Harbor of Refuge.

(13)　　The mean range of tide is 2.4 feet at Cape Charles. The tidal currents set across the entrance to and across the southwest section of the dredged channel, but farther north they follow the general direction of the axis. See the Tidal Current prediction service at *tidesandcurrents.noaa. gov* for specific information about times, directions, and velocities of the current at numerous locations throughout the area. Links to a user guide for this service can be found in chapter 1 of this book. The channel is exposed to westerly winds but is partially protected by the flats to the westward and seldom is too rough for motorboats. However, during severe west weather, heavy surges may occur in the harbor. Ice may hinder navigation in the harbor during severe winters.

(14)　　Due to the limited maneuvering room in the channel and the harbor, larger vessels and tows are sometimes a hazard to small craft. The larger commercial vessels and tugs that handle the floats barges, monitor VHF-FM channels 13 and 16.

(15)　　There is public access to the bulkheads and slips at the eastern end of the harbor. Anchoring is forbidden in any part of the harbor or the basins. A "no-wake" **speed limit** is enforced. A **harbormaster** enforces harbor regulations, and a **dockmaster** supervises docking at the municipal facilities. Gasoline, diesel fuel and water are available. Some marine supplies may be obtained in town. A yacht center adjacent to the Coast Guard Station at the head of Mud Creek has dry storage and a 75-ton travel lift; hull, engine and other repair services available.

(16) **Cherrystone Channel** is a passage inside Old Plantation Flats that leads from deep water 2 miles south-southeastward of Old Plantation Flats Light northward to Kings Creek and Cherrystone Inlet. The route follows part of the dredged channel to Cape Charles Harbor for about 1 mile. That part of Cherrystone Channel southward of the dredged channel to Cape Charles Harbor is unmarked and little used. Cherrystone Channel above Cape Charles Harbor is marked by lights and daybeacons to the vicinity of **Sandy Island**. This part of the channel has depths of about 10 feet but is narrow in places, and local knowledge is required to carry the best water. The recommended southerly approach to Kings Creek and Cherrystone Inlet is via the marked dredged channel to Cape Charles Harbor, which was discussed earlier in this chapter.

(17) **Kings Creek**, about 1 mile northward of Cape Charles Harbor and eastward of Sandy Island, has depths of 3.5 feet for 1 mile upstream. The shoal that extends out from the north side of the entrance bares at low water. The entrance into the creek is marked by lights and daybeacons. The creek is used extensively by fishermen and pleasure craft. Gasoline, diesel fuel, berths and marine supplies are available at a marina just inside the entrance.

(18) **Cherrystone Inlet**, which extends northeastward from Sandy Island, has depths of 5 feet for 2 miles, thence 4 to 2 feet to the upper end. The channel in the inlet sometimes is marked by bush stakes, but it is narrow and difficult to navigate without local knowledge.

(19) Boats bound for Kings Creek or Cherrystone Inlet can leave the Cape Charles Harbor channel west of the jetty on the north side of the harbor entrance and proceed northward in marked Cherrystone Channel. Depths of 2 to 4 feet over the flats that extend southward for 2 miles along the west side of Cherrystone Channel from Sandy Island limit the draft that can be carried over that area from westward and northwestward. The area between Sandy Island and **Wescoat Point**, 0.3 mile to the northward, bares at low water.

(20) A **fish haven**, marked by private buoys, is about 1.8 miles northwest of Wescoat Point.

(21)
**ENC - US5VA10M**
**Chart - 12226**

(22) **Hungars Creek** and **Mattawoman Creek** have a common outlet (37°23.7'N., 75°59.4'W.) to the bay 8 miles northward of Cape Charles Harbor. Hungars Creek is marked by lights, lighted buoys, daybeacons and bush stakes and Mattawoman Creek by bush stakes. Both creeks are difficult to follow without local knowledge.

(23) Hungars Creek extends about 4 miles in a northeasterly direction to **Bridgetown**. Depths of 3 feet

are available in the narrow entrance channel, thence decreasing to 1 foot to Bridgetown.

(24) Mattawoman Creek extends about 2 miles in a southeasterly direction and has several branches at its head. The best approach is to follow the lights at the entrance of Hungars Creek to the light off **Wilsonia Neck**, then follow the bush stakes southeastward and southward along the shore. The controlling depth is about a foot to the head of navigation. The overhead power cables near the head of the creek have a minimum clearance of 33 feet.

(25) A **danger zone** for naval firing begins about 12 miles north-northwestward of Cape Charles Harbor and extends northward to Tangier Sound Light, just south of **Tangier Island**. (See **33 CFR 334.220**, chapter 2, for limits and regulations.)

(26) **Nassawadox Creek**, 13 miles northward of Cape Charles Harbor and about 5 miles northward of the entrance to Hungars Creek and Mattawoman Creek, extends about 5 miles to the northeast. The controlling depth across the bar is about 1 foot, thence 4 feet for 4 miles upstream. The channel is marked by daybeacons for about 1.6 miles, but local knowledge is necessary to carry the best water. An overhead power cable with a clearance of 38 feet crosses the creek about 3 miles above the mouth. The flats on either side of the entrance are nearly bare at low water, are covered by marsh grass in the summer and are usually well defined. **Bayford**, on the southeast side of the creek 1.5 miles above the mouth, has a wharf. The several creeks that branch off from Nassawadox Creek have depths of 3 feet or less. A marine railway at **The Saltworks**, on the north side of the creek, can handle boats up to 35 feet for hull and engine repairs.

(27) **Occohannock Creek** (37°33.0'N., 75°56.3'W.) flows into Chesapeake Bay from eastward 18 miles northward of Cape Charles Harbor; a fixed bridge 5.4 miles above the entrance is the head of navigation. Inside the creek, depths of about 5 feet can be carried to **Morley Wharf**, on the south side 4 miles above the entrance, with lesser depths to the fixed bridge. The bridge has a horizontal clearance of 30 feet and vertical clearance of 4 feet.

(28) The channel over the bar of Occohannock Creek is marked by lights and daybeacons, but it is narrow and tortuous and difficult to navigate without local knowledge. The channel within the creek also is narrow, but the ends of the shoals are marked by daybeacons all the way to Morley Wharf. A public pier and boat ramp are at Morley Wharf. Gasoline, hull and engine repairs, a 25-ton travel lift and limited marine supplies are available at **Davis Wharf**, on the north side of the creek.

(29) **Nandua Creek**, 23 miles northward of Cape Charles Harbor and about 5 miles northward of Occohannock Creek, is entered through a channel marked by lights, buoys and daybeacons, which leads across the bar to the mouth of the creek. The bar channel is narrow and shifting; local knowledge is required to carry the best water. The

shoals at the entrance usually can be distinguished by the difference in water color, except in rough weather when the water is clouded. Buoys and daybeacons mark the critical parts of the channel to **Nandua.**

(30)        **Back Creek**, on the north side of Nandua Creek, 1 mile above the mouth, has depths of 3 feet to the village of **Hacksneck.**

(31)        **Pungoteague Creek**, 3 miles northeastward of Nandua Creek, has depths of 8 feet to the pier at **Harborton**, 2 miles above the mouth, and thence 4 feet to the ruins of **Boggs Wharf**, 3 miles above the mouth. Above this point the creek shoals rapidly. The entrance and inside channel are marked as far as Harborton. Barges load pulpwood at Harborton for delivery to West Point on York River.

(32)

## ENC - US5VA16M
## Chart - 12228

(33)        **Onancock Creek** (37°43'24"N., 75°51'06"W.), 38 miles north of Cape Charles, has traffic in petroleum products, sand and gravel. A marked dredged channel leads across the entrance bar and up the creek to an anchorage basin off the town of **Onancock**, about 4.3 miles above the mouth, thence to channels in the **North Branch** and **Central Branch** at the head of the creek.

(34)        Water and electricity are available at the public dock at Onancock. Gasoline is available at the oil wharf opposite the town dock. Diesel fuel is available by truck. The **harbormaster** makes berthing assignments and monitors VHF-FM channel 16.

(35)        **Chesconessex Creek** is 2 miles northward of Onancock Creek. In 1976, shoaling to an unknown extent was reported in the approach to the creek between Chesconessex Buoy 1 and Light 2. Above Light 2, depths are about 8 feet for 1 mile above the mouth to the middle of **Tobacco Island**, thence in 1997, favoring the south side of the channel, 6 feet to **Chesconessex**, about 2 miles above the mouth of the creek; thence in 2001, depths of about 1 to 3 feet could be carried to about 0.4 mile above the town. The creek is used by small local boats.

(36)        The approach to Chesconessex Creek from eastward of **Watts Island Rocks Warning Light** is marked by lights and a buoy; the channel above the entrance is marked by daybeacons and sometimes bush stakes.

(37)        The southern and main entrance to **Pocomoke Sound**, between the southern end of **Watts Island** and **Pocomoke Sound Light 6** (37°47'49"N., 75°50'19"W.), is 40 miles northward of Cape Charles. Extensive flats occupy most of the sound. A channel, wide and deep at the entrance but comparatively shallow in its most northerly part, leads to Pocomoke River, the most important tributary.

(38)        The shores of Pocomoke Sound are low and without prominent natural landmarks. The critical points along the main channel between the entrance and the mouth of Pocomoke River are marked by lights and buoys. The Virginia-Maryland boundary line is marked by diamond-shaped white daybeacons with orange reflective borders.

(39)        The sound is used by many local oyster and fishing boats and by some tugs and barges. Small boats can enter from northwestward in Tangier Sound by way of Broad Creek, which is discussed later.

(40)        A large area of shallow water separates the lower part of Pocomoke Sound from Tangier Sound on the westward. **Watts Island**, at the southernmost end of the area, is marshy and wooded. Watts Island Rocks Warning Light is 0.6 mile south-southwestward of the island.

(41)        **Great Fox Island**, 6 miles northward of the entrance to Pocomoke Sound, consists of a group of low islands, the northeasternmost of which is marked by a large building.

(42)        Just north of Pocomoke Sound Light 6, a marked crooked tributary channel with depths of 8 feet or more leads between shallow flats for 5 miles into a dredged channel in Deep Creek. The channel, marked by lights and daybeacons, leads for 2¼ miles to a turning basin at the town of **Deep Creek.** Gasoline, diesel fuel, marine supplies and a 25-ton travel lift are available at a boatyard in Deep Creek.

(43)        Deep Creek is used only by small local boats, many of which enter from Hunting Creek on the eastward by way of **The Notch**, a passage behind the 1.5-mile chain of islands that separates the outer parts of the two creeks; the controlling depth in The Notch is about 2 feet; the channel is marked by bush stakes.

(44)        Another tributary channel, 3.5 miles northeastward of Pocomoke Sound Light 6, leads to **Hunting Creek** along the south side of **Guilford Flats** and southward through **The Thorofare** to the wharf at **Hopkins** on the east side of Hunting Creek, 2.5 miles above the mouth. The marked channel has depths of 7 feet or more to within 0.7 mile of Hopkins, thence 2.5 feet to the wharf.

(45)        **Guilford Creek** is 2.5 miles northeastward of Hunting Creek, with which it has a common approach from the main channel as far as the light on the southwest end of Guilford Flats. The channel to Guilford Creek continues eastward along the flats, then turns northeastward and rounds a light off the mouth of the creek; the total distance from the main channel is about 8 miles. In 2016, the controlling depth was 2.4 feet to the turning basin, thence 4.0 feet in the basin.

(46)        **Messongo Creek** empties into the east side of Pocomoke Sound 8 miles northeast of Pocomoke Sound Light 6. The unmarked approach to Messongo Creek is from west-southwestward. In 2009, depths had shoaled to less than 2 feet at the mouth of the creek to about 1 foot at the village of **Marsh Market,** 2.5 miles above; extreme caution is advised. The creek is used only by small local boats.

(47)        **Starling Creek** is on the southeast side of Pocomoke Sound, 9 miles northeast of Pocomoke Sound Light 6. A dredged channel, marked by lights and daybeacons, leads from the sound to a harbor basin on the north side of the creek. **Saxis,** on the northeast side of the creek, is

the center of a considerable shellfish industry. Gasoline and diesel fuel can be obtained at the bulkhead, and some groceries are available in the town.

(48)

## ENCs - US5VA16M, US4MD20M
## Charts - 12228, 12230

(49)     **Pocomoke River** flows into the northeast end of the Pocomoke Sound 15.5 miles above Pocomoke Sound Light 6. The river has traffic in sand and gravel, pulpwood and some fish products. The marked approach through Pocomoke Sound has natural depths of 7 feet or more for 12.5 miles above the southern entrance, then the route passes through a marked dredged cut to the mouth of Pocomoke River. In 2010, the midchannel controlling depth in the dredged section was 2.8 feet. The cut is subject to continual shoaling, and lesser depths may be found, particularly on the southerly side of the channel.

(50)     Pocomoke River has depths of 7 feet or more from the mouth for 14 miles to Pocomoke City, thence 5 feet or more for 12 miles to Snow Hill. Navigation is easy for 20 miles, but the remainder of the channel to Snow Hill is narrow and requires local knowledge to carry the best water. Freshets cause a rise of 1 to 5 feet at Snow Hill but are not dangerous. The water is fresh above **Rehobeth**, 7.5 miles above the mouth.

(51)     **Shelltown** is a village on the west bank of Pocomoke River 1 mile above the mouth. Gasoline, diesel fuel and some supplies can be obtained in the village. Marine railways at Shelltown can handle craft up to 40 feet long.

(52)     **Pocomoke City**, on the east bank 14 miles above the mouth, has bus and rail communication and all kinds of supplies. There are public landings at the highway bascule bridge. Electricity, water and pumpout facilities are available.

(53)

**Structures across Pocomoke River**

| Name | Type | Location | Clearances (feet) Horizontal | Clearances (feet) Vertical* |
|---|---|---|---|---|
| Overhead cable | power | 38°04'09"N., 75°34'44"W. | | 82 |
| Pocomoke City Railroad bridge **See Notes 1 and 2** | swing | 38°04'18"N., 75°34'28"W. | 60 | 4 |
| Pocomoke City Highway bridge **See Note 1** | bascule | 38°04'36"N., 75°34'14"W. | 65 | 3 |
| U.S. Route 13 | fixed | 38°04'43"N., 75°34'15"W. | 55 | 35 |
| Overhead cable | power | 38°05'09"N., 75°33'30"W. | | 56 |
| Overhead cable | power | 38°06'28"N., 75°30'53"W. | | 57 |
| Overhead cables | power | 38°10'43"N., 75°23'40"W. | | 48 |
| State Route 12 **See Note 1** | bascule | 38°10'43"N., 75°23'40"W. | 40 | 2 |

**Structures across Pocomoke River**

| Name | Type | Location | Clearances (feet) Horizontal | Clearances (feet) Vertical* |
|---|---|---|---|---|

\* Clearances are referenced to Mean High Water
**Note 1** – See **33 CFR 117.1** through **117.59** and **117.569**, chapter 2, for drawbridge regulations.
**Note 2** – The best water is in the western opening.

(54)     A dredged channel about 22 miles above the mouth of Pocomoke River leads southerly from the river to **Shad Landing State Park**; a marina and turning basin are at the head of the channel. The channel is marked by a light and a daybeacon. Gasoline and some supplies are available.

(55)     **Snow Hill**, the town on the east bank 26 miles above the mouth, has rail freight service. The river is navigable for 2 miles above the bridge. Gasoline and some supplies are available in the town.

(56)     A line of marshy islands and flats, with Tangier Island at the south end, separates Tangier Sound from Chesapeake Bay to the westward; the principal thorofares between the islands are Kedges and Hooper Straits.

(57)     The danger zone of a naval missile target area is centered about 3.5 miles west-southwest of **Tangier Island**. (See **33 CFR 334.210**, chapter 2, for limits and regulations.) Sunken ships and other obstructions are within the area.

(58)     **Tangier Island** is low, sparsely wooded in the middle and bare on the north and south ends. **Tangier** is the village midway along the eastern side of the island; a church spire and two television towers are prominent. Oystering, crabbing and fishing are the principal industries. The island has telephone and motorboat communication with Crisfield.

(59)     **Tangier Sound Light** (37°47'17"N., 75°58'24"W.), 45 feet above the water, is shown from a white square tower with a black and white diamond-shaped daymark on piles, in depths of 5 feet. The light is 53.3 miles above the Virginia Capes.

(60)     **Tangier Sound**, its main entrance 1 mile northeastward of Tangier Sound Light, affords a broad and deep channel extending the 28-mile length of the sound. Extensive flats border the sound, but the critical points are marked by lights and buoys.

(61)     The town of Tangier can be reached from either Chesapeake Bay or Tangier Sound through well-marked dredged channels. A federal project provides for a 7-foot depth from the Chesapeake Bay to an anchorage basin with 7 feet in the basin and 8 feet from the anchorage basin to Tangier Sound. (See Notice to Mariners and latest edition of chart for controlling depths.)

(62)     (**Note** that the numbering system of marking the aids to navigation in the channel from Chesapeake Bay to Tangier Sound and from Tangier Sound to Chesapeake Bay is not continuous but changes in about 37°49'54"N., 75°59'49"W.)

(63)     Gasoline, diesel fuel and some marine supplies are available at Tangier; a marine railway here can handle craft up to 50 feet for hull and engine repairs.

(64)     The flats between Tangier Island and Smith Island, on the north, are shallow and can be navigated only by very small boats at high water.

(65)
## ENC - US5VA21M
## Chart - 12231

(66)     **Smith Island** consists of a large group of marshy islands separated by narrow thorofares; travel from place to place is mostly by boat. **Tylerton, Ewell** and **Rhodes Point** are small villages along the interior channels; crabbing, oystering and fishing are the principal industries. Gasoline and diesel fuel are available at Ewell and only diesel fuel at Rhodes Point; some supplies can be obtained at the villages. The island has telephone and motorboat communication with Crisfield. A marine railway at Rhodes Point can haul out boats up to 40 feet for hull repairs.

(67)     A well-marked 5-mile channel with several dredged sections extends from Tangier Sound through **Big Thorofare** to Ewell, thence northwestward in **Levering Creek** and again through Big Thorofare to Chesapeake Bay.

(68)     A marked channel leads southward from Big Thorofare through **Tyler Ditch** to Tylerton, about 1.7 miles above the entrance.

(69)     Another marked dredged channel leads from Tylerton to Rhodes Point. Local fishermen in shallow-draft boats sometimes approach Tylerton from southward at high water, leaving the main channel in Tangier Sound 7 miles north of Tangier Sound Light and following the deeper water northward into Tyler Creek. The depth in the southern approach is about 4 feet.

(70)     **Sheep Pen Gut** is the approach to Rhodes Point from the west. A dredged channel marked by daybeacons leads from Chesapeake Bay through the gut. Several other thorofares lead westward from the interior of Smith Island to Chesapeake Bay. Navigation of these channels requires local knowledge.

(71)     **Kedges Straits**, between Smith Island on the south and uninhabited **South Marsh Island** on the north, is used by vessels bound from northward in Chesapeake Bay to points southward of Manokin River in Tangier Sound. The inner approach to the straits is about 16 miles north of Tangier Sound Light. A depth of 10 feet can be carried through the marked straits.

(72)     **Holland Island Bar Light** (38°04'07"N., 76°05'45"W.), 37 feet above the water, is shown from a skeleton tower with a black and white diamond-shaped daymark on piles in depths of 9 feet on the north side of the bay approach to Kedges Straits. The light is 6.3 miles due east of a point on the bay ship channel 72.6 miles above the Virginia Capes.

(73)     **Solomons Lump Light** (38°02'53"N., 76°00'54"W.), 47 feet above the water, is shown from a brown octagonal dwelling, with a white square tower, on a brown cylindrical base, in depths of 7 feet on the Smith Island side of Kedges Straits.

(74)     Easterly winds raise the water and northwesterly winds lower it sometimes as much as 2 feet below the normal level. In severe winters, floating ice makes navigation of the straits dangerous.

(75)     **Holland Straits**, on the north side of Kedges Straits between South Marsh Island on the south and **Bloodsworth Island** and other smaller uninhabited low marshy islands on the north, is generally shallow and should not be used without local knowledge. Sandbars obstruct the Chesapeake Bay side and patches of eel grass uncover in the Tangier Sound entrance on the lower tides. Bloodsworth Island is within a **danger zone** for naval firing and bombing. A **prohibited area,** within the danger zone and with a radius of 0.5 mile, is close off the western side of the island. (See **33 CFR 334.190**, chapter 2, for limits and regulations of the danger zone and prohibited area.)

(76)     **Okahanikan Point Light** (38°11'42"N., 76°05'35"W.), 25 feet above the water, is shown from an concrete pile off the northwest side of Bloodsworth Island about 1.5 miles south of the bay entrance to Hooper Strait.

(77)     **Hooper Strait**, between Bloodsworth Island on the south and Hooper Islands and Bishops Head on the north, is the most northerly direct passage from Chesapeake Bay into Tangier Sound and is used by vessels bound from northward in the bay to tributaries at the north end of the sound. The inner approach to the strait is 27 miles north of Tangier Sound Light.

(78)     The channel through Hooper Strait is narrow, crooked and well marked; strangers should have little difficulty if close attention is given to the chart. **Hooper Strait Light** (38°13'36"N., 76°04'32"W.), 41 feet above the water, is shown from a skeleton tower with a black and white diamond-shaped daymark in depths of 9 feet midway along the north side of the channel.

(79)     <Deleted Paragraph>

(80)     Fall and winter continual northerly winds may lower the water as much as 2 feet below normal level. The current velocity is about 1.5 knots; the current floods eastward through Hooper Strait. In the winter vessels navigating Hooper Strait are in danger from running ice.

(81)
## ENCs - US5VA21M, US5VA16M
## Charts - 12231, 12228

(82)     **Little Annemessex River** (37°58'00"N., 75°53'48"W.), the approach to the town of Crisfield, empties into Tangier Sound 10 miles north of Tangier Sound Light. The entrance to the river is 0.8 mile wide between **Great Point** on the south and **Island Point**, the southwest end of **Janes Island**, on the north. The current velocity in Little Annemessex River is 0.9 knot.

(83)     A **fish haven** is about 1.3 miles west-southwestward of Great Point.

(84)     The main entrance to Crisfield is through the well-marked dredged channel of Little Annemessex River. (See Notice to Mariners and latest edition of the chart for controlling depths.) The southerly approach to Crisfield from Pocomoke Sound, used extensively by oyster boats, is through crooked **Broad Creek**. The northerly approach from Big Annemessex River is through marked **Daugherty Creek** and **Daugherty Creek Canal**. The tidal current floods northward in the canal and ebbs southward; the velocity is reported to be about 1.3 knots. See the Tidal Current prediction service at *tidesandcurrents.noaa. gov* for specific information about times, directions, and velocities of the current at numerous locations throughout the area. Links to a user guide for this service can be found in chapter 1 of this book.

(85)     **Jenkins Creek**, which enters Little Annemessex River close northeastward of Broad Creek, is used by fishermen and crabbers. Depths of 3 feet can be carried 0.5 mile above the mouth of the creek, thence 2 feet for 0.5 mile farther to the highway bridge with a 16-foot fixed span and a clearance of 6 feet; small boats pass through the bridge to piers on the north shore. The creek is marked by private daybeacons.

(86)     **Crisfield**, on the east side of Little Annemessex River 2 miles above the mouth, is a fish and seafood processing and tourist center. Waterborne commerce consists chiefly of seafood and petroleum products. The harbor is used by many oyster, fish and crab boats with drafts of 2 to 6 feet. Small freight and passenger boats operate daily to Tangier and Smith Islands.

(87)     The Crisfield waterfront is largely built up with bulkhead wharves and timber piers, most of which are privately owned but open to the public on equal terms. Some of the terminals have mechanical freight-handling equipment, but most of the freight is transferred by hand.

(88)     **Somers Cove** is a well-protected basin on the south side of Crisfield. A state-owned full-service marina is on the north side of the cove. A Coast Guard station is on the south side of the cove.

(89)     Marine supplies, gasoline and diesel fuel are available at Crisfield. Mobile lifts to 50 tons are also available.

(90)
**ENC - US5VA21M**
**Chart - 12231**

(91)     **Big Annemessex River** (38°02'54"N. 75°52'18"W.) joins Tangier Sound 15 miles north of Tangier Sound Light. The river has depths of 8 feet for 4 miles, thence 5 feet for 1 mile, and thence 3 feet for 1 mile. The channel is marked as far as Colbourn Creek.

(92)     **Daugherty Creek**, already described, enters the south side of Big Annemessex River 1.3 miles above the mouth. **Jones Creek**, close eastward of the canal, has depths of 2 feet for about 1.5 miles above the mouth. The channel is narrow and crooked; private daybeacons and a buoy mark the channel.

(93)     **Colbourn Creek**, on the south side of Big Annemessex River 3.5 miles above the mouth, has depths of 4 feet for about 0.7 mile, thence 2 feet for 0.5 mile. Excellent storm anchorage with good holding ground is available in depths of 5 feet in midstream 0.3 mile above the entrance.

(94)     **Manokin River**, on the east side of Tangier Sound 16 miles north of Tangier Sound Light, is directly across the sound from Kedges Straits, described earlier. The entrance to the river is 3.5 miles wide between **Hazard Point** on the southeast and low **Little Deal Island** on the northwest but is obstructed by numerous shoals.

(95)     The main channel of Manokin River is narrow and crooked and favors the southeast shore. The channel has depths of about 9 feet to abeam of **St. Pierre Island**, on the north side 4 miles above the mouth, thence 6 feet to within 0.5 mile of **Locust Point**, on the northwest side 7 miles above the mouth, and thence 1 foot to **Princess Anne**, 15 miles upstream.

(96)     The channel is marked to a point about 6 miles above the mouth. The lower of the two fixed highway bridges, 14 miles above the mouth, has a clearance of 3 feet. Most of the piers and wharves along the river are in poor condition.

(97)     **Goose Creek**, on the south side of Manokin River 1.3 miles above Hazard Point, is used by local fishermen and pleasure craft. A channel, marked by lighted buoys and daybeacons, leads to the village of **Rumbley** on the northeast side of the creek. Goose Creek has considerable traffic in crabs and oysters. Berths, gasoline, diesel fuel and marine supplies are available. Hull and engine repairs can be made; a 15-ton mobile lift is available.

(98)     **St. Peters Creek**, used mostly by fishing boats, is on the north side of Manokin River 5.5 miles above the mouth. A marked dredged channel leads to a basin and public wharf 1 mile above the entrance.

(99)     A marked dredged channel, 21 miles north of Tangier Sound Light, leads through **Lower Thorofare** between **Little Deal Island** and **Deal Island** to a mooring basin with bulkhead and several small piers at the fishing village of **Wenona**. Gasoline, diesel fuel and some supplies can be obtained at the village.

(100)     Another marked dredged channel, 25 miles north of Tangier Sound Light, leads through the west end of **Upper Thorofare** to an anchorage basin at the north end of Deal Island. A highway bridge crosses the thorofare and has a fixed span with a clearance of 25 feet. A boatyard just east of the bridges has a mobile lift that can handle boats up to 15 tons for repairs. Gasoline, diesel fuel, berths and some supplies are available. Beyond the bridge, least depths are about 1 foot southeastward for 2.5 miles to Manokin River.

(101)

## ENC - US5MD23M
## Chart - 12261

(102)    **Wicomico River** flows into the north end of Tangier Sound eastward of the inner approach to Hooper Strait, described earlier, and 26 miles north of Tangier Sound Light. The entrance to Wicomico River is 1.5 miles wide between **Long Point** on the south and Nanticoke Point on the north. Waterborne commerce is largely in fish, shellfish and fish byproducts.

(103)    **Great Shoals Light** (38°12'52"N., 75°52'46"W.), 37 feet above the water, is shown from a white skeleton tower with a black and white diamond-shaped daymark on piles in depths of 4 feet on the north side of the channel, 0.5 mile above the mouth.

(104)
### Current

(105)    Strong tidal currents set across the main channel off Monie Bay; the current velocity in the entrance to the river is 0.6 knot on the flood and 0.9 knot on the ebb. See the Tidal Current prediction service at tidesandcurrents.noaa.gov for specific information about times, directions, and velocities of the current at numerous locations throughout the area. Links to a user guide for this service can be found in chapter 1 of this book.

(106)
### Ice

(107)    Ice usually forms on the river as far down as Whitehaven; in ordinary winters the channel usually is open to navigation, but in severe winters it is often closed for extended periods.

(108)    **Monie Bay** is a large cove on the southeast side close within the mouth of Wicomico River. The bay has depths of 4 feet to the head but is used only by small local boats.

(109)    **Webster Cove** is on the south side of the Wicomico River, 3.5 miles from the mouth. A dredged channel leads southeast to a public wharf inside. The channel is marked by a buoy and daybeacon.

(110)    **Whitehaven**, on the north bank 6.5 miles above the entrance, has some supplies. Most of the docks are in poor condition. A marine railway can haul out boats up to 150 feet.

(111)    A cable ferry crosses the river at Whitehaven. The ferry operates only during daylight hours. The cable is picked up as the ferry moves from bank to bank and is dropped to the bottom when the ferry is not operating. The crossing is unmarked. Caution should be exercised while navigating in the area. **DO NOT ATTEMPT TO PASS A MOVING CABLE FERRY.**

(112)    **Wicomico Creek**, on the south side of Wicomico River 8.5 miles above the mouth, is navigable for small craft for several miles. The marked entrance channel has a controlling depth of about 4 feet with deeper water inside. A small yacht club on the north side of the entrance has gasoline and diesel fuel. A marina about 2.3 miles above the entrance has gasoline, diesel fuel, berths and marine supplies. Hull and engine repairs can be made; a mobile lift is available.

(113)    An overhead power cable about 14 miles above the mouth of Wicomico River has a clearance of 75 feet.

(114)    A cable ferry crosses the Wicomico River at **Upper Ferry**, 15 miles above the mouth. The ferry operates only during daylight hours. The cable, held taut by winches ashore, is suspended at or near the water's surface at all times during daylight hours but dropped to the bottom during nondaylight hours. The signal for lowering the cable is one blast on the whistle by a transiting vessel. The ferry slips are marked as a ferry crossing and warning signs are posted up and downstream of the crossing. Caution should be exercised when navigating in the area. **DO NOT ATTEMPT TO PASS A MOVING CABLE FERRY.**

(115)    Fishing boats use the large wharf on the south bank, 16.5 miles above the mouth; water is available. An overhead power cable, 17.7 miles above the mouth, has a clearance of 75 feet.

(116)    **Shad Point** is 18 miles above the mouth on the southeast side.

(117)    **Salisbury**, the head of navigation 20 miles above the mouth, is a major trading center of the Eastern Shore. Wicomico River forks at the city; the **North Prong**, in 1976–1977, had a controlling depth of 7.5 feet or 10 feet at midchannel to the fixed bridge 0.4 mile upstream, but **South Prong** is rarely used. The Main Street highway bridge and the U.S. 50 highway bridge over the entrance to North Prong have 40-foot-wide bascule spans with a minimum clearance of 1 foot. The bridgetenders monitor VHF-FM channel 16 and work on channels 13 and 68; call signs KZA-869 and KYU-697, respectively. (See **33 CFR 117.1** through **117.59** and **117.579**, chapter 2, for drawbridge regulations.)

(118)    Salisbury is a **customs station.**

(119)    Most of the commercial wharves are below the fork, but there are some in North Prong. Traffic to Salisbury consists of petroleum, aggregates, grain and fertilizer.

(120)
### Weather

(121)    Salisbury is in a region about midway between the rigorous climates of the north and the mild climates of the south and located on the Delmarva Peninsula immediately south of Delaware.

(122)    Rainfall distribution throughout the year is rather uniform with the spread between the wettest month (August) and the driest month (October) being only 2.07 inches (52.6 mm). The average annual precipitation for Salisbury is 44.87 inches (1140 mm). The greatest 24-hour rainfall occurred in October 1980 when 4.93 inches (125.2 mm) fell. The average annual snowfall for Salisbury is 11.4 inches (289.6 mm), of which most falls in January and February. Snow has fallen in each month October through April, and the greatest 24-hour snowfall was 11.7 inches (297.2 mm) in February 1996.

(123)     In summer, the area is under the influence of the large semipermanent high-pressure system commonly known as the Bermuda High. Based on climatology, it is usually centered over the Atlantic Ocean near latitude 30°N. This high-pressure system brings a circulation of warm, humid air masses over the area from the deep south. The proximity of large water areas and the inflow of southerly winds contribute to high relative humilities during much of the year.

(124)     January is the coolest month, and July, the warmest. The average annual temperature at Salisbury is 56.4°F (13.6°C) with an average high of 66.3°F (19.1°C) and an average low of 45.9 (7.7°C). The warmest temperature on record at Salisbury is 102°F (38.9°C), last recorded in July 1993. The coldest temperature on record is -6°F (-21.1°C). last recorded in January 1987. Each month October through May has recorded temperatures below freezing (0°C), while only June and July have seen temperatures in excess of 100°F (37.8°C).

(125)     **Nanticoke River** flows into the north end of Tangier Sound 29 miles north of Tangier Sound Light. Waterborne commerce is mostly in petroleum products, but there is also sizable traffic in fertilizers, corn, soybeans, pulpwood, shellfish and shells.

(126)     **Mileages** on Nanticoke River, such as Mile 11W, 19.6E, etc., are the nautical miles above the entrance that is between Nanticoke Point on the east side and **Clay Island** on the west. The letters N, S, E or W following the numerals indicate the side of the river by compass direction where each feature is located.

(127)     A depth of about 10.1 feet can be carried to Sharptown; local knowledge is advised. From the mouth to Wetipquin Creek, the river is more than 1 mile wide and is obstructed by extensive shoals, most of which are marked. The deepest water is usually near the points rather than in the bends.

(128)
**Current**

(129)     The current velocity in Nanticoke River is 1.2 knots in the entrance. The water is fresh above Vienna. Ice forms on the river in winter, but ordinarily there is enough traffic to keep the channel open. Spring freshets do not interfere with navigation.

(130)     **Nanticoke**, Mile 2.5E, has two packing plants. A dredged channel, marked by a buoy and lights, leads to a small boat harbor, protected by jetties, at the village.

(131)     **Bivalve** is at Mile 5.4E. A marked dredged channel leads to a municipal small-boat basin, 0.4 mile northeastward of the village. The basin is protected by jetties. Gasoline, diesel fuel, berths and limited marine supplies are available.

(132)     **Wetipquin Creek**, Mile 7.0E, is entered through an unmarked dredged channel to the wharf at **Tyaskin** on the south side of the creek just inside the entrance. A surfaced launching ramp is available.

(133)     **Vienna**, Mile 19.6W, has a public bulkhead wharf. A launching ramp is 100 yards below the bridge. Gasoline and some supplies can be obtained nearby.

(134)     The overhead power cables crossing the river at the electric power plant at Mile 19.6 have a clearance of 135 feet. The highway bridge at Mile 20.1 in Vienna has a fixed span with a clearance of 50 feet.

(135)     **Marshyhope Creek**, Mile 24.1W, has depths of 5 feet to the Harrison Ferry bridge, 9 miles above the entrance, above which point the creek is obstructed by snags and debris. The highway bridge at **Brookview**, 5 miles above the entrance, is kept in the closed position with a clearance of 11 feet. (See **33 CFR 117.1** through **117.59** and **117.563**, chapter 2, for drawbridge regulations.)

(136)     **Sharptown**, Mile 26.1E, has a bulkhead wharf but little waterborne commerce. Pulpwood is loaded at the south end of town for West Point on York River. The highway bridge over the river at the town has a fixed span with a clearance of 50 feet.

(137)     The Maryland-Delaware boundary line on Nanticoke River is at about Mile 27.5.

(138)     **Broad Creek**, DE, Mile 29.0E, is marked with daybeacons from the entrance to about 0.5 mile above Bethel. The fixed highway bridge at **Bethel**, 3.5 miles above the entrance, has a clearance of 30 feet. The overhead power cables close eastward of the bridge have a least clearance of 50 feet. **Laurel**, 6 miles above the entrance, has a fertilizer plant and several mills. The railroad bridge at Laurel has a swing span with the north opening obstructed; the south opening has a width of 40 feet and a clearance of 14 feet. Between this bridge and the dam, 0.3 mile upstream, are two drawbridges and a fixed bridge which have a minimum that of 37 feet and clearance of 2 feet. (See **33 CFR 117.1** through **117.59** and **117.233**, chapter 2, for drawbridge regulations.) There are several power cables and a telephone cable crossing the creek near the bridges at Laurel, which have a minimum clearance of 20 feet.

(139)     The vehicular cable ferry over Nanticoke River at **Woodland**, Mile 31.3W, operates during daylight hours only. The cable held tight by a winch ashore is suspended at or near the water surface at all times during ferry crossings and dropped when loading or unloading cars at the slips and during non-daylight hours. The ferry slips are marked, and warning lights and signs are posted facing up and downstream. Caution should be exercised while navigating in the area. **DO NOT ATTEMPT TO PASS A MOVING CABLE FERRY.**

(140)     A power cable crossing at Mile 33.7 has a clearance of 75 feet.

(141)     **Seaford**, DE, Mile 34.7N, has several mills and factories. Gasoline, diesel fuel and some supplies are available in town. The Norfolk Southern Railway Bridge at Mile 34.4 has a swing span with a width of 47 feet in the southeast opening and no vertical clearance. (See **33 CFR 117.1** through **117.59** and **117.243**, chapter 2, for drawbridge regulations.)

(142)    **Fishing Bay** is at the north end of Tangier Sound 28 miles north of Tangier Sound Light. The entrance to the bay is 3 miles wide between Clay Island on the east and **Bishops Head Point** on the west. The partially marked channel in Fishing Bay has depths of 9 feet for 2 miles, thence 13 to 30 feet for 4 miles, and thence 4 to 3 feet to the head, 9 miles above the mouth.

(143)    **Tedious Creek,** on the west side of the bay 2 miles above Bishops Head Point, has depths of 4 feet for 0.5 mile from the mouth, then for 0.7 mile shoals gradually to 1 foot at the head. The entrance is marked by a light. The cove at **Crocheron,** a village on the south side of the creek just inside the entrance, has a county wharf and ramp.

(144)    **Goose Creek**, on the west side of Fishing Bay 3 miles above the entrance, has a marked dredged channel to the wharves just inside; gasoline is available. **McCreadys Creek**, on the east side of Fishing Bay 4 miles above the entrance, has a marked dredged channel which, in 2007, had a controlling depth of 3.9 feet to the head of the project. Gasoline and some supplies are available at the village of **Elliott**, 0.6 mile inland.

(145)    **Farm Creek**, on the west side of Fishing Bay 5 miles above the entrance, has a marked dredged channel.

(146)    **Honga River** extends northwestward from the western part of Hooper Strait for 14 miles between the mainland on the northeast and the Hooper Islands on the southwest; the river is more than 1 mile wide for most of its length. Honga River has sizable traffic in shellfish and shellfish products.

(147)    The southern and main entrance to Honga River is between Hooper Strait Light on the east and Honga River Light 1H on the west. The narrow crooked channel in the river has depths of 13 to 55 feet as far as **Wroten Island**, on the east side 8.5 miles above the southern entrance, and thence 8 feet for 1.5 miles to the improved channel, described later, leading northwestward and westward to Fishing Creek. Depths northward of the Fishing Creek channel are 4 to 5 feet, shoaling gradually to 2 feet at the head. The river is marked as far as Fishing Creek.

(148)    **Fox Creek** is on the northeast side of Honga River 2.5 miles above the entrance. A light marks the east side of the creek entrance, and a daybeacon marks the point of a shoal that extends southeastward from **Paul Point**. The creek has depths of 8 feet to a line from Paul Point to **Wingate Point**, on the east side 2 miles above the entrance, then shoals gradually to 1 foot at the head, 1 mile farther up.

(149)    **Duck Point Cove**, on the east side just inside the entrance of Fox Creek, has general depths of 1 to 5 feet. A dredged channel leads northeastward into **Hearns Cove** to a basin at the town of **Wingate**. The oyster-packing plants here have small wharves for the oyster boats. Gasoline is available in town.

(150)    A 2-foot channel marked by private stakes leads to a boat ramp in **Insley Cove**, known locally as **Kirwins Wharf**, at the northeastern end of Fox Creek. The concrete ramp is 26 feet wide; parking and restrooms are nearby.

(151)    The three **Hooper Islands** divide Honga River from Chesapeake Bay and Tar Bay. Middle and Upper Hooper Islands are connected with each other and with the mainland by bridges. **Hoopersville** is a village with general stores and packing plants on Middle Hooper Island, 3.5 miles above the southern entrance of Honga River. A dredged channel in **Muddy Hook Cove**, marked by daybeacons, leads to a fish company-owned wharf at the village. In 2011, the controlling depth was 3 feet in the channel with 1 to 3 feet in the basin. A charted wreck just north of the channel covers at high water and is hazardous to navigation. Gasoline and diesel fuel are available at the wharves.

(152)    The highway bridge over the passage between **Middle Hooper Island** and **Upper Hooper Island**, at **Ferry Point**, has a fixed span with a clearance of 35 feet. The marked passage through the bridge from Honga River to Chesapeake Bay has a controlling depth of about 2 feet, but greater depths can be carried with local knowledge.

(153)    **Back Creek**, midway along the inner side of Upper Hooper Island 8.8 miles above the river mouth, has a marked dredged channel that leads to a basin at its head. Oysterhouses and a marine railway are along the creek; boats up to 45 feet can be hauled out for repairs. A boat yard in Back Creek has gasoline, diesel fuel, water, ice, a pump-out facility, hull and engine repairs and lifts up to 60 tons.

(154)    **Wallace Creek** empties into the eastern side of Honga River 12 miles above the mouth. A privately dredged channel, marked by daybeacons, leads from Honga River to a public landing and a marina at **Crossroads**, 1.9 miles above the entrance. In 1988, the reported controlling depth was 2.5 feet. Berths, gasoline, diesel fuel and some supplies are available.

(155)

## ENCs - US5MD21M, US5MD23M
## Charts - 12264, 12261

(156)    A 4-mile dredged channel connects the upper part of Honga River and the Chesapeake Bay via Fishing Creek and Tar Bay. The channel is marked by a light at the entrance from the Chesapeake Bay side and by daybeacons.

(157)    **Fishing Creek** lies between Upper Hooper Island and **Meekins Neck.** The highway bridge over the creek has a fixed span with a clearance of 24 feet. The overhead power cable just west of the bridge has a clearance of 65 feet.

(158)

### Current

(159)    The current velocity in Little Choptank River is estimated to be 3 knots.

(160)    A public wharf and several private wharves are along the creek.

(161)     A dredged channel in **Tyler Creek**, just west of the bridge and on the north side of Fishing Creek, leads to an anchorage basin in Tyler Cove. The channel to the basin is marked by daybeacons. The largest marine railway can handle boats up to 45 feet for repairs; some supplies can be obtained at **Honga**, on the south side at the bridge. A marina 0.3 mile west of the bridge has gasoline, diesel fuel and berths; the narrow entrance channel, marked by bush stakes, has depths of about 3 feet.

(162)     **Tar Bay**, west of Meekins Neck and Upper Hooper Island, is separated from Chesapeake Bay by Barren Island and a smaller island to the northward. The bay is shallow and unimportant except for the channel that leads through it from Honga River to Chesapeake Bay.

(163)
**ENCs - US5MD1AM, US5MD16M**
**Chart - 12266**

(164)     A group of rocks at about 38°37.0'N., 76°21.8'W., sometimes awash at low tide, is all that remains of **Sharps Island**. Submerged pilings are about 0.2 mile southward of the rocks.

(165)     **Fish havens** with an authorized minimum depth of 15 feet are about 4 miles south-southwestward of Sharps Island.

(166)     **Little Choptank River** joins the eastern side of Chesapeake Bay 6 miles south-southeastward of Sharps Island. Although obstructed by shoals, the river has depths of 11 feet in a crooked channel for 7 miles and the tributaries have depths of 5 feet for considerable distances. The river is marked as far as Fishing Creek, above which it is difficult to carry more than 7 feet without local knowledge. The tributary channels are usually marked by bush stakes, but navigation is difficult without some local information.

(167)
**Tide and currents**
(168)     The current velocity is about 0.3 knot. The river carries some commercial traffic in shellfish and shells.

(169)     The entrance to Little Choptank River is between **James Island** on the southwest and **Hills Point** on the northeast. James Island is subject to rapid erosion. Good anchorage is available in depths of 12 to 18 feet in the bight between James Island and **Hooper Point**, which is on the west side of the entrance to Slaughter Creek.

(170)     **Slaughter Creek**, on the south side of Little Choptank River 4 miles above the mouth, has depths of 2.5 feet over the bar, thence 6 feet to the bridge at the village of **Taylors Island**, 2 miles above the entrance. The creek is marked by lights, buoys and daybeacons. The creek is used by oyster tongers and crab fishermen. A marina on the east side of the creek just north of the bridge has gasoline, diesel fuel, some supplies and berths; a 25-ton mobile hoist is available for repairs.

(171)     **Brooks Creek**, on the north side of Little Choptank River 5 miles above the mouth, has depths of 10 to 4 feet in a narrow channel for 2 miles then depths decrease to 2 feet at the head. The narrow entrance is marked, but local knowledge is required to carry the best water. There are small-craft facilities on the west side of the creek along Hills Point Neck. A marine railway can handle boats up to 40 feet for repairs.

(172)     **Hudson Creek**, on the north side of Little Choptank River 6 miles above the mouth, has depths of 5 feet for 3.2 miles to just below **Hudson**, a village at the head. The entrance is marked, and the upper reaches usually are bush-staked. The wharves at Hudson are in poor condition.

(173)     **Madison Bay**, on the south side of the river opposite Hudson Creek, has depths of 1 to 9 feet. The entrance to the bay is marked by a light. A dredged channel, marked by daybeacons, leads through the upper part of the bay to a turning basin. The east end of the turning basin is connected to an anchorage basin at **Madison**, a village at the head of the bay. Gasoline, diesel fuel and some supplies are available at the wharf at Madison.

(174)     **Fishing Creek**, on the southeast side 7 miles above the river mouth, has a controlling depth of 5 feet for 4 miles to the forks at the head. The channel is narrow and crooked and difficult to navigate without local knowledge. There are several small piers along the creek, which is used extensively by boats bound for Church Creek, the principal tributary. The entrance is marked by daybeacons, and the upper reaches usually are marked by bush stakes. **Northeast Branch** and **Southeast Branch** have depths of 3 feet.

(175)     **Church Creek**, on the south side of Fishing Creek 2.5 miles above the latter's mouth, has depths of 6 feet for 0.8 mile, thence 4 feet for 0.8 mile, and thence 1 to 3 feet for 0.3 mile to **Church Creek**, a village near the head.

(176)     Other tributaries of Little Choptank River have depths of 2 to 5 feet and are used by small local boats.

(177)     **Choptank River** flows into the Chesapeake Bay 2 miles northeastward of Sharps Island and is navigable for 53.4 miles to the town of Greensboro. Traffic on the river consists chiefly of petroleum products, shells, grain, soybeans, fertilizer, fish and shellfish.

(178)     **Mileages** on Choptank River, such as Mile 8N, 13S, etc., are the nautical miles above the entrance between Blackwalnut Point on the north and Hills Point on the south. The letters N, S, E or W following the numerals indicate by compass direction the place where each feature is located.

(179)     The southern approach to Choptank River is through a buoyed channel leading south of Sharps Island; the controlling depth is about 25 feet. The northern approach, between designated fishtrap areas, has a least depth of 10 feet.

(180)     The Choptank River main channel has depths of 19 to 25 feet to Cambridge, 15 miles above the mouth, thence in 1975, a controlling depth of 5 feet to Denton and a centerline controlling depth of 2 feet to the fixed bridge at Greensboro. The channel is marked by lights, daybeacons and lighted and unlighted buoys from the entrance to Cambridge; thence by lights, daybeacons and

(189)

Knapps Narrows and Tilghman, Maryland
Image courtesy of NOAA / John Doroba (2019)

—N—

buoys to Warwick River, 4.5 miles above Cambridge. Above Warwick River, the river channel is marked by lights and daybeacons to Denton, and above Denton, private buoys mark the channel.

(181)
### Current

(182)    The river water is fresh above the town of Choptank. The current velocity is about 0.7 knot in the entrance off Cook Point. In Choptank and Tred Avon Rivers the current velocity is less than 1.0 knot.

(183)    **Caution**–It has been reported that during the winter many of the buoys marking the main river channel from the entrance to Cambridge may be moved off station due to ice conditions. It has been further reported that several vessels have grounded on the charted 12-foot shoal close westward of the main river channel in (38°37'37"N., 76°08'15"W.), about 0.2 mile southward of Lighted Buoy 18; mariners are advised to give this area a good berth.

(184)    Two miles above Hills Point, on the south side of the entrance, is shallow **Trippe Bay**, which is little used except by small oyster and fishing boats.

(185)    **Tilghman Island**, north of the entrance to Choptank River, has a substantial crabbing, oystering and fishing industry. The island, 3 miles long in a north-south direction, is subject to rapid erosion on its western side.

(186)    **Blackwalnut Cove**, at the south end of Tilghman Island, is well sheltered except from the south and is used

extensively by small boats. A marked dredged channel leads to a basin at the upper end of the cove. A public pier at the south end of **Fairbank** has depths of 3 feet at the outer end. In 2021, obstructions were reported with a least depth of 3 feet about 0.5 mile southeast of the cove entrance; caution is advised.

(187)    **Dogwood Harbor** is on the eastern side of Tilghman Island, 0.7 mile south of Knapps Narrows. A dredged channel in the upper part of Dogwood Harbor leads northwestward to an anchorage basin at Tilghman; no services are available in the harbor. The channel is marked by a light at the entrance, daybeacons and a lighted buoy to the basin.

(188)    **Knapps Narrows**, between the mainland and the northern end of Tilghman Island, affords passage from Choptank River to Chesapeake Bay. The 42-foot highway bridge over the narrows has a bascule span with a clearance of 12 feet. The bridgetender monitors VHF-FM channel 16 and works on channels 13 and 68; call sign KZA-868. The current at the bridge is reported to be 2 knots. The channel through the narrows is marked, proceeding from each entrance, and reverses at the bridge.

(190)    The village of **Tilghman** is on the south side of Knapps Narrows. The bulkheaded sides of the turning basin on the west side of the southerly abutment of the bridge are available for public use. Full service marinas and boatyards are on either side of the narrows.

(191)     **Harris Creek** empties into Choptank River at Mile 2.3N, along the east side of Tilghman Island. The channel has depths of 10 feet, with local knowledge, and is marked as far as Cummings Creek, 5.5 miles above the mouth. Above this point the narrow and crooked channel has depths of 6 feet to the forks, thence 5 feet in a channel marked by private stakes for 1 mile up **Northeast Branch**, and thence 2 feet for 1 mile to the head of the branch, 9 miles above to the mouth of the creek. **Northwest Branch** also extends 2 miles from the forks and has a controlling depth of about 2 feet to its head.

(192)     **Sherwood** is a village on the west side of Harris Creek 4.5 miles above the mouth. The county wharf at the village, available for public use, has depths of 3 feet alongside.

(193)     **Cummings Creek** empties into the northwest side of Harris Creek 5.5 miles above the mouth. A depth of about 5 feet can be carried up Cummings Creek to the county wharf at **Wittman**. The larger of two boatyards along the prongs just eastward of Cummings Creek can handle boats up to 40 feet for hull repairs.

(194)     **Broad Creek**, Mile 4.4N, has depths of 16 feet as far as **Edge Creek**, on the east side 3 miles above the mouth. Above Edge Creek, the winding channel has depths of 9 feet for 3 miles, then shoals gradually to depths of 2 feet at the head, 7.5 miles above the entrance. The wide entrance channel is marked, but some local knowledge is needed in the narrow unmarked upper reaches.

(195)     **Balls Creek**, on the west side of Broad Creek 1 mile above the entrance, has depths of 6 to 7 feet almost to its head; the narrow entrance is marked by a light and the channel by daybeacons. **Neavitt** is a village on the southwest side near the head.

(196)     **Grace Creek**, on the west side of Broad Creek 2.3 miles above the entrance, is marked by daybeacons. A marine railway on the south side near the head of the creek can handle boats up to 40 feet.

(197)     **St. Michaels**, a town with its main waterfront on Miles River, can be reached from Choptank River by way of Broad Creek, thence southeastward in Edge Creek for 0.7 mile, and thence northward in **San Domingo Creek** for 2.3 miles to its head, 6 miles from the mouth of Broad Creek. San Domingo Creek has depths of 7 feet or more for most of its length and a controlling depth of 4 feet to St. Michaels. In 1978, shoaling to an unknown extent was reported in 38°45'45"N., 76°13'52"W. In 1991, shoaling to an unknown extent was reported in about 38°45'08"N., 76°13'38"W. The channel is marked by daybeacons. Berthing, electricity, ice, gasoline, diesel fuel, marine supplies, water, pump-out station, engine, electronic and hull repairs are available; lift to 30 tons.

(198)     **Irish Creek**, Mile 4.7N, has depths of 7 feet for 1.4 miles, then shoals gradually to 2 feet at its head, 2 miles above the entrance. In 2004, shoaling to 2.5 feet was reported in the channel in about 38°41'35"N., 76°13'24"W., and 38°41'47"N., 76°13'25"W. The creek is used only by small local boats.

(199)     **Tred Avon River**, Mile 7.9N, has natural depths of 16 feet or more for 5 miles, thence 11 feet for 1 mile to **Peachblossom Creek**, thence in 2011, there was a midchannel controlling depth of 8 feet in the dredged channel to Easton Point, 8.5 miles above the mouth. The channel is marked as far as Easton Point. Shoals extend off **Watermelon Point**, on the east side 7 miles above the mouth; above this point midchannel courses can be steered. Caution should be exercised if going beyond Easton Point because of abrupt shoaling. Traffic in the river consists chiefly of petroleum products, shellfish and pleasure craft.

(200)     **Choptank River Light** (38°39'21"N., 76°11'04"W.), 35 feet above the water, is shown from a skeleton tower with small white house on piles in depths of 16 feet, 0.6 mile outside the entrance to Tred Avon River. A Coast Guard station is about 1.5 miles north-northeast of the light near Oxford..

(201)     Small motorboats can find anchorage near midchannel of any of the larger tributaries of Tred Avon River. The river bottom is quite firm, but the bottom in the tributaries is mostly soft mud. There is usually excellent protection from the wind; the brush and trees that line most of the banks provide some protection.

(202)     **Oxford** is on the east side of Tred Avon River, 2 miles above the mouth. The principal facilities are along Town Creek on the east side of the town. A marina is on the river side 2 miles above Choptank River Light; the marked entrance channel has a controlling depth of about 4 feet. The ferry landing on the river side of Oxford has depths of 14 feet at the face. Year-round ferry service is maintained to Bellevue, on the opposite side of the river. A public landing nearby has fuel.

(203)     **Town Creek** enters Tred Avon River east of Oxford and comprises the waterfront area of the town. A marked dredged channel leads from the entrance to a turning basin at the head of the creek. Two anchorage basins on the west side of the channel, 0.3 mile and 0.5 mile above the entrance, had depths of 9 feet and 7 feet, respectively.

(204)     Several packing houses have wharves along the west bank of Town Creek, and small piers are scattered on both sides.

(205)     **Bellevue**, across the river from Oxford, is the site of several oyster-packing plants in ruins but prominent as landmarks. A municipal mooring basin is immediately north of the ferry landing.

(206)     **Easton Point**, at the head of Tred Avon River 8.5 miles above the mouth at the junction of **North Fork** and **Papermill Pond**, is 1 mile west of **Easton**. A public wharf and the wharves of the oil terminals are on the point. A marina here has gasoline, diesel fuel, some supplies and slips. A 12-ton lift can haul out boats for repairs.

(207)     **Lecompte Bay**, Mile 10.0S, has depths of 7 to 13 feet. A narrow channel, marked at the entrance by a buoy, leads to a boatyard 0.5 mile inside **Lecompte Creek**, on the west side of the bay. A marine railway can haul out boats up to 50 feet for repairs.

(208)    **La Trappe Creek**, Mile 10.6N, has depths of 10 feet for 0.5 mile, thence 5 feet to the bulkhead at **Trappe Landing**, 3 miles above the mouth. The entrance is marked.

(209)    **Cambridge**, Mile 15.2S, is the center of a large agricultural area with related industries serving the Delmarva Peninsula. It is the second deepest port in Maryland and has an extensive maritime history. The town has services and facilities for both commercial and recreational mariners. Taxi, bus, truck and air services are available.

(210)    A dredged entrance channel leads from deep water in the Choptank River to a turning basin at the mouth of **Cambridge Creek**. Another dredged channel continues from the west corner of the turning basin through Cambridge Creek for about 0.7 mile to a turning basin at the head of the project. Anchorage basins are on each side of the channel about 0.2 mile inside the entrance.

(211)    Most of the waterfront facilities inside the creek have depths of 8 to 12 feet alongside. The Market Street Bridge, 0.3 mile above the harbor entrance, has a bascule span with a clearance of 8 feet. The bridgetender monitors VHF-FM channel 16 and works on channels 13 and 68; call sign KZA-695; telephone 410-228-8311. (See **33 CFR 117.1** through **117.59** and **117.549**, chapter 2, for drawbridge regulations.)

(212)    Marine repairs, services and supplies are available at two boatyards on Cambridge Creek. Dockage is available at the municipal boat basin and along the public bulkhead on the creek below the drawbridge, with anchorage permitted in the basin at the head of the project. Marine railways capable of handling vessels up to 100 feet and travel lifts up to 60 tons are also available. Fuel can be delivered by truck at the public wharf on the north side of the municipal boat basin.

(213)
**ENC - US5MD19M**
**Chart - 12268**

(214)    The highway bridge over Choptank River at Mile 15.5 has a fixed span over the main channel with a vertical clearance of 50 feet. The approaches of the former swing bridge, just to the southeast, have been retained as recreational fishing piers. A hotel marina about 1.1 miles southeast of the bridge and on the south side of the river has gasoline, diesel fuel, berths, electricity, pump-out station, marine supplies and electrical repairs available.

(215)    **Warwick River**, Mile 20.4E, is entered through a marked dredged channel which leads to the bulkhead wharves at **Secretary**, 1 mile above the entrance. A marine railway on the south side of the entrance to the river can haul out boats up to 60 feet for repairs; gasoline is available.

(216)    **Cabin Creek**, Mile 22.6E, has depths of 3 feet to the fixed highway bridge, 1 mile above the entrance, thence 2 feet for 0.5 mile nearly to the head. The bridge has a

horizontal clearance of 17 feet and vertical clearance of 7 feet.

(217)    **Hunting Creek** at Mile 25.2E has depths of 3 feet for 3 miles. A fixed highway bridge, 0.4 mile above the mouth, has a horizontal clearance of 17 feet and vertical clearance of 7 feet.

(218)    **Choptank** is a village at Mile 25.6N. The small yacht harbor at Choptank has depths of 2 to 3 feet behind its wooden bulkheads. A 6 mph, no-wake **speed limit** is enforced. Gasoline is available.

(219)    The overhead power cable at Mile 30.7 has a clearance of 139 feet.

(220)    Dover Bridge, Mile 33.0, has a swing span with a vertical clearance of 10 feet. (See **33 CFR 117.1** through **117.49**, and **117.553**, chapter 2, for drawbridge regulations.) The bridge is under construction (2016).

(221)    **Tuckahoe Creek** is at Mile 39.5N. The channel in the creek has depths of 8 feet for 2.7 miles, thence 5 feet for 6 miles, thence less than a foot to the fixed highway bridge from **Hillsboro** to **Queen Anne**, at the head of navigation 11 miles above the entrance. The channel is unmarked, crooked and difficult to navigate in places without local knowledge. The flats are covered with tuckahoes or marsh grass in the summer. The creek is used only by small fishing and pleasure boats. Tuckahoe Bridge, 7 miles above the entrance, has a fixed span with a vertical clearance of 20 feet. Overhead power and telephone cables just north of the bridge have a clearance of 25 feet. The overhead power cable across the creek about 6 miles above the mouth has a clearance of 32 feet.

(222)    **Williston** is a small settlement with a bulkhead landing at Mile 42.0E.

(223)    Choptank River is constricted by **Pealiquor Shoal** at Mile 44.3. A dredged channel has been cut through the shoal area.

(224)    **Denton** is a town at Mile 46.6E. The highway bridge over the river here has a fixed span with a vertical clearance of 25 feet. The railroad bridge 0.4 mile above the highway bridge has a swing span with a vertical clearance of 6 feet. The fixed bridge 0.4 mile above the railroad bridge has a vertical clearance of 25 feet. (See **33 CFR 117.1** through **117.59** and **117.553**, chapter 2, for drawbridge regulations.) The least clearance of the overhead power cables crossing Choptank River at Denton and above is 47 feet.

(225)    **Greensboro** is a town at the head of navigation at Mile 53.4W. A dredged channel is in the river between **Chapel Branch** and **Forge Branch**. The fixed highway bridge at Greensboro has a width of 37 feet and a clearance of 10 feet. Gasoline and some marine supplies can be obtained in town.

(226)
**ENCs - US5MD13M, US5MD17M**
**Chart - 12270**

(227)    **Eastern Bay**, the approach to Claiborne, St. Michaels, Miles River and other tributaries, is entered

between the southerly tip of Kent Island and the northerly end of Poplar Island, 2.2 miles southward.

(228)     The shores are low and have few prominent marks. Light-draft vessels also can enter from southward through Poplar Island Narrows and from Chester River on the north by way of Kent Island Narrows.

(229)     **Bloody Point Bar Light** (38°50'02"N., 76°23'30"W.), 54 feet above the water, is shown from a brown tower on a cylindrical foundation about 1 mile westward of the south end of Kent Island. The light is about 1 mile east of a point on the main ship channel 120.2 miles above the Virginia Capes.

(230)     The bay is used extensively by oystermen and fishing craft, as well as by increasing numbers of pleasure craft. The channel is wide and deep; within the bay are large shoal areas, but depths of 25 feet can be taken without difficulty to the mouths of most of the tributaries.

(231)
### Current
(232)     East of Poplar Island the current velocity is 1.0 knot on the flood and 0.6 knot on the ebb. Throughout Eastern Bay the current velocity is less than 1.0 knot.

(233)     **Poplar Island**, on the south side of the main entrance to Eastern Bay, is a dredged material placement site. The dredged material is contained within the site by rock dikes which surround the current footprint of the island. Expansion of the site is underway on the north end. Mariners are cautioned to stay clear of this area and remain vigilant when navigating near the site. The dredged access channels on the north and south sides of the the island are to be used for construction purpose only. **Jefferson Island**, east of Poplar Island, and **Coaches Island,** east of the southern end, once were part of the original island.

(234)     **Poplar Island Narrows** has a least width of 1 mile between Coaches Island and the mainland to the eastward. A marked channel leads through the narrows. A mooring field, consisting of several private lighted mooring buoys, is on the west side of the narrows—mariners are urged to use caution when navigation this area.

(235)     **Ferry Cove**, on the mainland side of Poplar Island Narrows, is entered through a channel that leads to a turning basin on the south side of **Lowes Wharf** at the head. The channel is marked by a light and daybeacon. A marina at the wharf provides water, ice, a pump-out station, berths with electricity, gasoline, diesel fuel, wet storage, a launching ramp and some supplies.

(236)     **Claiborne** is a village on the southeast side of Eastern Bay 5 miles by deep channel from the main entrance. A combination pier and jetty extends 0.2 mile west-southwestward from the Claiborne waterfront. The former ferry landing is south of the pier. In 2020, the channel to Claiborne, marked by a light and private buoys, had a controlling depth of 0.5 feet in the channel to the basin.

(237)     **Kent Point**, the northerly entrance point of Eastern Bay, is the southernmost extremity of **Kent Island**, which

has a north-south length of 12.5 miles and a greatest width of 5.5 miles.

(238)     **Cox Creek** flows southward from the interior of Kent Island into Eastern Bay between **Long Point**, 2 miles northeast of Kent Point, and **Turkey Point**, 3 miles farther to the northeastward. The channel has depths of 22 feet for 1.5 miles, thence 11 feet for 2 miles, thence 7 feet for 2 more miles, and then shoals gradually to 2 feet at the head of navigation, a fixed highway bridge 6.5 miles above the mouth.

(239)     A landing at **Romancoke**, 1.5 miles northward of Long Point, has depths of about 4 feet off its end but is in poor condition. Above Romancoke, Cox Creek has no villages on its shores and is used mostly by oyster boats. The channel is very narrow in places, and shallow water is close to the edges. The shoals are unmarked, and local knowledge is needed to avoid them.

(240)     **Crab Alley Bay** joins Eastern Bay between **Bodkin Island**, 0.8 mile east-southeastward of Turkey Point, and **Parson Island**, 2 miles eastward of Turkey Point. Bodkin Island is very small with sparse vegetation and is protected by a bulkhead. Larger Parson Island is sparsely wooded and has a ragged appearance.

(241)     Crab Alley Bay is 8 miles by deep channel from the Eastern Bay main entrance. The principal channel in Crab Alley Bay is marked and has depths of 8 feet for 2.5 miles to Crab Alley Creek, in the northwestern part of the bay.

(242)     The mouth of **Crab Alley Creek**, between **Cox Neck** on the west and **Johnson Island** on the east, is partly obstructed by very shallow areas that extend out from both sides. The channel within the creek has depths of 6 feet for 1 mile, then shoals gradually to 1 foot at the head. In 1978, shoaling to an unknown extent was reported on the west side of Johnson Island in about 38°55.8'N., 76°17.6'W.

(243)     **Little Creek**, northeast of Johnson Island, is entered through a marked dredged channel that leads to a basin about halfway up the creek.

(244)     Small-craft facilities are on the east side of Crab Alley Creek and in Little Creek and can provide transient berths, electricity, water, marine supplies, storage, pump-out and a launching ramp. Lifts to 25 tons are available for hull, engine and electricity repairs and a marine railway can haul out boats up to 45 feet.

(245)     **Prospect Bay**, in the northeastern part of Eastern Bay, is entered between Parson Island and **Piney Neck Point**, 2 miles to the east-southeastward. The entrance is 9 miles by deep channel from the main Eastern Bay entrance.

(246)     Prospect Bay extends northward for 5 miles to the U.S. Route 50/301 highway bridge over Kent Island Narrows. The channel has natural depths of 21 feet for 2 miles, thence 11 feet for 1 mile, and thence 7 feet to the beginning of the marked approach to the narrows, which is described later in connection with Chester River.

(247)     **Greenwood Creek**, entered on the southeast side of Piney Neck Point east of Prospect Bay entrance, has

depths of 5 feet for nearly 3 miles inside, but only about 3 feet can be taken over the bar.

(248)     **Miles River** flows into the eastern part of Eastern Bay from southeastward, between **Tilghman Point**, at the northeastern end of **Rich Neck**, and **Bennett Point**, 2.3 miles east-southeastward. The entrance is 8.5 miles by deep channel from the main entrance to the bay.

(249)     Miles River channel has depths of 20 feet or more for 6 miles, thence 10 feet to the highway bridge 11 miles above the mouth, and lesser depths to the head 14.5 miles above the mouth. A shallow middle ground, about 2 miles above the entrance, is well marked on all sides by buoys and daybeacons; the river channel is marked as far as the bridge. The small trade on the river is chiefly in shellfish and shells.

(250)     **Tilghman Creek** is on the west side of the entrance along the southeast side of Tilghman Point and Rich Neck. The outer end of Tilghman Point is heavily wooded. The narrow entrance, marked by a light and daybeacons, has depths of about 8 feet; depths of 11 to 8 feet are inside the creek for the remainder of its 1-mile length. A vessel must stay in midchannel to carry the best water. At the upper end of the creek, slips are available at a county wharf; depths to 3 feet alongside were reported in 2003.

(251)     **Wye River** flows into the east side of Miles River entrance, just inside **Bennett Point.** The approach can be made either around the middle ground or to the north of it. The northerly approach is shorter by 2 miles but is limited to depths of 8 feet; the southerly encircling approach has depths of 30 feet or more. Both approaches are marked.

(252)     Small local boats are the principal users of Wye River and its several branches. The twisting channels, some partially marked by private buoys and daybeacons, require local knowledge. The channel in the river proper has depths of 30 feet or more for 2 miles, thence 10 feet for 4 miles, thence 6 feet for 1.5 miles and shoaler depths, thence to the head 9.5 miles above the mouth. Oyster bars are along the channel edges in the vicinity of **Wye Island**. There are several landings along the river and its branches.

(253)     A **special anchorage** is in a small cove along the western side of Wye River, opposite **Drum Point**. (See **33 CFR 110.1** and **110.71b**, chapter 2, for limits and regulations.)

(254)     **Wye Narrows**; which branches eastward 4 miles above the mouth of Wye River, follows the north side of Wye Island for 4 miles to its junction with **Wye East River**. The channel through the narrows has a controlling depth of 6 feet. Midway along the narrows is a fixed highway bridge with a width of 43 feet and a clearance of 10 feet.

(255)     **Long Haul Creek**, on the west side of Miles River 5 miles above the entrance, has depths of 9 feet or more in most of its 0.6-mile length. The Miles River Yacht Club maintains the **285°** range that marks the channel into the small club harbor in the creek. The range is lighted from April through November and reportedly cannot be seen in daylight.

(256)     **St. Michaels**, a town at the head of a small harbor on the west side of Miles River 6 miles above the entrance, has a marked entrance with depths of more 10 feet. In 1983, the harbor had depths of 7 to 10 feet in the middle with lesser depths towards the shores, thence in 2008, a controlling depth of 5.6 feet was in the channel leading southward from the head of the harbor to a basin with a depth of 4.2 feet at the end of the channel.

(257)     The **Chesapeake Bay Maritime Museum** is at St. Michaels.

(258)     Small-craft supplies, gasoline, diesel fuel, a pump-out station, electricity, water, ice and slips are available at St. Michaels. Largest haul-out equipment for repairs is a 30-ton lift.

(259)     **Leeds Creek**, marked at the entrance by a daybeacon, is directly across Miles River from St. Michaels. **Fairview Point**, on the north side of the entrance, is thickly wooded. The creek has depths of 5 feet for 2 miles to the village of **Tunis Mills**, then shoals gradually to 3 feet at the head, 0.5 mile farther up. In 1972, shoaling to an unknown extent was reported in Leeds Creek in about 38°47'56"N., 76°11'39.5"W. and 38°48'05"N., 76°11'35.5"W. The fixed highway bridge from Tunis Mills to **Copperville**, on the northwest side of the creek, has a width of 19 feet and a clearance of 6 feet. An overhead power cable just below the bridge has a clearance of 18 feet.

(260)     **Oak Creek**, on the south side of Miles River 8 miles above the entrance, is privately marked by buoys and daybeacons. The creek has depths of 2 feet in the mouth, thence 3 to 5 feet for about 0.6 mile to the village of **Royal Oak** at the head of the creek. The fixed highway bridge at the entrance has a horizontal clearance of 24 feet. Overhead power cables just southward of the bridge have a reported clearance of 36 feet. Above the wharves at **Newcomb**, on the west side just above the bridges, the creek is obstructed by grass.

(261)     **Hunting Creek**, directly across Miles River from Oak Creek, has depths of 5 feet for 2.5 miles. The peninsula on the west side of lower Hunting Creek has a breakthrough with a depth of 3 feet, 0.8 mile above the entrance.

(262)     The highway bridge over Miles River 11 miles above the entrance has a 40-foot bascule span with a vertical clearance of 18 feet. (See **33 CFR 117.1** through **117.59** and **117.565**, chapter 2, for drawbridge regulations.)

(263)     The Chesapeake Bay shore of Kent Island is low and wooded. Marinas 3.8 and 4.8 miles north of Kent Point can provide supplies, gasoline, diesel fuel, berths, electricity, storage and a pump-out station. The southerly marina has a 20-ton lift and the northerly marina has a 35-ton lift available for hull, engine and radio repairs. In 2010, the reported controlling depth was 5 feet in the southerly and northerly marina. Both entrances are protected by jetties. It is reported that submerged pilings are at the ends of the jetties protecting the southerly marina.

(264)     **Matapeake**, 7 miles north of Kent Point, is the site of a former ferry terminal. The jettied entrance channel has a reported controlling depth of about 8 feet leading to

(266)

Chester River, Maryland
Image courtesy of Waterway Images (2004)

a pier of the Maryland Marine Police. The waters inside the jetties are available as a state harbor of refuge in an emergency; a launching ramp is available.

(265)    A marina, 1.7 miles north-northeast of Matapeake, is entered through a privately dredged channel marked by private lights. The marina can provide gasoline, diesel fuel, limited supplies and repairs; a mobile lift to 70 tons is available. The William P. Lane, Jr. Memorial (Chesapeake Bay) Bridge, 9 miles north of Kent Point, is described in chapter 13.

(267)

**ENC - US5MD18M**
**Chart - 12272**

(268)    **Love Point Light** (39°03'25"N., 76°17'01"W.), 31 feet above the water, is shown from a skeleton tower with a red and white diamond-shaped daymark, 1.4 miles northeast of Love Point.

(269)    The main entrance to **Chester River** is between **Love Point**, the northern end of Kent Island, and Eastern Neck Island, 3 miles to the eastward. The approach is northward and eastward of Love Point Light.

(270)    A fish haven, marked by a buoy, is in the approach to Chester River about 0.8 mile north-northwest of Love Point Light.

(271)    Light-draft vessels can also enter from Eastern Bay and Miles River on the southward by way of Kent Island

Narrows. Traffic on the river consists chiefly of petroleum products and shellfish.

(272)    **Mileages** on Chester River are designated Mile 7S, 11W, etc., which are the nautical miles above the entrance. The letters N, S, E or W, following the numerals indicate the side of the river by compass point direction where each feature is located.

(273)    Chester River is marked by lighted and unlighted buoys to Chestertown. Above Chestertown, deepest water is difficult to follow except with local knowledge and extreme caution.

(274)

**Current**

(275)    The current velocity is less than 1.0 knot. The river is usually closed to navigation by ice for extended periods during ordinary winters; in mild winters the channel is kept clear most of the time by powerboats. The river water is fresh above Chestertown.

(276)    **Love Point** is a village on the point on the west side of the entrance to Chester River. Shells are received by barge at the old railroad pier on the river side of the village.

(277)    **Eastern Neck Island**, on the east side of the entrance, is about 3 miles long in a northwest-southeast direction. The island is sparsely wooded with extensive grassy flats along the south shore. It is connected with the mainland over **Eastern Neck Narrows** by a fixed highway bridge with a horizontal clearance of 23 feet

and vertical clearance of 6 feet. Eastern Neck Narrows is narrow and little used.

(278)     At Mile 2.7S, a privately marked channel leads to a basin with a marina on its south side. In 2004, 8 feet was reported in the approach and 6 feet alongside. Gasoline, diesel fuel, berths, electricity, water, ice, some marine supplies and a pump-out station are available.

(279)     **Kent Island Narrows** entrance is at Mile 4.0S. A marked channel leads from Chester River to Prospect Bay. Very heavy traffic can be expected through the channel during the summer months, especially on weekends.

(280)     The State Route 50/301 highway bridge over the narrows has a fixed span with a vertical clearance of 65 feet. Immediately south of the fixed highway bridge is the State Route 18 (old State Route 50/301) bascule bridge with a 48-foot span and a vertical clearance of 18 feet. The bridgetender monitors VHF-FM channel 16 and works on channels 13 and 68; call sign KXE-254. (See **33 CFR 117.1** through **117.59** and **117.561**, chapter 2, for drawbridge regulations.) The nearby overhead power cable has a clearance of 85 feet. Temporary mooring areas for vessels awaiting bridge openings have been established by the State of Maryland on the west side of the channel about 50 yards north of the bridge and 100 yards and 650 yards south of the bridge.

(281)     The current velocity of **Kent Island Narrows** is 1.0 knot on the flood and 0.9 knot on the ebb at the bridge.

(282)     Two detached nearly parallel breakwaters, 700 and 1,500 feet long in a northwest-southeast direction, are about 0.3 mile southward of the highway bridge crossing the narrows and about 0.1 mile southwestward of the channel entrance to Wells Cove.

(283)     **Wells Cove**, on the east side of the narrows 0.4 mile southeast of the bridge, has general depths of 1 to 5 feet. A marked dredged channel leads to a basin in the cove.

(284)     **Jackson Creek**, Mile 5S, has depths of 2 to 7 feet at the entrance and is used as an anchorage by oyster boats; the channel is marked. The bottom is covered with grass.

(285)     **Queenstown Creek**, Mile 6.1E, is entered through a marked channel that leads to a turning basin at **Queenstown**, on the southeast side of **Little Queenstown Creek**. The entrance channel is bordered by very shallow grassy flats.

(286)     **Grays Inn Creek,** Mile 10.7W, has depths of 8 feet for 2.3 miles to a small settlement on the west side, then shoals gradually to 1 foot. About 1.8 miles above the mouth, a marina on **Skinners Neck** has a marine railway that can haul out craft up to 45 feet for repairs; gasoline is available.

(287)     **Langford Creek**, Mile 11.3N., has depths of 12 feet over the bar and deeper water inside to the forks 1.7 miles above the mouth; the channel is buoyed to **Drum Point**. An unmarked shoal extends southwestward from small **Cacaway Island** toward the junction of the two fork channels; above the shoal the unmarked forks are clear in midchannel. **East Fork** has depths of 10 feet for 3 miles, thence 7 feet for 1 mile to within 1 mile of the head. **West Fork** has depths of 8 feet for about 3 miles, thence 6 feet for 0.7 mile.

(288)     **Long Cove**, on the west side of Langford Creek 0.7 mile above the mouth, has depths of 4 feet to the head; the entrance to the cove is marked by daybeacons. The largest marine railway in the cove can haul out boats up to 50 feet for repairs; the largest lift is 70 tons. Gasoline, diesel fuel, launching ramp, a pump-out station and some supplies are available.

(289)     **Davis Creek**, on the west side of Langford Creek 1.5 miles above the mouth, has depths of 9 feet to a marina on the south side near the entrance. A private daybeacon marks the entrance to the creek. Gasoline, diesel fuel, berths with electricity, a pump-out station, water and ice are available. Repairs can be made; a 40-ton lift is available.

(290)     The common entrance to **Reed Creek** and **Grove Creek** at Mile 10.7E is marked by two buoys. The channel to the fork 0.3 mile above the common mouth has a depth of 6 feet. In 1984, a shoal was reported encroaching the channel from eastward about midway between Buoys 1 and 2. Reed Creek extends southeastward and has depths of 7 feet for about 0.6 mile above the fork, then shoals gradually to 1 foot 1 mile farther up. The channel in Grove Creek is only about 60 feet wide 0.3 mile above the fork but has depths of 3 feet through the narrows and 5 feet for a mile above that.

(291)     **Corsica River** is at Mile 11.9E. The channel in the upper part of the river has been dredged to the public wharf at **Centerville Landing**, 5 miles above the mouth. The lower part of the river is marked, but it is difficult to stay in the upper channel without local knowledge. Some supplies and gasoline can be obtained at Centreville, 0.5 mile inland of the landing. The main wharf at the landing is in poor condition, but a smaller wharf is available.

(292)     **Southeast Creek**, Mile 19.8S has depths of 4 feet for 1.8 miles, then shoals to 1 foot at the head of navigation 0.4 mile farther up. **Island Creek**, which empties into the south side of Southeast Creek, 0.5 mile above the mouth, has depths of 3.5 feet in the entrance and 4 feet or more for 2 miles to a fixed highway bridge. Both creeks are marked by bush stakes in the difficult reaches. Gasoline, berths with electricity, water and some supplies are available at **Kennersley Wharf**; a 30-ton lift can handle boats for repairs.

(293)     A marina is at **Rolphs**, Mile 20.7E. Some supplies, gasoline, diesel fuel, water, ice, a pump-out station, a 7-ton lift and berths with electricity are available. Small engine repairs are available.

(294)     A **special anchorage** is in the Chester River southeast of Chestertown. (See **33 CFR 110.1** and **110.72a**, chapter 2, for limits and regulations.)

(295)     **Chestertown**, Mile 23.8W, is a county seat and has bus and rail transportation. Water commerce consists chiefly of barged petroleum products.

(296)     The highway bridge over the river at Chestertown has a bascule span with a clearance of 12 feet. (See **33 CFR 117.1** through **117.59** and **117.551**, chapter 2, for

(302)

Rock Hall Harbor and Swan Creek, Maryland
Image courtesy of Waterway Images (2004)

drawbridge regulations.) The county wharf, 0.1 mile below the bridge has depths of 5 feet reported alongside. The marina 0.2 mile below the bridge has depths of 14 feet at the outer end and 6 feet at the inner face. Water, ice, electricity, gasoline, diesel fuel, slips, a 25-ton lift, a pump-out station, supplies and some repairs are available.

(297) Between Chestertown and Crumpton the channel is very narrow in places. Though marked in the more critical places, it is difficult to navigate without local knowledge and is more easily followed at low water.

(298) **Morgan Creek**, Mile 25.7N, in 1979, had reported depths of 2 to 3 feet over the bar at the entrance and 2 to 5 feet for about 2 miles in a narrow crooked channel. The entrance is a narrow slough between flats almost awash at low water. A fixed highway bridge, 0.6 mile above the entrance, has reported clearances of 30 feet horizontal and 6 feet vertical. The overhead power cable close northward of the bridge has a clearance of 32 feet.

(299) A public wharf is at **Deep Landing**, Mile 30S. **Crumpton** is at Mile 32S. The highway bridge at the town has a 40-foot fixed span with a clearance of 14 feet. The overhead power cable on the east side of the bridge has a clearance of 28 feet.

(300) Above Crumpton, the channel in Chester River is difficult to follow without local knowledge, but navigation is possible to Jones Landing, at about Mile 37S.

(301) **Rock Hall Harbor**, north of the entrance to Chester River and 5 miles north-northeastward of Love Point

Light, is the base for local fishing vessels and pleasure craft. The entrance channel leads north between converging breakwaters to two channels within the harbor. One channel leads to an anchorage basin at the west end of the harbor, thence eastward paralleling the waterfront at **Rock Hall** to a basin at the east end of the harbor. The Rock Hall waterfront is a 500-foot long bulkhead permitting overnight tie-up. No facilities are at the bulkhead. There is a boat ramp west of the bulkhead. The second channel leads northeast from inside the entrance and connects with the channel paralleling the waterfront. The approach to the harbor is marked by a buoy and lights, and daybeacons mark the channels inside the harbor.

(303) Numerous small-craft facilities are in Rock Hall Harbor. Berthing, water, electricity, gasoline, diesel fuel, pump-out station, launching ramp, storage and marine supplies are available. Repairs can be made with a marine railway that can haul out craft up to 50 feet and lifts to 30 tons.

(304) **Swan Creek** is 1 mile northwestward of Rock Hall Harbor and 0.7 mile southeastward of **Swan Point**, which is 139 miles above the Virginia Capes. The entrance channel is marked by lighted and unlighted buoys and a light, northward to **Deep Landing**. Inside the creek, the channel is privately marked by buoys and a daybeacon, eastward, to **The Haven**. Mariners should use caution when passing **Little Neck Island**, west of the entrance

channel, as it reportedly is visible only at extreme low water. Mariners are advised to pass close to the private moorings on the south side of the channel as the water shoals quickly to the northwest.

(305)    The shallow flats that extend 0.4 mile south-southeastward from Little Neck Island are marked by a buoy.

(306)    Several small-craft facilities are at **Gratitude**, 0.5 mile above the entrance to Swan Creek. Transient berths, electricity, water, ice, gasoline, diesel fuel, pump-out station, storage, limited marine supplies and lifts to 40 tons for marine repairs are available.

(307)    The area in Swan Creek just north of **Deep Landing** and in **The Haven** provides a good small-boat refuge in heavy weather.

(308)    The eastern shore of Chesapeake Bay above Swan Point is described in chapter 15.

## Chart Coverage in Coast Pilot 3—Chapter 15

NOAA's Online Interactive Chart Catalog has complete chart coverage
http://www.charts.noaa.gov/InteractiveCatalog/nrnc.shtml

# Baltimore to Head of Chesapeake Bay

(1)    This chapter describes the northern part of Chesapeake Bay and the many tributaries that empty into it, including the more important Patapsco, Elk and Susquehanna Rivers. Also described is the major port of Baltimore and several smaller ports and landings in this part of the bay.

(2)
**COLREGS Demarcation Lines**
(3)    The lines established for Chesapeake Bay are described in **33 CFR 80.510**, chapter 2.

(4)
**ENC - US4MD82M**
**Chart - 12273**

(5)    Patapsco River forms Baltimore Harbor, and Elk River is the approach to the Chesapeake and Delaware Canal. The other tributaries that empty into this part of the bay are seldom used by vessels drawing more than 12 feet. The shores are mostly wooded in the undeveloped areas and rise to considerable heights in the vicinity of Northeast and Susquehanna Rivers.
(6)    There are extensive shoal areas in the upper part of the bay, and **fishtraps** are numerous in season; fishtrap limits are shown on the chart. All of the tributaries are usually closed by ice for extended periods during the winter.

(7)
**ENC - US5MD12M**
**Chart - 12278**

(8)    Sandy Point Shoal Light and Baltimore Light, respectively 131.5 and 134.2 miles above the Virginia Capes, were described in chapter 13. The channel to Baltimore and the channel to the head of Chesapeake Bay divide at 0.5 mile eastward of Sandy Point Shoal Light.
(9)    **Sevenfoot Knoll Light** (39°09'19"N., 76°24'33"W.), 58 feet above the water, is shown from a skeleton tower on the northeast side of the channel to Baltimore, 140.1 miles from the Capes.
(10)    **Caution**–Large vessels transiting Craighill Channel Upper Range and Brewerton Channel Eastern Extension in the vicinity of Sevenfoot Knoll Light may generate large and dangerous wakes; waves as high as 10 to 12 feet have been reported. Small craft in the area are advised to use extreme caution.
(11)    **Baltimore Harbor** consists of the entire Patapsco River and its tributaries; a part of the waterfront thus included lies outside the municipal limits of Baltimore, but by state law is within the jurisdiction of the Maryland Port Administration.
(12)    **Patapsco River** joins the west side of Chesapeake Bay between Bodkin Point and **North Point**, 4 miles to the northward; the midchannel point in the entrance, 2 miles northwest of Sevenfoot Knoll Light, is 142.1 miles above the Virginia Capes, and 54 miles from Delaware River by way of the Chesapeake and Delaware Canal.

(13)
**Channels**
(14)    Federal project depths are 50 feet in Craighill Entrance Channel to Ferry Bar Channel, thence 49 feet in East Channel and 40 feet in West Channel, both in Northwest Harbor. Ferry Bar Channel has a project depth of 42 feet and Curtis Bay Channel has a project depth of 50 feet. The federal project in the main channel between the Delaware Capes and Baltimore via the Chesapeake and Delaware Canal is 35 feet.
(15)    The channels are maintained at or near project depths. For detailed channel information and minimum depths as reported by the U.S. Army Corps of Engineers (USACE), use NOAA Electronic Navigational Charts. Surveys and channel condition reports are available through a USACE hydrographic survey website listed in Appendix A.
(16)    **Bodkin Point** is the low northeastern extremity of **Bodkin Neck**, on the south side of the entrance to Patapsco River. Shoals extend northward and eastward from the point to the edge of the main channel.
(17)    **Bodkin Creek**, which flows into Patapsco River along the inner side of Bodkin Neck, has depths of 9 feet in the approaches and 7 to 9 feet for considerable distances into its branches. The channel is very narrow at the mouth and leads between extensive shoals. Shoaling to 3 feet is reported in the entrance to the creek between Daybeacon 9 and Light 11; mariners are urged to use caution in this area.
(18)    **Back Creek** is on the northeast side of Bodkin Creek just inside the mouth. A boatyard is in the upper part of the creek. Gasoline and slips are available. Hull and engine repairs can be made; marine railway, 50 tons; lift, 5 tons.
(19)    **Main Creek** is separated from Back Creek by **Spit Neck**. Both branches have depths of 7 to 9 feet almost to their heads and are much used by pleasure craft.
(20)    Several marinas are on **Graveyard Point**, on the south side of Main Creek 0.2 mile above the mouth. Gasoline, diesel fuel, slips and some marine supplies can be obtained. Hull and engine repairs can be made. Largest haul-out capacities are railway, 55 feet; lift, 5 tons.

(21)     A marina at the entrance to **Perry Cove**, 1.3 miles above the mouth of Main Creek, has gasoline and some marine supplies. Hull and engine repairs can be made; lift, 30 tons.

(22)     **Rock Point** is on the southwest side of Patapsco River 3 miles above Bodkin Point. A pier extends out from the Rock Creek side to depths of 5 feet or more. **White Rocks**, 0.6 mile northwest of Rock Point, are about 15 feet high and marked by a light; the deepest water is north and west of the rocks.

(23)     **Rock Creek**, on the northwest side of Rock Point, has depths of 11 feet almost to the head. The creek is marked by lights and daybeacons. A light on the east side of the creek marks the narrow part of the channel off **Fairview**, 0.5 mile above the mouth.

(24)     **Wall Cove** empties into the southeast side of Rock Creek along the south side of Fairview. In 1991, centerline controlling depths of about 10 feet were reported available for most of its length, but gradual shoaling to about 5 feet had occurred near the head of the cove. The Maryland Yacht Club piers on the Fairview side of the entrance have depths of about 13 feet at their outer ends.

(25)     There are several marinas and boatyards in Wall Cove and along Rock Creek where marine supplies, gasoline, diesel fuel, pump-out station, launching ramp, storage, water and ice can be obtained. Largest haul-out capacities for hull and engine repairs are marine railway, 60 feet; lift, 50 tons.

(26)     **Stony Creek**, on the southwest side of Patapsco River 5 miles above Bodkin Point, has depths of 12 feet or more almost to the head. The entrance channel into the creek is about 70 yards wide and marked by lights, buoys and daybeacons. The creek mouth on the east side is obstructed by rocks, some of which bare at all stages of the tide. The State Route 173 highway bridge 0.8 mile above the mouth of Stony Creek has a 40-foot bascule span with a clearance of 18 feet. The bridgetender monitors VHF-FM channel 16 and works on channels 13 and 68; call sign KAJ-667. (See **33 CFR 117.1** through **117.59** and **117.573**, chapter 2, for drawbridge regulations.) A marina on the north side just above the bridge has gasoline.

(27)     **Nabbs Creek**, a tributary on the northwest side of Stony Creek, 1 mile above the mouth, has depths of 12 feet almost to the head. A marina near the head of the creek has gasoline, diesel fuel, berths and marine supplies. Hull and engine repairs can be made. A marine railway can handle craft up to 60 feet; a 15-ton lift is available.

(28)     **Back Cove**, on the north side of Nabbs Creek near the mouth, has depths of 12 feet to a boatyard 0.3 mile above the entrance. The marine railway can handle craft up to 60 feet for hull and engine repairs; gasoline is available.

(29)     **Old Road Bay**, which empties into the north side of Patapsco River along the west side of North Point, has general depths of 7 to 10 feet. A light marks the edge of a shoal that extends westward from North Point. A dredged channel, marked by buoys and a **353.6°** lighted range, leads north from Brewerton Channel to a turning basin

off the east side of Sparrows Point. A **cable area** extends from the west side of North Point, across the bay and through the turning basin, to the east shore of Sparrows Point.

(30)     **North Point Creek** and **Jones Creek**, which empty into the northeast and northwest corners of Old Road Bay, respectively, have depths of 3 to 6 feet. The approach to North Point Creek is marked by lights, and the approach to Jones Creek is marked by lights and daybeacons. Approach both creeks by passing eastward of Jones Creek Light 1, being careful to avoid the reported underwater obstruction about 150 yards south of the light. Small-craft facilities are in both creeks.

(31)
## ENCs - US5MD11M, US5MD12M
## Charts - 12281, 12278

(32)     **Baltimore**, one of the major ports of the United States, is at the head of tidewater navigation on Patapsco River. The midharbor point, at the intersection of Fort McHenry and Ferry Bar Channels 0.6 mile southeast of Fort McHenry, is 8 miles from the mouth of the river, 150 miles above the Virginia Capes, and 62 miles from Delaware River.

(33)     Principal imports of the port are general cargo, petroleum products, coke of coal, iron ore, aluminum manganese, inorganic chemicals, salt, gypsum, lumber, motor vehicles, fertilizers and sugar. Principal exports are chiefly general cargo, coal, automobiles and machinery. Coastwise receipts include petroleum products, sand, cement, fertilizers, sulfur, sugar and lumber; shipments are petroleum and metal products.

(34)
### Channels
(35)     Federal project channels were discussed at the beginning of the chapter. The branch channels will be covered in the descriptions of the tributaries.

(36)
### Anchorages
(37)     General and dead ship anchorages are in Baltimore Harbor. (See **33 CFR 110.1** and **110.158**, chapter 2, for limits and regulations.)

(38)
### Tides and currents
(39)     Prolonged winds of constant direction may cause substantial variation in the tide. Currents in the harbor are 0.8 knot on the flood and ebb.

(40)
### Weather
(41)     Baltimore is in a region about midway between the rigorous climates of the north and the mild climates of the south and adjacent to the modifying influences of the Chesapeake Bay and Atlantic Ocean to the east and the Appalachian Mountains to the west. The net effect is to produce a more equable climate compared to inland locations of the same latitude.

(50)

Baltimore Harbor, Maryland
Image courtesy of Waterway Images (2006)

— N —

(42)    Rainfall distribution throughout the year is rather uniform; however, the greatest intensities are confined to the summer and early fall, the season for hurricanes and severe thunderstorms. Rainfall during this period occurs principally in the form of thundershowers, and rainfall totals during these months vary appreciably, depending on the number of thundershowers that occur largely by chance in a given locality. Hurricane-force winds, however, may occur on rare occasions due to a severe cold front or a severe thunderstorm. The greatest damage by hurricanes is that produced along waterfronts and shores by the high tides and waves.

(43)    In summer, the area is under the influence of the large semipermanent high-pressure system commonly known as the Bermuda High and centered over the Atlantic Ocean near latitude 30°N. This high-pressure system brings a circulation of warm, humid air masses over the area from the deep south. The proximity of large water areas and the inflow of southerly winds contribute to high relative humidities during much of the year.

(44)    January is the coldest month, and July, the warmest. Winter and spring have the highest average windspeeds. Snowfall occurs on about 25 days per year on the average; however, an average of only 9 days annually produce snowfalls greater than 1.0 inch. Although heaviest amounts of snow generally fall in February, occasional heavy falls occur as late as March. Records for the period, August 1950 through December 1967, indicate that the average date of the last temperature as low as 32° in the spring is April 15, while the average date of the first temperature as low as 32° in the autumn is October 26.

(45)    Glaze or freezing rain occurs an average of two to three times per year, generally in January or February. However, some occurrences have been noted in November and December. Some years pass without the occurrence of freezing rain, while in others it occurs on as many as 8 to 10 days. Sleet is observed on about 5 days annually. The sleet season begins as early as November in some years and ends as late as March in some cases, with the greatest frequency of occurrence in January.

(46)    The National Weather Service office is at Baltimore-Washington International Airport, about 7 miles southward of Baltimore. Barometers may be compared there or by telephone/internet.

(47)    **Fogs** occur chiefly from October to March, inclusive. From April to September there are only a few days with dense fogs. Very light winds clear the fog away.

(48)

### Ice

(49)    Baltimore Harbor is frozen over during severe winters, but the ice-breakers and the larger power-driven vessels keep the dredged channels open so that self-propelled vessels seldom have difficulty in entering the harbor. Ice conditions in the main channel are most severe in the vicinity of Sevenfoot Knoll Light, where ice moving from the northern end of Chesapeake Bay tends

to collect in packs. Navigation from Baltimore to the upper end of the bay and the Chesapeake and Delaware Canal is likely to be interrupted by ice for short periods during an average winter.

(51)

### Pilotage, Baltimore

(52) Pilotage is compulsory for all foreign vessels and for U.S. vessels under register in the foreign trade bound to or from the port of Baltimore. Pilotage is optional for U.S. vessels under enrollment in the coastwise trade that have on board a pilot licensed by the Federal Government for these waters.

(53) The Association of Maryland Pilots has an office in Baltimore (telephone: 410–276–1337, fax: 410–276–364, telex: 87–574 MARPILOTS BALTIMORE, cable address: MARPILOT BALTIMORE). They provide service to any port in Maryland and service between Baltimore and the entrance of the Chesapeake Bay at Cape Henry, VA. The pilot office also monitors VHF-FM channel 11.

(54) The Chesapeake and Interstate Pilots Association offers pilot services to U.S. vessels engaged in the coastwise trade and public vessels to or from Baltimore via the Chesapeake Bay if the vessel is entering from sea at Cape Henry or transiting between any port or place on the Chesapeake Bay and its tributaries. Pilot service is also offered to vessels to or from Baltimore that are transiting the Chesapeake and Delaware Canal. Pilots will meet vessels upon prior arrangement at Cape Henlopen or any port or place on the Delaware Bay and River, at Cape Henry or any port or place on the Chesapeake Bay and its tributaries. Pilots will also provide all pilot services required from the port of departure to the port of arrival. Arrangements for pilots may be made through the ships' agents or the pilot office in Norfolk (telephone, 757–855–2733).

(55) Interport Pilots Agency, Inc., offers pilotage to public vessels and private vessels in the coastal trade operating between Baltimore Harbor and many northeast ports via the Chesapeake and Delaware Canal. The 24-hour telephone number is 732–787–5554 and the email address is *interport@verizon.net*. Additional information about Interport Pilots can be obtained at *interportpilots. com.*

(56) Pilotage information for incoming vessels is given in chapters 6, 7 and 9.

(57)

### Towage

(58) Tugs up to 3,800 hp are available at all times to assist vessels arriving or departing, in docking or undocking and in shifting within the harbor. Long-distance towage is also available. Tug services are usually arranged far in advance through ships' agents.

(59)

### Quarantine, customs, immigration and agricultural quarantine

(60) (See chapter 3, Vessel Arrival Inspections, and appendix for addresses.)

(61) **Quarantine** is enforced in accordance with regulations of the U.S. Public Health Service. (See Public Health Service, chapter 1.)

(62) Baltimore is a **customs port of entry.**

(63)

### Harbor regulations

(64) The Maryland Port Administration has general jurisdiction over the physical operation of Baltimore Harbor and issues rules and regulations pertaining to the use of the public wharves and piers. The Port Administration office is at the World Trade Center Baltimore, Baltimore, MD 21202.

(65)

### Wharves

(66) Baltimore has more than 200 piers and wharves at Locust Point, Port Covington, Fairfield, Curtis Bay, Hawkins Point, Sparrows Point, Dundalk, Lower Canton, Canton and Lazaretto Point and in the Inner Harbor. For information of the latest depths contact the Maryland Port Administration. All of the facilities have direct highway connections, and most have railroad connections. Water and electrical shore-power connections are available at most piers and wharves.

(67) General cargo at the port is usually handled by ship's tackle. There are 22 traveling container cranes with lift capacities from 27.5 to 50 long tons and 5 full-portal gantry cranes with lift capacities up to 100 tons at the Port of Baltimore. Numerous warehouses and cold storage facilities adjacent to the waterfront are available. Several municipal piers, administered by the city harbormaster whose office is on Municipal Pier 4, are used mainly by coastwise vessels.

(68)

### Supplies

(69) Marine supplies of all kinds are available in the Port of Baltimore. All grades of heavy marine bunker fuel, lubricants and diesel oil can be obtained. Vessels may bunker directly at marine oil terminals or may be serviced by barge at anchor. Most of the piers and wharves described have water and shore power connections. Water can also be delivered by waterboat anywhere in the harbor.

(70)

### Repairs

(71) Marine railways can haul out vessels up to 125 feet and up to 300 tons. Shafts of any size required can be produced in the port. Several smaller repair facilities along the tributaries cater to yachtsmen and small-boat operators.

(72) Baltimore has extensive facilities for wrecking and salvage. In addition to equipment especially designed for salvage operations, there are heavy hoisting facilities

(90)

Patapsco River (Francis Scott Key Bridge), Maryland
Image courtesy of Waterway Images (2006)

—N➤

which, though primarily designed for private industrial purposes, are available in case of need.

(73)

**Communications**

(74) Nearly all the piers and wharves in Baltimore Harbor are near the center of the city, and all are connected to it by wide paved streets. Most of the piers and wharves have direct connections with mainline railroads whose tracks are connected with all parts of the port area.

(75) The Port of Baltimore is served by two Class I railroads. The Canton Railroad is a terminal line that operates about 35 miles of track in the port area and connects with the major railroads.

(76) More than 100 shipping companies connect Baltimore with principal U.S. and foreign ports by regular sailings in the overseas, coastwise and intercoastal trades. About 150 truck carriers service the port.

(77) Several major airlines provide frequent scheduled services between **Baltimore-Washington International Thurgood Marshall Airport**, inland about 7 miles southwestward of Fort McHenry, and domestic and overseas points.

(78) The **Baltimore Maritime Exchange**, located at the Maritime Center, provides to its members information concerning ship movements, local harbor conditions, weather data and various other services. The Exchange operates on VHF-FM channel 11 from 0400 to 1900, call sign WHX-654. Members are requested to contact the

Association of Maryland Pilots on VHF-FM channel 11 at other than previously mentioned times; call sign KMC-290.

(79) **Sparrows Point**, the former site of a large industrial area, is a projection of land on the northeast side of Patapsco River, 3 miles above the mouth. Access to the wharves at Sparrows Point are through two dredged channels leading north from Brewerton Channel to the south side of the point. Channels also lead to wharves on the west side. These channels are well-marked with lights and lighted and unlighted buoys.

(80) **Bear Creek**, on the northeast side of Patapsco River 4 miles above the mouth, has channel depths of 8 feet or more almost to the head, 3.5 miles above the mouth. Rocks, covered 2 feet, are southeast of Sollers Point in about 39°13'10"N., 76°31'01"W. Numerous piles and obstructions are in the entrance to the creek between Coffin Point and Lloyd Point. A fixed highway bridge with a clearance of 55 feet crosses Bear Creek from the northern side of **Coffin Point** to the opposite shore. An overhead power cable close south of the bridge has an authorized clearance of 46 feet, with 75 feet between the charted lights.

(81) **Peachorchard Cove**, on the west side of Bear Creek about 0.8 mile above the entrance, has depths of 7 feet for 0.4 mile to within 0.1 mile of its head.

(82) The Peninsula Expressway Bridge, 2.1 miles above the mouth of Bear Creek, has a bascule span with a

clearance of 25 feet. (See **33 CFR 117.1** through **117.59** and **117.543**, chapter 2, for drawbridge regulations.) The railroad bridge, just northeast of the expressway bridge, has a swing span with a clearance of 8 feet.

(83)       **Lynch Cove**, on the northwest side of Bear Creek 2.4 miles above the mouth, has general midchannel depths of 8 feet or more for about 0.6 mile, thence shoaling to 1 foot to the head of the cove. There are several small-craft facilities in Lynch Cove.

(84)       **Schoolhouse Cove**, 3.2 miles above the mouth, has depths of 7 feet to near the head. A small boatyard in the cove can haul out boats up to 45 feet for hull and engine repairs. A yacht club is on the east side of Bear Creek just below Schoolhouse Cove.

(85)       The highway bridge over Bear Creek just above Schoolhouse Cove, has a bascule span with a clearance of 12 feet. (See **33 CFR 117.1** through **117.59** and **117.543**, chapter 2, for drawbridge regulations.)

(86)       A 6 mph **speed limit** is enforced in Bear Creek above Lynch Cove on Saturdays, Sundays and holidays.

(87)       **Fort Carroll** is a stone-and-concrete structure on the northeast side of Patapsco River main channel 4.4 miles above the mouth. The white tower of the abandoned lighthouse is on the west front of the fort.

(88)       **Hawkins Point**, on the southwest side of Patapsco River 4.5 miles above the mouth, is at the southeastern limits of Baltimore. There are many obstructions surrounding the point. A privately dredged and marked 33-foot channel leads to a 720-foot-long cargo pier with rail and truck connections 0.4 mile northwestward of the point.

(89)       The **Francis Scott Key Bridge**, a fixed highway bridge with a clearance of 185 feet, crosses the Patapsco River between Hawkins Point and Sollers Point.

(91)       **Curtis Bay**, on the southwest side of Patapsco River 6 miles above the mouth, is the approach to large coal and oil wharves and to several plants. The entrance is between Leading Point and Fishing Point, 0.8 mile to the northwestward. The federal project depth in Curtis Bay Channel is 50 feet. (See Notices to Mariners and latest editions of charts for controlling depths.)

(92)       A privately dredged channel leads to the gypsum pier with mooring dolphins and conveyor belt 0.2 mile west of Leading Point.

(93)       The petroleum terminals on **Fishing Point**, the ore pier on the southwest side of **Stonehouse Cove,** the coal pier at the head of Curtis Bay and the other deep-draft facilities in Curtis Bay are listed in the facilities table earlier in this chapter.

(94)       **Curtis Creek** empties into the head of Curtis Bay from southward between **Sledds Point** and **Ferry Point**. A dredged channel in the creek has a federal project depth of 35 feet in the lower reach and 22 feet in the middle and upper reaches. (See Notice to Mariners and the latest edition of the charts for controlling depths.) The channel is marked by lighted and unlighted buoys.

(95)       **Cabin Branch**, on the west side of Curtis Creek just south of Ferry Point, has depths of 17 feet or more to within 0.1 mile of a fixed bridge 0.4 mile above the entrance.

(96)       A shipyard on the west side of Curtis Creek just north of the Pennington Avenue bridge has a marine railway that can handle vessels up to 125 feet for hull and engine repairs; cranes to 65 tons are available.

(97)       Curtis Creek is crossed by the three bascule bridges, 1 mile above the mouth at Walnut Point. The Pennington Avenue bridge has a vertical clearance of 40 feet. Just south are the east and west bound spans of the I-695 bridges, both with a vertical clearance of 58 feet. The railroad bridge, 1.3 miles above the mouth, has a swing span with a clearance of 13 feet. (See **33 CFR 117.1** through **117.59** and **117.557**, chapter 2, for drawbridge regulations.)

(98)       **Arundel Cove** is on the east side of Curtis Creek 1.6 miles above the entrance. The Coast Guard yard is on the north side of the cove. A highway bridge 0.4 mile above the entrance to the cove has a 28-foot fixed span with a clearance of 6 feet.

(99)       A depth of 13 feet can be carried up Curtis Creek from Arundel Cove to the forks 2.3 miles above the entrance. **Furnace Creek**, the west fork, in 1976, had reported depths of 11 feet or more for 0.8 mile, then shoals gradually to 4 feet at the fixed highway bridge 0.4 mile farther up; the bridge has a clearance of 8 feet. Overhead power cables about 0.1 mile above the bridge have a least clearance of 46 feet. **Marley Creek**, the middle fork, in 1997 had a reported controlling depth of 5 feet for 1.6 miles, thence 3.5 feet to the fixed bridge about 0.4 mile farther up; the bridge has a clearance of 9 feet. Overhead power cables crossing Marley Creek have a least clearance of 28 feet.

(100)       A marine service pier on the west side of Marley Creek 1.3 miles above the forks has depths of 12 feet at the face; gasoline and water are available. A marine railway can handle boats up to 50 feet for hull and engine repairs.

(101)       The **Fairfield** section of Baltimore begins 6.5 miles above the mouth of Patapsco River and extends upriver along the southwest side for more than 1 mile. Most of the piers and wharves handle paper, petroleum products, sulfur, chemicals, fertilizers, scrap metal and lumber. The deep-draft facilities at Fairfield are listed in the facilities table earlier in this chapter.

(102)       **Dundalk Marine Terminal,** on the east side of Patapsco River 6.5 miles above the mouth, is accessed through a channel leading northeast from Fort McHenry Channel. The channel is marked by lighted and unlighted buoys and a **032.8°** private lighted range. Several cranes have been lost overboard and some ships have parted their lines while berthed at Dundalk Marine Terminal during extreme wind conditions. Mariners should contact Maryland Port Administration for details about safety requirements. The facilities at the terminal are listed in the facilities table earlier in this chapter.

(107)

Baltimore, Maryland
Image courtesy of Waterway Images (2006)

N

(103)　　A dredged channel leads into **Colgate Creek** for about 0.3 mile and is used to access the facilities on the west side of Dundalk Marine Terminal.

(104)　　The **Lower Canton** section of Baltimore begins on the north side of Patapsco River, 7.5 miles above the mouth, and extends westward from the Seagirt Marine Terminal to **Lazaretto Point**. Dredged and buoyed channels lead to the principal piers, which handle general cargo, grain, ore and chemicals. The deep-draft facilities in this section are listed in the facilities table earlier in this chapter.

(105)　　Patapsco River turns sharply westward at the intersection of Ferry Bar Channel and main Fort McHenry Channel 7.8 miles above the mouth. About 0.7 mile wide between **Fort McHenry** on the north and Fairfield on the south, the river narrows to a width of 150 yards 10 miles above the mouth and meanders off to the southwestward while the deeper channel continues westward into **Middle Branch.**

(106)　　**Ferry Bar** is a point on the north side of Ferry Bar Channel 1.5 miles westward of Fort McHenry.

(108)　　Ferry Bar Channel (East Section) is marked by lighted buoys and has a project depth of 42 feet. (See Notice to Mariners and latest editions of the charts for controlling depths.)

(109)　　A marked channel leads from the west end of Ferry Bar Channel to the Hanover Street bascule bridge.

(110)　　The **South Locust Point Marine Terminal** begins 0.8 mile west of Fort McHenry and extends west and southwestward to include Port Covington near Ferry Bar. The approach is 1.2 miles westward along Ferry Bar Channel. The deep-draft facilities of the marine terminal are listed in the facilities table earlier in this chapter.

(111)　　Depths of about 5 to 8 feet are at the outer ends of piers at the boatyards northwestward of Ferry Bar. Hull and engine repairs can be made. The largest marine railway can handle boats up to 60 feet; largest mobile lift, 20 tons. Gasoline, diesel fuel, slips and some marine supplies are available.

(112)　　The Hanover Street bridge over Middle Branch 0.3 mile above Ferry Bar has a bascule span with a clearance of 38 feet at the center and 23 feet for a central width of 150 feet. The Western Maryland Railway bridge, 1 mile above Ferry Bar, has a swing span with a clearance of 9 feet. (See **33 CFR 117.1** through **117.59** and **117.566**, chapter 2, for drawbridge regulations.)

(113)　　Most of the marine facilities in Middle Branch are used by small vessels and barges for delivery of petroleum and coal for local consumption.

(114)　　**Northwest Harbor**, the northerly branch of Patapsco River, is entered between Fort McHenry and Lazaretto Point, 8.2 miles above the mouth of Patapsco River. East Channel, a dredged channel with a project depth of 49 feet, extends north from the entrance for about 0.7 mile to a turning basin. West Channel, with a project depth of

40 feet, branches northwest from East Channel for about 0.8 mile to a turning basin. (See Notice to Mariners and latest editions of the charts for controlling depths.) Above the West Channel turning basin, depths of about 25 to 21 feet can be carried to the head of Northwest Harbor at Inner Harbor.

(115)     **Fort McHenry Tunnel** crosses under the entrance to Northwest Harbor, extending from Lazaretto Point to a point about 0.2 mile westward of Fort McHenry.

(116)     The **North Locust Point Marine Terminal** is on the southwest side between Fort McHenry and Locust Point. Most of the piers handle general cargo, but some also handle bulk. The piers and wharves on the east and north sides of Northwest Harbor handle general cargo, coal, petroleum products, chemicals and fertilizers. The deep-draft facilities in this section are listed in the facilities table earlier in this chapter.

(117)     The ship repair facilities in Northwest Harbor can handle large ocean-going vessels. The graving dock on the southwest side of the harbor 0.4 mile above Fort McHenry is 460 feet long, 58 feet wide at the bottom, with a water depth of 18 feet. A shipbuilding basin, 1,200 feet long and 198 feet wide, is on the west side of Sparrows Point.

(118)     **Inner Harbor**, at the head of Northwest Harbor, has a marina on the south side with depths of 12 feet or more at the slips. Berths, electricity, gasoline, diesel fuel and some marine supplies are available.

(119)     A 6-knot **speed limit** is enforced in Inner Harbor.

(120)

## ENC - US5MD12M
## Chart - 12278

(121)     **Swan Point** (39°08'41"N., 76°16'44"W.), on the east side of Chesapeake Bay opposite Patapsco River entrance, has been mentioned in chapter 14.

(122)     **Tolchester Beach**, on the east side of Chesapeake Bay 4.5 miles north-northeast of Swan Point, has a privately dredged entrance channel and basin. In 2003, the reported approach and alongside depth was 6 feet. Gasoline, diesel fuel, marine supplies, pump-out station, storage, water, ice, electricity and limited berths are available. A 55-ton mobile lift is available for repairs.

(123)     **Fairlee Creek**, on the east side of Chesapeake Bay 8.5 miles north-northeastward of Swan Point, has a narrow entrance between a jetty on the east and a long, low hook on the west. The privately buoyed entrance has depths of about 6 feet. In 2007, shoaling to 3.3 feet was reported in the entrance. A marina with berthing facilities is on the east side of the creek just inside the entrance; gasoline, diesel fuel, pump-out station and some marine supplies are available. A 50-ton mobile lift is available for hull and engine repairs.

(124)     **Worton Point** is 152.5 miles above the Virginia Capes.

(125)     About 1.5 miles southward of Worton Point is **Worton Creek**, which has depths of 10 to 12 feet in the broad bight at the entrance and 7 feet inside for 1.4 miles. Good anchorage, protected from easterly winds, is available in depths of 11 to 12 feet just inside the entrance. The channel into the creek is marked by a lighted buoy and daybeacons.

(126)     A marina at **Green Point Wharf**, on the east side of Worton Creek about 1.1 miles above the mouth, has gasoline, diesel fuel, berths with electricity, a pump-out station, a 15-ton lift, water, ice and some marine supplies; limited engine repairs can be done. The marina at **Buck Neck Landing**, on the east side of the creek 1.4 miles above the entrance, has gasoline, diesel fuel and berthing facilities and marine supplies are available. Lifts to 70 tons are available for repairs. The public bulkhead adjoining the fuel pier has depths of about 6 feet alongside.

(127)     **Pooles Island**, 10 miles northeastward of Baltimore Harbor entrance, is a portion of the Aberdeen Proving Ground complex constituting prohibited land areas and dangerous contiguous water areas. Landing is prohibited to all personnel and boats, primarily because of the presence of hazardous unexploded ordnance and because such landings violate federal regulations. (See **33 CFR 334.140**, chapter 2, for limits and regulations of the **restricted area**.) **Pooles Island Light** (39°17'26"N., 76°15'59"W.), 38 feet above the water, is shown from a stone tower on the northwest side of the island.

(128)

## Local magnetic disturbance

(129)     Differences of as much as 5° from the normal variation have been observed in the channel from Pooles Island to Howell Point.

(130)     **Pooles Island Bar Light** (39°15'42"N., 76°16'41"W.), 27 feet above the water, is shown from a black skeleton tower on a cylinder base, in depths of 15 feet 0.8 mile south-southwestward of the island; the light is 147.1 miles above the Virginia Capes.

(131)     A buoyed lane extends southwestward between fishtrap areas from eastward of Pooles Island to the Baltimore channel 1 mile southward of North Point. Mariners are cautioned that the southwest end of the lane runs over a discontinued spoil area. Pooles Island Bar Light, a sector light for the channel, is on the northwest side of the lane.

(132)     The approach to the rivers between North Point (39°11'42"N., 76°26'38"W.) and Pooles Island is through a buoyed side lane southwestward of Pooles Island Bar Light.

(133)     **Hawk Cove**, 5 miles north-northeastward of North Point, has depths of 8 to 11 feet and is a good anchorage.

(134)     A shallow passage known as **Pleasure Island Channel**, 3 miles northeast of North Point, leads to Hawk Cove. In 2010, the controlling depth was 7.5 feet. The channel is marked by lights and daybeacons.

(135)     **Back River**, which flows into the southwest end of Hawk Cove, has depths of 7 to 4 feet for 6 miles to a fixed highway bridge with a clearance of 16 feet; overhead power cables above and below the bridge have

a clearance of 34 feet. Even the smallest boats seldom go above the bridge. The channel, marked by private buoys and day beacons, is clear except for a 4-foot middle ground about halfway between Hawk Cove and the bridge.

(136)    There are small-craft facilities on both sides of Back River.

(137)
### ENCs - US5MD12M, US5MD14M, US4MD82M
### Charts - 12278, 12274, 12273

(138)    **Middle River**, 6.5 miles north-northeastward of North Point, is entered through a marked dredged channel thay leads to an anchorage basin at the Martin Marietta Company plant at the head of **Dark Head Creek**, the east fork of the river 3.2 miles above the mouth. The west fork of Middle River has depths of 7 feet to within 0.5 mile of a fixed bridge near the head.

(139)    A 6 mph. **speed limit** is enforced on Saturdays, Sundays and holidays.

(140)    **Sue Creek**, on the south side of the entrance to Middle River, has depths of about 7 feet to the yacht club just inside the entrance, thence depths of 5 to 3 feet for 1 mile inside. The entrance is marked by a light.

(141)    **Galloway Creek**, a broad cove on the north side of Middle River just inside the entrance, has depths of 8 to 5 feet except along the shoreline.

(142)    **Frog Mortar Creek**, on the northeast side of Middle River 1.5 miles above the mouth, has depths of 6 to 8 feet. A 12-foot marked channel leads from Middle River to the Martin Marietta seaplane basin on the west side of the creek 0.5 mile above the entrance. A 6 mph **speed limit** is enforced on Saturdays, Sundays and holidays.

(143)    **Warning**–Small-craft operators in Frog Mortar Creek are advised to use caution in the vicinity of Martin State Airport. Small-craft with masts exceeding 37 feet in height above the waterline create an obstruction to low-flying aircraft. Operators of such vessels transiting Frog Mortar Creek should contact Martin State Airport Control Tower by telephone at 410–682–8848 when visibility is less than 1.0 statute mile so approaching aircraft can be warned. Tower operations are from 0600 to 2200 daily.

(144)    **Hopkins Creek**, on the southwest side of Middle River 2.6 miles above the mouth, has depths of 8 to 5 feet.

(145)    Numerous small-craft facilities are at the upper end of Middle River and in most of the tributaries.

(146)    **Seneca Creek**, 8 miles north-northeastward of North Point, has depths of 8 feet in the entrance and 5 to 6 feet into the several arms. A light marks the outer end of the shoal on the east side of the entrance. Gasoline, slips and some marine supplies can be obtained at several marinas along the creek. Lifts to 25 tons are available for hull and engine repairs.

(147)    **Gunpowder River**, 9 miles northeastward of North Point, is entered through a channel marked by lighted buoys and lights. **Spry Island Shoal**, in mid-entrance, is east of the entrance channel and reported to be covered 2 to 4 feet and should be avoided. In 1998, the river channel

had reported depths of 8 feet for 2 miles, thence 2 to 9 feet for 4 miles, thence 3 feet in a privately dredged channel leading to a creek below **Joppatowne**. In 1998–2001, depths of 5 feet were in the middle of the creek below Joppatowne; thence in 1998–2000, depths range from 3 to 6 feet in the middle of the marina basin at Joppatowne.

(148)    The fixed railroad bridge 6.3 miles above the mouth has a 19-foot channel span with a clearance of 11 feet. An overhead power cable at the bridge has a clearance of 37 feet.

(149)    Above the bridge, Joppatowne Marina has slips, gasoline, launching ramps, bath houses and some marine supplies.

(150)    Spry Island Shoal and most of Gunpowder River are within the **Aberdeen Proving Ground** complex, a **restricted area**, shown on the charts. Some waters of the Aberdeen Proving Ground are closed to the public at all times. Others have a limited access during specified hours. (See **33 CFR 334.140**, chapter 2, for limits and regulations.) The area is marked by private seasonal buoys.

(151)    It is stressed that opening these restricted and dangerous waters to navigation in the Aberdeen Proving Ground complex does not include the privilege of landing personnel or boats on any of the government property. All these land areas constitute an extremely hazardous risk due to the presence of unexploded ordnance. Any landings constitute punishable federal offenses.

(152)    Additional information on this subject is contained in the pamphlet "Boater's Guide to Restricted Water Zone," published by Aberdeen Proving Ground. This pamphlet is available at most local marinas in the area.

(153)
### ENC - US5MD14M
### Chart - 12274

(154)    **Bush River** is on the northwest side of Chesapeake Bay 152 miles above the Virginia Capes. The lower 5 miles of the river are within the Aberdeen Proving Ground complex constituting prohibited land areas and restricted and dangerous water areas.

(155)    The river has minimum depths of 7 feet to the railroad bridge 6.3 miles above the mouth, thence 5 to 6 feet for another 1.5 miles. The approach to the river and the channel inside are marked by lighted and unlighted buoys and a light to **Doves Cove**. Lights mark wrecks near **Redman Cove** and just north of **Tapler Point**. A lighted warning buoy marks a submerged pipe on the west side of the river between **Wilson Point** and **Beach Point**. A submerged pipe, marked by a private light and two daybeacons, is on the east side of the river, near **Sod Run**.

(156)    The railroad bridge 6.3 miles above the mouth of Bush River has a 35-foot bascule span with a vertical clearance of 12 feet. (See **33 CFR 117.1** through **117.59** and **117.547**, chapter 2, for drawbridge regulations.) The power cable at the bridge has a clearance of 35 feet. A

power cable about 200 yards below the bridge has a least clearance of 25 feet and is supported by towers on either bank and a tower near midriver; the towers are marked by private lights.

(157) **Otter Point Creek**, on the west side of Bush River 0.5 mile above the railroad bridge, has depths of 3 feet for 1 mile above the entrance. The overhead power cable across the creek has an authorized clearance of 49 feet. The towers that support the cable are marked by private lights.

(158) Marinas in Otter Point Creek and on the eastern shore of the Bush River just above the bridge have slips, gasoline, launching ramps and some marine supplies. Hull and engine repairs can be made; the largest haul-out capacities are: railway, 45 feet; lift, 12 tons.

(159) **Still Pond** (39°20'25"N., 76°08'30"W.), a bight on the southeast side of Chesapeake Bay 154.7 miles above the Virginia Capes, has general depths of 9 to 11 feet and is a good anchorage for small craft during easterly winds. **Churn Creek**, which empties into the southwest corner of the bight, has depths of 2 feet in the very narrow entrance and deeper water inside.

(160) **Stillpond Creek**, at the southeast corner of the bight, is entered through a narrow privately dredged channel. The entrance channel is marked by lights, buoys and daybeacons. Stillpond Creek entrance channel is subject to frequent shoaling; local knowledge is advised.

(161)

**Coast Guard**

(162) **Stillpond Coast Guard Station** is on the north side of the entrance to Stillpond Creek.

(163) **Sassafras River** joins Chesapeake Bay from eastward 159 miles above the Virginia Capes. The entrance is between **Howell Point** and **Grove Point,** 3.5 miles east-northeastward; the entrance width normal to the channel is about 1 mile. The river is used by vessels drawing up to 12 feet, but the usual draft is 6 feet or less.

(164) The river channel has depths of 13 feet or more to a point 1 mile above the U.S. Route 213 bascule bridge, thence 7 to 3 feet for another 2 miles. The channel is broad and straight for the first 4 miles, then is narrow and crooked in places but is marked as far as the highway bridge 10 miles above the mouth.

(165) **Betterton** is a village on the south side of Sassafras River 2 miles eastward of Howell Point. The principal wharf has depths of 9 feet at the outer end. Excursion boats from Baltimore call at the wharf during the summer. Gasoline and some supplies are available in the summer.

(166) **Turner Creek**, on the south side of Sassafras River 4.5 miles above the mouth, has depths of at least 7 feet in the very narrow entrance and 5 feet for 0.6 mile upstream. The entrance is marked by a seasonal buoy. The creek has several small landings along its shores and is much traveled by local pleasure boats.

(167) **Kentmore Park** is a small community on the south side of Sassafras River 5 miles above the mouth. The community wharf has depths of 7 feet at the upper end.

(168) **Fredericktown**, on the north side, and **Georgetown**, on the south side of Sassafras River 10 miles above the mouth, are connected by a highway bridge that has a 40-foot bascule span with a clearance of 5 feet. The bridgetender monitors VHF-FM channel 16 and works on channels 13 and 68; call sign KYU-699. (See **33 CFR 117.1** through **117.59** and **117.570**, chapter 2, for drawbridge regulations.) Many yachts and pleasure craft harbor here. The **speed limit** is 6 miles per hour in Sassafras River in an area extending about 0.5 mile above and 0.5 mile below the highway bridge.

(169) There are numerous small-craft facilities on both sides of the river just below the bridge. Berthing, electricity, water, gasoline, diesel fuel, pump-out station, storage and marine supplies can be obtained at these marinas. Mobile lifts are available to 45-tons for hull and engine repairs.

(170) The unmarked channel in Sassafras River above the bridge is narrow in places and difficult to follow without local knowledge. A marina on the south side of the river 1 mile above the bridge has gasoline and some supplies; an 18-ton lift can haul out boats for hull and engine repairs.

(171) **Spesutie Narrows** (39°25.2'N., 76°05.7'W.), on the northwest side of Chesapeake Bay 159 miles above the Virginia Capes, is between the mainland and **Spesutie Island**, close to the eastward. A privately dredged channel leads from the flats off the southern entrance into and along the narrows to a basin at the Army landings at Mulberry Point. In 2001, the reported controlling depth was 6 feet to the basin with 4 to 7 feet at the landings. The entrance channel is marked by buoys and privately maintained lighted ranges, and the inner channel is marked by daybeacons.

(172) The upper end of the narrows is closed by a solid-fill causeway.

(173) Spesutie Island and Spesutie Narrows are within the Aberdeen Proving Ground complex constituting prohibited land areas and restricted and dangerous contiguous water areas. (See **33 CFR 334.140**, chapter 2, for limits and regulations.)

(174) **Elk River**, on the east side of Chesapeake Bay 162 miles above the Virginia Capes, is the approach to the Chesapeake and Delaware Canal, which is described in chapter 7. The entrance to the river is between **Grove Point** and **Turkey Point**, 3 miles north-northeastward; the latter point is a thinly wooded bluff with abrupt slopes at the south end. The entrance width normal to the channel is about 1 mile.

(175) **Note**–Mariners are required to observe the federal speed regulation when navigating throughout Elk River, Back Creek and Chesapeake and Delaware Canal. (See Navigation Regulation **33 CFR 162.40(b)**, chapter 7, for the regulated speed limit and other warnings.)

(176) A **special anchorage** is on the east side of Turkey Point in **Jacobs Nose Cove**. (See **33 CFR 110.1** and **110.71**, chapter 2, for limits and regulations.)

(177) The current velocity is 0.8 knot.

(192)

Susquehanna River, Maryland
Image courtesy of Waterway Images (2006)

(178)
**Local magnetic disturbance**

(179)     Differences of 3° to 8° from normal variation have been observed in Elk River channel from Grove Point to Courthouse Point.

(180)     **Bohemia River**, on the east side of Elk River 5 miles above the mouth, has depths of 7 feet or more for 4 miles to the junction of **Great Bohemia Creek** and **Little Bohemia Creek**, thence 6 to 4 feet for 1.5 miles in Great Bohemia Creek and 7 feet for 1 mile in Little Bohemia Creek. The channel is broad and easy to follow for 2 miles above the entrance, then becomes very narrow and crooked. In 1980, shoaling to an unknown extent was reported in the entrance to the Bohemia River in about 39°28'45"N., 75°56'13"W.

(181)     The cove on the southwest side of Bohemia River 3 miles above the entrance has depths of 3 to 5 feet and is much used as a small-boat anchorage.

(182)     A highway bridge 4.0 miles above the mouth at Bohemia River has a 40-foot fixed span with a clearance of 30 feet. The **speed limit** is 6 miles per hour from the highway bridge to a point about 1 mile downstream in Bohemia River.

(183)     There are several small-craft facilities along the north side of Bohemia River, about 1.5 miles above the entrance and along the south side of the river below the bridge.

(184)     **Old Town Point Wharf**, on the southeast side of Elk River 7 miles above the mouth, has depths of 10 feet at the outer end. This is a government wharf and a vessel identification and monitoring station for the west end of the Chesapeake and Delaware Canal. (See **33 CFR 207.100**, chapter 7, for navigation regulations.)

(185)     **Back Creek**, on the east side of Elk River 9 miles above the mouth and 171.4 miles above the Virginia Capes, is the route of the Chesapeake and Delaware Canal and has been described in chapter 7.

(186)     Above Back Creek, the natural channel in Elk River is marked by private buoys to just above **Locust Point** (39°33'54"N., 75°50'56"W.). Depths in the narrow crooked channel vary considerably, ranging from about 10 feet at the south end to about 1 foot off Locust Point; the chart is the best guide. In 1978, a depth of 1 foot was reported to be available in the winding channel above Locust Point. For a distance of about 0.4 mile northward of Locust Point and about 0.2 mile southward of **Whitehall Point**, the channel is reported to be marked by private stakes. Mariners bound for Elkton are advised to seek local knowledge when transiting the channel.

(187)     Small-craft facilities are on both sides of Elk River 5 miles above Old Town Point Wharf.

(188)     **Big Elk Creek**, on the east, and **Little Elk Creek**, on the west, have depths of 3 feet to the fixed highway bridges 0.6 and 0.4 mile above their respective mouths. The channels in each are narrow and crooked with

numerous snags and shoals that are unmarked. Extreme caution is advised beyond the junction. **Elkton**, between the creeks and 16 miles above the mouth of Elk River, is on the main line of the Penn Central Railroad and has several industrial plants.

(189)      The natural channel of Chesapeake Bay turns northward off the mouth of Elk River and splits into two branches between Turkey Point and Spesutie Island, 2.3 miles to the westward. One branch rounds Spesutie Island and continues northward to Susquehanna River; the other hugs the west side of Turkey Point and high thickly wooded **Elk Neck**, and continues to Northeast River. The flats between the two branches are very shallow, and large areas bare at low water.

(190)      **Swan Creek**, on the western shore of Chesapeake Bay, just north of Spetsutie Island, has depths of 4 feet in the entrance and 3 to 10 feet inside for about 2 miles. The creek is little used except by boats of the U.S. Army. An overhead power cable with a reported clearance of 38 feet crosses the northern part of the creek.

(191)      **Susquehanna River** empties into the head of Chesapeake Bay from northwestward, 170.1 miles above the Virginia Capes. The entrance is between **Concord Point** and **Perry Point**, 1 mile east-northeastward. A marked dredged channel leads through the flats from deep water in Chesapeake Bay to Havre de Grace. A side channel leads to a basin at City Park at Havre de Grace. It is reported that the river is usually closed by ice for a few weeks during the winter, but ice gorges and freshets are infrequent because of the dams upstream.

(193)      A **seaplane landing area** is in the middle of the entrance to Susquehanna River; mariners are advised to use caution.

(194)      **Havre de Grace**, on the west side of the entrance to the Susquehanna River, is on the main lines of Amtrak and the CSX Transportation, Inc. The town has many pleasure craft and a significant amount of tug and barge traffic. Most wharves along the waterfront are in poor condition.

(195)      A rock covered 6 feet and marked by buoys on the east, west and south sides, is about 200 yards off the Havre de Grace wharves and 500 yards below the drawspan of the first bridge. There are said to be several other rocks between this rock and the wharves that require local knowledge to avoid. In 1967, a submerged rock was reported just north of the first bridge in 39°33'20"N., 76°04'58"W., about 200 yards east-northeastward of the charted rock.

(196)      The railroad bridge 0.8 mile above the mouth has a swing span with a clearance of 52 feet. (See **33 CFR 117.1** through **117.59** and **117.575**, chapter 2, for drawbridge regulations.) The overhead power cable on the lower side

of the bridge has a clearance of 127 feet. Stone piers of a former highway bridge, just below the railroad bridge, stand 15 feet above high water. The remaining three fixed bridges between Havre de Grace and Port Deposit have minimum clearance of 85 feet.

(197)      There are berthing and repair facilities for small craft at Havre de Grace. One of the basins is protected by old railroad barges sunk in place.

(198)      **Perryville**, on the opposite side of the river from Havre de Grace, has berthing facilities for small craft above the first bridge. Storage, some marine supplies and engine repairs are available; largest lift, 20 tons.

(199)      Above Havre de Grace, depths of 13 feet to 50 feet are in the channel of Susquehanna River to Port Deposit, on the northeast side 4 miles above the mouth; the river is obstructed by rocks above this point. In 1977, rocks were reported in about 39°35.8'N., 76°07.2'W., about 3.6 miles above the mouth.

(200)      **Garrett Island**, 0.8 mile long and 0.4 mile broad, high and wooded, is in midriver 1 mile above the mouth. The favored channel is west of the island; however, mariners are advised to use caution because of the numerous rocks, shoals, logs and submerged pilings in this area.

(201)      **Port Deposit** has a large manufacturing company that builds barges, derricks and boats. The marinas at the south end of the town have berthing, storage, launching ramp and engine repair facilities; largest lift, 12 tons. Gasoline and some supplies are available.

(202)      **Conowingo Dam** is about 10 miles above the mouth of the Susquehanna River.

(203)      **North East River** empties into the head of Chesapeake Bay 4.5 miles eastward of Susquehanna River and 169.1 miles above the Virginia Capes. The entrance is between **Red Point**, which is 5 miles north-northeastward of Turkey Point, and **Carpenter Point**, on the west. The commercial traffic on the river is in seafood products and gravel shipped by barges; yachtsmen use it extensively.

(204)      Extensive small-craft facilities are at **Hance Point**, on the east side of North East River 2 miles above the mouth; at **Charlestown**, on the west side 2.5 miles above the mouth; and at **Northeast Heights**, on the east side 3 miles above the mouth.

(205)      A **special anchorage** is westward of Northeast Heights. (See **33 CFR 110.1** and **110.70a**, chapter 2, for limits and regulations.)

(206)      **North East**, a town at the head of navigation 4.5 miles above the mouth of North East River, has good rail and highway connections. The river narrows considerably at North East. A dredged channel leads through this section of the river to a basin. Gasoline and some supplies are available at a few of the fish piers.

# Navigation Rules

(1)      Following is an amalgamation of the **International (72 COLREGS) and Inland Navigation Rules**, their Annexes, and associated Federal rules and regulations.

(2)      Text unique to Inland Rules is *italicized* and set apart in a text box or within 《 *double angle brackets* 》. International Rules are set apart in a text box or denoted with 〈 single angle brackets 〉.

(3)      Text within {curly brackets} denotes additions made by the U.S. Coast Guard Office of Navigation Systems.

(4)      Disparate paragraph or section numbering are shown side by side separated by a dagger, i.e. (a)†(b).

(5)      Instances of "…§§83.xx / in / with / of … this section / subpart / part of this Rule, etc." are redacted, and herein are shown as the enumerated rule(s) they referred to, i.e. 72 COLREGS Rule 18(e) states: "...with the Rules of this Part" and the same Inland Rule states: "...with the Rules of this Subpart (Rules 4-19) (§§83.04 through 83.19)", but, herein it is stated as "...with Rules 4-19.

(6)      Instances of paragraph / section (x) are redacted, and herein are shown as §(x).

(7)      Rules denoted with an asterisk also have an associated implementing or interpretative rule (i.e. 33 CFR 81-90), which can be found in chapter 2.

(8)
## Part A—General

(9)

### Rule 1—Application (International)

(a) These Rules shall apply to all vessels upon the high seas and in all waters connected therewith navigable by seagoing vessels.

(b) Nothing in these Rules shall interfere with the operation of special rules made by an appropriate authority for roadsteads, harbors, rivers, lakes, or inland waterways connected with the high seas and navigable by seagoing vessels. Such special rules shall conform as closely as possible to these Rules.

(c) Nothing in these Rules shall interfere with the operation of any special rules made by the Government of any State with respect to additional station or signal lights, shapes or whistle signals for ships of war and vessels proceeding under convoy, or with respect to additional station or signal lights or shapes for fishing vessels engaged in fishing as a fleet. These additional stations or signal lights, shapes or whistle signals shall, so far as possible, be such that they cannot be mistaken for any light, shape, or signal authorized elsewhere under these Rules.

### Rule 1—Application (International)

(d) Traffic separation schemes may be adopted by the Organization for the purpose of these Rules.

(e) Whenever the Government concerned shall have determined that a vessel of special construction or purpose cannot comply fully with the provisions of any of these Rules with respect to number, position, range or arc of visibility of lights or shapes, as well as to the disposition and characteristics of sound-signaling appliances, such vessel shall comply with such other provisions in regard to number, position, range or arc of visibility of lights or shapes, as well as to the disposition and characteristics of sound-signaling appliances, as the Government shall have determined to be the closest possible compliance with these Rules in respect to that vessel.

(10)

### Rule 1—Application (Inland)

*(a) These rules apply to all vessels upon the inland waters of the United States, and to vessels of the United States on the Canadian waters of the Great Lakes to the extent that there is no conflict with Canadian law. These Rules have preemptive effect over State or local regulation within the same field.*

*(b)(i)These rules constitute special rules made by an appropriate authority within the meaning of Rule 1(b) of the International Regulations for Preventing Collisions at Sea, 1972, including annexes currently in force for the United States ("International Regulations").*
*(ii) All vessels complying with the construction and equipment requirements of the International Regulations are considered to be in compliance with these Rules.*

*(c) Nothing in these Rules shall interfere with the operation of any special rules made by the Secretary of the Navy with respect to additional station or signal lights and shapes or whistle signals for ships of war and vessels proceeding under convoy, or by the Secretary with respect to additional station or signal lights and shapes for fishing vessels engaged in fishing as a fleet. These additional station or signal lights and shapes or whistle signals shall, so far as possible, be such that they cannot be mistaken for any light, shape or signal authorized elsewhere under these Rules. Notice of such special rules shall be published in the Federal Register and, after the effective date specified in such notice, they shall have effect as if they were a part of these Rules.*

*(d) Traffic separation schemes may be established for the purposes of these Rules. Vessel traffic service regulations may be in effect in certain areas.*

## Rule 1—Application (Inland)

*(e) Whenever the Secretary determines that a vessel or class of vessels of special construction or purpose cannot comply fully with the provisions of any of these Rules with respect to the number, position, range, or arc of visibility of lights or shapes, as well as to the disposition and characteristics of sound-signaling appliances, the vessel shall comply with such other provisions in regard to the number, position, range, or arc of visibility of lights or shapes, as well as to the disposition and characteristics of sound-signaling appliances, as the Secretary shall have determined to be the closest possible compliance with these Rules. The Secretary may issue a certificate of alternative compliance for a vessel or class of vessels specifying the closest possible compliance with these Rules. The Secretary of the Navy shall make these determinations and issue certificates of alternative compliance for vessels of the Navy.*

*(f) The Secretary may accept a certificate of alternative compliance issued by a contracting party to the International Regulations if it determines that the alternative compliance standards of the contracting party are substantially the same as those of the United States.*

*(g) The operator of each self-propelled vessel 12 meters or more in length shall carry, on board and maintain for ready reference, a copy of these Rules.*

(11)

## Rule 2—Responsibility

(12)     (a) Nothing in these Rules shall exonerate any vessel, or the owner, master, or crew thereof, from the consequences of any neglect to comply with these Rules or of the neglect of any precaution which may be required by the ordinary practice of seamen, or by the special circumstances of the case.

(13)     (b) In construing and complying with these Rules due regard shall be had to all dangers of navigation and collision and to any special circumstances, including the limitations of the vessels involved, which may make a departure from these Rules necessary to avoid immediate danger.

(14)

## Rule 3—General Definitions

(15)     For the purpose of these Rules, except where the context otherwise requires:

(16)     (a) The word "vessel" includes every description of watercraft, including non-displacement craft, WIG craft, and seaplanes, used or capable of being used as a means of transportation on water.

(17)     (b) The term "power-driven vessel" means any vessel propelled by machinery.

(18)     (c) The term "sailing vessel" means any vessel under sail provided that propelling machinery, if fitted, is not being used.

(19)     (d) The term "vessel engaged in fishing" means any vessel fishing with nets, lines, trawls, or other fishing apparatus which restrict maneuverability, but does not include a vessel fishing with trolling lines or other fishing apparatus which do not restrict maneuverability.

(20)     (e) The term "seaplane" includes any aircraft designed to maneuver on the water.

(21)     (f) The term "vessel not under command" means a vessel which through some exceptional circumstance is unable to maneuver as required by these Rules and is therefore unable to keep out of the way of another vessel.

(22)     (g) The term "vessel restricted in her ability to maneuver" means a vessel which from the nature of her work is restricted in her ability to maneuver as required by these Rules and is therefore unable to keep out of the way of another vessel. The term "vessels restricted in their ability to maneuver" shall include but not be limited to: (i) A vessel engaged in laying, servicing, or picking up a navigational mark, submarine cable or pipeline; (ii) A vessel engaged in dredging, surveying or underwater operations; (iii) A vessel engaged in replenishment or transferring persons, provisions or cargo while underway; (iv) A vessel engaged in the launching or recovery of aircraft; (v) A vessel engaged in mine clearance operations; (vi) A vessel engaged in a towing operation such as severely restricts the towing vessel and her tow in their ability to deviate from their course.

(23)

### Rule 3h (International)

(h) The term "vessel constrained by her draft" means a power-driven vessel which because of her draft in relation to the available depth and width of navigable water is severely restricted in her ability to deviate from the course she is following.

(24)     (i) The word "underway" means that a vessel is not at anchor, or made fast to the shore, or aground.

(25)     (j) The words "length" and "breadth" of a vessel mean her length overall and greatest breadth.

(26)     (k) Vessels shall be deemed to be in sight of one another only when one can be observed visually from the other.

(27)     (l) The term "restricted visibility" means any condition in which visibility is restricted by fog, mist, falling snow, heavy rainstorms, sandstorms, or any other similar causes.

(28)     (m) The term "Wing-In-Ground (WIG)" craft means a multimodal craft which, in its main operational mode, flies in close proximity to the surface by utilizing surface-effect action.

(29)

### Rules 3n–3s (Inland)

*(n) "Western Rivers" means the Mississippi River, its tributaries, South Pass, and Southwest Pass, to the navigational demarcation lines {30 CFR 80} dividing the high seas from harbors, rivers and other inland waters of the United States, and the Port Allen-Morgan City Alternate Route, and that part of the Atchafalaya River above its junction with the Port Allen-Morgan City Alternate Route including the Old River and the Red River.*

**Rules 3n–3s (Inland)**

*(o) "Great Lakes" means the Great Lakes and their connecting tributary waters including the Calumet River as far as the Thomas J. O'Brien Lock and Controlling Waters (between mile 326 and 327), the Chicago River as far as the east side of the Ashland Avenue Bridge (between mile 321 and 322), and the Saint Lawrence River as far east as the lower exit of Saint Lambert Lock.*

*(p) "Secretary" means the Secretary of the Department in which the Coast Guard is operating.*

*(q) "Inland Waters" means the navigable waters of the United States shoreward of the navigational demarcation lines {30 CFR 80} dividing the high seas from harbors, rivers and other inland waters of the United States and the waters of the Great Lakes on the United States side of the International Boundary.*

*(r) "Inland Rules" or "Rules" means these Inland Navigational Rules and the annexes thereto, which govern the conduct of vessels and specify the lights, shapes, and sound signals that apply on inland waters.*

*(s) "International Regulations" means the International Regulations for Preventing Collisions at Sea, 1972, including annexes currently in force for the United States.*

(30)     **Implementing Rule**—See **33 CFR 89.25**, chapter 2, for regulations.

(31)

# Part B—Steering and Sailing Rules

(32)

## I—Conduct of Vessels in Any Condition of Visibility

(33)

### Rule 4—Application

(34)     Rules 4 through 10 apply in any condition of visibility.

(35)

### Rule 5—Lookout

(36)     Every vessel shall at all times maintain a proper look-out by sight and hearing as well as by all available means appropriate in the prevailing circumstances and conditions so as to make a full appraisal of the situation and of the risk of collision.

(37)

### Rule 6—Safe Speed

(38)     Every vessel shall at all times proceed at a safe speed so that she can take proper and effective action to avoid collision and be stopped within a distance appropriate to the prevailing circumstances and conditions. In determining a safe speed the following factors shall be among those taken into account:

(39)     (a) By all vessels:

(40)     (i) The state of visibility; (ii) The traffic density including concentrations of fishing vessels or any other vessels; (iii) The maneuverability of the vessel with special reference to stopping distance and turning ability in the prevailing conditions; (iv) At night, the presence of background light such as from shore lights or from back scatter from her own lights; (v) The state of wind, sea and current, and the proximity of navigational hazards; (vi) The draft in relation to the available depth of water.

(41)     (b) Additionally, by vessels with operational radar:

(42)     (i) The characteristics, efficiency and limitations of the radar equipment; (ii) Any constraints imposed by the radar range scale in use; (iii) The effect on radar detection of the sea state, weather and other sources of interference; (iv) The possibility that small vessels, ice and other floating objects may not be detected by radar at an adequate range; (v) The number, location and movement of vessels detected by radar; (vi) The more exact assessment of the visibility that may be possible when radar is used to determine the range of vessels or other objects in the vicinity.

(43)

### Rule 7—Risk of Collision

(44)     (a) Every vessel shall use all available means appropriate to the prevailing circumstances and conditions to determine if risk of collision exists. If there is any doubt such risk shall be deemed to exist.

(45)     (b) Proper use shall be made of radar equipment if fitted and operational, including long-range scanning to obtain early warning of risk of collision and radar plotting or equivalent systematic observation of detected objects.

(46)     (c) Assumptions shall not be made on the basis of scanty information, especially scanty radar information.

(47)     (d) In determining if risk of collision exists the following considerations shall be among those taken into account:

(48)     (i) Such risk shall be deemed to exist if the compass bearing of an approaching vessel does not appreciably change.

(49)     (ii) Such risk may sometimes exist even when an appreciable bearing change is evident, particularly when approaching a very large vessel or a tow or when approaching a vessel at close range.

(50)

### Rule 8—Action to Avoid Collision

(51)     (a) Any action taken to avoid collision shall be taken in accordance with Rules 4 through 19 and shall if the circumstances of the case admit, be positive, made in ample time and with due regard to the observance of good seamanship.

(52)     (b) Any alteration of course and/or speed to avoid collision shall, if the circumstances of the case admit, be large enough to be readily apparent to another vessel observing visually or by radar; a succession of small alterations of course and/or speed should be avoided.

(53)     (c) If there is sufficient sea room, alteration of course alone may be the most effective action to avoid a closequarters situation provided that it is made in good time, is substantial and does not result in another close-quarters situation.

(54)     (d) Action taken to avoid collision with another vessel shall be such as to result in passing at a safe distance. The

effectiveness of the action shall be carefully checked until the other vessel is finally past and clear.

(55)     (e) If necessary to avoid collision or allow more time to assess the situation, a vessel shall slacken her speed or take all way off by stopping or reversing her means of propulsion.

(56)     (f)(i) A vessel which, by any of these Rules, is required not to impede the passage or safe passage of another vessel shall, when required by the circumstances of the case, take early action to allow sufficient sea room for the safe passage of the other vessel.

(57)     (ii) A vessel required not to impede the passage or safe passage of another vessel is not relieved of this obligation if approaching the other vessel so as to involve risk of collision and shall, when taking action, have full regard to the action which may be required by Rules 4 through 19.

(58)     (iii) A vessel, the passage of which is not to be impeded remains fully obliged to comply with Rules 4 through 19 when the two vessels are approaching one another so as to involve risk of collision.

(59)

## Rule 9—Narrow Channels

(60)     (a) ‹‹‹(i)›› A vessel proceeding along the course of a narrow channel or fairway shall keep as near to the outer limit of the channel or fairway which lies on her starboard side as is safe and practicable.

(61)

### Rule 9a (Inland)

*(ii) Notwithstanding Rule 9(a)(i) and Rule 14(a), a power-driven vessel operating in narrow channel or fairway on the Great Lakes, Western Rivers, or waters specified by the Secretary, and proceeding downbound with a following current shall have the right-of-way over an upbound vessel, shall propose the manner and place of passage, and shall initiate the maneuvering signals prescribed by Rule 34(a)(i), as appropriate. The vessel proceeding upbound against the current shall hold as necessary to permit safe passing.*

(62)     (b) A vessel of less than 20 meters in length or a sailing vessel shall not impede the passage of a vessel ‹ which ›‹‹that›› can safely navigate only within a narrow channel or fairway.

(63)     (c) A vessel engaged in fishing shall not impede the passage of any other vessel navigating within a narrow channel or fairway.

(64)     (d) A vessel ‹ shall ›‹‹must›› not cross a narrow channel or fairway if such crossing impedes the passage of a vessel which can safely navigate only within that channel or fairway. The latter vessel ‹ may ›‹‹must›› use the signal prescribed in Rule 34(d) if in doubt as to the intention of the crossing vessel.

(65)

### Rule 9e (International)

(e)(i) In a narrow channel or fairway when overtaking can take place only if the vessel to be overtaken has to take action to permit safe passing, the vessel intending to overtake shall indicate her intention by sounding the appropriate signal prescribed in Rule 34(c)(ii). The vessel to be overtaken shall, if in agreement, sound the appropriate signal prescribed in Rule 34(c)(i) and take steps to permit safe passing. If in doubt she may sound the signals prescribed in Rule 34(d).

### Rule 9e (Inland)

*(e)(i) In a narrow channel or fairway when overtaking, the power-driven vessel intending to overtake another power-driven vessel shall indicate her intention by sounding the appropriate signal prescribed in Rule 34(c) and take steps to permit safe passing. The power-driven vessel being overtaken, if in agreement, shall sound the same signal and may, if specifically agreed to, take steps to permit safe passing. If in doubt she shall sound the signal prescribed in Rule 34(d).*

(66)     (e)(ii) This rule does not relieve the overtaking vessel of her obligation under Rule 13.

(67)     (f) A vessel nearing a bend or an area of a narrow channel or fairway where other vessels may be obscured by an intervening obstruction shall navigate with particular alertness and caution and shall sound the appropriate signal prescribed in Rule 34(e).

(68)     (g) Any vessel shall, if the circumstances of the case admit, avoid anchoring in a narrow channel.

(69)

## Rule 10—Traffic Separation Schemes

(70)     (a) This Rule applies to traffic separation schemes ‹ adopted by the Organization › and does not relieve any vessel of her obligation under any other rule.

(71)     (b) A vessel using a traffic separation scheme shall:

(72)     (i) Proceed in the appropriate traffic lane in the general direction of traffic flow for that lane.

(73)     (ii) So far as is practicable keep clear of a traffic separation line or separation zone.

(74)     (iii) Normally join or leave a traffic lane at the termination of the lane, but when joining or leaving from either side shall do so at as small an angle to the general direction of traffic flow as practicable.

(75)     (c) A vessel, shall so far as practicable, avoid crossing traffic lanes but if obliged to do so shall cross on a heading as nearly as practicable at right angles to the general direction of traffic flow.

(76)     (d)(i) A vessel shall not use an inshore traffic zone when she can safely use the appropriate traffic lane within the adjacent traffic separation scheme. However, vessels of less than 20 meters in length, sailing vessels and vessels engaged in fishing may use the inshore traffic zone.

(77)     (ii) Notwithstanding Rule 10(d)(i), a vessel may use an inshore traffic zone when en route to or from a port, offshore installation or structure, pilot station or any other place situated within the inshore traffic zone, or to avoid immediate danger.

(78)    (e) A vessel, other than a crossing vessel or a vessel joining or leaving a lane shall not normally enter a separation zone or cross a separation line except:

(79)    (i) in cases of emergency to avoid immediate danger;

(80)    (ii) to engage in fishing within a separation zone.

(81)    (f) A vessel navigating in areas near the terminations of traffic separation schemes shall do so with particular caution.

(82)    (g) A vessel shall so far as practicable avoid anchoring in a traffic separation scheme or in areas near its terminations.

(83)    (h) A vessel not using a traffic separating scheme shall avoid it by as wide a margin as is practicable.

(84)    (i) A vessel engaged in fishing shall not impede the passage of any vessel following a traffic lane.

(85)    (j) A vessel of less than 20 meters in length or a sailing vessel shall not impede the safe passage of a power-driven vessel following a traffic lane.

(86)    (k) A vessel restricted in her ability to maneuver when engaged in an operation for the maintenance of safety of navigation in a traffic separation scheme is exempted from complying with this Rule to the extent necessary to carry out the operation.

(87)    (l) A vessel restricted in her ability to maneuver when engaged in an operation for the laying, servicing or picking up of a submarine cable, within a traffic separation scheme, is exempted from complying with this Rule to the extent necessary to carry out the operation.

(88)

## II—Conduct of Vessels in Sight of One Another

(89)

### Rule 11—Application

(90)    Rules 11 through 18 apply to vessels in sight of one another.

(91)

### Rule 12—Sailing Vessels

(92)    (a) When two sailing vessels are approaching one another, so as to involve risk of collision, one of them shall keep out of the way of the other as follows:

(93)    (i) when each has the wind on a different side, the vessel which has the wind on the port side shall keep out of the way of the other;

(94)    (ii) when both have the wind on the same side, the vessel which is to windward shall keep out of the way of the vessel which is to leeward;

(95)    (iii) if a vessel with the wind on the port side sees a vessel to windward and cannot determine with certainty whether the other vessel has the wind on the port or on the starboard side, she shall keep out of the way of the other.

(96)    (b) For the purposes of this Rule, the windward side shall be deemed to be the side opposite that on which the mainsail is carried or, in the case of a square-rigged vessel, the side opposite to that on which the largest foreand-aft sail is carried.

(97)

## Rule 13—Overtaking

(98)    (a) Notwithstanding anything contained in the Rules 4 through 18, any vessel overtaking any other shall keep out of the way of the vessel being overtaken.

(99)    (b) A vessel shall be deemed to be overtaking when coming up with a another vessel from a direction more than 22.5 degrees abaft her beam, that is, in such a position with reference to the vessel she is overtaking, that at night she would be able to see only the sternlight of that vessel but neither of her sidelights.

(100)   (c) When a vessel is in any doubt as to whether she is overtaking another, she shall assume that this is the case and act accordingly.

(101)   (d) Any subsequent alteration of the bearing between the two vessels shall not make the overtaking vessel a crossing vessel within the meaning of these Rules or relieve her of the duty of keeping clear of the overtaken vessel until she is finally past and clear.

(102)

## Rule 14—Head-on Situation

(103)   (a) «*Unless otherwise agreed*» when two power-driven vessels are meeting on reciprocal or nearly reciprocal courses so as to involve risk of collision each shall alter her course to starboard so that each shall pass on the port side of the other.

(104)   (b) Such a situation shall be deemed to exist when a vessel sees the other ahead or nearly ahead and by night she could see the masthead lights of the other in a line or nearly in a line and/or both sidelights and by day she observes the corresponding aspect of the other vessel.

(105)   (c) When a vessel is in any doubt as to whether such a situation exists she shall assume that it does exist and act accordingly.

(106)

### Rule 14d (Inland)

*(d) Notwithstanding Rule 14(a), a power-driven vessel operating on the Great Lakes, Western Rivers, or waters specified by the Secretary, and proceeding downbound with a following current shall have the right-of-way over an upbound vessel, shall propose the manner of passage, and shall initiate the maneuvering signals prescribed by Rule 34(a)(i), as appropriate.*

(107)

## Rule 15—Crossing Situation

(108)   (a) When two power-driven vessels are crossing so as to involve risk of collision, the vessel which has the other on her own starboard side shall keep out of the way and shall, if the circumstances of the case admit, avoid crossing ahead of the other vessel.

(109)

## Rule 15b (Inland)

*(b) Notwithstanding Rule 15(a), on the Great Lakes, Western Rivers, or water specified by the Secretary, a power-driven vessel crossing a river shall keep out of the way of a power-driven vessel ascending or descending the river.*

(110)

## Rule 16—Action by Give-way Vessel

(111) Every vessel which is directed to keep out of the way of another vessel shall, so far as possible, take early and substantial action to keep well clear.

(112)

## Rule 17—Action by Stand-on Vessel

(113) (a)(i) Where one of two vessels is to keep out of the way, the other shall keep her course and speed.

(114) (ii) The latter vessel may, however, take action to avoid collision by her maneuver alone, as soon as it becomes apparent to her that the vessel required to keep out of the way is not taking appropriate action in compliance with these Rules.

(115) (b) When, from any cause, the vessel required to keep her course and speed finds herself so close that collision cannot be avoided by the action of the giveway vessel alone, she shall take such action as will best aid to avoid collision.

(116) (c) A power-driven vessel which takes action in a crossing situation in accordance with Rule 17(a)(ii) to avoid collision with another power-driven vessel shall, if the circumstances of the case admit, not alter course to port for a vessel on her own port side.

(117) (d) This Rule does not relieve the give-way vessel of her obligation to keep out of the way.

(118)

## Rule 18—Responsibilities Between Vessels

(119) Except where Rules 9, 10, and 13 otherwise require:

(120) (a) A power-driven vessel underway shall keep out of the way of: (i) a vessel not under command; (ii) a vessel restricted in her ability to maneuver; (iii) a vessel engaged in fishing; (iv) a sailing vessel.

(121) (b) A sailing vessel underway shall keep out of the way of: (i) a vessel not under command; (ii) a vessel restricted in her ability to maneuver; (iii) a vessel engaged in fishing.

(122) (c) A vessel engaged in fishing when underway shall, so far as possible, keep out of the way of: (i) a vessel not under command; (ii) a vessel restricted in her ability to maneuver.

(123)

## Rule 18d (International)

(d)(i) Any vessel other than a vessel not under command or a vessel restricted in her ability to maneuver shall, if the circumstances of the case admit, avoid impeding the safe passage of a vessel constrained by her draft, exhibiting the signals in Rule 28.

(ii) A vessel constrained by her draft shall navigate with particular caution having full regard to her special condition.

(124) (e) A seaplane on the water shall, in general, keep well clear of all vessels and avoid impeding their navigation. In circumstances, however, where risk of collision exists, she shall comply with Rules 4 through 19.

(125) (f)(i) A WIG craft shall, when taking off, landing and in flight near the surface, keep well clear of all other vessels and avoid impeding their navigation;

(126) (ii) a WIG craft operating on the water surface shall comply with Rules 4 through 19 as a power-driven vessel.

(127)

## III—Conduct of Vessels in Restricted Visibility

(128)

## Rule 19—Conduct of Vessels in Restricted Visibility

(129) (a) This Rule applies to vessels not in sight of one another when navigating in or near an area of restricted visibility.

(130) (b) Every vessel shall proceed at a safe speed adapted to the prevailing circumstances and conditions of restricted visibility. A power-driven vessel shall have her engines ready for immediate maneuver.

(131) (c) Every vessel shall have due regard to the prevailing circumstances and conditions of restricted visibility when complying with Rules 4 through 10.

(132) (d) A vessel which detects by radar alone the presence of another vessel shall determine if a closequarters situation is developing and/or risk of collision exists. If so, she shall take avoiding action in ample time, provided that when such action consists of an alteration in course, so far as possible the following shall be avoided:

(133) (i) An alteration of course to port for a vessel forward of the beam, other than for a vessel being overtaken;

(134) (ii) An alteration of course toward a vessel abeam or abaft the beam.

(135) (e) Except where it has been determined that a risk of collision does not exist, every vessel which hears apparently forward of her beam the fog signal of another vessel, or which cannot avoid a close-quarters situation with another vessel forward of her beam, shall reduce her speed to be the minimum at which she can be kept on her course. She shall if necessary take all her way off and in any event navigate with extreme caution until danger of collision is over.

(158)

## Rules 21 and 22—Definitions and Visibility of Lights

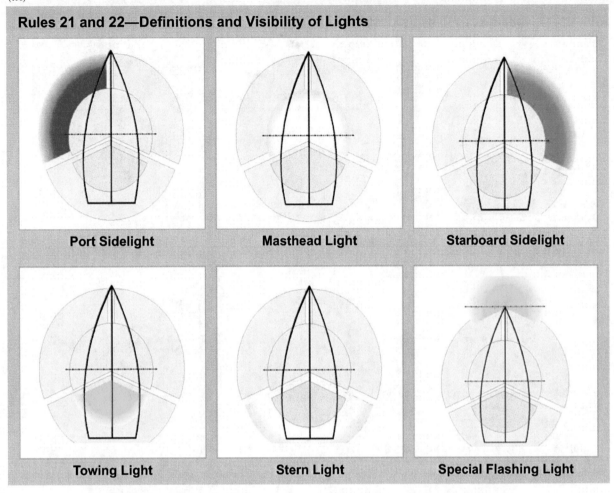

| Port Sidelight | Masthead Light | Starboard Sidelight |
| --- | --- | --- |

| Towing Light | Stern Light | Special Flashing Light |
| --- | --- | --- |

(136)

## Part C—Lights and Shapes

(137)

### Rule 20—Application

(138)    (a) Rules 20 through 31 shall be complied with in all weathers.

(139)    (b) The Rules concerning lights shall be complied with from sunset to sunrise, and during such times no other lights shall be exhibited, except such lights which cannot be mistaken for the lights specified in these Rules or do not impair their visibility or distinctive character, or interfere with the keeping of a proper look-out.

(140)    (c) The lights prescribed by these Rules shall, if carried, also be exhibited from sunrise to sunset in restricted visibility and may be exhibited in all other circumstances when it is deemed necessary.

(141)    (d) The Rules concerning shapes shall be complied with by day.

(142)    (e) The lights and shapes specified in these Rules shall comply with the provisions of Annex I of these Rules.

(143)

### Rule 20f (Inland)

*(f) A vessel's navigation lights and shapes may be lowered if necessary to pass under a bridge.*

(144)

### Rule 21—Definitions

(145)    (a) "Masthead light" means a white light placed over the fore and aft centerline of the vessel showing an unbroken light over an arc of the horizon of 225° and so fixed as to show the light from right ahead to 22.5° abaft the beam on either side of the vessel *‹‹except that on a vessel of less than 12 meters in length the masthead light shall be placed as nearly as practicable to the fore and aft centerline of the vessel ››.*

(146)    (b) "Sidelights" means a green light on the starboard side and a red light on the port side each showing an unbroken light over an arc of the horizon of 112.5° and so fixed as to show the light from right ahead to 22.5° abaft the beam on its respective side. In a vessel of less than 20 meters in length the sidelights may be combined in one lantern carried on the fore and aft centerline of the vessel *‹‹, except that on a vessel of less than 12 meters in length the sidelights when combined in one lantern*

(166)

## Rule 23—Power-driven Vessels Underway

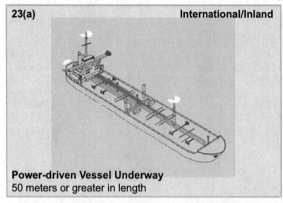

**23(a)** International/Inland

**Power-driven Vessel Underway**
50 meters or greater in length

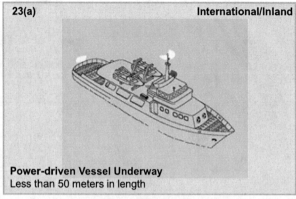

**23(a)** International/Inland

**Power-driven Vessel Underway**
Less than 50 meters in length

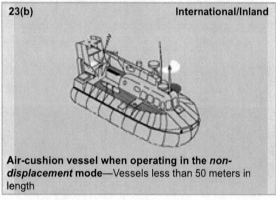

**23(b)** International/Inland

**Air-cushion vessel when operating in the *non-displacement* mode**—Vessels less than 50 meters in length

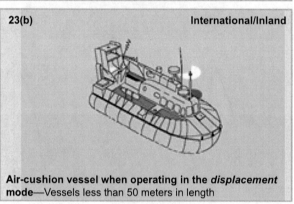

**23(b)** International/Inland

**Air-cushion vessel when operating in the *displacement* mode**—Vessels less than 50 meters in length

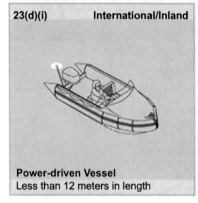

**23(d)(i)** International/Inland

**Power-driven Vessel**
Less than 12 meters in length

**23(d)(ii)** International

**Power-driven Vessel**
Less than 7 meters in length

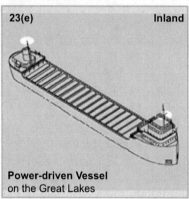

**23(e)** Inland

**Power-driven Vessel**
on the Great Lakes

shall be placed as nearly as practicable to the fore and aft centerline of the vessel ››.

(147)    (c) "Sternlight" means a white light placed as nearly as practicable at the stern showing an unbroken light over an arc of the horizon of 135° and so fixed as to show the light 67.5° from right aft on each side of the vessel.

(148)    (d) "Towing light" means a yellow light having the same characteristics as the "sternlight" defined in Rule 21(c).

(149)    (e) "All-round light" means a light showing an unbroken light over an arc of the horizon of 360°.

(150)    (f) "Flashing light" means a light flashing at regular intervals at a frequency of 120 flashes or more per minute.

(151)

### Rule 21g (Inland)

*(g) "Special flashing light" means a yellow light flashing at regular intervals at a frequency of 50 to 70 flashes per minute, placed as far forward and as nearly as practicable on the fore and aft centerline of the tow and showing an unbroken light over an arc of the horizon of not less than 180 degrees nor more than 225 degrees and so fixed as to show the light from right ahead to abeam and no more than 22.5 degrees abaft the beam on either side of the vessel.*

(152)

### Rule 22—Visibility of Lights

(153)    The lights prescribed in these Rules (Subpart C) shall have an intensity as specified in Annex I to these

Rules (33 CFR part 84), so as to be visible at the following minimum ranges:

(154)     (a) In a vessel of 50 meters or more in length: (i) a masthead light, 6 miles; (ii) a sidelight, 3 miles; (iii) a sternlight, 3 miles; (iv) a towing light, 3 miles; (v) a white, red, green or yellow all-round light, 3 miles; *«and (vi) a special flashing light, 2 miles. »*

(155)     (b) In a vessel of 12 meters or more in length but less than 50 meters in length: (i) a masthead light, 5 miles; except that where the length of the vessel is less than 20 meters, 3 miles; (ii) a sidelight, 2 miles; (iii) a sternlight, 2 miles; (iv) a towing light, 2 miles; (v) a white, red, green or yellow all-round light, 2 miles; *«and (vi) a special flashing light, 2 miles. »*

(156)     (c) In a vessel of less than 12 meters in length: (i) a masthead light, 2 miles; (ii) a sidelight, 1 mile; (iii) a sternlight, 2 miles; (iv) A towing light, 2 miles; (v) a white, red, green or yellow all-round light, 2 miles; *«and (vi) a special flashing light, 2 miles. »*

(157)     (d) In an inconspicuous, partly submerged vessel or objects being towed: (i) A white all-round light, 3 miles. (ii) [Reserved]

(159)

### Rule 23—Power-driven Vessels Underway

(160)     (a) A power-driven vessel underway shall exhibit: (i) a masthead light forward; (ii) a second masthead light abaft of and higher than the forward one; except that a vessel of less than 50 meters in length shall not be obliged to exhibit such a light but may do so; (iii) sidelights; and (iv) a sternlight.

(161)     (b) An air-cushion vessel when operating in nondisplacement mode shall, in addition to the lights prescribed in Rule 23(a) Air Cushion Vessel in Displacement Mode, exhibit an all-round flashing yellow light*«, where it can best be seen»*.

(162)     (c) A WIG craft only when taking off, landing and in flight near the surface shall, in addition to the lights prescribed in Rule 23(a), exhibit a high intensity allround flashing red light.

(163)     (d)(i) A power-driven vessel of less than 12 meters in length may in lieu of the lights prescribed in Rule 23(a) exhibit an all-round white light and sidelights.

(164)

---

**Rule 23d (International)**

(ii) a power-driven vessel of less than 7 meters in length whose maximum speed does not exceed 7 knots may in lieu of the lights prescribed in Rule 23(a) exhibit an all-round white light and shall, if practicable, also exhibit sidelights.

(iii) the masthead light or all-round white light on a power-driven vessel of less than 12 metres in length may be displaced from the fore and aft centre line of the vessel if centreline fitting is not practicable, provided that the sidelights are combined in one lantern which shall be carried on the fore and aft centre line of the vessel or located as nearly as practicable in the same fore and aft line as the masthead light or the all-round white light.

---

**Rule 23e (Inland)**

*(e) A power-driven vessel when operating on the Great Lakes may carry an all-round white light in lieu of the second masthead light and sternlight prescribed in Rule 23(a). The light shall be carried in the position of the second masthead light and be visible at the same minimum range.*

---

(165)     Regulations containing specifics on **Law Enforcement** and **Public Safety Vessel** lighting are in **Annex V–Pilot Rules, 33 CFR 88.05** and **33 CFR 88.07**, chapter 2.

(167)

### Rule 24—Towing and Pushing

(168)     (a) A power-driven vessel when towing astern shall exhibit: (i) instead of the light prescribed in Rule 23(a)(i) or 23(a)(ii), two masthead lights in a vertical line. When the length of the tow, measuring from the stern of the towing vessel to the after end of the tow, exceeds 200 meters, three such lights in a vertical line; (ii) sidelights; (iii) a sternlight; (iv) a towing light in a vertical line above the sternlight; and (v) when the length of the tow exceeds 200 meters, a diamond shape where it can best be seen.

(169)     (b) When a pushing vessel and a vessel being pushed ahead are rigidly connected in a composite unit they shall be regarded as a power-driven vessel and exhibit the lights prescribed in Rule 23.

(170)     **Interpretive Rule**—See **33 CFR 90.3** and **33 CFR 82.3**, chapter 2, for regulations.

(171)     (c) A power-driven vessel when pushing ahead or towing alongside, except ‹ in the case of a composite unit ›*«as required by Rules 24(b) and (i)»*, shall exhibit: (i) instead of the light prescribed in Rule 23(a)(i) or 23(a)(ii), two masthead lights in a vertical line; (ii) sidelights; and (iii) ‹ a sternlight ›*«two towing lights in a vertical line»*.

(172)     (d) A power-driven vessel to which paragraphs (a) or (c) of this Rule applies shall also comply with Rule 23 *«(a)(i) and»* (a)(ii).

(173)     (e) A vessel or object being towed, other than those ‹ mentioned ›*«referred»* in Rule 24(g), shall exhibit: (i) sidelights; (ii) a sternlight; (iii) when the length of the tow exceeds 200 meters, a diamond shape where it can best be seen.

(174)     (f) Provided that any number of vessels being towed alongside or pushed in a group shall be lighted as one vessel *«except as provided in Rule 24(f)(iii)»*.

(175)     (i) a vessel being pushed ahead, not being part of a composite unit, shall exhibit at the forward end, sidelights, and *«a special flashing light»*;

(176)     (ii) a vessel being towed alongside shall exhibit a sternlight and at the forward end, sidelights, and *«a special flashing light»*;

(188)

## Rule 24—Towing and Pushing (International/Inland)

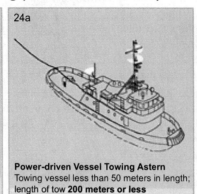

**24a**
**Power-driven Vessel Towing Astern**
Towing vessel less than 50 meters in length; length of tow **exceeds 200 meters**

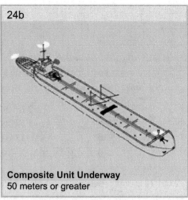

**24a**
**Power-driven Vessel Towing Astern**
Towing vessel less than 50 meters in length; length of tow **200 meters or less**

**24b**
**Composite Unit Underway**
50 meters or greater

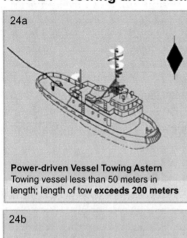

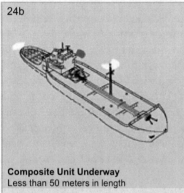

**24b**
**Composite Unit Underway**
Less than 50 meters in length

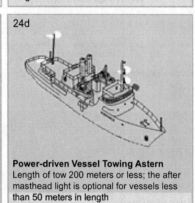

**24d**
**Power-driven Vessel Towing Astern**
Length of tow 200 meters or less; the after masthead light is optional for vessels less than 50 meters in length

**24d**
**Power-driven Vessel Towing Astern**
When masthead lights for towing are exhibited aft, a forward masthead light is required

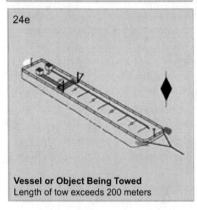

**24e**
**Vessel or Object Being Towed**
Length of tow exceeds 200 meters

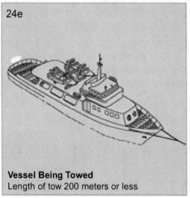

**24e**
**Vessel Being Towed**
Length of tow 200 meters or less

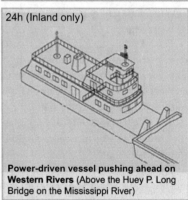

**24h (Inland only)**
**Power-driven vessel pushing ahead on Western Rivers** (Above the Huey P. Long Bridge on the Mississippi River)

(177)

### Rule 24f (Inland)

*(iii) when vessels are towed alongside on both sides of the towing vessel a sternlight shall be exhibited on the stern of the outboard vessel on each side of the towing vessel, and a single set of sidelights as far forward and as far outboard as is practicable, and a single special flashing light;*

(178)    (g) An inconspicuous, partly submerged vessel or object, or combination of such vessels or objects being towed, shall exhibit:

(179)    (i) if it is less than 25 meters in breadth, one all-round white light at or near the forward end and one at or near the after end except that dracones need not exhibit a light at or near ‹ the forward ›《each》 end.

(180)

### Rule 24g (International)

(ii) if it is 25 meters or more in breadth, two additional all-round white lights at or near the extremities of its breadth;

### Rule 24g (Inland)

*(ii) if it is 25 meters or more in breadth, four all-round white lights to mark its length and breadth;*

(181)    (iii) if it exceeds 100 meters in length, additional allround white lights between the lights prescribed in Rule 24(g)(i) 《and (ii)》 and so that the distance between the lights shall not exceed 100 meters. 《*Provided that any*

<sup>(196)</sup>

## Rule 25—Sailing Vessels Underway and Vessels Under Oars (International/Inland)

**Sailing Vessel Underway**

**Sailing Vessel Underway**
Less than 20 meters in length

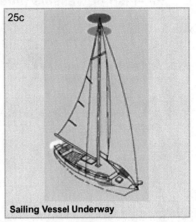

**Sailing Vessel Underway**

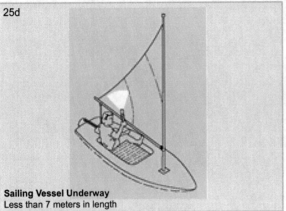

**Sailing Vessel Underway**
Less than 7 meters in length

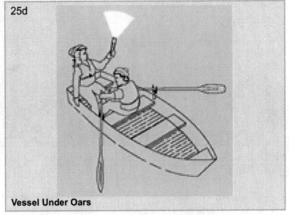

**Vessel Under Oars**

*vessels or objects being towed alongside each other shall be lighted as one vessel or object››.*

<sup>(182)</sup> (iv) a diamond shape at or near the aftermost extremity of the last vessel or object being towed; and ‹ if the length of the tow exceeds 200 meters an additional diamond shape where it can best be seen and located as far forward as is practicable. ›

<sup>(183)</sup>

### Rule 24g (Inland)

*(v) the towing vessel may direct a searchlight in the direction of the tow to indicate its presence to an approaching vessel.*

<sup>(184)</sup> (h) Where from any sufficient cause it is impracticable for a vessel or object being towed to exhibit the lights or shapes prescribed in Rule 24(e) or (g), all possible measures shall be taken to light the vessel or object towed or at least to indicate the presence of ‹ such ›‹‹the unlighted›› vessel or object.

<sup>(185)</sup> **Interpretive Rule**—See **33 CFR 90.7** and **33 CFR 82.7**, chapter 2, for regulations.

<sup>(186)</sup> (i) Where from any sufficient cause it is impracticable for a vessel not normally engaged in towing operations to display the lights prescribed by paragraph (a), (c), *«or (j)»* of this Rule, such vessel shall not be required to exhibit those lights when engaged in towing another

vessel in distress or otherwise in need of assistance. All possible measures shall be taken to indicate the nature of the relationship between the towing vessel and the vessel being towed ‹ as authorized by Rule 36, in particular by illuminating the towline ›*«and the vessel being assisted. The searchlight authorized by Rule 36 may be used to illuminate the tow».*

<sup>(187)</sup>

### Rule 24j (Inland)

*(i) Notwithstanding paragraph (c) of this Rule, on the Western Rivers (except below the Huey P. Long Bridge at mile 106.1 Above Head of Passes on the Mississippi River) and on waters specified by the Secretary, a power-driven vessel when pushing ahead or towing alongside, except as paragraph (b) of this Rule applies, shall exhibit: (i) sidelights; and (ii) two towing lights in a vertical line.*

<sup>(189)</sup>

### Rule 25—Sailing Vessels Underway and Vessels Under Oars

<sup>(190)</sup> (a) A sailing vessel underway shall exhibit: (i) sidelights; (ii) a sternlight.

<sup>(191)</sup> (b) In a sailing vessel of less than 20 meters in length the lights prescribed in Rule 25(a) may be combined in one lantern carried at or near the top of the mast where it can best be seen.

(210)

## Rule 26—Fishing Vessels (International/Inland)

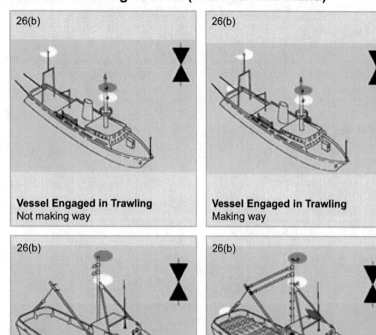

26(b)

**Vessel Engaged in Trawling**
Not making way

26(b)

**Vessel Engaged in Trawling**
Making way

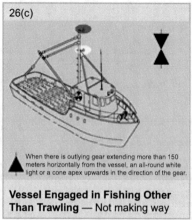

26(c)

When there is outlying gear extending more than 150 meters horizontally from the vessel, an all-round white light or a cone apex upwards in the direction of the gear.

**Vessel Engaged in Fishing Other Than Trawling** — Not making way

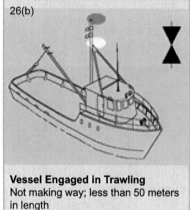

26(b)

**Vessel Engaged in Trawling**
Not making way; less than 50 meters in length

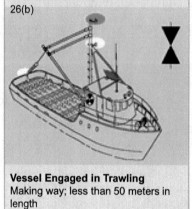

26(b)

**Vessel Engaged in Trawling**
Making way; less than 50 meters in length

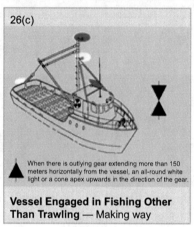

26(c)

When there is outlying gear extending more than 150 meters horizontally from the vessel, an all-round white light or a cone apex upwards in the direction of the gear.

**Vessel Engaged in Fishing Other Than Trawling** — Making way

(192)     (c) A sailing vessel underway may, in addition to the lights prescribed in Rule 25(a), exhibit at or near the top of the mast, where they can best be seen, two allround lights in a vertical line, the upper being red and the lower green, but these lights shall not be exhibited in conjunction with the combined lantern permitted by Rule 25(b).

(193)     (d)(i) A sailing vessel of less than 7 meter in length shall, if practicable, exhibit the lights prescribed in Rule 25(a) or (b), but if she does not, she shall *«exhibit an all around white light or »* have ready at hand an electric torch or lighted lantern showing a white light which shall be exhibited in sufficient time to prevent collision.

(194)     (ii) A vessel under oars may exhibit the lights prescribed in this rule for sailing vessels, but if she does not, she shall *«exhibit an all around white light or»* have ready at hand an electric torch or lighted lantern showing a white light which shall be exhibited in sufficient time to prevent collision.

(195)     (e) A vessel proceeding under sail when also being propelled by machinery shall exhibit forward where it can best be seen a conical shape, apex downwards. *«A vessel of less than 12 meters in length is not required to exhibit this shape, but may do so.»*

(197)

## Rule 26—Fishing Vessels

(198)     (a) A vessel engaged in fishing, whether underway or at anchor, shall exhibit only the lights and shapes prescribed in this Rule.

(199)     (b) A vessel when engaged in trawling, by which is meant the dragging through the water of a dredge net or other apparatus used as a fishing appliance, shall exhibit: (i) two all-round lights in a vertical line, the upper being green and the lower white, or a shape consisting of two cones with their apexes together in a vertical line one above the other; (ii) a masthead light abaft of and higher than the all-round green light; a vessel of less than 50 meters in length shall not be obliged to exhibit such a light but may do so; (iii) when making way through the water, in addition to the lights prescribed in this paragraph, sidelights and a sternlight.

(200)     (c) A vessel engaged in fishing, other than trawling, shall exhibit: (i) two all-round lights in a vertical line, the upper being red and the lower white, or a shape consisting of two cones with their apexes together in a vertical line one above the other; (ii) when there is outlying gear extending more than 150 meters horizontally from the vessel, an all-round white light or a cone apex upwards in

the direction of the gear; (iii) when making way through the water, in addition to the lights prescribed in this paragraph, sidelights and a sternlight.

(201)

### Rule 26d (International)

(d) The additional signals described in Annex II to these Regulations apply to a vessel engaged in fishing in close proximity to other vessels engaged in fishing.

(202) (e) A vessel ‹when› not engaged in fishing shall not exhibit the lights or shapes prescribed in this Rule, but only those prescribed for a vessel of her length.

(203) *« (f) Additional signals for fishing vessels in close proximity. »* {Same as International Rules Annex II}

(204) 1 ☐ (i) The lights mentioned herein shall ‹, if exhibited in pursuance of Rule 26(d),› be placed where they can best be seen. They shall be at least 0.9 meters apart but at a lower level than lights prescribed in Rule 26. ‹(b)(i) and (c)(i)› The lights shall be visible all round the horizon at a distance of at least 1 mile but at a lesser distance from the lights prescribed by ‹these Rules›*«Rule 26(a)-(c)»* for fishing vessels.

(205) 2 ☐ (ii) Signals for trawlers.

(206) (a) ☐ (1) Vessels ‹of 20 meters or more in length› when engaged in trawling, whether using demersal or pelagic gear, ‹shall›*«may»* exhibit: (i) ☐ (A) when shooting their nets—two white lights in a vertical line; (ii) ☐ (B) when hauling their nets—one white light over one red light in a vertical line; (iii) ☐ (C) when the net has come fast upon an obstruction—two red lights in a vertical line.

(207) (b) ☐ (2) ‹A›*«Each»* vessel ‹of 20 meters or more in length› engaged in pair trawling ‹shall›*«may»* exhibit: (i) ☐ (A) by night, a searchlight directed forward and in the direction of the other vessel of the pair; (ii) ☐ (B) when shooting or hauling their nets or when their nets have come fast upon an obstruction, the lights prescribed in Rule 26(f)(2)(a) ☐ (f)(ii)(1).

(208) 3 ☐ (iii) Signals for purse seiners.

(209) (a) ☐ (1) Vessels engaged in fishing with purse seine gear may exhibit two yellow lights in a vertical line. These lights shall flash alternately every second and with equal light and occultation duration. These lights may be exhibited only when the vessel is hampered by its fishing gear.

(211)

### Rule 27—Vessels Not Under Command or Restricted in Their Ability to Maneuver

(212) (a) A vessel not under command shall exhibit: (i) two all-round red lights in a vertical line where they can best be seen; (ii) two balls or similar shapes in a vertical line where they can best be seen; (iii) when making way through the water, in addition to the lights prescribed in this paragraph, sidelights and a sternlight.

(213) (b) A vessel restricted in her ability to maneuver, except a vessel engaged in mineclearance operations, shall exhibit: (i) three all-round lights in a vertical line where they can best be seen. The highest and lowest of

these lights shall be red and the middle light shall be white; (ii) three shapes in a vertical line where they can best be seen. The highest and lowest of these shapes shall be balls and the middle one a diamond; (iii) when making way through the water, a masthead light(s), sidelights and a sternlight in addition to the lights prescribed in Rule 27(b)(i); (iv) when at anchor, in addition to the lights or shapes prescribed in Rule 27(b)(i) and (ii), the light, lights, or shapes prescribed in Rule 30.

(214) (c) A power-driven vessel engaged in a towing operation such as severely restricts the towing vessel and her tow in their ability to deviate from their course shall, in addition to the lights or shape prescribed in Rule 27(b)(i) and (ii), exhibit the lights or shape prescribed in Rule 24.

(215) (d) A vessel engaged in dredging or underwater operations, when restricted in her ability to maneuver, shall exhibit the lights and shapes prescribed in Rules 27(b)(i), (ii) and (iii) and shall in addition when an obstruction exists, exhibit: (i) two all-round red lights or two balls in a vertical line to indicate the side on which the obstruction exists; (ii) two all-round green lights or two diamonds in a vertical line to indicate the side on which another vessel may pass; and (iii) when at anchor, the lights or shapes prescribed in this paragraph instead of the lights or shapes prescribed in Rule 30.

(216)

### Rule 27d (Inland)

*(iv) Dredge pipelines that are floating or supported on trestles shall display the following lights at night and in periods of restricted visibility.*

*(1) One row of yellow lights. The lights must be: (A) flashing 50 to 70 times per minute, (B) visible all round the horizon, (C) visible for at least 2 miles, (D) not less than 1 and not more than 3.5 meters above the water, (E) approximately equally spaced, and (F) not more than 10 meters apart where the pipeline crosses a navigable channel. Where the pipeline does not cross a navigable channel the lights must be sufficient in number to clearly show the pipeline's length and course.*

*(2) Two red lights at each end of the pipeline, including the ends in a channel where the pipeline is separated to allow vessels to pass (whether open or closed). The lights must be: (A) visible all round the horizon, and (B) visible for at least 2 miles, and (C) one meter apart in a vertical line with the lower light at the same height above the water as the flashing yellow light.*

(217) (e) Whenever the size of a vessel engaged in diving operations makes it impracticable to exhibit all lights and shapes prescribed in Rule 27(d), the following shall be exhibited: (i) Three all-round lights in a vertical line where they can best be seen. The highest and lowest of these lights shall be red and the middle light shall be white; (ii) a rigid replica of the International Code flag "A" not less than 1 meter in height. Measures shall be taken to ensure its all-round visibility.

(221)

# Rule 27—Vessels Not Under Command or Restricted in Their Ability to Maneuver (International/Inland)

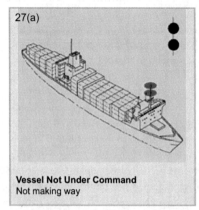

**27(a)**

**Vessel Not Under Command**
Not making way

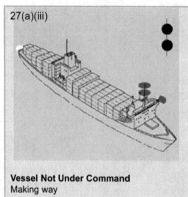

**27(a)(iii)**

**Vessel Not Under Command**
Making way

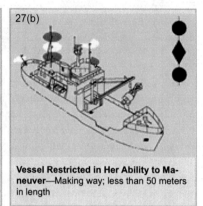

**27(b)**

**Vessel Restricted in Her Ability to Maneuver**—Making way; less than 50 meters in length

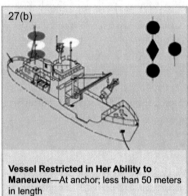

**27(b)**

**Vessel Restricted in Her Ability to Maneuver**—At anchor; less than 50 meters in length

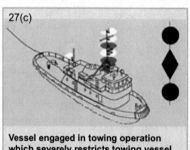
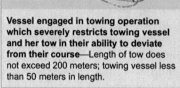

**27(c)**

**Vessel engaged in towing operation which severely restricts towing vessel and her tow in their ability to deviate from their course**—Length of tow does not exceed 200 meters; towing vessel less than 50 meters in length.

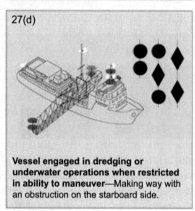

**27(d)**

**Vessel engaged in dredging or underwater operations when restricted in ability to maneuver**—Making way with an obstruction on the starboard side.

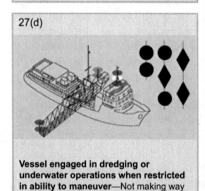

**27(d)**

**Vessel engaged in dredging or underwater operations when restricted in ability to maneuver**—Not making way with an obstruction on the starboard side.

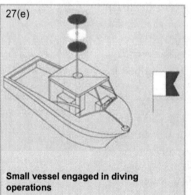

**27(e)**

**Small vessel engaged in diving operations**

**27(e)**

**Small vessel engaged in diving operations**

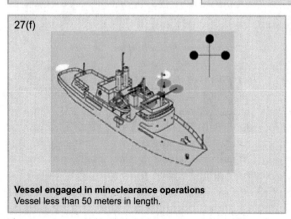

**27(f)**

**Vessel engaged in mineclearance operations**
Vessel less than 50 meters in length.

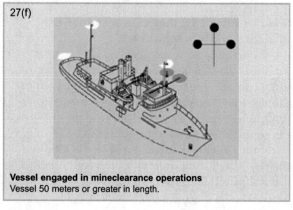

**27(f)**

**Vessel engaged in mineclearance operations**
Vessel 50 meters or greater in length.

(224)

## Rule 28—Vessel Constrained by Their Draft (International)

A vessel constrained by her draft may, in addition to the lights prescribed for power-driven vessels in Rule 23, exhibit where they can best be seen three all-round red lights in a vertical line, or a cylinder.

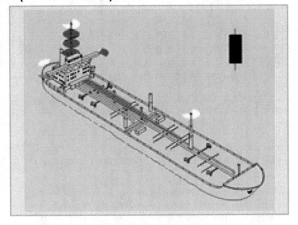

(218)    (f) A vessel engaged in mine clearance operations shall, in addition to the lights prescribed for a power-driven vessel in Rule 23 or to the lights or shape prescribed for a vessel at anchor in Rule 30 as appropriate, exhibit three all-round green lights or three balls. One of these lights or shapes shall be exhibited near the foremast head and one at each end of the fore yard. These lights or shapes indicate that it is dangerous for another vessel to approach within 1000 meters of the mineclearance vessel.

(219)    (g) Vessels of less than 12 meters in length, except ‹ those ›«*when* » engaged in diving operations, ‹ shall not be ›«*is not* » required to exhibit the lights ‹ and ›«*or* » shapes prescribed in this Rule.

(220)    (h) The signals prescribed in this Rule are not signals of vessels in distress and requiring assistance. Such signals are contained in Annex IV to these Rules.

(222)

### Rule 28—Vessels Constrained by Their Draft

(223)    See graphic, **Rule 28—Vessels Constrained by Their Draft.**

(225)

### Rule 29—Pilot Vessels

(226)    (a) A vessel engaged on pilotage duty shall exhibit: (i) at or near the masthead, two all-round lights in a vertical line, the upper being white and the lower red; (ii) when underway, in addition, sidelights and a sternlight; (iii) when at anchor, in addition to the lights prescribed in Rule 29(a)(i), the light, lights, or shape prescribed in Rule 30 for vessels at anchor.

(227)    (b) A pilot vessel when not engaged on pilotage duty shall exhibit the lights or shapes prescribed for a similar vessel of her length.

(228)

### Rule 30—Anchored Vessels and Vessels Aground

(229)    (a) A vessel at anchor shall exhibit where it can best be seen: (i) in the fore part, an all-round white light or one ball; (ii) at or near the stern and at a lower level than the light prescribed in Rule 30(a)(i), an all-round white light.

(230)    **Interpretive Rule**—See **33 CFR 90.5** and **33 CFR 82.5**, chapter 2, for regulations on vessels at anchor.

(231)    (b) A vessel of less than 50 meters in length may exhibit an all-round white light where it can best be seen instead of the lights prescribed in Rule 30(a).

(232)    (c) A vessel at anchor may, and a vessel of 100 meters and more in length shall, also use the available working or equivalent lights to illuminate her decks.

(233)    (d) A vessel aground shall exhibit the lights prescribed in Rule 30(a) or (b) and in addition, if practicable, where they can best be seen: (i) two all-round red lights in a vertical line; (ii) three balls in a vertical line.

(234)    (e) A vessel of less than 7 meters in length, when at anchor not in or near a narrow channel, fairway or where other vessels normally navigate, shall not be required to exhibit the lights or shape prescribed in Rule 30(a) and (b).

(235)    (f) A vessel of less than 12 meters in length, when aground, shall not be required to exhibit the lights or shapes prescribed in Rule 30(d)(i) and (ii).

(236)

### Rule 30 (Inland)

*(g) A vessel of less than 20 meters in length, when at anchor in a special anchorage area designated by the Coast Guard, shall not be required to exhibit the anchor lights and shapes required by this Rule.*

*(h) The following barges shall display at night and if practicable in periods of restricted visibility the lights described in Rule 30(i):*
*(i) Every barge projecting into a buoyed or restricted channel.*
*(ii) Every barge so moored that it reduces the available navigable width of any channel to less than 80 meters.*
*(iii) Barges moored in groups more than two barges wide or to a maximum width of over 25 meters.*
*(iv) Every barge not moored parallel to the bank or dock.*

*(i) Barges described in Rule 30(h) shall carry two unobstructed all-round white lights of an intensity to be visible for at least 1 nautical mile and meeting the technical requirements as prescribed in Annex I.*

### Rule 30 (Inland)

*(j) A barge or a group of barges at anchor or made fast to one or more mooring buoys or other similar device, in lieu of the provisions of Rule 30, may carry unobstructed all-round white lights of an intensity to be visible for at least 1 nautical mile that meet the requirements of Annex I and shall be arranged as follows:*
*(i) Any barge that projects from a group formation, shall be lighted on its outboard corners.*
*(ii) On a single barge moored in water where other vessels normally navigate on both sides of the barge, lights shall be placed to mark the corner extremities of the barge.*
*(iii) On barges moored in group formation, moored in water where other vessels normally navigate on both sides of the group, lights shall be placed to mark the corner extremities of the group.*

*(k) The following are exempt from the requirements of Rule 30:*
*(i) A barge or group of barges moored in a slip or slough used primarily for mooring purposes.*
*(ii) A barge or group of barges moored behind a pierhead.*
*(iii) A barge less than 20 meters in length when moored in a special anchorage area designated in accordance with 33 CFR 109.10.*

*(l) Barges moored in well-illuminated areas are exempt from the lighting requirements of Rule 30. These areas are as follows:*

#### CHICAGO SANITARY SHIP CANAL

| | |
|---|---|
| *(1) Mile 293.2 to 293.9* | *(15) Mile 314.6* |
| *(2) Mile 295.2 to 296.1* | *(16) Mile 314.8 to 315.3* |
| *(3) Mile 297.5 to 297.8* | *(17) Mile 315.7 to 316* |
| *(4) Mile 298 to 298.2* | *(18) Mile 316.8* |
| *(5) Mile 298.6 to 298.8* | *(19) Mile 316.85 to 317.05* |
| *(6) Mile 299.3 to 299.4* | *(20) Mile 317.5* |
| *(7) Mile 299.8 to 300.5* | *(21) Mile 318.4 to 318.9* |
| *(8) Mile 303 to 303.2* | *(22) Mile 318.7 to 318.8* |
| *(9) Mile 303.7 to 303.9* | *(23) Mile 320 to 320.3* |
| *(10) Mile 305.7 to 305.8* | *(24) Mile 320.6* |
| *(11) Mile 310.7 to 310.9* | *(25) Mile 322.3 to 322.4* |
| *(12) Mile 311 to 311.2* | *(26) Mile 322.8* |
| *(13) Mile 312.5 to 312.6* | *(27) Mile 322.9 to 327.2* |
| *(14) Mile 313.8 to 314.2* | |

#### CALUMET SAG CHANNEL

*(28) Mile 316.5*

#### LITTLE CALUMET RIVER

| | |
|---|---|
| *(29) Mile 321.2* | *(30) Mile 322.3* |

#### CALUMET RIVER

| | |
|---|---|
| *(31) Mile 328.5 to 328.7* | *(34) Mile 331.4 to 331.6* |
| *(32) Mile 329.2 to 329.4* | *(35) Mile 332.2 to 332.4* |
| *(33) Mile 330 west bank to 330.2* | *(36) Mile 332.6 to 332.8* |

#### CUMBERLAND RIVER

| | |
|---|---|
| *(37) Mile 126.8* | *(38) Mile 191* |

(237)
### Rule 31—Seaplanes

(238) Where it is impracticable for a seaplane or a WIG craft to exhibit lights or shapes of the characteristics or in the positions prescribed in Rules 20 through 31 she shall exhibit lights and shapes as closely similar in characteristics and position as is possible.

(239)
## Part D—Sound and Light Signals

(240)
### Rule 32—Definitions

(241) (a) The word "whistle" means any sound signaling appliance capable of producing the prescribed blasts and which complies with the specifications in Annex III to these Rules.

(242) (b) The term "short blast" means a blast of about one seconds duration.

(243) (c) The term "prolonged blast" means a blast of from four to six seconds duration.

(244)
### Rule 33—Equipment for Sound Signals

(245) (a) A vessel of 12 meters or more in length shall be provided with a whistle, a vessel of 20 meters or more in length shall be provided with a bell in addition to a whistle, and a vessel of 100 meters or more in length shall, in addition be provided with a gong, the tone and sound of which cannot be confused with that of the bell. The whistle, bell and gong shall comply with the specifications in Annex III to these Regulations. The bell or gong or both may be replaced by other equipment having the same respective sound characteristics, provided that manual sounding of the prescribed signals shall always be possible.

(246) (b) A vessel of less than 12 meters in length shall not be obliged to carry the sound signaling appliances prescribed in Rule 33(a) but if she does not, she shall be provided with some other means of making an efficient signal.

(247)
### Rule 34—Maneuvering and Warning Signs (International)

(a) When vessels are in sight of one, a power-driven vessel underway, when maneuvering as authorized or required by these Rules, shall indicate that manoeuvre by the following signals on her whistle:
–One short blasts to mean "I am altering my course to starboard"
–Two short blasts to mean "I am altering my course to port"
–Three short blasts to mean "I am operating astern propulsion"

(b) Any vessel may supplement the whistle signals prescribed in Rule 34(a) by light signals, repeated as appropriate, while the maneuver is being carried out:
(i) these signals shall have the following significance:
(ii) the duration of each flash shall be about one second, the interval between flashes shall be about one second, and the interval between successive signals shall not be less than ten seconds.
(iii) the light used for this signal shall, if fitted, be an all-round white, visible at a minimum range of 5 miles, and shall comply with the provisions of Annex I to these Regulations.
–One flash to mean "I am altering my course to starboard"
–Two flashes to mean I am altering my course to port"
–Three flashes to mean "I am operating astern propulsion".

## Rule 34—Maneuvering and Warning Signs (International)

(c) When in sight of one another in a narrow channel or fairway:

(i) a vessel intending to overtake another shall in compliance with Rule 9(e)(i) indicate her intention by the following signals on her whistle:

–Two prolonged blasts followed by one short blast to mean "I intend to overtake you on your starboard side"

–Two prolonged blasts followed by two short blasts to mean "I intend to overtake you on your port side".

(ii) the vessel about to be overtaken when acting in accordance with Rule 9(e)(i) shall indicate her agreement by the following signal on her whistle:

–one prolonged, one short, one prolonged and one short blast, in that order.

(d) When vessels in sight of one another are approaching each other and from any cause either vessel fails to understand the intentions or actions of the other, or is in doubt whether sufficient action is being taken by the other to avoid collision, the vessel in doubt shall immediately indicate such doubt by giving at least five short and rapid blasts on the whistle. Such signal may be supplemented by at least five short and rapid flashes.

(e) A vessel nearing a bend or an area of a channel or fairway where other vessels may be obscured by an intervening obstruction shall sound one prolonged blast. This signal shall be answered with a prolonged blast by any approaching vessel that may be within hearing around the bend or behind the intervening obstruction.

(f) If whistles are fitted on a vessel at a distance apart of more than 100 meters, one whistle only shall be used for giving maneuvering and warning signals.

(248)

## Rule 34—Maneuvering and Warning Signs (Inland)

*(a) When power-driven vessels are in sight of one another and meeting or crossing at a distance within half a mile of each other, each vessel underway, when maneuvering as authorized or required by these Rules,*

*(i) shall indicate that maneuver by the following signals on her whistle:*

*–One short blasts to mean "I intend to leave you on my port side"*
*–Two short blasts to mean "I intend to leave you on my starboard side"*
*–Three short blasts to mean "I am operating astern propulsion"*

*(ii) upon hearing the one or two blast signal of the other shall, if in agreement, sound the same whistle signal and take the steps necessary to effect a safe passing. If, however, from any cause, the vessel doubts the safety of the proposed maneuver, she shall sound the signal specified in Rule 34(d) and each vessel shall take appropriate precautionary action until a safe passing agreement is made*

*(b) Any vessel may supplement the whistle signals prescribed in Rule 34(a) by light signals:*
*(i) these signals shall have the following significance:*
*(ii) the duration of each flash shall be about one second.*
*(iii) the light used for this signal shall, if fitted, be an all-round white or yellow, visible at a minimum range of 2 miles, synchronized with the whistle and shall comply with the provisions of Annex I to these Regulations.*
*–One flash to mean "I intend to leave you on my port side"*
*–Two flashes to mean "I intend to leave you on my starboard side"*
*–Three flashes to mean "I am operating astern propulsion"*

## Rule 34—Maneuvering and Warning Signs (Inland)

*(c) When in sight of one another:*
*(i) a power-driven vessel intending to overtake another power-driven vessel shall indicate her intention by the following signals on her whistle:*
*–One short blast to mean "I intend to overtake you on your starboard side"*
*–Two short blasts to mean "I intend to overtake you on your port side"*
*(ii) the power-driven vessel about to be overtaken shall, if in agreement, sound a similar sound signal. If in doubt she shall sound the signal prescribed in Rule 34(d).*

*(d) When vessels in sight of one another are approaching each other and from any cause either vessel fails to understand the intentions or actions of the other, or is in doubt whether sufficient action is being taken by the other to avoid collision, the vessel in doubt shall immediately indicate such doubt by giving at least five short and rapid blasts on the whistle. Such signal may be supplemented by at least five short and rapid flashes.*

*(e) A vessel nearing a bend or an area of a channel or fairway where other vessels may be obscured by an intervening obstruction shall sound one prolonged blast. This signal shall be answered with a prolonged blast by any approaching vessel that may be within hearing around the bend or behind the intervening obstruction.*

*(f) If whistles are fitted on a vessel at a distance apart of more than 100 meters, one whistle only shall be used for giving maneuvering and warning signals.*

*(g) When a power-driven vessel is leaving a dock or berth, she shall sound one prolonged blast.*

*(h) A vessel that reaches agreement with another vessel in a head-on, crossing, or overtaking situation, as for example, by using the radiotelephone as prescribed by the Vessel Bridge-to-Bridge Radiotelephone Act (85 Stat. 164; 33 U.S.C. 1201 et seq.), is not obliged to sound the whistle signals prescribed by this Rule, but may do so. If agreement is not reached, then whistle signals shall be exchanged in a timely manner and shall prevail.*

(249)

## Rule 35—Sound Signals in Restricted Visibility

(250) In or near an area of restricted visibility, whether by day or night the signals prescribed in this Rule shall be used as follows:

(251) (a) A power-driven vessel making way through the water shall sound at intervals of not more than 2 minutes one prolonged blast.

(252) (b) A power-driven vessel underway but stopped and making no way through the water shall sound at intervals of no more than 2 minutes two prolonged blasts in succession with an interval of about 2 seconds between them.

(253) (c) A vessel not under command, a vessel restricted in her ability to maneuver «*whether underway or at anchor*», ‹ a vessel constrained by her draft ›, a sailing vessel, a vessel engaged in fishing and a vessel engaged in towing or pushing another vessel shall, instead of the signals prescribed in Rule 35(a) or (b), sound at intervals of not more than 2 minutes three blasts in succession, namely one prolonged followed by two short blasts.

(268)

## Rule 37—Distress Signals (International/Inland)

**RED STAR SHELLS**

**FOG HORN CONTINUOUS SOUNDING**

**FLAMES ON A VESSEL**

**GUN FIRED AT INTERVALS OF 1 MINUTE**

**ORANGE BACKGROUND BLACK BALL AND SQUARE**

SOS

SOS

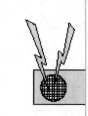
**"MAYDAY" BY RADIO**

**PARACHUTE RED FLARE**

**DYE MARKER (ANY COLOR)**

**CODE FLAGS NOVEMBER CHARLIE**

**SQUARE FLAG AND BALL**

**WAVE ARMS**

**RADIO-TELEGRAPH ALARM**

**RADIO-TELEPHONE ALARM**

**POSITION INDICATIONG RADIO BEACON**

**SMOKE**

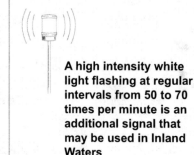
A high intensity white light flashing at regular intervals from 50 to 70 times per minute is an additional signal that may be used in Inland Waters

(254)

**Rule 35d (International)**

(d) A vessel engaged in fishing, when at anchor, and a vessel restricted in her ability to maneuver when carrying out her work at anchor, shall instead of the signals prescribed in Rule 35(g) sound the signal prescribed in Rule 35(c).

(255)   (e) A vessel towed or if more than one vessel is towed the last vessel of the tow, if manned, shall at intervals of not more than 2 minutes sound four blasts in succession, namely one prolonged followed by three short blasts. When practicable, this signal shall be made immediately after the signal made by the towing vessel.

(256)   (f) When a pushing vessel and a vessel being pushed ahead are rigidly connected in a composite unit they shall be regarded as a power-driven vessel and shall give the signals prescribed in Rule 35(a) or (b).

(257)   (g) A vessel at anchor shall at intervals of not more than 1 minute ring the bell rapidly for about 5 seconds. In a vessel 100 meters or more in length the bell shall be sounded in the forepart of the vessel and immediately after the ringing of the bell the gong shall be sounded rapidly for about 5 seconds in the after part of the vessel. A vessel at anchor may in addition sound three blasts in succession, namely one short, one long and one short blast, to give warning of her position and of the possibility of collision to an approaching vessel.

(258)   (h) A vessel aground shall give the bell signal and if required the gong signal prescribed in Rule 35(g) and shall, in addition, give three separate and distinct strokes on the bell immediately before and after the rapid ringing of the bell. A vessel aground may in addition sound an appropriate whistle signal.

(259)   (i) A vessel of 12 meters or more but less than 20 meters in length shall not be obliged to give the bell

signals prescribed in Rule 35(g) and (h). However, if she does not, she shall make some other efficient sound signal at intervals of not more than 2 minutes.

(260)　　(j) A vessel of less than 12 meters in length shall not be obliged to give the above mentioned signals but, if she does not, shall make some other efficient sound signal at intervals of not more than 2 minutes.

(261)　　(k) A pilot vessel when engaged on pilotage duty may, in addition to the signals prescribed in Rule 35(a), (b) or (g), sound an identity signal consisting of four short blasts.

(262)

### Rule 35 (Inland)

*(l) The following vessels shall not be required to sound signals as prescribed in Rule 35(g) when anchored in a special anchorage area designated by the Coast Guard:*

*(i) a vessel of less than 20 meters in length; and*

*(ii) a barge, canal boat, scow, or other nondescript craft.*

(263)

### Rule 36—Signals to Attract Attention

(264)　　If necessary to attract the attention of another vessel, any vessel may make light or sound signals that cannot be mistaken for any signal authorized elsewhere in these Rules, or may direct the beam of her searchlight in the direction of the danger, in such a way as not to embarrass any vessel.

(265)

### Rule 36 (International)

Any light to attract the attention of another vessel shall be such that it cannot be mistaken for any aid to navigation. For the purpose of this Rule the use of high intensity intermittent or revolving lights, such as strobe lights, shall be avoided.

(266)

### Rule 37—Distress Signals

(267)　　When a vessel is in distress and requires assistance she shall use or exhibit the signals described in Annex IV to these Rules. (See graphic, **Rule 37—Distress Signals**).

(269)

## Part E—Exemptions

(270)

### Rule 38—Exemptions (International)

Any vessel (or class of vessel) provided that she complies with the requirements of — the International Regulations for the Preventing of Collisions at Sea, 1960, the keel of which is laid or is at a corresponding stage of construction before the entry into force of these Regulations may be exempted from compliance therewith as follows:

(a) The installation of lights with ranges prescribed in Rule 22, until 4 years after the date of entry into force of these Regulations.

(b) The installation of lights with color specifications as prescribed in §7 of Annex I to these Regulations, until 4 years after the entry into force of these Regulations.

(c) The repositioning of lights as a result of conversion from Imperial to metric units and rounding off measurement figures, permanent exemption.

(d)(i) The repositioning of masthead lights on vessels of less than 150 meters in length, resulting from the prescriptions of §3 (a) of Annex I to these Regulations, permanent exemption. (ii) The repositioning of masthead lights on vessels of 150 meters or more in length, resulting from the prescriptions of §3 (a) of Annex I to these Regulations, until 9 years after the date of entry into force of these Regulations.

(e) The repositioning of masthead lights resulting from the prescriptions of §2(b) of Annex I to these Regulations, until 9 years after the date of entry into force of these Regulations.

(f) The repositioning of sidelights resulting from the prescriptions of §2(g) and 3(b) of Annex I to these Regulations, until 9 years after the date of entry into force of these Regulations.

(g) The requirements for sound signal appliances prescribed in Annex II to these Regulations, until 9 years after the date of entry into force of these Regulations.

(h) The repositioning of all-round lights resulting from the prescription of §9(b) of Annex I to these Regulations, permanent exemption.

(271)

### Rule 38—Exemptions (Inland)

*Any vessel or class of vessels, the keel of which was laid or which is at a corresponding stage of construction before December 24, 1980, provided that she complies with the requirements of —*

*(a) The Act of June 7, 1897 (30 Stat. 96), as amended (33 U.S.C. 154-232) for vessels navigating the waters subject to that statute;*

*(b) §4233 of the Revised Statutes (33 U.S.C. 301-356) for vessels navigating the waters subject to that statute;*

*(c) The Act of February 8, 1895 (28 Stat. 645), as amended (33 U.S.C. 241-295) for vessels navigating the waters subject to that statute; or*

### Rule 38—Exemptions (Inland)

*(d) §§3, 4, and 5 of the Act of April 25, 1940 (54 Stat. 163), as amended (46 U.S.C. 526 b, c, and d) for motorboats navigating the waters subject to that statute; shall be exempted from compliance with the technical Annexes to these Rules as follows:*

*(i) The installation of lights with ranges prescribed in Rule 22, vessels of less than 20 meters in length are permanently exempt;*

*(ii) The installation of lights with color specifications as prescribed in §7 of Annex I to these Rules, until 4 years after the effective date of the Inland Navigational Rules Act of 1980 (Pub. L. 96-591), except that vessels of less than 20 meters in length are permanently exempt;*

*(iii) The repositioning of lights as a result of a conversion to metric units and rounding off of measurement figures, are permanently exempt.*

*(iv) The horizontal repositioning of masthead lights prescribed by Annex I to these Rules, vessels of less than 150 meters in length are permanently exempted.*

*(v) Power-driven vessels of 12 meters or more but less than 20 meters in length are permanently exempt from the provisions of Rule 23(a)(i) and 23(a)(iv) provided that, in place of these lights, the vessel exhibits a white light aft visible all-around the horizon.*

(272) **Implementing Rule**—See **33 CFR 81.20**, chapter 2, for regulations.

(273)

## Part F—Verification of Compliance with the Provisions of the Convention

(274)

### Rule 39—Definitions

(275)

#### Rule 39 (International)

(a) "Audit" means a systematic, independent and documented process for obtaining audit evidence and evaluating it objectively to determine the extent to which audit criteria are fulfilled.

(b) "Audit Scheme" means the IMO Member State Audit Scheme established by the Organization and taking into account the guidelines developed by the Organization*.

(c) "Code for Implementation" means the IMO Instruments Implementation Code (III Code) adopted by the Organization by resolution A.1070(28).

(d) "Audit Standard" means the Code for Implementation.

(276)

### Rule 40—Application

(277)

#### Rule 40 (International)

Contracting Parties shall use the provisions of the Code for Implementation in the execution of their obligations and responsibilities contained in the present Convention.

(278)

### Rule 41—Verification of Compliance

(279)

#### Rule 41 (International)

(a) Every Contracting Party shall be subject to periodic audits by the Organization in accordance with the audit standard to verify compliance with and implementation of the present Convention.

(b) The Secretary-General of the Organization shall have responsibility for administering the Audit Scheme, based on the guidelines developed by the Organization*.

(c) Every Contracting Party shall have responsibility for facilitating the conduct of the audit and implementation of a programme of actions to address the findings, based on the guidelines developed by the Organization*.

(d) Audit of all Contracting Parties shall be:

(i) based on an overall schedule developed by the Secretary-General of the Organization, taking into account the guidelines developed by the Organization*; and

(ii) conducted at periodic intervals, taking into account the guidelines developed by the Organization*.

* Refer to the Framework and Procedures for the IMO Member State Audit Scheme, adopted by the Organization by resolution A.1067(28).

(280)

## Annex I—Positioning and Technical Details of Lights and Shapes

(281)

### Definitions

(282) (a) The term "height above the hull" means height above the uppermost continuous deck. This height shall be measured from the position vertically beneath the location of the light.

(283)

#### Annex I (Inland)

*(b) High-speed craft means a craft capable of maximum speed in meters per second (m/s) equal to or exceeding: $3.7\nabla^{0.1667}$; where $\nabla$ = displacement corresponding to the design waterline (cubic meters).*

*Note: The same formula expressed in pounds and knots is maximum speed in knots (kts) equal to exceeding $1.98(lbs)$ $3.7\nabla^{0.1667}$; where $\nabla$=displacement corresponding to design waterline in pounds.*

*(c) The term "practical cut-off" means, for vessels 20 meters or more in length, 12.5 percent of the minimum luminous intensity (Table 14(b)) corresponding to the greatest range of visibility for which the requirements of Annex I are met.*

*(d) The term "Rule" or "Rules" has the same meaning as in Rule 3(r).*

(284)
## Vertical Positioning and Spacing of Lights

(285)    (a) On a power-driven vessel of 20 meters or more in length the masthead light shall be placed as follows: (i) The forward masthead light, or if only one masthead light is carried, then that light, at a height above the hull of not less than ‹ 6 ›«*5*» meters, and, if the breadth of the vessel exceeds ‹ 6 ›«*5*» meters, then at a height above the hull not less than such breadth, so however that the light need not be placed at a greater height above the hull than ‹12 ›«*8*» meters; (ii) when two masthead lights are carried the after one shall be at least ‹ 4.5 ›«*2*» meters vertically higher than the forward one.

(286)    (b) The vertical separation of the masthead lights of power-driven vessels shall be such that in all normal conditions of trim the after light will be seen over and separate from the forward light at a distance of 1000 meters from the stem when viewed from ‹ sea ›«*water*» level.

(287)    (c) The masthead light of a power-driven vessel of 12 meters but less than 20 meters in length shall be placed at a height above the gunwale of not less than 2.5 meters.

(288)

### Annex I (International)

(d) A power-driven vessel of less than 12 meters in length may carry the uppermost light at a height of less than 2.5 meters above the gunwale. When, however, a masthead light is carried in addition to sidelights and a sternlight or the all-round light prescribed in Rule 23(d)(i) is carried in addition to sidelights, then such masthead light or all-round light shall be carried at least 1 meter higher than the sidelights.

### Annex I (Inland)

*(d) The masthead light, or the all-round light described in Rule 23(d), of a power-driven vessel of less than 12 meters in length shall be carried at least 1 meter higher than the sidelights.*

(289)    (e) One of the two or three masthead lights prescribed for a power-driven vessel when engaged in towing or pushing another vessel shall be placed in the same position as either the forward masthead light or the after masthead light, provided that ‹ , if carried on the after mast, › the lowest after masthead light shall be at least ‹ 4.5 ›«*2*» meters vertically higher than the «*highest*» forward masthead light.

(290)    (f)(i) The masthead lights or lights prescribed in Rule 23(a) shall be so placed as to be above and clear of all other lights and obstructions except as described in §(f)(ii).

(291)    (ii) When it is impracticable to carry the all-round lights prescribed by Rule 27(b)(i) ‹ or Rule 28 › below the masthead lights, they may be carried above the after masthead light(s) or vertically in between the forward masthead light(s) and after masthead light(s), provided that in the latter case the requirement of §3(c) shall be complied with.

(292)    (g) The sidelights of a power-driven vessel shall be placed at ‹ a height above the hull not greater than three quarters of that ›«*least 1 meter lower*» of ‹ the ›«*than*» forward masthead light. They shall not be so low as to be interfered with by deck lights.

(293)

### Annex I (International)

(h) The sidelights, if in a combined lantern and carried on a power-driven vessel of less than 20 meters in length, shall be placed not less than 1 meter below the masthead light.

(294)    (i) When the Rules prescribe two or three lights to be carried in a vertical line, they shall be spaced as follows: (i) On a vessel of 20 meters in length or more such lights shall be spaced not less than ‹ 2 ›«*1*» meter apart, and the lowest of these lights shall, except where a towing light is required, be placed at a height of not less than 4 meters above the hull. (ii) On a vessel of less than 20 meters in length such lights shall be spaced not less than 1 meter apart and the lowest of these lights shall, except where a towing light is required, be placed at a height of not less than 2 meters above the gunwale. (iii) When three lights are carried they shall be equally spaced.

(295)    (j) The lower of the two all-round lights prescribed for a vessel when engaged in fishing shall be at a height above the sidelights not less than twice the distance between the two vertical lights.

(296)    (k) The forward anchor light prescribed in Rule 30(a)(i), when two are carried, shall not be less than 4.5 meters above the after one. On a vessel of 50 meters or more in length this forward anchor light shall be placed at a height or not less than 6 meters above the hull.

(297)
## Horizontal Positioning and Spacing of Lights

(298)    (a) «Except as specified in §1(e), » when two masthead lights are prescribed for a power-driven vessel, the horizontal distance between them must not be less than one- ‹ quarter ›«*half*» of the length of the vessel but need not be more than ‹ 100 ›«*50*» meters. The forward light must be placed not more than one- ‹ quarter ›«*half*» of the length of the vessel from the stem.

(299)    (b) On a power-driven vessel of 20 meters or more in length the sidelights shall not be placed in front of the forward masthead lights. They shall be placed at or near the side of the vessel.

(300)    (c) When the lights prescribed in Rule 27(b)(i) ‹ or Rule 28 › are placed vertically between the forward masthead light(s) and the after masthead light(s), these all-round lights shall be placed at a horizontal distance of not less than 2 meters from the fore and aft centerline of the vessel in the athwartship direction.

(301)    (d) When only one masthead light is prescribed for a power-driven vessel, this light must be exhibited forward of amidships. For a vessel of less than 20 meters in length, the vessel shall exhibit one masthead light as far forward as is practicable.

(302)

### Annex I (Inland)

*(e) On power-driven vessels 50 meters but less than 60 meters in length operated on the Western Rivers, and those { waters specified by the Secretary }, the horizontal distance between masthead lights shall not be less than 10 meters.*

(303)

### Details of Location of Direction-Indicating Lights for Fishing Vessels, Dredgers and Vessels Engaged in Underwater Operations

(304)    (a) The light indicating the direction of the outlying gear from a vessel engaged in fishing as prescribed in Rule 26(c)(ii) shall be placed at a horizontal distance of not less than 2 meters and not more than 6 meters away from the two all-round red and white lights. This light shall be placed not higher than the all-round white light prescribed in Rule 26(c)(i) and not lower than the sidelights.

(305)    (b) The lights and shapes on a vessel engaged in dredging or underwater operations to indicate the obstructed side and/or the side on which it is safe to pass, as prescribed in Rule 27(d)(i) and (ii), shall be placed at the maximum practical horizontal distance, but in no case less than 2 meters, from the lights or shapes prescribed in Rule 27(b)(i) and (ii). In no case shall the upper of these lights or shapes be at a greater height than the lower of the three lights or shapes prescribed in Rule 27(b)(i) and (ii).

(306)

### Screens ‹ For Sidelights ›

(307)    (a) The sidelights of vessels of 20 meters or more in length shall be fitted with ‹ inboard screens painted › matt black, *«inboard screens»* and meet ‹ ing › the requirements of §‹ 9 ›*«15»*. On vessels of less than 20 meters in length, the sidelights, if necessary to meet the requirements of §‹ 9 ›*«15»*, shall be fitted with ‹ inboard › matt black *«inboard»* screens. With a combined lantern, using a single vertical filament and a very narrow division between the green and red sections, external screens need not be fitted.

(308)

### Annex I (Inland)

*(b) On power-driven vessels less than 12 meters in length constructed after July 31, 1983, the masthead light, or the all-round light described in Rule 23(d) shall be screened to prevent direct illumination of the vessel forward of the operator's position.*

(309)

### Shapes

(310)    (a) Shapes shall be black and of the following sizes: (i) A ball shall have a diameter of not less than 0.6 meter; (ii) a cone shall have a base diameter of not less than 0.6 meter‹s› and a height equal to its diameter; ‹ (iii) a cylinder shall have a diameter of at least 0.6 meter and a height of twice its diameter; › (iv)☐(iii) a diamond shape shall consist of two cones as defined in §(a)(ii) having a common base.

(311)    (b) The vertical distance between shapes shall be at least 1.5 meter ‹ s ›.

(312)    (c) In a vessel of less than 20 meters in length shapes of lesser dimensions but commensurate with the size of the vessel may be used and the distance apart may be correspondingly reduced.

(313)

### Color Specification of Lights

(314)    (a) The chromaticity of all navigation lights shall conform to the following standards, which lie within the boundaries of the area of the diagram specified for each color by the International Commission on Illumination (CIE). ‹ , in the "Colors of Light Signals", which is incorporated by reference. It is Publication CIE No. 2.2. (TC-1.6), 1975, and is available from the Illumination Engineering Society, 345 East 47th Street, New York, NY 10017 and is available for inspection at the Coast Guard, Shore Infrastructure Logistics Center, Aids to Navigation and Marine Environmental Response Product Line (CGSILC-ATON/MER), 2703 Martin Luther King, Jr. Ave SE, Mailstop 7714, Washington, DC 20593-7714. It is also available for inspection at the National Archives and Records Administration (NARA). For information on the availability of this material at NARA, call 202–741–6030, or go to: *http://www.archives.gov/federal_register/code_of_federal_regulations/ibr_locations.html.* This incorporation by reference was approved by the Director of the Federal Register. ›

(315)    (b) The boundaries of the area for each color are given by indicating the corner coordinates, which are as follows:

(316)

| (i) White | | | | | |
|---|---|---|---|---|---|
| x | 0.525 | 0.525 | 0.452 | 0.310 | 0.310 | 0.443 |
| y | 0.382 | 0.440 | 0.440 | 0.348 | 0.283 | 0.382 |

| (ii) Green | | | |
|---|---|---|---|
| x | 0.028 | 0.009 | 0.300 | 0.203 |
| y | 0.385 | 0.723 | 0.511 | 0.356 |

| (iii) Red | | | |
|---|---|---|---|
| x | 0.680 | 0.660 | 0.735 | 0.721 |
| y | 0.320 | 0.320 | 0.265 | 0.259 |

| (iv) Yellow | | | |
|---|---|---|---|
| x | 0.612 | 0.618 | 0.575 | 0.575 |
| y | 0.382 | 0.382 | 0.425 | 0.406 |

(317)

### Intensity of Lights

(318)    (a) The minimum luminous intensity of lights shall be calculated by using the formula:

(319)

$$I = 3.43 \times 10^6 \times T \times D^2 \times K^{-D}$$

I is luminous intensity in candelas under service conditions.

**T** is threshold factor 2 x 10⁻⁷ lux.

**D** is range of visibility (luminous range) of the light in nautical miles.

**K** is atmospheric transmissivity. For prescribed lights the value of K shall be 0.8, corresponding to a meteorological visibility of approximately 13 miles.

(320)      (b) A selection of figures derived from the formula is given in the following table:

(321)

| Range of visibility (luminous range) of light in nautical miles D | Minimum luminous intensity of light in candelas for K = 0.8 I |
|---|---|
| 1 | 0.9 |
| 2 | 4.3 |
| 3 | 12 |
| 4 | 27 |
| 5 | 52 |
| 6 | 94 |

(322)      ‹ Note: The maximum luminous intensity of navigation lights should be limited to avoid undue glare. This shall not be achieved by a variable control of the luminous intensity. ›

(323)

**Horizontal Sectors**

(324)      (a)(i) In the forward direction, sidelights as fitted on the vessel shall show the minimum required intensities. The intensities shall decrease to reach practical cut-off between 1 and one degrees outside the prescribed sectors.

(325)      (ii) For sternlights and masthead lights and at 22.5 degrees abaft the beam for sidelights, the minimum required intensities shall be maintained over the arc of the horizon up to 5 degrees within the limits of the sectors prescribed in Rule 21. From 5 degrees within the prescribed sectors the intensity may decrease by 50 percent up to the prescribed limits; it shall decrease steadily to reach practical cut-off at not more than 5 degrees outside the prescribed sectors.

(326)      (b)(i) All-round lights shall be so located as not to be obscured by masts, topmasts or structures within angular sectors of more than 6 degrees, except anchor lights prescribed in Rule 30, which need not be placed at an impracticable height above the hull *« , and the allround white light described in Rule 23(e), which may not be obscured at all»*.

(327)      (ii) If it is impracticable to comply with §(b)(i) by exhibiting only one all-round light, two all-round lights shall be used suitably positioned or screened so that they *«to»* appear, as far as practicable, as one light at a *«minimum»* distance of 1 *«nautical»* mile.

(328)      *«Note: Two unscreened all-round lights that are 1.28 meters apart or less will appear as one light to the naked eye at a distance of 1 nautical mile.»*

(329)

**Vertical Sectors**

(330)      (a) The vertical sectors of electric lights as fitted, with the exception of lights on sailing vessels underway *«and on unmanned barges»*, shall ensure that: (i) At least the required minimum intensity is maintained at all angles from 5 degrees above to 5 degrees below the horizontal; (ii) at least 60 percent of the required minimum intensity is maintained from 7.5 degrees above to 7.5 degrees below the horizontal.

(331)      (b) In the case of sailing vessels underway the vertical sectors of electric lights as fitted shall ensure that: (i) At least the required minimum intensity is maintained at all angles from 5 degrees above to 5 degrees below the horizontal; (ii) at least 50 percent of the required minimum intensity is maintained from 25 degrees above to 25 degrees below the horizontal.

(332)

**Annex I (Inland)**

*(c) In the case of unmanned barges the minimum required intensity of electric lights as fitted shall be maintained on the horizontal.*

(333)      (c)☐(d) In the case of lights other than electric lights these specifications shall be met as closely as possible.

(334)

**Intensity of Non-electric Lights**

(335)      Non-electric lights shall so far as practicable comply with the minimum intensities, as specified in the *«Intensity of Lights»* Table.

(336)

**Maneuvering Light**

(337)      *«Notwithstanding the provisions of §2(f)»*, the maneuvering light described in Rule 34(b) shall be placed *«approximately»* in the same fore and aft vertical plane as the masthead light or lights and, where practicable, at a minimum height of ‹ 2 ›*«1.5»* meter vertically above the forward masthead light, provided that it shall be carried not less than ‹ 2 ›*«1.5»* meter vertically above or below the after masthead light. On a vessel where only one masthead light is carried, the maneuvering light, if fitted, shall be carried where it can best be seen, not less than ‹ 2 ›*«1.5»* meters vertically apart from the masthead light.

(338)

**High-speed Craft**

(339)      (a) The masthead light of high-speed craft may be placed at a height related to the breadth *«of the craft»* lower than that prescribed in §2(a)(i), provided that the base angle of the isosceles triangle formed by the sidelights and masthead light when seen in end elevation is not less than 27 degrees.

(340)      (b) On high-speed craft of 50 meters or more in length, the vertical separation between foremast and mainmast light of 4.5 meters required by §‹ 2(a)(ii) ›*«2(k)»* may be modified provided that such distance shall not be less than the value determined by the following formula:

(341)

$$y = \frac{y = (a+17\Psi)\ C}{1000} + 2$$

**y** the height of the mainmast light above the foremast light in meters.

**a** is the height of the foremast light above the water surface in service condition in meters

**Y** is the trim in service condition in degrees.

**C** is the horizontal separation of masthead lights in meters.

Note: Refer to the International Code of Safety for High-Speed Craft, 1994 and the International Code of Safety for High-Speed Craft, 2000.

(342)

### Approval

(343) The construction of lights and shapes and the installation of lights on board the vessel ‹ shall be to the satisfaction of the appropriate authority of the State whose flag the vessel is entitled to fly ›*«must satisfy the Commandant, U. S. Coast Guard»*.

(344)

# Annex II—Additional Signals for Fishing Vessels Fishing in Close Proximity

(345) See Rule 26(f).

(346)

# Annex III—Technical Details of Sound Signal Appliances

(347) (a) Frequencies and range of audibility. The fundamental frequency of the signal shall lie within the range 70-700 Hz. The range of audibility of the signal from a whistle shall be determined by those frequencies, which may include the fundamental and/or one or more higher frequencies, which lie within the range 180-700 Hz (+/- 1 percent) for a vessel of 20 meters or more in length, or 180-2100 Hz (+/- 1 percent) for a vessel of less than 20 meters in length and which provide the sound pressure levels specified in §1(c).

(348) (b) Limits of fundamental frequencies. To ensure a wide variety of whistle characteristics, the fundamental frequency of a whistle shall be between the following limits: (i) 70-200 Hz, for a vessel 200 meters or more in length; (ii) 130-350 Hz, for a vessel 75 meters but less than 200 meters in length; (iii) 250-700 Hz, for a vessel less than 75 meters in length.

(349) (c) Sound signal intensity and range of audibility. A whistle fitted in a vessel shall provide, in the direction of maximum intensity of the whistle and at a distance of 1 meter from it, a sound pressure level in at least one onethird octave band within the range of frequencies 180-700 Hz (+/- 1 percent) for a vessel of 20 meters ‹ or more in length, or 180-2100 Hz (+/- 1 percent) for a vessel of less than 20 meters in length ›, of not less than the appropriate figure given in the table below.

(350)

| Length of vessel in meters | One-third octave band level at 1 meter in dB referred to $2 \times 10^{-5} N/m^2$ | Audible range in nautical miles |
|---|---|---|
| 200 or more | 143 | 2 |
| 75 but less than 200 | 138 | 1.5 |
| 20 but less than 75 | 130 | 1 |
| Less than 20 | 120*<br>115**<br>111*** | 0.5 |

\* When the measured frequencies lie within the range 180-450 Hz
\*\* When the measured frequencies lie within the range 450-800 Hz
\*\*\* When the measured frequencies lie within the range 800-2100 Hz

(351) The range of audibility in the table is for information and is approximately the range at which a whistle may be heard on its forward axis with 90 percent probability in conditions of still air on board a vessel having average background noise level at the listening posts (taken to be 68 dB in the octave band centered on 250 Hz and 63 dB in the octave band centered on 500 Hz). *«It is shown for informational purposes only.»* In practice, the range at which a whistle may be heard is extremely variable and depends critically on weather conditions; the values given can be regarded as typical but under conditions of strong wind or high ambient noise level at the listening post the range may be reduced.

(352) (d) Directional properties. The sound pressure level of a directional whistle shall be not more than 4 dB below the ‹ prescribed › sound pressure level ‹ on the axis at ›, *«specified in §(c)»* any direction in the horizontal plane within +/- 45 degrees of the axis. The sound pressure level at *«of the whistle in»* any other direction in the horizontal plane shall be not more than 10 dB ‹ below the prescribed ›*« less than the »* sound pressure level ‹ on the ›*« specified for the forward »* axis, so that the range *« audibility »* in any direction will be at least half the range *«required»* on the forward axis. The sound pressure level shall be measured in that one-third octave band which determines the audibility range.

(353) (e) Positioning of whistles.

(354) (i) When a directional whistle is to be used as the only whistle on ‹ a vessel, it shall be installed with its maximum intensity directed straight ahead ›*«the vessel and is permanently installed, it shall be installed with its forward axis directed forward»*.

(355) (ii) A whistle shall be placed as high as practicable on a vessel, in order to reduce interception of the emitted sound by obstructions and also to minimize hearing damage risk to personnel. The sound pressure level of the vessel's own signal at listening posts shall not exceed 110 dB(A) and so far as practicable should not exceed 100 dB(A).

(356) (f) Fitting of more than one whistle. If whistles are fitted at a distance apart of more than 100 meters, ‹ it shall be so arranged that they are ›*«they shall»* not *«be»* sounded simultaneously.

(357)

### Annex IIIg (International)

(g) Combined whistle systems.

If due to the presence of obstructions the sound field of a single whistle or of one of the whistles referred to in §(f) is likely to have a zone of greatly reduced signal level, it is recommended that a combined whistle system be fitted so as to overcome this reduction. The whistles of a combined system shall be located at a distance apart of not more than 100 meters and arranged to be sounded simultaneously. The frequency of any one whistle shall differ from those of the others by at least 10 Hz.

### Annex IIIg (Inland)

*(g) Combined whistle systems.*

*(i) A combined whistle system is a number of whistles (sound emitting sources) operated together. For the purposes of the Rules a combined whistle system is to be regarded as a single whistle.*

*(ii) The whistles of a combined system shall:*

*(1) Be located at a distance apart of not more than 100 meters;*

*(2) Be sounded simultaneously;*

*(3) Each have a fundamental frequency different from those of the others by at least 10 Hz; and*

*(4) Have a tonal characteristic appropriate for the length of vessel which shall be evidenced by at least 2-thirds of the whistles in the combined system having fundamental frequencies falling within the limits prescribed in §(b) of this section, or if there are only two whistles in the combined system, by the higher fundamental frequency falling within the limits prescribed in paragraph (b) of this section.*

*Note: If, due to the presence of obstructions, the sound field of a single whistle or of one of the whistles referred to in §(f) of this section is likely to have a zone of greatly reduced signal level, a combined whistle system should be fitted so as to overcome this reduction.*

(358) For the purposes of the Rules a combined whistle system is to be regarded as a single whistle. ‹ (ii) › The whistles of a combined system shall:

(359) (1) Be located at a distance apart of not more than 100 meters;

(360)

### Annex III(h) (Inland)

*(h) Towing vessel whistles*

*A power-driven vessel normally engaged in pushing ahead or towing alongside may, at all times, use a whistle whose characteristic falls within the limits prescribed by §1(b) for the longest customary composite length of the vessel and its tow.*

(361)

### Bell or Gong

(362) (a) Intensity of signal. A bell or gong, or other device having similar sound characteristics shall produce a sound pressure level of not less than 110 dB at ‹ a distance of › 1 meter ‹ from it ›.

(363) (b) Construction. Bells and gongs shall be made of corrosion-resistant material and designed to give clear tone. The diameter of the mouth of the bell shall be not less than 300 mm for vessels of 20 meters or more in length. Where practicable, a power-driven bell striker is recommended to ensure constant force but manual operation shall be possible. The mass of the striker shall be not less than 3 percent of the mass of the bell.

(364)

### Approval

(365)

### Annex III (International)

The construction of sound signal appliances, their performance and their installation on board the vessel shall be to the satisfaction of the appropriate authority of the State whose flag the vessel is entitled to fly.

(366)

## Annex IV—Distress Signals

(367)

*«Need of Assistance»*

(368) The following signals, used or exhibited either together or separately, indicate distress and need of assistance:

(369) (a) a gun or other explosive signal fired at intervals of about a minute;

(370) (b) a continuous sounding with any fog-signaling apparatus;

(371) (c) rockets or shells, throwing red stars fired one at a time at short intervals;

(372) (d) a signal made by any signaling method consisting of the group . . . - - - . . . (SOS) in the Morse Code;

(373) (e) a signal sent by radiotelephony consisting of the spoken word "Mayday";

(374) (f) the International Code Signal of distress indicated by N.C.;

(375) (g) a signal consisting of a square flag having above or below it a ball or anything resembling a ball;

(376) (h) flames on the vessel (as from a burning tar barrel, oil barrel, etc.);

(377) (i) a rocket parachute flare or a hand flare showing a red light;

(378) (j) a smoke signal giving off orange-colored smoke;

(379) (k) slowly and repeatedly raising and lowering arms outstretched to each side;

(380) (l) a distress alert by means of digital selective calling (DSC) transmitted on: (i) VHF channel 70, or (ii) MF/HF on the frequencies 2187.5 kHz, 8414.5 kHz, 4207.5 kHz, 6312 kHz, 12577 kHz or 16804.5 kHz;

(381) (m) a ship-to-shore distress alert transmitted by the ship's Inmarsat or other mobile satellite service provider ship earth station;

(382) (n) signals transmitted by emergency position-indicating radio beacons;

(383) (o) approved signals transmitted by radiocommunication systems, including survival craft radar transponders *meeting the requirements of 47 CFR 80.109»*.

(384) *«(p) A high intensity white light flashing at regular intervals from 50 to 70 times per minute.»*

(385)
### *«Exclusive Use»*

(386) The use or exhibition of any of the foregoing signals except for the purpose of indicating distress and need of assistance and the use of other signals which may be confused with any of the above signals is prohibited.

(387)
### *«Supplemental Signals»*

(388) Attention is drawn to the relevant sections of the International Code of Signals, the International Aeronautical and Maritime Search and Rescue Manual, Volume III, ‹ the International Telecommunication Union Radio Regulations, › and the following signals:

(389) (a) A piece of orange-colored canvas with either a black square and circle or other appropriate symbol (for identification from the air);

(390) (b) A dye marker.

(391)
## Annex V—Pilot Rules

(392)
### §88.01 Purpose and applicability.

(393) This part applies to all vessels operating on United States inland waters and to United States vessels operating on the Canadian waters of the Great Lakes to the extent there is no conflict with Canadian law.

(394)
### §88.03 Definitions.

(395) The terms used in this part have the same meaning as the terms defined in part 83 of this subchapter.

(396)
### §88.05 Law enforcement vessels.

(397) (a) Law enforcement vessels may display a flashing blue light when engaged in direct law enforcement or public safety activities. This light must be located so that it does not interfere with the visibility of the vessel's navigation lights.

(398) (b) The blue light described in this section may be displayed by law enforcement vessels of the United States and the States and their political subdivisions.

(399)
### §88.07 Public safety activities.

(400) (a) Vessels engaged in government sanctioned public safety activities, and commercial vessels performing similar functions, may display an alternately flashing red and yellow light signal. This identification light signal must be located so that it does not interfere with the visibility of the vessel's navigation lights. The identification light signal may be used only as an identification signal and conveys no special privilege. Vessels using the identification light signal during public safety activities must abide by the Inland Navigation Rules, and must not presume that the light or the exigency gives them precedence or right of way.

(401) (b) Public safety activities include but are not limited to patrolling marine parades, regattas, or special water celebrations; traffic control; salvage; firefighting; medical assistance; assisting disabled vessels; and search and rescue.

(402)
## Implementing Rules

(403) **Alternative Compliance**—see **33 CFR 81** and **33 CFR 89**, chapter 2, for regulations.

(404) **Vessel Bridge-to-Bridge Radiotelephone Regulations**—see **33 CFR 26**, chapter 2, for regulations.

# Appendix A

## Sales Information

(2)      NOAA publications, nautical charts and unclassified National Geospatial-Intelligence Agency (NGA) nautical charts are sold by authorized sales agents in many U.S. ports and in some foreign ports. Information on obtaining charting products and a listing of authorized agents can be found at *nauticalcharts.noaa.gov*.

(3)
## Products and Services–NOAA

(4)
### Reporting corrections to Nautical Charts and Coast Pilots
(5)      Users are requested to report all significant discrepancies or additions to NOAA navigational products, including depth information in privately maintained channels and basins; obstructions, wrecks and other dangers; new, relocated or demolished landmarks; uncharted fixed private aids to navigation; deletions or additions of small-craft facilities and any other information pertinent to safe navigation. This information may be submitted using the NOAA Office of Coast Survey site *https://www.nauticalcharts.noaa.gov/customer-service/assist/*

(6)
Department of Commerce, NOAA
Nautical Data Branch
N/CS26, Station 7505
1315 East-West Highway
Silver Spring, Maryland 20910
*ocs.ndb@noaa.gov*

(7)
### Nautical Charts
(8)      NOAA maintains the nautical charts and publications for the coast of the United States and the Great Lakes. Over a thousand charts cover 95,000 miles of shoreline and 3.4 million square nautical miles of water. Access to charts, publications and chart catalogs is available through *www.nauticalcharts.noaa.gov*.

(9)
### Dates of Latest Editions
(10)      Information concerning the dates of the latest editions for the full suite of NOAA's nautical charts and U.S. Coast Pilot volumes can be found at *www.nauticalcharts.noaa.gov/mcd/dole.htm*.

(11)
## Coast Pilots
(12)
U.S. Coast Pilot 1—Atlantic Coast: Eastport to Cape Cod
U.S. Coast Pilot 2—Atlantic Coast: Cape Cod to Sandy Hook
U.S. Coast Pilot 3—Atlantic Coast: Sandy Hook to Cape Henry
U.S. Coast Pilot 4—Atlantic Coast: Cape Henry to Key West
U.S. Coast Pilot 5—Gulf of Mexico: Puerto Rico and Virgin Islands
U.S. Coast Pilot 6—Great Lakes: Lakes Ontario, Erie, Huron, Michigan, Superior and St. Lawrence River
U.S. Coast Pilot 7—Pacific Coast: California
U.S. Coast Pilot 8—Alaska: Dixon Entrance to Cape Spencer
U.S. Coast Pilot 9—Alaska: Cape Spencer to Beaufort Sea
U.S. Coast Pilot 10—Pacific Coast: Oregon, Washington, Hawaii, and Pacific Islands

(13)
## Distance Tables
(14)      Distances Between United States Ports is available at    *www.nauticalcharts.noaa.gov/publications/docs/distances.pdf*

(15)
## National Ocean Service Center for Operational Oceanographic Products and Services
(16)
1305 East-West Highway
Silver Spring, Maryland 20910
301–713–2815 (phone)
301–713–4500 (fax)
*www.tidesandcurrents.noaa.gov*

(17)
## National Weather Service Offices
(18)      The following offices provide forecasts, current conditions, local information and climatological data. This data can be accessed through the websites listed after each office below.

(19)
**Maryland/Virginia**

NWS Forecast Office Baltimore/Washington
*www.weather.gov/lwx*
44087 Weather Service Road, Sterling, VA. 20166

**Pennsylvania/New Jersey**

NWS Forecast Office Philadelphia/Mount Holly
*www.weather.gov/phi*
732 Woodlane Road, Mount Holly, NJ. 08060

(20)

## NOAA Weather Radio

(21)    National Weather Service VHF-FM radio stations provide mariners with continuous FM broadcasts of weather warnings, forecasts, radar reports and surface weather observations. Reception range is up to 40 miles from the antenna site, depending on the terrain, type of receiver and antenna used. The VHF-FM radio stations with locations of antennas in or near the area covered by this Coast Pilot are listed in the table.

(22)

| Call Sign | Station | Location | Frequency |
|-----------|---------|----------|-----------|
| KWO-35 | New York, NY | 40°46'N., 73°59'W. | 162.55 |
| KIH-28 | Philadelphia, PA | 40°03'N., 75°14'W. | 162.475 |
| KHB-38 | Atlantic City, NJ | 39°22'N., 74°26'W. | 162.40 |
| WXJ-94 | Lewes, DE | 38°47'N., 75°09'W. | 162.55 |
| WXK-97 | Sudlersville, MD | 39°11'N., 75°55'W. | 162.50 |
| KEC-83 | Baltimore, MD | 39°23'N., 76°43'W. | 162.40 |
| KHB-36 | Washington, DC | 38°38'N., 77°26'W. | 162.55 |
| KEC-92 | Salisbury, MD | 38°30'N., 75°38'W. | 162.475 |
| WXM-57 | Heathsville, VA | 37°54'N., 76°28'W. | 162.40 |
| KHB-37 | Norfolk, VA | 36°48'N., 76°28'W. | 162.55 |
| WXF-65 | Richmond, VA | 37°30'N., 77°32'W. | 162.475 |

(23)    The National Weather Service provides **Radio Facsimile Weather Information** for east coast waters through the Coast Guard Communication Station Boston (NMF). Broadcasts are made on the following frequencies: 4235 (02z, 08z), 6340.5, 9100, 12750 (14z) kHz. For carrier frequency, subtract 1.9 kHz. Fax schedules are transmitted at 0243 and 1405 GMT and provide area coverage and descriptions of services. For further information on Marine Radiofax Charts, visit: *https://www.weather.gov/marine/radiofax_charts*

(24)    **Coastal Marine Forecasts** are issued four times daily by National Weather Service Offices. For further information on coastal marine forecasts as well as additional types of forecasts, visit: *https://weather.gov/marine/forecast -and- https://nowcoast.noaa.gov/*

(25)

## Space Weather Prediction Center (SWPC)

(26)    The Space Weather Prediction Center provides real-time monitoring and forecasting of solar and geophysical events that impact satellites, power grids, communications, navigation and many other technological systems.

(27)

NOAA, National Weather Service
National Centers for Environmental Predictions
Space Weather Prediction Center, W/NP9
325 Broadway
Boulder, Colorado 80305
*www.swpc.noaa.gov*

(28)

## National Weather Service Port Meteorological Officers (PMOs)

(29)    Port Meteorological Officers provide assistance on matters of weather chart interpretation, instruments, marine weather communications and requirements affecting ship operations. (See **National Weather Service**, chapter 1, for further details.) PMO offices in the area covered by this Coast Pilot are as follows:

(30)    Baltimore, MD – P.O. Box 3667, Frederick, MD 21701

(31)    Norfolk, VA – 104 Hemlock Court, Yorktown, VA 23693-4544

(32)

## Products and Services–Other U.S. Government Agencies

(33)    A partial list of publications and charts considered of navigational value is included for the ready reference of the mariner. In addition to the agents located in the principal seaports handling publication sales, certain libraries have been designated by the Congress of the United States to receive the publications as issued for public review.

(34)

## Government Publishing Office

(35)

U.S. Government Publishing Office
710 North Capitol Street, NW
Washington, DC 20401-0001
202-512-1800
866-512-1800
*www.gpo.gov/*
ContactCenter@gpo.gov

(36)

## Hydrographic Surveys

(37)    U.S. Army Corps of Engineers hydrographic survey activity is available at: *https://www.mvr.usace.army.mil/Missions/Navigation/Hydrographic-Surveys/HydrographicSurveysMap/*

(38)

## Nautical Charts

(39)    **Apalachicola, Chattahoochee and Flint Rivers Navigation Charts**, **Alabama River Charts** and **Black Warrior-Tombigbee Rivers River Charts**—available from the U.S. Army Corps of Engineers Mobile District for purchase in bound hard copy or as a free download in PDF at *www.sam.usace.army.mil*.

(40)    **Flood Control and Navigation Maps of the Mississippi River, Cairo, IL to the Gulf of**

**Mexico**— available from the U.S. Army Corps of Engineers Memphis District as a free download in PDF at *www. mvm.usace.army.mil*.

(41) **Upper Mississippi River Navigation Charts (Mississippi River, Cairo, Illinois to Minneapolis, Minnesota)** and **Charts of the Illinois Waterway, from Mississippi River at Grafton, Illinois to Lake Michigan at Chicago and Calumet Harbors**—available from the U.S. Army Corps of Engineer Rock Island District for purchase in hard copy format or as a free download in PDF at *www.mvr.usace.army.mil*.

(42)

## Publications and Services

(43) **Local Notices to Mariners** are posted weekly by the U.S. Coast Guard Navigation Center at *www.navcen. uscg.gov*. The National Geospatial-Intelligence Agency, U.S. Notice to Mariners are available at *msi.nga.mil/ NGAPortal/MSI.portal*.

(44) **Special Notice to Mariners** are issued annually in National Geospatial-Intelligence Agency Notice to Mariners 1. These notices contain important information of considerable interest to all mariners. Interested parties are advised to read these notices.

(45) **Light List**—maintained by the United States Coast Guard and available online at *www.navcen.uscg.gov*. Also see **Light List**, chapter 1, for additional information.

(46) **List of Lights, Sailing Directions, Radio Navigational Aids (Pub. 117), American Practical Navigator (Pub. 9)** and **International Code of Signals (Pub. 102)**—issued by the National Geospatial-Intelligence Agency and available at *msi.nga.mil/ NGAPortal/MSI.portal*.

(47) **The Nautical Almanac**, the **Air Almanac** and **Astronomical Almanac**—available through the United States Naval Observatory—*https://www.public.navy. mil/fltfor/cnmoc/Pages/usno_test_page.aspx* -and- *https://bookstore.gpo.gov/agency/united-states-naval-observatory-usno*

(48) **Dissemination of Marine Weather Information**, maintained by National Weather Service on the internet at *https://www.weather.gov/marine/nws_dissemination* -and- **NWS Marine Weather Services** at *https://www. weather.gov/marine/*

(49) **Navigation Rules and Regulations Handbook**, publication produced by the United States Coast Guard Navigation Standards Branch, which contains International and Inland Rules of the Road and Navigation Regulations. Available for download or viewing at *www. navcen.uscg.gov*. Navigation Rules are also found near the end of each individual Coast Pilot volume.

(50)

## Offices and Services–Other U.S. Government Agencies

(51)

### U.S. Army Corps of Engineers (USACE) Offices

(52)

| District/Division Office | Information |
|---|---|
| North Atlantic Division Office 302 General Lee Avenue Brooklyn, NY 11252 | www.nad.usace.army.mil |
| Philadelphia District Office The Wanamaker Building 100 Penn Square East Philadelphia, PA 19107-3390 | www.nap.usace.army.mil |
| Baltimore District Office City Crescent Building 10 South Howard Street Baltimore, MD 21201 | www.nab.usace.army.mil |
| Norfolk District Office Public Affairs Office 803 Front Street Norfolk, VA 23510 | www.nao.usace.army.mil |

(53)

### Environmental Protection Agency (EPA) Offices

(54)

| Regional Areas, States and Information |
|---|
| **Region 1** New Hampshire, Vermont, Maine, Massachusetts, Connecticut, Rhode Island www.epa.gov/aboutepa/epa-region-1-new-england |
| **Region 2** New Jersey, New York, Puerto Rico, Virgin Islands www.epa.gov/aboutepa/epa-region-2 |
| **Region 3** Delaware, Maryland, Virginia, District of Columbia, Pennsylvania www.epa.gov/aboutepa/epa-region-3-mid-atlantic |
| **Region 4** Alabama, Florida, Georgia, Mississippi, South Carolina, North Carolina www.epa.gov/aboutepa/epa-region-4-southeast |
| **Region 5** Illinois, Indiana, Michigan, Minnesota, Ohio, Wisconsin www.epa.gov/aboutepa/epa-region-5 |
| **Region 6** Louisiana, Texas www.epa.gov/aboutepa/epa-region-6-south-central |
| **Region 9** California, Hawaii, Guam www.epa.gov/aboutepa/epa-region-9-pacific-southwest |
| **Region 10** Alaska, Oregon, Washington www.epa.gov/aboutepa/epa-region-10-pacific-northwest |

(55)

### U.S. Coast Guard Navigation Center (NAVCEN)

(56) The Coast Guard Navigation Center provides cutting-edge services for safe, secure and efficient maritime transportation. The center operates the Navigation Information Service (NIS), the Maritime Differential GPS (DGPS) and the developing Nationwide Differential Global Positioning System (NDGPS). In addition, NAVCEN serves as the civilian interface for the Global Positioning System and manages other navigation-related projects.

(57)     For further information and/or operational questions regarding GPS and DGPS, visit *navcen.uscg.gov*, or contact:

(58)

Commanding Officer
U.S. Coast Guard Navigation Center
NAVCEN MS 7310
7323 Telegraph Road
Alexandria, VA 20598-7310

(59)

## Coast Guard District Offices

(60)

### Districts, Boundary Description and Contact Information

**First Coast Guard District**
Maine, New Hampshire, Vermont, Massachusetts, Rhode Island, Connecticut, New York except that part north of latitude 42°N. and west of longitude 74°39'W.; that part of New Jersey, north of latitude 40°18'N., east of longitude 74°30.5'W., and northeast of a line from 40°18'N., 74°30.5'W., north-northwesterly to the New York, New Jersey and Pennsylvania boundaries at Tristate; all U.S. Naval reservations on shore at Newfoundland; the ocean area encompassed by the Search and Rescue boundary between Canada and the United States easterly to longitude 63°W.; thence due south to latitude 41°N.; thence southwesterly along a line bearing 219°T to the point of intersection at 37°N., 67°13'W., with a line bearing 122°T from the New Jersey shoreline at latitude 40°18'N., (just south of the Shrewsbury River); thence northwesterly along this line to the coast.

408 Atlantic Avenue
Boston, MA
02110-3350
617–223–8356

**Fifth Coast Guard District**
North Carolina, Virginia, District of Columbia, Maryland, Delaware, that part of Pennsylvania east of a line drawn along longitude 78°55'W. south to latitude 41°00'N. thence west to longitude 79°00'W. and thence south to the Pennsylvania/Maryland boundary; that portion of New Jersey that lies south and west of a line drawn from the New Jersey shoreline at latitude 40°18'N. (just south of the Shrewsbury River), thence westward to 40°18'N., 74°30.5'W. thence north-northwesterly to the junction of the New York/New Jersey/Pennsylvania boundaries at Tristate; and the ocean area encompassed by a line bearing 122°T from the coastal end of the First and Fifth Districts' land boundary at the intersection of the New Jersey shoreline and latitude 40°18'N. (just south of the Shrewsbury River) to the southernmost point in the First Coast Guard District (approximately 37°N., 67°13'W.); thence along a line bearing 219°T to the point of intersection with the ocean boundary between the Fifth and Seventh Coast Guard Districts, which is defined as a line bearing 122°T from the coastal end of the Fifth and Seventh Districts' land boundary at the shoreline of the North Carolina/South Carolina border (approximately 30°55'N., 73°W.); thence northwesterly along this line to the coast.

431 Crawford Street
Portsmouth, VA
23704-5004
757–398–6486

(61)

## Coast Guard Sector Offices

(62)     Note: A Sector Office combines the functions of the Captain of the Port and Marine Inspection Office.

(63)

| Sectors | Contact Information |
|---|---|
| Sector Delaware Bay | One Washington Avenue Philadelphia, PA 19147 215–271–4800 |
| Sector Maryland-National Capital Region | 2401 Hawkins Point Road Baltimore, MD 21226 |
| Sector Hampton Roads | 4000 Coast Guard Boulevard Portsmouth, VA 23703 |

(64)

## Coast Guard Stations

(65)     The stations listed are in the area covered by this Coast Pilot. They have search and rescue capabilities

and may provide lookout, communication and/or patrol functions to assist vessels in distress. The National VHF-FM Distress System provides continuous coastal radio coverage outwards to 20 miles on channel 16. After contact on channel 16, communications with the Coast Guard should be on channel 22. If channel 22 is not available to the mariner, communications may be made on channel 12. Selected stations guard the International Radiotelephone Distress, Safety and Calling Frequencies.

(66)

| Delaware | |
|---|---|
| Station Indian River Inlet | Inside the inlet, on the north shore. |
| **Maryland** | |
| Station Ocean City | 0.6 mile inside the inlet on the southwest side of Ocean City. |
| Station Crisfield | Aids to Navigation Team on the south side of Somers Cove. |
| Station Stillpond | On the north side of the entrance to Stillpond Cove. |
| Station Baltimore | At Curtis Bay Coast Guard Yard in Arundel Cove. |
| Station Annapolis | On the west side of Fishing Creek, about 1 mile northwestward of Thomas Point. |
| Station St. Inigoes | On the west side of the entrance to Molls Cove. |
| **New Jersey** | |
| Station Sandy Hook | On the bay side, 0.5 mile south of the point of the hook. |
| Station Shark River | About 500 yards west of the entrance, on the north side of Shark River Inlet. |
| Station Manasquan Inlet | On the south side of the inlet, quarter mile west of the entrance. |
| Station Barnegat Inlet | On Long Beach at Barnegat City, 0.5 mile south-southeast of abandoned light tower. |
| Station Beach Haven | At Beach Haven, 3 miles north of Beach Haven Inlet. |
| Station Atlantic City | Near Absecon Inlet entrance, on north side of Clam Creek, opposite Gardiner Basin. |
| Station Great Egg | Inside Great Egg Harbor Inlet at Ocean City, 0.4 mile southward of bridge. |
| Station Townsend Inlet | North side of the inlet, 2.3 miles southwest of Ludlum Beach Light (manned during summer months only.) |
| Station Cape May/ Cape May Air Station | On the south side of Cape May Harbor |
| **Pennsylvania** | |
| Station Philadelphia | Search and Rescue boats on the west side of Delaware River at the foot of Washington Avenue. |
| **Virginia** | |
| Station Chincoteague | On the east side of Chincoteague Channel, 0.3 mile south of the bridge. |
| Station Wachapreague | In the town of Wachapreague, about 4.0 miles west-northwest of Wachapreague Inlet. |
| Station Cape Charles | On the spit between Mud Creek and Harbor of Refuge. |
| Station Milford Haven | About 0.4 mile eastward of Narrows Point. |
| Station Little Creek | About 1 mile south of the entrance to Little Creek, 4.5 miles west of Lynnhaven Inlet. |
| Station Portsmouth | On the west side of the entrance to Craney Island Creek. |

(67)
## Coast Guard Radio Broadcasts

(68)      Urgent, safety and scheduled marine information broadcasts are made by Coast Guard stations. In general, these broadcasts provide information vital to vessels operating in the approaches and coastal waters of the United States including the Great Lakes, Puerto Rico and U.S. Virgin Islands. Types of broadcasts are as follows:

(69)      **Scheduled broadcasts**–U.S. Coast Guard stations make scheduled broadcasts on a prepublished schedule of 12-hour intervals. After the preliminary announcements on VHF-FM channel 16, the station advises shifting to working frequency VHF-FM channel 22.

(70)      **Safety broadcasts**–U.S. Coast Guard stations that make scheduled broadcasts issue safety broadcasts upon receipt and on the next scheduled broadcast. Safety broadcasts are preceded by the safety signal SECURITY. After the preliminary signal on VHF-FM channel 16, the station may announce shifting to working frequency VHF-FM channel 22A.

(71)      **Urgent broadcasts**–U.S. Coast Guard stations that make scheduled broadcasts issue urgent broadcasts upon receipt and on schedule until canceled. Urgent broadcasts are preceded by the urgent signal, PAN-PAN. Both the urgent signal and message may be transmitted on VHF-FM channel 16.

(72)

| Coast Guard Radio Station | Scheduled Broadcast Times (EST) |
|---|---|
| Baltimore, MD (NMX) | 0705 and 2030 (VHF-FM channel 22A) |
| Atlantic City, NJ (NMK) | 0603 and 1803<br>(VHF-FM channel 22A and 2670 kHz) |
| Philadelphia, PA (NMK-2) | 0735 and 1935 (VHF-FM channel 22A) |
| Eastern Shore (NMN-70) | 0645 and 2100 (VHF-FM channel 22A)<br>0903 and 2133 (2670 kHz) |
| Hampton Roads, VA (MNM-80) | 0620 and 2130 (VHF-FM channel 22A)<br>0833 and 2103 (2670 kHz) |
| USCG Activites New York<br>(NMY-3) | 1050 and 2250<br>(VHF-FM channel 22A and 2670 kHz) |

(73)
## U.S. NAVTEX Transmitting Stations

(74)      NAVTEX is an international automated medium frequency direct-printing service informing mariners of navigational and meteorlogical warnings and forecasts, as well as urgent marine safety information. Coverage is reasonably continuous to 200 NM off the U.S. East, Gulf and West Coasts; Puerto Rico; Southwest Alaska; Hawaii; and 100 NM off Guam. U.S. Coast Guard NAVTEX broadcast stations and message content for the areas covered by this Coast Pilot are shown below.

(75)

| Station | ID | Broadcast Schedule (UTC) |
|---|---|---|
| Boston (NMF) | F | 0050, 0450, 0850, 1250, 1650, 2050 |
| Chesapeake (NMN) | N | 0210, 0610, 1010, 1410, 1810, 2210 |
| Charleston (NMN) | E | 0040, 0440, 0840, 1240, 1640, 2040 |
| Miami (NMA) | A | 0000, 0400, 0800, 1200, 1600, 2000 |
| San Juan (NMR) | R | 0250, 0650, 1050, 1450, 1850, 2250 |

| Station | ID | Broadcast Schedule (UTC) |
|---|---|---|
| New Orleans (NMG) | G | 0100, 0500, 0900, 1300, 1700, 2100 |

(76)
## Customs Ports of Entry and Stations

(77)      Vessels arriving in the United States from a foreign port or place are required to report their arrival to Customs and Border Protection immediately. Field Operations Offices and contact information is listed below.

(78)

| Field Operations Office | Contact Information |
|---|---|
| Philadelphia | 2$^{nd}$ and Chestnut Streets<br>Room 102<br>Philadelphia, PA 19106<br>215–717–5800 |
| Baltimore | 40 South Gay Street<br>Baltimore, MD 21202<br>410–962–2666 |
| Wilmington | 908 New Churchman's Road<br>Suite C<br>New Castle, DE 19720<br>302–326–0600 |
| Norfolk-Newport News | 101 East Main Street<br>Norfolk, VA 23510<br>757–533–4200 |

(79)
## Public Health Service Quarantine Stations

(80)

| Quarantine Stations and Addresses |
|---|
| **CDC Philadelphia Quarantine Station**<br>Philadelphia International Airport<br>Terminal A West, 3$^{rd}$ floor, International Arrivals<br>Philadelphia, PA 19153 |
| **CDC Washington D.C. Quarantine Station**<br>Dulles International Airport<br>C Terminal, Gate C-1<br>Mezzanine Level<br>Dulles, VA 20166 |

(81)      At other ports, quarantine and/or medical examinations are usually performed by Public Health Service contract personnel or by quarantine inspectors from the nearest quarantine station. Inquiries concerning quarantine matters should be directed to the nearest quarantine station.

(82)

(83)
## Department of Agriculture, Animal and Plant Health Inspection Service (APHIS)

(84)      Information on the importation of plants, animals, and plant and animal products is available from APHIS, Department of Agriculture, 4700 River Road, Riverdale, MD 20737. Visit *aphis.usda.gov* for more information.

(85)

| USDA Animal and Plant Inspection Service |
|---|
| **Animal Import Centers:** |
| **Los Angeles Animal Import Center (LAAIC)**<br>222 Kansas Street<br>El Segundo, CA 90245<br>310-955-3311 |

| USDA Animal and Plant Inspection Service | |
|---|---|
| **Animal Import Centers:** | |
| **Miami Animal Import Center (MAIC)** 6300 NW 36th Street Miami, FL 33122 305-876-2200 | |
| **New York Animal Import Center (NYAIC)** 474 Animal Import Center Newburg, NY 12550 845-838-5500 | |
| **John F. Kennedy Airport Office** 230-59 Rockaway Blvd. Suite 100, Room 101 Jamaica, NY 11413 718-553-3570 | |
| **Agriculture Select Service Agents** 4700 River Road, Unit 2 Riverdale, MD 20737 AgSAS@aphis.usda.gov 301-851-3300 (select option 3) | |

(86)

## U.S. Citizenship and Immigration Services

(87)

| New Jersey | |
|---|---|
| Newark Field Office | Peter Rodino Federal Building 970 Broad Street Newark, NJ 07102 |
| Mount Laurel Field Office | 530 Fellowship Road Mount Laurel, NJ 08054 |
| **Delaware, Pennsylvania** | |
| Dover Field Office | 250 Gateway S. Boulevard Suite 270 Dover, DE 19901 |
| Philadelphia Field Office | 30 N. 41st Street Philadelphia, PA 19104 |
| **Maryland** | |
| Baltimore Field Office | 3701 Koppers Street Baltimore, MD 21227 |
| **Washington, D.C., Virginia** | |
| Washington Field Office | 2675 Prosperity Avenue Fairfax, VA 22031 |
| Norfolk Field Office | 5678 East Virginia Beach Blvd. Norfolk, VA 23502 |

(88)

## Food and Drug Administration (FDA) Regional Offices

(89)

| Northeast Region | 158-15 Liberty Avenue Jamaica, New York 11433 718-340-7000 |
|---|---|

| Central Region | 20 North Michigan Avenue Suite 510 Chicago, Illinois 60602 215–597–4390 |
|---|---|
| Pacific Region | 1301 Clay Street Room 1180N Oakland, California 94612 510–287–2700 |
| Southeast Region | 60 Eighth Street NE Atlanta, Georgia 30309 404–253–1171 |
| Southwest Region | 4040 North Central Expressway Suite 900 Dallas, Texas 75204 214–253–4901 |

(90)

## Federal Communications Commission Offices

(91) **District field offices**

(92) Philadelphia, PA: One Oxford Valley Office Bldg., Room 404, 2300 East Lincoln Hwy., Langhorne, PA 19047-1859.

(93) Columbia, MD: 9200 Farm House Lane, Columbia, MD 21046.

(94) Atlanta, GA: 3575 Koger Blvd., Ste. 320, Duluth, GA 30096-4958.

(95) Telephone toll free: 888–225–5322; (888–CALL–FCC) to report radio communications interference issues.

(96)

## Stations Transmitting Medical Advice

(97) To obtain radio medical advice by reliable voice radio communications, urgent calls for assistance may be broadcast using the normal Urgency prowords PAN-PAN as follows:

(98)

| Broadcast Language | Details |
|---|---|
| PAN PAN | (3 times) |
| All Stations | (3 times or specific station if known) |
| This is ship name | (3 times) |
| Call sign | (call sign) |
| In Position | (give position) |
| I require medical advice | |
| Over | |

# Weekly Record of Updates

| Week of | Action | Chapter | Paragraph(s) | User notes |
|---|---|---|---|---|
| 07 DEC 2021 | | | | U.S. Coast Pilot 3, 55th Edition has been issued. |
| 12 DEC 2021 | **No Correction** | | | |
| 19 DEC 2021 | **No Correction** | | | |
| 26 DEC 2021 | **No Correction** | | | |
| 02 JAN 2022 | **Change** | 8 | 52 | |
| 09 JAN 2022 | **No Correction** | | | |
| 16 JAN 2022 | **No Correction** | | | |
| 23 JAN 2022 | **No Correction** | | | |
| 30 JAN 2022 | **No Correction** | | | |
| 06 FEB 2022 | **No Correction** | | | |
| 13 FEB 2022 | **No Correction** | | | |
| 20 FEB 2022 | **No Correction** | | | |
| 27 FEB 2022 | **No Correction** | | | |
| 06 MAR 2022 | **Change** | 14 | 79 | |
| | **Change** | 14 | 236 | |
| 13 MAR 2022 | **Insert** | 9 | 149.0010 | |
| 20 MAR 2022 | **No Correction** | | | |
| 27 MAR 2022 | **No Correction** | | | |
| 03 APR 2022 | **No Correction** | | | |
| 10 APR 2022 | **No Correction** | | | |
| 17 APR 2022 | **No Correction** | | | |
| 24 APR 2022 | **No Correction** | | | |
| 01 MAY 2022 | **No Correction** | | | |

This record is intended as a log for critical updates applied to this volume. For online versions or Print on Demand (POD) copies, all weekly critical updates issued and applied to this edition at time of download or purchase are listed.
Affected paragraphs within the chapters are indicated by a gray highlight for ease of identification; e.g. (215)

Updates are available from NOAA at https://nauticalcharts.noaa.gov/publications/coast-pilot/index.html.

| Week of | Action | Chapter | Paragraph(s) | User notes |
|---------|--------|---------|--------------|------------|
|         |        |         |              |            |

| Week of | Action | Chapter | Paragraph(s) | User notes |
|---------|--------|---------|--------------|------------|
|         |        |         |              |            |

| Week of | Action | Chapter | Paragraph(s) | User notes |
|---------|--------|---------|--------------|------------|
|         |        |         |              |            |

This record is intended as a log for critical updates applied to this volume. For online versions or Print on Demand (POD) copies, all weekly critical updates issued and applied to this edition at time of download or purchase are listed.
Affected paragraphs within the chapters are indicated by a gray highlight for ease of identification; e.g. (215)

Updates are available from NOAA at https://nauticalcharts.noaa.gov/publications/coast-pilot/index.html.

# Index

## T

## U

## V

# Y